PLANT AND ANIMAL BIOLOGY
VOLUME I

PLANT AND ANIMAL BIOLOGY

VOLUME I

BY

A. E. VINES, B.Sc. (Hons.)

*Formerly Head of Science Department
and Principal Lecturer in Biology
The College of St. Mark and St. John, Chelsea*

AND

N. REES, B.Sc. (Hons.)

*Formerly Senior Lecturer in Biology
The College of St. Mark and St. John, Chelsea*

FOURTH EDITION

Longman Group UK Limited,
Longman House, Burnt Mill, Harlow,
Essex CM20 2JE, England
and Associated Companies throughout the world.

First published by Pitman Publishing Limited 1959
First published by Longman Group UK Limited 1986
Fourth edition 1972
Fifteenth impression 1986

Printed in Great Britain
at The Bath Press, Avon

ISBN 0 582 35598 2

PREFACE TO THE FOURTH EDITION

WE have again endeavoured to give some account of important modern work in these topics considered necessary at the level of this textbook, and to include more recent interpretation of some older ideas. Most of the additions and amendments appear in Volume II; they concern physiology, cytochemistry, genetics and behaviour. In the more classical biology of Volume I, there has been less need for amendment; the most important changes occur in the endocrinology of vertebrates and the higher invertebrates, with somewhat more emphasis on neurosecretion.

S.I. units are used throughout both volumes; this has necessitated redrawing of certain figures bearing scale measurements. A number of minor errors, pointed out by perspicacious students, have been gratefully noted and corrected. Some of the older examination questions have been substituted by more recent examples, and a number of questions on current topics have been added. It is hoped that the volumes will continue to be of use to students of the biological subjects.

We take this opportunity of thanking our publishers, and particularly the Technical Editor, for continued whole-hearted co-operation and encouragement. For the typing of the new material in Volume I and some parts of Volume II, we are greatly indebted to Mrs Rees.

A.E.V.
N.R.

CAVENDISH,
SUFFOLK.
26 *November*, 1971

v

PREFACE TO THE FIRST EDITION

WE hope that this and its companion volume, in scope and presentation, reflect the main purposes for which they were written. Our chief aims were to present to the Advanced Level student an approach to the biological subjects through an integration, and to bring within his reach a more modern outlook towards biological problems. There is at least one valid reason for the integration. There exists but one living world, and, although we may choose for convenience to recognize and study separately the two main classes of its inhabitants, we cannot escape from the fact that all exist under the same conditions afforded by this planet, are intermingled, have the same corresponding life processes and are largely interdependent. We feel that at this level of study it is still too early to make a completely rigid separation between Botany and Zoology. To do so, in some measure at least, defeats the object of trying to teach a proper understanding of the processes involved in the maintenance of life, surely the most important of all teaching aims. In the past there has been a sad lack of emphasis on other than very elementary physiology due undoubtedly for the most part to paucity of accurate, understandable information relating to this subject. But as chemists and physicists have increasingly provided biologists with better techniques of investigation, much of what was once obscure can now be explained in terms well within the comprehension of the sixteen- to eighteen-year-old student, providing that he studies physics and chemistry as parallel subjects. We foresee a radical change in the pattern of biology teaching and hope that our effort, if only to a small degree, may speed its coming. We do, however, recognize that there will always be the necessity for morphological study, particularly in a comparative way, and in the field as far as possible, since this is an essential background. We believe that a great deal more of this kind of work could be undertaken at the Ordinary Level if students commenced serious biological study at an early enough stage in their science career. There is presented first, therefore, a variety of type studies from which the student can select according to his needs. We recommend that all should be treated, if some only for interest rather than for examination purposes. These types have been described in a way which does not preclude the purely Botanical or Zoological study if that is desired.

It was our original intention to attempt a complete coverage in one volume, and our first scheme was prepared accordingly. As the work progressed, it became increasingly evident that, unless many important topics were to receive scanty treatment, the book would become far too cumbersome. To avoid pruning the content too heavily, our publisher generously allowed us to modify our original plan and the subject-matter has been divided into two sections. This first volume is mainly systematic, with the types presented as a series showing gradation in complexity, and transition from fully aquatic to fully terrestrial forms. The free-living organisms are treated first, and then in their proper perspective, the parasitic, saprophytic and other modes of living are described. Our second volume consists chiefly of physiology but it includes also the topics of general biology with which it is necessary for the Advanced Level student to be familiar.

This division into two volumes necessitated some rearrangement of the sequence of topics from that which we considered to be best from both learning and teaching viewpoints. We had intended that the introductory chapters to the physiology should appear before the detailed studies of types. However, if the volumes are used in conjunction with one another, and this is borne in mind, it is still possible to follow the scheme as we first prepared it.

In the treatment of some topics we may be accused of erring by giving too detailed an account, but our decision to do so was influenced by three main considerations. First, we have taken into account how much the student can be expected to learn and understand and at the same time be fitted for University study. We have assumed that he will already have gained some introduction at the Ordinary Level, and in most cases we have presented the facts without undue worry. On the other hand, there have been occasions when we were unable to find a suitable bridge between a very elementary approach and a much more complicated modern interpretation. In such cases, perhaps we have expanded beyond the bounds of what is necessary, but then we have always had in mind the greater requirements of the Scholarship student. Our second consideration has been the extent of the knowledge which it would appear that examiners expect of the student. We have studied many examination papers, and have concluded that a candidate can do well only if he possesses a real understanding of his subject-matter. A superficial knowledge of facts alone is not often sufficient. This is an excellent thing, but it invariably calls for a deeper than elementary study. The third influence was the extent to which a student might be expected to make use of the text as an aid to his work. Too frequently, it has been our experience that the textbook is used only to check classroom notes. We have tried to produce a text which will amplify these and not always be subsidiary to them.

During our own reading in preparation of the manuscript, we have found instances of confused terminology and some conflict of factual statements. It has been no part of our plan to attempt to "put the house in order," but we have tried always to make the best use of the terms customarily used and to employ authoritative sources for our facts. Here we must pay tribute to the originators of our information, having possession now of a much clearer comprehension of what tenacity of purpose their work must have entailed.

Of the figures to the text, we would say that neither of us lays claim to any special artistic qualifications, but, with few exceptions, we have managed to complete the illustrations without assistance. Some figures are, of course, purely diagrammatic representations, but wherever it was possible, these have been constructed from actual specimens. All illustrations are line drawings and almost invariably relate to matters in the text. We could have used photographs in many cases but felt that these would have detracted from rather than increased the clarity of meaning.

We gratefully acknowledge those to whom we are indebted for aid in the completion of our work in preparing Volume I. Our wives must stand high in the list for their patience and ministrations during the many hours of toil, and special thanks must go to Mrs. Rees, who so competently and speedily completed all the typing. To the technical Editors of Sir Isaac Pitman & Sons, Ltd., we give our thanks for their ready advice and assistance in matters of preparation of which we started out with no knowledge. To Dr. V. Fretter, of Reading University, we are grateful for advice and criticism after reading some of the manuscript, and to Mr. R. C. Bullock, B.Sc., Biology Master, Sexey's Boys School, Bruton, for his encouragement and sympathy. Among others who made more material assistance we must acknowledge Prof. Gough, of the Department of Pathology, Cardiff University, for his gift of animal histology slides, Mr. C. B. Wyatt, of Southend-on-Sea High School for Boys, who prepared the originals for Figs. 4, 16, 17, 18, 19, 21, 22, 23, 24, of Chapter 29, all those who made loans of examination papers, and the various University Examination Boards who are listed in the heading to the Examination Questions, for their kind permission to use them.

A. E. V.
N. R.

SOUTHEND-ON-SEA.
22nd February, 1959

CONTENTS

CONTENTS

CHAPTER 1

UNITS OF LIVING SUBSTANCE: CELLS

RECORDS of the study of plants and animals date from the time of the Greek philosophers Theophrastus, Aristotle and others, but prior to the invention of the compound microscope by Jensen in 1590 and its development and use by Leeuwenhoek in the period 1650 to 1700, no observers had recorded any comments on the nature of the substance to which the property of being alive is now attributed. It was not till well after Leeuwenhoek's time that the continued use of the instrument led more observant students to conclude that there did exist a definite substance, then described as a "living jelly," and that it could be associated with many of the animate objects under examination. No recordings of note concerning this substance were made until 1665, when Robert Hooke, in coining the term "cells" for the box-like structures he found in thin sections of plant material, dismissed their contents as "nourishing juices." One hundred and seventy years later, in 1835, Dujardin, a French student of microscopic animals, named their body substance "sarcode" and described it as "a substance, viscid, translucent, homogenous, elastic and contractile." In 1838, Schleiden and Schwann enlarged on a "cell-theory" previously conceived by Turpin in 1826. This was further extended by Naegeli (1854) and Virchow (1858) who stated that the bodies of living things were constructed of units each of which owed its origin to the pre-existence of another such unit, and indicated also that the plant "cells" previously described were merely the outer coverings of a substance of infinitely greater significance.

In 1859, Purkinje coined the word "protoplasm," to name this living jelly, which by that time was so frequently associated with animal bodies. Shortly afterwards, von Mohl applied the same term to the slime-like substance which he recorded as circulating inside some plant cells. Schulze (1861) reported on the similarity between the protoplasm of plants, of animals, and of the sarcode of protozoa and proposed that the same term should be applied to all these cases. Thus *protoplasm* became recognized as the physical basis of all life and the fundamental similarity between plants and animals was established. Except for convenience of study, there is no valid reason for treating them separately. Collectively they make up the living world and they all possess the special characters of living things, merely performing their functions in different ways and employing different structures for similar purposes.

1

Living things exist in a vast variety of forms, but in the majority of cases, it can be seen that their bodies are constructed of small, individual masses of protoplasm, to which the name *cells* has been given. Hooke's first use of the term was inept and can be confusing, but he must be forgiven, since he had no conception of the real nature of the living substance. Not all living things can be said to be composed of cells in the forms about to be described. Other protoplasmic units will be described later.

GENERALIZED CELL STRUCTURE

The term, *cell*, is now in general use to describe a protoplasmic unit or *protoplast*, whether plant or animal, together with any substance it may form in or around itself. Because of some inherent differences in the activities of plant and animal protoplasm the general appearance of plant and animal cells is strikingly different. Whereas plant protoplasts almost invariably construct around themselves rigid walls of dead material, animal cells are separated by an intercellular substance which varies greatly in thickness and consistency according to the type of cell producing it. This separating layer may easily be overlooked. Because of the constancy of the rigid wall, the term cell as applicable to plants, can be used to describe any one of several things—

An uncovered protoplast.

The more usual construction of the living protoplast surrounded by its dead wall.

The dead wall only, after the living contents have disappeared.

In animals, *cell* has a more definite application, almost always denoting the living protoplast alone.

Any protoplast whether of plant or animal origin has fundamentally three distinct parts. There is an outer protoplasmic membrane of sub-microscopic dimensions, known as the *plasma-membrane* (*cell membrane* or *plasmalemma*), which encloses the mass of the protoplasm. Inside this surface layer, the protoplasm is differentiated into two distinct regions. There is an apparently more fluid and often granular *cytoplasm* in which will be seen a more dense and somewhat hyaline *nucleus*, consisting of *nucleoplasm*. It may be discoid or globular in shape.

There are protoplasts which may differ from this simplified pattern in several ways, but these are exceptions and will be referred to later.

The Living Cell of a Plant

Plant cell structure in a simple form may be elucidated by examining, with the aid of a microscope, convenient tissue prepared in a suitable way. Such preparations may include thin strips of cells such as may be torn from some outer covering of a plant, thin sections cut with a razor by hand or on a microtome, or loose cells resulting from the maceration of bulky pieces. Any of these preparations may be suitably treated with dyes and other reagents to distinguish the main cellular parts more clearly, but will not truly represent the living condition.

If a preparation of mature epidermal cells of the fleshy leaf of an onion bulb is made by stripping it gently from the underlying cells, and examined in surface view under the microscope, it will appear as in

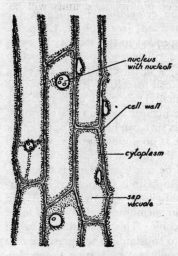

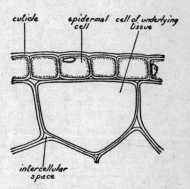

Fig. 1.1. Surface view of cells o epidermis stripped from the fleshy leaf base of an onion bulb. Diagram to show the main parts of the cells.

Fig. 1.2. Vertical section of cells of onion leaf epidermis with some underlying cells.

Fig. 1.1. If a preparation of the same material is made by sectioning the leaf base with a razor at right angles to the surface, and examined, it will appear as in Fig. 1.2. In either case, it will be seen that this layer of cells is composed of a very large number of more or less similar units clearly marked from one another by an intervening wall. Each wall delimits a cell and is known as the *cell wall*. If the student can now combine the picture in the one plane with the picture in the other plane at right angles to it, it must become obvious that each of these cells has three dimensions and is in fact a comparatively long (300–600μ), narrow (about 60μ) and shallow (about 50μ) box-like structure somewhat as in Fig. 1.3.

The student should remember that all cells have three dimensions and that it is always useful to make preparations of material in at least two suitably chosen planes at right angles to one another, in order to appreciate fully the dimensions and shape of any cell. Careful focusing of the microscope at different levels in a preparation can also assist greatly in giving a better understanding of cell shape and contents.

The examination will also reveal that within the boundary of each cell wall, a living protoplast is contained. This appears as a lining to the wall and closely adheres to it at all points, leaving a clear central space or *vacuole.* For the most part this living substance appears colourless but slightly granular. This is the *cytoplasm.* Frequently, the granules can be seen in Brownian movement (*see* Vol. II, Chap. 2). Located either against one wall or suspended in the vacuole by cytoplasmic threads is the *nucleus.* Its shape will depend upon the direction from which it is viewed. It is generally a biconvex disc but the exact size and shape may vary slightly from cell to cell. Within its outline may be seen one or more (up to three usually) very much more refractive bodies of small dimensions. These are nuclear components known as *nucleoli.* No clear limiting membrane as such can be seen around either the cytoplasm or the nucleus, but there is no doubt that the cytoplasm is distinct from the cell wall and that the nuclear substance is clearly definable from the cytoplasm. As will be seen later, there is considerable evidence for supposing that the cytoplasm is surrounded by a surface plasma membrane where it is contiguous with the cell wall, and there is reason to believe that a similar membrane exists on its inner face delimiting it from the central vacuole. This membrane is called the *tonoplast.* Similar evidence exists to substantiate the presence of a superficial layer, called the *nuclear membrane,* separating the *nucleoplasm* from the cytoplasm.

A closer examination of the intervening wall between two cells will show that it is not a single thickness but a double one. This may not be very evident in the epidermal cells themselves since the walls are extremely thin and very great magnification is required to show this detail. But when the epidermal cells are examined in the vertical section in relation to the larger cells underneath, and when these are examined in relationship to one another, the double thickness becomes evident at once. This is due to the fact that every protoplast has secreted its own cell wall independently of the surrounding protoplasts. Adjacent cell walls are cemented to one another by an intervening substance common to both cells. This is known as the *middle lamella.* Where cell walls do not touch one another, and this can be seen very clearly at points where the epidermal cells are in contact with the underlying cells, are spaces devoid of any plant substance. They are *intercellular spaces* and in most cases will be air filled. The substance of which the cell wall is made can be shown to be *cellulose.* It can be demonstrated in younger cells that the cell wall is perforated by very fine channels or *pits* through which adjacent protoplasts are in continuity with one another by means of cytoplasmic connexions called *plasmodesmata* (*see* Fig. 2.6 (*b*)). These will not be revealed in untreated living cells of the onion but such connexions can more easily be shown in other plant material.

In the case of onion leaf epidermal cells, as in fact with the outermost layer of the majority of plants, it will be seen that the whole of the outer face of the tissue is covered by a common overlying substance which gives the outer walls of the cells a thickness much greater than the inner walls. This outer layer is composed of a substance, different from the cell wall itself, and known as a *cuticle* (*see* p. 250). It is composed of a waxy material known as *cutin* but such an extra layer is not produced by all types of plant cells.

If an epidermal strip is lightly stained with methylene blue the important parts of the cell can be picked out more clearly. A phase-contrast attachment for the microscope can be put to good use in studying live, unstained cells. Cell parts with different refractive indices will stand out clearly from one another.

The Origin and Development of the Mature Cell

The structure just described is that of a mature cell. It must be clearly understood that whilst it had the same fundamental components all its

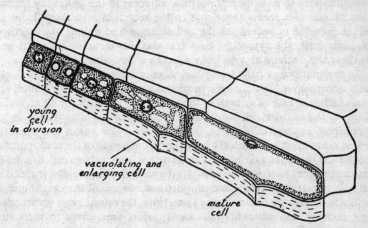

Fig. 1.3. Diagram of the origin and differentiation of the cells of the onion leaf epidermis.

life, it did not appear thus in the early stages of its development. Fig. 1.3 illustrates the development of the mature cell from its young stages which appear at the base of the leaf where the cells are in constant division to form a meristematic region. It will be seen that the young cell, produced by division of an already existing one, has much smaller dimensions. It is roughly cubical in shape, a property common to most young plant cells, and the cavity within the wall is completely filled by the richly granular protoplast in which the nucleus appears to be large in relation to the size of the cell. Such a cell proceeds to grow in size and develops a shape peculiar to its own type. It is said to *differentiate*. As will be seen, the characteristic shapes of plant cells are many and varied. Both the cell wall and the protoplast are affected by the developmental changes. The protoplast, being the active part of the cell, is responsible for the changes and the wall is modified by the changing protoplast. During these changes, the wall is easily moulded, physically and chemically, and only after cell maturity is attained is a fully-developed and permanent wall present. Details of cell division, separation and wall formation will be found in Chap. 2.

In the maturing of the protoplast, many changes occur. They may be summarized briefly, as follows. The nucleus appears to be reduced in proportion to the size of the cell, whilst the cytoplasm develops as a much less richly granular substance. At various places within the cytoplasm fluid-filled cavities appear. They are the vacuoles, which ultimately run together to form one large central vacuole which restricts the cytoplasm to a peripheral position adjacent to the wall. The formation of vacuoles seems to be due to the secretion of watery droplets, which increase in volume as the cell enlarges and finally run together. In some cells, the cytoplasm may traverse the vacuole as strands and in these the nucleus may be suspended in a central position.

In the maturing of the wall, there occurs increase in area and thickness accompanied by changes in chemical and physical structure. In most cells, the rate of growth of the wall is not uniform for all areas. If it were, the mature cell would have roughly equal dimensions in all directions, i.e. be isodiametric. In the case of the onion leaf epiderm cell, it is obvious that greatest growth occurs in length of the walls parallel to the longitudinal axis of the leaf, so that the mature cell is usually six to ten times as long as broad. Its depth and width, whilst increasing slightly, never reach the same proportions. Since all the neighbouring cells are increasing in size at the same time, they must exert pressure on one another and adjacent walls must adjust themselves to their surroundings. Growth brings about changes in the relative positions of the walls. This is clearly demonstrated by the onion epidermal cells where the elongation tends to force the ends of one cell between the two cells on either side of these extremities. When all the cells are developing together in this way, the result is, that the end faces of cells are set obliquely to the longitudinal axis, giving a very characteristic zig-zag effect. In order to achieve their final positions, the adjacent walls must have slipped alongside one another; such a phenomenon may be referred to as *sliding growth* of the cells. This simple conception cannot be used to explain all such peculiarities and no satisfactory comprehensive explanation has yet been made.

The Living Cell of an Animal

Many types of animal cells may be examined under the microscope while still in the living condition. Protozoa are normally studied in this way; the developing eggs of many animals may be inspected periodically. Cells of the blood, and small pieces of many tissues may be kept alive long enough for thorough examination. Such living specimens are best mounted in saline solutions which are similar to their cell contents.

By the technique of tissue culture, pieces of animal tissue can be kept alive for long periods, provided that due attention is paid to aseptic precautions, nutrient materials and oxygenation. Thus the growth of cells, their division and many particular processes such as those of ossification and tooth formation, have been carefully observed.

The standard method of study of animal cells, as with plants, is that of fixation, staining, permanent mounting and then examination, but this involves death of the cells. For animal tissues there are four principal types of permanent preparation. Smears are used for concentrations of small animals such as *Monocystis*, and for separate cells such as are found in blood and saliva. Thin sections are cut of softer tissues, and ground sections of material such as bone. Fibrillar structures such as striated muscle and nerve are finely teased with needles. Thin extensible sheets, as are found in bladder and mesentery, are examined as stretch preparations.

As with plant cells, so with animal cells there are often very great differences in the shape, size, structure and functions of mature cells. Here will be described a cell from the inside of the human cheek, mainly because of its availability, and because of its relatively simple nature. Such cells may easily be scraped from the inside of the cheek and examined alive. They are regularly shed into the mouth and may thus be found in smears of saliva.

There is some variation in the size and shape of these cells, but they are often irregularly oval in surface view, and their size averages $110\mu m \times 80\mu m$. Viewed under the light microscope, the living cell appears perfectly transparent, and apart from an obvious and highly refractive nucleus near the centre, there is no apparent differentiation (*see* Fig. 1.4).

A single nucleolus may sometimes be seen within the nucleus.

Vertical sections of fixed material, when stained and mounted, show the thickness of these cells in various planes. The greatest thickness is in the region of the nucleus and is approximately 15μ. At the edges, the cytoplasm tapers to a point.

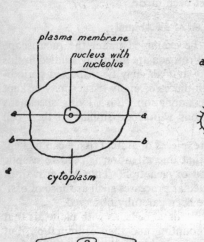

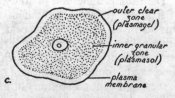

Fig. 1.4. (*a*) Surface view of untreated epidermal cell of the human cheek (inside mouth). (*b*) Sectional views of the same cell in the planes indicated.

Fig. 1.5. Diagram of human cheek cells to show (*a*) and (*b*), inter-cellular substance, protoplasmic fibrils and (*c*), granular and non-granular cytoplasm.

If the upper few layers of cells in a vertical section are carefully examined, it will be seen that the cells are separated by narrow zones of intercellular material. Across these zones there are fine protoplasmic connexions. Their main function in this tissue is probably to afford some mechanical strength by binding the cells together. Sections cut in other planes will show that these protoplasmic connexions run in all directions (*see* Fig. 1.5). In a well-stained smear preparation, some differentiation of the cytoplasm into an outer clear zone, and an inner granular zone may be seen. There are no vacuoles present.

Origin and Development of the Mature Cell

The cells we have described are those which are cast off into the mouth. They are the outermost cells of a stratified epithelium which consists of ten to fifteen layers of cells (*see* Fig. 1.6).

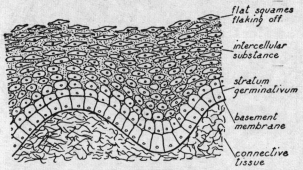

flat squames flaking off

intercellular substance

stratum germinativum

basement membrane

connective tissue

Fig. 1.6. Vertical section through stratified epithelium of human cheek. Diagrammatic.

The deepest layer of cells abuts on connective tissue of the submucosa layer, beneath which is the buccinator muscle of the cheek. This lowest layer of the epithelium is known as the stratum germinativum and from it all the outer-lying cells arise. The cells of the stratum germinativum frequently divide in a plane parallel to the surface. The outermost cell of the two is gradually pushed by later-formed cells, towards the surface, from whence it is eventually cast.

The cells of the stratum germinativum are columnar, normally with six faces. The longest axis is at right angles to the surface, though the cells are often almost isodiametric. There is a prominent nucleus with at least one nucleolus visible. All the cells are bound together by minute protoplasmic connexions across the intercellular substance.

As the cells are forced towards the surface by the continued development of further cells beneath, they become progressively more and more flattened. Nearer the surface, owing to mutual pressure and often distortion, many of the protoplasmic connexions become broken. Finally, the flat thin squames are loose on the surface, whence they are washed off by saliva, or rubbed off by friction with tongue and teeth.

PROTOPLASMIC COMPONENTS AND INCLUSIONS

What has been described has particular reference to the epidermal cells of the onion leaf and human cheek, but nevertheless it is true in general terms for all plant and animal cells respectively. The many varieties of cell which the student will encounter, are the results of the different ways

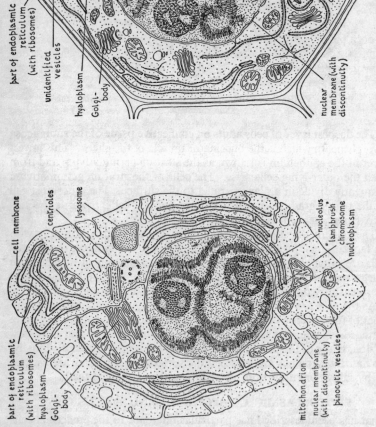

cell wall

mitochondria

part of endoplasmic
reticulum
(with ribosomes)

unidentified
vesicles

hyaloplasm

Golgi-
body

nucleolus
'lampbrush'
chromosome

nucleoplasm

nuclear
membrane (with
discontinuity)

Fig. 1.8. Diagram of a generalized plant cell to show some of the possible components and inclusions.

cell membrane

centrioles

lysosome

part of endoplasmic
reticulum
(with ribosomes)

hyaloplasm

Golgi-
body

nucleolus
'lampbrush'
chromosome

nucleoplasm

mitochondrion

nuclear membrane
(with discontinuity)

pinocytic vesicles

Fig. 1.7. Diagram of a generalized animal cell to show some of the possible components and inclusions.

in which protoplasm may conduct its activities, according to differences in its constitution. Some of these differences are directly reflected by the size and shape of the cell and the precise nature of the protoplasmic structures. The wide variety of cell construction and an account of the various activities of protoplasm are treated elsewhere. It will suffice here to give an account of the components of protoplasts that can be found in general cases. Such components are of two kinds. There are those which form part of the protoplasmic substance and are therefore part of the living system, and those which are merely the non-living products of the chemical activity of these.

Living Components of the Cytoplasm

In both plant and animal cells, the cytoplasm consists of a more or less homogeneous ground substance, known as *hyaloplasm*, in which occur numerous granular bodies. So far, no details of the structure and composition of the hyaloplasm have been discovered beyond the fact that extending through it is a complex system of membrane-bound vesicles, forming a meshwork and referred to as the *endoplasmic reticulum*. This was thought to be similar to and continuous with the plasma membrane, but it could be that it is not so (*see* Vol. II, Chap. 2). Much more has been learnt about the granular inclusions of the cytoplasm by the application of centrifuge techniques which separate them for detailed chemical and physical analysis, and by studies of electron micrographs in which they can be observed at extremely high magnifications. By these means, there have been distinguished a number of clearly different kinds of particles, each of which can be associated with some specific metabolic activity of the cell.

The smallest of the particles are *microbodies* and *ribosomes*. The former are small vesicular structures with a diameter of 300 to 600 nm; the thickness of the membrane is about 6 nm. They are known to contain catalase and also certain enzymes concerned with uric acid metabolism (*see* Vol. II, Chap 5). Ribosomes are smaller still; they consist chiefly of ribonucleic acid and are arranged alongside the endoplasmic reticulum. They are the sites where assemblage of amino acids into proteins is carried out.

Among some of the larger cytoplasmic structures are those termed *mitochondria*. Samples from a wide variety of both plant and animal cells indicate that all have a common basic composition although occurring in a variety of sizes and forms. Each is bounded by a double membrane with the inner folded to form shelf-like or tubular processes or *cristae* penetrating into the central fluid matrix. They vary in shape from small spherical masses to elongated filamentous strands, and in size from about 1μm to 15μm long. They have been seen to fuse together and to divide transversely into two or more parts, each part then developing into a new mitochondrion. They are, therefore, living, self-replicating structures. Biochemists have discovered that the mitochondria are the sites at which the respiratory energy transformations of the cell are carried out, that is, the enzymically controlled chemical changes which transfer the energy of respiratory substrates such as glucose, to the energy-rich bonds of ATP (*see* Vol. II, Chap. 11). All living cells so far investigated show the presence of mitochondria but they occur in much greater numbers in cells taken from rapidly metabolizing tissues.

The *Golgi apparatus*, which was once believed to be peculiar to animal cells, is now known to be present in all cells, though its actual size varies widely. It consists of membranous vesicular structures arranged in series to appear like a coiled tubule. Each separate vesicular structure has a central vacuole bounded by a pile of five or six flattened ring like plates called *cisternae*; these are separated from each other by minute microtubules which appear to open into the central vacuole. The outer portions of the cisternae lead to a complex meshwork of tubules, and peripherally these tubules periodically bud off small membranous vesicles called *primary lysosomes* (*see* Vol. II, Chap. 2). The membranes throughout the whole structure are about 7 nm thick, and in the pile of cisternae, they are roughly 14 nm apart. The whole apparatus has two major functions as far as is known at present; the budded lysosomes are containers in which enzymes are packaged, especially proteolytic enzymes which are eventually secreted by the cell (*see* Vol. II, Chap. 14). These enzymes are synthesized on the ribosomes of the endoplasmic reticulum and merely packaged by the Golgi apparatus. Also associated with the Golgi are enzymes concerned with linking of sugars with proteins to form glycoproteins (*see* Vol. II, Chap. 4). It is thought that the apparatus plays a part in the formation of the extra lengths of plasma membrane which are necessary after cell division.

An inclusion almost universal in animal cells, but found only in the cells of some lower plants, e.g. algae and fungi, is the *centrosome*, or the *central body* or *cytocentre*. The light microscope reveals a minute granule, obviously most active at the time of cell division when it divides into two parts, each becoming the centre of an "aster" (*see* p. 22). Electron microscope studies show that it is composed of two parts at right angles to one another. Each is called a *centriole;* it consists of a cylinder of 9 outer and 2 central microtubules, 400 nm long and 150 nm diameter; between them is a ring of 9 very fine microtubules. Undoubtedly the centrosome is actively concerned with spindle formation during cell division. In the motile green algae, a similar structure has an intranuclear origin and is associated with the flagella in young cells.

Lysosomes, present in animal cells, have not been demonstrated in plants. They package secreted enzymes and isolate cytolytic enzymes which break down material brought in by vacuoles. The post-lysosomes may remain inert in the cell, or may extrude the contents to the exterior. *Basal bodies* (basal granules, blepharoplasts, kinetosomes), present at the bases of cilia and flagella, have a structure like that of centrioles. The fibres of all cilia and flagella are microtubules with the 9–9–2 arrangement.

Occurring in all types of plants except the fungi, but not in animals, are structures described as *plastids*. They are often the most easily visible of all cell inclusions since many of them contain pigment, and may be referred to as *chromoplasts*. They are sometimes very large in proportion to the size of the cell; they are denser than the surrounding cytoplasm but do not appear to be separated from it by any definite membrane. Among the commonest, are the *chloroplasts* of green plants; these contain the green pigment *chlorophvll* and are very variable in size and shape in some plant groups, particularly the green algae. In the higher plants however, they are much more uniform, being usually small biconvex discoid structures, often very numerous. In mature cells, they can increase in number by division, but appear to arise originally from minute granules (pro-plastids) in young cells. It is interesting to note that in moss plants, the material of which they are composed is passed on from one generation to the next in the female reproductive structure. Whilst in many cases the pigment is not formed in the absence of light, there appears to be nothing definite about this, since some plant embryos may form chloroplasts in darkness.

The plastid seems to be of a gel consistency and the body or *stroma* is colourless but includes numerous *grana* composed of protein and lipid, containing the chlorophyll (*see* Vol. II, Chap. 2).

There are chromoplasts which contain pigments other than chlorophyll. Xanthophyll and carotene are common plastid pigments which have a yellowish colouring effect. They are insoluble in cell sap, but others which are soluble in the cell sap are mentioned on p. 15. Any plastids which contain no pigment at all are called *leucoplasts*. They may form pigment if subjected to the right conditions; for example, chlorophyll may be formed in them in potato tuber cells exposed to light. Few plastids seem to be permanent cell structures and their origin is not easy to trace since the pro-plastids cannot be distinguished clearly from other cytoplasmic granules, particularly mitochondria.

An inclusion within the chloroplasts of the green algae and in the liverwort genus *Anthoceros*, is the structure known as a *pyrenoid*. This again is not a permanent structure since it can appear and disappear under varying conditions of nourishment and light. Sometimes they are characteristic in position and number but there are cases in which a pyrenoid can divide into two when fully formed. They are generally considered to be centres of metabolic activity. The centre of the pyrenoid is a structureless granule of protein substance and surrounding this is usually an envelope of starch plates or grains forming a more or less complete covering. Pyrenoids have been considered as centres of starch production but this is open to dispute; sometimes they appear to have no outer starchy envelope and very frequently starch formation does not only occur around pyrenoids in the chloroplast, the larger granules appearing in the stroma. Pyrenoids often disappear rapidly if starvation sets in.

Non-living Inclusions of the Cytoplasm

These are materials secreted by the cytoplasm either as reserve substances or as by-products of metabolism. *Fats* and *oils* occur in some animal cells as globules and are usually compounds of oleic, palmitic or stearic acids. They may also be found as ethereal oils in many plant cell vacuoles. *Glycogen* is a common animal carbohydrate inclusion and occurs as granules or may be in solution in the cytoplasm. It may sometimes occur in fungal cells but otherwise is rare in plants. In mucus-secreting cells of animals, a substance called *mucinogen* may appear as clear globules. These concentrate over a period and are then passed externally, i.e. secreted as mucus, often leaving the cell with a characteristic goblet shape after its discharge. *Yolk* is another cell inclusion peculiar to animals. This is held as a reserve substance by the ova of many animals and is a mixture of protein, fats, lecithin and cholestrin. Generally speaking, the solid inclusions in plant cells are more variable and the following may be numbered among them. The food product *starch* is probably the commonest and occurs as grains in storage cells of cortex, pith and phloem of many plants. *Inulin*, another carbohydrate food, is stored by some Compositae either in solution or as sphaero-crystals. Fruits of the cereals, and many seeds, include special cells where protein is stored in the form of *aleurone grains*. Each consists of an amorphous protein mass in which are embedded two kinds of bodies. One is an angular crystalloid structure composed of protein, the other globose and composed of protein combined with a double phosphate of calcium and magnesium. Crystals of various substances are commonly found in plant cells also. They appear to be by-products of metabolism and include *calcium oxalate* in bunches of needle-like crystals or *raphides*, or globose masses of needle crystals forming *druses* or *sphaeroraphides*. *Calcium carbonate* is sometimes found deposited on ingrowths of the cell wall forming the characteristic *cystoliths*. Other crystalline materials of varying shapes and sizes have been identified as one or other of silica, gypsum, or organic crystals of carotin, berberin, saponin and nitrogenous substances such as asparagine. An almost universal part of plant cells is the *cell sap*. This is a watery solution of very varied constituents including several of the following: *organic acids*, e.g. citric, malic, tartaric, oxalic, etc.; *alkaloids*; *amides, glucosides, glycogen, inulin, mucilage, pigments*, e.g. anthocyanins (red), anthoxanthins or flavones (ivory to yellow), *sugars,*

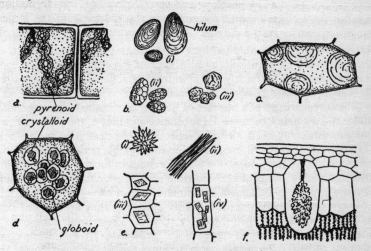

Fig. 1.9. Plant cell structures and inclusions.

(*a*) Pyrenoids of *Spirogyra* chloroplast. (*b*) Starch grains of: (i) potato tuber, (ii) rice-grain endosperm, (iii) pea cotyledon. (*c*) Inulin crystals of *Dahlia* (*d*) Aleurone grains of castor oil endosperm. (*e*) Various crystals of inorganic substances: (i) druse (ii) raphides, (iii) and (iv) rhombohedrons. (*f*) Cystolith in epidermis of *Ficus elastica* leaf.

tannins, proteins, mineral salts and *enzymes*. It is not unusual to find in the cavities of non-living cells of plants such substances as *gums, resins, tannins* and crystals of various sorts which were deposited there by the living protoplasts before these were reabsorbed by other parts of the plant.

Components of the Nucleus

Within the nuclear membrane is the clear *nuclear sap* with a variety of bodies suspended in it. The nuclear sap appears to be a homogeneous fluid or weak gel containing desoxyribose nucleic acid and protein which is chiefly histone in most cases. It may be protamine in some fish spermatozoa. Salts of calcium and magnesium are considered to be present also. It is slightly alkaline with a pH of 7·5. Within the nuclear sap are generally to be seen one or more structures of a denser nature. These are collectively termed *nucleoli* and may be considered to be of two kinds at least. The *plasmosomes* (synonymous with nucleoli) are regularly spherical in shape and are so-called because they have similar staining properties to cytoplasm. They contain largely ribose-nucleoprotein. Micro-incineration shows an iron content also. The *karyosomes* or heterochromatic granules are more irregular in shape and stain differently from plasmosomes. Seen easily with the light microscope during cell division are the *chromosomes*. At this period they appear as short, spiralized, easily stainable bodies, but in a non-dividing nucleus they have no such appearance. Only the electron microscope has been able to show their "resting" state but even then there seems to be no absolute uniformity of structure. Basically, each is composed of an extremely thin spiralized axial filament bearing paired thicker and denser regions, the *chromomeres*. The chromosome axis is probably made up of a number of fibrillar units called *chromonemata*, and is not a single structure. Its substance and that of the chromomeres has unmistakably been identified chemically as deoxyribonucleic acid (DNA). Along each chromosome is an unstainable region known as the *centromere* or *kinetochore*. On chromosomes in the dividing condition they are clearly points of chromosome spindle attachment, but nothing definite appears to be known of their structure or chemical composition.

When the chromosomes are readily apparent, they are seen to exist as two sets, the sets being exactly paired. Their total number is a constant for each species, e.g. man 46, *Drosophila* 8. The whole complement of paired chromosomes constitutes the *diploid* condition of the nucleus. It will be seen later that as a result of two types of division, a new nucleus derived from an existing nucleus may have an exact duplication of this diploid set, or alternatively a halving of the total number may occur, when the nucleus is said to be in the *haploid* condition. The significance of these two types of division will become apparent later, for it is generally regarded that the inheritable potentialities are carried on the chromosomes. The particulate structures representing these potentialities are known as *genes*. It seems clear now that the precise arrangements of parts of the DNA molecules, of which the chromosomes are composed, spell out the genetic messages which are passed from cell to cell and from generation to generation. For more detail of cell structure and physiology, *see* Vol. II, Chap. 2.

DIFFERENCES BETWEEN PLANT AND ANIMAL CELLS

From the foregoing account, it will be realized that all cells, whether plant or animal, have the same common fundamental plan. Nevertheless, in mature cells, there are generally certain obvious physical and chemical differences. Plant cells, with their more rigid and obvious walls, are readily distinguished from animal cells. Further, the chemical nature of the investing substance is much more constant in plants than animals. In plants, cellulose is almost universal, and, together with certain impregnations, it gives the wall a range of purposes. In animals, the intercellular substance may be very variable in nature and consistency, and may often be completely invisible. There is a wide range of purpose served by such a variety of substances as, for example, the intercellular substance of bone, cartilage or blood.

Another difference between the two types of cell is the presence of a large sap vacuole in plant cells which has no counterpart in animal cells. This is probably bound up with the differences in distribution of body fluids between the two classes. Certain cell components and inclusions are also characteristic of either plant or animal. Higher plant cells lack centrosomes. Only young plant cells show Golgi-bodies. Coloured plastids are peculiar to plant cells, pigmentation being diffused through the cytoplasm in animal cells. Certain food storage compounds are also characteristic of one or the other, particularly carbohydrate. Plants in general store starch, animals store glycogen. Lastly, whereas crystals of various kinds are normally found in many plant cells, only abnormally do they occur in animals.

The differences between plants and animals are not as fundamental as was once thought. Their different structures, both macroscopic and microscopic, are no more than reflections of subtle differences in their protoplasm and hence in its potentialities for performing its essential functions under various conditions.

OTHER TYPES OF PROTOPLASMIC UNITS

There are some plants and animals, and possibly parts of all plants and animals, which do not consist of cells. It is possible for units of protoplasm to exist in two other forms. The commonest of these may be called a *non-cellular* or *acellular* body and is typified by many of the protozoa and lower algae. The distinction between such non-cellular structures and single cells is hard to draw. We may imagine the primitive protoplast as a simple structure, capable of three major lines of development. First, there is the differentiation of structures within the single unit to produce a completely self-supporting organism which could divide to form more equally independent protoplasts. The second line of development could presumably have arisen as the result of the ability of the primitive cell to give rise to multicellular masses composed of many cells which eventually became differentiated for particular purposes, each type of cell becoming more and more specialized to perform one particular function and co-dependent with all the others for the performance of all the vital functions. A third evolutionary line has led to the development of protoplasmic masses of no definite size limits and without separation into the fundamental cell units. The body is thus a single large protoplast containing many nuclei. Such a structure is called a *coenocyte* or *syncytium*. In plants this is exemplified by the plasmodia of the Myxomycetes (slime fungi) which are unprotected by any external covering, and the multinucleate filaments of some algae and fungi which develop outer protective walls. In animal coenocytes, there is not unlimited growth, but there are multinucleate masses of protoplasm varying in size from minute protozoa to the long muscle fibres of the vertebrates.

GRADES OF COMPLEXITY

Of the three lines of evolution suggested above, from the point of view of numbers, it is the non-cellular structures which predominate. On the other hand, from the point of view of complexity, size and differentiation, it is the multicellular structures which show the greatest advances. It appears that with increasing bulk, cellularization becomes a necessity for two possible reasons. One is the maintenance of a suitable surface area/volume ratio which maintains all the protoplasm of the plant or animal in correct relationship with its environment by offering the correct proportion of surface area for the necessary exchanges to occur. The second is the cytoplasm/nucleus ratio which governs the sphere of influence of a nucleus within the protoplast and hence the metabolic activity of the whole structure. Thus it is that the most complex living things, capable of the greatest variety of activity, are the multicellular plants and animals which form a graded series culminating in the flowering plant and man.

We may consider the simplest kind of living thing to be that which shows differentiation within the single protoplasmic unit of *organelles*, which are specialized portions of the protoplasm designed for a particular function. Examples of this type of differentiation are found in species of *Chlamydomonas*, *Amoeba* and *Paramecium*.

With the achievement of the multicellular condition, we find whole cells specialized for particular functions. Examples are seen in the genera *Hydra*, *Obelia*, *Oedogonium*, *Ulothrix*. The next level of differentiation is in the formation of *tissues*, where large numbers of similar cells are aggregated together for the better performance of one or more functions. In *Hydra*, some parts achieve this level, as in the musculo-epithelial tissue, and in the seaweed *Fucus* a similar level of tissue development is found. When one tissue is co-ordinated with others for the performance of a major function, an *organ* results. For example, many types of cell may be working together in the excretory function of the kidney or in the light-perceiving function of the eye. Similarly, several different types of cell may compose a plant organ, e.g. a leaf, which performs one main function. Where several organs are co-ordinated so as to perform one prime function, the status of *system* is achieved. For example the kidneys, ureters, bladder and ducts constitute the system primarily responsible for nitrogenous excretion in a mammal. Similarly we may speak of the root or shoot system of a plant.

Finally, in the aggregate of organelles in the non-cellular case, or in organs and organ systems in the multicellular case, when all are co-ordinated to work harmoniously for the benefit of the whole structure, we have the living *organism*, which possesses certain characteristics not shared by any inanimate object. It is by the possession of these characteristics that we judge them to be alive.

THE SPECIAL CHARACTERISTICS OF LIVING ORGANISMS

Whatever the degree of complexity, all organisms, and indeed their individual cells, possess certain special abilities. They are *able to nourish themselves*, so obtaining the materials necessary for energy release, for growth, for manufacture of secretory substances and for provision for the offspring. Processes involved in material intake are termed *nutritional*. Cells are *able to bring about chemical reactions by which energy is released* for their own purposes; we say that they *respire*. Some of this energy *is used for making movements*. All protoplasm moves about the cell. In most animals and a few plants, the whole body moves; this we term *locomotion*. All organisms *have the power of growth*. During its development, a non-cellular organism increases the amount of its protoplasm. Multicellular organisms increase the number of cells as well as increasing the amount of protoplasm within them. All living things are *able to eliminate the waste products of their chemical activities*; we say that they *excrete*. An organism is *able to perceive and to respond to changes in its external and internal conditions*; we say that it is *irritable* or exhibits *sensitivity*. Lastly, every type of living creature is *able to increase its numbers* and so perpetuate its kind; it *reproduces*.

The above seven special abilities of living things are sometimes known for convenience as the seven functions of life and may be enumerated as nutrition, respiration, movement, growth, excretion, irritability and reproduction. In ensuing chapters we shall get a glimpse of the complexity of the living world as we encounter a few of the ways in which these processes are accomplished by a limited range of its inhabitants.

CHAPTER 2

THE FORMATION OF NEW PROTOPLASMIC UNITS: CELL DIVISION

A SURVEY of the plant and animal kingdoms indicates that all individuals, by whatever means produced, have their origin in a single protoplasmic unit. This unit inherits from its immediate progenitors, three vitally important bequests. They are, the ability to continue its existence, a sufficient store of potential energy for its use until it is able to obtain its own supplies, and the capacity for development in the same mould as its antecedents when in a suitable environment. The building of a multicellular body from a single cell is achieved by repeated self-propagation by the original cell and its descendants. The process is known as *cell division*, which implies a breaking into parts, but as will be seen, the process is complicated and involves a duplication of some of the cell substance already present before there is any division into new units. Cell duplication might be a more descriptive term, but to avoid confusion the customary name for the phenomenon will be used.

When a cell divides, there are normally three consecutive events. These are *division of the nucleus, cleavage of the cytoplasm* and *cell separation*, in that order.

Nuclear division in almost all organisms takes one of two forms according to the ultimate destiny of the new cells produced. *Mitosis* is the type of division by which all the cells of the body or *soma*, as distinct from certain reproductive parts, are produced. It is sometimes known as *somatic cell division. Meiosis* or *reduction division* occurs in the formation of the gametes in animals and some plants, or the formation of spores in others. A third form of nuclear division, referred to as *amitosis*, is said to occur in a few instances, when the nucleus apparently splits into two parts without the preliminary changes which are clearly apparent in the other processes. Mitosis ensures that all the nuclei of the somatic cells are maintained in a condition in which they contain exactly the same chromosome complement and genetic constitution as the parent nucleus which produced them. Meiosis is the special case in which a diploid cell produces four cells, each in the haploid condition.

Following nuclear division, there is usually cleavage of the cytoplasm into zones representing the sphere of influence of each nucleus. This cleavage may take place immediately, as is found in the development

20

of organisms from eggs and in the meristems of plants. There are cases when cleavage may be delayed, in which event many nuclear divisions may occur before the cytoplasm is distributed. This is found to happen in the formation of the endosperm in seeds, and in gamete formation in *Monocystis* for example. In coenocytic organisms, repeated nuclear division is very rarely accompanied by cytoplasmic cleavage and the resulting structure is a mass of cytoplasm not apportioned to the numerous nuclei. *Mucor* is an example of such construction, and striated muscle fibres have the same characteristics.

A cell, when completely divided from its parent, will usually have enclosed itself in an outer layer of its own making. Thus, as soon as cytoplasmic cleavage is complete, each new protoplast proceeds to secrete a substance peculiar to its own type. In plants, the cells are first separated by a common middle lamella, upon which each daughter cell lays a new wall of cellulose or similar material. In most animals, merely an outer plasma membrane bounds the newly-formed cells, which then proceed to secrete an intercellular jelly-like substance. It is not unusual for cytoplasmic continuity to persist by means of proto-plasmic fibrils between adjacent cells. In *Amoeba*, *Chlamydomonas* and many other small organisms, there is total separation of the cells into complete and independent individuals.

Details of these processes in plant and animal cells will now be given.

MITOTIC DIVISION OF ANIMAL CELLS

Nuclear Division

The reader should recall the cytology of the animal cell given in the first chapter. It is necessary that this should be understood in order that the changes occurring in the nucleus during its division shall be properly comprehended. There is little doubt that before the nucleus commences its greatest visible activity, the chromosomes composed principally of DNA, have already duplicated themselves and that the more easily demonstrable stages of the division about to be described, involve only the separation of the nuclear material into two identical portions. The final result is that the two daughter nuclei will have each a complement of chromosomes alike in all respects and, what is more, each new set will be an exact replica of the chromosomes of the parent nucleus. Observation has shown that there is variability in the details of the process between species, but in all known cases it follows a general pattern which is common to all animals and, it may be noted, to all plants as well. Under natural conditions, nuclear division is a continuous process and the stages into which it is sometimes separated are purely for convenience of study.

The division is said to commence when the long, attenuated chromosome threads of the nucleus during its non-dividing phase duplicate their structure and become paired threads, each pair joined at a common centromere. Until this time, the chromosomes have been too fine to be visible with the light microscope but as the process continues, they coil or spiralize to become highly condensed, comparatively short, stout threads. Gradually they become clearly demonstrable by staining techniques or by the use of the phase contrast microscope. Concurrently, each of the centrioles of the centrosome replicates and the two

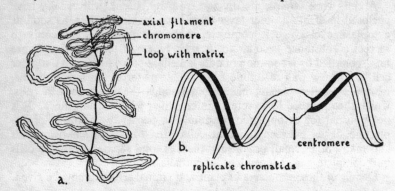

Fig. 2.1. Chromosome structure. (a) Part of "lamp brush" chromosome. (b) Diagram of spiralled, replicate chromatids.

centriole pairs begin to move away from one another towards opposite ends of an axis through the cell which is at right angles to the plane of final cell division. During this migration, fibril-like striations appear to radiate from the centrioles to give them a star-like appearance, whence they are called *asters*. When the centrioles have reached their final positions, these striations in the cytoplasm extend through the nuclear area blending with others from the centromeres of the chromosomes and joining one centriole pair with the other. This brings into existence a structure termed the *spindle*, the shape of which may be described as a pair of cones with bases together at the centre and apices at the centrioles. The slant edges of the cones are slightly bowed outwards. The apices of the spindle are referred to as its *poles* and the central region as the *spindle equator*.

During this spindle-forming activity the nuclear membrane undergoes such changes that it can no longer be demonstrated and the nucleolar substance is dispersed so that each of these loses its identity completely.

The spindle is now completed and the chromosomes have attained their maximum thickness and minimum length. They are double structures and each half is termed a *chromatid*. Up to this point, there has been little movement of the chromosomes from their positions of

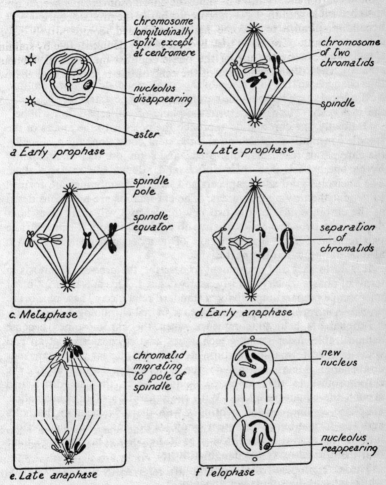

Fig. 2.2. Mitotic nuclear division in an animal cell. Diagram.

formation, but now they migrate to arrange themselves at the circumference of the equatorial plate of the spindle, attached to the spindle fibres by their centromeres, and loosely supported externally to the spindle, by the cytoplasm.

When all the chromosomes have thus arranged themselves, each separates into two independent chromatids, the separation commencing at the centromere and gradually extending away from this point in both directions. As the divergence of the chromatids continues and as the spirals disengage, the characteristic ◊ and ◖ chromosome shapes can be seen. With centromeres leading, the chromatids, formed from each chromosome, now continue to move towards opposite poles of the spindle at a steady rate. As they separate, further fibrous structures appear between them, and the spindle axis elongates. The spindle shape is thus changed, so that the region of the equatorial plate is pulled out into a cylindrical shape between the chromatids. This new structure is termed the *stem body*. Across its centre the plane of cell separation will lie.

Gradually, the chromatids approach the poles with the apices of the spindle constantly diminishing and the stem body elongating. Finally, the chromatids reach the polar areas, and soon lose their individuality by changing back into their diffuse and attenuated "resting" state. The nucleolus gradually reappears and nuclear membranes are formed to delimit the new nuclear areas. The chromatids are now considered as the chromosomes of the two new nuclei and will themselves later duplicate as two chromatids at any subsequent division. Each centriole pair remains outside the membrane of its associated nucleus and will also be duplicated at the next division.

It is customary and convenient to describe the process of mitosis in terms of phases which are fairly clearly defined. This aids description of microscope preparations, giving a standard reference. These phases are *prophase, metaphase, anaphase, telophase*, in that chronological sequence.

Prophase is held to commence when the chromosomes become demonstrable under staining techniques, and is considered at an end when spindle formation is complete and the nuclear membrane has disappeared. Metaphase includes the movement and attachment of the chromosomes to the completed spindle where they lie distributed around the equatorial plate. With the separation of the chromatids, anaphase commences and continues with the movement to the poles and the formation of the stem body. Telophase, the final period, includes the arrival of the chromatids at the polar areas and the details of the re-formation of the daughter nuclei.

The term *interphase* is sometimes used to describe the period during which nuclear division is not apparent.

Cytoplasmic Cleavage

The final effect of cleavage is to form at each new cell surface a layer of firm cortical protoplasm and a plasma membrane continuous with those of the parent cell.

It has been demonstrated that in the absence or distortion of the asters, no cytoplasmic cleavage will take place. Whilst it is certain that the asters control the process, there is no indication as to their precise function in this respect. The cleavage is brought about by the formation of new cortical material on either side of a furrow which completely encircles the old cell about its plane of division. The furrow is initiated by the transformation of the outer cortex into the sol condition and a gradual flowing inwards to cause an ever-deepening groove. As this groove deepens, cortical protoplasm flows in on each side, extending towards the cell centre. This new cortical protoplasm is derived by

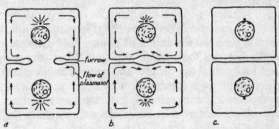

Fig. 2.3. Cleavage and cell separation in an animal cell. Diagram.

the transformation of the more fluid plasmasol in the region of the asters, and the flow is maintained until the new cell surfaces are completed.

The advancing furrow exists as a ring-like fluid-filled cavity in the cytoplasm, of ever-decreasing diameter, as it approaches the centre of the old cytoplasmic mass. The cavity is due to the adjacent faces of the furrow remaining apart for a short time whilst each new cell face forms its plasma membrane. Finally, there is merely a disc-like cavity in the centre, which disappears as the last portions of the plasma membranes are formed.

Cell Separation

The final separation into two cells is effected by the production of intercellular substance by both cells. In young cells, this substance is the jelly-like hyaluronic acid, secreted in response to the activity of an enzyme, hyaluronidase. Later, other substances may permeate this layer.

MITOTIC DIVISION OF PLANT CELLS

Nuclear Division

It cannot be too strongly emphasized that in all the main essentials nuclear division in plants follows the same pattern of events as in animals. No full description will be needed here; only one difference need be pointed out. This lies in the apparent absence of a centrosome in the higher plant cell. Consequently, the appearance of a spindle during prophase cannot be associated visibly with its activities as in animals. The suggestion is that the centromeres of the chromosomes may control spindle formation in this case. Since no centrioles are evident, there is no aster formation to be seen. In all other respects, particularly in the formation and behaviour of the chromosomes, the processes are exactly equivalent. If the centrosome and asters are omitted from the drawings for the preceding section, they will serve also to illustrate mitosis in plant cells.

Cytoplasmic Cleavage

Cleavage begins with the formation of minute fluid droplets around the central spindle fibres in the equatorial plane. Soon after telophase, the spindle loses its original appearance in this area as the fibres lose their identity. The result is a construction of fibres gradually losing their nature at the centre and reforming further and further outwards towards the cell perimeter. The barrel-shaped spindle in this condition

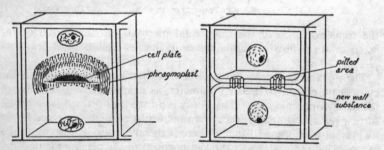

Fig. 2.4. Cleavage and cell separation in a plant cell. Diagram.

is known as the *phragmoplast*. Droplet formation follows behind the expanding phragmoplast, in a centrifugal manner across the plane of cell separation, which was the equatorial plane of the spindle. This contrasts with the centripetal development of the furrow in animal cells. Coalescence of these droplets gives a continuous fluid layer across the plane of division and it is known as the *cell plate*. On the cytoplasmic surfaces bordering the cell plate, plasma membranes are formed, but complete separation is not achieved, since continuity is often preserved between the two protoplasts by plasmodesmata. The precise nature of the cell plate is not fully known but it is thought to be the fore-runner of a special inter-cellular region. This is the

middle lamella, which cements cell walls together, and through it pass
the plasmodesmata. By development outwards from the centre, the
middle lamella proceeds to merge into the corresponding structure
between the original parent cell and its neighbours (*see* Fig. 2.5).

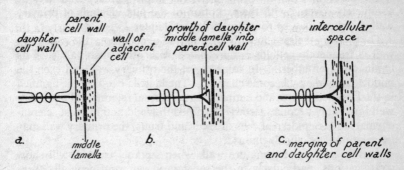

Fig. 2.5. Diagram to show development of the middle lamella during separation
of plant cells.

Cell Separation

Cell separation is completed by the laying down on the middle lamella
of a primary cell wall. This is deposited as long fine fibres of cellulose.
Deposition of the primary wall is uneven, and the unevenness sets off
thin areas known as *primary pit-fields*; at this stage, abundant protoplasmic connexions between the protoplasts separated by the new walls,
are evident in these regions. The mesh-like wall is probably freely
penetrated by cytoplasmic projections but they have not been clearly
demonstrated. In this state, the young wall is plastic and very adaptable
to changing volume and shape, allowing for growth of the young
protoplast. With the attainment of full size and form in the cell, the
primary wall becomes mature and may thicken further. In the areas of
the primary pit-fields, thin portions persist as pits. It is interesting to
note that such a thin area produced by one protoplast is exactly apposed
to a similar thin area in the wall developed by the other protoplast of
the new pair. Such pits may persist throughout the whole life of the
cell, and often exhibit characteristic shapes.

In many cell types, further thickening of the wall takes place after the
cell has reached full size; the wall then formed is the secondary wall.
Whereas the primary wall is plastic and easily moulded, the secondary
wall is incapable of increase in area, and any modifications which may
arise in the cell owing to its presence are irreversible. The primary wall
ensheathes the protoplast except where the plasmodesmata occur; the

secondary wall is formed over the primary wall except in the neighbour-
hood of pits. The secondary wall is usually much thicker than the
primary and may vary considerably in surface coverage, e.g. in protoxylem cells it may be no more than a series of annuli or a single
spiral band, whereas in fibrous cells, the whole primary wall may be
completely covered with the exception of the pits. Details of primary
wall structure may be found in Vol. II, Chapter 2.

The primary wall is generally constructed of cellulose; the secondary
wall is frequently cellulose impregnated with other materials such as
lignin, cutin or suberin. In some cases, the primary wall and even the
middle lamella may become changed. The lamella can become lignified
in thick-walled tissues and cutinized in epidermal regions. The primary
wall invariably becomes strongly lignified in wood and in most sclerenchyma. In the epidermal cells of seeds and fruits, the primary wall may
be gelatinous or mucilaginous.

A cross-section of a mature wall, when suitably treated, will show
stratifications, particularly in the secondary wall, and generally three
layers can be made out in each secondary wall. Thus, making up the
wall between two protoplasts, or between the lumina of empty cells,
there are nine major layers; six secondary layers, two primary walls
and the middle lamella (see Fig. 2.6 (a)).

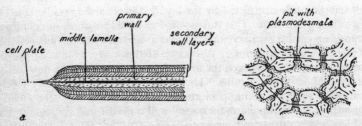

Fig. 2.6. Plant cell wall. (a) Diagram representing deposition of primary and
secondary layers. (b) Pits and plasmodesmata in stained preparation of date
endosperm. H.P. drawing.

When examining tissues, it is easy to overlook the existence of the
middle lamella. While nine layers will only be visible in very special
cases, the student should practically always be able to see the three
main layers, the middle lamella and the composite walls on each side
of it. It is important that drawings should show these characteristics
where they are visible.

Duration of Mitosis

The time taken for a complete mitosis varies considerably in different
species, in different regions of the same species, at different points in the

life cycle, and under different conditions. Under the best conditions the process has been timed from twenty minutes in *Acanthamoeba* to six hours in erythroblasts of the newt. In the stigmas of the grass *Arrhenatherum*, the process takes about one hundred minutes at 19°C. Where conditions are abnormal, mitosis is seriously hampered. Absence of oxygen acts as a complete inhibitor, whilst several chemical inhibitors may be used to prevent it, or to prolong stages for observation purposes. At low temperatures, the process is very slow or may not occur at all.

MEIOTIC DIVISION OF CELLS

Before attempting to learn the details of meiotic division, the student must recall and fix firmly in his mind the following facts. Each somatic nucleus of an organism contains the same number of chromosomes. These can be arranged in homologous pairs, each pair consisting of one maternal and one paternal chromosome, i.e. originating one from the male gamete and the other from the female gamete from which the zygote was formed. The total of these chromosomes is the diploid number. Meiosis differs from mitosis in that it produces four new cells in each of which this diploid number is halved. The process is brought about by two nuclear divisions but only one duplication of the chromosomes. We refer to these two divisions as the first and second meiotic divisions.

During the first meiotic division, we may say broadly that the same phases occur in the same sequence as they do in mitosis. But in the prophase of meiosis, the behaviour of the chromosomes is significantly different from that in mitosis. For ease of description, a number of distinct stages are recognized in the meiotic prophase. We describe meiosis in animal cells, but except for the activity of the centrosome, the same description can be applied to meiotic division in plants.

Prophase 1. *Leptotene* (thin thread stage). The chromosomes become fixable as long thin threads in the nucleus. In two respects they differ from the appearance of the chromosomes in the prophase of mitosis. First, they are simple threads, not longitudinally split into chromatids. Secondly, the chromomeres are much more apparent as heavily stainable granules connected by non-staining material.

Prophase 2. *Zygotene* (pairing stage). The maternal and paternal chromosomes come together in their homologous pairs and lie closely approximated to each other, centromere to centromere and chromomere to chromomere along their whole length. Such a pairing never occurs in mitosis. The chromosomes begin to shorten and thicken very noticeably, are spiralized, and easily stainable. Such a double structure of two whole chromosomes is referred to as a *bivalent*, to distinguish it from the double chromatid structure seen in the prophase of mitosis. At the end of zygotene, the pairs of homologous chromosomes are tightly spiralled on one another.

Prophase 3. *Pachytene* (thickening stage). After formation of the bivalents, each chromosome continues to shorten and thicken and each of the individuals of the bivalent is now seen as a duplicate structure, becoming longitudinally split into two chromatids except at the centromeres. Thus each chromosome is now a double structure spiralled on the other, like four strands twisted in pairs. Now, the chromosomes being split longitudinally, have reached the stage at which they first appear in mitosis. For this reason, many authorities regard meiosis as

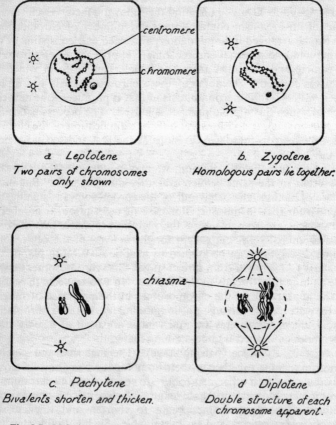

a. Leptotene
Two pairs of chromosomes only shown

b. Zygotene
Homologous pairs lie together.

c. Pachytene
Bivalents shorten and thicken.

d Diplotene
Double structure of each chromosome apparent.

Fig. 2.7. Meiotic nuclear division in an animal cell. Leptotene, zygotene, pachytene and diplotene stages of prophase. Diagram.

being a nuclear division brought into activity by some unknown stimulus before they have duplicated their structure as chromatids.

Prophase 4. *Diplotene* (duplication stage). When the partners of a bivalent have each split longitudinally as described above, they are said to have reached the diplotene stage. Following this is the tendency of the split chromatids of each bivalent to draw apart from one another. This is not usually effected rapidly or easily since the four twisted strands appear to hold together at one or more points in addition to the centromeres. Up to twelve of these junctions have been recorded in some species. These points are termed *chiasmata*, where two of the four chromatids form a cross. These chiasmata mark places along the spirals where stresses have caused the chromatids to break, and in easing the stress, to become unwound. When joining up once more, the broken end of a chromatid is united with the corresponding broken end of a chromatid from the other homologous chromosome. Its own broken piece will in turn unite with the remaining odd piece of the other chromatid. In effect, an exchange of chromatid material has occurred between the pairs of homologous chromosomes. This is known as *crossing over*. It is referred to again in Vol. II, Chap. 18, when its full significance will be better understood. It should be appreciated from what has been said here, that when crossing over occurs, despiralization of the two pairs of chromatids will inevitably lead to a chiasma which must be passed along each chromosome until its end is reached. This movement is known as *terminalization* and it may be accompanied by a rotation of the arms of the cross through an angle of up to 180°. The chiasmata never pass over the centromere. Depending on the position of the centromere in the chromosome, and the positions and numbers of chiasmata, complicated but often characteristic crosses and chain-like formations of separating bivalents may be visible.

Prophase 5. *Diakinesis* (moving apart stage). This stage is characterized by the final separation and moving apart of the homologous chromosomes, i.e. partners of a bivalent, which once more appear to return to their unsplit condition by further shortening and thickening.

In cells where a centrosome is present, it will, by this time, have divided. The two resulting asters will have taken up their positions at opposite ends of the cell, prior to spindle formation. The nuclear membrane can no longer be demonstrated. Shortly after diakinesis, the spindle appears and prophase is completed.

Metaphase. Each member of a pair of homologous chromosomes comes to lie at an equal distance from the equatorial plane of the spindle as its partner but on the opposite side. Each is attached, as in mitosis, by its centromere.

Anaphase. The centromeres move towards opposite poles of the spindle, each dragging its two chromatids with it and completing terminalization if not already accomplished. It is well to remember here that these centromeres do not divide at this stage in meiosis as they would have done in mitosis. They are still the centromeres of whole chromosomes.

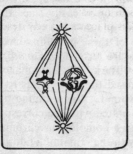

a Diakinesis
Partners of each bivalent
separate. Chromatid material
exchanged at cross-overs

b. Metaphase

c. Anaphase of
first division

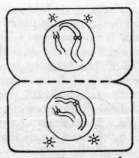

d. Prophase of
second division.

Fig. 2.8. Meiotic nuclear division in an animal cell. Diakinesis, metaphase and anaphase of the first division and prophase of the second division. Diagram.

Telophase. When the chromosomes have reached their appropriate poles, a telophase may or may not be completed according to conditions and species. Sometimes two new nuclei may be formed which both enter into a short interphase. Alternatively both nuclei may enter the second meiotic division immediately. In the latter case, a second prophase may be completely eliminated with the exception of the formation of two new spindles. These lie with their axes at right angles to the first spindle axis, which will have disappeared as cytoplasmic cleavage between the two new cells is completed.

Metaphase: second division. In each new cell, the chromosomes, each now present as two chromatids, group themselves around the equator of the spindle.

Anaphase: second division. The centromeres divide and the chromatids move away from each other as in mitosis.

Telophase: second division. This takes place as already described for mitosis.

Thus, from the original single nucleus, there will be derived four groups of nuclear material each consisting of the haploid number of

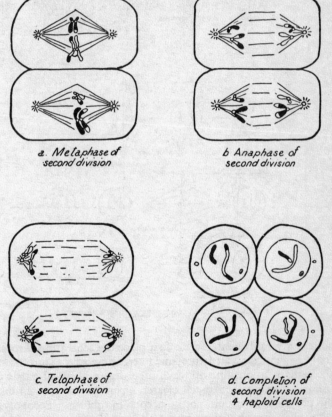

Fig. 2.9. Meiotic nuclear division in an animal cell. Metaphase anaphase, telophase and completion of second division. Diagram.

chromosomes. In addition, interchange of material may have taken place, so that each nucleus may be different from the others in its exact make-up. The spindles disappear; cleavage of the cytoplasm and cell separation result in the formation of four new cells.

It is common to regard the second meiotic division as a mitosis following a meiosis. A little consideration will show that the two cases

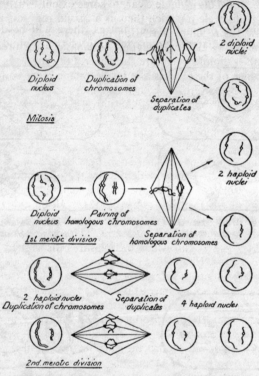

Fig. 2.10. Diagrams comparing mitosis with meiosis.

are not exactly equivalent. In the first place the separating chromatids may not be identical in structure, due to crossing over. Thus they have not the same relationship with each other as an identical pair would. This shows visually as a much clearer separation of the chromatids during prophase than ordinarily occurs in mitosis. Secondly, the dividing cells have only the haploid number of chromosomes, and so the starting points of the two processes are different.

THE SIGNIFICANCE OF MITOSIS AND MEIOSIS

The sequence of events in these types of cell division appears to follow an invariable pattern in all organisms in which they occur. Though the details may vary slightly between species, the general story is always the same. The ubiquity of the processes and their similarity in all species surely indicate that they are events of some considerable importance and significance. This is made clear, to some extent, when it is realized that in every life cycle in which there is a sexual reproductive process, there is always a regular alternation of meiosis and fertilization, i.e. diploid structure → meiosis (halving) → haploid structure → fertilization (fusion) → diploid structure, as generation succeeds generation. The significance of the processes is further made more comprehensible when it is remembered that the chromosomes are the vehicles by which the factors (genes) representing inheritable characters are transferred from parent to offspring.

Every somatic cell in the body of any organism originates as a mitotic descendant of a single cell which may be a diploid zygote or a haploid spore according to the organism. Thus every body cell of an individual receives chromosome material identical with all the others, together with some cytoplasm. By this means each cell receives potentialities for development and function compatible with all the other cells which eventually make up the mature structure. The fact that cells of different regions of the body may differentiate in different ways may be bound up with the precise way in which cytoplasm is distributed at each cell division (see Vol. II, Chap. 19).

There are two points of significance in meiosis which can be coupled with the fact that it occurs only at divisions *preceding* the development of haploid reproductive cells. Sometimes the meiosis occurs immediately before the gametes are produced, as in nearly all animals (some of the sporing protozoa are the only exceptions); sometimes the meiosis may occur well before the gametes are formed, as in many plants. In this latter case, the gametes are finally produced by a specialized haploid generation of the plant concerned, by mitotic divisions, but in all cases, plant and animal, a reduction division will have occurred in the life cycle *before* the sex cells are formed, so that they are *always haploid*. Since each sexually-produced individual is the result of fusion of two haploid gametes, the meioses which preceded their formation ensure that the chromosome complement of an individual is the same as that of its parents. If there were no meiosis in the life cycle, each succeeding generation produced by sexual means would possess double the chromosome number of its parents. The meiotic division before gamete production thus ensures that the chromosome number of a species is maintained in constancy throughout successive generations. The second feature of significance can only be appreciated fully when some knowledge of genetics has been gained. It may be stated briefly here that the random distribution of maternal and paternal chromosomes together with the reshuffling of chromosome material during crossing over, both of which may occur in meiosis, lead to the production of variance between individuals of a species. Variation is important, since it provides the raw material for natural selection to operate upon. These matters are more fully discussed in Vol. II, in the chapters on genetics and evolution and cannot profitably be pursued further here.

RETENTION AND SUPPRESSION OF THE POWER OF CELLS TO DIVIDE

The capacity for division is not always retained permanently by all cells. There are cells which perform no other function than to produce more cells. Examples are found in the germinal epithelium of the ovary and testis, in the stratum germinativum of the skin, and in the meristems of plants. Others, though specialized for different functions may retain the power of division; in the higher animals, practically all cells can divide as harmonious growth of all the parts of the organism proceeds. When an animal grows, its liver, kidneys, lungs, eyes, etc., all grow.

Many types of cells after full development, have apparently lost the power of division, and do not normally divide again, but it is often found that various stimuli will set the division process in motion once more. Such renewal of dividing activity can be brought about by outside agencies. A common stimulus is that of injury, when many types of cells may divide to produce a complete new structure. A crayfish can develop a complete new limb in replacement of a severed one: the seaweed, *Fucus*, can develop new fronds from damaged pieces. When damaged or lost tissues are replaced by cell formation in this manner, we call the process *regeneration*. It may range from the development of a whole body from a few cells as in the sponges, in *Hydra* and in *Funaria*, to the healing of a small wound in the skin of a mammal. Insects frequently stimulate plants into rapid gall formation as a result of their injections. Application of chemical compounds such as β-indolyl-acetic acid to plant parts frequently results in hypertrophy. Often an internal stimulus will reactivate cells to divide. Examples are found in the abscission layer at leaf fall forming cork, and in the endogenous origin of roots from a pericycle.

Some cells in the mature state are incapable of division by reason of the fact that they no longer contain any living substance. Such are exemplified by the stratum corneum of mammalian skin and the corky

cells of the bark of a tree. Certain others, whilst they are definitely
alive, have never been known to divide once they are formed. Such are
the nerve cells of animals. Cell division may be suppressed as a result
of particular environmental conditions. Interference with metabolic
activity due to shortage of nutrients and oxygen, or presence of certain
inhibiting substances may prevent cells from dividing when they otherwise would do so.

COMMENTS CONCERNING SOME OF THE CELL DIVISION PHENOMENA

In recent years certain acceptable explanations of the visible changes occurring
in dividing cells have been put forward. Some of these are given below, but
not all cell division phenomena have yet been made intelligible.

Chromosome Structural Changes during Division

Electron microscope studies have shown that during the interphase period,
the chromosomes are extended through the nucleoplasm as extremely fine
axial filaments, interrupted at short intervals by pairs of denser swellings, the
chromomeres (*see* Fig. 2.1). These appear to be regions of the axis where it is
densely spiralized, but at each chromomere a pair of thin filaments, encased
in matrix, leave the main axis and pass out as loops, one on each side, and
then return to it at the second chromomere of the pair. Chromosomes in
this condition have been called "lamp brush" chromosomes. The chromosome axis, the chromomeres and the lateral loops consist of double helices of
deoxyribonucleic acid (DNA). The matrix enclosing the loops is composed
of ribonucleic acid (RNA) and protein.

As the nucleus approaches division, the chromosomes greatly change in
appearance, becoming easily stainable and readily visible with the light
microscope. However, unless and until each chromosome has replicated its
DNA substance, no division will occur. This replication takes place during the
interphase period and its completion appears to trigger off the other cell-
division activities. A nucleus not destined to divide again does not perform
the chromosome replication process. The DNA required to effect the replication is synthesized in the cell and when it is ready, each original DNA double
helix splits longitudinally, except at the centromere. The new DNA nucleotides then take up their positions on each of the "halves" to reconstitute two
identical axial filaments where there was previously only one. The precision
with which the replication is effected is due to the fact that the base portions
of the nucleotide molecules, i.e. adenine, thymine, cytosine and guanine can
pair in the following way only; adenine—thymine and cytosine—guanine
(*see* p. 87, Vol. II), thus ensuring that always the correct nucleotides are
selected for perfect genetic identity between the replicates.

Once this replication has taken place, each pair, still united at a common
centromere, condenses into the visible threads by which the early stage of
prophase is characterized. The condensation appears to be simply one of
shortening of the chromosomes by tight spiralization of the axes. The coiling

seems to be of the "coiled coil" form and what was once a collection of extremely long, delicate, tangled threads, are compacted into discrete short, stout bundles, well separated and capable of independent and unhindered movement.

The Origin and Nature of the Spindle

In animal cells, where centrosomes seem to occur universally, there is no doubt that spindle formation is very much bound up with the activities of these. Early during the division, apparently long before the chromosomes are replicated, each of the pair of centrioles regenerates another. These pairs subsequently separate under unexplained forces to points in the cell at which the chromosome replicates will eventually aggregate, i.e. the spindle poles. It has become clear that if the regeneration of centrioles is prevented, then the spindle apparatus cannot be formed in the normal way and the nuclear division is also blocked.

When the spindle is completely formed at metaphase, it is seen under the light microscope as a collection of "fibres" connecting pole to pole, lying in a matrix of undefined clear substance. In this state the spindle has a more or less rigid structure and by micro-manipulation may be displaced or even completely dislodged with the chromosomes attached to it. It has elastic properties and recovers its shape after deformation. Electron microscope preparations show the spindle "fibres" as very fine straight filaments connecting the centromeres of the chromosomes with the centrioles. The filaments have been described as tubular with a diameter of about 15 nm. The polarizing microscope shows that the molecular units of the spindle "fibres" are oriented parallel to the long axis of the spindle.

It seems that the centrioles initiate and control the concentration of the molecular substances of the spindle from the surrounding cytoplasm, or in some cases from the area of the nucleus, and that these then become aggregated into the visible "fibres." In plant cells, where similar centrioles have never been observed, there is as yet no indication as to what influences the spindle formation. Since, however, plant cell spindles seem to resemble those of animal cells in all other respects, it is possible that specialized cell organelles, corresponding in function to centrioles, will yet be discovered.

Direct attempts to isolate the spindle in order to examine its molecular composition have never been very successful due to its chemical instability. In the cell there appears to be some kind of stabilizing influence which is lost when the spindle is extracted. This "protection" can be simulated by the addition of substances containing sulphur to sulphur bonds and spindles so isolated have been examined in some detail. Much of the spindle substance is protein, mostly of one kind, containing thiol (—SH) groups. This is apparently manufactured prior to the nuclear division, not during the actual spindle formation. RNA also seems to be associated with the protein. RNA is normally involved with protein synthesis, but since this is not actually occurring during spindle formation it could play a part presumably only in the construction of the apparatus from the already formed protein. It may have been held previously in the nucleoli. Fatty substances also occur in the spindle, but their precise relationship to the rest of the structure is not known.

The rigidity of the completed spindle has been attributed to the formation of unstable chemical bonds between sulphur atoms on adjacent protein molecules and it has been suggested that the assembly of the spindle is really the formation of such bonds between previously formed proteins. The evidence suggesting this is the increasing concentration of sulphur-containing proteins in the regions of the centrioles during early spindle formation and their subsequent disappearance later.

Separation and Movement of Chromatids

The initial separation of the chromosome replicates, involves first the division of the common centromere which holds them together and the dissociation of the tightly spiralled halves. The movement which follows during anaphase is in straight lines converging on the poles. These may also move farther apart, but this happens most commonly only when the chromatids have completed their movements. The shapes of the chromatids during movement indicate that they are being pulled individually to the poles and then dragged as groups farther apart as the poles push away from one another. This activity undoubtedly necessitates the expenditure of energy. The isolation of an ATP-splitting enzyme from the spindle substance suggests that ATP is the energy source and this has tempted some to postulate that the apparent dragging forces applied to the chromatids by the spindle "fibres" may be similar to those which would occur if the fibres had some similarity to contractile muscle fibres. There is little doubt that the fibrillar appearance of the spindle is due to the occurrence of real fibrils and cannot be dismissed as artifact occasioned by previous treatment, thus the "muscle-contraction" theory is a very attractive one. However, it does not explain the process fully enough. The chromatid-to-pole "fibres" shorten to a much greater extent than any known muscle fibres do, and may even vanish. The pole-to-pole "fibres," on the other hand, lengthen considerably. In neither case do the "fibres" alter in diameter or lose their straightness. One explanation of this is that shortening is due to the removal of molecules from some part of the fibril and that lengthening is due to the addition of molecules somewhere along it. Clearly, the removal or addition of molecules could account for the alterations in lengths of the fibrils, but cannot be used so easily to account for the movements of the chromatids and the poles. One acceptable suggestion to account for most of the observable phenomena is that the spindle region is composed of molecules which can exist in oriented or disoriented states. In the former condition they make up the visible and well-formed fibrils with their specific dimensions, in the latter condition they constitute a formless mass. The conversion fron one state to another, energized by ATP, might result in the movements which are observed.

CHAPTER 3

INTRODUCTION TO THE STUDY OF TYPE ORGANISMS

THE student is advised to read this chapter before systematic study commences, despite the fact that much of its content can be fully appreciated only when the greater part of the study is completed. The latter part of the chapter may be referred to after the study of each type, so that conceptions concerning its more important features may be formed with greater success.

In the preceding chapters, some mention has been made of the living characteristics of protoplasm. A much fuller account of its physical and chemical properties is given in Vol. II, Chap. 2. In most cases, protoplasm exists in units called cells. It has been indicated that a single cell can exist as an individual organism, but that in most cases, an organism is composed of numerous cells, often showing considerable variation in structure and function. By his systematic study, the biologist aims to survey, as widely as possible, the great ranges of variation which occur in the structure of the bodies of organisms and the ways in which the parts function. In addition, he attempts to elucidate the finer points of relationship between an organism and its environment, and the interrelationships between organisms themselves. Such a comprehensive picture of living creatures is not possible unless a large number of types are studied in detail.

The complete description of any organism will involve some knowledge of all the major subdivisions of biology, as applied to that organism. *Natural history* includes the general description of the habitat and habits of the type. This involves knowledge of where it spends its life, the prevailing conditions there, and what it may be expected to be doing at different times of the day and seasons of the year.

A knowledge of the form and functions of an organism's mature body is essential. *Morphology* is the study of the general form of the creature and of its organs; it is particularly applied to visible form, and in some connexions, it is used of external features alone. *Anatomy* applies particularly to the manner in which the organs are arranged, and how they are related to each other. Detailed composition of tissues is studied as *histology*, and the minute details of individual cells as *cytology*. The manner in which the various cells, tissues, and organs function, is described as *physiology*. Further knowledge of the individual is gained from the study of its development from the fertilized egg. Such study is termed *embryology*. Examination of the organism in its natural surroundings is designed to elucidate the special adaptations which enable it to exist there. This study, together with its relationships in form and function to the prevailing environmental conditions, is known as *ecology*.

From these considerations, which may be said to apply to the organism as an individual, we next formulate ideas concerning its relationships with other living creatures. Comparative study of its features permits *classification* by *taxonomic* principles. *Genetics* is the study of its inherited characteristics. Its *evolution* concerns the nature of its possible ancestors, and how they may have given rise to new forms. Lastly, the scope may be extended into the field of *applied biology*, where the relationships between the organism and man are considered, so that man may exercise intelligent control in the attempt to bring about desirable effects and avoid evil ones.

In order to assist the student in assimilating all the knowledge that he should acquire, it is intended in this book to adhere to a standard and consistent presentation of the facts concerning each type organism as far as this is possible. The differing disciplines of botanists and zoologists demand that plants and animals be treated somewhat differently, but as will be appreciated with wider study, the common characteristic that they are all living things welds them together to such an extent that any such separation is a man-made convenience.

In animal studies, the following descriptive sequence will be adopted—

Habitat and habits
External features
Structure and functions of the body wall
The skeleton or other supporting structures
Organs concerned with nutrition and storage
Organs concerned with respiration
Locomotive activity
Growth of the organism
Organs concerned with excretion
Organs concerned with sensitivity and co-ordination
Organs of reproduction; dispersal, and survival under adverse conditions
Development into maturity
Adaptation to environment
Classification
Special features of biological importance

In the study of plants, corresponding treatment is not suitable, since their structure is very different from animals and the majority have much more complicated life cycles. Many plants complete the full life cycle existing in two forms alternating with one another, and they may together form a composite structure, but they often are separate individuals, each with an independent existence. It is therefore most convenient, where applicable, to treat each phase of the life cycle separately, commencing with the form which possesses the more persistent vegetative structure. The following sequence of description will therefore be adopted in most cases—

Persistent vegetative form
    Habitat
    Morphology and anatomy of vegetative parts
    Physiology, including growth and development of vegetative parts
    Morphology and anatomy of reproductive parts
    Physiology and development of reproductive parts
Development of the alternate form
Alternate form
    Morphology and anatomy of vegetative parts
    Physiology, including growth and development of vegetative parts
    Morphology and anatomy of reproductive parts
    Physiology and development of reproductive parts
Development of the persistent vegetative form
The complete life cycle
Adaptation to environment
Special features of biological importance

(Note that classification, detailed beyond that given in the next chapter, is not considered necessary.)

The student will be well advised to learn the facts according to some similar plan.

As an organism is studied, the realization must be borne in mind that each is an integral part of the vast panorama of living creatures. Its position in the picture, relative to other organisms, depends on its possession of certain broad features of biological significance. In order to help the student understand what these features are, a general guide is set out here. It is in the form of questions to which he should attempt to supply the answers as he completes his study of each type organism. Full answers will not always be forthcoming at the start, but as more and more organisms come under survey, more gaps can be filled.

1. *What is the mode of life and how are the necessities of life obtained?*

To maintain its existence, any organism must obtain its requirements of energy-yielding and body-building substances. If it is successful in this respect, we can say it is "making a living." The manner in which an organism makes its living, whether independent of other living things or dependent upon them in varying degrees, we call its *mode of life*. Thus the mode of life of an organism can be described largely in terms of how and from whence it obtains sufficient substances of nutritional value to ensure its continued well-being.

Within almost every major group of plants and animals of every habitat, there are to be encountered many different structural and functional features associated with different modes of life. It is necessary to recognize and describe such features as they are found in every type of living thing.

As a more and more detailed knowledge has accrued of the ways in which living things are morphologically and physiologically adapted to sustain their bodies from the materials at their disposal, so terms have been coined to describe them. Some terms have been used to describe broadly the various modes of living, some have been applied to distinguish types of feeding according to the source and nature of the food, others have been applied to describe specific mechanisms of food ingestion and still others to describe a particular form of diet or nutritional requirement. With the present terms in use, having regard to the fact that many were first brought into use prior to a more complete understanding of the diversity of living things (the micro-organisms in particular), it is not always possible to convey a precise distinction since some of them have been used with various shades of meaning.

The terms which are used in this text, with the meanings they are intended to convey, are explained below and the figure may assist in showing the interrelationships between one class of organisms and the others.

With reference to the immediate source of energy which an organism uses, it can be said to belong to one of two classes, the *autotrophes* or the *heterotrophes*. Unfortunately, neither of these terms seems suited to its common usage today; autotrophe means literally "self-feeder," and appears to have been applied originally to green plants; heterotrophe seems to have been applied originally to plants which absorb diverse forms of organic material as a means of nourishment. The term autotrophe, in this text, describes an organism which derives the energy initially needed for its synthesizing processes from sources other than organic compounds. As far as biologists are aware, only two such sources have been tapped by living things. These are radiant energy in the form of light, and the energy released during oxidation of inorganic compounds in reactions initiated by the organisms themselves. It is possible therefore to distinguish between the *photo-autotrophes*, which include the pigmented plants and some pigmented bacteria, and the *chemo-autotrophes*, of which there are a few bacterial representatives. Both these forms are able to synthesize organic compounds from inorganic raw materials, using, in the first instance, the energy which they

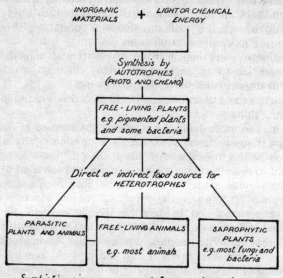

Fig. 3.1. The interrelationships between organisms with different modes of living.

trap or release for themselves. They are said to feed *holophytically*, if indeed they can be said to feed at all in the sense that animals do.

A heterotrophic organism is one which, in the absence of the ability to use the sources of energy mentioned above, must rely on the energy-fixing ability of the autotrophes and obtain its energy in the chemical form in the organic compounds on which it feeds. It can then release and utilize this energy for its own purposes. To this class belong all the animals (except a few pigmented flagellate forms), the fungi and the large majority of the bacteria.

It follows from this distinction between autotrophes and heterotrophes, that most plants and a few bacteria can lead entirely independent existences, but that most animals, the fungi, and most bacteria, must always associate themselves with their source of food materials.

The degree to which they are tied is variable and depends upon their special methods of obtaining requirements often in a particular form. We may distinguish several modes of life among these heterotrophic organisms.

The *free-living* animals are those which take organic matter in the form of the bodies of other organisms or their derivatives, either by roaming freely among their potential food source or by affixing themselves in such a position that their food comes into their grasp. Such organic matter is then, if necessary, internally digested as a preliminary to absorption. We may distinguish between methods of feeding within the free-living animals by describing those which ingest particulate matter as *holozoic* feeders, and those which absorb only separate organic compounds in solution in the environment as *saprozoic* feeders.

The *saprophytes* are plants whose food source is the dead tissue of some other organism. The saprophyte is bound to its food source in order that it may externally digest it as a preliminary to absorbing its requirements. This mode of life in plants is the counterpart of what actually occurs in most holozoic animals, the difference being that in the animal case, where locomotive activities are usually very much in evidence, the feeder is able to find and kill its food if necessary, ingest the substance, carry it away, and render it soluble and diffusible inside its own body at its later convenience. The saprophytic plant, lacking locomotive powers and a comparable digestive apparatus, must lie bathed in the products of its own digestive activities in order to absorb them.

The *parasites* are plants, animals and bacteria, which are also very closely tied to their food source, which is the substance of another living organism or the food it has managed to manufacture or catch and ingest for itself. The parasite, by strict definition, must not only obtain its food from the living body of another organism, the host, but must cause it to be at some disadvantage. This distinguishes the condition of parasitism from the conditions of symbiosis and commensalism. These last are defined below. A parasite is often so highly exacting in its food requirements that only one kind of organism can serve as its host and sometimes only particular tissues of a host can be utilized. A parasitic animal may still be said to feed holozoically or saprozoically since it may ingest and digest its food for itself or absorb already digested substances. A parasitic plant may externally digest its host tissues or alternatively establish tissue-connexions with the host through which it may draw off its requirements. Parasites which kill the host may sometimes be able to continue to make use of the dead host tissues as a food source. These are described as *facultative parasites* as distinct from the *obligate parasites* which must die when the host dies.

In addition to these more common modes of living, there are numerous instances of partnerships between pairs of organisms, in which mutual benefit is derived from the association. Such partners are termed *symbionts* and the condition of organisms existing in co-operation with one another is called *symbiosis*.

Finally, there is the condition in which one organism may derive benefit from its association with another without apparent contribution to its well-being or obvious indications of injurious effects. Such an organism is termed a *commensal* and the association is one of *commensalism*.

Besides these more or less clearly defined modes of life, there are intermediate forms. For example, the phenomenon of *partial parasitism* is not uncommon among plants. The precise nature of *mycorrhizal associations* may be something between symbiosis and controlled parasitism. The *insectivorous plants* are able to augment their food source by digesting animal tissues and absorbing the products.

In the succeeding chapters are described examples of all these forms. The free-living plants and animals illustrate the widest range of structure and function in existing organisms and it is believed that from these the other forms have been derived. The student must always attempt to relate structure and function with the mode of life.

2. *What degree of complexity has the body of the organism attained by comparison with the other members of its kingdom and what are the details of its structure?*

The study of a wide variety of types will show that all conceivable degrees of complexity exist, from free-living single cells to the intricate structure of a tree or mammal. Increasing complexity cannot be traced in its entirety, but certain levels can be clearly seen and general trends can be outlined. For every type studied, its level of organization should be determined, bearing in mind that modifications may be superimposed on the general pattern according to the organism's mode of living and its environment.

3. *What degree of complexity have the bodily functions attained and how are they accomplished?*

Various creatures perform the essential functions in various ways. With increasing differentiation of parts, there is increasing division of labour among the parts. Function, like structure, shows varying degrees in intricacy of pattern; the two are obviously closely correlated. The student must examine this correlation in each case and make some attempt to be comparative in his study of physiology.

4. *How is the organism fitted to maintain its existence in its natural environmental conditions?*

In assessment of adaptation, parallel study of the organism and its environment is necessary. From primitive self-sufficient forms in an aquatic environment, organisms have evolved which are capable of making a living in one of several ways and in almost every conceivable degree of desiccation. To enable them to cope with different conditions, modifications in structure and function must have occurred. For each type, it is necessary to note and compare the more obvious adaptive features to the way of life and the environmental conditions.

5. *What structures and methods of function has it that are analogous with those of other organisms of different kinds which exist in similar situations?*

Every major type of environment shows a considerable diversity of population. Indeed, in some environments, representatives of all the great plant and animal groups may be found. Each has the same conditions to contend with. An effort should be made to appreciate the various ways in which different forms are adapted to achieve the same ends.

6. *What variations from the generalized pattern of its group does an organism show, and how does its group compare with other groups?*

The gradual development of the whole field of biological knowledge has led to the understanding that organisms can be classified in groups, all members of a group possessing certain common characters which indicate relationship. For example, we distinguish plants from animals, and within the plants, mosses from conifers; within the animals, worms from birds. Not very long ago, *Hydra* was considered to be a plant, and the group Vermes included nematode, nemertine, platyhelminth and annelid worms. The extent of modern knowledge and understanding is such that fairly complete natural classifications of plants and animals can be made.

Within each group, are often countless variations of a similar theme. With as much knowledge as can be gained from study of representatives of each major classification unit, comparison between forms should be attempted.

7. *From what type of ancestor may the organism have evolved?*

It is generally agreed that all modern types of organism have developed from pre-existing forms: in other words, that evolution has occurred. A close study of a type organism and of its individual development, and comparison with other modern types, coupled with knowledge gained from study of the remains of past forms, enable the formulation of probable lines of evolutionary change. It is not often possible to determine evolutionary sequences with accuracy, but thoughtful consideration of the possibilities is always profitable.

8. *In what ways may the organism be controlled for the benefit of man?*

Man has learnt to control his competitors to an ever-increasing extent; to put them to his own use, and to prevent or lessen their interference with his well-being. He has based his control on a knowledge of their habits. It is unfortunate that often the control has not been intelligent nor the knowledge complete enough. However remote the impact on man may appear, it should always be considered, so that through the efforts of biologists, man may exercise his control in an increasingly intelligent way.

The types selected for study are presented in a sequence designed to assist the student in his fuller appreciation of the features of biological significance just outlined. The whole selection of types has been divided into two groups, the free-living examples and those with other modes of life. Among the free-living organisms, a distinction is first made between an autotrophe and a heterotrophe, using as examples a simple alga (*Chlamydomonas*) and a protozoon (*Amoeba*). Following this, is an account of an indeterminate type, a pigmented flagellate (*Euglena*). All these show a comparatively simple structure. Then follow two series to illustrate advancing complexity from the single cell to colonial and ultimately multicellular bodies. These are typified by examples from the algae among plants and the protozoa, sponges and coelenterates among the animals. So far, all are illustrative of purely aquatic organisms. Then follow the forms which have conquered the land to a greater or lesser extent. First are the plants, and of these are described a liverwort and a moss, which illustrate some primitive adaptations to the land habit, together with advances in complexity of body structure beyond any yet exemplified. The plant story is then continued by illustrations of the gradual development of the complicated life cycle, the outline of which is sketched in the treatment of the algae, and the increasing structural and reproductive adaptations to the land environment. The ferns and lycopods form the introduction and the tale is completed with reference to the seed-bearing plants. The animal kingdom is then returned to, and the story is taken up with reference to worms, which illustrate the more primitive adaptations to less watery conditions. Following these, come the arthropods and more primitive chordates, which are illustrative of variations along different lines of a fundamental body plan which has been successful both on the land and in the water. The free-living animal series is completed by those animals showing the highest grades of organization, namely, the terrestrial vertebrates.

Then follow the plants and animals exhibiting parasitic and saprophytic modes of life, together with examples of more unusual methods of existence. The bacteria and other micro-organisms are described last, being regarded as a distinct group of such wide diversity as to warrant separate treatment. The parasitic and saprophytic organisms are treated in such a way as to emphasize their specialized modes of living.

It is necessary to point out here that complete details of physiology will not be found necessarily with each type. Where functional details seem to be of wide application, the student is referred to Vol. II which deals with physiological processes at some length. It should also be remembered that not always is it possible to illustrate a particular group of plants or animals with types best suited to the purpose. Availability of material for practical work must be considered and examination syllabuses are always framed in relation to this important point. We have attempted to cover as much ground as syllabuses demand and as is compatible with practical possibilities.

CHAPTER 4

THE PRINCIPLES OF CLASSIFICATION: CLASSIFICATION TABLES

THE study which deals with the principles on which a classification is based is known as *taxonomy*. A biological classification has two other aspects; *systematics* fixes the groups to be used in the classification and *nomenclature* deals with the naming of individuals and groups of individuals. Since it is impossible for man to keep in mind separately all the millions of organisms which exist, he must of necessity arrange them into groups. Modern biological classification is the result of many years of study and discussion, and both botanists and zoologists have learnt to classify living creatures in a rational manner. Both branches of biology use essentially the same plan which is, in effect, a vast filing system with a pigeon-hole for every minor group.

The history of classification goes back to early man, who distinguished between one group and another by purely personal and practical criteria. For example, he would think of plants as harmful or harmless, edible or inedible, and somewhat the same standards would be used in judging animals. We still talk of weeds and flowers, of fruits and vegetables, and of herbivores and carnivores. Early attempts at written classification by such men as Aristotle and Theophrastus, followed similar lines. In the Middle Ages, in the herbals, plants were classified according to their uses for making tinctures, decoctions, cordials and ointments. It was not until the seventeenth century that John Ray advocated a system of classification based on natural affinities rather than arbitrary relationships. Linnaeus, the Swedish botanist with a genius for classifying and indexing, also recognized this better method, but later discarded it to a large extent, in favour of a more artificial system usable for identification purposes. In the middle of the nineteenth century, de Candolle made a great contribution to the progress of taxonomy, by examining and interpreting the existing methods of classification. He recognized that there are two ways of classifying organisms. By the empirical method, they can be divided into groups without any reference to their nature. Thus an alphabetical catalogue of plants is a useful method of classification for reference, but it has no connexion whatever with their characteristics. On the other hand, there are rational methods of classification which have some real connexion with the nature of the organisms classified. Of rational methods, de Candolle recognized three; a practical system, considering the properties of organisms which are of value to the human race; an artificial classification purely to make easy the identification of newly-discovered organisms, and a third based on the natural affinities between living creatures. Of these, de Candolle gave greatest weight to the natural system.

An artificial classification is based on purely arbitrary criteria. It is, as it were, imposed on the organisms from without. By contrast, a natural classification is one which exists already within the framework of living things, only waiting to be discovered. The natural system, therefore, is not only useful for identification and reference in the same way as an artificial one would be, but will also express the evolutionary relationships between one organism and another. Its "naturalness" resides in the fact that present-day living things are related to a greater or lesser extent and can be grouped accordingly because they are the ultimate ends of evolutionary paths which all stem from a common trunk. Whilst it may be considered that the purely natural system of classification is the ideal to be aimed at, modern opinion is that it is unlikely to be achieved in a complete state, since the "phylogenetic tree" is never likely to be traced in its entirety. The tendency is, therefore, to make some compromise and to produce a classification which is primarily orderly and practically convenient, and at the same time makes use of all the information on natural affinities which can be made available.

UNITS OR CATEGORIES OF CLASSIFICATION

The basic unit in this system is that which Ray attempted to define, namely, the *species*. Linnaeus, in his *Systema Naturae* of 1758, adopted this unit as the basis of biological classification and it has been used ever since.

A species has never been defined to the satisfaction of all biologists, but when applied to a group of organisms, it indicates that they have certain common characteristics. An attempt to define a species has been made as follows—

1. A species is a group of organisms which do not differ from one another more than the offspring of a single pair may do.

2. Gradations from one species to a closely related one, do not occur. There are no intermediate forms, but sharp and distinct differences between each species and any other.

3. Members of a species can interbreed freely with one another, but not usually with members of another species; if they do, the hybrid offspring are infertile.

4. Usually, the geographical locations inhabited by a particular species, are distinct from those inhabited by most nearly-related species.

It must be pointed out that there are exceptions to each of these attributes, and that for any particular case, often one or more of the four characteristics have to be modified. There is no clear definition which will suit all cases. Perhaps the commonest method of distinction is the non-interbreeding characteristic.

From the species, we may group organisms in an upward manner. A group of *species*, which are obviously closely-related form a *genus*, and genera are further grouped into a *family*. Families with close relationship are placed in the same *order* and orders into a *class*. With each higher category, relationship becomes less and less obvious. Similar classes are placed in a *phylum*, and phyla into a *kingdom*. Each higher category includes a wider range of species. Where necessary, sub-groupings are made. In botany, *tribe* may be inserted between genus and family; in both botany and zoology, we may find *sub-order* between family and order, *sub-class* between order and class, *sub-phylum* between class and phylum, and *sub-kingdom* between phylum and kingdom. The introduction of sub-categories appears to be almost a personal matter, and many taxonomists have used them according to their private opinions. In some cases, this has led to considerable confusion which has been increased by the use of *grade*, *cohort* and *branch*. It would perhaps be advisable for the student at this level to concentrate on the essential seven categories: kingdom, phylum, class, order, family, genus, species. In botanical nomenclature the category *division* has replaced phylum.

In a similar manner, we may subdivide organisms downward from the species, into *sub-species* or *varieties*. In agriculture, the practice has grown of dividing varieties into *strains*. In the fungi particularly, species are divided into *races*, and in the bacteria we have *serological types* within the species.

NOMENCLATURE

Any system of classification demands a method of naming. Any method of naming things is arbitrary, though in biology many of the names refer to some characteristic or property of the organism. The scheme which is universally adopted is the *binomial system*, devised by Linnaeus, and used in his *Systema Naturae*, which was written in Latin, since this was the international language for communication between scholars. Under the binomial system, each species has two names, *generic* and *specific*. The generic name indicates the genus to which it belongs; *this name is always written with a capital letter*, but care should be taken to see that the generic name is used correctly. When it is used as a common name or noun, it should be written with a small letter. For example: "In *Amoeba* . . ." "An amoeba . . ." The second name is the specific name, designating the species to which the organism belongs. No two species can have the same specific name. Normally its initial letter is a small one, except where it has been previously used as a generic name, or, in botany, where it is a man's surname. For sub-species, a third name may be applied.

The generic name is a Latin or latinized substantive in the nominative case. The specific name is either an adjective agreeing grammatically with the generic name, or another substantive in apposition with it, or it may be a substantive in the genitive case, e.g. *Rana temporaria* (agreement), *Amoeba proteus* (apposition), *Entamoeba coli* (genitive). Synonyms frequently occur, owing to continuous revision of names. Where it is intended to imply synonymous generic names, the one should follow the other, and be enclosed in square brackets, e.g. *Oryctolagus* [*Lepus*], and *Dryopteris* [*Nephrodium*]. Generic and specific names are normally printed in italics, except as the title of a paragraph or in a list. Where it is desired to give the author of a specific name, it should follow the name without a comma and should be printed in roman type, e.g. *Caltha palustris* L., and *Primula vulgaris* Hudson. It must be borne in mind that the author thus quoted is the one who first applied the specific name to the species in question in a printed publication, and not necessarily the one who first employed the particular combination of generic and specific names that is being used. Abbreviations for authors' names are frequently used, but are of little value unless the reader is a specialist. The initial L. is, however, in general use for Linnaeus.

Attempts have been made to establish universal name-endings for the higher categories, but except in a few instances, no real agreement has been reached. In zoology, names of families are formed by adding the termination -*idae* to the stem of the name of the type genus, e.g. Ranidae, from *Rana*, the frog. Sub-family names in zoology are formed by adding -*inae* to the stem, e.g. Fasciolinae, from *Fasciola*, the liver-fluke. In botany there is a somewhat wider range of agreement; family names usually end in -*aceae*, though a few have -*ae*, e.g. Ranunculaceae, from *Ranunculus*, the buttercup; orders end in -*ales*, e.g. Filicales, the ferns; divisions end in -*phyta*, e.g. Spermatophyta, the seed-bearing plants.

There is no uniformity in the size of categories; any group may contain from one to many hundreds, e.g. the family Adoxaceae contains one species, *Adoxa moschatellina*, while the family Compositae contains upwards of 23,000 species.

Below is a summary of the classification of one plant and one animal, using no sub-categories.

	Plant	*Animal*
Kingdom:	Plantae	Animalia
Division or phylum:	Spermatophyta	Annelida
Class:	Angiospermae	Oligochaeta
Order:	Rosales	Megadrili
Family:	Rosaceae	Lumbricidae
Genus:	*Rosa*	*Lumbricus*
Species:	*Rosa canina*	*Lumbricus terrestris*

RULES OF NOMENCLATURE

In both botany and zoology, there have been numerous international congresses for the purpose of establishing universal standard methods for naming species. For zoology, the first International Commission on Nomenclature was appointed at the Leyden Congress of 1895. It has continued intermittently ever since. For botany, the Paris Congress of 1867, instructed de Candolle to draw up a list of rules, which became known as the "Paris code." In 1912, international rules for botanical classification were published; since that date, up to the congress at Amsterdam in 1935, only minor changes were made. The International code of botanical nomenclature, drawn up in 1950, sought to clarify many of the existing problems.

The work of standardizing nomenclature has been extremely complicated. Difficult cases are constantly being discovered, and both in botany and zoology, the commissions have issued a large number of opinions on individual cases. As a example of the difficulties encountered, we quote the case of the genus *Cobra*. In 1768, Laurenti placed the African puff-adders in the genus *Cobra*, of the family Colubridae. In 1842, Gray placed them in the genus *Bitis*, of the family Viperidae. By the rule of priority then, these puff-adders should be placed in the genus *Cobra*, but since the seventeenth century, cobra has been the name in common usage for the hooded snakes. The fact that the poisons produced by puff-adders and hooded snakes are different, entails the use of different antidotes and the use of conflicting names might lead to serious errors in administration of serum. Therefore, the Zoological Commission decided that the name *Bitis* should be used for puff-adders and the name *Cobra* withdrawn. Such cases are constantly coming to light, and the confirmed names are known as "*nomina conservanda*."

The present rules for botanical and zoological nomenclature show only minor variations, and may be summarized thus—

1. Every plant and animal can have only one scientific name.

2. The binomial system of generic and specific names is to be used.

3. If several different names have been given to an organism, the earlier is the valid one; the rule does not apply to names used before the system of Linnaeus.

4. The generic name must bear a capital letter and the specific name a small letter. The exceptions in botanical specific names are disappearing, and there is a tendency to conform to small letter for species. The Copenhagen conference of 1953 recommended that there should be no *ii* endings.

5. A full specific name should include the name of the author.

6. From 1st January, 1935, a name is not legitimate, unless accompanied by a suitable published description, which, except in the case of bacteria, must be written in Latin.

7. *Nomina conservanda* are valid if authorized by the commissions, even though the rule of priority may be broken.

TAXONOMIC METHODS

The earliest efforts at natural classification were based on three lines of investigation, comparative morphology, comparative anatomy and palaeontology. These are now supplemented by comparative physiology, cytology and genetics, serology, ecology and geography.

In both animals and plants, morphology and anatomy are the most widely-used instruments of classification. By their use, major features of organisms can be assessed rapidly, and in the majority of cases, newly-discovered forms can be quickly allocated to their respective categories. In lower organisms, such as bacteria and fungi however, similar appearance may be deceptive, since there may be wide physiological differences. For example, two sorts of bacteria which look similar, may cause quite different diseases. There is need for the newer methods in these lower groups.

Evidence of phylogeny based on existing organisms can never be complete because many ancestral forms have become extinct. Palaeontology therefore has been of great value, especially where sufficient fossils have been discovered to provide a chronological record of the evolution of a particular group. There are many cases where fossil discoveries have confirmed classification based on morphology of present forms. Though the fossil record is but fragmentary, new finds will continue to fill in the present "missing links."

Cytology, by microscopic examination of cells, is a modern way of supplementing results obtained by the older methods. It is of particular use in the lower groups. Genetics, by chromosome counts and inter-breeding techniques, has helped to confirm and even to correct earlier opinions.

Physiology is nowadays of particular importance in systematics. In some of the lower groups, it is the only method of value. Comparison of substrates utilized and of enzymes produced is of very great value in classifying bacteria and fungi. Even in the higher groups, quantitative and qualitative physiological comparison has been utilized to confirm the older morphological findings. Serology is a branch of physiology, inasmuch as it is an interpretation of physiological reactions. It has been of particular use in separation of lower categories, and of indicating nearness of relationship in higher categories.

Ecological studies and geographical distribution indicate the interaction between the environment and the individual and provide supplementary evidence of phylogenetic relationships.

CLASSIFICATION TABLES

The following tables for the plant and animal kingdoms indicate major groupings only, with their principal diagnostic characters. More detailed classifications of some types described in this book will be given in the appropriate chapters.

The kingdom Animalia is divided into three sub-kingdoms, namely, Protozoa, Parazoa and Metazoa. The first two of these include one phylum each, the Protozoa and the Porifera respectively. In the last are included all the remaining animal phyla. These are Coelenterata, Platyhelminthes, Nematoda, Rotifera, Polyzoa, Brachiopoda, Annelida, Arthropoda, Mollusca, Echinodermata and Chordata.

PHYLUM: **Protozoa.** Usually small units of protoplasm not divided into cells. Organization on the protoplasmic level not the cellular level. There may be considerable differentiation into organelles, not organs.

CLASS RHIZOPODA [Sarcodina]. Movement and food-capture by pseudopodia in the adult phase. Comparatively little differentiation, e.g. *Amoeba, Polystomella, Sphaerozoum.*

CLASS MASTIGOPHORA [Flagellata]. Movement by flagella in the adult phase. Usually a pellicle present. Reproduction usually by binary fission, e.g. *Euglena, Noctiluca, Trypanosoma, Trichonvmpha.*

CLASS CILIOPHORA. Movement by cilia arranged in definite tracts. Meganucleus and micronucleus usually present. High degree of differentiation. Asexual reproduction by binary fission; sexual reproduction by conjugation, e.g. *Paramecium, Vorticella, Stentor.*

CLASS SPOROZOA. All parasitic. Amoeboid or having no external organs of locomotion in the adult phase. Production of large numbers of spores after syngamy, e.g. *Monocystis, Plasmodium.*

PHYLUM: **Porifera.** Multicellular; sessile; aquatic. Single body cavity, the gastric cavity. Two layers of cells, an outer pinacoderm, an inner choanoderm. Choanoderm consists mainly of collared flagellate cells.

Water enters the gastric cavity through numerous pores, and passes out through a single osculum. Usually a skeleton of calcareous or siliceous spicules, or of horny fibres of spongin. No nervous system. Asexual reproduction by budding. Unique embryonic development.

CLASS CALCAREA. Skeleton of spicules made of calcium carbonate, e.g. *Sycon, Grantia.*

CLASS HEXACTINELLIDA. A siliceous skeleton made of six-rayed spicules. Deep sea. For example, *Hyalonema* (the glass-rope sponge) and *Euplectella* (Venus' flower basket).

CLASS DEMOSPONGIA. Skeleton siliceous, or silica and spongin, or spongin alone, e.g. *Euspongia* (the bath sponge), *Halichondria* (the crumb-of-bread sponge), *Spongilla* (a freshwater genus).

PHYLUM: **Coelenterata.** Radially symmetrical metazoa. Diploblastic. A single body cavity, the enteron. A single opening, the mouth. A structureless jelly separates ectoderm and endoderm; often cells migrate into this. Nervous system is a network. Asexual reproduction by budding. Sexual reproduction produces a characteristic planula larva.

CLASS HYDROZOA. Usually alternation of two phases, hydroid and medusoid. Often large zoophyte colonies which give rise to the medusa. This is the sexual phase; the zygotes produce new hydroid colonies, e.g. *Hydra, Tubularia, Obelia, Physalia* (Portuguese man-of-war).

CLASS SCYPHOZOA. The jelly-fishes. Adult stage medusoid. Where a hydroid form is present, it buds off medusae. Enteron divided into pouches; extensive network of radial canals, e.g. *Aurelia, Cyanea arctica* (the largest jelly-fish, diameter 1·5 to 2·0 m).

CLASS ANTHOZOA. Hydroid form only, solitary or colonial. Enteron divided by vertical partitions. A stomodaeum (gullet) is present. Gonads endodermal, e.g. *Actinia* (a sea anemone), *Alcyonium digitatum* (dead men's fingers), *Tubipora* (organ-pipe coral), *Pennatula* (sea-pen), *Gorgonia* (sea-fan).

CLASS CTENOPHORA. Variously grouped as an order, class, sub-phylum, and in the opinion of some authorities, they should form a separate phylum. Sea gooseberries. Solitary, transparent, globular animals. Locomotion by cilia. Only one genus has a planula larva, e.g. *Hormiphora, Cestus veneris* (Venus' girdle).

PHYLUM: **Platyhelminthes.** Bilaterally symmetrical, triploblastic Metazoa. Single opening to the alimentary canal, the mouth. Excretory system of branched tubules ending in flame cells. Reproductive organs are complicated; usually hermaphrodite. The flat-worms.

CLASS TURBELLARIA. Free-living, ciliated, aquatic mainly. Ectoderm ciliated, e.g. *Planaria, Convoluta.*

CLASS TREMATODA. The flukes. All are parasitic. Thin, leaf-like body. Thick cuticle. Suckers present. No cilia. For example, *Polystomum* (in bladder of frog), *Fasciola hepatica* (in liver of sheep), *Schistosoma* (in abdominal veins of man).

CLASS CESTODA. The tapeworms. All are parasitic. No alimentary canal. Thick cuticle. No cilia. Fixation by hooks. suckers or both. Enormous powers of reproduction. For example, *Taenia solium* (the pork tapeworm of man), *Dipylidium caninum* (the dog tapeworm).

PHYLUM: **Nematoda.** Bilaterally symmetrical, triploblastic Metazoa. Free-living or parasitic. Elongated body pointed at both ends. Alimentary canal has mouth and anus. Thick elastic protein cuticle; no cilia. Excretory system of two intracellular tubes. Sexes separate. Many are serious parasites of animals and plants. For example, *Ancylostoma* (the hookworm), *Ascaris lumbricoides* (the pig nematode), *Oxyuris vermicularis* (the thread-worm common in children), *Tylenchus tritici* (the wheat eelworm), *Heterodera* (root eelworms).

PHYLUM: **Rotifera.** The wheel animals. Minute, aquatic, triploblastic animals. A ciliated anterior disc for locomotion and food collection. Complicated alimentary canal with mouth and anus. Excretory system of canals ending in flame cells. Nervous system very simple. Sexes separate: two types of females—female-producers (parthenogenetic), and male-producers. For example, *Hydatina* (in puddles and ponds), *Callidina* (in roof-gutters).

PHYLUM: **Polyzoa.** The sea mats. Triploblastic, coelomate, unsegmented. Most are colonial and marine. Few are freshwater. A ring of ciliated tentacles around the mouth. U-shaped alimentary canal. Nervous system of a single ganglion with many nerves. Excretory canals ending in flame cells. Hermaphrodite. For example, *Flustra* (one of the sea mats), *Plumatella* (freshwater). The two classes, Endoprocta and Ectoprocta are very dissimilar and may justify two separate phyla.

PHYLUM: **Brachiopoda.** The lamp shells. Triploblastic, coelomate, unsegmented. Marine only. Enclosed in a bivalve shell always attached to the substratum. Ciliated organ around the mouth for feeding. Two coelomoducts function as excretory and genital outlets. Sexes usually separate. Simple blood system. Nervous system of two ganglia joined by connectives, forming a ring round anterior end of gut. For example, *Lingula* (intertidal zones of tropical seas), *Terebratula* (deep water off British coast).

PHYLUM: **Annelida.** The segmented worms. Metamerically segmented, triploblastic, bilaterally symmetrical, coelomate. The perivisceral coelom is well developed. Body wall consists of a thin chitinous cuticle, a glandular epidermis, circular and longitudinal muscle. Central nervous system has paired cerebral ganglia from which paired commissures around the gut lead to a double ventral nerve cord, expanded to form a ganglion in every segment. Segmentally arranged chaetae are typical. Nephridia are the typical excretory organs.

CLASS POLYCHAETA. Marine bristle worms. Chaetae are numerous and borne on segmental outgrowths called parapodia. Often well-marked cephalization. Sexes usually separate; external fertilization. The larva is a trochosphere. For example, *Nereis* (the rag-worm), *Arenicola* (the lugworm), *Chaetopterus* (a tube-living worm).

CLASS OLIGOCHAETA. The earthworms and a few freshwater forms. No parapodia and relatively few chaetae. Reduced cephalization. Hermaphrodite, with few gonads in definite anterior segments. Genital products passed out of coelomoducts. Cross-fertilization during a process of copulation. Eggs laid in a cocoon; no larval stage in development. For example, *Lumbricus* (common earthworms), *Megascolides* (the giant Australian earthworm), *Tubifex* (freshwater blood-worm).

CLASS HIRUDINEA. The leeches. No parapodia, and usually no chaetae. Shortened body and small number of segments each showing many annuli. All are ectoparasites with anterior and posterior suckers. Coelom reduced to two longitudinal canals, the rest filled with mesenchyme. Hermaphrodite; eggs laid in cocoons; no larval stage. For example, *Hirudo* (the medicinal leech), *Haemopis* (the common horse-leech).

CLASS ARCHIANNELIDA. Small marine worms. Simplified structure; usually no parapodia or chaetae. Seem to be derived by reduction from Polychaeta. For example, *Polygordius*, *Histriobdella* (parasitic on lobster eggs). The Echiuroidea and Sipunculoidea are sometimes treated as classes of the Annelida, and sometimes as distinct phyla. They show little segmentation, but a well-developed coelom. Echiuroids have one pair of chaetae, and sipunculoids have none. Both have a trochosphere larva. For example, *Bonellia viridis*, with pronounced sexual dimorphism, the small ciliated male living within the female body; *Sipunculus*.

PHYLUM: **Arthropoda.** Metamerically segmented, triploblastic, bilaterally symmetrical, coelomate. Chitinous cuticle thickened or impregnated to form a strong exoskeleton. Thin chitinous articular membranes between the segments. Segmental jointed limbs, at least one pair functioning as jaws. Coelom reduced to small cavities in the gonads and in the excretory organs. The perivisceral cavity is a haemocoel. No nephridia. No cilia except in one genus (*Peripatus*). Pronounced cephalization. Central nervous system of paired cerebral ganglia, commissures around the gut, and typically, paired segmental ganglia joined by commissures. A contractile dorsal heart lying in a pericardial, haemocoelic cavity.

CLASS ONYCHOPHORA. Sometimes treated as a separate phylum. Terrestrial; breathing by tracheae. Thin, soft cuticle. Head of three segments, not distinctly marked and only one pair of jaws; remaining segments all alike, each with one pair of appendages. Cilia in the excretory tubules and in parts of the genital tract, e.g. *Peripatus*.

CLASS TRILOBITA. Sometimes treated as a sub-phylum. Oval, flattened arthropods with five pairs of head appendages. All were marine, becoming extinct after the Silurian period. Fossils are plentiful. For example, *Triarthrus*.

CLASS CRUSTACEA. Mainly aquatic; breathing by gills. Exoskeleton often considerably thickened. Two pairs of antennae. Three pairs of head appendages, and often some thoracic appendages serve as jaws.

Very diverse specialization of the limbs. For example, *Daphnia* (the water-flea), *Argulus* (the fish-louse), *Balanus* (a barnacle), *Astacus* (a crayfish), *Cancer* (a crab).

CLASS MYRIAPODA. Terrestrial, breathing by tracheae. Numerous similar limb-bearing segments. Clearly-marked head with one pair of jaws. For example, *Lithobius* (a centipede), *Iulus* (a millipede; two pairs of appendages in each apparent segment).

CLASS INSECTA. Mainly terrestrial, breathing by tracheae. Three distinct regions in the body; head, thorax and abdomen. Head of six segments, with one pair of antennae. Three thoracic segments, each with a pair of walking limbs. Eleven abdominal segments with no walking limbs. A larval stage with a metamorphosis is characteristic of most orders. There are some two dozen major orders of insects. The Orthoptera (cockroaches), Hemiptera (aphides), Lepidoptera (butterflies and moths), Coleoptera (beetles), Hymenoptera (bees and wasps), Diptera (flies), will be treated more fully elsewhere.

CLASS ARACHNIDA. Body divided into two regions, the prosoma and opisthosoma. In the prosoma, the first segment bears prehensile chelicerae, the second, sensory or prehensile pedipalps, and the remaining four segments each bear a pair of walking limbs. The opisthosoma consists of thirteen segments. Respiration is by tracheae, lung-books or gill-books. For example, *Scorpio* (a scorpion), *Limulus* (a king-crab), *Epeira* (a common web-spinning spider), *Boophilus* (a cow-tick).

PHYLUM: **Mollusca**. Unsegmented, triploblastic, usually bilaterally symmetrical, coelomate animals. The body consists of a head, a muscular foot and a visceral hump. The skin is soft and not cuticularized; skin covering the visceral hump is extended into folds forming the mantle; the mantle secretes the shell. There is a heart and an open haemocoelic blood system. Coelom consists of pericardial cavity, renal cavities and gonadial cavities, often also a perivisceral coelom. Nervous system of ganglia joined by commissures. The larva is often a trochosphere.

CLASS AMPHINEURA. The chitons or coat-of-mail shells. Bilaterally symmetrical. Entirely marine. Body elongated, with anterior mouth and posterior anus. A shell of eight calcareous plates, or calcareous spicules only. For example, *Chiton* and *Craspedochilus* (both living in the intertidal zone).

CLASS GASTROPODA. Terrestrial, marine and freshwater. The visceral hump undergoes torsion so that the anus is anterior. Not bilaterally symmetrical. A distinct head with eyes and tentacles. For example, *Patella* (limpet), *Buccinum* (whelk), *Helix* (land snail), *Planorbis* (freshwater snail), *Limax* (slug), *Littorina* (winkle).

CLASS SCAPHOPODA. Elephant's-tusk shells. Long worm-like body enclosed in a tubular shell open at both ends. Small foot used for burrowing in sand. Poorly-developed head with a number of thread-like tentacles, e.g. *Dentalium*.

CLASS LAMELLIBRANCHIATA. Bilaterally symmetrical; the body compressed laterally and completely enclosed by the mantle which secretes the bivalved shell. Greatly extended plate-like gills. For example, *Mytilus* (the mussel), *Ostrea* (the oyster), *Anodonta* (the freshwater mussel), *Pecten* (the scallop), *Teredo* (the ship-worm).

CLASS CEPHALOPODA. Bilaterally symmetrical. Head highly developed, with complex eyes. An exhalant siphon formed from part of the foot; tentacles possibly formed from the foot. The shell is either well developed, reduced or absent. For example, *Loligo* (the squid), *Sepia* (the cuttle-fish), *Octopus* and *Nautilus* (the pearly Nautilus).

PHYLUM: **Echinodermata.** Triploblastic, coelomate animals. Larva segmented, adult unsegmented; larva shows bilateral symmetry, the adults a five-rayed radial symmetry. Coelom in the adult consists of a perivisceral cavity and a water vascular system which dilates the numerous tube feet. Exoskeleton of dermal calcareous ossicles. Nervous system reduced, remaining in contact with the ectoderm. No specialized excretory organs. Sexes usually separate; pelagic larvae.

CLASS ASTEROIDEA. Free-living, star-shaped, with a flattened body. The arms contain blind pouches of the gut: mouth ventral. For example, *Asterias, Asterina* (common British star-fishes).

CLASS OPHIUROIDEA. Free-living; star-shaped with no pouches of the gut in the arms. For example, *Ophiura, Ophiothrix* (brittle-stars).

CLASS ECHINOIDEA. Free-living, globular or discoid. Five-rayed but the arms folded in to form the globe or disc. For example, *Echinus, Echinocardium,* (sea-urchins).

CLASS HOLOTHUROIDEA. Free-living, cucumber-shaped with no external spines. For example, *Holothuria, Cucumaria* (sea-cucumbers).

CLASS CRINOIDEA. Attached during part or all of the life by an aboral stalk. Branched arms with ciliated food-grooves running towards the mouth. No spines. For example, *Antedon, Actinometra* (sea-lilies or feather-stars).

PHYLUM: **Chordata.** A notochord is present at least in some stage of the life history. The pharynx has visceral clefts. There is a tubular, dorsal central nervous system. There is a closed blood system in which the main lines of flow are forward ventrally and backward dorsally. Commissural vessels connect ventral vessel to dorsal, flowing in the arches between the visceral clefts. There is a post-anal, metamerically segmented tail. Limbs, when present, are formed of more than one body segment.

SUB-PHYLUM ACRANIA. Chordates which have no true brain or skull, heart or kidneys.

CLASS HEMICHORDATA. Body divided into a pre-oral proboscis, a collar and a trunk. Notochord represented by a short portion in the proboscis. The nerve cord is usually in contact with the epidermis. For example, *Balanoglossus Dolichoglossus* (burrowing marine worms).

CLASS UROCHORDATA. Chordate features most obvious in the larvae; notochord lost at metamorphosis, nerve-cord degenerates, gill slits multiply to form a large perforated pharynx which becomes a ciliary feeding mechanism. The coelom is always absent. Sexes separate or combined; asexual budding and colony formation are common. For example, *Cionia* (a shallow-water sea-squirt), *Oikopleura* (a pelagic form which retains the larval characteristics).

CLASS CEPHALOCHORDATA. Small fish-like animals. No specialized head, no paired limbs or heart. Notochord extends the whole length of the body. Pharynx large with numerous ciliated bars which form the feeding mechanism. The gill slits between the bars open into an atrium. Nephridia are the organs of nitrogenous excretion. Segmental myotomes are clearly marked. For example, *Amphioxus*, *Asymmetron* (lancelets).

SUB-PHYLUM CRANIATA [VERTEBRATA]. Chordates with a well-developed head and brain. Internal skeleton of bone or cartilage. Visceral clefts are few in number, and often lost in the adult. Kidneys are the organs of nitrogen excretion. A muscular heart develops from part of the ventral vessel. Usually two pairs of limbs. The craniates are usually subdivided into the branch *Agnatha* and the branch *Gnathostomata*. The Agnatha are round-mouthed and do not possess jaws. The skull is peculiar. The notochord is retained throughout life.

CLASS CYCLOSTOMATA. Contains the modern lampreys and hagfishes, with a slimy skin and no placoid scales. There is a single median hypophysial aperture from the outside world leading to the median olfactory organ and to the hypophysis of the pituitary body. For example, *Petromyzon* (the lamprey), *Myxine* (the hagfish). The class also includes the Ostracodermi, with a very substantial endoskeleton, and an exoskeleton of placoid scales, e.g. *Cephalaspis*.

In the branch *Gnathostomata*, the animals have jaws and the hypophysis does not open to the exterior. There are paired nostrils and olfactory organs. The notochord is not retained complete, though traces of it are always present. Paired limbs are marked features; they are, in some groups, secondarily lost.

CLASS PISCES. A huge group which includes all the fishes. They show very thorough adaptation to aquatic life. The paired limbs are pectoral and pelvic fins. The visceral clefts persist in the adult as gill-clefts. Lateral line system is well developed. Besides an endoskeleton, there is an exoskeleton of placoid or cycloid scales. There is no middle or external ear.

The classification of the vastly different forms of fishes is a complex and vexed subject. Many systematists hold the view that if we are to maintain natural classification, then the present class Pisces should be abolished, and at least three groups, the Aphetohyoidea, the Chondrichthyes and the Osteichthyes, elevated to the status of class.

SUB-CLASS APHETOHYOIDEA. Primitive fishes of the Palaeozoic era. They were characterized by the simplicity of the jaws and the completeness of the hyoid arch and the hyoid cleft. The tail was heterocercal, e.g. *Pterichthys*, *Acanthodes*.

SUB-CLASS CHONDRICHTHYES. An endoskeleton of cartilage and an exoskeleton of placoid scales. The hyoid arch plays an important part in jaw suspension, and the hyoid cleft is reduced to the spiracle.

ORDER SELACHII: No operculum covering the gills; many teeth which are continually being replaced, e.g. *Scyliorhinus* (the dogfish), *Selache* (the basking shark), *Raia* (the ray), *Torpedo* (the electric ray).

THE ORDER BRADYODONTI includes the modern chimaeras and many fossil forms. The gills are covered by an operculum and the spiracle is absent. The teeth are few in number. For example, *Chimaera* ("the king of the herrings").

SUB-CLASS OSTEICHTHYES. The bony fishes, in which the skeleton is almost entirely of bone; there is an exoskeleton of bony plates. An air-bladder derived as an outgrowth of the gut is usually present.

THE ORDER COELACANTHINI is of interest because of the recently-discovered modern genera *Latimeria* and *Malania*; the order was thought to have been extinct since the Cretaceous period. They possess hollow spines (coel-acanth), no internal nares and the tail is diphycercal. For example, *Latimeria* (discovered 1938), *Macropoma* (extinct).

THE ORDER DIPNOI consists of the lung-fishes. The skeleton is reduced and the tail is diphycercal. Internal nares are present. As well as gills, there are efficient lungs. The upper jaw is fused to the cranium and the teeth united to form crushing plates. For example, *Ceratodus* (the Burnett Salmon of Queensland), *Protopterus* (the mud-fish of South Africa).

THE ORDER TELEOSTEI includes most of the modern bony fishes. The endoskeleton is reduced, and the exoskeleton consists of thin bony plates, the cycloid scales. The function of the air-bladder is hydrostatic. The tail is homocercal. For example, *Salmo* (the salmon), *Gadus* (the cod), *Exocoetus* (the flying-fish), *Hippocampus* (the sea-horse).

CLASS AMPHIBIA. Craniates with pentadactyl limbs. The skin is soft; usually with no scales. Gills are present in the tadpole larva, and lungs in the adult. The middle ear is present but there is no external ear.

THE ORDER STEGOCEPHALIA comprises the large extinct Amphibia of the Permian period. The endoskeleton is massive and there is a stout exoskeleton of bony scales. For example, *Cacops*.

THE ORDER URODELA: The limbs are short and the tail persists. Often the adults retain the gills, e.g. *Triton* (the newt), *Salamandra* (the salamander), *Amblystoma* (the axolotl).

THE ORDER ANURA contains the frogs and toads. The adults possess neither tail nor gills. The limbs are well developed especially the long powerful hind-limb, e.g. *Rana* (the frog), *Bufo* (the toad).

THE ORDER GYMNOPHIONA: Amphibia which burrow like worms. There are no girdles, limbs or tail. Small scales are embedded in the dermis. The eggs of some are large and yolky and are laid on land. In these cases the larval stage is omitted, e.g. *Coecilia*.

CLASS REPTILIA. Craniates with pentadactyl limbs. Skin is dry and bears horny scales and sometimes bony plates. The respiratory organs are lungs; the visceral clefts never develop gills. Large heavily-yolked eggs with a calcareous shell are laid. There is no larval stage, and the embryo develops an amnion and allantois.

The Mesozoic was the great age of reptiles and the majority are now extinct. Present reptiles are a poor remnant of this once-magnificent class. The extant orders are—

ORDER CHELONIA including the tortoises and turtles.

ORDER RHYNCOCEPHALIA with one surviving genus—*Sphenodon* (the New Zealand tuatara).

ORDER LACERTILIA: The lizards.

ORDER OPHIDIA: The snakes.

ORDER CROCODILIA: The crocodiles and alligators.

CLASS AVES. Warm-blooded craniates with pentadactyl limbs, the front pair forming the wings. The skin bears feathers, except on the legs where there are horny scales, a relic of their reptilian ancestry. Lungs are the sole respiratory organs; the visceral clefts never bear gills, Large yolky eggs in calcareous shells are laid. There is no larval stage, and the embryo develops an amnion and allantois.

Primitive toothed birds of the sub-class Archaeornithes are all extinct. Of the sub-class Neornithes, two orders remain.

ORDER RATITAE: Large running birds with very small wings, e.g. *Struthio* (the ostrich), *Dromaeus* (the emu), *Casuarius* (the cassowary), *Apteryx* (the kiwi).

ORDER CARINATAE: The flying birds, e.g. *Columba* (the pigeon), *Gallus* (the fowl), *Turdus* (the thrush).

CLASS MAMMALIA. Warm-blooded craniates with pentadactyl limbs. The skin bears hair and has two types of glands, sebaceous and sudoriparous. The young are fed on milk produced in the mother's mammary glands. Except in two genera, the eggs are minute and developed within the mother. There is no larval stage, and the embryo develops the amnion and allantois. The respiratory organs are lungs; the visceral clefts never develop gills. There is an external ear; the middle ear bears three auditory ossicles. The buccal cavity is roofed by a secondary bony palate; the pharynx has an epiglottis and the glottis leads into a larynx. A partly-muscular diaphragm separates thorax from abdomen.

There are three sub-classes of extant mammals: the Monotremata include the duck-billed platypus and the spiny ant-eater, both of which lay large yolky eggs and do not possess true mammary glands; the Metatheria are the marsupials of Australasia and South America; the young are born in a immature state and move to the pouch, where the mammary glands nourish them with the milk. In the sub-class Eutheria, viviparity is highest developed. The main orders of extant Eutheria are

ORDER INSECTIVORA: Shrew, mole and hedgehog.

ORDER RODENTIA: Mouse, porcupine, rat, squirrel, lemming, beaver.

ORDER LAGOMORPHA: Rabbit, hare.

ORDER CARNIVORA: Cat, dog, weasel, otter, badger, bear, seal.

ORDER ARTIODACTYLA: The even-toed ungulates; cow, goat, deer, giraffe, sheep.

ORDER PERISSODACTYLA: The odd-toed ungulates; rhinoceros, tapir, horse, zebra.

ORDER SUBUNGULATA: Elephant, hyrax; the sea-cows sometimes form an order—SIRENIA.

ORDER CETACEA: Whale and dolphin.

ORDER CHIROPTERA: Bats.

ORDER PRIMATES, divided into two sub-orders: the sub-order Lemuroidea includes the lemurs. The sub-order Anthropoidea includes the monkeys, apes and man.

For many years the kingdom Plantae has been treated systematically as separable into four major divisions only—Thallophyta (algae, fungi, lichens, bacteria), Bryophyta (liverworts, mosses), Pteridophyta (lycopods, horsetails, ferns) and Spermatophyta (gymnosperms, angiosperms). More detailed study of the physiology, biochemistry and the fine structure of cells as revealed by the electron microscope, indicates that the plants once aggregated as thallophytes are too heterogeneous an assemblage to be grouped in this way. The modern treatment recognizes this by elevating to division status most of the classes that once comprised the single division. The name Thallophyta is often discarded but some still use it to designate a sub-kingdom, separated from another, the Embryophyta, on the criterion that in the latter group the members possess an embryonic stage nurtured in the parent for at least some part of the life cycle, whereas in the former this does not occur.

Below are given the main features by which the more recently defined groups can be recognized. The more detailed breakdown relates to those forms that are referred to somewhere in the later text and are not repeated there.

ALGAL FORMS. Note that although this term now has no systematic significance it is still frequently used to describe those plants that conform to the broad general characters as follows.

Mostly aquatic, all with photosynthetic pigments; unicellular, colonial, filamentous and thalloid forms, not differentiated into root, stem and leaf and with little cellular differentiation. Classified primarily by five major criteria: nature of photosynthetic pigments (chlorophylls, carotenoids, biloproteins); nature of food reserves; nature of cell wall components; types of flagella; details of fine cell structure. Features of vegetative structure and reproductive processes are used only in separating smaller groups. Sexual reproduction generally well defined, from isogamy to advanced oogamy, but sex organs very rarely other than unicellular. Fertilization zoidogamous in nearly all cases. Asexual reproduction by vegetative cell division, fragmentation and specialized spores, most commonly zoospores. Life cycles variable; some haplonts (zygote only diploid), some diplonts (gametes only haploid), some diplohaplonts (alternating diploid and haploid phases, i.e. showing alternation of generations). Fossils scarce but with a history back to the Proterozoic era. Considered the most primitive of plants.

DIVISION: **Cyanophyta [Myxophyta]** (blue-green algae)

CLASS CYANOPHYCEAE (sometimes placed with bacterial forms as Schizophyceae in Division Protophyta, *see* p. 1244). Marine, freshwater and wet surfaces. Unicellular or simple filaments, often in a gelatinous matrix. No internal cell membranes separating nuclear material, chlorophyll, mitochondria, etc. from the cytoplasmic background, i.e. procaryotic. No flagella but some show characteristic gliding motility. Pigments include chlorophyll *a*, the biloproteins, *c*-phycocyanin and *c*-phycoerythrin and some highly specific carotenoids. Storage compounds: cyanophycin (proteinaceous), oil and glycogen. No sexual reproduction but possibly some genetic interchange between individuals. Asexual reproduction by amitotic cell division, fragmentation, non-motile resting spores or vegetative cells. Some form characteristic cells, heterocysts, of no proven function. Colonizers of fresh ground. Frequently in association with higher plants, possibly as symbionts. Commonly algal partners in lichens. Some nitrogen-fixers, e.g. *Anaboena, Nostoc, Oscillatoria.*

DIVISION: **Chlorophyta**

CLASS CHLOROPHYCEAE (green algae). Mostly freshwater, few marine, occasionally terrestrial. Unicellular, colonial, filamentous and expanded thalloid forms. Pigments include chlorophylls *a* and *b*, carotenes, xanthophylls, but no biloproteins. Food reserve starch. Cell walls always cellulosic. Flagella two or four, equal, always smooth or "whiplash", i.e. acronematic, when present. Cells eucaryotic, i.e. internal membranes present. Chloroplasts of various forms and pyrenoids often included within them. Sex organs unicellular, process varying from isogamy to oogamy with always motile male gametes. Asexual spores commonly zoospores. Most species are haplonts but some show isomorphic alternation of generations, i.e. alternating phases identical.

ORDER VOLVOCALES: Mainly freshwater. Motile unicellular or coenobial forms; body haploid. A single chloroplast in each cell and very commonly an eye-spot. Asexual reproduction by zoospores in most cases, these forming daughter coenobia prior to release in colonial forms. Sexual reproduction from isogamy to well-defined oogamy, e.g. *Chlamydomonas, Pandorina, Eudorina, Volvox.*

ORDER CHLOROCOCCALES: Mainly freshwater (plankton). Haploid solitary cells or colonial forms, non-motile. Never filamentous. Asexual reproduction by zoospores usual. Sexual reproduction isogamous by motile gametes, e.g. *Chlorella, Scenedesmus, Pediastrum, Hydrodictyon.*

ORDER ULOTRICHALES: Mainly freshwater. Body usually a simple filament of haploid cells. Chloroplast usually a single parietal band in each cell. Fixed to substratum at least in young stages. Asexual reproduction by various types of zoospores. Sexual reproduction from isogamy to well-defined oogamy, e.g. *Ulothrix, Cylindrocapsa.*

ORDER ULVALES: Marine or brackish water. Initially uniseriate filaments similar to Ulotrichales and members are sometimes placed in this order. By longitudinal divisions of cells, body becomes expanded to a sheet-like thallus, anchored to substratum by a holdfast. Chloroplast single, parietal. Asexual reproduction by zoospores, quadriflagellate. Sexual reproduction isogamous, gametes biflagellate. Some genera exhibit isomorphic alternation of generations with meiosis at zoospore formation, e.g. *Ulva, Enteromorpha*.

ORDER OEDOGONIALES: Freshwater. Fixed, at least when young. Filamentous, haploid body with unique method of cell division ("cap cell" formation). Single reticulate chloroplast in each cell. Asexual reproduction by multiflagellate zoospores. Sexual reproduction oogamous. Some species nannandrous, i.e. develop dwarf male plants from special androspores, e.g. *Oedogonium, Oedocladium, Bulbochaete*.

ORDER ZYGNEMATALES (CONJUGALES): Freshwater. Free-floating solitary cells or unbranched filamentous haploid body with distinctive chloroplast structure, e.g. spiral bands, lobed or stellate. No asexual reproductive process beyond fragmentation. Sexual reproduction isogamous by non-flagellate, amoeboid gametes; conjugation often through tubular connexions between pairing cells, e.g. *Spirogyra, Zygnema*. Other genera of interest form the unicellular desmids.

ORDER CLADOPHORALES: Freshwater and marine. Fixed, usually branched filamentous haploid or diploid body of multinucleate cells. Chloroplast reticulate. Asexual reproduction by quadriflagellate zoospores. Sexual reproduction isogamous to oogamous. Isomorphic alternation of generations exhibited by some species with meiosis at zoospore formation, e.g. *Cladophora, Chaetomorpha*.

OTHER ORDERS generally recognized are: Tetrasporales, Chaetophorales, Sphaeropleales, Prasiolales, Acrosiphonales, Siphonocladales, Dasycladales, Caulerpales (Siphonales).

CLASS CHAROPHYCEAE (stoneworts). Freshwater. Fixed and very characteristic multicellular haploid thallus of erect, branched axis, with well-defined nodal and internodal zones. Numerous discoid chloroplasts in each multinucleate cell. No asexual reproductive process. Sexual reproduction elaborate oogamy involving multicellular sex organs, the exception to the general algal case, e.g. *Chara, Nitella*.

DIVISION: **Xanthophyta**

CLASS XANTHOPHYCEAE (yellow-green algae). Almost all freshwater. Separated from the Chlorophyceae by possession of chlorophylls *a* and, in some cases, *c*, and more carotenoid pigment. Food storage is oil; no starch in the cells. These are eucaryotic and cell walls may be absent, but when present have a high pectic content and may be silicified. Motile forms biflagellate, unequal; longer, pantonematic, i.e. with rows of fine processes, otherwise known as "flimmer" or "tinsel"; shorter, acronematic. Other forms are amoeboid, palmelloid, multicellular and coenocytic filamentous, some with uninucleate cells, others multinucleate. Asexual reproduction by vegetative division, aplanospores or zoospores, these multiflagellate in some cases. Sexual reproduction varying from isogamy to very advanced oogamy, e.g. *Vaucheria, Botrydium.*

DIVISION: Bacillariophyta

CLASS BACILLARIOPHYCEAE (diatoms). Marine, freshwater and almost any damp surface. Constitute much of the phytoplankton, free-floating and epiphytic. Unicellular or in chains or groups of cells. Unique wall form in two overlapping halves (petri dish), silicified, sculptured. Some genera motile by presumed cytoplasmic streaming mechanism. Eucaryotic and some sexual stages motile with a single pantonematic flagellum. Pigments include chlorophylls *a* and *c* with xanthophylls, including fucoxanthin. Foods stored are oils and chrysolaminarin (leucosin), a carbohydrate polysaccharide different from starch in the glucose linkages. Asexual reproduction by cell division in which generations beome successively smaller. Smallest cells reproduce sexually either isogamously or oogamously. Parent cells diploid, gametes produced meiotically, i.e. diplontic. Zygote develops into an enlarged auxospore that gives rise to a full-sized vegetative cell. Cell walls persist long after death and form deposits of diatomaceous earth, used commercially as kieselguhr, e.g. *Pinnularia, Navicula, Asterionella, Melosira, Cyclotella.*

DIVISION: Phaeophyta

CLASS PHAEOPHYCEAE (brown algae). Almost entirely marine seaweeds of the littoral shore zone. Forms range from fixed branched filamentous to partially organized expanded thallus with hapteron, stipe and blade showing some cellular differentiation. Cells are eucaryotic with usually numerous discoid chloroplasts, uninucleate, with centrosomes at mitosis. Pigments are chlorophylls *a* and *c*, the characteristic xanthophylls, fucoxanthin and diatoxanthin, but no biloproteins. Food reserves are laminarin and mannitol. So-called fucosan vesicles of unknown significance are frequently present in active cells. Cell walls are of inner cellulose identical with higher plants with outer gelatinous layer of mucilaginous alginic and fucinic acids. Motile reproductive stages, asexual and sexual, are distinctively pear-shaped, bearing two laterally inserted flagella, one forward, longer, pantonematic, other hind, shorter (or granule only), acronematic and possessing eyespots. Members show a well-marked alternation of generations in all except one order.

SUB-CLASS ISOGENERATAE (five orders). Isomorphic alternation of generations, e.g. *Dictyota.*

SUB-CLASS HETEROGENERATAE (five orders). Heteromorphic alternation of generations, e.g. *Laminaria.*

SUB-CLASS CYCLOSPOREAE. No alternation of generations.

ORDER: FUCALES (only). Marine. On rocky coasts, mostly between tide levels. Diploid thallus fixed and differentiated into holdfast, stipe and blade of varying tissue structure. No asexual reproduction. Sexual reproduction oogamous with sex organs carried in special conceptacles, e.g. *Fucus, Ascophyllum, Pelvetia.*

OTHER DIVISIONS OF THE ALGAL FORMS. Rhodophyta Chrysophyta, Pyrrophyta, Cryptophyta, Euglenophyta.

FUNGAL FORMS. Note that the name fungi no longer applies to a single group and lacks any systematic significance.

Mainly terrestrial, but lower forms widespread in aquatic conditions. The vegetative body shows a range including naked plasmodia, unicellular and filamentous or hyphal forms. The filamentous fungal body is termed a mycelium and may occur as a loose weft of hyphae or as a compacted mass of pseudo-tissue form (plectenchyma), particularly in the spore-producing parts. Some possess features by which they can be related to the algae, but all differ in lacking completely the photosynthetic pigments. Colour may be present but is due to pigmentation in cell walls, cytoplasm or oil globules in the cells. The mode of life is generally saprophytic or parasitic but some form apparently symbiotic associations with higher plants (mycorrhizae) and some form natural symbiotic unions with algae (lichens). Few have cellulosic cell walls, a form of chitin or fungal cellulose occurring more commonly. The primary classification is based on morphology, whether plasmodial, unicellular or hyphal construction and if the latter whether, during active growth, these are septate or non-septate. The septate forms are further separated according to whether the characteristic spores are endogenously or exogenously produced. Almost all show an asexual or "imperfect" spore stage and many reproduce sexually at a "perfect" stage, through true sexual fusion of gametes produced either in special sex organs, by fusion of the contents of two specialized hyphae or by the fusion of two nuclei in a vegetative cell. Many produce highly characteristic "fructifications" after sexual fusion. Life cycles are variable. Fossil representatives scarce and origins difficult to trace; no doubt the fungi are phylogenetically diverse.

DIVISION: **Myxomycophyta** (slime fungi). Vegetative body a multinucleate, naked protoplasmic mass or plasmodium that concentrates to form spores. Each spore gives rise to a flagellated swarm cell or zoospore. After multiplication these act as gametes, fusing in pairs to grow into a fresh plasmodium. Meiosis occurs at spore formation. The group is sometimes referred to as the Mycetozoa and regarded as of animal origin, related to the Protozoa.

DIVISION: **Eumycophyta** (true fungi).

CLASS PHYCOMYCETES. Many aquatic or damp-loving forms, fewer fully terrestrial. Simple organization with some bearing resemblances to the filamentous algae. Mycelium haploid, generally of non-septate hyphae with multinucleate protoplasts. Some become septate on ageing and when reproducing. Cell walls often cellulose; food reserves oil and glycogen. Asexual reproduction by zoospores, sporangiospores or conidiospores. Sexual reproduction is either oogamous with male cells sometimes motile or by conjugation of similar non-motile gametic structures. Further classification is based primarily on the presence or absence of a motile stage in the life cycle and the flagellation of motile cells.

SUB-CLASS UNIFLAGELLATAE. Mostly parasites. Body not a true mycelium or of coenocytic form. Asexual reproduction by zoospores with a single flagellum or sometimes with a very reduced second flagellum, in some cases acronematic, others pantonematic. Sexual reproduction varies from isogamy by naked uniflagellate gametes to advanced oogamy. Five orders, e.g. *Synchytrium, Plasmodiophora, Spongospora.*

SUB-CLASS BIFLAGELLATAE. Parasites or saprophytes. Mycelium mostly non-septate. Asexual spores may be zoospores and when so these always possess two laterally placed flagella (forward short, pantonematic; hind long, acronematic) or conidia. Sex organs antheridia and oogonia. Fertilization may be through a conjugation tube.

ORDER PERONOSPORALES. Highly specialized parasites mainly on land plants. A few persist as saprophytes on dead host tissue. They are eucarpic, i.e. external to the substrate, obtaining nourishment by means of haustoria (a holocarpic fungus is contained entirely in a host cell). Cellulose cell walls. Asexual reproduction by air-borne conidia from which biflagellate zoospores may be developed under wet conditions. In some genera, zoospore formation may not occur, and the conidia germinate by germ tubes. Sexual reproduction by oogonia, fertilized from antheridia through a conjugation tube, e.g. *Pythium, Phytophthora, Peronospora, Albugo [Cystopus].*

OTHER ORDERS: Saprolegniales, Leptomitales, Lagenidiales.

SUB-CLASS APLANATAE [AFLAGELLATAE]. Parasites and saprophytes. Mostly latter. Mycelium mostly non-septate. Asexual spores never flagellate. Sexual reproduction by union of two equal or unequal gametangia to form zygospores.

ORDER MUCORALES: Saprophytic moulds on many substrates, occasionally parasitic on members of the same order. Chitin in the cell walls, e.g. *Mucor, Rhizopus, Pilobolus, Absidia.*

OTHER ORDERS: Entomophthorales, Zoopagales.

CLASS ASCOMYCETES. Terrestrial saprophytes and parasites, often highly specialized. Mycelium of septate hyphae; the protoplasts are usually uninucleate or binucleate; haploid nuclei. Often, the hyphae are compacted into pseudoparenchymatous "fruiting" structures of easily recognizable form. Cell walls of "fungal cellulose." Asexual reproduction by non-motile spores usually conidiospores. Sexual reproductive organs characteristically antheridia and ascogonia; these frequently reduced or absent. All have a distinctive reproductive structure, the ascus, formed after nuclear fusions; usually eight ascospores. Asci are generally borne inside or on ascocarps, either cleistothecia (closed), perithecia (flask-shaped) or apothecia (disc- or saucer-shaped).

SUB-CLASS PROTOASCOMYCETES [HEMIASCOMYCETES]. Parasites or saprophytes. Body sometimes reduced to a single cell. Asci developed singly or in irregular groups, directly on mycelium or formed from a specialized ascogenous cell.

ORDER ENDOMYCETALES: Mainly saprophytes. Asexual reproduction by conidia, oidia, by "budding" of sprout cells or by transverse fission. Each ascus may arise directly from a zygote or a cell derived from a zygote by asexual reproduction and having a diploid nucleus, e.g. *Saccharomyces*. There is one other order.

SUB-CLASS EUASCOMYCETES. Parasites or saprophytes. Asci in ascocarps from ascogenous hyphae; cleistothecia or perithecia.

ORDER PLECTASCALES [ASPERGILLALES] [EUROTIALES]: Chiefly saprophytic fungi. Mycelium usually of multinucleate cells. Asexual reproduction by conidiospores. Asci are enclosed irregularly in an indehiscent cleistothecium, e.g. *Aspergillus, Penicillium.*

ORDER ERYSIPHALES [PERISPORIALES]: Mainly external parasites on leaves. Mycelium rarely compacted. Asexual reproduction by conidiospores. Sexual reproduction by well-defined sex organs in some cases; in others, vegetative cells function in this capacity. Fruiting body is a cleistothecium or perithecium, with asci regularly arranged, e.g. *Erysiphe, Sphaerotheca*. There are thirteen other orders in this sub-class and two other sub-classes.

CLASS BASIDIOMYCETES. Widespread saprophytes and parasites, often highly specialized. Mycelium septate; frequently shows anastomoses and "clamp connexions." Cells usually binucleate with haploid nuclei; this is the "fruiting" or secondary mycelium achieved by fusion of primary mycelia which are haploid and uninucleate. Two fusing primary mycelia are derived from spores which are usually of different strains (heterothallic). Fructifications usually of binucleate cells only; compacted, pseudoparenchymatous and of easily recognizable form. Cell walls of fungal cellulose. Some have asexual reproduction by conidiospores. No special sex organs formed, but nuclear fusion occurs in special cells, basidia, borne on a fertile layer, the hymenium. Each basidium usually forms four basidiospores exogenously.

SUB-CLASS HOMOBASIDIOMYCETES. Number of basidiospores definite, usually four. The basidia are non-septate.

ORDER AGARICALES: Mainly saprophytes. Hymenium borne on gills of a clearly recognizable sporophore (the "toadstool" form). Many are in mycorrhizal association with higher plants, e.g. *Agaricus, Coprinus, Amanita*. There are nine other orders.

SUB-CLASS HETEROBASIDIOMYCETES. Basidia septate or deeply cleft or if one-celled arising from a special teleutospore stage. Includes the smuts and rusts, e.g. *Puccinia.*

CLASS FUNGI IMPERFECTI. Conidium-bearing fungi existing habitually without any other kind of spore formation; imperfect stage only.

SUB-DIVISION LICHENES. Naturally occurring composite parasitic or doubtfully symbiotic associations of algal cells and a fungal mycelium.

CLASS ASCOLICHENES. The fungi concerned are Ascomycetes. Common genera are *Xanthoria*, *Physcia* and *Peltigera*. *Cladonia rangiferina* is the "reindeer moss."

CLASS BASIDIOLICHENES. The fungi concerned are Basidiomycetes. There are no British species.

DIVISION: **Bryophyta**. The persisting vegetative body is attached to the substratum and differentiated into attaching and absorptive organs, rhizoids, and aerial parts which may or may not show a stem and leaf-like organization. Dichotomous branching is common. Growth from a single apical cell or row of cells. Photosynthetic pigments as in higher plants. There may sometimes be a low degree of differentiation of the tissues. Always well-defined sexual reproduction. Multicellular sex organs are formed, male antheridia and female archegonia. Fertilization is always zoidogamous with biflagellate male gametes. Clear-cut heteromorphic alternation of generations. The persisting plant body is the haploid gametophyte; the diploid sporophyte (sporogonium) is always wholly or partially dependent on the gametophyte. Spores always of one kind only, i.e. homosporous. Spores may germinate into a highly characteristic structure, the protonema. Chiefly terrestrial, but seldom able to withstand any degree of desiccation; a few are purely aquatic. Fossil representatives are scarce, but history goes back to the Palaeozoic era. The first step towards land colonization; possible origin in the green algae.

CLASS HEPATICAE. The liverworts. Gametophyte dorsiventral, frequently prostrate and thalloid in nature; dichotomously branched. Rhizoids unicellular. More advanced representatives may develop an axis bearing leaf-like structures. Growth from an apical cell or row of cells. Sporophyte simple; little sterile tissue, no chlorophyll, and wholly dependent on the gametophyte (except in the Anthocerotales). Spores from inner tissue of capsule (endothecium), except in Anthocerotales. Spore dispersal aided by elaters. Spores never develop into protonemata.

ORDER METZGERIALES: Gametophyte not differentiated to any great extent; air chambers never present. Rhizoids always unicellular and smooth walled. Sex organs in groups on parts of the gametophyte which show no morphological differentiation. Sporogonium a simple capsule of definite growth, dehiscing by four valves, e.g. *Pellia*.

OTHER ORDERS: Sphaerocarpales, Marchantiales, Calobryales, Jungermanniales, Anthocerotales.

CLASS MUSCI. The mosses. Gametophyte with erect habit in most cases and differentiated into an axis with leaf-like structures above ground, and multicellular rhizoids with oblique cross-walls, below ground. Growth always apical from a single cell. Sex organs apical. Sporophytes often show a high degree of differentiation, possessing stomatal apertures and chlorophyll-bearing tissues. Usually dehisce by teeth and do not form elaters. Spores develop from inner (endothecial) tissue of capsule, except in Sphagnales. Spores always develop into protonemata.

SUB-CLASS BRYIDAE. Includes twelve orders containing most moss families and genera, with the above general characteristics, e.g. *Funaria*. There are four other sub-classes with five orders including the distinctive Sphagnales, Andreaeales and Polytrichales.

DIVISION: Pteridophyta. The persisting vegetative body in nearly all cases is differentiated into root, stem, and leaf systems. Dichotomous branching is common. High degree of internal tissue differentiation. There is a conducting system of xylem and phloem. Xylem elements are always tracheids. Growth from an apical cell. Pigments are chlorophylls *a* and *b* with carotenoids. Well-defined sexual reproduction with antheridia and archegonia. Fertilization is zoidogamous with biflagellate or multiflagellate male gametes. Clear-cut alternation of generations. The persisting plant is the diploid sporophyte, independent of the haploid gametophyte at maturity. Heteromorphic alternation of generations. Spores of the sporophyte may be all identical (homosporous) or of two kinds (heterosporous). Gametophytes in the former case always nutritionally independent of the sporophyte, not always in the latter case. Chiefly terrestrial with few aquatic representatives. Fossil forms are very common. History goes back to the Silurian period of the Palaeozoic era. Very richly represented in the Carboniferous (coal measures) period. Much more fully adapted to terrestrial conditions. Origin obscure.

CLASS LYCOPSIDA. A few living and some fossil forms of world-wide distribution. Sporophyte differentiated into root, stem and leaf, but leaves always small in relation to stem size (microphyllous). No leaf gaps in the stele. Homosporous and heterosporous representatives. Sporangia aggregated into cones or strobili, usually at the ends of branches.

ORDER LYCOPODIALES: Two extant genera; mostly tropical. Leaves without ligules (eligulate). Homosporous, e.g. *Lycopodium*.
ORDER SELAGINELLALES: One extant genus; mostly tropical. Leaves with ligules (ligulate). Heterosporous, e.g. *Selaginella*.
OTHER ORDERS: Isoetales, with one living genus, *Isoetes* (the quillwort). Protolepidodendrales and Lepidodendrales fossils only.

CLASS PTEROPSIDA (applied here only to the large-leaved Pteridophyta). World-wide distribution. Many living and fossil forms. Sporophyte differentiated into root, stem and leaves, except in one or two cases where roots may be lacking on mature plants. Leaves always large in relation to stem (macrophyllous) and spirally arranged. Leaf gaps in the stele in most cases. Homosporous except in one family (Salviniaceae). Sporangia borne on margins or abaxial faces of leaves, usually in clusters or sori, except in one group of fossil forms.

SUB-CLASS LEPTOSPORANGIATAE. Sporangium with a jacket one cell thick, and developed from a single cell.

ORDER FILICALES: Homosporous, leptosporangiate ferns.

FAMILY DENNSTAEDTIACEAE: Includes nearly all British wild ferns. Annulus of sporangium in same plane as stalk, and does not completely encircle the sporangium, e.g. *Dryopteris* (sub-family, Dryopteroideae). Nine other families.

OTHER ORDERS: Marsileales (pillworts); Salviniales (water ferns).

SUB-CLASS EUSPORANGIATAE. Sporangium develops from a group of cells. Includes the living British order, Ophioglossales (adders' tongues and moonworts), and the tropical order Marattiales.

SUB-CLASS OSMUNDIDAE. Characters intermediate between the above sub-classes. Contains one living order, the Osmundales (royal ferns) with many fossils back to the Permian.

SUB-CLASS PRIMOFILICES. Sporangia borne singly at ultimate leaf dichotomy, elongated. Jacket more than one cell thick, dehiscing by pore or slit. Fossil forms only.

CLASS PSILOTOPSIDA. Sporophyte rootless, and shoot composed of branches only, or with small leaves spirally arranged. No leaf gaps in the stele. Homosporous. Sporangia borne singly at the tips of branches. One order Psilotales.

CLASS PSILOPHYTOPSIDA. Only fossil order Psilophytales.

CLASS SPHENOPSIDA. Sporophyte differentiated into root, stem and leaf. Leaves nearly always microphyllous and arranged in whorls. No leaf gaps in the stele. Sporangia homosporous and borne on distinctive sporangiophores in a strobilus.

The order Equisetales includes the living horsetails, e.g. *Equisetum*, and the fossil genus, *Calamites*. There are three fossil orders, Hyeniales, Sphenophyllales and Calamitales.

DIVISION: **Spermatophyta.** The persisting vegetative body always differen-tiated into root, leaf and stem systems. Dichotomous branching is rare. They show the highest degree of internal tissue differentiation. Stele has clearly defined conducting elements; the xylem elements may be tracheids or vessels. Growth from an apical meristem. Secondary thickening is common. Pigments are chlorophylls *a* and *b* with carotenoids. Well-defined sexual reproduction; the sex organs may be antheridia and archegonia in the more primitive groups. Clearly-defined alternation of generations. Fertilization is by means of a pollen-tube (siphonogamous). The male gametophyte is shed as a pollen grain and borne by air-currents or insects to the female gametophyte which develops in the sporophyte (cf. Bryophyta and Pterido-phyta). Both gametophytes are very reduced structures. Male gametes may be ciliate in primitive forms. Reproductive parts borne in highly specialized structures; strobili in the lower groups and flowers in the higher. After fertilization, the resulting mature structure is a seed. Seeds may be borne naked or in a closed structure developed by the sporophyte to form a true fruit. Chiefly terrestrial but with some obviously derived aquatic representatives. Fossils common; history goes back to the Devonian period of the Palaeozoic era. Now the world's dominant vegetation and the most thoroughgoing of all land plants. Possible origin in the early pteridophytes. Fossil representatives found alongside the pteridophytes in Palaeozoic rocks.

CLASS GYMNOSPERMAE. Mostly trees and shrubs of world-wide distribution, but relatively few different forms. Xylem elements always tracheids (except in one order where primitive vessels may be found). Flowers mostly of strobiloid construction and unisexual. Seeds with one integument and borne naked. Endosperm of female gametophyte origin.

ORDER CYCADALES: Small group in warmer climates. Nine genera only. Very abundant in Mesozoic era. Relatively primitive. Some show palm habit. Usually large male and female cones. Dioecious. Male gamete ciliated, e.g. *Cycas, Zamia, Encephalartos*.

ORDER CONIFERALES: Much the largest order of the class. Nearly all evergreen trees or shrubs. Represented most fully in the northern hemisphere; they reach the northernmost limit and highest altitude of all tree forms. Female parts in strobili in nearly all cases.

SUB-ORDER ABIETINEAE: Large trees with needle-like leaves, e.g. *Pinus* (the pines), *Larix* (the deciduous larches), *Picea* (the spruces), *Abies* (the firs), *Cedrus* (the cedars).

OTHER SUB-ORDERS: Araucariineae, broad-leaved with large cones, e.g. *Araucaria* (the monkey puzzle); Podocarpineae, female parts not in cones, e.g. *Podocarpus*; Taxodineae, large trees with narrow spine-like leaves, e.g. *Taxodium* and *Sequoia*; Cupressineae, trees or shrubs with small flattened leaves, e.g. *Cupressus* and *Juniperus*.

ORDER TAXALES: Small group with only three genera. Dioecious. No female cones. Ovules borne singly, e.g., *Taxus*.

ORDER GINKGOALES: A single living species, *Ginkgo biloba*.

ORDER GNETALES: Show more advanced characteristics than most gymnosperms. Ovules enclosed. Primitive xylem vessels. Three genera only, *Gnetum, Ephedra, Welwitschia*.

OTHER ORDERS: Cordaitales and Bennettitales. Fossils only, some with hermaphrodite flowers, e.g. *Cycadeoidea*.

CLASS ANGIOSPERMAE. Dominate the world's vegetation in practically all habitats. Represent the greatest advance in evolution towards a vegetation of fixed habit adapted to life on land. Great diversity of form. Anatomically unique in possessing true xylem vessels. Most characteristic feature is the flower consisting usually of whorls of sterile and fertile parts. Usually hermaphrodite. Male gametophyte represented only by the pollen grain. Female gametophyte reduced to an embryo-sac usually containing eight nuclei only. Fertilization siphonogamous. Endosperm unique; formed as a result of a triple fusion in which both male and female cells take part. Seeds with two integuments enclosed in specialized carpels, forming an ovary which ripens into a true fruit.

SUB-CLASS MONOCOTYLEDONES. Most are herbaceous; a few of palm habit but no true trees. Adventitious root systems; usually parallel-veined leaves. Vascular bundles irregularly arranged in the stem; rarely secondary growth. Flower parts in threes or multiples of three. Single cotyledon in the seed. Nine orders, twenty-five families, including:

ORDER LILIIFLORAE: e.g., Liliaceae, Iridaceae.
ORDER GLUMIFLORAE: e.g., Gramineae.

SUB-CLASS DICOTYLEDONES. Herbs, shrubs and trees. Net-veined leaves usually. Vascular bundles arranged in a ring or rings; secondary growth is usual. Flower parts in fours or fives or multiples of these. Two cotyledons in the seed (rarely one, by reduction).

ARCHICHLAMYDEAE: Petals free or absent, rarely united.

ORDER RANALES: e.g., Ranunculaceae.
ORDER RHOEADALES: e.g., Cruciferae.
ORDER CENTROSPERMAE: e.g., Caryophyllaceae.
ORDER LEGUMINOSAE: e.g., Papilionaceae [Leguminosae].
ORDER ROSALES: e.g., Rosaceae.
ORDER SALICALES: e.g., Salicaceae. Twenty-one other British orders, with sixty-five other families.

METACHLAMYDEAE: Petals united, very rarely free or absent.
ORDER TUBIFLORAE: e.g., Scrophulariaceae, Labiatae.
ORDER ASTERALES: e.g., Compositae. Seven other British orders with twenty-seven other families.

CLASS PTERIDOSPERMAE [CYCADOFILICALES]. All fossil forms with a history back to the Devonian period. Pteridophyte (fern-like) body forms bearing microsporangia and megasporangia, the latter developing as seeds. Sporophylls like foliage leaves; no flowers formed.

Note. This classification of plants is one now commonly used, but must not be regarded as perfect or final. As more discoveries are made, opinions concerning relationships will change. Some variations from the above exist. For example, the divisions Pteridophyta and Spermatophyta are sometimes grouped in one, the Tracheophyta, on the primary criterion that all members of both possess a vascular system, the seed habit being of secondary importance. Some taxonomists would regard all simpler organisms, whether autotrophic or heterotrophic, as belonging to a separate kingdom, the Protista. In this group are then placed the bacterial forms and blue-green algae as lower protists, these having no true nucleus or intracellular membranes, whilst the higher protists include algae and protozoans with the fungi and slime moulds somewhere between them. The higher plants and animals then form two other kingdoms as at present.

While biologists are still making discoveries that affect the systematic placings of different forms, rejecting some older ideas as to what constitutes a valid criterion for separating one group from another and renaming groups, there are bound to be some differences of opinion between those regarded as authorities in taxonomy. These differences will be expressed in their various writings and unless the beginner understands that what is written is often a matter of opinion only, with no real right or wrong, he can become very confused. To reduce confusion to a minimum, the reader is advised to adhere initially to one classification, such as the above, and to consider the merits of others in relation to it.

CHAPTER 5

UNICELLULAR GREEN PLANTS: CHLAMYDOMONAS, CHLORELLA

THESE plants illustrate the simplest types of structure and life history in the algae. The species of *Chlamydomonas* may be considered the more primitive because they are flagellate, a feature usually associated with the ancestral forms. *Chlorella*, made famous by its use in the study of photosynthesis by green plants, is a very simple non-motile, unicellular green alga. It represents about the lowest limit of simplicity of body structure found in green plants.

CHLAMYDOMONAS

The genus is of world-wide distribution and includes about 150 species of which twenty may be found in Great Britain.

Habitat

The majority of species are inhabitants of stagnant, freshwater pools, ponds or ditches, and are very frequently found in such vast numbers that their presence causes the water to appear a cloudy green colour. A few species are wholly marine, whilst a few others may occur in water less saline, above high-tide mark. Some species may be found in wet soil, but none can exist in a habitat that is not predominantly wet. The sudden appearance of such large numbers of them in a hitherto untenanted pool, may give cause for surprise, but it reflects only their remarkable capacity for rapid reproduction when growth conditions are good. Their transfer from one pool to another could be effected by the agencies of birds and other animals carrying them in droplets of water, or alternatively by their dispersal by air currents whilst in a resting, resistant condition after a pool has dried up.

Vegetative Structure

Here a description will be given of a generalized member of the genus *Chlamydomonas*. Since variation is not too wide among the species, it may be taken as applying to most of them. Specific differences are based on a number of small details which need not concern us.

The whole organism is but a single cell. This, in most species, is roughly ovoid in shape and about 20μ long by about 10μ wide.

Opposite ends can be distinguished by shape as well as by other features. The anterior end is slightly pointed; the posterior is more rounded.

The cell is clearly defined by its *cell wall* which is a delicate covering, sometimes of two layers, an inner of pure cellulose and an outer coat of mucilage. At the anterior end, this wall may be perforated to allow an extrusion of the cell contents to form an *apical papilla* of clear cytoplasm through which pass two equal cytoplasmic threads or *flagella*

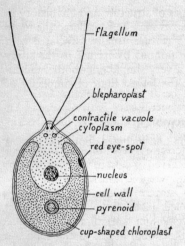

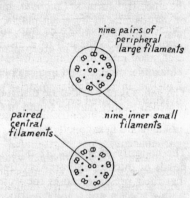

Fig. 5.1. *Chlamydomonas* plant in optical section.

Fig. 5.2. Diagram to show internal fibrillar (tubular) structure of flagellum as seen with electron microscope × 30,000.

extending into the water to a length which may approach twice that of the cell itself. When no apical papilla is present, the flagella extend to the outside through minute pores in the cell wall.

The cell contents may be divided into several clearly recognizable structures, although very high magnification is required to elucidate detail in most cases. The most prominent of these is the single large *chloroplast* which almost fills the cell. Although superficial examination may not disclose this, it is cup-shaped, with its base towards the posterior and its rim reaching nearly to the apex of the cell. There is left only a small region of clear cytoplasm at the anterior end. Embedded in the thickened base of the chloroplast is a shining refractive structure known as a *pyrenoid*.

Near the anterior border of the chloroplast can be observed a minute pigmented spot, reddish in colour. This is the *red eye-spot* or *stigma*. It is sometimes possible to distinguish species by the relative position of this structure. Also in the clear cytoplasm may be seen two, or very occasionally, four, *contractile vacuoles*, so-called because of their ability to expand and contract in volume alternately. Only the structures so far named will be visible to the student. The *nucleus* will not be seen, since it lies in the central cytoplasm filling the hollow of the cup-shaped chloroplast.

Electron microscope studies have elucidated much of the fine detail hitherto unknown. The flagella, for example, are known to be of the "smooth," "whiplash" or *acronematic* type (as distinct from the process-bearing, "flimmer," "tinsel" or *pantonematic* form). Each contains the 9 outer, 9 inner and 2 central microtubules common to all plant and animal flagella and cilia (*see* Fig. 5.2). Each flagellum is attached inside the cell to a distinct basal body (blepharoplast). The cell membrane, in common with the general case, is two-layered. The chloroplast is enclosed in a membrane which contains pigment-bearing lamellae in a granular matrix, starch grains, red eye-spot and the pyrenoid. The red eye-spot at the anterior of the chloroplast consists of two or three concentrically placed curved plates of which the components are hexagonally packed. The pyrenoid consists of a refractive proteinaceous core surrounded by starch plates. The contractile vacuoles are the only distinct water-filled spaces in the cytoplasm which otherwise shows an endoplasmic reticulum structure and includes among is granules clearly-defined mitochondria and Golgi bodies or *dictyosomes*. The nucleus is also membrane-bound and contains a nucleolus. Cells in which the cytoplasmic structures are discretely separated by membranes are described as *eucaryotic* in contradistinction to the *procaryotic* case in which there are no intracellular membranes.

Some species may be found in a condition different from that described. They may occur in a resting form where the flagella are lost; the cells are rounded, with a thickened wall and sometimes a red pigment (haematochrome) may be secreted.

It is known that the nucleus is haploid, that is, it contains only half the double set of chromosomes (*see* p. 16). Chlamydomonas plants therefore can be described as being haplont since in the vegetative stage the nucleus is in the haploid condition.

Physiology

Functionally, *Chlamydomonas* plants are free-living autotrophic structures, possessing all the characteristics attributable to living things.

The possession of photosynthetic pigments of the same composition as those of higher plants, is sufficient indication that the nutritional processes must at least be fundamentally similar. The chief product of photosynthesis is starch and the pyrenoid with its starch sheath is regarded as being a centre of starch production. After periods of bright illumination, the chloroplast contains many comparatively large starch grains that disappear when the plants are kept in darkness. The movement of materials into and out of the cell must also be regarded as occurring in a way similar to that in higher plants (*see* Vol. II, Chap. 3).

Unless delicate tests are devised to illustrate the intake of oxygen and the output of carbon dioxide, there is no way of demonstrating that respiration is proceeding. It may be considered that *Chlamydomonas* plants respire aerobically, that is to say, they require the presence of oxygen (*see* Vol. II, Chap. 11). Continued absence of oxygen from the water, causes them to cease active movement and soon results in their death.

Growth is manifested by the increase in size of the cell up to a limit. All parts appear to enlarge in proportion except the nuclear material and there is no change in form, the miniature plant resembling the mature one in all respects.

Chlamydomonas plants will respond to changes in external conditions usually by making locomotive movements described as tactic (*see* Vol. II, Chap. 16). Those most frequently studied are in response to changes in light intensity. It can clearly be demonstrated that the plants will move from regions of too high or too low a light intensity to a region selected by them as suitable for their requirements. These changes in light intensity and the direction from which incident light is coming, are detected by the red eye-spot. Locomotive movement is effected by means of the flagella, and there is presumably some co-ordinating link between the locomotor apparatus and the red eye-spot, although none so far has been successfully demonstrated. The forward progression of the cell is accompanied by rotation about its long axis, so that it might be described as corkscrew-like. The mechanism of flagellar movement in *Chlamydomonas* has been investigated but so far no clear explanation has emerged. It is suggested that the flagellum obtains traction by undergoing alternate expansion and contraction thus creating a sine-wave from base to apex. Flagella detached from the cell will continue to beat if supplied with the energy source, ATP, but can be made to undergo a paralysis by chemical treatment. Flagellar chemical composition is comparable with that of muscle proteins, actin and myosin (*see* p. 587).

A condition necessary to the proper functioning of all living cells is that they shall be correctly balanced, osmotically, with their chemical environments (*see* Vol. II, Chap. 3). In *Chlamydomonas*, the contractile vacuoles are considered to function for this purpose. As water enters the cell in excess from outside, or accumulates as a result of internal activities such as respiration, it is collected into the vacuoles which fill to a regular capacity and then are discharged through the cell wall to the exterior. It is interesting to note that mutant forms of *Chlamydomonas* can be obtained, lacking contractile vacuoles. These can live only in media of constant osmotic pressure near 150 kN m^{-2} (about 1·5 standard atm) presumably isotonic with the cell. When normal plants are grown in the same media, they do not form contractile vacuoles, a feature of marine species. When normal freshwater forms are placed in media of gradually increasing osmotic pressure, the frequency of action of the vacuoles is lowered.

Chlamydomonas species exhibit both *asexual* and *sexual* forms of reproduction but there are no special structures associated with either process. The former involves the formation by the parent cell of a variable number of new organisms identical with the parents in all respects except size. The latter involves the formation from the parent of new cells often very similar in form to the parent cells, but they are unable to develop further until the protoplasm of one has been fused with that of another. Such specialized cells are termed *gametes* and the fusion cell from which a new generation can arise is the *zygote*.

Asexual Reproduction

A mature cell comes to rest and in most cases the flagella are absorbed into the cell cytoplasm and the blepharoplasts lose their structure. The whole protoplast becomes less closely applied to the interior of the cell wall and proceeds to divide longitudinally into two, the chloroplast cleaving with the rest. During the process, the red eye-spot does not divide but usually remains in one of the two new cells. Nuclear division is mitotic and an intra-nuclear centrosome divides at the same time. This cleavage is usually followed by a second in which both of the new protoplasts take part simultaneously. This may be followed by yet a third longitudinal cleavage simultaneously by the four new protoplasts. Thus 2, 4, 8 or more new individuals may arise within the parent cell, depending upon its previous nutritive activities. Each of these proceeds to develop into a miniature *Chlamydomonas* plant complete with all the essential features. A new cell wall is produced around each and a red eye-spot quickly takes form. A new locomotive apparatus is developed by activity of the centrosome which extrudes part of itself to the exterior of the nucleus from whence it migrates to the anterior of the cell and there proceeds to divide into two blepharoplasts, each of which becomes the originating point of a new flagellum. Finally, the parent wall gelatinizes and the new cells are released as free swimmers or *zoospores* to continue their activities precisely as their parent did, and eventually to reach its size and form

Under certain conditions, the daughter cells may be inhibited from developing into motile cells. They remain within the parent envelope and produce copious masses of a gelatinous substance. Continuous division and redivision of these non-motile cells together with increasing quantities of the gelatinous matrix produces an irregularly shaped mass containing sometimes thousands of cells. This is the so-called "Palmella-stage" (*Palmella* is another genus of unicellular but non-motile green algae which usually occurs in this condition). These palmelloid

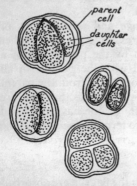

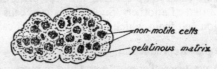

Fig. 5.3. Asexual reproduction in *Chlamydomonas*.   Fig. 5.4. Palmelloid form of *Chlamydomonas*.

cells may regain their motility at any time and continue as normal organisms.

Sexual Reproduction

According to species, *Chlamydomonas* illustrates differing forms of sexual reproduction which, whilst essentially the same, display a trend of advancement in complexity of the nature and origin of the gametes. As described for most species of *Chlamydomonas*, a parent plant may divide into 8, 16, 32 or even more biflagellate gametes which are all of equal size and which appear generally similar in structure with the parent cell except that they are naked, i.e. have no cell wall, and are much smaller. When the gametes are released they do not often unite in pairs from the same parent cell, indicating that many species are *heterothallic*, i.e. exist as more than one strain (cf. *homothallic*), sexual compatibility being achieved only between different strains. Groups of compatible gametes clump together and then separate in pairs with their flagella adhering. The gametes then merge into one zygote which develops a thick wall, i.e. encysts, and becomes a *zygospore*. This is later followed by a division of the contents, typically into four proto-plasts each of which changes into a biflagellate *Chlamydomonas* cell. This division is known to be meiotic and hence it can be assumed that all normal *Chlamydomonas* cells are haploid, the zygote only being diploid. These cells are released and eventually mature into the adult vegetative structure. Such sexual reproduction is described as *isoga-mous* since all fusing gametes are morphologically identical.

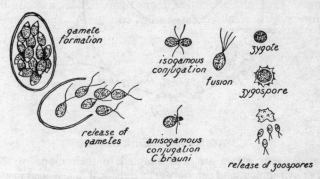

Fig. 5.5. Sexual reproduction in *Chlamydomonas*.

In *C. monoica*, the procedure is identical with the above, except that the gametes are not naked. When fusion occurs, the contents of one cell are passed into the other through the region where the cell walls break down on contact.

In *C. brauni*, different individuals produce gametes of unequal sizes and sometimes slightly differing characteristics. The smaller ones are called *micro-gametes* and the larger ones *macro-* or *mega-gametes*. When fusion occurs, it is always between one large gamete and one small one. Such fusion of gametes is referred to as *anisogamous*.

Lastly, in *C. coccifera*, there is considerable difference in the mode of origin of the gametes. One type is formed as are those in *C. brauni*, but the other type consists of the whole of an ordinary cell which undergoes no division, but enlarges, loses its flagella and becomes non-motile. We shall see in more advanced algae that this condition in which one gamete is large and non-motile when compared with the other, is a much more constant feature and that such a gamete is produced in a specialized cell called an *oogonium*, so that the condition is referred to as *oogamous* Some would consider that the mode of sexual reproduction in *C. coccifera* represents a very simple and primi-tive form of oogamy.

Life Cycle

The life cycle of *Chlamydomonas* may be summarized diagrammatically as shown below.

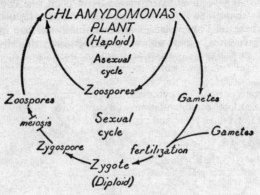

Adaptation to Environment

Chlamydomonas plants are well adapted to their mode of life in a watery environment and can only exist outside it in a special resting and resistant form. The main activities are concerned with obtaining and utilizing materials for food manufacture and in reproduction. Nutrients may not have to be sought, but in finding a good position in the light, the locomotive apparatus in conjunction with the red eye-spot serve their purpose. The contractile vacuoles ensure a balance between internal and external osmotic conditions. Gamete motility favours their coming together to effect fertilization, whilst the resistant zygospore condition affords a means of survival during bad conditions and possible dispersal to new freshwater localities.

Classification

The taxonomic position of the genus is clearly outlined in Chap. 4, and will not be repeated here. To complete his knowledge of each plant type genus, the student is referred to that chapter for its classification in this and every subsequent case.

Special Features of Biological Importance

Chlamydomonas plants serve well to illustrate a number of features of biological importance. These include the existence of single cells as complete self-sufficient units, and a consequent high degree of cytoplasmic differentiation associated with special functions; photo-autotrophism; motility in plants; plant reproductive processes; the haplont vegetative plant body.

The Unicellular Condition

Chlamydomonas plants exist as single protoplasmic units capable of performing all the functions of living things. When compared as a whole plant body with the highly-differentiated multicellular plant, the condition must be regarded as simple and primitive. But when compared as a cell with any particular cell of the higher plant, the condition is not one of simplicity. Rather it is the reverse, because whereas the higher plant cell is usually highly specialized to perform one particular function, only the unicell is able to perform them all. Consequently its protoplasm shows a complexity of differentiation not shared by the cells of more complex plants. For example, we can recognize parts of the cytoplasm specially concerned with nutritional activity, locomotion, osmoregulation and irritability and in addition the whole is able to respire, grow and reproduce. Such a cell cannot be simple. It must be regarded as representing the highest degree of complexity capable of being reached by a single mass of protoplasm. If the cells of higher plants are to be compared with this, then they must represent a reduced but specialized condition in which the cell has developed to perform no more than one or two of these functions with consequently a lower degree of protoplasmic differentiation, but a capacity for performing its special functions with a much higher degree of efficiency. We see in the higher plants aggregations of specialized cells, co-ordinated to act in harmony for the benefit of all, a *division of labour*. In a *Chlamydomonas* plant we see the wholly self-sufficient single mass of protoplasm.

Photo-autotrophism

Such a plant is entirely self-sufficient in the sense that it is able to synthesize all its requirements using light as a source of energy and inorganic substances found in its environment for materials. We say it is photo-autotrophic. It is able to live in this way by reason of its powers to synthesize the pigment chlorophyll, a characteristic of most plant forms. Animals, unable to develop chlorophyll in their cells, must rely on the synthesizing powers of the plants and can build their substance only from energy-rich compounds ultimately derived from plants. We say they are heterotrophic.

Motility in Plants

Motility of the vegetative plant body is to be found only in those showing the lowest grade of organization; the unicellular or small colonial plants. It must be regarded as another primitive characteristic. The higher plants, in evolving to their successful sedentary condition, have lost all locomotive powers except in the reproductive cells, where at least one of the gametes is freely motile in every type of plant except the most highly-evolved land plants.

Plant Reproductive Processes

Reproductive processes in plants can be described as sexual or asexual (non-sexual). The former process implies the development of specialized cells which cannot continue to develop further unless fused with a comparable cell, the two then developing as one. Such cells are called gametes. The latter process implies any other means of reproduction whereby single cells or groups of cells may be formed, which can develop into a new generation without any fusion process having to occur. There are two fairly clearly distinguishable cases of asexual reproduction. First, there is the case in which individual cells (spores) are developed solely for the purpose of reproduction in special structures (sporangia). Secondly, a plant may reproduce by separating parts composed of many cells of the vegetative body. Both cases, strictly speaking, are asexual processes, but it is convenient to distinguish between them by referring to the first as asexual reproduction and the second as vegetative reproduction.

Chlamydomonas plants exhibit both the sexual and asexual processes by these definitions. In the sexual process, we see within the genus a gradual trend of advance from the simplest condition of isogamy to anisogamy, coupled in one instance with the loss of motility by one of the gametes. In addition it is to be noted that even in the isogamous cases, only rarely do the isogametes from the same parent cell fuse. This indicates the condition of *heterothallism*, meaning that there are at least two body forms. Morphologically this is not evident so we must assume that it is some physiological difference between the cells which gives rise to the formation of complementary gametes. Where a species is anisogamous, this difference is clearly manifested at gamete production, where some cells produce the micro-gametes and others the mega-gametes, but never both. In higher unisexual organisms, the distinction between the body forms is often clearly morphological as well as physiological and is manifested as *sexual dimorphism* (*see* Vol. II, Chap. 17).

The Haplont Vegetative Plant

In plants, the life cycle may include only one form of vegetative plant, or there may be two separate vegetative phases within the same cycle, one producing gametes and the other reproducing asexually by spores. A plant existing in only one vegetative form is said to be *haplobiontic* and its nuclear condition may be haploid or diploid. When existing in two forms, it is said to be *diplobiontic* and in such a case one of the bodies is haploid and the other diploid, the two regularly alternating with each other in the cycle. *Chlamydomonas* plants clearly illustrate the first case and are in fact haplont. We shall see cases illustrating each of these varying conditions in plant life cycles.

CHLORELLA

This genus includes about nine British species. *C. vulgaris* is an example.

Habitat

The plants are of very common occurrence and abound in ponds and ditches and other stagnant water, but not in clean open lakes and seas.

The surface of wet soil is also their home and many can be found actively alive at some depth below the soil surface. The green, powdery growth on tree trunks and damp walls is often composed of millions of chlorella plants. *C. conductrix* occurs in the cells of some protozoans, e.g. *Stentor*, and of *Chlorohydra viridissima*, where it lives symbiotically, (*see* p. 179).

Vegetative Structure

Each young plant, of the simplest possible structure, consists of a single spherical cell of about 5–10μ diameter, with a thin outer wall (*see* Fig. 5.6). The cell wall is probably not of pure cellulose, but of

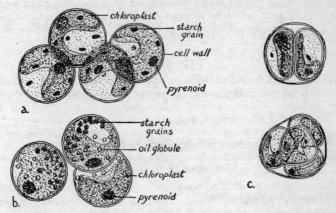

Fig. 5.6. *Chlorella.* (a) Young plants. (b) Old plants. (c) Reproduction.

some allied polysaccharide. The protoplast is non-vacuolated, except in older cells, and embedded in the peripheral cytoplasm is a single curved, plate-like chloroplast. In older cells, the chloroplast may extend to line the wall completely except for a small opening on one side. In *C. pyrenoidosa* a conspicuous pyrenoid is present. A single, small, haploid nucleus occurs near the centre of the cell. Old cells may contain starch grains and possess cell walls substantially thicker than those of young ones.

Physiology

Much study has been made of the metabolic activities of chlorella plants, with particular reference to photosynthesis (*see* Chap. 10, Vol. II). For photosynthesis to occur the plants must be given, in the presence of light, the necessary mineral substances including nitrates or ammonium compounds, sulphates, phosphates, potassium and magnesium and in trace amounts, iron and manganese, as well as carbon dioxide and water. When all the necessary nutrients are available and the cells are at the right temperature (20–25° C), they can double their organic content in about 15 hours. In addition to this photo-autotrophic way of life, chlorella plants can exist heterotrophically. Given the right kinds of organic substances in their culture medium, they can grow perfectly well in total darkness. In most cases, the cells do not even lose their chlorophyll and can become photo-autotrophic again as soon as light is available. This heterotrophic capacity accounts for the green cells being found at some depth in the soil where suitable organic compounds are present. As a result of its metabolism, each cell increases in size up to a maximum, changing form slightly as it does so. It then undergoes mitotic division so that one mature cell becomes two young ones.

Reproduction

This is vegetative by cell division as described above. No spores of any kind are produced and there is no gamete formation.

Life Cycle

The diagram below summarizes the life cycle.

Adaptation to Environment

There are no such obvious adaptations to a watery environment as may be seen in *Chlamydomonas*. The cells lack locomotive apparatus, eye-spots and contractile vacuoles. Nevertheless, the delicate cells can multiply only in water or in very damp situations. They can exist in an inactive state, however, under dry conditions when the cells become extremely resistant to desiccation. This presumably results from internal physiological changes. Cells in such a state can clearly be dispersed by air over great distances to new sites of active growth.

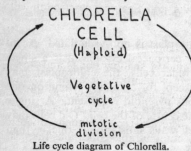

Life cycle diagram of Chlorella.

Special Features of Biological Importance

The unicellular, non-motile condition of plants may be taken as a starting point for the evolution of higher green plants, since it seems reasonable to suppose that such plants could only have arisen from ancestral forms which had already lost motility of vegetative parts.

CHAPTER 6

A SIMPLE PROTOZOAN: AMOEBA

THE subject of this and the preceding chapter show sharp distinction in their modes of life. Structural and physiological differences reflect this in many ways. By these differences we distinguish, in general, between free-living plants and animals.

AMOEBA

The amoeba was first recorded by von Rosenhof in 1755. He referred to it as "the little Proteus." Linnaeus gave it the rather impressive name of *Chaos chaos*. The lack of visible differentiation led early observers to regard it as an extremely simple animal. Its simplicity is deceptive; its tiny protoplasmic mass possesses all the essential capabilities of the higher animals. It is not to be regarded as primitive, as much as a very specialized animal, suitably adapted for its particular niche in the world.

There are many species of *Amoeba* known. They vary in size from a minimum diameter of about 10μ to 1 mm. The species usually cultured and supplied by dealers is *A. proteus*, though diligent search of ponds may reveal any of the three other large species, *A. discoides*, *A. kerri*, or *A. lescherae*. The four are much alike, and a general description will suffice for all.

Habitat and Habits

They may be found creeping on the mud of shallow ponds and slow-flowing streams, especially where there is plentiful decaying organic material. Sometimes they drift at various levels in the water. When conditions are suitable there is ceaseless erratic motion in reaction to favourable or unfavourable stimuli. The full-grown amoeba divides into two; old amoebae sporulate. In unfavourable conditions there is encystment.

Damp soil harbours many small species and several types occur in man. *Entamoeba gingivalis* is the mouth amoeba; it is said to feed on bacteria at the bases of the teeth. *E. coli* feeds on bacteria in the large intestine. *E. histolytica* is a parasite, consuming the cells lining the lower part of the gut. It causes amoebic dysentery. (*see* Chap. 32).

General Features

The animal is just visible to the unaided eye as a white speck. The young adults normally studied will be about 0·1 mm diameter. Viewed under the microscope, it appears as an irregularly-lobed mass of greyish jelly. The protoplasm shows differentiation into three distinct zones. There is an outer, clear, thin zone of *plasmagel*, which appears to be of firmer consistency than the rest of the protoplasm. Within this plasmagel is the more fluid *plasmasol*, packed with granules of various sizes. In the plasmasol is a biconvex *nucleus*, which in the living animal is clear and shining. Projecting from the general body surface are the *pseudopodia*, again consisting of plasmagel and plasmasol. They are concerned with locomotion, and with food capture.

The most obvious inclusion in the protoplasm is the *contractile vacuole*, a clear spherical structure at some point near the external surface. It is 30μm to 50μm in diameter and it will be seen to discharge its fluid contents periodically into the surrounding water. Scattered throughout the plasmasol are *food vacuoles* of different sizes; some are

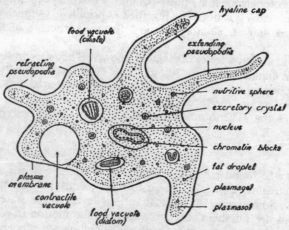

Fig. 6.1. An amoeba seen in optical section.

large, containing recently-ingested food particles; some contain food particles in various stages of digestion; still others contain the indigestible remains of food. Smaller vacuoles contain nutritive spheres of a stored food product consisting of a carbohydrate allied to starch. Yet other vacuoles contain crystals of various shapes and sizes which are excretory materials. Besides these larger inclusions, there are very numerous minute granules packed into a hyaline matrix.

Outer Layer of the Body

The body is bounded by a delicate *plasma membrane*; it cannot be resolved by the light microscope. There is evidence that it is probably composed of lipoid and protein molecules arranged in a definite pattern, not more than four molecules thick, possessing little intrinsic strength but considerable elasticity. It has some measure of control over exchange of substances; it prevents the animal sticking to the substratum and it maintains the protoplasm as a coherent unit. If the amoeba is torn with a fine needle, the cytoplasm begins to flow out into the water, but a fresh covering of plasma membrane is quickly formed, and soon, beneath it, plasmagel appears.

Support

Since an amoeba does not maintain a definite shape, it merely has to keep its protoplasm from dispersing. The plasmagel and plasma membrane suffice for this purpose. Since it can creep along the substratum or float, with equal facility, its specific gravity can be little different from that of the water, and hence its weight in water is negligible. Thus no specialized skeletal or supporting structures are necessary.

Nutrition and Food Storage

The larger amoebae will ingest both plant and animal material. Rotifers, flagellates, ciliates, diatoms, desmids, bacteria and any kind of

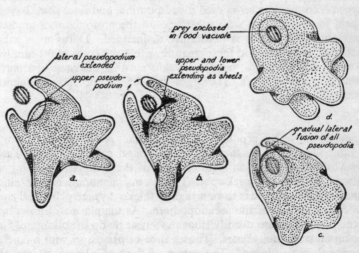

Fig. 6.2. An amoeba capturing a ciliate.

plant or animal debris, are all utilized. It is said that they thrive best on and even show preference for animal material, especially small ciliates and flagellates. A hollow pseudopodium or food cup flows round the food particle and then is closed. Thus the particle is trapped in the amoeba's body together with a drop of water. This whole structure is a food vacuole and within it, digestion takes place by means of enzymes secreted by the protoplasm. Micro-injection of harmless indicators has shown that the fluid in the vacuole has at first an acid reaction, and later is alkaline. It is interesting to note that these two successive phases of digestion are found even in man, where there is an acid phase in the stomach and an alkaline phase in the small intestine.

The digested material, soluble and diffusible, passes into the surrounding protoplasm and undigested portions are eliminated by the simple process of leaving them behind as the animal moves. There is no definite anal spot; faecal matter may be egested at any point on the surface. An amoeba flows round its food, and flows away from its faeces.

Storage products consist of minute fat droplets and nutritive spheres of an insoluble polysaccharide. These spheres increase in size as the animal grows, and at sporulation they disappear entirely.

Respiration

An amoeba is aerobic and thus requires a supply of free oxygen from the surrounding medium. It is obtained by diffusion in solution and this necessitates the establishment of a diffusion gradient. Since internal oxygen is continually being used for respiration, and since some oxygen is held in combination with substances in the protoplasm, a gradient from outside to inside is constantly maintained. Diffusion is rapid over small distances, and for a creature with a thickness of 0·1 mm will take only a few seconds, but for a creature with a thickness of 1 mm it would take several hours. The largest amoebae will not have a thickness greater than 0·1 mm.

Locomotion

Amoebae move by producing pseudopodia. At the point where a pseudopodium is to be formed, the plasmagel softens and plasmasol flows towards this region from the rest of the cytoplasm, causing an outward bulge at this weak spot. The plasma membrane is maintained intact, and there appears to be a slightly thicker hyaline plasmagel zone protecting the end of the pseudopodium. As the plasmasol flows into it, the pseudopodium steadily elongates; near its tip the plasmasol fans out on all sides and gelates. Thus a tube of plasmagel with a core of plasmasol is developed. The cause of flow of plasmasol into the pseudopodium is not certainly known. Three possible explanations have been suggested. Firstly, the plasmagel in the posterior region may contract and squeeze the plasmasol forward. Secondly, the plasmasol gelating in the anterior region may contract and suck or pull the rest of

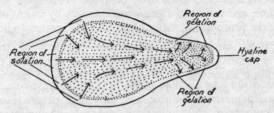

Fig. 6.3. Changes of state and directions of flow of cytoplasm during pseudopodium formation by an amoeba.

the plasmasol towards it. Thirdly, the fixed molecules on the inner face of the plasmagel may push the plasmasol molecules along by a kind of ratchet or shearing action. (*see* Ch. 12, Vol. II). Several pseudopodia may be developing at the same time; their shape is a diagnostic character for distinguishing the species.

If unidirectional movement is maintained, the whole of the body will have flowed into the pseudopodium, and thus the amoeba will have changed position as well as shape. This unidirectional movement is rare; it is far more usual for the animal to probe its environment with several pseudopodia simultaneously, and thus a very erratic course is pursued. It must be noted that pseudopodia are not projected in one plane only; often a lateral view will show the animal with the tips of

Fig. 6.4. Lateral view of an amoeba showing the body raised from the substratum and supported on the tips of the pseudopodia.

pseudopodia touching the substrate, so that it appears to be walking on tentacles.

Recent study of the movement of an amoeba seems to indicate that there are definite anterior and posterior regions and that it normally progresses with a particular region leading. Simultaneous production of a number of pseudopodia tends to obscure this.

Growth

From digested food, the amoeba selects the requisite amino-acids and other components necessary for synthesizing more of its own protoplasm. Thus the body grows to a maximum which is determined partly by the area/volume ratio and partly by the age of the culture. Then division ensues. In a fresh culture, this maximum size is less than it is in an older culture. After cell separation, the daughter-cells begin the process of growth again.

Excretion

The carbon dioxide resulting from respiration is excreted by diffusion. Since there is constant production of carbon dioxide within the animal, there will be a greater concentration in its protoplasm than there is in the surrounding water and hence the net movement of carbon dioxide molecules will be outward. The nitrogenous excretory materials are said to be ammonium compounds, possibly ammonium carbonate, but some investigators report an increase in uric acid or urates in water containing amoeba cultures.

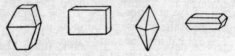

Fig. 6.5. Excretory crystals of *Amoeba*.

A young amoeba, emerging from a spore, does not contain excretory crystals. They soon appear and gradually increase in size as the culture ages, and then, at sporulation, the crystals are discarded. It is probable that most of the nitrogenous excretory material is isolated from the protoplasm by crystallization in these small vacuoles.

Osmoregulation

Freshwater species of *Amoeba* must absorb considerable quantities of water by osmosis. In addition there will be excretory water produced by respiration. To cope with this continual increase of internal water, the organelle known as the contractile vacuole has been evolved. Under normal conditions it fills and empties every few minutes. There is a fairly accurate relationship between the quantity of water expelled by the vacuole, and the difference in osmotic pressure between the internal and external fluids. Since the vacuole fills against an osmotic gradient, work has to be done. This involves expenditure of energy, and it is significant that if the animal's oxygen supply is reduced, the vacuolar rate slows down. One would expect that if the vacuole is purely an osmoregulatory apparatus, then placing the amoeba in a stronger solution would slow down the vacuolar frequency. This is found to be the case. Marine species, living in a fluid which is isotonic with their internal solution, do not possess contractile vacuoles.

Gradual introduction of these species into freshwater brings the need for osmoregulation and contractile vacuoles are formed. Since the quantity of water expelled is considerable in relation to the size of the amoeba, there must be incidental excretion via the contractile vacuole.

Sensitivity and Behaviour

The amoeba has no visible organelles specialized for the perception of stimuli; the whole of the protoplasm shows generalized sensitivity. It prefers the dim, diffuse light to be found in its natural habitat. If a bright beam of light is directed on it, it slows down, then stops, and finally proceeds in the reverse direction, though erratically. If an intermittent fine beam is repeatedly shone on the tip of a pseudopodium, the amoeba reacts by first putting out a number of small lateral pseudopodia; these are withdrawn, and finally a large pseudopodium causes movement in the reverse direction. If the same stimulus is repeated after an interval of twenty-four hours or less, then the amoeba will respond by putting out the reverse pseudopodium, omitting the tentative lateral ones. The animal may be said to have learnt by experience, and this may be adduced as evidence of a very feeble power of memory.

Stimulus with very dilute chemical solutions causes the production of pseudopodia towards the stimulus. With stronger solutions, the animal comes to a halt, and then proceeds in the reverse direction. It shows selectivity in its choice of food and will actually pursue moving prey. In this connexion, we may note that it varies the size of its food cup, opening it widely for catching motile prey, while diatoms and other immotile food particles are closely enveloped. Violent jolting or an electric shock will cause withdrawal of all pseudopodia and the assumption of a spherical shape. Stimulus by the touch of a fine needle will bring the animal to a halt, and if the irritation persists, it will move in some other direction.

In general, it may be said that although its responses are sluggish, it does perceive and react to the same major stimuli as do the higher animals. All its behaviour is adaptive and conducive to its survival.

Reproduction—Binary Fission

Young adult amoebae, living in a favourable environment, divide by binary fission every three or four days. The whole process takes from fifteen to twenty minutes, the nucleus dividing by a rather peculiar mitosis. The chromosomes are extremely small and there are over five hundred present. Separation of the chromatids in anaphase appears to be achieved almost entirely by the enormous elongation of the region between the two daughter nuclei. Thus, as telophase is approaching, the daughter nuclei appear to be joined together by a long narrow bridge, even when cell separation is almost completed. The nuclei still appear to be in telophase when the daughter cells have separated.

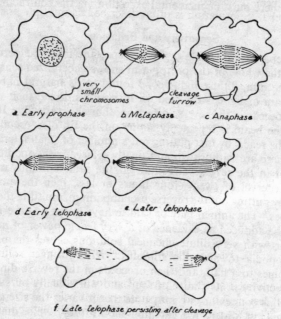

a. *Early prophase*   b *Metaphase*   c *Anaphase*

d *Early telophase*   e *Later telophase*

f *Late telophase persisting after cleavage*

Fig. 6.6. Stages in binary fission in *Amoeba*.

However, the normal interphase nucleus is quickly restored, and the daughter amoebae are soon actively engaged in feeding.

Reproduction—Sporulation

Before each successive binary fission, the size of the amoebae is slightly increased. The nutritive spheres and the excretory crystals become larger. After several months, the full-grown amoebae seem to lose the power of binary fission; they feed less frequently; the protoplasm assumes a yellowish tint and becomes more viscous; their bodies are less transparent, and in general, they show signs of senescence. Such individuals then begin the process of sporulation. The nuclear membrane disintegrates at one or more points and chromatin blocks migrate into the cytoplasm and aggregate in small groups. A portion of cytoplasm envelops each group, and thus a large number of small spores, often several hundreds, appear within the body. Each spore develops its own tough, resistant wall, forming a cyst, while the residual cytoplasm containing the excretory crystals, disintegrates, and the liberated spores remain quiescent for varying periods. Spore formation has also been described as occurring within a large cyst formed by the old amoeba. Sporulation is often described as multiple fission.

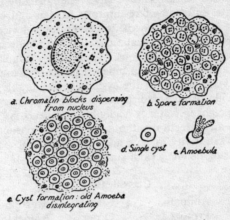

a. Chromatin blocks dispersing from nucleus

b. Spore formation

d. Single cyst

e. Amoebula

c. Cyst formation: old Amoeba disintegrating

Fig. 6.7. Diagram of sporulation in *Amoeba*.

In the encysted state, the protoplasm can withstand a considerable period of desiccation, and temperatures well below the freezing point of water. Thus the race survives periods of drought, when the pond may be completely dried up, and also is able to withstand the rigours of winter. When the cysts are again covered with water at a suitable temperature, very small amoebulae emerge, and the active stage of the life begins again. Dispersal takes place in the encysted state by means of dust blown from dried-up ponds, or in mud on the feet of various animals; it is very effective since pond amoebae are ubiquitous in distribution.

The process of sporulation is not necessarily a response to environmental conditions. It is known to occur invariably in cultures kept in consistently favourable conditions and a fairly regular rhythm has been observed. The sporulation phases, when no active amoebae are to be found, probably account for the "depression" periods which have been often described. No sexual process has been observed in any of the freshwater species mentioned earlier. Some workers have bred and observed *A. proteus* for hundreds of generations and found no evidence of sexual reproduction. Possible sexual processes have been described for certain parasitic amoebae.

Adaptation to Environment

The very small size of the animal, its neutral colour against the background of mud, and its preference for dimly-lit situations, all conspire to give it a good measure of protection against predators. Its sluggish movement is not to be discerned easily. The normally flattened form ensures adequate diffusion of respiratory oxygen and excretory substances, and the contractile vacuole is an admirable device for pumping out excess water. It is not specialized in its food requirements; indeed it may be described as omnivorous. The amoeba population is maintained by the rapid succession of binary fissions in favourable periods, and by the survival powers of the cysts in unfavourable periods. The cysts also provide means of dispersal and thus colonization of fresh territory. Its weight in water is negligible and hence pseudopodia can be projected in any direction without the need for particular stiffening. Its generalized sensitivity and its adaptive behaviour both contribute towards increasing its chances of survival.

Classification

Kingdom:	Animalia	Class:	Rhizopoda (Sarcodina)
Sub-kingdom:	Protozoa	Order:	Amoebina
Phylum:	Protozoa	Family:	Amoebidae
		Genus:	*Amoeba*
		Species:	*A. proteus*, etc.

Members of the order Amoebina are characterized by blunt pseudopodia not uniting to form networks, and by the absence of vacuolar structures in the plasmagel. Their reproduction is usually by binary or multiple fission and dispersal takes place during the encysted stage. The family Amoebidae is distinguished from others in this order by the absence of a shell. In the genus *Amoeba*, there is a contractile vacuole, and in the species *A. proteus* the pseudopodia are often very long and sometimes branched; in the single nucleus, the chromatin is present in scattered granules.

Special Features of Biological Importance

Some topics of biological importance arising from the study of *Amoeba* are heterotrophism; the protoplasmic level of organization; the duration of life; the incidence of amoeboid motion; the importance of the nucleus.

Heterotrophism

The amoeba illustrates clearly the essential characteristics of heterotrophes. It cannot synthesize all its components from simple inorganic chemicals, and therefore is dependent upon its intake of already-elaborated substances.

These have to be broken down into soluble and diffusible form, then useful components are incorporated into the body and useless and undigested materials are eliminated. There is thus a necessity for organelles for food capture and for digestion. It has marked sensitivity to the presence of suitable food material and a method of placing itself within grasping distance of it.

The Protoplasmic Level of Organization

An amoeba carries out all its functions and contains all its multifarious components within one single unit of protoplasm. Compared with some other groups of Protozoa, it shows but little differentiation. Being of a non-cellular nature, we do not describe any specialized portions of the body as organs, but as organelles. Such are the contractile vacuole, the food vacuoles, and the vacuoles containing nutritive spheres and excretory crystals. The pseudopodia are to be regarded as temporary organelles. Finally, it possesses the basic constituents of all protoplasts, the plasma membrane, the plasmagel and plasmasol, and a nucleus bounded by the nuclear membrane. Within the nucleus are the vitally important chromosomes bearing the genes.

The Duration of Life

An amoeba does not suffer natural death. At the senescent stage, sporulation takes place, and from the protoplasm of the old individual, hundreds of amoebulae are fashioned. In all animals at the metazoan level of organization, special germ cells are set aside for the continuance of the race by individuals produced from sexual union. No germ cells are produced by an amoeba but the greater part of the body has the potential immortality of the germ cells of Metazoa. Amoebae which die, do so by accident; they are eaten by predators; the drought lasts too long; the cysts alight on an unsuitable substratum, or the pond is polluted.

Incidence of Amoeboid Motion

While amoeboid motion is possibly not the most primitive type, it is interesting to note how common it is in the animal kingdom. Many members of the two protozoan classes, Flagellata and Sporozoa, show this type of movement at some stage of the life. The leucocytes (white corpuscles) of blood, not only move as an amoeba does, but also ingest particles in the same manner. In embryonic formative movements, often described as "streaming of cells," the actual movement of each cell is performed by means of pseudopodia. Wounds in the bodies of metazoan animals are healed by the pseudopodial activity of cells at the cut surfaces reaching out across the gaps. Finally, the technique of tissue culture has shown that many types of cells which are extremely specialized when in position in the body, can behave like an amoeba if grown in suitable media.

Importance of the Nucleus in Amoeba

The absence of a firm external covering, and the power of reforming plasma membrane and plasmagel after damage, have both helped to make the amoeba a good subject for experiments in micromanipulation, especially of the nucleus.

If an amoeba is cut into two approximately equal portions, with one containing the nucleus, the nucleated half will soon begin to function normally and will grow to the original size. The other portion will be capable of slow movement and will ingest food particles, but cannot digest them. Hence it will eventually perish. This suggests that the nucleus is either the source of the digestive enzymes or instigates their development in the cytoplasm. De Fonbrune performed some famous experiments on amoebae at the Pasteur Institute. He showed that the nucleus could be removed and replaced by a nucleus of another amoeba of the same species. The animals thus treated, soon recovered and functioned normally. In recent years, many experiments have been carried out on the interchange of nuclei between *A. proteus* and *A. discoides*. The results seem to indicate that while the types of molecules which a cell can make are determined entirely by nuclear factors, the arrangement of structural and functional systems in the cell is principally effected by cytoplasmic determinants. In the nuclear interchanges mentioned above, viable amoebae were produced which showed some of the characteristics of the two species concerned. Further reference to cytoplasmic determinants is made in Ch. 19, Vol. II.

The Position of Amoeba in the Animal Kingdom.

The amoeba is sometimes regarded as being the most primitive of existing animals and has even been considered the ancestral type from which all animals evolved. There is, however, some evidence that the flagellate form is the more primitive. Certain amoebae have flagella-like pseudopodia, and several species can change from the amoeboid to the flagellate form, but no adult flagellates ever possess pseudopodia. Many flagellates have chlorophyll and live autotrophically; a few are capable of both autotrophic and heterotrophic modes of life. Some flagellates possess contractile vacuoles and eye-spots, often regarded as typical animal characteristics, while still living the typically autotrophic existence of green plants. From these facts, it seems that the flagellate form is more primitive than the amoeboid. The question of the original ancestral animals must remain largely a matter of speculation.

The little Proteus, named after a mythical god who was presumed to be capable of adopting many forms, is a modern animal, adapted to its environment, but showing little differentiation or division of labour.

CHAPTER 7

AN INDETERMINATE ORGANISM: EUGLENA

WE have seen the characteristics of simple plant and animal forms in the genera *Chlamydomonas* and *Amoeba* respectively. This chapter deals with a type of organism which possesses a mixture of both.

EUGLENA

Both botanists and zoologists have described this genus and it may be found in classifications of the plant and animal kingdoms.

Habitat and Habits

During the warmer months of the year, both green and colourless euglenae are plentiful in ponds and puddles, especially where there is likely to be organic nitrogenous material in solution. They abound in the vicinity of farmyards where the drainage water is rich in manurial substances. There are also a few species of brackish and salt waters. The water is often green in colour, due to the enormous numbers of these little organisms. The species described here, *Euglena viridis*, is a minute spindle-shaped creature, swimming in a rotatory manner by means of its single flagellum. It is a photosynthesizer, reproduces by asexual means only, and it encysts during cold or dry periods.

General Features

There is great variation in size among the species of *Euglena*, the length ranging from 30μm to 200μm; an average for *E. viridis* is about 130μm. The anterior end is bluntly pointed, the posterior end more acute. Radiating from a central zone are rod-shaped *chloroplasts*. The large and prominent nucleus is nearer the posterior end. In front, a narrow *gullet* leads into a spherical *reservoir*. Around the gullet entrance is a thickened rim inside the outer covering, the *pellicle*. This rim may act as a sphincter. In the cytoplasm, near the base of the gullet, is a prominent red carotinoid pigment spot, or *stigma*. The single *flagellum* is about the length of the body. It bifurcates in the gullet, and one of the branches bears a lens-like thickening opposite the stigma. The two branches of the flagellum cross near the base of the reservoir, pass separately into the cytoplasm and appear to end in two basal bodies. In some species, the threads appear to travel through the cytoplasm to a granule just behind the nucleus. In the cytoplasm just behind the gullet, but slightly out of centre, is a small pulsating *vacuole*, fed by many tributary canals. At the centre of the radiating chloroplasts is a mass of granules consisting of a polysaccharide called *paramylum* $(C_6H_{10}O_5)_n$, which differs from starch and glycogen in giving no colour

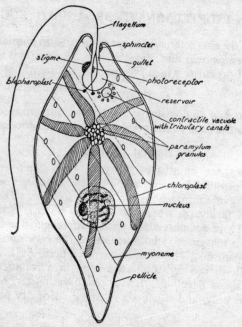

Fig. 7.1. *Euglena viridis* as seen in optical section and at very high magnification.

reaction with iodine. Similar discoid paramylum granules are scattered throughout the cytoplasm. In some species of *Euglena*, very fine spirally-arranged contractile threads can be distinguished beneath the pellicle; they are known as *myonemes*.

Outer Layer of the Body

The body is invested by a thin clear pellicle consisting of non-living material secreted by the cytoplasm. It is flexible enough to allow of the characteristic euglenoid movements brought about by contraction of the myonemes, but firm enough to preclude the formation of pseudopodia. The plasma membrane abuts on the pellicle, then there is a narrow zone of plasmagel and finally the granular plasmasol, which has a distinctly vacuolated appearance.

Skeleton and Support

The shape of the body is maintained by the pellicle, which may be regarded as an *exoskeleton*. The weight of the organism in water is negligible, and it appears to be able to swim with equal facility at varying depths.

Nutrition and Food Storage

Euglena viridis is a photosynthesizer, deriving its carbon dioxide from the pond water and trapping the energy of sunlight with its chloroplasts. In some species, definite pyrenoids are associated with the chloroplasts. The nitrogenous portion of the food appears to be derived from soluble organic compounds such as amino-acids. In *E. viridis*, the gullet does not serve as an aperture for the intake of solid particles, though in some species and in several related genera, the flagellum causes a vortex into the gullet and thus small organisms are taken into the reservoir and engulfed by the cytoplasm which is here devoid of the pellicle. Some species of *Euglena* are colourless and appear to nourish themselves saprozoically by the extracellular digestion of organic compounds. Green euglenae lose their chlorophyll when kept in darkness, but continue to flourish if there is sufficient organic material in solution.

The carbohydrate storage product is paramylum, and proteins accumulate in the pyrenoids. In encysted forms, oil droplets are present.

Respiration

Most euglenae are aerobic, the oxygen being absorbed from the aqueous medium. Green euglenae produce oxygen during photosynthesis, and thus help to make good any lack of oxygen in the somewhat stagnant water they inhabit. Some colourless species, found in the rectum of the frog, live where oxygen is scarce and possibly exist anaerobically.

Locomotion

The flagellum pulls the organism forward. Waves pass along the flagellum from the base to the tip at the rate of twelve per second. Along the flagellum. the waves proceed in a spiral manner, thus causing rotation of the body once per second. The body also gyrates around its posterior end. Thus the anterior end traces out a spiral path about a straight line, rotating about its anterior-posterior axis. As waves pass towards the tip of the flagellum they gain velocity and amplitude, and therefore energy must be expended by the flagellum itself. If the energy for each beat came from the attached end, then the velocity and amplitude would decrease towards the tip. The distance covered by the organism in one second is less than half a millimetre, or about four times its own length.

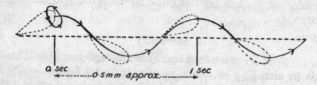

Fig. 7.2. Diagram representing movement in *Euglena*.

The broken line represents the general direction; the full line (spiral) shows the path traced out by the anterior end in gyration; the small ellipse shows the direction of rotation. Four positions of the organism are shown.

As a euglena swims along, waves of contraction may pass along its body from anterior to posterior. These are due to the action of the myonemes; the sequence of changes being known as *euglenoid motion*.

Fig. 7.3. Different shapes of the body seen during euglenoid movement.

A euglena is unable to reverse the direction of motion; it cannot swim backwards. Nevertheless, change of direction is quickly effected by violent flexure of the anterior part of the body.

Growth

From its food, the organism synthesizes all the materials necessary for increase of its body substance. The maximum size achieved is partly dependent upon environmental conditions, but even in the most favourable circumstances it rarely exceeds 300μ in length, the limit being imposed by the area/volume ratio. At the maximum size, it divides longitudinally to form two separate individuals.

Excretion

In green species, there will be little excretory carbon dioxide during the daylight hours, since photosynthesis is proceeding at the same time as respiration. At any time, however, carbon dioxide not utilized for photosynthesis will escape from the general body surface. Nitrogenous excretion also takes place over the whole surface.

The vacuole is fed by radiating smaller tributary canals which discharge their contents into the large one and then are quickly re-formed.

The main vacuole discharges into the reservoir whence the liquid escapes via the gullet. This vacuole system is probably mainly concerned with osmoregulation, though the fluid discharged must also contain excretory materials.

Sensitivity

Euglena viridis is sensitive to favourable and unfavourable stimuli and responds by changing its direction of motion by flexure of the body. It reacts, as do all the protozoa, to light, chemicals, touch, oxygen and carbon dioxide concentration. Its reaction to light stimuli is particularly interesting since, in the stigma and the thickening on the flagellum,

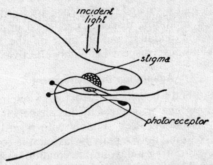

Fig. 7.4. Diagram of the anterior of *Euglena*, showing the position in which the photoreceptor is completely shaded by the stigma.

it possesses a rudimentary optic organelle. Normally it swims parallel to the light rays and towards their source. Other stimuli however often cause it to change its course with respect to the incident light. When the light rays are at right angles to the body, there will be, during the rotation, a position at which the stigma intercepts the light reaching the photoreceptor on the flagellum. At this point, the anterior region bends towards the light source, and the organism is soon swimming parallel to the incident light again.

Reproduction, Survival and Dispersal

Reproduction is by binary fission; there is no authenticated case of sexual reproduction. The organism comes to rest and secretes a mucilaginous covering; often large numbers of euglenae form a mucilaginous mass on the surface of the water. The flagellum is normally withdrawn, and it does not divide. Division appears to begin at the blepharoplasts, then the nucleus undergoes mitosis. Cytoplasmic cleavage is longitudinal, proceeding from the reservoir. Sometimes one daughter organism retains the old flagellum, and the other develops a new one from the blepharoplast. In other cases, the old flagellum seems to be completely absorbed, and both offspring develop new ones.

Palmella forms like those in *Chlamydomonas* may be formed, by repeated binary fission within the mucilage. Eventually the euglenae free themselves from the mucilage and proceed to lead the normal active life.

During the winter and in periods of drought, *Euglena viridis* encysts within a hard resistant covering. The cysts are spherical and red in colour, due to the presence of the pigment haematochrome. In this condition, the organisms can remain dormant for long periods. Binary fission may occur within the cyst. With the return of favourable conditions, the cysts split open and the euglenae are freed.

In the encysted condition, dispersal is effected in dust blown from dried-up ponds and puddles, and in mud on the feet of animals. Euglenae are ubiquitous; dispersal is highly effective.

Adaptation to Environment

The shape of the body is well adapted for swimming, and the firm pellicle obviates any major changes in this shape. It has an efficient mechanism for orientating itself suitably with regard to the incident light. The ability to multiply rapidly in favourable conditions, and to form resistant cysts during unfavourable conditions, are both adaptations to its normal environment. Alternative autotrophic or heterotrophic modes of living give it greater scope in environment.

Classification

Because of its mixture of plant and animal characteristics, as has been stated, *Euglena* is included in both zoological and botanical classification.

Zoological		*Botanical*	
Phylum:	Protozoa		
Class:	Flagellata	Division:	Euglenophyta
Sub-class:	Phytomastigina	Class:	Euglenophyceae
Order:	Euglenoidina	Order:	Euglenales
Family:	Euglenidae	Family:	Euglenaceae
Genus:	*Euglena*	Genus:	*Euglena*
Species:	*E. viridis*, etc.	Species:	*E. viridis*, etc.

Zoological Classification

The sub-class Phytomastigina includes the plant-like flagellates which either possess chloroplasts or other types of chromatophore or are colourless.

They never have more than four flagella. Members of the order Euglenoidina have a firm pellicle which restricts all but "euglenoid" movements effected by the myonemes; they have a single flagellum which arises from the body in the reservoir. The Euglenidae are characterized by their spindle-like shape with the posterior end more pointed than the anterior end. In the genus *Euglena* there is a red eye-spot, and a posterior nucleus. In the species *E. viridis*, there are radiating chloroplasts, pyrenoids, and paramylum granules.

Botanical Classification

Because of the simple body with no distinction into root, stem or leaf, the organism is placed in the division Thallophyta. Aquatic thallophytes with chlorophyll belong to the sub-division Algae. The absence of a definite cell wall, the possession of flagella and pulsating vacuoles place *Euglena* in the Euglenophyceae. The order Euglenales contains pigmented or colourless organisms with a single flagellum, reproducing by binary fission only. Further classification into genus and species is based on the criteria given above.

Special Features of Biological Importance

The peculiar characteristics of *Euglena* provide several topics for discussion. It shows a mixture of plant and animal features, and the ability of certain species to exist autotrophically or heterotrophically affords an interesting field of speculation as to the origin of both plants and animals.

Plant and Animal Characteristics

Plant	Animal
(a) Chloroplasts	(a) Myonemes and euglenoid movement
(b) Pyrenoids	(b) Utilization of amino-acids, peptones or poly-peptides as sources of nitrogen (some species)
(c) Utilization of NO_3 or NH_3 for nitrogen requirements (some species)	(c) Gullet with sphincter and reservoir
(d) Palmella forms	(d) Heterotrophic (some species)
(e) Autotrophic (some species)	

Modes of Life

Some species of *Euglena* are permanently heterotrophic, absorbing all their requirements from the water, while related genera such as *Copromonas*, *Cyathomonas* and *Peranema* take in solid food through the gullet. *E. gracilis*, *E. stellata*, *E. viridis*, *E. anabaena*, *E. deses* and *E. pisciformis* are all autotrophic in the presence of light but they show great variation in their nitrogen requirements. The first three can utilize amino-acids as well as nitrates; *E. anabaena* requires ammonia or ammonium compounds; *E. deses* requires the presence of specific amino-acids, while *E. pisciformis* cannot utilize any of these sources of nitrogen, but must have peptones or polypeptides. There is some evidence that colourless forms may originate by unequal division of green forms, whereby one of the two offspring obtains no chlorophyll. However, most green species appear to be able to survive, if not to flourish,

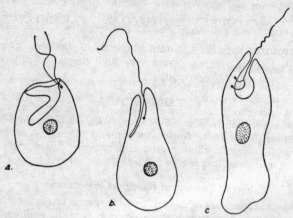

Fig. 7.5. Three common colourless holozoic flagellates. (a) *Cyathomonas*; (b) *Copromonas*; (c) *Peranema*.

in the absence of light. Thus, we have in various members of the Euglenoidina, some which are holozoic, some which are saprozoic and some which are holophytic. All the modes of nutrition possible for free-living forms are exemplified.

The Position of Euglena in the Living World

Some members of the Euglenoidina are typical animals, some have very marked plant characteristics, and some are in an intermediate position. It is probably best to regard them in general, as intermediate forms with a slight leaning to the animal side of the fence. It has already been stated that of the present protozoa, it is likely that the flagellates are the most primitive, though not the least differentiated. The study of *Euglena* will tend to confirm this impression, though it must be emphasized that arguments about probable ancestors of the phylum Protozoa cannot be settled with certainty.

CHAPTER 8

A COMPLEX PROTOZOAN: PARAMECIUM

NOT all protozoa have the apparent simplicity of *Amoeba*. This chapter deals with a form which shows a very high degree of differentiation within a single unit of protoplasm.

PARAMECIUM

This genus is among the most highly evolved of the non-cellular animals. The species, *P. caudatum*, will be described here.

Habitat and Habits

Various species of *Paramecium* are plentiful in freshwater ponds, especially where there is decaying organic matter. A few species are found in sea-water pools.

The animals swim with a slow rotation and frequent changes of direction. Occasionally they may be seen in a stationary position apparently attached to a fragment of vegetation. In good conditions, binary fission takes place two or three times a day, and a peculiar process of conjugation between two individuals, may be observed in crowded cultures.

General Features

The animals have been called the slipper-animalcules because of their undoubted resemblance in shape to a flattened slipper. The blunter end is anterior, and the more pointed end posterior. The size varies considerably in different species, and even in the same species under different conditions. In the common *P. caudatum*, the length is about 240μ. This species is visible to the unaided eye as a greyish-white speck. When the animal is stationary, the ventral surface shows an *oral groove* starting in the left anterior part of the body. The groove narrows inward and backward to a *gullet* which tapers like a long cone inward to the *cytostome* or *cell mouth*, situated in the mid-line of the body about two-thirds of the distance from the anterior end. This ventral surface is somewhat flattened while the dorsal surface is slightly convex. An outer *pellicle* encloses the protoplasm.

The body is covered with *cilia*, arising in pairs from basal granules in the plasmagel and emerging through the pellicle by fine pores. In the gullet are several closely-packed rows of cilia, often referred to as the *undulating membrane*, though evidently no such structure exists. Also embedded in the plasmagel are small spindle-shaped objects called *trichocysts* which discharge long fine threads when the animal is irritated by chemicals, but their probable function is one of attachment while feeding. There are longitudinal *myonemes* in the plasmagel which effect change of shape and enable the animal to squeeze through small apertures. The plasmasol is a homogeneous, granular, dilute gel. The basal granules of cilia and trichocysts are joined by *neuronemes*.

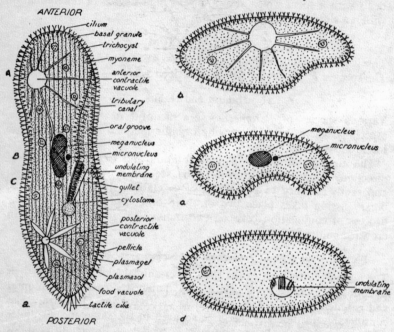

Fig. 8.1. (*a*) Optical section of *Paramecium*, seen from the right side. (*b*), (*c*) and (*d*), vertical sections at the planes indicated by *A*, *B* and *C* respectively.

In the centre of the body, dorsal to the gullet, are a large bean-shaped *meganucleus* and a very small spherical *micronucleus*. There are two *contractile vacuoles* both nearer the dorsal than the ventral surface; the anterior vacuole is one-quarter of the distance from the front end, and the posterior vacuole a similar distance from the hind end. They empty alternately, and each is fed by long radiating canals in the plasmasol.

Food vacuoles circulate in the plasmasol and faecal material is passed out at a fixed *anal pore* on the ventral surface near the posterior end.

Outer Layer of the Body

The pellicle is tough but elastic and is perforated by numerous apertures for the cilia and trichocysts. It bears a well-marked pattern of hexagonal pits separated by narrow ridges. A pair of cilia emerge from the centre

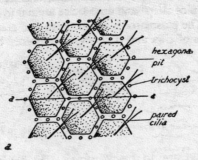

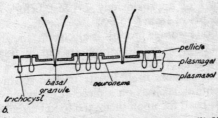

Fig. 8.2. Outer layer of *Paramecium*. (*a*) Surface view. (*b*) Vertical section through *a–a*.

of each pit and beneath the ridges lie the trichocysts. Under the pellicle is a firm cortical layer of plasmagel which contains the basal granules, the neuronemes, the myonemes and the trichocysts.

As in *Euglena*, the only skeletal material is the pellicle, which is an exoskeleton.

Nutrition

The main food consists of bacteria, though any kind of small organic particle will be ingested. Under normal active conditions, a paramecium requires over one thousand bacteria an hour. The cilia of the oral groove draw a cone of water towards the gullet, and any particles contained in the water are drawn down the gullet by the cilia of the undulating membrane. At the base of the gullet is a crossed arrangement of cilia which prevents the passage of large particles. Beyond this filter there is an area of soft plasmasol where a globule of water containing food particles gradually increases in size until it is pinched off by closure of the plasmasol above it. The process is then repeated.

The food vacuoles follow a constant path round the body though no definite canal can be distinguished. From the cytostome, the path makes one turn of a spiral around the gullet, then describes the major part of a figure eight. Undigested particles are finally eliminated at an

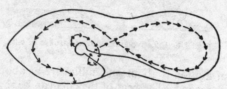

Fig. 8.3. Diagram to show the path of food vacuoles in *Paramecium*.

anal pore almost ventral to the cytostome. The liquid in the vacuoles shows first an acid phase with a pH around 4 and finally an alkaline phase with a pH of approximately 7. Just before defaecation the contents show a pH of from 6 to 6·5.

The carbohydrate storage product is glycogen; the granules accumulate under good feeding conditions, but are rapidly used up, even with a short period of starvation.

A paramecium anchors itself by its trichocysts in an area where bacteria are plentiful, such as on a piece of decaying vegetation. The cilia continue to beat, for upon them, the food current depends.

Respiration

Oxygen is absorbed from the water over the whole surface and its circulation in the body is assisted by the passage of the food vacuoles. The oxygen is utilized for respiratory processes which must be very efficient, for a great deal of energy is used in locomotion. It is to be noted that the respiratory enzymes, at least in part, must be different from those of higher animals, since they are not poisoned by cyanide.

Locomotion

The cilia beat diagonally backwards from left to right, giving rise to the spiral motion. They are almost rigid on the backward power stroke, but limp on the forward recovery stroke. Each cilium is a fraction of a second later in its beat than the one in front of it and thus a rapid series of waves sweeps successively from anterior to posterior. The rhythm is known as *metachronal*; it resembles the passage of successive puffs of wind along a field of wheat. For structure of cilia *see* Fig. 5.2.

The cilia of the oral groove beat more strongly than the rest, and cause the anterior end to gyrate around the posterior end. The end result of the motion is very similar to that of a euglena; it moves forward in a spiral path about a straight line, with the anterior end tracing out a wider spiral than the posterior end.

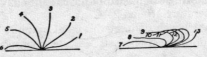

Fig. 8.4. Effective and recovery strokes of cilia.

The speed of motion is about one millimetre or about four times its own length, per second. The beat of the cilia can be reversed, enabling the animal to swim backwards. When this occurs, the cilia are all halted before the backward motion begins. A paramecium can also use its cilia for gliding over a solid substratum.

Growth

Growth of the individual takes place by synthesis of all the components of the body, until a maximum size is attained. Then binary fission follows and there is growth of the population.

Excretion and Osmoregulation

Carbon dioxide is excreted over the whole surface. The nitrogenous excretory product is urea; it passes out through the pellicle. The problem of osmoregulation is solved by the contractile vacuoles. It has been estimated that a paramecium passes out its own volume of water every half-hour. The vacuoles are fed by long narrow canals which radiate out into the cytoplasm. These tributary canals gradually disappear as the main vacuole swells, but before it bursts, they are again visible as narrow ducts. The posterior vacuole has a faster rate of filling and emptying than the anterior one, since the extra surface provided by the gullet means that there is more endosmosis posteriorly.

Sensitivity

Apart from a few long tactile cilia at the posterior end, there are no special sense organelles. The animal is sensitive to dissolved chemicals, oxygen and carbon dioxide concentrations, light, touch and temperature, over the whole surface. The strong beat of the oral groove cilia ensures that it is always sampling the water ahead of it and thus it has advance perception of conditions in front. It reacts to unfavourable stimuli by complete cessation of the cilia for a few seconds, then they beat in reverse, the front end swings round in a wide arc, and the animal tries some other direction. Thus, by trial and error, the paramecia tend to congregate in the most favourable location. They negotiate obstacles by a similar trial and error method, reversing at a slight angle and trying a different direction until a clear path is found. Experiments with cultures in tiny glass tanks show that they prefer a moderate light, and a temperature around 25°C.

The neuronemes which connect the basal granules also play some part in the control of the trichocysts. All the neuronemes originate at

Fig. 8.5. A paramecium circumventing an obstacle by the trial and error method.

Fig. 8.6. End portions of two discharged trichocysts of *Paramecium* showing transverse banding and thorn-like end.

a small darkly-staining granule called the *motorium*, near the gullet; this appears to be a control centre and is appropriately near the position where advance notice of future conditions is received. The system is very highly developed and is sometimes compared with the nervous system of higher animals.

The trichocysts in *Paramecium* appear to be used for the purpose of attachment only, though in some other ciliates they are used for offence, defence and other purposes. The animal will swim purposively towards a concentration of bacteria, then anchor itself by discharging trichocysts. Once ejected, they are broken off the body when it moves away, and are regenerated, probably by the activity of the basal granules.

Paramecium caudatum has been credited with some discernment as to its choice of food particles, not only with regard to size, but also to their nature. It is said to prefer protein and carbohydrate materials and to avoid fats except in conditions of food shortage. It is even stated to prefer some types of bacteria to others.

Reproduction, Dispersal, and Survival

With optimum conditions, asexual reproduction by transverse binary fission takes place two or three times a day. The micronucleus divides mitotically, a very elongated spindle forming within the nuclear membrane. Finally the chromosomes are aggregated at the two ends which

break off and form new micronuclei. The meganucleus divides amitoti-
cally, i.e. random sharing of chromosomes. Then the cytoplasm divides,
and the two daughter individuals separate, and quickly form all the
organelles necessary for active life.

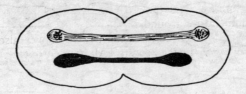

Fig. 8.7. Mitotic division of the micronucleus and amitotic division of the
meganucleus in *Paramecium*.

A sexual process involving *mating* or *conjugation* may often be
observed in cultures. Two paramecia become attached by their ventral
surfaces. Within each conjugant, the meganucleus gradually disintegrates, while the micronucleus performs two successive divisions. Of
the four micronuclei thus formed, three disintegrate, and the sole
surviving nucleus again divides. Thus each member of the pair has two
micronuclei remaining. These act as gametes, and from each paramecium, one nucleus passes over into the mate, where it fuses with the
stationary nucleus to form a zygotic nucleus. The passage of these
nuclei takes place through a small area where the pellicle is broken
down. After this exchange of nuclei, the two animals separate.

It is to be noted that so far there has been no reproduction, and that
a meiosis occurred at some stage before the last division. The fusion
nucleus in each paramecium now divides mitotically three times, so
that eight nuclei are formed and then the body divides transversely, so
that each half has four nuclei. Then there is a further transverse
division, so that from each paramecium we have, produced asexually,
four offspring each having two nuclei. Of the two nuclei, one remains
small and is the micronucleus, while the other increases in size and
becomes the meganucleus. It is known that this becomes polyploid.

Even well-kept cultures will not flourish indefinitely without conjugation or another type of sexual process called *autogamy*, which takes
place every three or four weeks. Unbalance in the chromosome complement of the meganucleus, caused by amitotic division at binary fission,
is responsible for the "depression." During autogamy, involving
paramecia singly, the meganucleus disintegrates, the micronucleus
divides twice, as in conjugation. Three micronuclei disappear and the
remaining one divides into two. These two nuclei now fuse, and binary

fission follows. Since the two fusion-nuclei are identical, then the resulting offspring will be genetically homozygous. Whereas conjugation gives possibilities of variation, autogamy gives pure lines (*see* Vol. II, Chap. 18). In a good culture, maintained for more than four weeks,

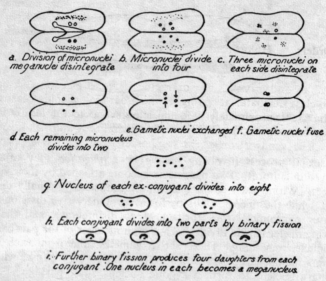

a. Division of micronuclei meganuclei disintegrate   b. Micronuclei divide into four   c. Three micronuclei on each side disintegrate

d. Each remaining micronucleus divides into two

e. Gametic nuclei exchanged   f. Gametic nuclei fuse

g. Nucleus of each ex-conjugant divides into eight

h. Each conjugant divides into two parts by binary fission

i. Further binary fission produces four daughters from each conjugant. One nucleus in each becomes a meganucleus.

Fig. 8.8. Conjugation in *Paramecium*.

every individual will be homozygous; there will be a number of strains, and it is probable that conjugation can take place only between members of different strains.

The details of conjugation vary in different species, the one described being as for *P. caudatum*.

Adaptation

The small size and neutral colour make the animal barely discernible against the background of the bottom of a pond or of the sky above. The rapid motion and ability to perceive the nature of the water ahead of it, ensure that it finds the most favourable conditions present in a particular body of water. The device of anchoring by trichocysts enables it to feed while stationary near a concentration of bacteria (it must be remembered that movement of the cilia is essential to feeding). The circulating vacuoles speed up the even distribution of food materials. The neuroneme system provides for co-ordination of the cilia. The ability to reverse the movement quickly, enables it to back out of danger without turning round. Close consideration of the various organelles will reveal many other adaptive features.

Classification

Phylum:	Protozoa	Family:	Paramecidae
Class:	Ciliophora	Genus:	*Paramecium*
Sub-class:	Euciliata	Species:	*P. caudatum*
Order:	Holotrichida		

The presence of cilia all over the body, a micronucleus and meganucleus, an oral groove, and contractile vacuoles place the animal in the sub-class Euciliata. It belongs to the order Holotrichida because all the cilia are approximately of equal length, and to the family Paramecidae because it is asymmetrical, free-swimming, and has a ventral gullet. The genus *Paramecium* is characterized by the slipper-like shape and the various species are separated by size and by the details of the conjugation process.

Special Features of Biological Importance

A number of important topics arise from the study of *Paramecium*. The high degree of differentiation as compared with *Amoeba* and even *Euglena* is remarkable; the relative importance of the micronucleus and meganucleus needs assessment, and the process of conjugation can be compared with sexual reproduction in higher animals. Also in view of the animal's importance in genetical investigations and in the study of plasmagenes, some mention of these will be made.

Differentiation

The degree of differentiation is best illustrated by a list of the organelles; associated with the various organelles are particular functions. Division of labour and differentiation are inevitably associated as below—

(a) cilia for locomotion and for creating feeding currents;

(b) closely-packed cilia (the undulating membrane) for wafting food particles down the gullet;

(c) straining cilia for particle selection at the base of the gullet;

(d) sensory cilia at the posterior end;

(e) the constant body shape ensured by the tough elastic pellicle;

(f) myonemes allowing slight changes of shape;

(g) neuronemes and the motorium for co-ordination and control of the cilia;

(h) trichocysts for attachment to particles holding large numbers of bacteria;

(i) the cytostome; a fixed cell mouth;

(j) the anal pore; a fixed point for defaecation;

(k) a constant path for circulation of food vacuoles;

(*l*) the two contractile vacuoles, and the efficient and widespread system of collecting canals;

(*m*) the meganucleus for control of somatic activities and the micronucleus for control of reproduction;

(*n*) the possession of plasmagenes, e.g. basal granules which quickly organize the formation of cilia, gullet and other organelles after division.

The Micro- and Meganuclei

The micronucleus contains the diploid number of chromosomes characteristic of the particular species. The meganucleus begins with this same number after either conjugation or autogamy, but then it proceeds to become polyploid owing to repeated multiplication of its chromosome pairs. Amitotic division of the meganucleus at binary fission gives unequal distribution of these chromosomes to the daughter individuals. This leads to unbalance in the normal bodily activities and hence to "depression." Both conjugation and autogamy lead to the production of new meganuclei and thus there is, for a time, normality in the meganucleus (rejuvenation). It seems that the meganucleus controls all bodily activities except reproduction, and that the micronucleus controls reproduction alone.

Comparison of Conjugation with Sexual Reproduction in the Higher Animals

Paramecium

(*a*) Two types of nuclei; meganuclei and micronuclei.

(*b*) Disintegration of meganucleus; potential immortality of micronucleus.

(*c*) Haploid gametic nuclei produced by meiosis.

(*d*) Fusion of two gametic nuclei of different origin to produce a zygotic nucleus.

(*e*) The gametic nuclei which fuse are derived from two different strains.

(*f*) The migratory gametic nucleus carries little or no cytoplasm.

(*g*) Growth of the population by cell multiplication and separation; by binary fission, a large number of individuals derived from each conjugant.

Higher Animals

(*a*) Two types of cells; somatic and germ cells.

(*b*) Death of the soma; potential immortality of the germ cells.

(*c*) Haploid gametes produced by meiosis.

(*d*) Fusion of two dissimilar gametes to produce a zygote.

(*e*) The gametes which fuse are derived from two different sexes.

(*f*) The sperm consists mainly of nucleus and contains very little cytoplasm.

(*g*) Growth of the organism by cell multiplication; all the cells derived from the zygote initially.

Cytoplasmic Determinants

It is becoming increasingly obvious that the genes or hereditary determinants are not confined to the nucleus. *Paramecium spp.* have been used extensively in experiments on cytoplasmic hereditary factors. Certain particles in the cytoplasm appear to arise only by division of pre-existing particles. Such are the basal granules of the cilia, which are known to contain RNA. After fission, these granules are apparently able to organize not only the cilia, but the neuronemes, trichocysts and the gullet.

The "kappa" particles which give rise to the so-called killer strains are now known to be bacteria with enlarged nuclei and little cytoplasm. These bacteria release an excretory product previously known as "paramecin." The strains of *Paramecium* which are able to tolerate the poison, can do so by reason of their possession of a particular nuclear gene. Other strains, not possessing this gene, are killed by the paramecin liberated into the water.

Further reference is made to cytoplasmic determinants in Ch. 19, Vol. II.

The Class Sporozoa

The three protozoan type genera so far studied, *Amoeba*, *Euglena* and *Paramecium*, representing the classes Rhizopoda, Flagellata and Ciliophora, are pre-eminently distinguished by the method of locomotion in the mature state, amoeboid, flagellate and ciliary. The last class of the Protozoa, the Sporozoa, contains only parasites, which are either amoeboid or have no external organs of locomotion. Two genera of the Sporozoa, *Plasmodium* and *Monocystis*, will be considered in Chap. 32 together with other parasitic Protozoa.

CHAPTER 9

SIMPLE MULTICELLULAR GREEN PLANTS: PANDORINA; VOLVOX; PEDIASTRUM; ULOTHRIX; OEDOGONIUM; SPIROGYRA; VAUCHERIA; ULVA; FUCUS

WE may regard species of *Chlamydomonas* and *Chlorella* as illustrative of the most simple forms of plant construction, reproductive processes and life cycles. Much greater complexity in vegetative structure and reproductive mechanisms is to be found within the algae. Advance in vegetative structure alone is along many lines with culminations in colonial, filamentous, expanded sheet and well-differentiated solid forms. The occurrence of very marked oogamy, often, but not always, accompanies the greater vegetative complexity. It is intended here to describe the structure, physiology and life histories of some examples illustrative of these more complicated algae.

MOTILE COLONIAL FORMS OF THE CHLOROPHYCEAE: PANDORINA, VOLVOX

In these genera, the vegetative body is composed of generally identical cells present in constant numbers in each species, and no growth by cell division occurs when the colony is fully formed. Any cell division is the commencement of a new reproductive phase. Such definitely integrated colonies with fixed numbers of cells, specifically arranged, are called *coenobia*. With increasing complexity of structure, there is frequently a limited degree of "division of labour," in that the colony may show definite anterior and posterior ends of differing construction; the anterior being generally more distinctly vegetative and the posterior only, developing the reproductive structures.

PANDORINA

This genus of three species is widely distributed but never in great abundance. The species described here is *P. morum*.

Habitat

It inhabits freshwater ponds and ditches, but seldom in very great numbers.

Vegetative Structure

The coenobium is composed of sixteen chlamydomonas-like cells (occasionally eight or thirty-two) which are pear-shaped and closely packed broad end outwards to form a spherical mass, enclosed in a well-defined envelope of mucilage (*see* Fig. 9.1). Each cell possesses a pair of flagella and the whole structure is motile. It does, however, show marked polarity in its movements in that one point is consistently the anterior and here the cells may vary slightly from the others in

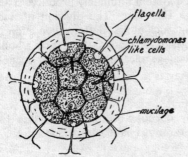

Fig. 9.1. Coenobium of *Pandorina*.

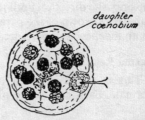

Fig. 9.2. Asexual reproduction in *Pandorina*. Daughter coenobia.

possessing larger eye-spots. There is no direct evidence that the cells are cytoplasmically connected with one another, as is known to be the case in some coenobia. Other than the enlarged red eye-spots there is no vegetative division of labour. When in motion, the whole coenobium rotates around its anterior-posterior axis.

Physiology

Each cell of the coenobium appears to function in ways comparable with a *Chlamydomonas* cell and independently of the rest, except that the locomotive apparatuses operate in unison to produce a steady and regular progression of the colony as a whole. The manner in which this co-ordination is achieved is unknown, since there is no evidence of intercellular connexions. The maturing of a coenobium is seen outwardly only as an increase in size, without increase in cell numbers by division. Under suitable conditions, when maximum size is reached, a reproductive phase is commenced. The coenobia are responsive to light stimuli and execute phototactic movements.

Reproductive Structures

There is never any development of specialized reproductive structures by any of the cells. All function alike reproductively and more or less independently. They are first vegetative and assume the reproductive role apparently without change.

Reproduction

Both asexual and sexual processes are employed.

Asexual Reproduction

Each cell rapidly divides into sixteen daughter cells within the confines of the parent, so that each coenobium ultimately produces sixteen miniature daughter coenobia (*see* Fig. 9.2). The division of a cell results in a curved plakea of cells, which at first flattens then curves in the opposite direction until the edges of the plate unite to form a hollow ball. Breakdown of the parent mucilage releases the daughter coenobia to an independent existence.

Sexual Reproduction

This is usually carried out by coenobia somewhat smaller than normal. Each cell of the parent develops as a gamete (*see* Fig. 9.3),

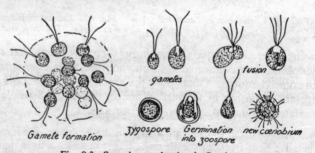

Fig. 9.3. Sexual reproduction in *Pandorina*.

but there is no external sign that the cells have changed their nature from vegetative to reproductive, until the naked protoplast is liberated. The gametes may vary in size, but apart from a tendency towards a greater number of fusions between a small and a large gamete, the process is isogamous. At least, the anisogamous condition is by no means fixed. The zygote resulting from the fusion may enlarge to some extent and then develop around itself a thick outer wall, which is partly of cellulose. Not infrequently, the green of the chloroplast may become obscured by the development of an orange pigmented substance, probably haematochrome. In this condition, as a zygospore, a rest follows. On germination, the zygospore contents divide into four and usually only one of these develops into a motile swarmer or zoospore which escapes and soon undergoes division to form a new coenobium of sixteen cells. Whilst it cannot be certain, there is every reason to suppose that the division of the zygote is meiotic so that the new coenobium is haploid. This is known for certain in the related genus *Gonium*.

Life Cycle

The following diagram summarizes the life cycle—

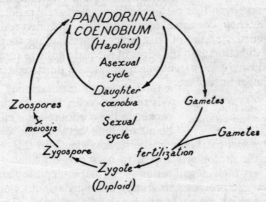

Adaptation to Environment

Bearing in mind the colonial construction of the members of the genus, the same observations apply as for *Chlamydomonas*.

Special Features of Biological Importance

Pandorina may be taken to illustrate a stage in the evolution of a more complex vegetative body from the motile unicell, that in which a fixed number of such cells are integrated into a unit structure or colony. In this genus, we see the least complicated of such colonial units. There is no distinction between the cells of the colony and all serve identical purposes both physiologically and reproductively. There is no division of labour among them. In the next genus, we shall see the greatest complexity which ever appears to have been reached along this evolutionary trend.

VOLVOX

This is a genus of some twelve or more species varying chiefly in the size and form of the coenobium. Several species are mentioned below.

Habitat

They inhabit freshwater pools and ditches, sometimes in very large numbers.

Vegetative Structure

The coenobium reaches the largest size of all colonial algae and is composed of a hollow sphere of cells arranged in a single layer at the outer surface, the whole being bounded by a delicate membrane through which the flagella protrude (*see* Fig. 9.4). The cells are very numerous and may be as many as 20,000 in *V. globator*. Each coenobium of this species is readily visible to the naked eye. When fully

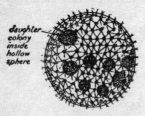

daughter
colony
inside
hollow
sphere

grown, it is as big as a pin's head. Each cell is composed of a small protoplast, with curved plate-like chloroplast containing pyrenoids, eye-spot, from two to six contractile vacuoles and two flagella.

The wall surrounding each protoplast is a thick layer of mucilaginous substance. Where these cells have become tightly packed as the coenobium has enlarged, the boundary lines between the cells can be

Fig. 9.4. Coenobium of *Volvox*.

seen as polygonal markings in the surface view. In this view of the coenobium, the protoplasts appear to be widely distributed in a clear matrix, but very high magnification shows that each protoplast possesses clear cytoplasmic processes traversing the mucilaginous wall to correspond with similar processes of all the adjacent cells. Thus there is cytoplasmic continuity between the cells.

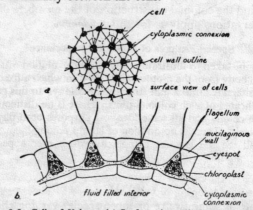

cell
cytoplasmic connexion
cell wall outline
surface view of cells
flagellum
mucilaginous wall
eyespot
chloroplast
fluid filled interior
cytoplasmic connexion
a
b

Fig. 9.5. Cells of *Volvox*. (*a*) Surface view. (*b*) In vertical section.

In an optical section it can be seen that each cell is bounded on the interior by the inner face of its own mucilaginous wall and that the centre is a fluid-filled cavity. The cytoplasmic processes uniting adjacent cells can be seen to lie in one plane only, parallel to the surface. There are small differences in structure in other species but basically the pattern is the same. In *V. aureus*, the cells usually number between 1,000–4,000 and the protoplasts are more like those of *Chlamydomonas*, the chloroplast being cup-shaped. Also the mucilaginous wall of each cell extends deeply into the interior cavity so that it is nearly occluded. In *V. tertius*, the cells number about 1,000 or less. The protoplasts are somewhat rounded and do not appear to show any interconnexions.

There is little or no difference between the vegetative structure of any of the cells in any coenobium but there is marked polarity. The coenobium moves always with one pole in front, and rotates about the axis through the anterior and posterior poles in an anti-clockwise manner. At the posterior pole, the sphere may show a small pore where it is not completely closed.

Physiology

The coenobium appears to have physiological characteristics similar to those of *Pandorina* but there is greater indication of a coordinating mechanism between the cells, i.e. cytoplasmic continuity. The plants make phototactic responses which are very easily demonstrated.

Reproductive Structures

There is no apparent specialization of reproductive cells but relatively few of the vegetative cells take part in reproductive processes.

Reproduction

Both asexual and sexual processes are employed.

Asexual Reproduction

In this method of reproduction, relatively few vegetative cells undergo divisions; each will form a new daughter coenobium. Each such initial cell is called a *gonidium* and soon enlarges to contrast with the others. It may enlarge sufficiently to be suspended in the hollow interior of the sphere. The manner of formation of each daughter coenobium is complicated but has been worked out in detail. The process is illustrated in Fig. 9.6, and may be described briefly as follows.

Each enlarged gonidium proceeds to divide in planes at right angles to the surface of the mother sphere and quickly a concave plate of cells is formed with its opening towards the outside. These cells are naked, attached laterally to form the plate and the anterior region of each is directed towards the inside of the concavity. Further divisions give an increasing number of such cells until a hollow sphere of naked cells, anterior poles still inwards, forms a miniature daughter coenobium. This is closed, except for one small aperture and is of course inside out. When this structure is completed, by an inversion of the sphere through its own aperture, the whole young coenobium is orientated correctly with the cell anterior regions outwards.

Each cell of the new coenobium proceeds to develop its own flagella and mucilaginous wall, maintaining contact nevertheless with adjacent cells by means of protoplasmic connexions. Thus the new daughter structure assumes the form of the parent. The aperture through which the coenobium inverted itself may eventually become closed. When

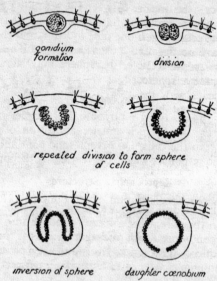

gonidium formation

division

repeated division to form sphere of cells

inversion of sphere

daughter coenobium

Fig. 9.6. Asexual reproduction in *Volvox*. Daughter coenobia.

complete it breaks away into the interior of the parent and along with several others, awaits release by the ultimate rupture and disintegration of the parent.

Sexual Reproduction

This is markedly *oogamous* with the gametes, male *antherozoids* and female *oospheres*, being quite different in form and behaviour. *V. globator* is *monoecious*, both types of gametes being formed on the same plant; *V. aureus* is most frequently *dioecious*, some plants male, others female. In *V. globator* cells of the posterior region only form gametes, but they appear not to be particularly specialized for this purpose. A cell which produces antherozoids is an *antheridium*; a cell which forms an oosphere is an *oogonium*.

A cell about to produce antherozoids, withdraws its flagella, enlarges and undergoes rapid successive divisions much as in the asexual development of a gonidium. These new cells remain in a flat plate in *V. globator*, but in *V. aureus* may undergo the same complicated inversion as in the asexual process. Each antherozoid forms two flagella. They are distinguishable from the vegetative cells by their elongated shape and very pale green chloroplasts. They are released as a complete plate or sphere, which breaks up in proximity with female organs.

antherozoid formation

The oospheres are developed singly from the much enlarged dark green protoplasts of separate cells. When mature, they have no flagella and hang downwards into the cavity of the parent sphere. They communicate with the exterior of the parent by a beak-like projection. The whole structure is functionally an oogonium.

oosphere   fertilization   oospore

Fig. 9.7. Sexual reproduction in *Volvox*. Oogamy.

Details of fertilization are not certain, but subsequent development of an oosphere gives rise to an *oospore* with a thick spiny outer wall and dark red contents in *V. globator*. The oospores remain *in situ* in the parent coenobium for some time. When released under suitable conditions, each undergoes meiosis; only one haploid zoospore is produced. This swims freely and then proceeds to develop into a new coenobium exactly as an asexually produced gonidium does.

Life Cycle

The following diagram summarizes the life cycle—

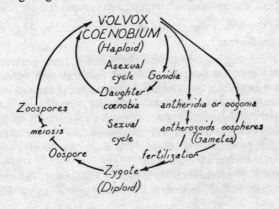

Adaptation to Environment

As for *Pandorina*.

Special Features of Biological Importance

Volvox exhibits clearly the condition in which a large, non-motile, female gamete is fertilized by a small, motile male gamete. This is described as the *oogamous* condition, from the name given to the female gamete, a large food-laden oosphere. It is a condition found in nearly all the more advanced algae and in many fungi, and involves the fertilization of the female gamete without its liberation from the parent cell. The advantages of this are discussed on p. 142. In monoecious species, the male gametes are formed and released before oospheres are formed. This *protandrous* condition prevents self-fertilization.

Volvox illustrates the culmination of a particular trend in evolution. We may derive the condition theoretically through the simpler colonial forms from the motile unicell. The size of the body, the slight division of vegetative and reproductive function between the cells, and the condition of oogamy in *Volvox* are the highest levels reached along this evolutionary dead-end. The restriction in size and form of the plant is no doubt imposed upon it by the retention of motility by all the cells. A larger, hollow body, fully motile, would be mechanically unstable. A larger, more complex, solid motile body would have to contend with complicated physiological difficulties; much greater division of labour would be necessary. It seems certain that the higher green plants have been derived from ancestors which lost motility of the vegetative cells and retained it only in some reproductive cells, finally to lose it here also, in their conquest of the land.

A NON-MOTILE COLONIAL FORM OF THE CHLOROPHYCEAE: PEDIASTRUM

The genus represents one of the simplest of multicellular non-motile plant forms.

Habitat

The species are widely distributed in fresh water where they are plank-tonic.

Vegetative Structure

The species vary in details of cell number and arrangement, but each plant is usually a disc, one cell thick, composed of closely-fitting cells. In *P. tetras* the number of cells is either four or eight; in *P. boryanum* there may be from 16 to 128 cells (*see* Fig. 9.8). In this case there are no gaps between the central, five-sided cells, but in some species, e.g. *P. duplex*, the adjacent cells touch only at points, leaving intercellular gaps. In most cases, the cells are arranged regularly to form a charac-teristic pattern and the marginal cells carry one or a pair of horn-like processes. These may bear fine gelatinous bristles in some species.

Each cell contains a single, parietal chloroplast with one or more pyrenoids. Older cells may contain more than one haploid nucleus.

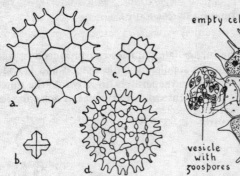

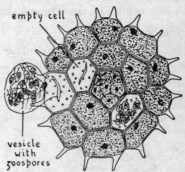

Fig. 9.8. *Pediastrum spp.*
(*a*) *P. boryanum.*
(*b*) and (*c*) 4 and 8-celled *P. tetras.*
(*d*) *P. duplex.*

Fig. 9.9. *Pediastrum boryanum.*
Asexual reproduction.

Physiology

Although forming a single unit, there is no indication that the fundamentally similar cells act other than independently in their physiological processes. Nutritionally, the plants are photoautotrophic and the chief storage product is starch. Growth is by enlargement of all cells until a maximum size is attained.

Reproductive Structures

There is no specialization of cells for reproductive purposes.

Reproduction

Both asexual and sexual processes occur.

Asexual Reproduction

When mature, any cell may undergo successive nuclear divisions, with cleavage of the protoplast, to form a number of separate small bodies. This number tends to be constant for a species but can vary. Each becomes an active, biflagellate, ovoid zoospore and all are released together into a delicate vesicle which is extruded through a slit in the parent wall (*see* Fig. 9.9). Within the vesicle the zoospores swim independently but soon become arranged in one plane in a single group, the form of which duplicates the arrangement of cells in the parent colony. Each zoospore then loses motility and a miniature non-motile daughter colony is formed. This is released from the vesicle to lead an independent existence. All the cells of the parent may undergo the same process in turn, so that mature plants may be seen with varying numbers of empty cells. Rarely, a cell may form a thick-walled, drought-resistant, non-motile spore, called a *hypnospore*, which later gives rise to a new colony by the formation of zoospores.

Sexual Reproduction

This is *isogamous* and the biflagellate gametes are produced in like manner to the zoospores, but are smaller, spindle-shaped and formed in greater numbers. They are released separately directly into the water through a pore (*see* Fig. 9.10). Pairs fuse to form zygotes. Each enlarges

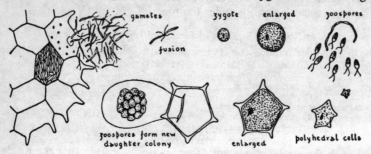

Fig. 9.10. *Pediastrum boryanum*. Sexual reproduction.

and then by a cleavage process, probably involving an initial meiosis, a number of zoospores are formed. On release, each swims freely, settles, loses motility and becomes a small polyhedral cell. This enlarges for a while and then acts as a normal vegetative cell in asexual reproduction. Its contents are transformed into zoospores which finally form a miniature colony inside a vesicle.

Life Cycle

The diagram below summarizes the life cycle.

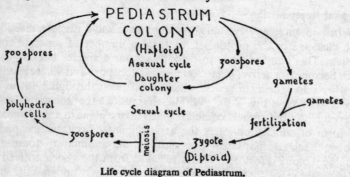

Life cycle diagram of Pediastrum.

Adaptation to Environment

These minute, freely-floating plants are clearly adapted to a planktonic existence. Retention of motility in the reproductive phases is in keeping with aquatic conditions.

The drifting forms of living things, plankton (cf. *nekton*—swimming, and *benthos*—attached to or crawling on the bottom), show certain special adaptations to their environments. Most phytoplankton (plant) forms are microscopic with a relative density very close to that of the medium in which they float and are thus virtually weightless in the water. Some possess parts, such as bristly outgrowths, which clearly offer resistance to sinking under the force of gravity.

Special Features of Biological Importance

The non-motile, multicellular but undifferentiated, body as the constant vegetative condition of the plant, distinct from the transitory "palmelloid" condition of some motile algae, constitutes a possible stage in the evolution of more complex forms. Any such suggestion is purely hypothetical, however.

FILAMENTOUS FORMS OF ALGAE: ULOTHRIX, OEDOGONIUM, SPIROGYRA (CHLOROPHYCEAE), VAUCHERIA (XANTHOPHYCEAE)

In the first three of these genera, the vegetative body is composed of all, or nearly all, identical cells joined end to end to form a *filament*, which may be branched in some cases. The plane of division of cells is confined to one direction, at right angles to the longitudinal axis of the cell. Thus increase in size, although unlimited, occurs in one direction causing elongation of the filament. In many members of the Chlorophyceae (and other algae), compacting of such filaments may give rise to sheet-like or solid structures of some complexity. The genus *Vaucheria* typifies the non-cellular filamentous growth in which a multinucleate protoplast is enclosed within a branched tubular wall.

ULOTHRIX

This genus contains about thirty species and is widely distributed.

Habitat

The species are usually found in all freshwater habitats. A common one, *U. zonata*, is characteristic of flowing streams, where it may form large areas of bright green growth in spring and autumn. Some species are marine and *U. flacca* is often found on salt marshes.

Vegetative Structure

The mature plant is composed of an indefinite number of cylindrical cells bounded by clear cellulose walls and joined end to end to form a single unbranched filament (*see* Fig. 9.11). In many species, this floats freely in still water although in the earlier stages of development it is attached to the substratum by the lowermost cell. In other species, the attachment may be permanent. The only differentiation between all the cells of the filament is in this lowermost cell, which becomes flattened to secure attachment and possesses no chloroplast. Every other cell consists of a vacuolate protoplast within the cell wall; it possesses a single nucleus and a characteristic single girdle-like chloroplast lying in the peripheral cytoplasm and extending from about half-way to fully around the cell according to species. The chloroplast may contain several pyrenoids and the central vacuole contains a watery sap. The filaments of *U. zonata* are extremely fine, measuring no more than 20–25μ in diameter. The length of the cells is usually even less than this, so that each has a somewhat characteristic squat appearance.

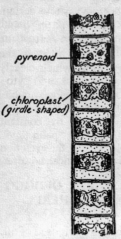

pyrenoid

chloroplast (girdle-shaped)

Fig. 9.11. Portion of filament of *Ulothrix*.

Physiology

The filament shows no division of labour. Every cell is apparently physiologically independent of all the others and exhibits no outstanding peculiarities. Starch seems to be the product of photosynthesis. Increase in size of the filament occurs by the division of any cell, except the basal cell, into two, with subsequent enlargement of the two daughter cells. Such growth, not being localized at any special points in the filament, is described as *intercalary*.

Reproductive Structures

There are no specialized reproductive structures produced. All cells seem to be capable of developing from a vegetative to a reproductive condition.

Reproduction

Both asexual and sexual reproductive processes are carried out, and in addition, vegetative reproduction may be effected by the fragmentation of a filament into individual cells or small chains, each of which may continue to develop as larger filaments.

Asexual Reproduction

This is brought about by zoospore development which may take place in any cell of the filament. It usually commences in the cells more apically placed and continues in each cell successively towards the base. As each cell produces its zoospores, its contents undergo change. The chloroplast extends to the end walls and the whole protoplast contracts slightly and rounds off. It then undergoes successive divisions to produce up to sixteen parts. These are then liberated into a small mucilage vesicle and develop their special nature as zoospores. They may be of two distinct types; quadriflagellate *macrozoospores* produced in small numbers, or quadri- or biflagellate *microzoospores* formed in larger numbers. Occasionally, in species with very small cells, a single zoospore may be formed from each cell.

Each zoospore is a naked structure composed of nucleus, and cytoplasm containing a single chloroplast, an eye-spot, contractile vacuole

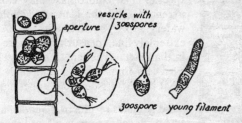

Fig. 9.12. Asexual reproduction in *Ulothrix*. Zoospore formation.

and flagella. The body is somewhat pear-shaped and the pointed anterior end consists of clear cytoplasm. All the zoospores are able to distinguish between high and low light intensities and thus make phototactic movements. The two kinds seem to favour different intensities to which they make positive responses; thus they tend to separate themselves out.

On being freed from the mucilage vesicle, the zoospores swim actively before settling to germinate. The microzoospores may swim freely for as long as several days in conditions of low temperature and bright light, whereas the macrozoospores cease movement in less than twenty-four hours. On settling, the macrozoospores broaden at the posterior end and become attached to the substratum. The zoospore loses its flagella and develops an outer wall to become a starting cell for a new filament. An attaching basal or rhizoidal cell is produced on one side and on the other, the vegetative cells. The microzoospores act in a similar manner, but the new filament is usually made of cells of much smaller diameter than those produced by a macrozoospore. There is evidence that microzoospores will germinate only at temperatures below 10°C so that asexual reproduction is restricted chiefly to the winter months.

Sexual Reproduction

Isogamous gametes, which fuse in pairs, are produced. The filaments concerned are usually distinct, so that heterothallism is exhibited. These gametes are very similar to microzoospores and are produced in the same way, but in the summer months. They always possess two flagella and are most often produced in groups of thirty-two per parent

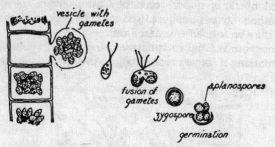

Fig. 9.13. Sexual reproduction in *Ulothrix*. Isogamy.

cell. A lateral fusion of two gametes results in a quadriflagellate zygote which soon settles, retracts its flagella, rounds off and secretes a wall, to become a resting zygospore (*see* Fig. 9.13). On germination, it divides into a number of non-flagellate cells or *aplanospores* which are then liberated to develop into new filaments. It is known that the divisions producing the aplanospores are meiotic, thus the vegetative filament is haploid.

Life Cycle

The following diagram summarizes the life cycle—

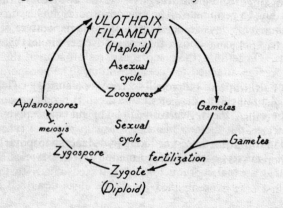

Adaptation to Environment

The delicate filamentous construction is compatible only with complete and constant submersion in water. The formation of motile reproductive structures helps to ensure dispersal of the plants through the environment. The resting stage in the sexual cycle, the zygospore, affords a means of tiding the plant over bad conditions for growth and development and dispersal to other favourable localities.

Special Features of Biological Importance

The thallus of *Ulothrix* illustrates the simplest form of filamentous structure. It shows no signs of motility and results from the property shared by all the cells of division only in the plane at right angles to the long axis of the filament. The unlimited intercalary growth results in a body of no particular size. The incidence of isogamous sexual reproduction may be regarded as primitive.

The Filamentous Plant

The undifferentiated single filament is not really an individual plant but a colony of cells in a particular form, each cell behaving independently both vegetatively and reproductively. Fragmentation has no ill effects and in some filamentous plants is a regular means of vegetative reproduction and dispersal. Such a delicate structure is fitted only for survival in a medium essentially wet, where support is afforded and desiccation never threatened. An evolutionary trend from this, has resulted in the compacting of filaments to form bulky plants such as some of the larger seaweeds, but in such cases the cells show considerable differentiation and division of labour.

OEDOGONIUM

This is a genus of some 285 species, representative of a very clearly-defined order of the green algae.

Habitat

The species are confined to fresh water, particularly ponds, ditches and water tanks, and rarely occur in running water.

Vegetative Structure

The plant body consists of a long unbranched filament which is generally free-floating in the older stages but attached during development. The cells of the filament are long cylinders and are usually all identical except the attaching cell. This is expanded and flattened to form a holdfast, and contains no chloroplast. In some species, the apical cell of the filament may be broadly rounded, in others it may bear a bristle. Each of the vegetative cells, within a cell wall, consists of a protoplast without a clear sap vacuole. Embedded in the clear cytoplasm is a single large nucleus and an elaborately-meshed reticulate chloroplast. This contains many scattered pyrenoids. Very characteristic of the genus is the occurrence of the so-called "cell-caps" which are produced during cell divisions. The cell wall is fairly thick and rigid and appears

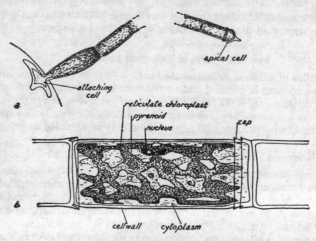

Fig. 9.14. (*a*) Filament of *Oedogonium*. (*b*) Single cell much enlarged.

homogeneous, but tests indicate a three-layered structure of inner cellulose, middle pectose substance and outer chitinized material.

Physiology

As is typical of such a filament, all cells seem to be physiologically independent except the attaching or rhizoidal cell. The product of photosynthesis is starch.

Growth of the filament is intercalary and is of interest because of the unique mode of new cell-wall formation at cell division (*see* Fig. 9.15). It leads to the formation of the cell caps mentioned above. When a cell is about to divide, the nucleus is situated about two-thirds of the distance from the basal end; it divides mitotically. During this nuclear division, a ring of cell wall material, completely encircling the inner face of the longitudinal wall, makes its appearance just below the end wall nearest the dividing nucleus. This ring of material thickens considerably and forms a ridge bulging into the cell contents. When fully formed, there appears a cavity within it all around its circumference, where it abuts on the old cell wall, and quickly the outer old wall splits immediately over this cavity. By this time mitosis is complete and soon there is a cleavage of the cytoplasm across the equatorial plane of the spindle separating the protoplast into two. Each new protoplast now elongates rapidly until approximately the length of the old cell. The one nearest the base pushes out until it reaches a mark just short of or level with the position of the ring of new material just formed. The other expands to keep pace with the activity of the newly inserted ring which proceeds to elongate until it is stretched out to a length about equal to the length

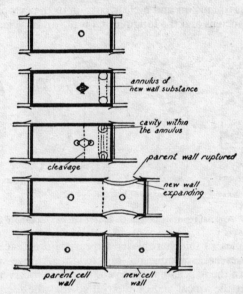

Fig. 9.15. Diagram to show the formation of "cell caps" in *Oedogonium*.

of the parent cell. This stretching of the new wall substance separates the broken edges of the old parent wall so that these appear as a ragged encircling ridge at either end of the upper of the two new cells. These are the so-called "caps." As the upper of the two newly-formed cells divides again, it will receive a cap at each new division and these can often be seen as a series on older cells. The lower cell of the two keeps the old parent wall. Between the two new protoplasts, a new transverse septum is developed to complete the separation. In some species only the terminal cell of a filament shows caps.

Reproductive Structures

These are developed from vegetative cells of the filament and there appears to be no part of the filament specially concerned.

Reproduction

A vegetative fragmentation often occurs and both asexual and sexual reproductive processes are carried out.

Asexual Reproduction

This is effected by zoospore formation (*see* Fig. 9.16). Each zoospore is formed from the complete protoplast of a cell. During development, the protoplast rounds off and a clear portion of the cytoplasm appears between the nucleus and the longitudinal wall. In this clear cytoplasm,

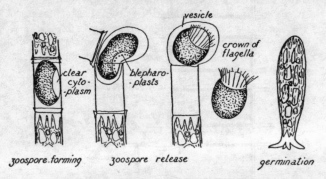

Fig. 9.16. Asexual reproduction in *O. concatenatum*. Zoospore formation.

minute granules or blepharoplasts appear. From each of these, a flagellum arises as a cytoplasmic outgrowth. An eye-spot may also appear. When the flagella have formed, there is a transverse split made in the wall at the apical end of the cell so that the filament becomes broken. Through the aperture, the zoospore is liberated, encased in a delicate vesicle which soon disrupts to release a freely motile swimmer. It swims for a short period and then comes to rest, hyaline end downwards. It retracts its flagella and becomes sessile by flattening itself on the substratum. This flattened portion becomes the holdfast and may appear as rhizoidal outgrowths in some species. The zoospore rapidly secretes a wall and from this a new filament is developed by cell division.

If a zoospore ceases to swim and does not effectively anchor itself, it will develop a wall, but will soon form again a motile zoospore which swims for a further period.

Some species of *Oedogonium* may form a type of spore described as an *akinete*. This is a non-motile resting structure developed from a protoplast within the parent cell wall and without any clearly-defined wall of its own. Many filamentous algae produce such structures and in addition, *aplanospores*, which are also non-motile cells but possessing distinct walls of their own secretion. The akinetes occur in chains of up to forty or more and are smaller than the normal vegetative cells, rich in stored starch and an orange-coloured oily substance. They are capable of germinating directly to produce new filaments.

Sexual Reproduction

This is markedly oogamous and is reported to occur only when the surrounding water is alkaline and deficient in nitrogenous substances. The sex organs are clearly distinguishable antheridia and oogonia, but the conditions of their development differ for the different species. There are two main cases. In one, the antheridia are developed from cells on the normal vegetative filament. These species are described as *macrandrous*. In the other, the antheridia are formed on specialized small filaments known as *dwarf male plants* or *nannandria*. These species are described as *nannandrous*.

The Macrandrous Species. The antheridia may be developed on the same filament as the oogonia, i.e. the plant is monoecious, or the organs may be developed on separate filaments, in which case the plant is dioecious. In either case, the antheridia occur in an intercalary position and are the result of the division of an antheridial mother-cell which divides repeatedly in the normal manner except that the upper cell is always much smaller than the lower cell. The repeated division of the lower cell may result in a chain of antheridia numbering forty or more. Along this chain can be seen the broken-up remains of the old longitudinal wall as loose rings of material around the young antheridia. In the general case, the contents of each antheridium cleave into two portions and each changes into a multiflagellate antherozoid. Each looks like a miniature zoospore, but has fewer flagella. In some species, the flagella may be very long. Liberation is effected by the breaking of the filament at points just below the transverse walls of the antheridia. Each antherozoid is invested in a mucilage vesicle at first, as are the zoospores.

Oogonia of the macrandrous species are formed by division of an oogonial mother-cell. This divides once and the distal cell develops into the oogonium, which therefore always has a "cap" at its upper end (*see* Fig. 9.17). The lower cell may divide again to produce yet another oogonium. This may be repeated, so that a short series of them may be produced. Each potential oogonium rounds off and becomes larger in diameter so that it stands out clearly in the filament. The protoplast changes into a single female gamete, an oosphere, with a centrally-placed nucleus which later migrates to a clear peripheral region of the cytoplasm just opposite a portion of the oogonial wall which opens by a fissure. It is through this opening that an antherozoid penetrates and

enters the oosphere at the clear receptive spot. The male and female
nuclei then fuse and the zygote is formed. It retracts from the wall and
begins to secrete a wall of its own, which is often ornamented with
sculpturings, reticulations and pits, according to species. As this
oospore ripens, it changes colour from green to reddish-orange because
of the accumulation of food-storage substances which include oil.
Eventually, the oospore is liberated as the oogonial wall decays and it

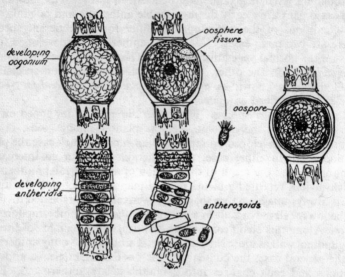

Fig. 9.17. Sexual reproduction in *O. bosci*. Macrandrous case.

may continue to rest for some time. During this rest, there is a reduction division of the zygotic nucleus to form four nuclei. Just before
germination, the protoplast regains its green colour and divides into
four parts; each of these is liberated as a zoospore. They develop in
the same manner as asexual zoospores. The new filament is haploid.

The Nannandrous Species. These produce dwarf filaments which bear
antheridia. The nannandria result from the germination of specialized
zoospores called *androspores*, produced in special zoosporangia called
androsporangia (*see* Fig. 9.18). These are developed on filaments
separate from those bearing oogonia in some species, whilst in others
they are borne on the same filaments. Androsporangia are formed in
the same way as are the antheridia in the macrandrous species, but the
contents of each cell form a single motile androspore comparable with
a normal asexual zoospore, but smaller and slightly yellowish. Each

androspore, when liberated, swims freely until it reaches the neighbour-hood of an oogonium. It settles either on the oogonium or on a cell adjacent to it and germinates to produce a holdfast and a short filament or nannandrium, usually of one cell. This develops at least one

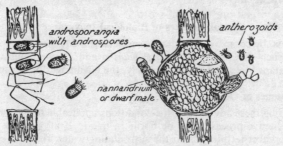

Fig. 9.18. Sexual reproduction in *O. ciliatum*. Nannandrous case.

flattened antheridium at its apex and from it are released two normal antherozoids. In a few nannandrous species, the antherozoids may be produced from the contents of a single cell forming the dwarf filament.

The oogonia are developed exactly as in the macrandrous species; the antherozoids function in the same way; zygote formation and further development are as described previously.

Life Cycle

The following diagram summarizes the life cycle—

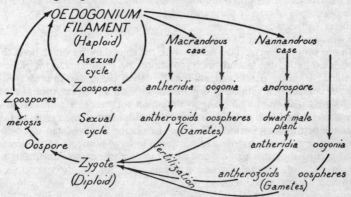

Adaptation to Environment

Oedogonium filaments can develop only in completely aquatic conditions. The onset of sexual reproduction and the consequent formation of resting oospores at times of nitrogen shortage, are interesting adaptations of frequent occurrence in freshwater organisms. Shortage of nitrogenous substances inhibits further vegetative growth; during the resting period, the decay of various plants and animals restores the essential nitrogen.

Special Features of Biological Importance

Oedogonium, by comparison with other genera less advanced in reproductive processes such as *Chlamydomonas*, *Pandorina* and *Ulothrix*, illustrates one very important biological feature, namely, the advantages of oogamy.

The Advantages of Oogamy

In assessing these advantages, the conditions applicable to the more primitive reproductive process must be borne in mind. If all gametes are to be released to effect fertilization in the surrounding water, then the chances of successful pairing can only be very good if the numbers of both kinds of gametes are high. Large numbers of gametes can be produced only by large numbers of vegetative cells dividing into large numbers of very small parts and these, once released, can no longer be nourished by other vegetative cells of the parent plant. The tendency is for the parent plant to cease its existence on gamete production and continuation of the species depends entirely on the ability of these minute self-supporting structures to find one another and pair off in reasonable numbers. But the zygote produced from such a chance pairing is also comparatively tiny and can contain no greater substance for its future development than was brought to it by the two gametes which formed it. Unless the conditions for its development are exceedingly good, it must run the risk of extinction before it develops sufficiently to be self-supporting. The death-rate of parent plants which give up their whole substance to the gametes, of the gametes themselves, and of the zygotes, must be very high and the whole process must be very wasteful.

In oogamous plants, on the other hand, the chief dangers which beset those species exhibiting the less advanced condition are eliminated. One gamete is retained within the parent cell, still on the parent plant, and thus escapes the risks of competition with other organisms. In such a position, it can be large, well-stored with food, and bring to the union with another gamete a supply of material which can be used in further development of the zygote to tide it over the first difficult period. Chances of its being fertilized can still be high if the other gamete is motile and produced in large numbers. Some method of attracting the other gamete and allowing ease of penetration through the parent cell wall is necessary and it seems usual for all oogonia to secrete substances through a break in the wall to which antherozoids can make chemotactic responses, thereby finding the oospheres with greater certainty. The whole process is much less wasteful of substance and has a much greater likelihood of success. Furthermore, in view of the smaller numbers of gametes involved, the parent plant need not commit the whole of its body to gamete production. Only certain specialized cells need be involved and the remainder can continue to exist, to repeat the process at intervals. This further advantage of the oogamous condition has been exploited by many plants and in these we see complete division of labour between the vegetative and reproductive cells (*see* p. 165).

It is interesting to note that a condition similar to oogamy is prevalent in animals, where a larger yolky non-motile female gamete awaits fertilization by a smaller non-yolky motile male gamete.

SPIROGYRA

This is a genus of many species and of world-wide distribution.

Habitat

The plants are most often encountered in small stretches of stagnant fresh water and the majority are floating. The bright green colour of the filaments and their sliminess to the touch are especially noticeable.

Vegetative Structure

The mature filament is unbranched and composed of identical long cylindrical cells in the floating species (*see* Fig. 9.19(*a*)). The few fixed

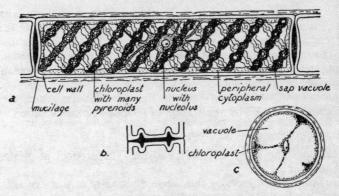

Fig. 9.19. (*a*) Cell of *Spirogyra* filament much enlarged. (*b*) Replicate septum. (*c*) T.S. cell in region of the nucleus.

species such as *S. adnata* have the lowermost cell modified as a holdfast. Each cell is bounded by a wall of three components. Internally there is a cellulose layer enclosed by a delicate cuticle. Externally there is a mucilaginous covering which accounts for the sliminess. Constant sloughing of the mucilage may prevent growth of epiphytic organisms on the cells. The middle lamella between cells is often biconvex in side view and the end walls of the cells therefore bulge inwards towards the cell cavity. In other species may be seen a collar-like ring of middle lamella substance on which the transverse wall has been laid down. This is known as a *replicate septum* (*see* Fig. 9.19(*b*)). Swelling of the biconvex lamella or the collar-like ring, causes disengagement of adjacent cells and effectively fragments the filament.

Within its wall, the vacuolated protoplast lies in the peripheral position. It exhibits a large nucleus, with one or more nucleoli, suspended by cytoplasmic threads in the sap vacuole. Embedded in the peripheral cytoplasm are one or more chloroplasts (according to species) containing many pyrenoids. The chloroplasts are very characteristic spiral bands. Under differing nutritional conditions, they may vary in appearance. Under poor conditions, they may be thin and attenuated with a straight margin and with the pyrenoids few and regularly spaced. Under the best conditions, they are broad and thick, with serrated margins, and they contain many scattered pyrenoids of various sizes. In some species, the chloroplast is T-shaped in cross-section with the stalk of the T directed inwards and connected to the nucleus by delicate cytoplasmic threads. In others it is grooved with the concave surface outwards and with the inner face similarly attached to the nucleus. Very rarely are the chloroplasts branched.

The pyrenoids can multiply in numbers within the chloroplasts by constriction into two pieces, but may also arise by some other means independent of existing pyrenoids. They are of the more common algal pattern and consist of a central protein mass surrounded by minute starch plates. Despite much investigation their exact role in the physiology of the cell is not clear.

The cell sap is frequently rich in dissolved tannins which can be precipitated as "ink" by application of ferrous sulphate solution.

Physiology

All cells are physiologically independent. The product of photosynthesis is starch.

Growth is intercalary, by transverse division of any cell of the filament. Two features of the division are unusual. The new separating septum is formed first at the peripheral region of the cleaving cytoplasm. As the septum proceeds to develop from all sides towards the centre, the chloroplasts divide into roughly equal pieces. The second feature of interest is that the nuclear division occurs within the nuclear membrane, which does not disappear. The spindle is therefore *intranuclear*. Some observers have recorded centrosomes associated with its formation.

Reproductive Structures

There are no specialized reproductive structures. All vegetative cells may act in this capacity.

Reproduction

Vegetative fragmentation frequently occurs but no other type of asexual reproduction is known. Sexual reproduction takes place by a process of *conjugation*, most commonly between two filaments. Flagellate gametes are never produced.

Vegetative Fragmentation

This occurs by the separation of cells either as individuals or in short chains. In species possessing replicate transverse septa, it is effected by the swelling of the pectic material of the middle lamella

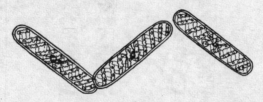

Fig. 9.20. Fragmentation of *Spirogyra* filament into separate cells.

which forces the cells apart. In others, where the septum is bowed (biconvex in side view), differences in turgor pressure between adjacent cells apparently cause alterations in the shapes of bulged ends and ultimately the cells are forced apart. After separation, the folds or concavities in the end walls evaginate and the cell takes on characteristically bulging ends.

Sexual Reproduction

This usually involves the conjugation of two filaments although three and even more may take part. It occurs when the filaments are vegetatively well-matured, under increasing alkalinity of the surrounding water, and only among filaments which are fairly closely crowded. Two filaments become ranged alongside one another, presumably by slow movement which has never been fully explained. Filaments placed in a shallow covered dish frequently show slow creeping movements up the side of the dish and even on to the cover where they are only wetted by capillary water. Secretion of mucilage may play some part in the process since other algae are believed to make movements as a result of secreting mucilage in a non-uniform manner. Resulting surface-tension differences could conceivably cause small movements of the whole or part of a filament. Only filaments with more recently divided cells conjugate and in these the cells are often shorter than normal.

At the beginning of conjugation the two filaments become closely adherent by their mucilage and the disposition of each is such that adjacent cells coincide very closely with one another. As soon as the cells are in position, short protuberances commence development at corresponding points on each of a pair of adjacent cells (*see* Fig. 9.21). The protuberances are in contact with one another by their tips from

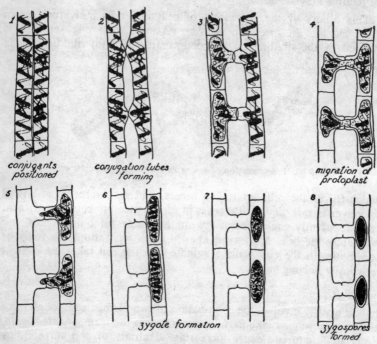

Fig. 9.21. Conjugation between filaments of *Spirogyra*. Sequence of stages numbered 1–8.

the start of their formation and as they elongate to form tubes, the conjugating filaments are slowly separated, being held together now only by the conjugation tubes whose tips adhere strongly. The appearance of the filaments is now ladder-like (scalariform), with the conjugation tubes forming the rungs. Meantime the protoplasts of the cells involved, become rich in starch.

When the conjugation tube of each cell is fully formed, the wall between them becomes partly dissolved and the two protoplasts which have extended into the tubes, come into contact through a small pore.

During the next part of the process, the protoplast of one of the conjugants passes into the cell cavity occupied by the other so that both lie within one cell wall. It is common to refer to the moving protoplast as the male gamete and the other as female. The filaments vary in this respect. Usually all cells of one produce male gametes and the other female. More rarely a filament may produce a mixture of both. Heterothallism is therefore not clearly defined.

Once the opening through the conjugation tube is clear, the male gamete, with little change in its structure, proceeds to contract from its cell wall by withdrawing liquid from its vacuole into a number of spherical contractile vacuoles which are then discharged into the enlarging space between the wall and the protoplast. As it gets smaller, without losing contact with the female gamete, it passes through the conjugation pore into the cell cavity of the female, which by this time has withdrawn from the conjugation tube and has contracted from its wall to allow space. The progress of the male gamete along the tube cannot be regarded as comparable with amoeboid movement and is considered to be due to the continuous action of the contractile vacuoles acting as a propelling agent.

As soon as both gametes are within the one cell wall, they fuse to form a zygote. It is notable that the gametes have no difference other than the motility of one of them. *Spirogyra* may be considered anisogamous for this reason, but it is not a clear-cut characteristic.

Once formed, the zygote promptly contracts until it becomes a dense ovoid body with no discernible chloroplast structure, and filled with brownish oil drops. It secretes a thick outer wall to become a resting zygospore. When fully ripened, this is easily recognized by its colour and position in the conjugating filaments.

Further development takes place some time later when the decayed parent wall has released the zygospore and conditions are correct. Zygospores must be fully immersed in water for germination to occur. On germination, the zygospore wall is ruptured and the contents pass out as a green cell which soon divides transversely, the lower cell forming a kind of holdfast in some species. It is well established that upon germination the zygotic nucleus divides into four by reduction division. Three of these abort, so that the first cell contains one haploid nucleus and the filament which develops from it will therefore be haploid.

The ladder or scalariform mode of conjugation does not always occur and conditions of lateral conjugation may be seen in which alternate protoplasts in the same filament act as male and female gametes, coming into communication with one another by side connexions. Lateral conjugation may also occur in filaments actively engaged in the scalariform process, whilst occasionally three or four filaments may be involved in the formation of a double or triple ladder.

Life Cycle

The following diagram represents the life cycle, omitting the vegetative fragmentation—

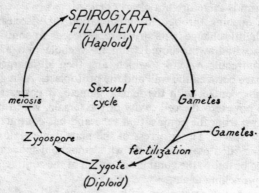

Adaptation to Environment

The same conditions apply as for other filamentous algae.

Special Features of Biological Importance

Spirogyra can be used to illustrate a biological feature which can be encountered over and over again, namely, the "evolutionary side-line." In their reproductive processes, they do not appear to be on the main track through which the corresponding processes in higher plants can be derived.

The "Evolutionary Side-line"

Most groups of algae exhibit clear-cut differences from all the others, indicating that each is an end-point or side-line from the main evolutionary trend towards higher plants. These differences may be morphological, physiological or reproductive. We have already seen the motile condition of the body which separates the Volvocales from all the others, the unique method of cell division and reproductive specialization by dwarf males in the Oedogoniales. The red algae stand apart by the development of different photosynthetic pigments. A fuller study of the algae would provide many more examples. The Zygnematales, of which the genus *Spirogyra* is representative, illustrate a side-line of evolution towards a method of sexual reproduction unique among the green algae.

VAUCHERIA

This is a genus of about thirty-five species.

Habitat

Many of the species are partially terrestrial and can be found as green felt-like masses on damp soil, e.g. *V. sessilis*, at the edges of ponds and ditches and even on well-watered greenhouse pots. The rest are aquatic but chiefly freshwater, only three or four species being marine.

Vegetative Structure

The thallus is not comparable with any other so far described in this text. It is tubular and filamentous with sparse branching, but the filament has no cross-walls. A single continuous wall encloses the whole living substance of the plant, which is multinucleate and there-

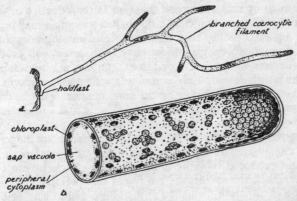

Fig. 9.22. (*a*) *Vaucheria* filament. (*b*) Filament tip much enlarged.

fore *coenocytic* (non-cellular body) (*see* Fig. 9.22). The filaments only become septate upon injury and at reproduction.

A single plant may increase in size within its wall until filaments several centimetres in length, but still microscopic in diameter, are developed. One end is fixed to the substrate by a lobed holdfast. The wall is comparatively thin and delicate, and constructed of cellulose. In some species, it may be encrusted with calcium carbonate, e.g. *V. debaryana*. Lining the wall throughout, and surrounding a central vacuole, is a layer of cytoplasm in which are embedded numerous nuclei and many small discoid chloroplasts. At the lower holdfast end, chloroplasts are few or absent and nowhere do they show pyrenoids. Within the cytoplasm may be seen countless oil drops. At the rounded tips of filaments and their branches the contents may be extremely dense, giving a dark green appearance to these younger parts.

Physiology

The whole plant behaves as a normal autotrophic green plant but does not form starch. The food reserve is oil.

Growth is made at the apices of filaments and branches by the addition of new protoplasm and secretion of new wall material continuous with that behind. During active growth, the apical nuclei repeatedly divide and some observers have recorded centrosomes as being associated with these nuclear divisions. Terrestrial species show marked phototropic responses (*see* Vol. II, Chap. 16).

Reproductive Structures

Specialized branches of the filament may become separated from the main filament by cross-walls and function as reproductive organs.

At the tips of some branches, club-shaped sporangia may be formed. In fully aquatic species, they produce free-swimming zoospores, and are therefore zoosporangia. Most terrestrial species will produce the same structures in very wet conditions. Others may develop similar sporangia which develop only non-motile walled aplanospores.

Borne on other branches or on the main filament, may be developed the organs of sexual reproduction, the oogonia and antheridia. These are formed as specialized branches on vegetative parts. The oogonia are short-stalked spherical cells, whilst the antheridia are longer-stalked and appear as miniature branches with less green contents. The sex organs are produced typically in mixed small groups by most species. In *V. terrestris*, the sex organs are found on special side branches of which the termination forms the antheridium and arising below it are several oogonia. *V. dichotoma* is dioecious.

Reproduction

Vaucheria can reproduce asexually and sexually and also multiplies vegetatively as a result of the development of broken-off pieces.

Asexual Reproduction

Each zoosporangium produces a single multiflagellate zoospore (*see* Fig. 9.23). When the zoosporangium is forming, many chloroplasts, nuclei, and much cytoplasm, stream into the tip of a branch, so that the vacuole almost disappears and the tip becomes very deep green. This portion is then separated from the rest by a cross-wall. Within the sporangium, movement of the chloroplasts and nuclei occurs, so that the latter come to lie in the cytoplasm in a position outside the chloroplasts, which fill the centre of the dark green mass. The contents now contract from the zoosporangium wall and opposite each nucleus are developed two short flagella. At the apex, the wall now gelatinizes to give an aperture; through this the motile zoospore is liberated. The zoospore, with a central vacuole and paired flagella opposite each nucleus, may be taken to represent a large number of uninucleate zoospores which have not become separated. Zoospores are regularly produced by the aquatic species and by the terrestrial species when flooded, but some, such as *V. uncinata*, rarely produce them. Instead, aplanospores are produced in sporangia which are more rounded than club-shaped; they split open to release the spores.

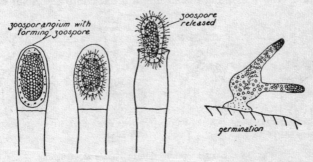

Fig. 9.23. Asexual reproduction in *Vaucheria*. Zoospore formation.

Zoospores are usually released shortly after day-break and make sluggish movements for a short while. They come to rest, withdraw the flagella, secrete a wall and germinate by sending out several filamentous protrusions, one of which develops as a holdfast. Aplanospores germinate in a similar manner and may even do so from the sporangium without liberation.

In a few species, another form of aplanospore development and germination is found. The whole filament may become septate with short segments, and within each, the protoplast secretes a thick wall. This *hypnospore* rests until conditions are right, when it develops into a new filament or the contents may divide into a number of thin-walled structures which on liberation make amoeboid movements before settling to germinate.

Sexual Reproduction

All species reproduce sexually and sex organs are developed simultaneously. The antheridia are produced as tightly curved tubes cut off from a lower outgrowth of the filament by a septum (*see* Fig. 9.24). According to species, they normally contain fewer chloroplasts than the vegetative parts or none at all, and the few nuclei originally present,

undergo division to produce many. As the organ matures, the cytoplasm divides into portions, each containing a single nucleus, and each
portion changes into a small, colourless, oval or pear-shaped antherozoid with two laterally inserted flagella. In the majority of cases, the
antherozoids are released through a single apical pore in the antheridium
and swim freely. Oogonium development commences with the production of a sessile or short-stalked outgrowth of the filament. This
rounds off and becomes densely filled with nuclei, oil and chloroplasts,
but finally contains only a single central nucleus which enlarges considerably. The remaining nuclei migrate back into the main filament

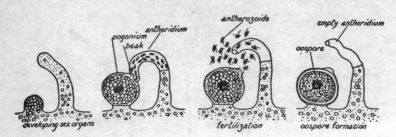

Fig. 9.24. Sexual eproduction in *Vaucheria*. Oogamy.

and in many cases a septum cuts off the oogonium. As it matures, it
forms a beak-like structure on one side and at the tip of this, by gelatini-
zation of the wall, a pore appears immediately over a clear receptive
spot of the cytoplasm, part of which may be extruded to the outside.
The chloroplasts and oil drops now tend to concentrate in the centre
of the ripening oosphere, leaving a clear peripheral zone of cytoplasm,
and the whole mass shrinks somewhat from the wall as the vacuole loses
water. Fertilization is effected by the penetration of an antherozoid
through the receptive pore and its ultimate fusion with the oosphere
nucleus. A wall now forms to close the receptive pore and the zygote
forms a thick resistant covering of its own, to become an oospore.
While this occurs, the oil accumulates centrally as two or three large
globules, the chloroplasts lose their identity and the whole spore may
become reddish-brown in colour. Oospores normally rest for several
months before germinating directly to form new filaments. It is now
generally accepted, though not conclusively proved, that the first
division of the zygotic nucleus is meiotic and the new thallus is thus
haploid.

Life Cycle

The life cycle may be summarized diagrammatically as shown on p. 153.

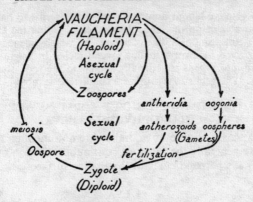

Adaptation to Environment

Some species may be regarded as sub-aerial but can exist only in the dampest of habitats. Neither in structure nor in reproductive processes are any of them adapted to normal dry-land conditions. The filaments die when subjected to desiccation and the male gametes and zoospores can move only in water films.

Special Features of Biological Importance

The genus *Vaucheria* illustrates two features of importance, first the occurrence of yet another form of plant-body construction and secondly, the formation of special cells set apart for reproduction. Comment on this latter condition is deferred (*see* p. 165).

The Coenocytic Plant

This also appears to be an evolutionary dead-end. Only the multicellular plant body, with great potentiality for differentiation and consequent great

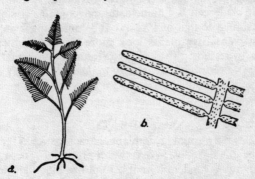

Fig. 9.25 *Bryopsis*. (*a*) Habit drawing.   *b*) Portion of thallus enlarged.

division of vegetative labour among its cells, ever seems to have dominated either in the water or on the land. Nevertheless, within the Chlorophyceae (Caulerpales) are examples like *Codium*, in which coenocytic branches become compacted to form a thallus several inches in height with external differentiation into organs superficially similar to the root, stem and leaf of higher plants. The genus *Bryopsis* has a characteristic moss-like appearance.

AN EXPANDED SHEET FORM OF THE CHLOROPHYCEAE: ULVA

Sheet-like expanses of vegetative thallus are not uncommon among the algae and are generally the result of continuous division of all the cells in planes always perpendicular to the thallus surface.

ULVA

The genus contains thirty species of which *U. lactuca* is the commoner of two British representatives and will be described here. The genus is important for study not only because of its body form but because of the details of the life cycle, which are different from those of any other alga described in this text. The student is well advised to make a study of *Ulva*, in order to appreciate more fully the significance of the discussion at the end of this chapter.

Habitat

Ulva lactuca is a marine alga occurring in the intertidal zone and in rocky pools. It is said to flourish in waters polluted by sewage.

Vegetative Structure

The thallus is a crinkled sheet, of two cells' thickness, bright green in colour and attached to the substratum by a holdfast composed of tightly compressed filamentous outgrowths of the lower cells (*see* Fig. 9.26). Each blade cell is uninucleate and contains a single laminate chloroplast similar to that of *Ulothrix* and containing a single pyrenoid. Although all vegetative plants look more or less identical, there are nevertheless two kinds. They differ cytologically, in that *one is composed of haploid cells and the other of diploid cells*. They differ also in their modes of reproduction and can only be distinguished during reproductive phases.

Physiology

The thallus has the normal green plant characteristics as far as is known. It seems to be unable to live in deep water presumably because its lack of accessory pigments renders it unable to utilize blue light to full advantage. Growth is indefinite and all cells are capable of successive division. The lower portions of a thallus may perennate, new growth being made by regeneration each year.

Reproductive Structures

All cells seem to be capable of producing reproductive bodies, except the lowermost. The type of structure produced, depends upon the kind of thallus producing it. In the case of the diploid thallus, any cell may be converted into a *zoosporangium*. In the case of the haploid thallus, any cell may be converted into a *gametangium* or gamete-producing cell.

Reproduction

Apart from the possible break-up of a thallus and eventual regeneration of whole new plants from the parts, asexual and sexual methods of

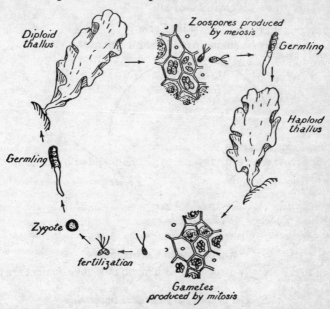

Fig. 9.26. Diagram of the structure and reproduction of *Ulva lactuca*. Alternation of generations.

reproduction occur. Each is peculiar to one type of thallus only and they follow one another in regular sequence, each being part of the full cycle of reproductive events. *Ulva spp.* are said to exhibit *alternation of generations*, a condition more fully described at the end of this chapter, and the life cycle is described as *diplobiontic*.

Commencing with the mature haploid thallus, the cycle of events is as follows. Any blade cell may produce eight or sixteen identical biflagellate gametes which are released through a pore to the outside. Here they meet exactly identical gametes from another thallus and proceed to fuse in pairs. Gametes from the same thallus do not fuse, indicating heterothallism. The process is clearly sexual. The fusion product, the zygote, loses motility, secretes a wall, rests for a short time and germinates into a diploid thallus, vegetatively identical, i.e. isomorphic, with the gamete-producing haploid thallus after a preliminary filamentous stage. When mature, the cells of the diploid thallus each produce four or eight quadriflagellate zoospores, which are the result of a meiotic division of the cell nucleus. They are therefore haploid. They are liberated and proceed to develop in much the same manner as the zygote, but their product is the haploid thallus once more. This process is clearly asexual.

Life Cycle
The life cycle may be summarized as shown below—

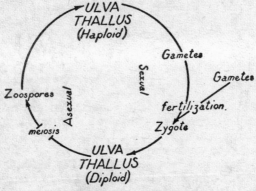

Adaptation to Environment
The features normally associated with an aquatic environment are to be seen.

Special Features of Biological Importance
The very clearly-defined alternation of generations in the life cycle is of extreme importance botanically, but discussion of this condition is best deferred till the end of this chapter when the details of the life cycle of the seaweed *Fucus* will have been described.

A PARENCHYMATOUS FORM OF THE PHAEOPHYCEAE: FUCUS

The parenchymatous, organized thallus reaches its climax in the algae in the Phaeophyceae. In these brown algae, the giant kelps exhibit the culmination of this evolutionary line. A common example is the strap-shaped seaweed *Laminaria*. The genus *Fucus* is closely related in form to this and is a suitable subject for study. This type of vegetative body can be achieved by the compacting of numerous filaments as is illustrated by members of the green and red algae, but in the case of the solidly constructed brown algae, the result is achieved by the property possessed by the meristematic cells of division in all three planes. This property is not often encountered in the algae as a whole, but is characteristic of all the more advanced types.

The genus contains many species, five of them British. These are *F. anceps*, *F. ceranoides* (three varieties), *F. spiralis* (two varieties), *F. serratus* (five varieties) and *F. vesiculosus* (nine varieties).

Habitat

Members of the genus are all marine and occur mainly in the intertidal zone of north temperate and arctic waters. The species of *Fucus* and related genera show zonation between high- and low-tide marks according to their ability to withstand longer or shorter periods of non-immersion.

Vegetative Structure

In all species the thallus is essentially similar in structure. *F. vesiculosus* will be described here. Specific variations will be noted later.

Morphology

The thallus is morphologically differentiated into three main regions. Lowermost is a *holdfast* or *hapteron* which is a flattened disc capable of adhering strongly to almost any solid substratum. Next is a short round *stalk* or *stipe*, which may appear to lengthen with age as the older wing-like extensions get worn away. Distally is the broadly-flattened *blade* of hard leathery texture, showing conspicuous *dichotomous branching* in one plane only. The margin of the blade is entire and centrally each branch shows the presence of a thickened midrib, except at the very young tips, at which can be seen a small indentation in the margin. Within the tissues of each branch are numerous prominent *air vesicles*. The whole plant is greenish-brown to black in colour (*see* Fig. 9.27).

A mature reproducing thallus shows further distinctive differentiation at the branch tips, which are markedly swollen due to abundant production of mucilage internally. These swollen portions, either green or orange in colour, are termed *receptacles* and on them can be seen small swellings marking the positions of chambers known as *conceptacles* in which the reproductive organs are developed.

Individual plants vary considerably in size according to age (reckoned

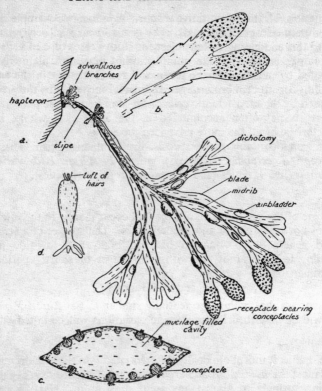

Fig. 9.27. Vegetative morphology of *Fucus*. (*a*) *F. vesiculosus* plant. (*b*) Receptacles of *F. serratus*. (*c*) Receptacle in transverse section. (*d*) Young *Fucus* plant.

to be a maximum of four or five years), and precise locality. Under the conditions prevalent at high-tide mark, the whole plant may be no more than 6 or 7 cm in length; lower in the tidal zone it may reach a metre or more.

Anatomy

By comparison with the algae already described, anatomical differentiation is very advanced. showing several different types of cells arranged to form distinct tissues. All cells are uninucleate. Fig. 9.28 illustrates the structure of a young thallus as seen in a section cut transversely through a distal winged branch. Externally there is a thin, outer, mucilaginous sheath or cuticle covering a layer of small, closely-packed, rectangular cells with many brownish plastids. It is in this layer that most of the photosynthetic activity is carried on. These cells are also meristematically active all their lives and add to the thickness of the thallus. Internal to this layer is a cortex of cells, also meristematic and containing a few plastids. The cortex is generally more loosely-packed towards the interior with a good deal of intercellular mucilage. The cells often contain stored carbohydrate and constitute a storage tissue. Innermost is a medulla of loose filamentous strands.

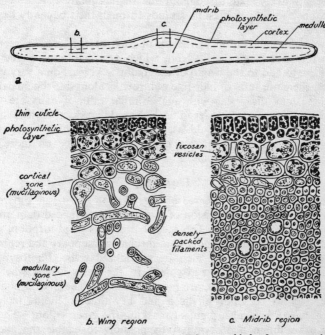

Fig. 9.28. Vegetative anatomy of *Fucus*. (*a*) T.S. young blade. Low power plan of tissue layout. (*b*) and (*c*) High power drawings of the regions indicated in (*a*).

In the wing of the blade, these filaments may be very loosely packed and all thick-walled. They are outgrowths of the inner cortical cells and traverse the blade in all directions, showing cross-connexions with one another. In the midrib region, similar but more tightly-packed outgrowths of the cortex, form a medulla of thick-walled threads interspersed with larger thin-walled medullary cells derived from the apex of the blade branch. All midrib medullary cells traverse the blade longitudinally and some may show perforated cross-walls comparable with sieve plates of vascular plants. This indicates a conducting function, as well as a mechanical function, which they undoubtedly serve.

In the stipe, the cross-section is generally comparable in all respects with the midrib region of the blade. The stipe is really no more than the final junction of all the midribs with thin layers of cortex and photosynthetic tissue continuous with those of the blade.

The holdfast is the expanded end of the stipe composed of densely-packed hyphae, thick-walled, hard and tough, and serving a mechanical function.

It seems likely that throughout the thallus many of the cells are interconnected by cytoplasmic strands through the frequently heavily-pitted cell walls.

Within the indentation at the tip of each branch can be seen the single four-sided apical cell, from which new cells are formed continuously, to add to the length of the thallus. At least on a very young thallus, there are tufts of hair-like outgrowths alongside the apical cell, but these may disappear with age. Similar tufts of hairs are to be found on older winged blades in flask-shaped depressed cavities known as *cryptoblasts*. Some would ascribe special absorbing functions to these hairy outgrowths but the cryptoblasts may be no more than sterile reproductive conceptacles.

Physiology

The comparatively high degree of organization and tissue differentiation clearly indicates a division of labour more advanced than any yet encountered in the algae. The special functions of absorption, nutritional activity, storage, conduction, mechanical support and reproduction are adequately performed by specialized cells. Photosynthetic activity seems to be confined chiefly to the outer layers, where the plastids, lacking pyrenoids, are most abundant. The plastid pigments are known to be chlorophylls *a* and *c* with carotenoids including *fucoxanthin*, a brownish pigment masking the green colour. The role of fucoxanthin in photosynthesis is possibly to enable the plant to take maximum advantage of blue light. The end-products of photosynthesis are not clearly determined. Small quantities of fat, and polysaccharide carbohydrates (*laminarin*) with the properties of dextrin, have been extracted. *Mannitol*, a sugar alcohol, appears with greater abundance, whilst a tannin-like substance, *fucosan*, having an undetermined significance, is most abundant. This substance appears in many cells of all the tissues in the form of *fucosan-vesicles* which are highly refractive colourless vacuoles in the cytoplasm. Cell extracts yield quantities of *iodine* bound in an organic form.

Growth of the thallus is unlimited and occurs in length as a result of continuous division of the apical cell at the tip of each branch, and in thickness as a result of the meristematic activity of the outer (*meristoderm*) and cortical layers. A mature apical cell is pyramidal and regularly and consecutively it cuts off daughter cells from each of its four faces and its base. The presence of centrosomes has been clearly associated with nuclear activity during division. Dichotomous branching is the result of a longitudinal division of the apical cell, each new daughter cell then adopting the role of an apical cell at a more or less equal rate, thus forming two identical branches from a bifurcation.

The healing of broken branches and the regeneration of new tissues is effected very readily by any portion containing medullary cells, which seem to play the major part. When a wound is healed by a callus-like growth of medulla, adventitious branches develop, to continue increase in size of the thallus. Such adventitious branches are not unusual on unwounded parts, particularly of the holdfast and stipe.

Air-bladders have a purpose in that they keep the whole plant buoyant. They are first formed a little way behind the apex, and result from a rupture of the medulla due to excessive surface growth of the outer and cortical layers. The gases of the bladder correspond closely with those of the atmosphere, but proportions of carbon dioxide and oxygen vary by day and night. Some botanists would ascribe a respiratory function to them.

Reproductive Structures

The only specialized reproductive structures are the conceptacles inside which the sex organs develop. *Fucus vesiculosus* is dioecious and fertile male and female plants may be readily distinguished by the orange coloration of the male conceptacles as opposed to the deep green of the female.

A conceptacle is a deep, hollow, flask-shaped chamber in the thallus tissues, opening to the exterior by a narrow pore or *ostiole*. Male and female conceptacles vary little in general structure, but greatly in the form and arrangement of the gamete-producing organs they develop (*see* Fig. 9.29).

The male conceptacle is lined with profusely branched hairs, some of which protrude through the ostiole. On the hairs are borne the antheridia, which when mature have a two-layered wall and contain sixty-four antherozoids each.

The female conceptacle is similarly lined with hairs, but generally these are unbranched and bear no reproductive parts. The female organs, oogonia, are borne directly on the walls of the chamber on short stalks among the bases of the hairs. Each oogonium has a three-layered wall and contains eight oospheres.

Both male and female conceptacles continue to produce new sex organs for some months and whilst engaged in this, they are filled with mucilage said to be formed by the hairs in the lower part.

The development of the fertile conceptacles at the tips of branches may take several months. When they are initiated, the apical cell ceases to function and the tip becomes heavily swollen with internal

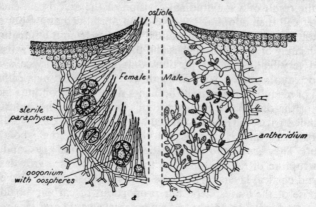

Fig. 9.29. Diagram of conceptacles of *Fucus*. (*a*) Female. (*b*) Male.

mucilage. The conceptacles then arise on the swelling tip, each from an initial cell in a slight depression. Upgrowth of the surrounding tissues forms the final flask-shaped cavity.

Reproduction

Apart from the possible regeneration of broken pieces to form new plants, the only method of reproduction is sexual; this is very markedly oogamous. The male gametes are very tiny, motile, and are produced in very large numbers. The female gametes are comparatively large, non-motile, and occur in smaller numbers.

Sexual Reproduction

The developing antheridium at first contains a single nucleus which divides by reduction division (meiosis) followed by four mitoses to produce sixty-four nuclei in the cell. The whole contents then divide into sixty-four uninucleate portions, each becoming a pyriform, naked antherozoid with large nucleus, small chloroplast, eye-spot, and two lateral, unequal flagella; the forward, shorter and pantonematic, the other acronematic (*see* Fig. 9.30).

Similarly, each developing oogonium at first contains only one nucleus. As the oogonium matures, the nucleus undergoes reduction division, followed by a mitosis, to produce eight nuclei, each of which becomes surrounded by a portion of the cytoplasm and develops as an oosphere. In young oogonia, these oospheres can be seen squeezed against one another as each proceeds to enlarge within the oogonium. The mature oosphere is a greenish spherical body, non-motile, surrounded by a delicate membrane, and charged with stored food material in the form of oil drops.

The method of liberation of the gametes is an adaptation to the intertidal environment. When the plants are exposed to the air between tides, they tend to dry and contract, thus squeezing out the conceptacle contents. Small globules of mucilage containing the differently

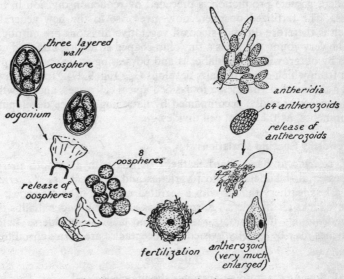

Fig. 9.30. Sexual reproduction in *Fucus*.

coloured male and female organs can be seen, extruded on the thallus surface. When the tide returns, this mucilage is washed off, carrying with it the gametes, still enclosed, into the water. On release from the conceptacle the antherozoids are retained together within the inner wall of the antheridium. the outer having ruptured within the conceptacle When wetted, this inner wall gelatinizes and the antherozoids are set free. When the oospheres are squeezed out of the conceptacles, they are retained within the two inner membranes of the oogonium. The outer of these gelatinizes on being wetted, whilst the inner ruptures and the oospheres are also freed into the water containing the antherozoids. Presumably as a result of some chemical attraction, the antherozoids swarm in large numbers around each oosphere. This swarming is easily seen when discharged oospheres and antherozoids are mixed in a watchglass and placed on the microscope stage.

Sooner or later, an antherozoid penetrates the oosphere membrane and its nucleus migrates across the cytoplasm and fuses with the oosphere nucleus. The remaining antherozoids cease to be attracted, stop swimming and die. During the nuclear fusion, two centrosomes appear, one from the oosphere and the other apparently from the male cell. The fusion nucleus is now the diploid zygotic nucleus which is reconstituted from the haploid nuclei of the gametes, since, it will be recalled, gamete production is preceded by reduction division in both cases. The fertilized oosphere now gives rise to the new generation which is therefore diploid, since all vegetative divisions are mitotic.

The very young thallus is a tiny club-shaped structure, attached at its base by outgrowing rhizoidal cells and possessing at its apex a depression from which a tuft of hairs develops (*see* Fig. 9.27). In this cavity, first a three-sided and then a four-sided apical cell arises, and growth in size proceeds rapidly, accompanied by flattening and the development of branches, as the apical cell divides.

Noteworthy Specific Variations

F. vesiculosus has a hard leathery thallus with a smooth margin, possesses air-bladders in most varieties and is dioecious. *F. serratus* has a less leathery thallus with a serrated margin; it is dioecious, but always lacks air-bladders. *F. spiralis* has a rather broader thallus than *F. vesiculosus*; it is smooth-margined and lacks air-bladders. Lateral branches may be spirally twisted. Conceptacles are hermaphrodite.

Life Cycle

The following diagram summarizes the life cycle—

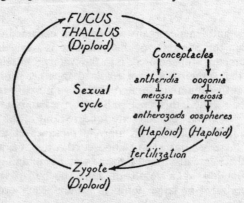

Adaptation to Environment

Structurally, *Fucus spp*. are adapted to maintaining a fixed position in the intertidal zone by the development of a powerful holdfast and at the same time the leathery but non-rigid body can withstand the repeated buffeting of the waves. Increase in surface area by a flattening of the thallus increases the volume of the plant which can be engaged in food manufacture by photosynthesis.

The development of the brown pigment fucoxanthin is said to enable the plant to make most use of blue light. The possession of any such pigment is an advantage where immersion in fairly deep water curtails the use of the longer red wavelengths, which tend to be absorbed rapidly by the water. It is to be noted that the deeper-lying seaweeds all produce pigments which will absorb blue light. The production of copious mucilage undoubtedly serves to store water for the periods when the plant is exposed to drying conditions.

In their reproductive processes, *Fucus* plants are adapted to the fully aquatic environment in possessing free-swimming male gametes and are also able to make use of the changing wet and dry conditions for the release of gametes into the water.

Special Features of Biological Importance

Fucus illustrates two important points. First, compared with other algae, a high degree of vegetative and reproductive division of labour is shown and secondly, the vegetative body is diplont.

Division of Labour

This term has been used several times previously and denotes the condition in a multicellular body in which cells have different structure and are set apart, more or less in groups, to carry out specific functions. It means a sharing-out of the work of the whole body among the tissues which are specially suited for one kind of work and no other. In the organisms so far described, the highest division of labour has been no more than a separation of the body parts into more or less identical vegetative cells (holdfasts excepted) and some wholly reproductive cells. A *Fucus* thallus shows a very clear functional differentiation between the vegetative cells and also develops cells wholly reproductive in function. We can recognize nutritive, storage and mechanical tissues of differing forms and a special apical cell from which growth is made. The division of labour is therefore much greater than in any plant so far encountered. However, it does not approach the state achieved by higher plants. The condition in which specialized cells are set apart for reproductive functions only, allows the vegetative structure to persist over long periods (perennate) so that the reproductive process can be repeated many times.

The Diplont Body

All the algae previously described, possess haplont bodies, except *Ulva*, which exists in both haplont and diplont conditions. The single vegetative plant in the *Fucus* life cycle is diplont and results from the germination of the zygote without a preliminary meiotic division. Many related brown algae exhibit very clearly, an alternation of generations in the life cycle. These brown algae exist as haplonts, which produce gametes to give a diploid zygote on fusion. This then develops into a diplont body, which produces spores by meiotic divisions, each spore then producing the haplont body once more. The diploid and haploid bodies may be isomorphic (*Dictyota*) or heteromorphic (*Laminaria*). The genus *Fucus* is considered to be derived from such brown algae. The derivation could have been accomplished by the loss of the haploid generation from the life cycle.

GENERAL TRENDS IN THE ALGAE

The algae as a group illustrate a number of trends from the simple to the more complex in structural, physiological and reproductive conditions. Those described in this text may be used to illustrate the following lines of advance.

Structural

1. There is a series ranging from the primitive motile unicell of *Chlamydomonas* to the complex coenobium culminating in *Volvox*, which must be regarded as an evolutionary dead-end, largely on grounds of its fragility.

2. Another series ranges from the non-motile unicell such as *Chlorella* to the filamentous colonies of *Spirogyra* and *Oedogonium*, and the flat sheet of *Ulva*. Such a form is not always an evolutionary end-point, since much more complicated branched and compacted filamentous structures are common in the algae.

3. The occurrence of the walled coenocyte, as in *Vaucheria*, derived from some unknown ancestral form.

4. The evolution of the parenchymatous, organized body, exhibiting morphological and tissue differentiation as in *Fucus*. This appears to be the most persistent and successful of all the algal types, presumably due to the specialization of cells and the permanent fixation of the thallus to a substratum. Both factors tend to lead to greater efficiency of the structure as a whole.

Physiological

In our present state of knowledge, it is impossible to recognize clear trends of physiological advancement except those which are manifest in the growth and developmental pattern. This shows an advance from indeterminate growth and division of all cells, to the localization of growth activity in a single cell.

Reproductive

1. The gradual advance in sexual reproductive processes can be traced from homothallic isogamy to heterothallic anisogamy, as illustrated by the various species of *Chlamydomonas*, *Pandorina* and *Ulothrix*, and further advance to very clearly-defined oogamy as in *Eudorina*, *Volvox*, *Vaucheria* and *Fucus*.

2. There is increasing complication of the life cycle to exhibit clear-cut alternation of generations (always assuming that the simple life cycle such as that of *Chlamydomonas* is the primitive condition).

It is important that every student at this stage should understand the sequence and significance of the phenomenon of alternation of generations, since the life histories of all the higher plants from the bryophytes upwards are variations on the same pattern. They exhibit a clearly-defined alternation of generations in which a haploid sexually-reproducing plant body known as the *gametophyte generation*, gives rise to a diploid asexually-reproducing structure known as the *sporophyte generation*. In its turn this gives back the haploid generation to complete the cycle. This sequence of events and the variations from it, can best be understood if it is realized at the outset that all sexual cycles always involve this regular sequence—

$\rightarrow$ Fertilization $\rightarrow$ Zygote $\rightarrow$ Meiosis $\rightarrow$ Gametes $\rightarrow$

At the same time, the interval with which one follows the other may be extended at one or both of two points by the development of a clearly-distinguishable plant body. These two points are: at the mitotic development of the zygote when a diploid sporophyte may arise; and at the development of the meiotic derivatives of the zygote when a haploid gametophyte may arise. For example, three cases may be cited—

1. $\rightarrow$ Fertilization $\rightarrow$ Zygote $\rightarrow$ Meiosis (spores) $\rightarrow$ **Haploid plant** (gametophyte) $\rightarrow$ Gametes.
2. $\rightarrow$ Fertilization $\rightarrow$ Zygote $\rightarrow$ **Diploid plant** (sporophyte) $\rightarrow$ Meiosis $\rightarrow$ Gametes.
3. $\rightarrow$ Fertilization $\rightarrow$ Zygote $\rightarrow$ **Diploid plant** (sporophyte) $\rightarrow$ Meiosis (spores) $\rightarrow$ **Haploid plant** (gametophyte) $\rightarrow$ Gametes.

The first case is exemplified by all the algae described here except

Ulva and *Fucus* and the life cycle may be summarized conveniently
thus—

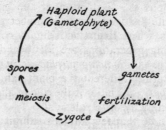

The second case is exemplified by *Fucus* and the life cycle may be
summarized conveniently thus—

The third case is exemplified by *Ulva* and the life cycle may be summarized conveniently thus—

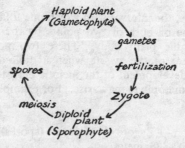

In the last case, the gametophyte and sporophyte generations are
equally vegetatively developed and functional. In the following
chapters, some plants will be described in which the gametophyte
assumes the dominant vegetative role, whilst the sporophyte is little
more than a spore-producing body. This is the case in the bryophytes.
More advanced plants show the condition in which the sporophyte is

the dominant vegetative phase of the life cycle, whilst the gametophyte is no more than a reduced gamete-producing structure as in the pteridophytes and spermatophytes. Reduction of the gametophyte is the general trend in the life histories of all the higher plants, culminating in the flowering plants, where reduction is finally complete.

When the alternating generations are identical in structure, as in *Ulva*, the plant is said to exhibit *homomorphic alternation of generations*. When they are structurally different the plant exhibits *heteromorphic alternation of generations*. The latter is the rule in all plants higher than the algae but occurs in many of the algae also.

It is interesting to note that few animals exhibit this alternation of generations in the life cycle (*see* Chap. 32).

CHAPTER 10

SIMPLE MULTICELLULAR ANIMALS:
SPONGES; HYDRA; OBELIA

INCREASE in bulk, in the animal kingdom, has followed three different lines. Some protozoans have achieved large masses by their colonial habit, but each unit in the colony is usually morphologically identical. There is rarely differentiation into various types of cells except that some may be physiologically specialized for reproduction. In the sponges, a multicellular body is achieved and there is differentiation to the extent that there are several types of cells subserving different functions. Nevertheless, there is no co-ordinating system, and to all intents and purposes each cell functions as an independent unit. All the remaining phyla constitute the Metazoa, and they form a series showing gradually increasing differentiation. In this chapter, we shall deal lastly with coelenterates which begin to show tissue differentiation with co-ordination centred in a primitive nervous system.

SOME COLONIAL PROTOZOA

Examples of colonial protozoa are found in the classes Rhizopoda, Flagellata and Ciliophora, but there are none in the class Sporozoa.

In the Rhizopoda, good examples of colonies are found in the orders Heliozoa and Radiolaria. In the Heliozoa, there are a number of colonial genera in which the zooids are joined by protoplasmic bridges, each zooid possessing stiff, radiating pseudopodia. The genus shown in Fig. 10.1 (*a*) is the stalked *Rhaphidiophrys*. The radiolarian genus *Collozoum* (*see* Fig. 10.1 (*b*)), consists of a firm mass of gelatinous protoplasm in which are embedded numerous capsules, each containing a single zooid. The colony may reach a length of three or four centimetres.

Three orders of flagellates, Chrysomonadina, Phytomonadina and Choanoflagellata, possess well-known colonial genera. In *Dinobryon* (Chrysomonadina), the zooids are contained in cups secreted by the protoplasm. When binary fission occurs, one of the products stays in the old cup, while the other creeps out, fixes itself on the edge of the old cup, and proceeds to secrete a new container. Thus, a symmetrical fan-like colony is built up (*see* Fig. 10.2 (*a*)). Two colonial genera of the order Phytomonadina, *Pandorina* and *Volvox*, are described as plants in Chap. 9. The order Choanoflagellata is interesting, not only for its colonial forms, but because each zooid consists of a collared-flagellate cell, which is present as the feeding type of cell in all sponges. The occurrence of this type of cell in these two groups and nowhere else, strongly suggests that the Porifera were evolved from choano-flagellates. By repeated branching, a tree-like colony is produced in

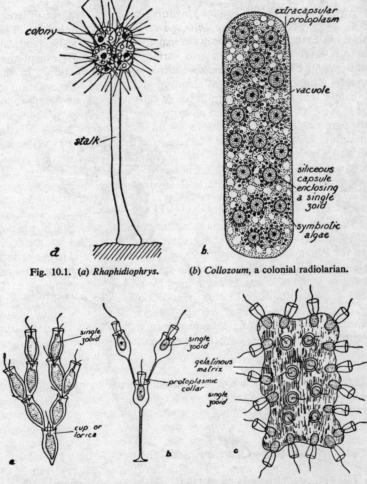

Fig. 10.1. (a) *Rhaphidiophrys*.   (b) *Collozoum*, a colonial radiolarian.

Fig. 10.2. (a) *Dinobryon*, a colonial flagellate. (b) *Polyoeca*, a colonial choano-flagellate. (c) *Proterospongia*, a colonial choano-flagellate.

Polyoeca (*see* Fig. 10.2 (*b*)). In *Proterospongia*, the zooids are enclosed in a common gelatinous matrix (*see* Fig. 10.2 (*c*)).

In the class Ciliophora, colonial forms are common in the order Peritricha, but rare in other orders. *Ophrydium* (*see* Fig. 10.3 (*a*)) consists of a colony of zooids embedded in an irregular gelatinous

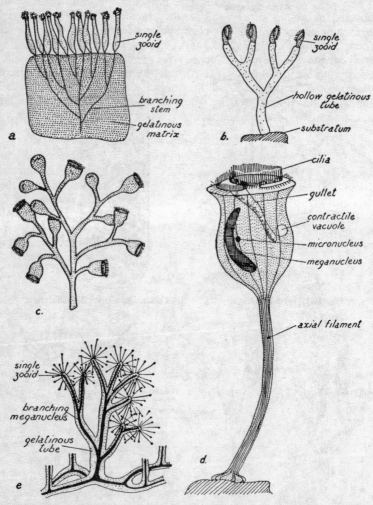

Fig. 10.3. (*a*) *Ophrydium*, a colonial ciliate. (*b*) *Stichotricha*, a colonial ciliate. (*c*) *Carchesium*, portion of a colony. (*d*) *Vorticella* (stalk somewhat reduced). (*e*) *Dendrosoma*, a colonial suctorian.

mass, often 8 or 9 centimetres in diameter. There is a delicate branching stem, each branch terminating in a zooid. *Stichotricha* (*see* Fig. 10.3(*b*)) has zooids at the ends of each branch of a hollow gelatinous tube. The beautiful freshwater *Carchesium* (*see* Fig. 10.3 (*c*)) consists of a branched colony of zooids, each individual being like the solitary *Vorticella* (*see* Fig. 10.3 (*d*)). The branches are protoplasmic and covered by a thin cuticle; all are contractile by means of a single branching myoneme. The sub-class Suctoria contains only one colonial form, *Dendrosoma* (*see* Fig. 10.3 (*e*)). The colony consists of a prostrate stem from which vertical branches arise, each branch terminating in a zooid with suctorian tentacles. An interesting and unusual feature of *Dendrosoma*, is the extent of the meganucleus, which ramifies as a branched axis throughout the whole colony. *Dendrosoma* may attain a length of two to three millimetres.

THE PHYLUM PORIFERA (SUB-KINGDOM PARAZOA)

All sponges are aquatic, the majority living in the sea where they are found at all depths from the intertidal zone to the deepest abysses. One family, the Spongillidae, contains only freshwater members; they inhabit rivers and lakes, practically all over the world.

In the life history of some sponges, a simple stage known as the *olynthus* (*see* Fig. 10.4) appears. It is probable that all sponges are modifications of this simple type. The olynthus is a vase-shaped

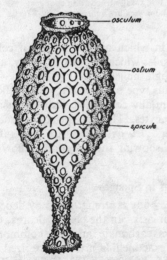

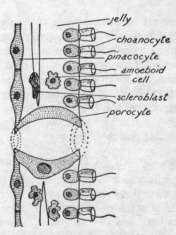

Fig. 10.4. An olynthus (*after Haeckel*).

Fig. 10.5. Vertical section through the body wall of a simple sponge.

structure attached to the substratum at the narrower end. The lateral surfaces are perforated by microscopic pores called *ostia*, which lead into a large cavity, the *paragaster*. At the free end is a single exhalant aperture, the *osculum*.

The outer surface is covered by flattened cells called *pinacocytes*, closely cemented together. The inhalant pores are perforated through single cells, the *porocytes*. Lining the internal surface are collared-flagellate cells, the *choanocytes*. The outer dermal and inner gastral

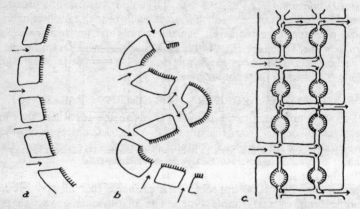

Fig. 10.6. The three principal grades of body wall structure in sponges: (*a*) Ascon. (*b*) Sycon. (*c*) Leucon. The choanocytes are represented by flagella only.

layers are separated by a stiff jelly in which are two types of cells. *Scleroblasts* secrete the tri-radiate spicules which support the body, and frequent amoeboid cells wander through the jelly (*see* Fig. 10.5).

No adult sponge retains the olynthus type of structure, but all show various modifications which are essentially concerned with increasing the area of surface occupied by choanocytes. The three principal grades of structure are the *ascon*, *sycon* and *leucon*. They are illustrated diagrammatically above, with arrows showing the direction of flow of the water currents.

Skeletal Elements in Sponges

The jelly which gives coherence to the body is strengthened by deposition of various elements by the scleroblasts. In the class Calcarea, the spicules are always made of calcium carbonate and are commonly tri-radiate (*see* Fig. 10.7 (*a*)). The Hexactinellida are characterized by siliceous spicules, of which there is a wide array (*see* Fig. 10.7 (*b*)). The shapes of these spicules are useful in classifying this group. Some members of the Demospongiae have siliceous spicules, but the more common skeletal material is a network of spongin fibres secreted by

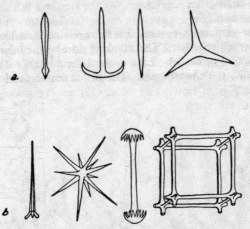

Fig. 10.7. (a) Calcareous spicules from various sponges. (b) Siliceous spicules from various sponges mainly Hexactinellida.

spongoblasts; this spongin in some genera is impregnated with spicules or granules of silica.

Physiology and Reproduction of Sponges

All sponges feed holozoically. The flagella of the choanocytes beat inwards, creating inhalant currents through the ostioles. Small food particles of many types are ingested by the choanocytes at the base of the protoplasmic collar. The exact manner in which ingestion takes place is not known. The food is digested intracellularly and it is presumed that the wandering amoeboid cells collect digested food from the choanocytes and distribute it to the other types of cells. Water containing defaecated particles and excretory materials is swept out through the osculum by the exhalant current.

Respiration is aerobic, diffusion of oxygen being fully effective since no cell is far removed from the water. Growth is interstitial; every type of cell is capable of division. Most sponges are colonial and extension takes place by means of horizontal outgrowths, giving a basal portion which secretes a cementing substance fastening the colony to the substratum. Then, at irregular intervals, vertical outgrowths give rise to upright branches.

Excretion of nitrogenous material is probably largely performed by the amoeboid cells. They are said to convey such materials from other cells and discharge them into the paragastral cavity. With such ready access to water, diffusion would suffice for all excretion of soluble and diffusible products.

Sponges have no nervous system or special receptor cells. Responses to stimuli, even if the latter are violent, are slow and local. In many species, there is an ability to effect slow closure of the inhalant pores by means of special contractile cells around their edges. These cells are stimulated to action by the cessation of water movement, and in still water, they contract slowly and effect closure. Thus they act both as receptors and effectors.

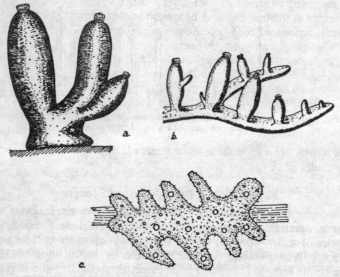

Fig. 10.8. (a) Small colony of *Sycon*, a sponge in Grade *b*. (b) Portion of colony of *Leucosolenia*, a sponge in Grade *c*. (c) *Euphydatia*, a common freshwater sponge, growing on a twig.

Reproduction occurs by asexual and sexual methods, though with many species, sexually-produced larvae have not been demonstrated. In asexual reproduction, external buds may become separated, or internal buds called *gemmules*, may develop. A gemmule is formed from a cluster of amoeboid cells; it becomes detached from the parent body and is drifted away to found another individual or colony.

Sperm and ova are produced from wandering amoeboid cells. All sponges are hermaphrodite and most are protandrous, so that cross-fertilization is probably the rule. One amoeboid cell divides many times to form a mass of small, tailed sperm. Each ovum is formed from a single cell which enlarges and becomes spherical. After fertilization, the zygote becomes invested with a layer of the parent's cells. Within this, the early stages of development take place.

After cleavage, an ovoid *blastula* is formed, wholly or partly covered with flagellated cells; this is released into the water as a free-swimming larva (*see* Fig. 10.9) and thus dispersal of the species is effected. Eventually the larvae settle down and by a remarkable process, the flagellated cells migrate through the inner cell layer and become the choanocytes, the internal cells passing out to form the coherent dermal layer. An aperture develops at the free end and becomes the osculum; special amoeboid cells become the porocytes; the jelly is secreted and growth begins.

Fig. 10.9. A sponge larva.

Having evolved a sedentary mode of life, sponges have developed suitable adaptations. Feeding, respiratory, and defaecating currents are set up by the constant inward beating of the flagella. The minute ostia prevent entry of particles too large for ingestion into the choanocytes, and the slow closure of the ostia may be a protective mechanism under certain conditions. There is effective dispersal by the swimming larvae. The sharp-pointed spicules, which frequently project from the surface, render them immune from predation; no aquatic animals are known to eat sponges.

Special Features of Biological Importance

The sponges have reached the cellular level of organization. Although there are few types of cells, two types cover a considerable proportion of the surface; they are the pinacocytes and the choanocytes. The lack of any co-ordinating mechanism precludes consideration of them as tissues. The presence of the highly-characteristic and peculiar choanocytes indicates strongly their probable line of descent from choanoflagellate protozoa.

The sponges possess remarkable powers of regeneration. Any small piece of the body can grow into a complete animal. If a sponge is forced through silk bolting-cloth into a dish of water, the cells soon aggregate into small clumps and each clump will develop slowly into the mature form.

Certain features distinguish the Porifera very clearly from the Metazoa. The principal and largest opening is exhalant. In all metazoan animals where there is a single large opening, it is inhalant primarily and exhalant secondarily. The minute pores of the sponges limit the food material to microscopic particles. Digestion is not a common function shared by a layer of cells all working in co-ordination, but each choanocyte acts as an independent unit. The complete absence of nervous system and sensory cells is another peculiarity. Finally, the migration of the flagellated cells from exterior to interior during development is found nowhere else.

The Porifera are a side-line in evolution. Because of their many peculiar features they may be considered a sub-kingdom, the Parazoa, which developed from the Protozoa by a different route from that which gave rise to the Metazoa.

HYDRA. A SIMPLE METAZOAN ANIMAL

The members of the phylum Coelenterata are all aquatic animals, the majority living in the sea. They exhibit variability in size and shape, but apart from the specialized ctenophores, they conform to a common plan which is well illustrated in the familiar genus *Hydra*. The sea supports a wide variety of coelenterates including the large jelly-fishes, minute medusae, delicate, branched zoophytes, the stony corals, sea-pens and sea-fans, and the colourful sea-anemones.

Habitat and Habits

A hydra was first described by Leeuwenhoek in 1703. Various species occur in ponds and slow-flowing streams; they are ubiquitous over the earth's surface except in the frigid zones. The species usually studied

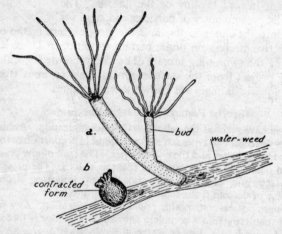

Fig. 10.10 *Hydra fusca.* (*a*) Expanded and (*b*) fully contracted. The expanded animal bears a mature bud.

is *Chlorohydra viridissima*, previously called *Hydra viridis*, but any of the hydrae will conform to this general account. Apart from the green hydra, *H. fusca* (brown), *H. grisea* (orange), *H. oligactis* and *H. attenuata* (colourless), are British species. The larger *Pelmatohydra* is a North American species.

The hydra is usually found with its basal disc attached to a stone or water-weed. Its slender cylindrical body hangs downwards with the thread-like tentacles writhing gently. Occasionally, it will contract suddenly, becoming a mere blob of jelly, then it will slowly expand. It feeds on small animals such as water-fleas, which it captures with its tentacles. The prey is swallowed with difficulty, causing great distension of the body. Undigested particles are expelled from the single aperture, the mouth. Unless conditions are markedly unfavourable, it shows little indication of locomotion. When it does move, it may loop, somersault, or drift freely. It reproduces asexually by means of buds, and also sexually. Survival over unfavourable periods is achieved by encystment of the embryo in a spiny chitinous shell.

General Features

The body consists essentially of a hollow cylinder, the cavity being a digestive and absorptive *enteron*. When fully extended, the cylinder may reach a length of twenty millimetres or so. The free end tapers to form a conical *hypostome* or *oral cone*, which is pierced by the small mouth. Around the wider base of the hypostome is a circlet of six to eight tentacles, which contain extensions of the enteron. The green colour of *Chlorohydra viridissima* is due to the presence of minute green algae of the genus *Chlorella*, which live in the cells lining the enteron. The association provides a good example of symbiosis (*see* Chap. 34).

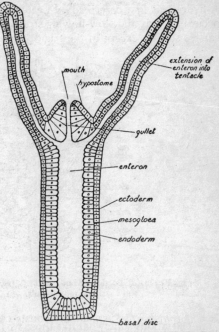

Fig. 10.11. Diagram of the body of *Hydra* in the median L.S. to show the general structure.

The Body Wall

There are two clearly-marked layers of cells, an outer *ectoderm* and an inner *endoderm*. They are separated by a thin layer of non-cellular jelly secreted by both ecto-derm and endoderm. Such a body structure is known as *diploblastic*. In more highly-differentiated animals, a third layer, the *mesoderm*, appears in the place of the jelly, giving a grade known as *triploblastic*.

The ectoderm consists of a number of types of cells. *Musculo-epithelial cells* cover most of the body. They are columnar cells, tapering towards the inner end and then extending at the base into muscle-tails which are fused to the *mesogloea*. These slender processes show

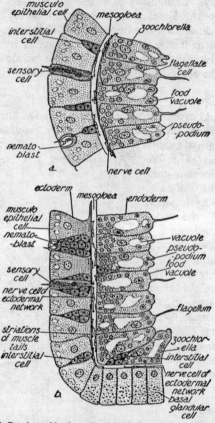

Fig. 10.12. (*a*) Portion of body wall of *Hydra* seen in T.S. The endoderm cells show striated muscle tails. (*b*) The same seen in L.S.

faint striations somewhat like those we find in muscle of higher animals. They are orientated in a plane such that by their contraction, the animal becomes squat. These musculo-epithelial cells form a coherent covering to the body and they provide the means whereby protective contraction of the whole body takes place. Unlike the pinacocytes of sponges, their movement is co-ordinated. hence they provide an example of an epithelial tissue to which is added the function of a muscular tissue (*see* Fig. 10.12 (*a*), (*b*)). Scattered among the musculo-epithelial cells are narrow columnar *sensory cells* each with a delicate protoplasmic process projecting into the water. From the base of each sensory

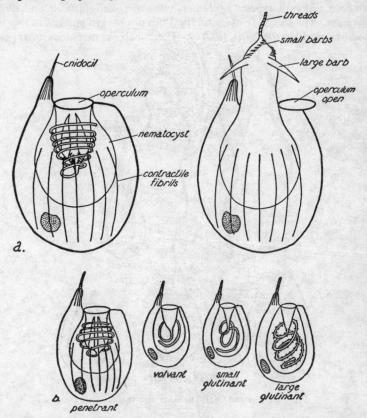

Fig. 10.13. (*a*) Nematoblast with penetrant thread before and after discharge. (*b*) The four types of nematoblasts of *Hydra* with threads undischarged.

cell, a fine nerve fibre leads into the mesogloea and there terminates in a number of branches which form a synapse with similar branches from a nerve cell. The peculiar stinging cells called *nematoblasts* are grouped in batteries on the tentacles, but are less plentiful elsewhere and are completely absent from the basal region. They develop in the middle one-third of the body, from undifferentiated interstitial cells, then migrate by amoeboid movement into their final situations, where development is completed. Most frequently they pierce the musculo-epithelial cells and project slightly beyond the general surface.

Each nematoblast contains near its outer surface, an ovoid cavity enclosing a coiled thread. The cavities are called *nematocysts* and there are four different types: *penetrant, volvant, small glutinant* and *large glutinant*. The structure of each type, both discharged and undischarged is shown in Fig. 10.13 (*a*), (*b*), (*c*). The penetrant nematocysts are the

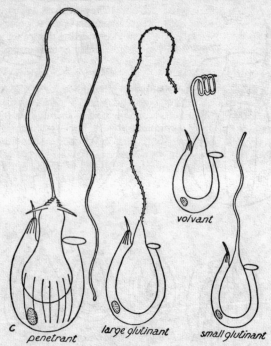

Fig. 10.13—(*contd.*) (*c*) The same with threads discharged.

most complex. Beneath the lid is an inverted cone which leads at its apex into a long coiled thread or tube. Around the cone are large and small barbs. Extending from the equatorial zone of the nematocyst to the base of the cell are a number of contractile fibrils. The exact method of discharge is not certainly known, but when suitable prey touches the sensitive *cnidocil*, the thread is shot out by inversion from narrow end to wide end. The process can be compared with blowing out the inverted finger of a rubber glove. The first part to strike the prey will be the barbed zone which lacerates the outer tissue. This is followed rapidly by the thread which contains a poisonous fluid causing paralysis of the prey It will be appreciated that the nematocysts are discharged in large numbers and the effect is to cause rapid paralysis of the hapless water-flea. All the types of nematoblast are most plentiful on the tentacles.

The volvant nematocysts discharge threads which coil around the bristles of the prey and help to hold it during its struggles. The glutinant nematocysts release, more slowly. threads which secrete a sticky material which in turn anchors the tentacles to the substratum while the hydra is performing its looping movements. Large glutinant nematocysts are discharged for defence; the threads have a plentiful supply of tiny barbs.

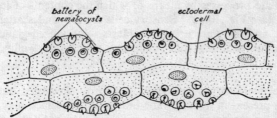

Fig. 10.14. Small portion of a tentacle of *Hydra*.

Aggregated in clusters in the gaps between the narrow inner ends of the musculo-epithelial cells. are small rounded cells, known from their location as *interstitial*. They are undifferentiated and their chief function appears to be that of replacing nematoblasts, though they also give rise to the gametes.

The cells at the base of the hydra are *glandular* cells, tall and columnar. They contain numerous granules of a sticky mucoid substance secreted to fix the animal. These cells are also capable of secreting a bubble of gas which is trapped by the mucus and this enables the hydra to float in an inverted position near the surface.

Beneath the ectoderm is the *ectodermal nerve net* consisting of a network of neurones which ramify over the whole outer edge of the mesogloea with perhaps a slightly higher concentration in the hypostome region. They communicate directly with the muscle-tails and by means of *synapses* with the sensory cells, with each other, and with the cells of the *endodermal nerve net* on the other side of the mesogloea.

Thus, in the ectoderm of a mature hydra, there are seven types of cells: musculo-epithelial, sensory, nematoblasts, interstitial, sex cells, nerve cells and basal glandular cells. Of these, the musculo-epithelial coat and the nerve net have certainly achieved the status of a tissue.

The mesogloea shows no visible structure and contains no cells. It is secreted by both ectoderm and endoderm layers.

In the endoderm there are fewer types of cells. All are columnar and larger than the musculo-epithelial cells. Their bases are prolonged into muscle-tails which are extended in the transverse plane. By their contraction, elongation of the body is effected. As with voluntary muscles of higher animals, the muscle-tails in a hydra work in two opposing sets; the ectodermal set cause contraction of the body and the endodermal set effect extension.

Most of the endoderm cells are glandular, secreting digestive juices which collect in small vacuoles preparatory to being passed into the enteron. There are also frequent amoeboid cells which ingest small particles for intracellular digestion. These cells can also produce long flagellate processes by means of which the contents of the enteron are mixed (see Fig. 10.12). Sensory cells are few and scattered in the endoderm, and there are no nematoblasts. Specialized glandular cells near the mouth secrete a sticky substance which aids swallowing.

Skeleton

Many coelenterates produce stony or horny skeletons, but there is none such present in hydrae. The only structure which may be called skeletal is the mesogloea. All the cells are attached to it, and by its elasticity it undoubtedly aids in extension of the body after contraction.

Nutrition

The food of hydrae consists mainly of small crustaceans such as *Daphnia* and *Cyclops*, two genera of "water-fleas." If the crustacean brushes against cnidocils on the tentacles, penetrant nematocysts are discharged. They paralyse the prey, and the volvant threads assist in holding it. The tentacle then bends over towards the mouth and the other tentacles also fold inwards. The mouth gapes widely due to the contraction of radially-disposed muscle-tails, and the prey is engulfed. Mucus, secreted by the glandular cells within the mouth, assists the process of swallowing.

The endodermal gland cells secrete enzymes which kill the prey and perform preliminary digestion. Thrashing of the flagella finally produces small particles which are then ingested by pseudopodia of the amoeboid cells. Digestion is completed intracellularly. The animal thus shows a combination of extracellular and intracellular digestion.

The digested products diffuse from the endodermal cells through the mesogloea to the ectodermal cells. It has been reported that endoderm cells or portions of them may break off and be carried bodily by currents caused by the flagella into the hollow tentacles where they are ingested. Some of the cells may also move in amoeboid fashion about the enteron and transport food in that manner. Defaecation takes place through the mouth and may be violent, by sudden contraction with the mouth open, or more gentle by directed movements of the flagella.

Respiration

A hydra is aerobic and obtains its oxygen by diffusion from the surrounding water. Both ectoderm and endoderm are normally bathed with the water, and no cell is far removed from it. In stagnant ponds, the respiration is assisted in some species by the symbiotic algae which produce oxygen as a result of their photosynthetic processes.

Locomotion

Hydrae move rarely and then usually only in response to hunger or persistent unfavourable stimuli. The method employed is known as looping, from its resemblance to the movement of "looper" caterpillars.

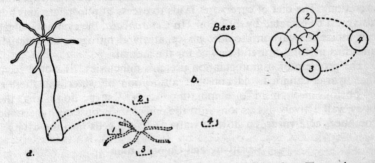

Fig. 10.15. Movement of *Hydra*. (a) Side view. (b) Plan view. The numbers show some of the positions in which the base may be placed.

The body is extended and bent over to one side so that the mouth end touches the substratum; the tentacles are then firmly attached by discharge of the small glutinant nematocysts. The base is then freed and drawn up closer to the mouth end. This looping movement may be repeated. Sometimes the base is moved round a quarter of a circle to a lateral position, and more rarely it may move through an arc of 180° to be put down on the opposite side. This has given rise to the idea of somersaulting.

Young hydrae often secrete bubbles of gas into the mucus at the base and then float up to the surface, where they remain in an inverted position, "fishing" with the tentacles. Sometimes a mature hydra will do this in response to repeated stimuli of an unfavourable nature. Faint gliding movements of the whole body by amoeboid action of the basal cells, have been observed.

A careful consideration of the looping movement will show that there must be considerably accurate co-ordination so that the muscle-tails in the various regions shall contract or relax in the correct succession.

Growth

After the developmental stages are completed, a hydra grows by division of all types of cells except nematoblasts. These are continually replaced from interstitial cells. Any portion of the body which is damaged is made good by migration of interstitial cells which can differentiate into any of the other forms.

Excretion

The hydra excretes the carbon dioxide resulting from respiration by diffusion into the surrounding water. The same is true of nitrogenous excretion. The diet of carnivores leads to excess of phosphate and this also must be excreted by diffusion. In *Chlorohydra*, the symbiotic algae can utilize the carbon dioxide, phosphates and nitrogenous materials and thus perform a useful service for the animal.

The problem of osmoregulation presents difficulties. It would seem that hydrae cannot avoid constant absorption of water, but there is no obvious mechanism for eliminating excess. A suggestion is that the body wall actively passes ions into the enteron. A constant hypertonic condition here ensures a flow of water from the cells into the cavity.

Sensitivity and Co-ordination

The nervous system of a hydra may be said to be the most primitive type. It consists of a *double nerve net*, one on each side of the meso-gloea (*see* Fig. 10.16). The *neurones* are multipolar and each *dendron* ends in a terminal *arborization*. There are no long axons, and hence no nerves (*see* Chap. 20). The majority of the neurones communicate with each other via synapses, but there may be direct connexions passing longitudinally, so that sudden contraction of the whole body may be effected. Usually, impulses seem to travel very slowly, but repetition of a stimulus will gradually cause more rapid conduction. The synapses are said to have become "facilitated" or easier of passage, after a number of impulses have been transmitted.

The nematoblasts may be described as receptor-effectors. They are directly stimulated by touch on the cnidocil and the discharge response is made without the intervention of the nervous system. Nevertheless, impulses do travel through the nerve net, because other nematocysts in the vicinity discharge their threads although their cnidocils have not been stimulated. The impulse, however, seems to fade out with distance from the point of disturbance, since only comparatively local nematocysts are discharged.

A hydra is sensitive to food materials, but the response is not purely automatic. If it is well fed, water-fleas may brush the cnidocils repeatedly and it will not respond. If hungry, brushing with a glass rod will not cause discharge of the nematocysts, but a drop of meat juice, placed in the water, will cause it to open its mouth widely. Some protozoa normally creep over its surface and it makes no response. The stimulus for active feeding is *glutathione*, a tripeptide almost universal in animal tissues (*see* index, Vol. II).

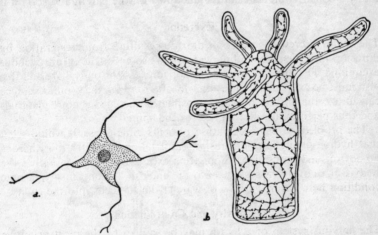

Fig. 10.16. Diagrams showing (*a*) a nerve cell and (*b*) the ectodermal nerve net in *Hydra*.

Its sensitivity to touch and to injurious chemicals is indicated by contraction. But the response to persistent unfavourable stimuli is not directional; it merely contracts and then it expands in a slightly different direction, which may even be closer to the source of the stimulus. Eventually it will move its body by looping, but again the movement is not directional. Its sensitivity to oxygen tension and to bluish light are adaptive in that it will frequent those regions of the water where its prey also congregate.

A remarkable experiment has been performed on a hydra by turning it inside out. The process was effected by pushing the base up through the mouth. Thus the ectoderm became the inside and the endoderm the outside covering. In a short time, the layers became correctly orientated by migration of all the cells through the mesogloea; the ectoderm cells passing outwards and the endoderm cells inwards.

Reproduction, Survival. Dispersal

Species of *Hydra* reproduce both asexually and sexually. Asexual reproduction is performed by a process known as budding. In favourable circumstances, the numbers will be multiplied thirty- or forty-fold in a few months. The buds arise somewhat nearer the base than the mouth end. They commence as outpushings of the enteron which cause all three layers to bulge out beyond the general surface (*see* Fig. 10.17). The bulge increases in size and becomes cylindrical. Shortly, tentacles and a mouth develop and soon the little hydra feeds. Eventually a constriction arises at its junction with the parent and soon it is

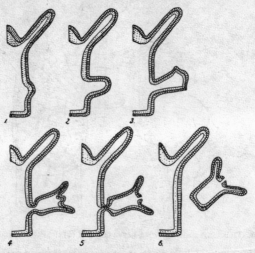

Fig. 10.17. Successive stages in the formation of a bud in *Hydra*.

pinched off, rises to the top of the water and remains there for some time before settling down. It has been recorded that the bud may help in separation by obtaining a hold on an object with its tentacles and actively pulling itself away from the parent.

Sexual reproduction is seasonal; in *Chlorohydra* and also in *H. grisea*, it occurs in early summer; in *H. fusca* it occurs in autumn. The gonads are not true organs but merely aggregates of gametes; all traces of them disappear, and they may arise in a different place again. Gametes develop from interstitial cells which aggregate in clumps, causing the ectoderm to bulge outwards. Several testes occur in the anterior third of the body. The cells divide many times, giving rise eventually to minute sperm with rounded heads, narrow middle-pieces, and long flagellate tails. A thin weakened area develops in the covering of ectodermal cells. This soon bulges slightly as a papilla; the ripe sperm are liberated by the bursting of this papilla. Normally only one ovary develops, in the posterior half of the body. It begins as a group of interstitial cells. One becomes much enlarged and finally consumes the others to form a large oocyte. It undergoes normal meiosis and polar bodies are extruded. The ripe ovum is relatively enormous and packed

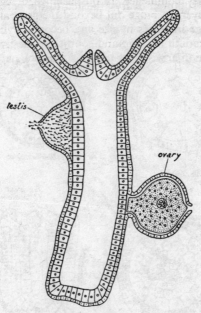

Fig. 10.18. L.S. of *Hydra* showing mature testis and ovary

with dark, spherical granules of yolk; it bursts the musculo-epithelial coat to form a wide pore through which the sperm swim. Most species of *Hydra* are protandrous; this ensures cross-fertilization.

The early stages of development take place while the zygote is still retained in the ovary. Eventually the embryo, contained in a spiny and thick horny shell, falls away and subsides to the bottom of the pond. There is usually a quiescent period when these cysts may be dispersed on the feet of wading animals. Further dispersal takes place when the young hydrae, sexually or asexually produced, float to the surface and remain there for some time; disturbance of the surface by winds will tend to spread the population.

The cysts are very resistant and will survive long periods of drought or very low temperatures. When conditions are favourable, each splits open and a young hydra emerges. Many species of *Hydra* can survive the winter in the adult condition, provided the water temperature remains above freezing point.

Development

Following fertilization, cleavage begins immediately, the zygote still remaining in the ruptured ovary attached to the parent's body. After

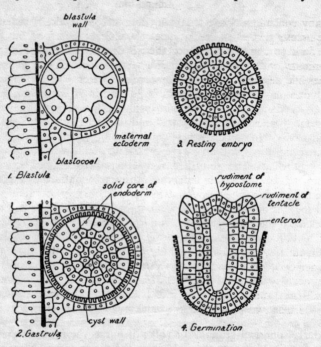

Fig. 10.19. Stages in the development of *Hydra* embryo.

many cell divisions, a *blastula* is formed. It consists of a single layer of cells surrounding a large fluid-filled cavity called the *blastocoel*. By divisions in tangential planes, these outer cells cut off other cells which accumulate in the blastocoel until they fill it. Thus a two-layered embryo is formed, with an outer covering of ectoderm and a solid core of endoderm; it is now a *gastrula*. The cells of the ectoderm secrete a colourless horny case beset with low spines. In this condition, the cyst is released; the parent often dies.

There is usually a resting period when the cyst lies at the bottom of the pond. In the case of those species which reproduce sexually in spring, the cyst may lie in dried mud. When favourable conditions occur, rise in temperature for winter cysts and the presence of water for summer cysts, the wall splits open and the young hydra emerges. Soon a central cavity appears in the endoderm; it widens to give rise to the enteron. The mouth appears at the distal end and the animal commences feeding and growth.

Adaptation

Many coelenterates are sedentary animals. A hydra is sedentary for the greater part of its life; it does not actively seek food but waits for the food to come to it. Hence there is distinct advantage in the radial symmetry with the very extensible tentacles which can probe a considerable distance into the surrounding water. In *H. oligactis* the tentacles may extend to a length of 20 cm; in *H. attenuata*, 5 cm, and in *C. viridissima*, 2 cm. Respiration by diffusion is facilitated by the extreme thinness of the body wall and the fact that there is an internal fluid cavity. In some species which inhabit stagnant waters, there is further aid to respiration by the symbiotic union with zoochlorellae or zooxanthellae. The ability to secrete gas bubbles and thus to float completely away from an unfavourable area, is conducive to its survival. The four types of nematocysts are adapted for four different purposes, and there is an adequate mechanism for their replacement, since once discharged they are lost to the body. Excretion is satisfactorily carried out by diffusion aided again by the symbiotic algae. All its behaviour is conducive to survival, and its preference for blue light and high oxygen content, urges it to move to those parts of the pond where its prey are also likely to foregather. The rapid rate of budding under good conditions, and the production of a resistant cyst, ensure survival and the maintenance of satisfactory numbers.

The hydra shows no special adaptations for the low salinity of freshwater; but the effect of pumping ions to maintain an osmotic gradient from outside to the enteron could be osmoregulatory.

Classification

Phylum: Coelenterata   Family: Hydrida
Class: Hydrozoa   Genera: *Hydra, Chlorohydra*
Order: Hydroidea   Species: *C. viridissima, H. fusca*

Members of the order Hydroidea are characterized by a life cycle in which a fixed hydroid phase is usually followed by a free medusoid stage with ectodermal sex organs. Genera in the family Hydrida show only the hydroid stage and do not produce medusae. The various genera and species are separated on characteristics such as colour, shape of the body, and size.

Special Features of Biological Importance

The study of *Hydra* reveals a number of features which show either advance on lower forms or specialization peculiar to the phylum.

Differentiation in Hydra

Whereas in the Protozoa we find the protoplasmic level of organization, and in the Porifera, the cellular level of organization, the coelenterates have achieved the tissue level. In a tissue, the cells are of the same kind and are grouped in coherent masses for the performance of one or more special functions. Further, the cells work in harmony; they are co-ordinated Such tissues, in *Hydra*, are the musculo-epithelial tissue, the nervous tissue the basal glandular tissue and almost the entire endoderm. With differentiation, there is division of labour. It must be remembered, however, that each cell still maintains the protoplasmic level of organization. Also, there are scattered cells and groups of cells not yet organized into tissues. Such are the sensory cells, the nematoblasts and the interstitial cells.

It is sometimes considered that the tentacles should be given the status of organs, consisting of several types of tissue co-ordinated for the performance of one or more functions. They consist of musculo-epithelial cells, sensory cells, interstitial cells, nematoblasts and endoderm cells. Their functions are the capture of food and its conveyance to the mouth, and they also play a part in the looping movements.

Regeneration

The hydra shows remarkable powers of regeneration, which, however, are not quite on a par with those of the sponges. A single hydra may be cut into fifty or more pieces, and provided that each piece contains a portion of ectoderm and endoderm, it will produce a complete animal.

Symbiosis

The details of symbiosis are discussed in Chap. 34. A great many coelenterates harbour symbiotic algae. In the case of *Chlorohydra*, zoochlorellae are plentiful in the endodermal cells. They benefit from the association by receiving carbon dioxide, phosphates and nitrogenous substances, all of which the hydra would otherwise excrete The algae are also provided with a sheltered habitat. The hydra benefits by receiving the oxygen produced by photosynthesis. Both partners can live without the other; the zoochlorellae are found free-living. In periods of continued food shortage, the hydra will digest the plant cells, and later ingest more living algae which it will not digest. Thus the union is not an obligatory symbiosis.

Nematoblasts

These cells, which bear the peculiar nematocysts, are not developed in any other phylum. It is interesting that they are sometimes found in the epidermis of free-living platyhelminthes. The flat-worms eat hydrae; they do not digest the nematoblasts, which migrate to the epidermis and so form a secondarily-acquired defensive mechanism. This is a remarkable case of natural implantation; cells derived from one animal, form an integral part of another.

OBELIA

Obelia is a genus of delicate marine zoophytes inhabiting the coastal zone from low water to more than 90 m deep. They occur in large fixed colonies of a cream or light brown colour on seaweeds, on shells, on rocks and on wooden piles. The branched colonies sway gently in the water with the very small *polyps* protruding from cups at the ends of the branches. They capture food in the same manner as a hydra does, and thus feed the whole colony. In the axils of the lower branches, asexual reproductive zooids called *blastostyles* bud off small swimming *medusae*. These reproduce sexually, the zygote developing into a free-swimming larva known as a *planula*. Eventually, the larva settles down to give rise to another hydroid colony.

General Features of the Colonial Form

The colony consists of a branching portion called the *hydrorhiza*, which is attached to the substratum. At intervals, this gives rise to upright stems, each constituting a *hydrocaulus*. Each hydrocaulus is made up of branches arranged in cymose fashion, each branch giving rise to the next. Thus the polyps are arranged alternately.

At the apex is an undifferentiated bud which will produce another polyp. Each vertical branch achieves a height of 3 to 5 cm (*see* Fig. 10.20).

Microscopic examination reveals that the living, hollow tube, the *coenosarc*, is enclosed in a thin chitinous exoskeleton, the *perisarc*. At the end of each branch, the perisarc expands into a small goblet-shaped container called a *hydrotheca*. This contains a polyp or *hydranth*, resting on a circular shelf near the base. Below each hydrotheca are

Fig. 10.20. Small portion of *Obelia* colony.

several annular constrictions, and one or two other constrictions occur above the point where each branch meets the main stem. They give a limited degree of flexibility to the whole structure. In the axils of the

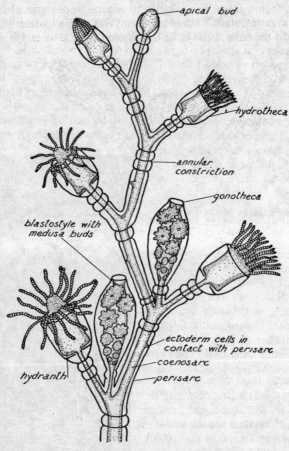

Fig. 10.21. *Obelia* hydranths and blastostyles.

lower branches, the perisarc forms vase-like structures called *gonothecae*, each having a small circular aperture at its free end. The gonothecae contain the blastostyles which bud off the medusae. The entire perisarc is secreted by the ectoderm of the coenosarc, but only a few of the cells touch it; some are extended to make contact, but the main part of the coenosarc has receded a little way from it (*see* Fig. 10.21).

The coenosarc has the typical coelenterate arrangement of ectoderm, mesogloea, endoderm and enteron. The enteron is a continuous cavity throughout the whole colony. The coenosarc produces two types of zooids, the hydranths and the blastostyles.

Each hydranth resembles a hydra in general appearance, but differs from it in certain details. There are about two dozen tentacles arranged in a circle at the base of the large hypostome. These tentacles are solid,

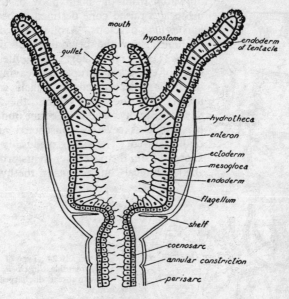

Fig. 10.22. Single hydranth of *Obelia* in L.S.

with an outer layer of ectoderm cells and a solid core consisting of a single row of large endoderm cells separated by a thickened layer of intercellular substance. The base of the hydranth rests on the circular shelf, but its enteron communicates by a somewhat constricted passage with the general enteron of the coenosarc. Each hydranth can withdraw itself almost completely into the hydrotheca, with its tentacles folded over the hypostome. Both in the hydranth and the coenosarc, there is a large proportion of flagellate cells in the endoderm (*see* Fig. 10.22).

The blastostyles have neither tentacles nor mouth; they are purely reproductive zooids. Each consists of a club-shaped hollow column. Medusae are budded off in succession from the apex downwards, and thus all stages in their development may be seen in a single blastostyle.

Each medusa is initiated as a small bud which becomes enlarged and almost spherical, communicating with the enteron by a narrow passage. The ectoderm of the outermost portion delaminates a disc of cells inwards. By further cell divisions, this disc becomes double in its central zone and a small cavity appears between these two layers of ectoderm. The cavity enlarges as development proceeds, and within it, projecting outwards from the main body of the young medusa, a raised cone destined to become the *manubrium*, develops. Around the edges, outpushings show the beginnings of the *radial canals* (*see* Fig. 10.23). The outer double layer of ectoderm is ruptured, leaving a small inwardly-projecting circular shelf called the *velum*. Outside the velum, the tentacles develop rapidly. Soon the connexion with the blastostyle is severely constricted and eventually severed. The young medusa is probably expelled from the pore by currents produced by the rhythmical contractions of the hydranths.

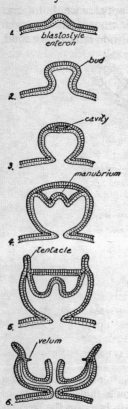

Fig. 10.23. Stages in the development of a medusa on the blastostyle of *Obelia*.

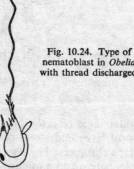

Fig. 10.24. Type of nematoblast in *Obelia* with thread discharged.

The types of cells in the hydranths are, in general, the same as those found in a hydra. Nematoblasts are confined to the tentacles, where they are arranged in annular groups, and to the hypostome. Only one type of nematocyst thread is present. It is similar to the penetrant type, with a few equal barbs radially arranged near its base (*see* Fig. 10.24). They arise from interstitial cells situated both in the coenosarc and in the basal region of the hydranth. Interstitial cells occur comparatively rarely.

Physiology of the Colonial Form

The hydranths are the feeding zooids and they supply the whole colony. Small organisms are captured by the nematocyst threads and brought to the mouth by the tentacles. Extracellular digestion reduces the food to a fine state of division. Circulation of these small particles throughout the general enteron is achieved by the movement of the flagella and also by the rhythmical contraction of individual hydranths which sends a current swirling through the whole colony. Most of the endoderm cells can ingest small particles by amoeboid action and digestion is completed intracellularly. Soluble food materials diffuse through the mesogloea to supply the ectodermal cells. Defaecation takes place through the mouths of the polyps.

Respiration is aerobic; the perisarc is permeable to water and thus the whole colony contains water inside the enteron and outside the ectoderm. Contraction of the hydranths and the flickering of the flagella keep the internal fluid moving. Oxygen is absorbed from the water.

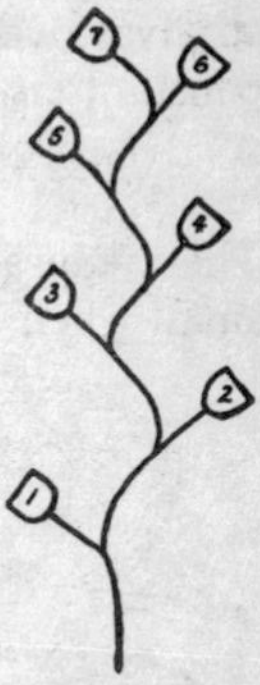

There is no locomotion of the colonial form.

Growth takes place in a somewhat peculiar manner. Each developing polyp can be regarded as giving rise to a short length of stem, and until the polyp is developed, no further branch can arise. With complete development, apical dominance is lessened, and a new branch grows out from the old branch. Each branch is comparable with a hydra bud, except that the successive buds remain attached to the older branches. In a similar manner, as the colony increases in size, branches of the hydrorhiza spread further along the substratum. The general mode of growth is thus very similar to that of a green plant with cymose branching, e.g. the iris inflorescence (*see* Fig. 10.25). When each vertical branch has reached a sufficient size, blastostyles originate in the axils of the lower branches, by a process exactly similar to that of a hydra budding. The stimulus which gives rise to blastostyle formation is not known. The interstitial cells are utilized mainly for replacement of nematoblasts.

Excretion is by diffusion, practically every cell being bathed by seawater. There is no problem of osmoregulation, the cell contents being isotonic with the water.

There is a double nerve net as in a hydra and a similar type of

Fig. 10.25. Sequence of development of polyps in *Obelia*.

sensory cell which is confined in distribution to the upper region of the hydranths, especially on the hypostome. Apart from the rhythmical contraction which aids circulation of water and food, the hydranths contract in reaction to touch or to unfavourable chemical conditions.

The colony cannot reproduce itself directly since it bears no germ cells and does not produce detached buds, apart from the medusae. These develop sexual organs and give rise to larvae which then settle down to produce new colonies. Each colony appears to be capable of indefinite survival by extension of the hydrocaulus and the appearance of an unlimited series of upright branches. There is no problem of survival over unfavourable periods since the seas provide a relatively constant environment.

The Structure of the Medusa

The medusae are liberated in spring or early summer. They are very small when freed and spend several months achieving full growth and

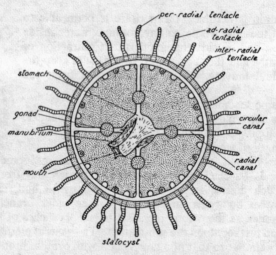

Fig. 10.26. *Obelia* medusa, sub-umbrellar view.

development of the gonads. When fully grown, they are transparent, saucer-shaped animals, about 3 mm in diameter. The convex upper surface is known as the *ex-umbrella* and the concave lower surface as the *sub-umbrella*. A short thick column hangs from the middle of the sub-umbrellar surface; it is the *manubrium* and corresponds to the hypostome of hydroid forms. At the lower end of the manubrium is the four-lobed *mouth*. The tentacles hang vertically downwards all round the edge of the medusa. There are twenty-four present when it is liberated from the blastostyle, but the number increases considerably. Within the ring of tentacles a circular shelf, the velum, projects into the cavity of the bell. It is small when the medusa is freed, and rapidly becomes almost vestigial, though in certain other medusae, it is a well-marked feature (*see* Fig. 10.23).

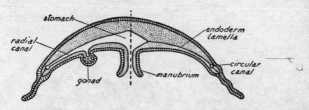

Fig. 10.27. Diagram of *Obelia* medusa in L.S. One half passes through a radial canal, the other half through the endoderm lamella.

The mouth leads into a short *gullet* which traverses the manubrium. The gullet leads into a *gastric cavity*, sometimes called the stomach. From this cavity, four radial canals lead out to the edge of the bell, where their ends are joined by a circular canal. All the canals bear numerous flagella, giving a ciliated appearance. The entire outer surface is covered by ectoderm, while the gullet, stomach and all canals are lined with endoderm. Each quadrant between the canals bears a flattened sheet of endoderm, known as the *endoderm lamella*. Below the endoderm lamella, the mesogloea is comparatively thin, while above the lamella it is considerably thickened (*see* Fig. 10.27).

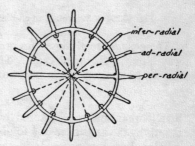

Fig. 10.28. The principal tentacles of an *Obelia* medusa.

The tentacles are solid and somewhat swollen at their inner ends where the endodermal core projects into the mesogloea above the circular canal. Below the tentacle, and just outside the circular canal, is a slight swelling caused by an accumulation of interstitial cells. They are used for replacement of the nematoblasts which are confined to the tentacles. The ectodermal cells at the bases of the tentacles may possess dark pigment spots said to be sensitive to light. They are probably granules of excretory material. The four tentacles opposite the radial canals are known as *per-radial tentacles*; on the bisectors of the per-radial angles are the *inter-radial* tentacles, and on the bisectors of the eight angles so formed are the *ad-radial* tentacles (*see* Fig. 10.28). Within the bases of the latter tentacles, just beneath the margin of the bell are the *statocysts*; they are sensory organs concerned with appreciation of changes in orientation (*see* Fig. 10.29).

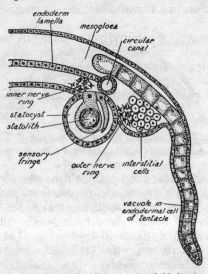

Fig. 10.29. V.S. through an ad-radial tentacle of *Obelia* showing statocyst.

The *gonads* are globose sacs protruding from the sub-umbrella, half-way along each radial canal. The medusae are unisexual; thus the gonads produce sperm in males and ova in females.

Physiology of the Medusa

Small organisms are captured by the tentacles and pushed into the mouth by the assistance of a folding inward of the bell margins. Extra-cellular digestion proceeds in the gastric cavity, and small particles circulate in the canals where they are ingested by amoeboid endoderm cells. Defaecation is effected through the mouth.

Respiration is aerobic; a respiratory current of water throughout the canal system can be maintained.

Although the medusa drifts passively for much of its time, it can swim actively by contractions of the bell. These contractions force water backward, thus driving the animal forward. They are effected by the plentiful musculo-epithelial cells whose muscle-tails are so pronounced that they almost constitute a separate tissue. Indeed, in certain special tracts on the sub-umbrellar side, the muscle-tails have separate nuclei and constitute a muscular tissue. Occasionally, the medusa will contract the upper surface making it concave, while the lower surface becomes convex. After any movement which involves alteration in shape, the normal form is attained largely by the elasticity of the mesogloea. Special circular and radial muscle tracts exist on the sub-umbrellar side.

The medusa grows comparatively little during its short life. During the period of growth and development all the cells, except possibly nerve cells, are capable of division. New tentacles begin as small buds. Discharged nematoblasts are replaced by interstitial cells from the clumps at the bases of the tentacles. The medusa dies after discharge of the gametes.

Excretion occurs by diffusion, and the pigment granules in the ectodermal cells at the bases of the tentacles may also be excretory in origin.

The nervous system shows a considerable advance on that of hydroid forms. Apart from the general double network, there is considerable concentration of nerve cells in two rings, one external to the circular canal and one internal. This concentration is probably developed in relation to the greater locomotive activity of medusae. The inner nerve ring is concerned mainly with control and co-ordination of the sub-umbrellar musculature, while the outer nerve ring deals with impulses from the statocysts. These are small fluid-filled sacs lying inside the margin of the bell, beneath the bases of the ad-radial tentacles. Thus there are eight statocysts. The sac is lined with ectoderm and hanging from the upper part is a single large cell which contains a granule of calcium carbonate, a *statolith*. On the outer side of the suspended granule are sensory protoplasmic processes forming a fringe. While the medusa is floating horizontally, none of the statoliths will touch a sensory process, but as soon as any part of the margin is inclined to the horizontal, one or more statoliths will touch a sensory process. Thus impulses are set up and transmitted by fine nerve processes to the outer nerve ring. This then re-transmits impulses to the inner nerve ring and thus the sub-umbrellar muscles are stimulated to restore the equilibrium. The whole mechanism causes swimming movements which prevent the medusa sinking too deeply. Many medusae possess undoubted ocelli but the pigmented cells in species of *Obelia* do not seem to have this function.

The gonads are pendulous ectodermal sacs into which folds of endoderm from the radial canals project. The germ cells have been traced from the ectoderm of the manubrium, where they arise, along the gullet and radial canals. There they pass through the endoderm and maturation divisions take place in the ectodermal sacs. When mature, the sacs burst and the gametes are liberated in the surface waters, where fertilization takes place.

After cleavage of the zygote, a blastula is formed, and converted into a gastrula by multiplication of cells at one pole; thus a larva called the *planula* is produced. It consists of a single layer of ciliated ectodermal cells which enclose a solid core of endodermal cells. It swims freely for

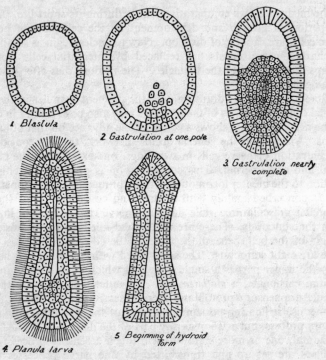

1. *Blastula*

2. *Gastrulation at one pole*

3. *Gastrulation nearly complete*

4. *Planula larva*

5. *Beginning of hydroid form*

Fig. 10.30. Development after cleavage in *Obelia*.

some time, during which a split appears in the endoderm. This split will enlarge to become the future enteron (*see* Fig. 10.30).

Soon, the planula settles down by its broader end; a branch grows out horizontally along the substratum to commence the hydrorhiza. The vertical portion develops tentacles and a mouth and becomes the first hydranth. Thus the sessile stage is inaugurated.

The particular adaptive features shown by the medusa, are connected essentially with dispersal Its transparency makes it almost invisible in the water; the swimming movements due to the perceptive powers of the statocysts keep it in the surface waters where plankton is more plentiful and where fertilization takes place. The swimming planula larva further aids dispersal.

Classification of Obelia

Phylum:	Coelenterata	Family:	Campanulariidae
Class:	Hydrozoa	Genus:	*Obelia*
Order:	Hydroidea	Species:	*O. geniculata*
Sub-order:	Leptomedusae		

Obelia is placed in the order Hydroidea because of the alternation of fixed hydroid and free-swimming medusoid phases, and because of the possession of ectodermal gonads. Coelenterates in the sub-order Leptomedusae have both hydrothecae and gonothecae, and bear the gonads beneath the radial canals. In the family Campanulariidae, cup-shaped thecae are borne at the ends of distinct branches. In the genus *Obelia*, the reproductive zooids are the free-swimming medusae. Species are distinguished by colour and size.

Special Features of Biological Importance

Topics worthy of further consideration in *Obelia* are the alternation of generations, polymorphism, the relationship between the hydroid and medusoid forms, and the colonial habit.

Alternation of Generations

In green plants, the term "alternation of generations" as exhibited notably by the Bryophyta (Chap. 11) and Pteridophyta (Chap. 13) has a precise meaning. A haploid generation producing gametes is succeeded by a diploid generation producing spores. As applied to *Obelia*, it has a different meaning. Both fixed and free forms are diploid; the haploid phase is represented only by the gametes. The colonial form, produced from the zygote via the planula larva, produces many hydranths before the blastostyles are developed and hence the medusae. The hydranths may be regarded as asexual buds which do not become detached. Since the colonial form does not produce any gametes, it may be considered the juvenile stage, while the medusae constitute the adults, now separated from the colony. Rather than describe the phenomenon as "alternation of generations," it is perhaps better to refer to it as *metagenesis*, meaning deferment of the power of generation.

In various groups of the Coelenterata there is great variation in the extent to which the hydroid or medusoid form predominates. In *Hydra*, there is only the hydroid form; in *Obelia*, both hydroid and medusoid forms are well developed; in the Scyphozoa, the hydroid form is much suppressed and in some is completely absent; in the Anthozoa, there is no medusoid form.

Polymorphism

The appearance of the same creature in various forms is known as *polymorphism*. In the great majority of animals, there is only sexual dimorphism, but in many coelenterates, various types of zooids are developed for specific functions. In *Obelia*, there are the feeding polyps, the asexual reproductive

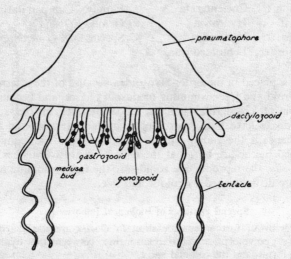

Fig. 10.31. *Physalia*, the Portuguese man-of-war.

zooids and the sexual reproductive zooids. The acme of polymorphism is achieved by certain members of the order Siphonophora of the class Hydrozoa. In *Physalia*, "the Portuguese man-of-war," there is a large pneumatophore for floating, dactylozooids for food capture, gastrozooids for feeding and gonozooids for reproduction (*see* Fig. 10.31).

Colonial Habit

It is difficult to decide whether *Obelia geniculata* is a single animal or a colony of individuals joined by living connexions. If we regard it as a single individual, then all the free medusae from one individual are part of it, and pursuing the argument to its limit, all the hydroid forms developed from the gametes of the medusae would be part of the same individual, since one single colony can produce both male and female medusae. On this reasoning, all the types of zooids are merely examples of *merism* or repetition of similar parts, which is a common phenomenon in certain groups of animals. On the other hand, if we regard *Obelia* as a colony of individuals organically connected, it constitutes a population of zooids which are genetically identical. Also, if we regard the hydranths as individuals, they have no reproductive organs, while the blastostyles have no feeding organs. Thus it seems more sensible to regard it as a colony of individuals in which the zooids have lost certain functions but are specialized for the needs of the whole colony. The medusae then become the sexual reproductive zooids, specialized also for dispersal.

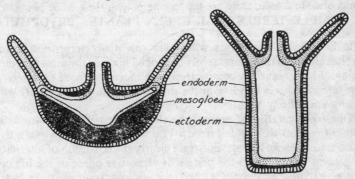

Fig. 10.32. Comparison of hydroid and medusoid forms of coelenterates.

Hydroid and Medusoid Forms

A little consideration will show that the medusoid form can readily be derived from the hydroid form. If a hydroid is progressively flattened, the enteron will be reduced to a small cavity into which the mouth and gullet lead (*see* Fig. 10.32). The radial and circular canals would represent further vestiges of the enteron. Thickening of the mesogloea and increase in the number of tentacles would thus produce the characteristic medusoid form.

CHAPTER 11

SIMPLE TERRESTRIAL GREEN PLANTS: BRYOPHYTA

THE bryophytes are plants which are essentially terrestrial in their habitat although they can scarcely be looked upon as the most thorough-going of land plants by comparison with more advanced examples. A few representatives can live in the driest of situations, however, whilst others are entirely aquatic.

One representative of each of the classes Hepaticae (liverworts) and Musci (mosses) will be described. The selected genera, *Pellia*, a liverwort, and *Funaria*, a moss, illustrate clearly the condition of alternation of generations in which the persistent vegetative phase of the life cycle is the haploid gametophyte, and the diploid sporophyte is but an ephemeral spore-producing body dependent for its development on the nutritional activity of the gametophyte.

PELLIA

This genus includes three species only, of which *P. epiphylla* occurs most commonly in Great Britain and will be described here. The other species are *P. neesiana* and *P. fabbroniana*.

Habitat

The usual sites for habitation are damp places such as banks of ditches and streams, on the ground in damp woods and under hedges where shady conditions prevail. Since many plants usually occur together, they may overlap one another to cover large patches of soil to the exclusion of all other sizeable plants.

Vegetative Structure of the Gametophyte Generation

All cells of the gametophyte body are haploid.

External Morphology

The body is *thallose*; it lacks any stem and leaf organization. It consists of a flattened, dichotomously branched and often deeply lobed plate whose size may vary with age from a mere speck up to 7 or 8 cm in length when in healthy mature growth. No definite size at maturity can be fixed, however, since the thallus continues to grow indefinitely outwards from its point of origin, the older parts dying away year by year. The upper surface is dark green, except where a midrib shows a brownish to purple colour. It has no vegetative appendages. The lower surface is lighter in colour and bears numerous hair-like *rhizoids* in the region of the midrib; by these rhizoids the thallus is fixed to the soil.

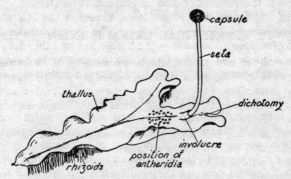

Fig. 11.1. *Pellia* gametophyte bearing spore capsule.

On a fertile thallus near the tips of branches are small pockets each covered by a bract or *involucre*; in them are located the female reproductive organs. The position of the male organs can be made out with a lens; they lie a little way behind the involucre as a patch of small dots.

Anatomy

A transverse section of the thallus shows the simple structure. It is composed entirely of closely-packed, uninucleate, haploid cells of polygonal form, except where the lowermost grow out as unicellular rhizoids (*see* Fig. 11.2). The upper and lower layers of cells are densely

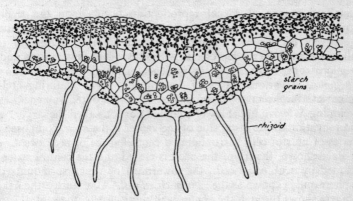

Fig. 11.2. T.S. of *Pellia* thallus.

crowded with small discoid chloroplasts, the middle layers containing very few, but all cells may carry starch grains as food reserve. The cells of the extreme outer layers in both upper and lower surfaces are smaller than the remainder and constitute an epidermis. It is not unusual to find fungal cells in the lower tissues of the thallus but the precise significance of these is not clear. The position of the midrib is marked by increased thickness in the tissues but no other very distinct difference is noticeable. The edges of the thallus may be no more than one cell thick, tapering away from the thickened midrib region.

Physiology of the Gametophyte

As far as is known, the plant has a nutritional mechanism comparable with that of green plants generally. The chlorophyll pigments are of normal composition and the end-product of photosynthesis is starch. There are no openings in the epidermis to allow of better aeration of the thallus. Special pores in the epidermis are a common feature in some other thallose liverworts, e.g. *Marchantia*. Absorption of water takes place through the rhizoids, from the soil, but all cells can absorb when their surfaces are wet enough.

Growth of the thallus is the result of divisions of a single large apical cell lying at the base of a small indentation at the tip. In the indentation may be found small mucilage-secreting hairs protecting the apical cell from desiccation. This has three "cutting-faces" and new cells are formed to each side and below, the last giving rise to the thicker midrib region. The dichotomous branching is the result of a longitudinal division of the apical cell, each new cell functioning independently to produce new growth.

Reproductive Structures of the Gametophyte

Specialized organs of sexual reproduction occur upon the thallus during early summer. It is to be noted that many liverworts reproduce vegetatively by *gemma* formation. Dissection or sectioning of the thallus in the involucral depression, with subsequent examination under the microscope, will disclose the presence of female organs known as *archegonia*, in various stages of development. The maturing archegonium has the structure shown in Fig. 11.4. An outer wall encloses a developing *oosphere* in the lower rounded portion called the *venter*. As a prolongation of the distal side of the venter is the *neck*, composed of a series of tiers of cells surrounding a central space or *neck canal*. At the stage shown, the tip of the neck is closed and the central space is occluded by *neck canal cells*, the lowermost of which surmounts the oosphere and is known as the *ventral canal cell*. At maturity the naked oosphere shows through the venter wall quite clearly, the ventral canal cell has disappeared and the neck is open along its full length due to disintegration of the neck canal cells. Only a mucilage-filled channel now separates the oosphere from the exterior.

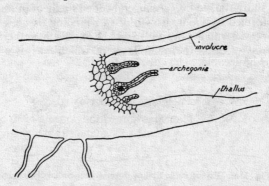

Fig. 11.3. T.S. of *Pellia* thallus through archegonial depression.

The archegonium shows considerable advance in structure over the oogonia described in the algae in being composed largely of sterile cells functioning to protect the female gamete from desiccation or other injury, and forming a direct channel through which fertilization can

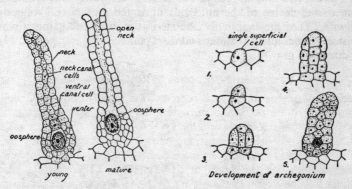

Fig. 11.4. Archegonia of *Pellia*.

Fig. 11.5. Diagram of the stages in the development of an archegonium of *Pellia*.

occur. Archegonia are formed from initial cells lying in groups just behind the thallus tip. The ridge on which they are situated is built up by the surrounding tissue behind and the involucre grows out from the top of this ridge to cover the depression so made. All cell divisions giving rise to all parts of the archegonium, including the oosphere, are mitotic.

A section through the thallus containing the male organs discloses them to be short-stalked *antheridia*, embedded singly or in small groups, in pockets formed by the upgrowth of surrounding tissue, but open to the exterior by a small pore (*see* Fig. 11.6). Each antheridium is a spherical mass of cells, the outer layer of which acts as a protective

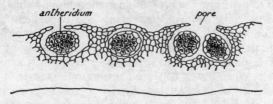

Fig. 11.6. T.S. of *Pellia* thallus through antheridial chambers.

covering to the inner fertile cells. Arising from a single cell initially, the inner mass first consists of *antherozoid mother-cells* produced by rapid successive mitotic divisions. As maturity is approached, each antherozoid mother-cell gives rise to two naked *antherozoids* each of which consists of a spirally-coiled nucleus covered with a little cytoplasm and bearing two long flagella at one end. The mature antherozoids lie freely in the cavity of the antheridium as the mother-cell walls disintegrate. They are eventually liberated as motile male gametes when the antheridium absorbs water and disrupts.

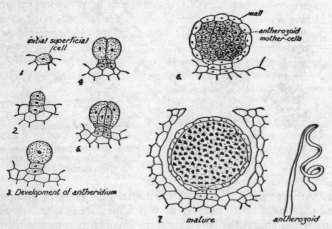

Fig. 11.7. Diagram of the stages in the development of an antheridium of *Pellia*.

Reproduction by the Gametophyte

Only sexual reproduction is exhibited by the vegetative thallus except that fragmentation by the death of a thallus up to a dichotomy can lead to the isolation of several new plants from one.

Sexual reproduction follows the normal pattern in which the motile antherozoid seeks out and fuses with the non-motile oosphere. This can be achieved only under wet conditions, for it is necessary for an antherozoid to penetrate the neck of an archegonium distantly situated from its own origin. Thus *Pellia* plants are dependent upon very watery conditions for their reproductive processes. The ability of the male gamete to find the oosphere, resides in its property of making a chemotactic response to protein substances secreted by the neck of the archegonium. When fusion between gametes in the venter of an archegonium has been completed, the diploid *zygote* is formed and this becomes an *oospore*. Rarely will more than one zygote be formed under each involucre.

Development of the Zygote into the Sporophyte Generation

Soon after its formation during the early summer period, the oospore commences its development and has reached a well-developed but resting condition by the end of autumn. The fully mature structure is known as a *sporogonium* and is entirely the product of zygote development, but it appears as an outgrowth of the vegetative thallus. This is because the young embryo develops in the venter of the old archegonium and establishes close connexions with the latter by means of its lower end. As a result of mitotic divisions of the diploid zygote, the young structure at first becomes a roughly ovoid mass of cells with an outer wall, the whole enclosed by the venter of the archegonium which enlarges considerably to keep pace with its growth. The enlarging archegonial sheath is known as the *calyptra*. Quickly, the embryonic structure establishes firm cell contacts with the old thallus by the simple means of growing backwards into the thallus tissue.

Structure, Physiology and Reproduction of the Sporogonium

The lower portion of the sporogonium is the *foot*; it is a conical mass of cells with a flanged base which in vertical section gives it the appearance of an arrowhead (*see* Fig. 11.8). The remainder of the sporogonium is differentiated into a lower short stalk or *seta* continuous with the foot, and an upper spherical, capsular structure known as the *theca* or *capsule*. The theca at first consists of a single-layered wall surrounding a mass of cells, the *archesporial tissue*. With continued development, the outer wall becomes two cells thick and the inner cells differentiate into *spore mother-cells*. From each of these latter, as a result of meiotic division, four cells are produced and each becomes a *spore*. It is recorded that centrosomes are associated with division of the archesporial cells. Below the main mass of archesporial tissue but within the capsule, the cells differentiate not into spore mother-cells but into very

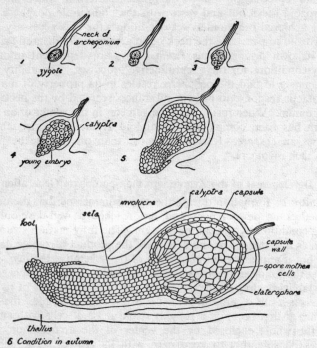

Fig. 11.8. Early stages in the development of *Pellia* sporogonium.

long thin cells, pointed at both ends and spirally thickened by two internal cutinized bands. They are the *elaters* and the whole differentiating structure is known as the *elaterophore*. At this stage of its development, still within the calyptra, the sporogonium rests during the winter. In very early spring of the next year (about February–March) it commences further development. The capsule wall cells become thickened with radial strips of cutinized material and their contents die. The spores are then surrounded by a dried-out layer of thickened cells, dark brown to black in colour. The seta, previously short, now elongates very rapidly to carry the ripening capsule upwards away from the thallus, rupturing the calyptra in the process. This period of seta elongation lasts no more than two or three days, but the seta may reach a length of as much as 8 cm. During this time, the spores also undergo a change and each becomes a group of a few cells containing chloroplasts. Each may be looked upon as a miniature thallus.

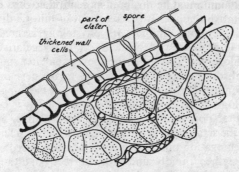

Fig. 11.9. *Pellia* capsule. Portion of wall enclosing spores and elaters.

The reproductive capacity of the sporogonium is purely asexual since the reproductive bodies are spores developed without an immediately previous formation and fusion of gametes. It must be noted that each

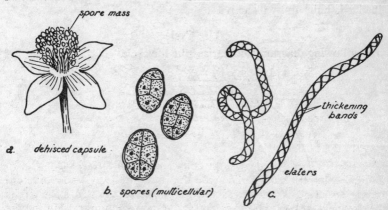

Fig. 11.10. *Pellia.* (*a*) Dehisced capsule and contents. (*b*) Multi-cellular spores. (*c*) Elaters.

spore is a haploid structure and on development reproduces the haploid vegetative thallus. The spores are liberated by the bursting of the capsule into four segments as a result of differential tensions in the wall at drying out. As the segments fold back from the apex, the elater and spore mass is exposed. The elaters with their peculiar thickenings execute hygroscopic movements and loosen the spores, which are then dispersed by air currents. This phase in the life cycle is entirely dependent on dry atmospheric conditions as opposed to the wet conditions necessary for motility of the male gametes.

The sporogonium must be regarded as a physiological entity distinct from the vegetative thallus. It is a resultant of mitotic divisions of the zygote and is therefore diploid. Its physiology is greatly different. Nutritionally it is entirely dependent on the vegetative thallus. It contains no chlorophyll (except in the spores at a later stage). The foot serves as an absorbing organ to pass food to the developing seta and capsule. It is not a parasite within the normal meaning of the term.

The physiology of its growth is not known, but it is certain that in early spring the sporogonium becomes light-sensitive, and the rapid elongation of the seta seems to be connected with this. The lengthening is due to cell elongation only, since the seta is composed of many short cells which lengthen rapidly under the correct conditions. The part played by auxins, if any, is not known.

Development of the Spores into the Gametophyte Generation

If it settles on damp soil, each spore germinates immediately without resting. One cell assumes the role of apical cell and gradually a new thallus is built up by its activity.

Life Cycle

The following diagram summarizes the life cycle.

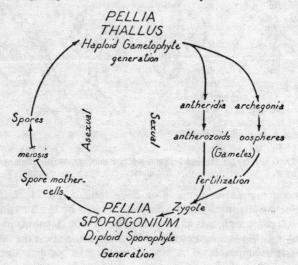

Adaptation to Environment

P. epiphylla cannot be said to be well adapted either structurally or in its reproductive processes to the full rigours of terrestrial conditions. In a continuously drying atmosphere, desiccation of the thallus occurs and death soon results, so that it flourishes only in moist shady localities. This is largely due to a lack of protective waterproof covering to resist rapid water loss, a feature of more fully adapted land plants. On the other hand, by anchoring itself to the soil with rhizoids which can absorb water and mineral salts, it illustrates a great step towards successful land colonization. Its ability to absorb water all over its surface, is an advantage in the moist conditions in which it exists. The success of the sexual reproductive process exhibited by the gametophyte is dependent upon very wet conditions, but it is noticeable that successful liberation and dispersal of the asexual spores demands a drying atmosphere. The mode of development of the sporophyte and the elevation of the capsule into the air both favour the appropriate degree of desiccation.

Special Features of Biological Importance

Pellia epiphylla illustrates several important features. These include the possession of multicellular sex organs and heteromorphic alternation of generations with retention of the developing oospore on the gametophyte.

It also illustrates the beginning of a trend which has been of major significance in the evolution of terrestrial plant life. This is the production of structures which not only serve the purpose of anchoring the plant in the soil, but are also able to absorb water and dissolved salts.

Bryophyte Antheridia and Archegonia

In none of the algae described is there a condition in which a multicellular wall surrounds the developing gametes. Both sex organs of *Pellia* show this condition. Such a state is very difficult to derive from the corresponding unicellular organs of the green algae. There are no transitional forms in existence. Thus, although the vegetative structure of the liverwort is not difficult to derive, the postulation that the bryophytes arose from the green algae is open to doubt. The possession of a sterile jacket around the developing gametes is obviously an advantage to the plant in its terrestrial surroundings. It helps to prevent desiccation of the sex cells. There are several other ways in which the gametes may be protected in the bryophytes; such are the embedding of the organs within the thallus, or the surrounding of the organs with accessory outgrowths such as the involucre.

Heteromorphic Alternation of Generations

The two generations of the cycle are clearly heteromorphic; they differ from one another morphologically. All plants higher than the Thallophyta exhibit this condition.

Lack of Independence of the Sporophyte

The total or partial dependence of the sporophyte on the gametophyte is strongly characteristic of the bryophytes. The sporogonium of *Pellia* shows not the slightest trend towards self-sufficiency. It is very largely reproductive in nature with no differentiation of chlorophyll-containing tissue. In the mosses the degree of dependence is not quite so complete. We shall see that all plants higher than this division show an increasing tendency to reverse the bryophyte condition; gradually the gametophyte becomes more and more dependent on the sporophyte.

FUNARIA

There are five British species, *F. hygrometrica*, *F. fascicularis*, *F. muehlenbergi*, *F. obtusa* and *F. attenuata*. The first is commonest and will be described here.

Habitat

The moss grows quite readily on damp patches of soil between other plants which may afford it shade, since exposed dry conditions are not very suitable for its growth. Sometimes, relatively extensive areas may be completely covered by it, particularly the sites of old bonfires in woodlands. The moss is often able to colonize such burnt patches remarkably quickly. This is an indication of its measure of success as a land plant.

Vegetative Structure of the Gametophyte Generation

All cells of the gametophyte body are haploid.

External Morphology

Each plant is erect in habit and quite small, measuring about 10 to 15 mm in length. If a whole plant, the lower portion of which has been washed free of soil, is examined, it will be seen to be differentiated into an upper "*stem*" with sessile ovate "*leaves*" spirally arranged along it in three rows, although twisting of the stem may hide this arrangement (*see* Fig. 11.11). From the base of the stem, grows a system of delicate *rhizoids*. These parts are not homologous with the stems, leaves and roots of higher plants since the whole structures are not comparable; this is a haploid gametophyte whilst the higher plant is a diploid sporophyte.

Branching of the stem is usual, but branches arise below the points of leaf insertion and not in their axils. The leaves are very delicate and are centrally thickened by a single midrib. The leaf margin is almost smooth, showing very slight indentations. At later stages of development, the uppermost leaves of a main axis show a distinctly different arrangement from those on a branch. *F. hygrometrica* is monoecious and bears the male and female sex organs separately. The male organs occur at the apex of a main axis and the female organs at the apex of a lateral branch. It is possible to recognize the male axis from the female by the disposition of the apical leaves. The male axis bears its leaves in the form of a widely expanded rosette, the centre portion of which is brownish in colour. On the female branch, the terminal leaves are

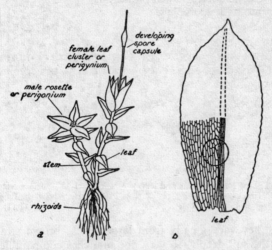

Fig. 11.11. (*a*) Habit drawing of *Funaria hygrometrica*. *b*) Low power drawing of leaf.

closely clustered around the apex, enclosing it completely. Leaves or similar enveloping structures of the sex organs in the bryophytes are called *perichaetia*. To distinguish male from female, the terms *perigonia* and *perigynia* are sometimes used. At still later stages of development, the female branch may be seen to carry at its apex the conspicuous spore capsule on a long stalk.

Anatomy

In sectional views, the stem is seen to consist of an outer small-celled and thick-walled epidermal layer surrounding a cortex of larger isodiametric cells; centrally placed in this cortex is a strand of smaller cells which are longitudinally elongated, forming possibly a conducting and mechanical tissue of a simple kind. The cells of the cortex contain small discoid chloroplasts. Each leaf is a single thickness of oblong cells, except at the midrib, where there is a strand of narrow elongated cells similar to the central strand of the stem. The cells of the blade of the leaf contain numerous discoid chloroplasts and form the chief assimilating tissue of the plant. The rhizoids are branched multi-cellular hair-like outgrowths from the base of the stem. The septa between the cells of the rhizoids are nearly always set obliquely.

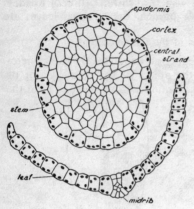 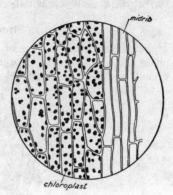

Fig. 11.12. T.S. of *Funaria* stem and leaf.   Fig. 11.13. Surface view of *Funaria* leaf. H.P. drawing of region indicated in Fig. 11.11. (*b*).

In size, they vary greatly from large, thick, brown strands which penetrate the soil deeply, to very fine branches comparable with root hairs, which permeate the soil in all directions.

Physiology of the Gametophyte

Nutritionally, the plant seems to be quite normal for green plants in general. Starch is the product of photosynthesis although the cell walls are constructed chiefly of hemicelluloses and pentosans instead of cellulose. Absorption of water and mineral salts from the soil undoubtedly occurs through the rhizoids, but investigations into the water-conducting capacity of the central strand of tissue in the stems of some mosses, have given indications that much of the water intake by the plant is through its external surfaces of leaves and stem from water rising by capillarity over the whole system. This would mean that the central strand is probably more mechanical than conducting in function. This is not necessarily true of those mosses in which the central stem tissues are much more specialized, as in *Polytrichum* for example.

Growth takes place by division of a tetrahedral apical cell which cuts off segments in regular sequence from its three faces. Each segment then undergoes a division parallel to the surface (periclinal) and the inner portion then becomes incorporated into the stem, whilst the outer portion develops into a leaf. Very early in development of each leaf, an apical cell is established which cuts off segments alternately to right and left to build up a blade of one cell thickness, except in the midrib region. Stem branches arise when the lower half of a divided leaf segment assumes the role of stem apex.

Reproductive Structures of the Gametophyte

The only specialized organs of reproduction produced on the gametophyte are the sex organs borne at the apices of the main axis or its branches. Many mosses develop small multicellular *gemmae* from the

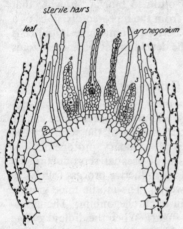

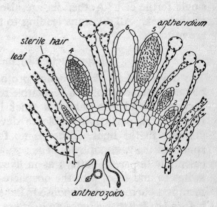

Fig. 11.14. *Funaria*. Diagram of apex bearing archegonia. The numbers indicate successive stages in their development.

Fig. 11.15. *Funaria*. Diagram of apex bearing antheridia. The numbers indicate the successive stages in their development.

leaf margins, midribs, stem apices or side branches, but this is not the case in the genus *Funaria*. However, *F. hygrometrica* can produce tiny bud-like structures on green filamentous growths which may arise from leaves, stems or rhizoids. Such a filament is known as a *protonema* and is always developed prior to the development of a gametophyte moss plant. Protonemata produced by a fully-grown gametophyte are known as *secondary protonemata* as a distinction from the *primary protonemata* developed from spores (*see* later). The sex organs are *antheridia* and *archegonia*. These can be examined microscopically by sectioning or teasing out apices of fertile branches. If a female apex is examined, it shows the archegonia as in Fig. 11.14. These are comparable in all respects with those of the liverworts but have more strongly-developed stalks and somewhat longer and often twisted necks. They are interspersed with sterile hairs or *paraphyses*. The archegonia are developed from single initial cells at the apex and at maturity the oosphere can be plainly seen in the venter and the neck is open.

The antheridia, similarly interspersed with paraphyses, which may aid in the retention of water by capillarity, are club-shaped bodies surmounting thick multicellular stalks (*see* Fig. 11.15). The internal fertile cells are protected externally by a single layer of cells forming a wall. During development, the inner mass of cells goes through the antherozoid mother-cell stage as in liverworts and each becomes a biflagellate antherozoid in much the same way. Antherozoid mother-cells can often be seen in polygonally outlined blocks, showing that each block has been derived separately from the repeated divisions of a single fertile cell. Antheridia are also derived from single initial cells of the apex. All divisions leading to the development of antherozoids are mitotic.

Reproduction by the Gametophyte

The development of secondary protonemata, on which new gametophytes arise, constitutes a vegetative reproductive process which can be very rapid and bring about a quick local spread of the species. The rhizoids are particularly able to develop secondary protonemata, if growing in the light. There is no form of asexual reproduction by spores in the gametophyte. The sexual reproductive process follows in essentials the same pattern as in liverworts. The motile male gamete swims to and fuses with the oosphere in the archegonium. The movement is a chemotactic response to cane sugar. When the diploid zygote is formed, it first becomes an oospore which soon commences development. Very rarely does more than one fertilized oosphere continue development at a single apex.

Development of the Zygote into the Sporophyte Generation

Oospore development results in a *sporogonium* comparable in essentials with that of the liverworts, being composed of capsule, seta and foot. It is, however, much more complicated in structure than the sporogonium of *Pellia*. The oospore first divides transversely into an upper and lower segment (*see* Fig. 11.16).

Each of these gives rise to a triangular flattened apical cell which proceeds to cut off other cells into a central elongating portion. The lowermost cells, derived from the lower apical cell, form the foot and grow back into the tissue of the parent plant to establish cellular contact. Thus they can function as an anchor and also absorb water and nutritional substances. The middle region becomes the seta, the inner cells of which become elongated and mechanical and conducting in function, whilst the outer ones become cortical and green. The upper portion becomes the capsule, which is at first not clearly defined from the seta. The outer cells of the developing capsule form a layer known as the *amphithecium*, surrounding an inner mass, the *endothecium*. From these layers, a very complicated structure is eventually differentiated.

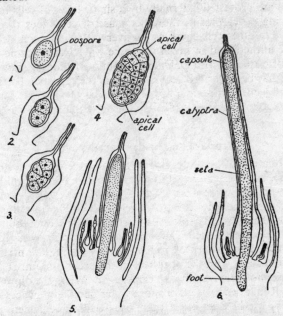

Fig. 11.16. Early stages in development of *Funaria* sporogonium.

As the whole upper portion enlarges and elongates away from the parent, the venter and neck of the archegonium increase in diameter and length to keep pace with it, thus forming a calyptra. With further elongation of the seta, the calyptra ruptures around its base and is carried upwards as a cap over the developing capsule, which when ripe is pendulous with the open end downwards.

Structure, Physiology and Reproduction of the Sporogonium

The foot of the sporogonium grows sufficiently into the gametophyte apex to establish contact with the central strand of the stem. It is bluntly rounded in shape and composed of soft absorbing tissue.

The seta may reach a length of 4 or 5 cm and in section is seen to be composed of a central mass of elongated cells surrounded by larger cortical cells containing chloroplasts. The outer cells of this layer are small and constitute an epidermis.

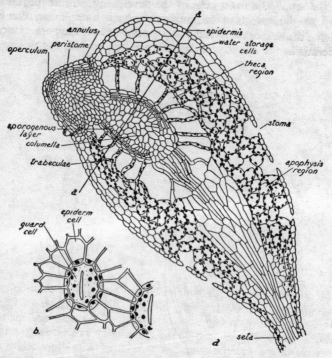

Fig. 11.17. (a) Diagram of *Funaria* capsule in L.S. (b) Surface view of stoma.

When the sporogonium is mature and dry the seta is markedly twisted. On wetting, it unwinds itself quite vigorously, carrying the capsule around with it. On drying out it once more becomes coiled.

The structure of the capsule can best be made out in longitudinal section (*see* Fig. 11.17). It is pear-shaped, with the stalk end blending with the seta. This end is solid and forms the *apophysis*. The upper portion is rounded, and centrally situated in a space traversed by a few filamentous threads or *trabeculae*, is the spore-bearing tissue on the outside of a central *columella* continuous with the inner tissue of the apophysis. The upper spore-bearing portion is known as the *theca*. It is surmounted by a complicated covering composed of an inner *peristome* and an outer *operculum*. The apophysis and all the outer layers of the theca are derived from the amphithecium, whilst the spores are developed from the outer layers of the endothecium, the columella being the inner portion of this.

Covering the apophysis region, and extending to enclose the upper portion, is an *epidermis*, clearly perforated by *stomata* in the lower part. The guard cells of the stomata appear as a single ring after break-down of the adjacent end walls at opposite ends of the pore. Under the epidermis in the apophysis, the cells are thin walled, roughly rounded

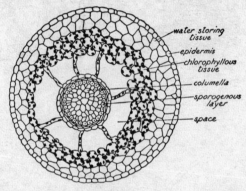

Fig. 11.18. Section of *Funaria* capsule in plane *a–a* of Fig. 11.17.

and have clear air spaces between them. They contain chloroplasts and are photosynthetic in function. Within this is a region of elongated cells continuous with the central strand of the seta and expanding upwards into the lower end of the columella. Immediately under the epidermis in the upper portion, is a layer of colourless cells forming possibly a water-storage tissue, and under this, and continuous with the chlorophyll-bearing cells of the apophysis, are more chlorophyll-bearing cells. Towards the inner layers of these, the cells become no more than filamentous structures to form the trabeculae traversing a wide air space. Within this space a few more normal amphithecial cells surround the endothecium.

The junction of the epidermis and the operculum is clearly seen where a ring of much larger cells, the *annulus*, stands out from the surface as a ridge. The opercular cells above this are normal epidermal cells forming a domed cap. Within the operculum, the innermost amphithecial cells form the peristome. When fully developed, this is composed of sixteen outer and sixteen inner segments, each of which is a peculiarly lignified strip of cell-wall material. All the peristome segments meet at a small central disc of unthickened cells.

The manner of the formation of the peristome can be followed by reference to Fig. 11.19.

The outer layer of the endothecium forms an *archesporial layer*; at first it is one, and later two cells thick. These are *spore mother-cells* and each undergoes meiotic divisions to form four haploid *spores*. No

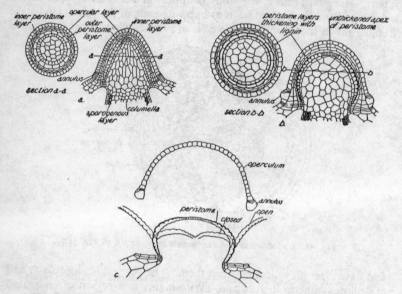

Fig. 11.19. Formation and function of operculum and peristome of *Funaria* capsule. (*a*) Peristome layers differentiating in the columella. (*b*) Lignification of the peristome layers. (*c*) Separation of the annulus and the movements of the peristome teeth.

elaters as in *Pellia* are formed. The reproductive capacity of the sporogonium is purely asexual, as in the liverworts.

With approaching maturity, the whole structure begins to dry out. The columella cells and the innermost amphithecial cells surrounding the ripening spores, break down to form a hollow spore sac closed at the upper end by the peristome and operculum. Inside this space, the spores lie as a powdery mass. Each spore, protected by a smooth, firm *exosporium*, contains oil and a little chlorophyll. As the capsule dries the calyptra falls away and the operculum is forced off by a movement of the annulus. This peels off as a strip, turned inside out, due to swelling of the innermost layer of cells which have mucilaginous walls. The peristome teeth show very remarkable hygroscopic movements, bending away from the centre when dry, and closing in again to close the opening when damp. By this time, the seta has bent back on itself just below the apophysis, so that the capsule hangs with the peristome downwards. In dry conditions, when the teeth are open, the ripe spores

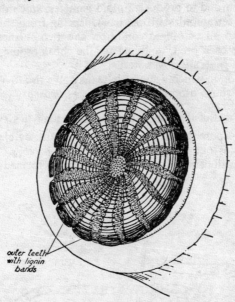

outer teeth
with lignin
bands

Fig. 11.20. Surface view of mature but unopened peristome of *Funaria* capsule.
Inner teeth not visible.

can fall out to be carried away on air currents. In a wet atmosphere, the peristome teeth are closed, retaining the spores within the spore sac.

There is no doubt that the sporogonium is partially self-supporting nutritionally, in that it can assimilate carbon, provided water and mineral salts are available. These are presumably supplied by the parent. There is no definite time of the year at which spore capsules ripen, as there is in *Pellia*. *Funaria* gametophytes may be found bearing the capsules in various stages of development at almost any time.

If on damp soil, wounded sporophyte tissue is capable of producing a *secondary protonema*. Such

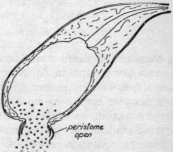

peristome
open

Fig. 11.21. Ripe capsule of *Funaria*
in L.S.

a protonema can only develop diploid gametophytes, but even so, they are still formed in exactly the same way as the haploid ones. In a related genus, *Mnium*, fertile diploid gametophytes have been known to occur and to produce diploid gametes which on fertilization give rise to a tetraploid sporophyte. Offspring from this, have eventually produced an octoploid condition and two further generations from this have been bred, doubling up the chromosome number each time. The last generation was sterile.

This condition in which a sporophyte may give rise to a gametophyte other than by spore production is known as *apospory* (*see* p. 278).

Development of the Spores into the Gametophyte Generation

A germinating spore first ruptures the exosporium by expansion from within and sends out two or three delicate *germ tubes*. One of these forms a cross-wall near the spore and the cell thus formed develops into

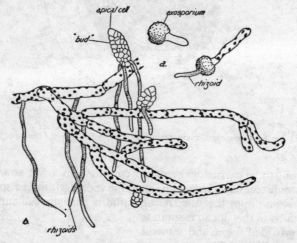

Fig. 11.22. (*a*) Spores of *Funaria* germinating. (*b*) Primary protonema.

a branched filamentous structure known as a *primary protonema*. This is very comparable in structure to a filamentous green alga, since its aerial cells contain numerous discoid chloroplasts. Some branches of the filament behave as rhizoids, penetrate the soil, lack chlorophyll, have brownish walls and oblique septa separating the cells. By these characteristics, the protonemata may be distinguished from algal filaments. After a period of spreading growth of the protonema, certain cells undergo rapid successive divisions to form a number of roughly spherical masses of cells usually called "buds." Within each "bud," an apical cell is differentiated and by the activity of this, a small moss plant with the characteristic stem, leaf and rhizoid arrangements, is developed.

Detailed studies of protonemata indicate that there may be two developmental stages. When first formed, and until about six weeks old, it is unable to form "buds" and all its cross-walls are transverse. It is called a *chloronema*. Eventually it becomes a *caulonema*, formed by vigorous growth of the apical cells of the chloronema filaments after most of the others have degenerated. Only the caulonema shows oblique cross-walls and develops "buds."

Life Cycle

The following diagram summarizes the life cycle—

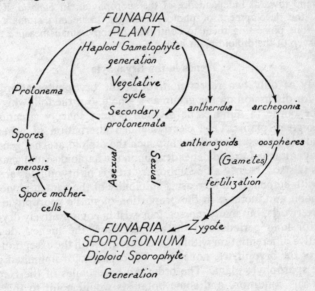

Adaptation to Environment

F. hygrometrica shows no greater adaptation to the terrestrial habitat than does *P. epiphylla*, except in one condition. That is in the differentiation of the moss aerial axis into erect stem with broadly-flattened appendages. This allows of a greater area of contact between the organs of photosynthesis and the atmosphere. It also means that there is greater photosynthetic area with smaller soil coverage. Individuals can be crowded with much less ill effect on one another. It is noticeable that all higher plants show analogous differentiation into root, stem and leaf systems and this seems to have been the most successful of all plant body forms on the land.

Special Features of Biological Importance

Funaria hygrometrica illustrates two features of major importance not found in the liverwort previously described. There is great contrast in vegetative complexity of both gametophyte and sporophyte generations. *Funaria* is much more suited vegetatively for a terrestrial existence, but it is still among the least well adapted of the moss genera. Many of them show a high degree of tissue differentiation into clearly-defined photosynthesizing tissue, mechanical and conducting tissue. It must be specially emphasized however, that none possess a vascular system structurally comparable with that of higher plants.

The second feature of major importance is that here we see the beginning of a trend towards independence of the sporophyte. In *Funaria*, it is only slight; the development of photosynthesizing tissue and stomata enable the regions possessing them to contribute in some small measure towards the upkeep of the diploid plant body.

Trends in the Bryophyta

A study of only two representatives of the bryophytes affords little scope for discussion on the group as a whole, but the following points may be borne in mind. The division is very sharply circumscribed among green plants. The clearly-defined alternation of generations common to all representatives, in which the diploid asexual generation is always attached to and dependent upon the haploid sexual generation makes this so. Nearly all evolutionary trends in bryophytes are structural with emphasis on increasing suitability of the gametophyte to the land habit and increase in the proportion of sterile sporophyte tissue. Few liverworts, but many mosses, can exist in comparatively dry conditions for long periods and these latter show the highest degree of vegetative differentiation within the division. With the exception of one order of the bryophytes, none show the capacity for unlimited growth by the sporophyte plant. The order Anthocerotales of the Hepaticae shows this condition, and some botanists would point to this as the possible origin of the characteristic which is possessed by the sporophytes of higher plants.

CHAPTER 12

HISTOLOGY OF VASCULAR PLANTS

PLANT cell structure has been described in Chapter 1 and the student will have had opportunity to see and study cells of varying but generally simple construction in the plants already described. Before progress can be made in the detailed study of more advanced types, it is necessary to comprehend the much wider range of tissue differentiation which occurs among them.

The evolution of the fully-erect land habit in plants has been the result of a capacity for great variation in cell types to meet the structural and functional requirements consistent with success in the terrestrial environment.

Three main types of cell differentiation have been evolved from the basic pattern to meet these requirements. First, *mechanical and supporting tissue* has evolved to counteract the lack of body support offered by the land conditions. Secondly, highly specialized *conducting or vascular tissues* have arisen to enable the spatially separated absorbing tissue (root system) and the photosynthetic tissues (leaves) to be in direct and continuous communication with one another. The vascular system found in all higher plants allows for conduction of materials to and from all parts of the plant and in many instances may lend additional support to the mechanical tissues; it may even supplant them entirely. Thirdly, outer specialized *epidermal layers* protect against desiccation by the drying atmosphere.

It is necessary to point out that the vague beginnings of the differentiation of cells according to such needs have been encountered in the gametophytes of mosses, but that no gametophyte of any plant shows the kind of tissue differentiation shown by the sporophyte of the vascular plants. It is the sporophyte generation which has evolved as the fully-adapted land plant, but from what origin is entirely unknown.

When studying the shape and size characteristics of the various kinds of plant cells as seen in thin sections, it is important to realize that the microscope can indicate structure in one plane only. It is therefore necessary to examine transverse and longitudinal sections of the same tissue. Macerates are very useful in the study of isolated cells.

TYPES OF TISSUES

It is usual to describe mature plant tissues under the following main functional categories—

1. Parenchyma or ground tissues.
2. Mechanical and supporting tissues.
3. Vascular or conducting tissues.
4. Outer protective tissues.

It is useful to consider them in this way because it emphasizes the differences in structure which may be associated with special functional requirements.

Parenchyma Tissues

The word *parenchyma* means literally "poured in beside" and suggests the gap-filling capacity visualized by earlier histologists, who thought that the cells occupying the spaces between the more solid components of plant parts had been formed merely to fill them. This is far from the truth, since mature parenchyma is as much a functional tissue as any other. It can also be regarded as the foundation of the plant body, since all cells produced from the meristems and regions of regeneration go through stages of development when they possess characters similar to parenchyma cells. In the evolutionary series, it is certain that this cell form has come first; primitive plant structure bears testimony to this. Functionally, the various forms of parenchyma are capable of a wide range of purposes such as photosynthesis, food storage and secretion; all metabolic activity occurs in their protoplasts.

It is now usual to regard any mature but relatively undifferentiated or unspecialized cell as parenchyma, in contrast to the much more highly specialized epidermal, mechanical or conducting cells. Nevertheless, parenchyma may show specialization according to its position in the plant. For example, inner leaf tissues are highly specialized for photosynthesis and root cortex for food storage. At the same time, parenchyma cells retain their ability to change their nature according to the needs of the plant, and this they frequently do.

In the higher plants, parenchyma cells usually form fairly clearly-defined tissues, although they may be associated with groups of more specialized cells to form mixed tissues. This condition occurs in the vascular regions, where parenchyma cells form vertical and horizontal strands among the conducting elements. Pith and cortex of stems and roots, mesophyll of leaves, succulent or fleshy storage tissues of any sort are all examples of regions chiefly parenchymatous. Cases will be frequently met however, where there is no clear distinction between parenchyma and other kinds of cell, since variation in shape, size and wall structure make it difficult to draw a sharp dividing line.

Parenchyma cells are extremely variable in shape. We may see them roughly isodiametric with many flattened or rounded faces. Alternatively, they may be considerably elongated along one axis to conform to the pattern of the so-called *prosenchyma*, a term applied to any elongated cells with tapering ends. The walls may be variously lobed or

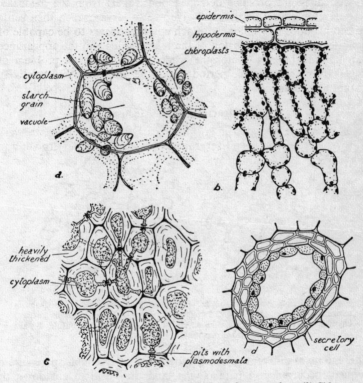

Fig. 12.1. Parenchyma. (*a*) Storage parenchyma of potato tuber. (*b*) Chlorenchyma from mesophyll of holly leaf. (*c*) Storage endosperm of date. (*d*) Secretory epithelium of *Pinus* resin duct.

folded (*see* Fig. 12.2). In fact, so great is the variation, that it is nearly impossible to generalize. However, assuming that the tissue is derived from cubical, box-like initial cells, all equal in size and all differentiating at the same speed, the mature constituent cells are polyhedral. Each such cell in the ideal case would possess fourteen faces, eight hexagonal in outline and six oblong (*see* Fig. 12.3). The conditions under which adjacent cells differentiate rarely remain constant The original cells are most often of unequal size; they are irregularly spaced, and they

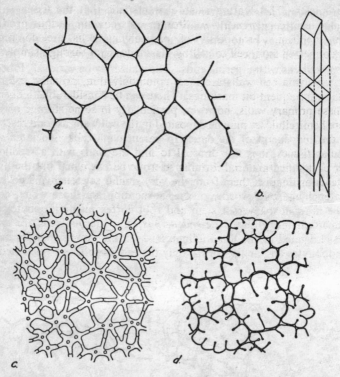

Fig. 12.2. Parenchyma cell shapes. (*a*) Roughly isodiametric polyhedrons in maize stem (T.S.). (*b*) Elongated cells in cambium of flowering plant (prosenchyma). (*c*) Lobed pith cells of the rush (T.S.). (*d*) Cells with infolded walls from mesophyll of pine leaf.

differentiate at different rates. Furthermore, intercellular spaces are of frequent occurrence in parenchyma, and they tend to cut down the number of cell contacts so that less than fourteen faces occur. Thus

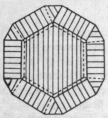

Fig. 12.3. Fourteen-sided polyhedron.

rarely, if ever, is the ideal shape achieved. However, in homogeneous parenchyma, the average number of cell faces is nearer fourteen than the twelve which would occur if the initial cells were spherical.

All parenchyma cells have a common characteristic. *They all possess living protoplasts* which have special features related to the main function of the cell. For example, the actively photosynthesizing leaf mesophyll contains abundant chloroplasts. This feature is so characteristic that the tissue is frequently termed *chlorenchyma*. Storage cells contain various products of metabolism. Protoplasts of parenchyma cells are commonly interconnected from cell to cell by plasmodesmata through simple pits in the walls.

Parenchyma cell walls are most commonly thin, primary, cellulose walls with frequent pit markings. There can be considerable thickening of these primary walls, however, particularly in some storage organs, where hemicelluloses may be deposited in the cell walls as food reserves, e.g. the endosperm of the date. In parenchyma cells associated with vascular tissues, it is not unusual to find the walls with a secondary layer of lignified material forming sclerotic parenchyma, but the living contents distinguish them from the very similar sclerenchyma cells.

Parenchyma cells worthy of special mention are those which occur as the innermost layer of stem and root cortex in pteridophytes and spermatophytes, forming the *endodermis*. Endodermal cells are somewhat elongated in the longitudinal axis. In the young endodermis of pteridophytes and angiosperms, only the radial walls are thickened by

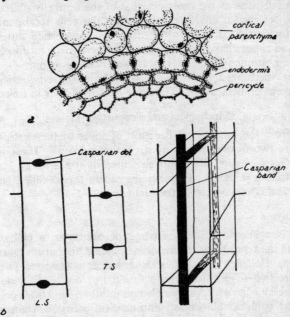

Fig. 12.4. (*a*) Endodermis and pericycle as seen in T.S. of young buttercup root. (*b*) Various views of endoderm cell (diagrammatic) to show Casparian band.

a narrow band of material composed of lignin or suberin or some related fatty substance. This band, the *Casparian band*, completely encircles the cell in the tangential plane (*see* Fig. 12.4). A few cells remain unthickened and are called *passage cells*. In the transverse section, the bands appear as thickened zones on the radial walls. In older regions of an endodermis, the thickening may extend to other parts of the cell. In monocotyledonous angiosperm roots the endodermis is characterized by having thick cutinized and sometimes partly lignified walls. This thickening may be all over the cell or restricted to the radial and inner tangential walls only. Endodermal cell walls are considered to be impervious to water in the radial direction, but the occasional unthickened passage cells break the continuity. In some stems, the more characteristic endodermis may be replaced by a layer of cells containing prominent starch grains forming the *starch sheath*. The functions of the endodermis are discussed in Vol. II, Chap. 7.

Another parenchyma cell layer in some stems and roots is the pericycle, a layer of cells inner to the endodermis, and clearly distinguishable from it by possessing no thickening of the walls. The pericycle may be regarded as the most external of the centrally-placed vascular tissues. Its special characteristic is that the cells retain their potentiality for further division after maturity, and certain outgrowths of roots and shoots have their origin in the pericycle. In appearance the cells are not much different from those of cortex or pith.

Other specialized parenchyma cells form the *companion cells* in angiosperm phloem tissue. These are described later in this chapter.

Mechanical and Supporting Tissues

Apart from the mechanical function of some of the vascular tissues, there are two distinct forms of strengthening cells. These are *collenchyma* (colla = glue, thick and glistening in appearance), and *sclerenchyma* (sclera = hard). Together they form the so-called *stereome* or mechanical tissue system of the plant.

Collenchyma

This is a simple tissue consisting of one type of cell only. The structure and position of the cells indicate the primary supporting function. Collenchyma can be regarded as specialized parenchyma, since the two tissues are always found in close association and frequently blend imperceptibly with one another. Further, collenchyma cells may contain chloroplasts and can, on occasion, change function and become meristematic.

In general shape, the cells are elongated parallel to the longitudinal axis of the organ in which they occur and possess tapering end walls (*see* Fig. 12.5). The cross-section shows a comparatively small lumen or cavity. Shape is variable however, and there may be transitions from the elongated tapering structure to quite short prismatic cells where the collenchyma blends into adjacent parenchyma. By far the most constant distinguishing character of collenchyma cells is the

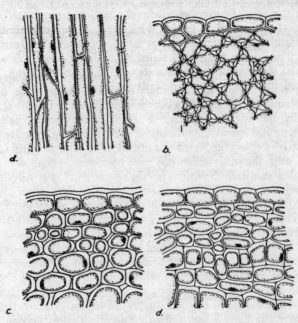

Fig. 12.5. Collenchyma. (*a*) Cells in L.S. (*b*) Angular collenchyma from dead-nettle stem. (*c*) Lacunar collenchyma from holly leaf midrib. (*d*) Lamellar collenchyma from *Aucuba* stem. ((*b*), (*c*) and (*d*) in T.S.)

structure of the walls. They are primary walls which are thickened irregularly by cellulose and pectic materials containing much water. This property causes them to shrink considerably when treated with dehydrating substances. There are three fairly clearly-recognizable patterns. In the first, sometimes known as *angular* collenchyma, the main deposition of wall material is in the angles of the cavities, the remainder of the wall remaining thin. At points where several such thickened cells are in contact, the effect is quite unmistakable, for no other cells are thickened in this way. The second form is sometimes known as *lamellar* collenchyma and wall thickening in this case is largely confined to the tangential walls of the cells, the radial walls remaining comparatively thin. In the third form, *lacunate* collenchyma, large air spaces exist between the cells, and wall thickening is in general confined to the areas adjacent to the spaces. In longitudinal sections, the walls show the variability in the thickening according to the precise direction of the cut. In all cases the walls show primary pit areas through both thin and thickened regions. At maturity, the thickened cell walls still enclose living protoplasts, and these frequently include chloroplasts.

Collenchyma occurs as the first-formed supporting tissue in growing organs, particularly young stems, leaves and flower parts. It may persist as the main supporting tissue everywhere in mature dicotyledonous herbaceous plants which do not develop secondary tissues. Some monocotyledons do not form it at all. Its position is nearly always peripheral, immediately beneath the epidermis or only separated from it by one or two parenchyma layers. It may form one or more continuous cylinders in rounded stems and petioles, or separate bundles along the ribs of organs which are ribbed or angular in outline. Occasionally, even the outer epidermis may be collenchymatous in nature. In some leaves it may be found on the upper and lower sides of veins and sometimes on the leaf margin.

Its flexible and plastic, i.e. mouldable, nature is admirably suited to the purpose it serves. Its plasticity allows it to stretch with the other rapidly elongating and expanding tissues of young parts without hindering their development. Stronger but less plastic tissues such as sclerenchyma would exert considerable forces to prevent such elongation and expansion of adjacent tissues. Collenchyma is also strong enough to withstand the bending and twisting strains to which young plant parts are constantly subjected by the external conditions. Once full differentiation of other tissues has ceased, the collenchyma becomes much harder, more brittle and less plastic. Finally, it becomes a sturdy mechanical tissue and may even become lignified with a secondary wall. In woody plants undergoing secondary thickening, it is often the case that the peripheral collenchyma keeps pace with expanding girth by active division and growth. At any time, collenchyma cells may revert to a more parenchymatous nature by diminishing their walls and becoming meristematic, particularly if injured. In a few cases, the periderm of woody plants has its origin in a peripheral layer of collenchyma.

Sclerenchyma

The structure and position of this tissue also indicate its primary strengthening function, but it is clearly distinguishable from collenchyma. Two widely diverse forms of sclerenchyma cell are generally recognized; the *fibre*, which is a long narrow cell, and the *sclereid*, a much shorter, almost isodiametric cell. Numerous intermediates between these occur.

The sclerenchyma fibre has a long, spindle-like shape with finely tapering ends in the general case, but blunt or even branched ends may be found to the cells (*see* Fig. 12.6). In cross-section the fibres are sharply polygonal in outline and usually closely packed, with little or no air-space between them. The cell walls are often comparatively

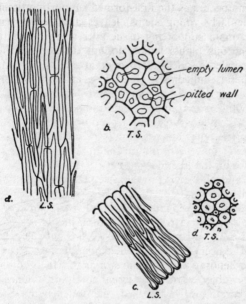

Fig. 12.6. Sclerenchyma. (*a*) and (*b*) L.S. and T.S. of sclerenchyma fibres (*c*) and (*d*) L.S. and T.S. sclereids of bean testa.

thick and each consists of a primary wall bearing heavy depositions of lignified secondary substance laid down in a laminated pattern. The lumen is usually no more than a small fraction of the total cell volume, having been occluded by the deposition of the secondary wall. Pitting is normal and there may be simple or bordered pits. Not always is the wall substance lignified; in flax the wall is almost pure cellulose. When the wall has been fully built up, the protoplast is reabsorbed by surrounding tissues and the lumen is therefore empty.

Fibres usually occur in isolated groups or as cylinders following the outline of the cortices of stems and roots and are also frequently associated with vascular tissues. In the outer cortical regions of ribbed stems, bundles of sclerenchyma cells may strengthen the ribs, and form an interlaced pattern connected with the epidermis. In many monocotyledon leaves, sclerenchyma cells form rigid strands, cross-connecting the epidermal layers in girder fashion. In association with vascular tissues, sclerenchyma fibres may form outer or inner caps to the vascular bundles or entirely ensheathe them. Fibres may occur, interspersed singly or in groups, in the primary and secondary xylem and

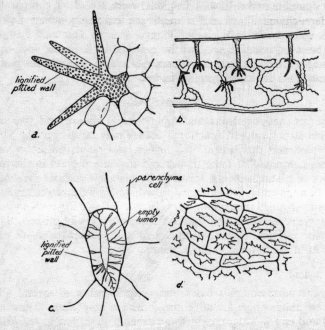

Fig. 12.7. Various forms of sclereid (*a*) Idioblast of water lily petiole. (*b*) Same in water lily leaf. (*c*) Stone cell of pear fruit. (*d*) Stone cells of hazel nut shell.

phloem conducting elements. This is highly characteristic of the angiosperms. In these higher vascular plants, sclerenchyma fibres are often described as xylem fibres, phloem fibres, cortical fibres or perivascular fibres according to their location.

Sclereids are too varied in form to be generalized. *Stone cells* are short and roughly isodiametric; they occur singly or in groups in the cortex, phloem and medulla of stems and in the flesh of fruits. *Macrosclereids* are elongated rod-like cells forming a close palisade to protect the outer surfaces of seeds and fruits. *Bone-form sclereids* (osteosclereids), are similar in function, but are columnar in shape, with enlarged ends. *Star-sclereids* are irregularly branched in outline and are found in some dicotyledonous plant leaves. Sclereids of various form may also occur in groups of xylem and phloem interspersed with fibres; distinction is often difficult, since fibres and sclereids may be intergraded. It is not unusual for parenchyma cells to become lignified and differentiated as sclereids; they join groups of fibres at the periphery of the vascular bundle system in stems. All sclereids have small empty lumina and thick heavily-pitted walls.

Sclerenchyma fibres and sclereids are extremely strong and tough when compacted as a tissue. Plants such as flax and hemp have long been cultivated to produce the material for linen and rope-making. Retting (rotting) by fungal and bacterial action, frees the tough fibrous strands from the softer ground tissues.

Vascular Tissues

These are heterogeneous and composite in nature and two clearly-defined structural and functional tissues may be discerned. They are the *xylem* and the *phloem*. All higher land plants possess a vascular system composed of these tissues and they are present in the primary bodies of all such plants, forming the primary vascular system. This may be augmented by secondary growth, to form the secondary vascular system. Named according to sequence of origin, protoxylem and metaxylem, protophloem and metaphloem, may be discerned in the primary vascular tissues. Protoxylem and protophloem are the first formed in the differentiation sequence.

The Xylem

In the more complex cases, the xylem consists of several different types of cells; some are alive and some are non-living. There are the dead and empty water-conducting elements, described as *tracheids* and *vessels*, the *fibres* and *sclereids* which lend added support, and *living parenchyma cells* of various function. In more lowly vascular plants, the xylem and phloem tissues may be much more homogeneous.

Tracheids and Vessels. In the mature state, the tracheid is an elongated element with finely tapering ends, heavily lignified and pitted secondary cell wall and no protoplast. Its only connexion with other elements is by way of the paired pits in the intervening walls (*see* Fig. 12.8).

When the vessel is mature, it is a long, open, pipe-like unit, composed of a number of *vessel members* whose intervening cross-walls have become perforated either completely or in strips or circular areas to allow the lumina to become continuous. The vessel is characteristically greater in diameter than the tracheid, proportionally less heavily thickened in the wall, and of wide lumen. Lateral interconnexion between adjacent cells may be achieved also through paired pits in the longitudinal walls (*see* Fig. 12.12).

The detailed structure of the deposited secondary wall is variable in the different xylem areas and from plant to plant, but conforms to certain generalizations.

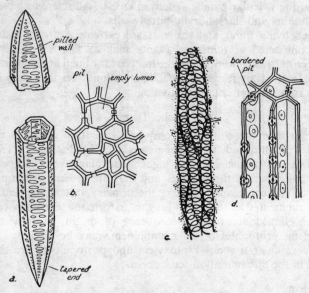

Fig. 12.8. Xylem. (*a*) and (*b*) Generalized tracheid whole and in T.S. (*c*) Spiral tracheids in leaf vascular bundle. (*d*) Tracheids of pine wood with bordered pits.

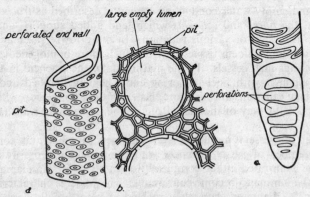

Fig. 12.9. Xylem. (*a*) Single vessel element (whole). (*b*) T.S. vessel. (*c*) Scalariform perforation in vessel end wall of vine stem.

In the xylem elements first to be differentiated, the protoxylem, only a small area of the primary wall is covered by lignified deposits as compared with the elements of the later metaxylem. There is, however, no set rule and various types of thickening may overlap or be intermixed. In protoxylem elements, thickening is usually deposited as lignified

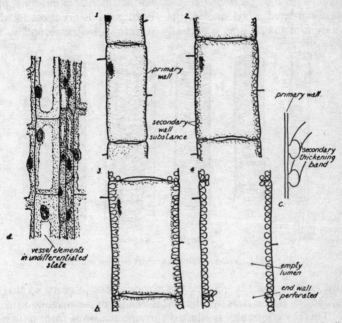

Fig. 12.10. Ontogeny of vessel. (a) Young vessel elements. (b) (1, 2, 3, 4) Stages in differentiation—lateral enlargement, secondary wall deposition, perforation of end walls, loss of living contents. (c) Attachment of secondary thickening bands.

rings or annuli, that is, they are *annularly thickened* (*see* Fig. 12.11). Elements formed slightly later, the first elements of the metaxylem, are thickened sometimes by rings, but more often by continuous helices and are said to be *spirally* or *helically thickened*. Slightly later, the young xylem may be thickened with interlacing helices to give the wall a ladder-like appearance and these are said to be thickened in a *scalariform* manner. These rings and helices are usually firmly attached to the primary wall by a narrow band (*see* Fig. 12.10 (*c*)). Xylem elements formed still later may have the secondary wall deposited as an irregular meshwork of lignified material and such are said to be *reticulately thickened*. It is difficult to decide between the last two forms when the meshes are elongated transversely across the wall. When the walls are still more extensively thickened so that only small pit areas are left, they are called *pitted* tracheids or vessels and these are characteristic of the last-formed primary xylem, and of the secondary xylem.

Pits in walls may be *simple*, *bordered* or *half-bordered* but most often they are bordered in xylem elements. Bordered pits are those in which the margin of the pit area is partially overgrown by the secondary wall

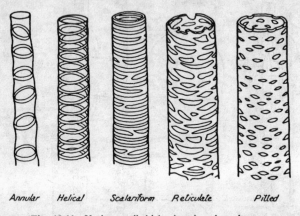

Annular   Helical   Scalariform   Reticulate   Pitted

Fig. 12.11. Various wall thickenings in xylem elements.

deposit (*see* Fig. 12.12). Pits nearly always occur in pairs, so that the pit in one cell wall is exactly adjacent to the pit in the neighbouring cell wall. Thereby continuity is effected through the walls from cell to cell except for the *pit membrane*. This is quite permeable to water, however. On the pit membrane separating a bordered pit pair may be a further small primary deposit known as the *torus*. Simple pits lack the overgrown border and the torus. Half-bordered pits are bordered on one side of the membrane and simple on the other. The type of pitting on a xylem vessel or tracheid is variable and depends to some extent on the nature of neighbouring cells. Between tracheid and tracheid, or tracheid and vessel, the large bordered pit is usual. Pit pairs between vessel or tracheid and parenchyma may be any of those mentioned above. Between a tracheid or vessel and a fibre, the pits may be absent altogether or may be very small and simple.

Functionally, the tracheids and vessels are chiefly concerned with water conduction through the plant, though they must lend additional support particularly in the case of tracheids, where they may be the only type of hard xylem element.

The nature of these conducting elements in vascular plants is of some evolutionary and phylogenetic significance. The primitive cell type is undoubtedly the tracheid and the vessel seems to be a much more advanced modification of this. With the exception of one or two pteridophytes (*Selaginella spp.*) and representatives of the gymnosperm order, the Gnetales, only the angiosperms have developed true vessel construction in their xylem components.

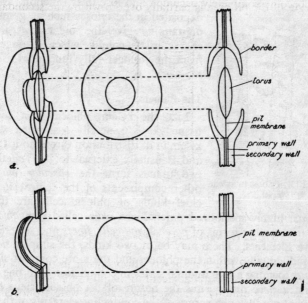

Fig. 12.12. (*a*) Bordered, and (*b*) simple pit seen in various views.

Fibres and Sclereids. These have been described as sclerenchyma. Among xylem elements, they are distinguished from the vessels and tracheids in possessing comparatively much thicker walls and smaller lumina. However, the fibres may grade imperceptibly into tracheids and it is sometimes impossible to separate them in a section, except by details of the pits, which have smaller borders or are simple. The fibres and sclereids are obviously primarily mechanical in function rather than conducting elements.

Xylem Parenchyma. Parenchyma cells always form part of both primary and secondary xylem. In the latter, they are recognizable as forming the radial strands or *medullary rays* and may form longitudinal strands through both kinds of xylem also. The cells of the medullary rays are called *ray parenchyma* and any living cells forming a longitudinal series through xylem are called *wood parenchyma*. These parenchyma cells are usually charged with stored food such as starch but may contain tannins and crystals of various kinds.

It is not unusual for the parenchyma cells to develop ingrowths into the adjacent tracheids or vessels through the paired pits. Such ingrowths are known as *tyloses* and are produced very frequently in older wood or in injured tissue. The conducting elements may eventually become completely occluded and lose their function. Materials deposited in the tyloses such as gums, resins or tannins give the older *heart-wood* its characteristic colour, which distinguishes it from the younger fully functional tissue, the *sap-wood*.

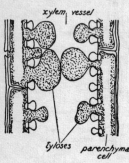

Fig. 12.13. Tyloses in xylem vessel.

The Phloem

Like the xylem, phloem is a composite tissue. It is generally associated with the xylem in its distribution throughout the plant and is usually external to it. Together, the two tissues form the *vascular bundles* or other components of the central *stele*. The chief kinds of phloem cells are the *sieve elements*, highly-specialized parenchyma cells called *companion cells*, and various other forms of *parenchyma cells, fibres* and *sclereids*.

Sieve Elements. These may be of two kinds, the simpler *sieve cells* lying individually within the phloem and the more complex *sieve-tube elements* forming a longitudinal series in conjunction with one another to form a *sieve tube*. Thus the nature of the phloem sieve elements somewhat parallels the nature of the conducting elements of the xylem, in that the less-specialized form of sieve cell tissue seems more primitive and corresponds to the tracheid, whilst the more-specialized sieve tube is more advanced and corresponds to the vessel. Sieve cells are to be distinguished from sieve tube elements by reason of the fact that they possess perforated regions known as *sieve areas*. These are of more or less uniform complexity and are generally evenly distributed over the walls adjacent to other phloem elements, but the sieve tube element possesses perforated areas, some of which are very much more specialized than others; they are localized on the adjacent end walls of a longitudinal series of such elements to form a *sieve plate*. The longitudinal series, connected by sieve plates, form the sieve tube (*see* Fig. 12.14). It is not unusual however to find sieve tubes laterally connected by sieve areas of less or equal complication as the sieve plates, so that an intricate intracellular connecting system is built up.

The sieve areas and sieve plates are regions of the otherwise thick primary cell walls where perforations are clustered together, and through which the protoplasts of the adjacent sieve elements are connected together by cytoplasmic strands (*see* Fig. 12.15 (*a*), (*b*)). They are specialized primary pit fields, as in parenchyma cells, through which

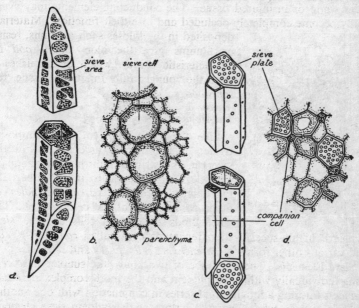

Fig. 12.14. Phloem. *a*) Generalized sieve-cell (whole). (*b*) T.S. sieve cells. (*c*) Generalized sieve-tube element and companion cell (whole). (*d*) T.S. sieve tubes and companion cells.

plasmodesmata pass and it is from such beginnings that the sieve areas differentiate. The specialization shows clearly that the interconnecting cytoplasmic strands are much more prominent than plasmodesmata and each connecting strand, where it passes through the perforation, is encased by a cylinder of a substance called *callose* laid down around the periphery of the pore (*see* Fig. 12.15 (*c*), (*d*)).

Callose is distinctly different from cellulose. This can be shown by its staining reactions. It shows up clearly when stained with aniline blue but its precise chemical nature is not certain. Sieve areas and sieve plates differ only in the degree of prominence of the cytoplasmic strands. Simple sieve areas may be no more than slightly more pronounced pit fields. Every functional sieve area or plate is double in structure like any other pit, since the walls of both adjacent cells must have entered into its construction.

Only fully active sieve elements possess the structures described above. As the elements age, changes occur in which considerably more callose is deposited in the pores and over the surface of the walls between the pores, so that the whole area becomes thickened and the

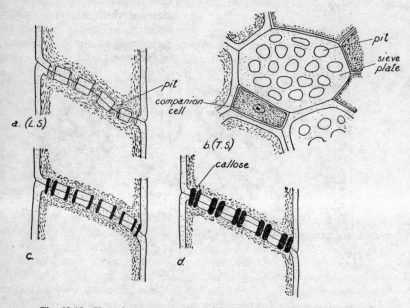

Fig. 12.15. Sieve plate structure. (*a*) and (*b*) Functional sieve plates in L.S. and T.S. (*c*) and (*d*) Ageing sieve plates.

connecting strands become thinner and thinner until they are no more than the finest of connexions. Even these finally disappear. The thickenings of callose form what is known as a *definitive callus*. It is to be noted that this callus bears no relation to the callus tissue formed at wounds, the word merely meaning "thickened." Finally, the protoplast of the ageing element is disorganized, the callus may separate from the sieve area and also disappear so that the sieve area becomes even more pronounced as a porous thin area in the walls. In this condition it is, of course, non-functional.

Sieve elements possess protoplasts with an outstanding characteristic. When fully functionally developed, there is *no nucleus in the cell*. This disappears during the differentiation of the element from a paren-chyma cell, but in some cases the nucleolus is extruded before dispersal of the nuclear material and may remain as a discrete body throughout the life of the cell. The cell vacuole in many dicotyledonous cases (less so in monocotyledons and lower vascular plants) is composed of a viscous substance called *slime*, believed to be protein in nature and originating in special cytoplasmic inclusions called *slime bodies*. These slime bodies lose their individual identity, pass into the vacuole from

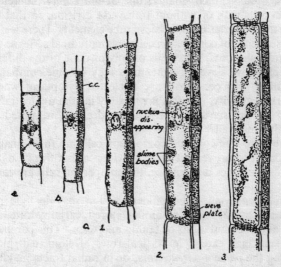

Fig. 12.16. Ontogeny of sieve tube. (*a*) and (*b*). Division to form sieve tube element and companion cell. (*c*) (1, 2, 3) stages in differentiation—elongation, lateral expansion, appearance of slime bodies, perforation of end walls and disappearance of nucleus.

the cytoplasm and run together as the slime at about the same time as the nucleus disorganizes. In many plants the cytoplasm also includes small disc-like plastids which appear to manufacture a carbohydrate allied to starch.

Functionally, the sieve elements are regarded as being concerned with translocation of materials, particularly the elaborated plant foods. The mechanism by which they may operate in this capacity is discussed in Vol. II, Chap. 9.

Within the different plant groups, we find that the lower vascular plants possess phloem of a simpler structure than the higher spermatophytes. The sieve cell construction is found in the pteridophytes whilst the fully-developed sieve tube system is found only in the angiosperms.

Companion Cells. Commonly associated with the sieve tube members in angiosperms only, are the companion cells, which appear to be highly specialized parenchyma cells (*see* Fig. 12.14 (*c*)). When they occur, they arise at the same time as the sieve tube member and from the same meristematic initial cell. We say they have the same *ontogeny*. The initial cell which gives rise to both, divides longitudinally into two or more cells. The largest of these becomes the sieve tube member and of the others, usually much smaller, one or more may differentiate into companion cells with or without transverse division, so that they may be as long as or shorter than the sieve tube element. There is not always a definite sequence of companion cells in longitudinal series as there is of the sieve tube elements, since cells on any or none of the different faces of two consecutive sieve tube members may become companion cells.

Companion cells contain dense nucleated cytoplasm when at the height of their activity, and this is probably in communication with the cytoplasm of the sieve tube by plasmodesmata in pitted areas of the thin dividing wall.

That the sieve elements and companion cells are functionally associated is difficult to prove, but there is evidence that this is so in the fact that when sieve tubes disorganize, the companion cells appear to do so as well.

Phloem Parenchyma. The phloem region may include numerous typical parenchyma cells containing stored carbohydrate and fatty materials and accumulations of tannin and resin. This parenchyma, as in the xylem, may extend in vertical rows of elongated, pitted cells, constituting the *phloem parenchyma*, or in radial tracts making up the *phloem rays*. The parenchyma cells are usually in communication with sieve elements and companion cells by pitted areas, which are adjacent to sieve areas on the longitudinal walls in the case of the former.

Phloem Fibres and Sclereids. These occur in both primary and secondary phloem and their general structure has been described. In some plants, lignification of the fibre walls may not occur, but all possess secondary walls, lignified or not. The walls are commonly pitted with simple or sometimes slightly bordered pits. In some species, e.g. *Tilia europaea*, the fibres are well developed early and function mechanically throughout their lives. In *Prunus spp.* the elements may develop only as fibres after the disorganization of the adjacent sieve tubes.

Epidermal and Peridermal Tissues

An *epidermis* is the outer layer of cells which covers the whole primary structure of a plant. A *periderm* is the layer of protective tissue which replaces the epidermis when that is eventually sloughed as a result of secondary growth or from some other cause. Functionally, they have the common purposes of protecting against injury or infection and of preventing drying-out of inner parts, but in structure and in origin they are very different. Various parts of an epidermis or periderm may be modified for a variety of other functions. It would be correct to say that all epidermal and peridermal cells are specialized parenchyma.

The Epidermis

This usually illustrates a wide variety of cell structure according to the position on the plant, but there is a fundamental pattern on which

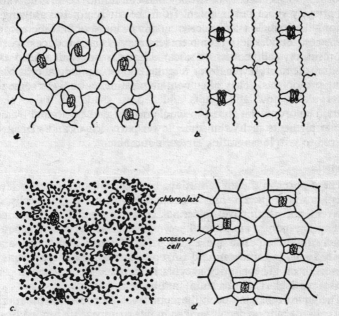

Fig. 12.17. Epidermis. Leaf epidermis of (a) house-leek (b) maize (c) *Dryopteris* (d) *Tradescantia*. Stomata are shown.

all types are based. There can be seen such diverse structures as *stomatal guard cells*, *secretory cells* and *hairs* or *trichomes* of numerous forms and functions. The typical protective epidermal cells are individually flat, plate-like cells, closely knit together, without intervening spaces except at stomatal apertures. The outlines of their walls in surface view may be of almost any shape, isodiametric or elongated, wavy or straight (*see* Fig. 12.17). In vertical section, the shallowness of the cell is apparent in most cases, though the outer layer of cells in a seed may have greater depth than breadth. The outer wall is most commonly convex, bulging outwards.

Wall structure is very variable in the epidermal cells of different plants. In the majority of cases, the outer wall is thickest and unpitted but it is not certain whether such walls are of primary or secondary origin. The thinner radial and inner walls are often pitted and may show plasmodesmata between cells. The most characteristic feature of epidermal cell walls is their impregnation with a waxy substance, *cutin*, and the deposition of this to form an outer superficial layer, the *cuticle* (*see* Fig. 12.18). Such a cuticle, thicker or thinner according to species and environmental conditions, covers the whole of the primary shoot but is absent from the surface of the growing root region. The cuticle may be smooth, spiny, ridged or cracked according to species. Besides cutin, some epidermal cells may produce deposits of oil, resin, crystalline salts or silica. Lignin is rarely deposited except by some members of the lower vascular plants. Epidermal cells contain living protoplasts. They often contain plastids, but only in some ferns, water plants and land plants addicted to shade, do these plastids contain chlorophyll. The sap vacuole may often be coloured by anthocyanin pigments such as in some flower parts, leaves and stems, where the red to purple coloration is very noticeable.

Stomata

These pores in the epidermis are bounded by specialized epidermal cells known as *guard cells*. In conjunction with the guard cells, other adjacent and distinctive epidermal cells may assist in opening and closing the pore. These are known as *accessory cells*. Stomata are usually found only on the aerial parts of stems and leaves and on flower parts, but underground rhizomes and some aquatic plants may possess them. They may be irregularly scattered or arranged in parallel rows; particularly is this so in parallel-veined leaves.

The guard cells may be at the same level, or above the other epidermal cells, or may be deeply sunken in pits to appear suspended from the accessory cells above them. In surface view, they are typically sausage-shaped and fit together as in Fig. 12.17, with the pore between them. Ridges of wall material may be developed around the edge of the pore (*see* Fig. 12.18). The outstanding characteristic of the guard cells is the irregular thickening of the walls, those adjacent to the pore being thick and those further displaced being thin. This irregularity is no doubt related to the changes in shape by which the pore is opened and closed (*see* Vol. II, Chap. 7). Variations in guard cell shape can be seen in different species. In grasses and sedges, the guard cells are dumb-bell shaped, placed side by side with the broad ends touching (*see* Fig. 12.17 (*b*)). In such cases the broad ends of the cells are thin-walled and the straight portions thick.

Guard cell and accessory cell walls are normally of cutinized cellulose with an outer cuticle, but in some conifers they may be partly lignified. Beneath each stomatal aperture, there invariably occurs a wide air space connected to smaller air spaces within. The cuticle of the epidermis

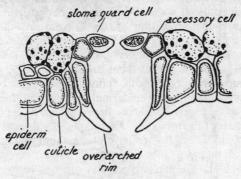

Fig. 12.18. Deeply sunken stoma of *Cycas*.

may extend over the guard cells to the cells around this air space and sometimes even further inside.

Hairs or Trichomes

These are epidermal appendages which may be uni- or multicellular, originating from the epidermal cells alone. They may occur on all parts of the plant and may persist alive, or may die and later fall away with age. Their shapes and sizes are too numerous to describe, but examples are illustrated in Fig. 12.19. The cell walls of hairs are usually of cellulose with a cuticle, except on some root regions. In function, they vary from being glandular and secretory to having no apparent function whatsoever. The specialized nature of *root hairs* marks them as worthy of special mention. The root hairs are typically unbranched, tubular outgrowths of the root epidermal cells produced just behind the growing apex in regular succession. They are uncuticularized and the cell walls are apparently of cellulose covered by a layer of calcium pectate which may be mucilaginous. Each cell has a normal vacuolate protoplast. Each hair arises first as a papilla which elongates from the tip quite rapidly until the hair may be a centimetre or more in length. During development, the nucleus is close to the advancing tip. In the soil, the cell outline may be of any shape but in moist air, the hair is usually straight and cylindrical. Root-hairs are generally short-lived, usually only a few days, and when they die, they collapse, and if the epidermal cells bearing them are not sloughed off to be replaced by

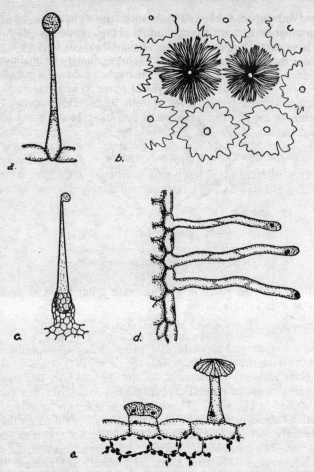

Fig. 12.19. Hairs or trichomes. (a) Leaf of *Pelargonium*. (b) Peltate hairs of leaf of sea buckthorn (*Hippophoe*). (c) Stinging hair of nettle. (d) Root hairs. (e) Glandular hairs of butterwort (*Pinguicula*) leaf.

another layer, the cell walls become suberized or lignified. Root-hairs are most certainly concerned with absorption of water and minerals from the soil.

The Hypodermis and Exodermis

The *hypodermis* is the name sometimes given to a layer of cells which lies immediately below an epidermis, but which is clearly distinct from deeper-lying tissues. An epidermis with hypodermis can be regarded as a compound or multiple epidermis. The hypodermis may be variously constructed to perform different functions. It may be composed of colourless cells acting in a water storage capacity as in some succulent leaves or in the velamen of aerial roots, or the cells may be small and heavily lignified as in the leaves of *Pinus*. The name *exodermis* is sometimes applied to the layer of cells immediately adjacent to the epidermis in a root when these cells become first suberized and later lignified (*see* Figs. 15.8 and 17.104).

The Periderm

When a primary plant body part such as root or stem commences secondary growth, its girth increases and the epidermal layer rarely

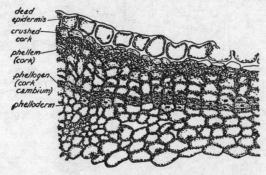

Fig. 12.20. T.S. of the bark and cortex of elder (*Sambucus*).

keeps pace with this expansion for long. Usually coincident with development of secondary vascular tissue within the vascular cambium (but sometimes delayed), a *periderm cambium* or *phellogen* arises, most often in the sub-epidermal layers. This has the power of dividing to produce cells from both its inner and outer faces so that the periderm is constructed eventually of three layers of cells, namely, an outer *phellem* or *cork layer*, the middle active *phellogen* and an inner *phelloderm* (*see* Fig. 12.20). In general, the cells of each layer are specialized parenchyma cells or their dead remains.

The cork cells are compactly arranged in radial rows showing their origin from the phellogen, and when young, they contain protoplasts which have the special function of depositing suberin in the cell walls before dying. Other substances such as lignin, fatty acids and tannins may be deposited to obliterate the cavity and give the cells their colour in many instances, but many cork cells may be filled with air only.

Collectively, the cork cells build up a deeper layer of waterproof, but dead tissue, in this way. As outer layers are sloughed, new cork cells are formed from within. A few cells of the corky layer may fail to suberize and these are recognizable as *phelloids*.

The phellogen is a layer of meristematically active cells whose nature and functions are more fully described under secondary growth in Chap. 17.

The phelloderm cells are almost indistinguishable from the cortical parenchyma in structure and contents but can be picked out by their radial arrangement, originating from the phellogen.

Perforating the periderm are *lenticels*. These are characterized by the loose arrangement of cells and lack of suberization. Their formation is described in Chap. 17. Their structure facilitates aeration of the internal tissues.

CHAPTER 13

VASCULAR TERRESTRIAL GREEN PLANTS: PTERIDOPHYTA

THIS division includes all those plants which have been aptly named "the vascular cryptogams"; vascular, because the vegetative structure shows always a clearly-defined vascular system composed of the highly specialized conducting elements xylem and phloem, and cryptogams, because the reproductive processes were once considered hidden by comparison with those of flowering plants. Alternation of generations is clearly marked, but in contrast to the bryophytes, the persistent vegetative structure is the sporophyte (diploid) generation and not the gametophyte (haploid) generation. Furthermore, the two generations lead independent existences. The sporophyte is morphologically differentiated into shoot and root systems consistent with land conditions and quite homologous with those of the more advanced flowering plants, whereas the partial differentiation of some bryophyte gametophytes shows only analogous structures.

It is possible here to describe examples of only three genera of the pteridophytes, *Dryopteris* (a fern), *Lycopodium* (a large club-moss) and *Selaginella* (a small club-moss). Unfortunately, this gives but a scanty impression of an ancient and very variable form of plant life.

DRYOPTERIS

This genus includes about 150 species with eight British representatives (some as several sub-species) and its generic name has variously been given as *Aspidium*, *Lastraea* and *Nephrodium*. The species *D. filix-mas*, the male fern, is described here.

It must be noted that the name *Dryopteris filix-mas* has for many years been used to describe what has now been recognized as a complex of species rather than a single distinct type. Investigations into the nuclear condition of the species complex, i.e. chromosome counts, have shown that the old name has in fact been used for three distinct ferns. These are now recognized as *D. filix-mas* ($n = 82$), *D. abbreviata* ($n = 41$), and *D. borreri* ($n = 82, 123, 164$ or 205). These three ferns differ morphologically from one another in some respects and it may help to dispel confusion if some of these are given briefly. *D. abbreviata* can be distinguished from *D. filix-mas* by its smaller stature, smaller average size of the sori (1 mm diameter as compared with

1·5 mm) and by the fact that the tips and edges of the leaves never become completely flattened even when the frond is fully developed. *D. borreri* can be distinguished from both these by a stature greater than either, the pinnules of the leaves are not completely separated at the base and the pinnule tips are much less tapering; there is a dark patch of pigment at the base of each pinna rachis where it meets the main axis, which is not seen in the other two. The collector may be still further confused by the fact that hybrids between these forms can occur.

Habitat

The fern is commonly found all over Great Britain in woods, copses and hedgerows, where it may achieve a stately habit in shady conditions. In cultivation, it is capable of flourishing remarkably well even in the sunniest of positions so that constant high humidity is not essential for good growth as is the case for many ferns.

Vegetative Structure of the Sporophyte Generation

External Morphology

The plant consists of a stubby underground stem axis or *rhizome*, usually unbranched and set obliquely in the soil. It bears a mass of tough, fibrous *adventitious roots* which penetrate the soil in all directions. At its slightly exposed apex is a cluster of large aerial *leaves* which break the ground surface and in diverging from the apex form a shape like an inverted cone (*see* Fig. 13.1). The rhizomes vary greatly in size according to age, since they perennate and increase in size from year to year. The older parts, more distant from the apex, are withered; as new annual growth is made, the older region dies. A good deal of the thickness of the underground structure is made up of the blackened bases of old dead leaves, which persist after the upper parts have fallen and decayed. If a rhizome has all these leaf bases carefully trimmed, it will appear as in Fig. 13.3, showing the obvious spiral arrangement of the leaves along the axis. Around the bases of the leaves are numerous brown, dry, scaly outgrowths or *ramenta* which fill the spaces between them and give the whole structure a more solid appearance.

The leaves, or *fronds*, are compound, each consisting of a main axis bearing leaflets called *pinnae*; these are subdivided into *pinnules*. The main axis is called the *rachis*. It has a thick base or *petiole* attached to the rhizome and gradually tapers to the end of the leaf. The fronds take two years to develop fully; various stages in development are found on the rhizome with the youngest nearest the apex. Mature fronds are furthest from the apex and may be 1 m in length; they are very much

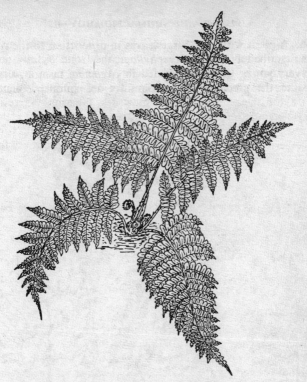

Fig. 13.1. Habit drawing of *Dryopteris filix-mas*.

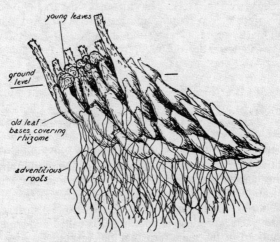

young leaves

ground
level

old leaf
bases covering
rhizome

adventitious
roots

Fig. 13.2. *Dryopteris*. Underground axis.

divided. A plant with such large leaves in proportion to the size of its stem is described as being *macrophyllous*.

The very young leaves are folded in *circinnate* fashion, the rachis, midribs of the pinnae and the pinnules are spirally coiled like a

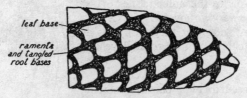

Fig. 13.3. *Dryopteris*. Older part of rhizome with leaf bases trimmed.

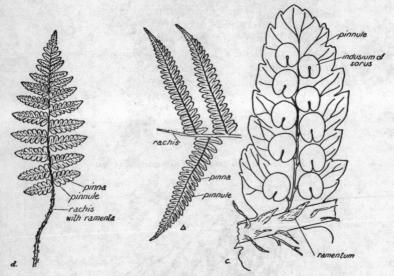

Fig. 13.4. Leaf structure of *Dryopteris*. (*a*) Whole young frond. (*b*) Several pinnae. (*c*) Underside of pinnule bearing sori.

bishop's crozier (*see* Fig. 13.5). Such a kind of leaf folding (vernation) is a primitive characteristic found in many of the pteridophyte plants. Very young leaves are completely covered by ramenta which afford them protection. Fully-developed leaves bear specialized reproductive structures, *sori of sporangia*, on their abaxial (lower) surfaces. A leaf, when bearing the reproductive sporangia, is called a *sporophyll* and it is to be noticed in the male fern that the vegetative leaves serve this purpose and that no specialized reproductive leaves are developed.

The roots on an older rhizome form a matted fibrous system, but if traced to their origins, they can be seen to arise in twos or threes from near the leaf bases. If the rhizome is almost horizontal in the ground, this arrangement may be hidden, since all the roots turn downwards as soon as they pierce the outer tissues of the rhizome. The very young fern possesses a single primary root, but this soon dies as the axis and its adventitious roots develop.

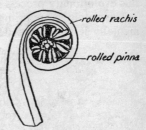

Fig. 13.5. Young leaf of *Dry-opteris* rolled circinnately.

Anatomy

The Rhizome. If an older part of a rhizome is cut transversely and longitudinally and the exposed surfaces examined, they will show the structures illustrated in Fig. 13.6. Within the solid part of the axis there is a broken ring of irregularly-shaped groups in the otherwise homogeneous tissue. This ring locates the position of the *stele*, or central vascular cylinder, which encloses a *medulla* and is surrounded by a *cortex*. In the longitudinal section, these parts of the stele form two

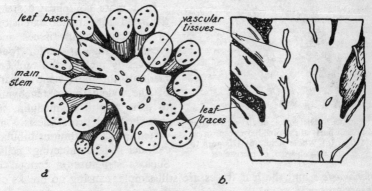

Fig. 13.6. Rhizome structure of *Dryopteris*. (*a*) T.S. with ramenta and roots removed. (*b*) L.S. part of rhizome.

parallel rows of irregularly-shaped groups. The views in the transverse and longitudinal sections combined, indicate immediately that the stele must have an intricate meshwork nature. It is illustrated in Fig. 13.7 when all the other softer tissues of cortex and medulla have been removed. In the rhizome section more vascular strands scattered in the cortex are visible. These are the *leaf traces* which originate at the main stele, cross the cortex and lead into the leaf bases.

The whole stele is described as a *dictyostele* and each apparently separate bundle of vascular tissue is called a *meristele*. The dictyostele is one of the more advanced types of stelar construction and its evolution from the primitive form is of great interest. The general trend in this evolutionary process may be outlined as follows—

The simple, more primitive stele, is known as the *protostele*. Fundamentally it is composed of a solid central mass of xylem with no pith, completely surrounded by phloem and bounded by a pericycle, the outermost of the stelar tissues (*see* Fig. 13.8 (*a*)). From this, leaf traces originate as simple strands to the leaves. The whole stele and its leaf traces are separated from the softer cortical tissues by the innermost layer of the latter, the endodermis, and nowhere is the vascular tissue interrupted by spaces or gaps.

In a more complicated stele, the need for greater extension of the conducting tissues and greater storage space for food reserves is met by the replacement of the more central part of the xylem by parenchyma to form a pith or medulla, so that the solid protostele is converted into a continuous tubular cylinder of conducting cells. Such a structure is termed a

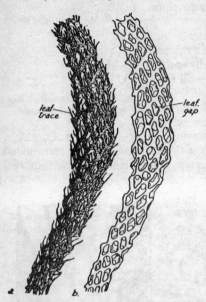

leaf trace

leaf gap

Fig. 13.7. Dictyostele of *Dryopteris* after all soft parts of rhizome have been rotted away. (*a*) Whole stele. (*b*) Diagram to show mesh-work of meristeles.

siphonostele and the leaf traces are still simple, causing no breaks or interruptions.

Further advance in this direction is evident in the *solenostele* as in Fig. 13.8 (*b*), in which the phloem, pericycle and endodermis together extend continuously from the outside to line the inner face of the xylem cylinder through gaps left in the tubular cylinder above the points where leaf traces originate. These leaf gaps in a solenostele are small, close up quickly, and do not overlap one another in the longitudinal direction. A transverse section can show only one leaf gap at any level. The leaf traces may be U-shaped in cross-section and often break up into several parallel strands on entering the leaf base.

Under conditions where the leaf gaps are large and the leaves closely crowded, the gaps overlap longitudinally, reducing the original continuous tube to a meshwork of vascular parts each surrounded on all sides by pericycle and endodermis. The whole stele is then termed a *dictyostele* and each of its small segments is a *meristele* (*see* Fig. 13.8 (*c*)). A fully dissected dictyostele of *Dryopteris* clearly shows this meshwork arrangement; the spaces represent leaf gaps and each leaf

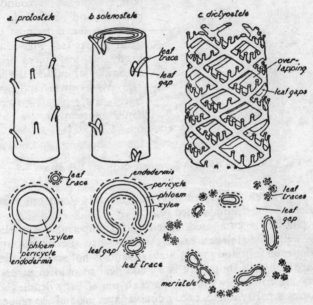

Fig. 13.8. Diagrams to show three types of stele.

is inserted so that its base sits over a gap, as it were, and its traces, no longer simple, can be seen as separate strands leaving the lower half of a meristele mesh, to enter the leaf as a U-shaped system with open end on the adaxial border of the petiole. In the development of the vascular system from the embryonic condition to that of the adult, these changes in complexity are recapitulated. Starting as a protostele, it becomes solenostelic and finally dictyostelic. An interesting experiment has been performed in which all leaf initials at the apex of a fern have been removed as they arise, resulting in the stelar tissues of the stem developing in no more complicated fashion than the protostele. The indications are that leaf development is a physiological condition essential to stelar differentiation.

Detailed examination of a meristele shows a central core of xylem composed mainly of scalariform tracheids, and xylem parenchyma surrounded by phloem, pericycle and endodermis in concentric arrangement. The tracheids for the most part are large, empty and polygonal in outline in the transverse section and constitute the metaxylem, but at one or two points within the main xylem group are small helically-thickened tracheids constituting the protoxylem. There are no xylem

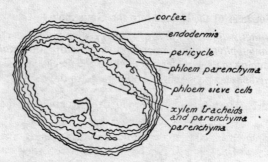

Fig. 13.9. Tissue layout in *Dryopteris* meristele. L.P. plan of T.S.

vessels anywhere. The xylem parenchyma cells stand out clearly as small, densely-filled, thin-walled cells.

The phloem is composed of elongated, tapering sieve elements showing well-defined sieve areas on the walls where the cells are adjacent. The strict tube formation as in higher plants is not seen and there are no companion cells, but there is a good deal of phloem parenchyma which makes continuity with the parenchyma of the xylem. The pericycle forms a partly single, partly double layer around the phloem and can be recognized by the thinner cell walls. The inner layer of the cortex, the endodermis, surrounds the whole and is composed of cells showing Casparian bands on the radial walls. In older parts, this is always thickened on the tangential walls also, so that the characteristic appearance of young endodermis is hidden.

External to the endodermis, the medulla and cortex are made up of large, thin-walled, parenchyma cells storing starch grains. Interspersed in this tissue are small cavities lined by glandular hairs which secrete a resinous substance valuable as a medicine against parasitic worms in animals, e.g. *Taenia*. Towards the periphery of the cortex, the cells gradually assume a thick-walled nature and at the extreme exterior they become lignified and sclerenchymatous. Finally, the epidermis, if still present, is a single layer with thick outer walls bearing the ramenta, which are dead scales of single cell thickness.

The Leaf. The cross-section of a leaf-base and a rachis show much the same structure as that of the rhizome except that they are circular in outline, flattened on the face next the stem, and contain from five to seven traces arranged in horseshoe fashion with the open end towards the flattened side (*see* Fig. 13.11). Each trace is like a meristele and the upper two larger ones give off branches to right and left into each pinna as they traverse the rachis. These in turn give off single vascular

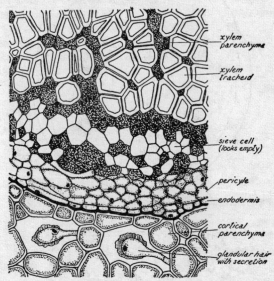

Fig. 13.10. Part of meristele and cortex of *Dryopteris* rhizome. H.P. drawing of T.S.

bundles forming the midribs of each pinnule. The ultimate venation of a pinnule is markedly dichotomous, with the bundles ending abruptly. This is an open arrangement in contrast to the closed reticulate meshwork of bundles found in the leaves of many higher plants.

The blade of each pinnule is constructed on lines to be found almost universally in leaves or leaf-like appendages (*see* Fig. 13.12). It is a broad, flattened, dorsi-ventral plate bounded externally by an epidermis within which is the mesophyll tissue ramified throughout by the smaller vascular bundles from the midrib. The epidermis of both upper and lower surfaces is composed of tightly-fitting but irregularly-shaped cells, cuticularized on their outer walls and containing protoplasts in which chloroplasts are much in evidence. This is characteristic of many shade plants and a few aquatic flowering plants and points to a function of the epidermis not primarily protective. The lower epidermis only is perforated at numerous points by stomata, the guard cells of which are of typical structure. The mesophyll is not clearly differen-

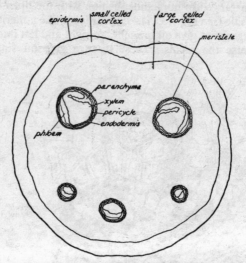

Fig. 13.11. *Dryopteris* rachis tissue layout in T.S. L.P. plan.

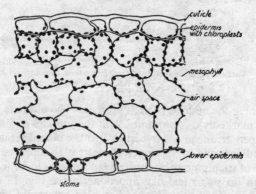

Fig. 13.12. *Dryopteris* leaf in V.S. H.P. drawing.

tiated into upper palisade and lower spongy layers as in the leaves of many plants, but is composed throughout of irregularly-shaped parenchyma cells containing abundant chloroplasts and interspersed with large air-spaces. This form of the mesophyll is also characteristic of many shade plants.

The Root. The root structure is simple by comparison with the stem. A transverse section appears as in Fig. 13.13. The central protostele is composed of xylem tracheids with two protoxylem groups, one at each end of the metaxylem group, i.e. in the *exarch* position. The xylem is

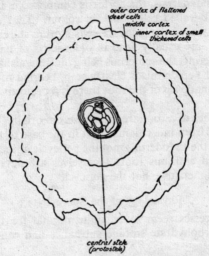

Fig. 13.13. Tissue layout in *Dryopteris* root. L.P. plan of T.S.

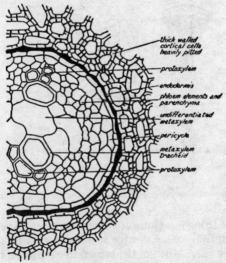

Fig. 13.14. Part of stele and cortex of *Dryopteris* root. H.P. drawing of T.S.

flanked by two phloem groups, one on either side and alternate with the protoxylem. The whole stele is surrounded by a double-layered pericycle and a single-layered endodermis. A root constructed with two protoxylem groups is said to be *diarch*.

Outside the endodermis, the cortex is composed in its inner parts of very small, thick-walled cells, dark in colour. They merge gradually into larger thin-walled parenchyma cells storing starch. These, at the extreme outside, are usually dead in older parts of the root and form a dark outer covering, the epidermis being indistinguishable. In younger parts of roots, the epidermis is clearly seen, bearing root-hairs. At the extreme meristematic tip of the root there is a protective sheath of cells, the *root cap*.

Lateral branches of a root are *endogenous* in origin. This means that they are derived from inner tissues, but in the case of the fern, the site of their origin is the endodermis, not the pericycle as in flowering plants. Similarly, the adventitious roots themselves are developed from the endodermis of a meristele, not the pericycle.

Physiology of the Sporophyte

Nutritional processes seem to be quite normal for the green plant. Starch is the carbohydrate storage substance and can be seen in leaf

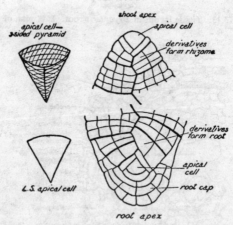

Fig. 13.15. Apical growing points of *Dryopteris* shoot and root. Diagrams.

cells and in the storage regions of stems and roots. The old leaf bases are also frequently used as storage structures until long after the leaf blade has died away. Much of the brownish coloration of cells of parts like the ramenta is due to the accumulation of phenolic compounds called *phlobaphenes*. These are chemically related to the plastic substance bakelite.

Growth of the sporophyte axis is by means of *single apical cells* located at the apex of the rhizome and at the tip of each adventitious root. The stem apical cell is like a minute tetrahedron, base uppermost (*see* Fig. 13.15). It cuts off new cells successively from each of its three side faces and these divide further before their products differentiate into the stem tissues. Each root apical cell is of similar shape and functions in the same way, but cuts off cells on its fourth face also, to contribute to the root cap. Each leaf is initiated at the stem apex from a single cell like a thin triangular prism; it produces all the tissue of the blade. There is no secondary growth of the plant body.

Reproductive Structures of the Sporophyte

The only specialized reproductive structures are the *sporangia*, which occur in clusters or *sori* on the abaxial faces of the mature pinnules.

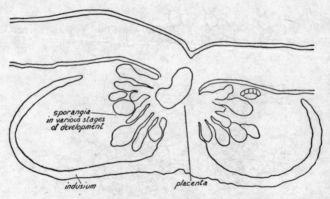

Fig. 13.16. V.S. through a sorus of *Dryopteris*.

The sori can be clearly located, since each is protected by a scale-like hood known as the *indusium* (*see* Fig. 13.16). The kidney-shaped outline of the indusium was responsible for the generic name *Nephrodium*. When the sorus ripens, the indusium changes from green to brown in colour and withers to expose the sporangia underneath. They are microscopic and all arise from a central protuberance on the pinnule known as the *placenta* (*see* Fig. 13.16). When ripe, a sporangium has the structure as shown in Fig. 13.17. It is a laterally-compressed, ovoid, hollow container on a multicellular stalk which often bears a glandular appendage, said to be concerned with water storage. Within the hollow upper portion are 48 or 64 dark brown *spores*. The sporangium wall is a single cell thick, but is clearly differentiated into distinct regions. From a point about half-way along one edge of the flattened

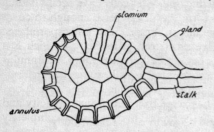

Fig. 13.17. *Dryopteris* sporangium.

structure, right over the apex and all along the other edge back to the stalk, a single row of cells stands out clearly. These form the *annulus* and each cell is heavily thickened on all but its outer face. Just below the point where the annulus commences on one edge, long narrow cells with their axes in the transverse direction of the sporangial wall meet to form the *stomium*. The remainder of the cells of the sporangial wall are flattened, plate-like cells.

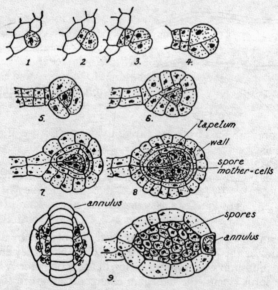

Fig. 13.18. Diagram of the developmental stages of *Dryopteris* sporangium.

Each sporangium arises as a single superficial cell of the placenta and by division forms a small protuberance (*see* Fig. 13.18). The central cell of this mass is tetrahedral in shape and is surrounded by a single outer layer of cells, the lowermost of which continues to divide to form the stalk and its water gland. The central cell is the *archesporial cell* and this divides several times in a direction parallel to the surface of the developing sporangium, to form a two- or three-celled layer around itself called the *tapetum.* Meanwhile, the outer cells have been dividing at right angles to the surface to form a wall extensive enough to cover the inner mass. When the tapetum is formed, the archesporial cell proper divides further into twelve or sixteen cells each of which is a *spore mother-cell.* The wall cells begin to differentiate into the annulus and stomium regions. Each spore mother-cell undergoes meiotic division to produce a tetrad of cells each of which becomes a spore. During this phase, the tapetum has acted in a nutritional capacity and by the time the spores are forming, the tapetal layer becomes completely disorganized to form a fluid in which the developing spores lie freely. All the spores on the male fern are identical, i.e. the plant is *homosporous.* Each spore is a unicellular structure with a double wall, the outer of which is thickened irregularly and is dark brown in colour.

Reproduction by the Sporophyte

Dryopteris plants are able to reproduce vegetatively and by spores. Vegetative propagation is achieved by the development of *adventitious buds* on the old leaf bases of matured rhizomes, and these buds develop into new fern sporophytes as the old rhizome decays. From the description of the sporangia and formation of the spores and the fact that these give rise directly to the next generation, it will be realized that the sporing process is asexual. No gametes are involved at this stage of the life cycle.

The spores are shed from the parent by the dehiscence of the sporangia and this is dependent upon the reactions of the cells of the annulus during drying-out. The dehiscence mechanism is illustrated in Fig. 13.19. It has been noted that the annulus cells are peculiarly thickened. When exposed to dry air, as the indusium shrivels, they begin to lose water by evaporation. Owing to the cohesive properties of the watery contents, and its adhesion to the inner wall faces as it shrinks in volume, it exerts an inward pull on all the cell faces. Only the thin outer wall can be appreciably bowed inwards and as this happens, it has the effect of pulling the radial walls of each annulus cell towards one another, so that the whole distance around the edge of the annulus tends to shorten and exert a strain in the wall in the plane of the annulus. As drying-out proceeds further and further, the stomium is gradually ruptured to ease this strain and the annulus curls back on itself so that it is inside out. It carries with it the fully-exposed spore mass in the remainder of the broken-down sporangium. Many of the spores will fall free of the ruptured structure. Drying proceeds to the point where the cohesive and adhesive forces exerted on the walls of the annulus cells are no longer great enough to hold the annulus in its "wound-up" condition. An air bubble appears in each cell and as these forces suddenly cease to exist, the wound-up annulus, by its own elasticity, snaps back

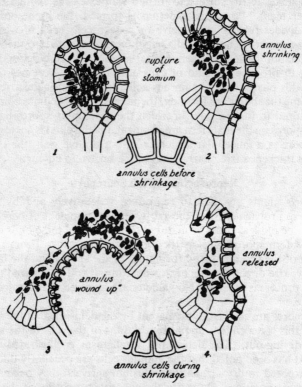

Fig. 13.19. Dehiscence of *Dryopteris* sporangium.

into its original position, catapulting the remaining spores outwards to a distance of several centimetres. The whole of this procedure can be watched under the microscope if ripe sporangia are placed on a warm slide. The dispersal mechanism is entirely dependent on warm, dry conditions. A large male fern plant may produce several hundred million spores in a season.

Development of the Spores into the Gametophyte Generation

After lying dormant for a while, and if in damp shady positions, the spores will germinate and produce a new generation of plants (*see* Fig.

13.20). Germination commences by the rupture of the spore wall and the growth of the spore contents into a green cell which quickly develops a colourless rhizoid to anchor it to the soil and to commence absorption of water and mineral salts. The green cell divides regularly to produce

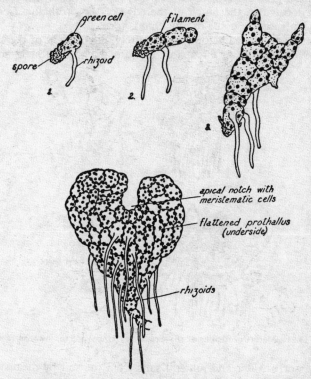

Fig. 13.20. Stages in the development of a *Dryopteris* gametophyte from the spore.

first a short filament of cells some of which produce more rhizoids. The apical cell of the filament then begins to cut off cells on its lateral faces to produce a flattened plate of cells, which is now the recognizable green fern *prothallus*. *It is the gametophyte generation of the life cycle.*

Structure, Physiology and Reproduction of the Prothallus

The gametophyte at maturity is roughly heart-shaped and rarely measures more than 1 cm along its greater axis (*see* Fig. 13.21). It is distinctly dorsi-ventral and from its under surface numerous unicellular attaching rhizoids are developed from a central cushion-like portion which is several cells thick. At the extreme edges, the plate tapers to one cell in thickness. The thicker central region is due to the dividing activity of a small group of cells, which are derivations of the original single apical growing cell, and which they replace. These meristematic cells are located in the notch at the edge of the prothallus (*see* Fig. 13.20). No vascular tissue of any kind is formed.

In every way, the gametophyte is entirely independent of the sporophyte. Nutritionally, it is capable of normal photosynthetic activity

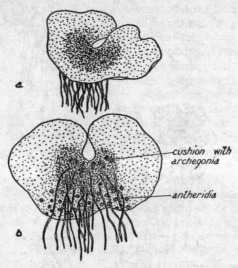

Fig. 13.21. Mature prothallus of *Dryopteris*. (*a*) Upper and (*b*) lower surfaces.

and it absorbs water and mineral salts from the soil by means of its rhizoids. Starch is its main carbohydrate product. It is, however, a delicate structure and not adapted to withstand drying atmospheric conditions. It develops no protective cuticle over its surface, so that its survival is only assured in the dampest of habitats, where the risk of desiccation does not arise.

By the time that the gametophyte has reached maturity, it has developed on its lower side the sex organs, in which the gametes are developed. The organs are clearly distinguishable as male *antheridia* and female *archegonia*. The antheridia commence development at quite an early stage. Archegonia may be found later on the cushion portion just behind the apical notch, whilst antheridia occur more widely scattered among the rhizoids further away.

Each antheridium develops from a single superficial cell on the lower side. This divides to isolate a single central colourless cell surrounded by a single layer of wall cells which at first contain chloroplasts (*see* Fig. 13.23). The wall cells divide further to develop as a single layer composed of two tiers surmounted by a discoid cap cell. The whole antheridium is mounted on a short stalk so that it forms a spherical protuberance on the prothallus. Within the wall, the central cell undergoes successive mitotic divisions to produce thirty-two smaller *antherozoid mother-cells*. From the contents of each of these, without further division, an *antherozoid* develops. It must be recalled that the gametophyte is haploid and thus there is no need

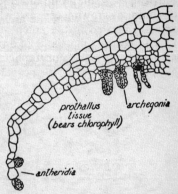

Fig, 13.22. V.S. of *Dryopteris* prothallus showing male and female sex organs.

for reduction division to occur when it produces its gametes. The reduction division of the life cycle has already occurred at spore formation by the sporophyte. The nucleus of the antherozoid mother-cell changes form into a tapering spiralled band with a vesicle of cytoplasm at one end. Attached to the other end along the edge of the band is a denser

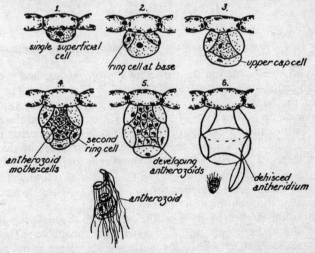

Fig. 13.23. Diagram of the stages in development of *Dryopteris* antheridium.

substance forming a blepharoplast. From this, a group of very long flagella are developed so that the antherozoid is actively motile when released. This is accomplished by the gelatinizing of the mother-cell walls which swell and force the lid cell of the antheridium clear. This normally occurs before the archegonia are mature, so that self-fertilization is not frequent.

Each archegonium also originates from a single superficial cell on the lower side. By division, it produces the characteristic pattern of

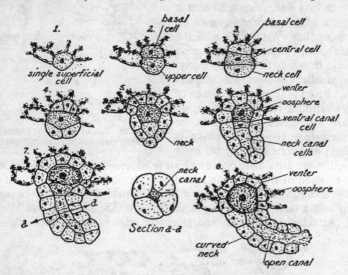

Fig. 13.24. Diagram of the stages in development of *Dryopteris* archegonium.

lower *venter*, embedded in the tissues of the prothallus, and a curved *neck*, projecting from the prothallus surface (*see* Fig. 13.24). The venter contains the female *oosphere*, and below it a *ventral canal cell*. The neck is made up of four rows of cells joined laterally around the central canal. Two of these rows are of five or six cells and the other two of four cells; this brings about the characteristic curvature of the neck. At first, the canal is blocked by *neck canal cells* and the tip is closed. When the archegonium is mature, the ventral canal cell and the neck canal cells disintegrate and the tip is ruptured, leaving a mucilage-filled passage through the neck up into the venter.

Fertilization is effected by a motile antherozoid swimming up the neck of the archegonium and fusing with the oosphere. The neck secretes malic acid to which the antherozoids respond by making chemotactic movements. After fusion, the zygote thus formed secretes a wall and becomes an *oospore*. Several oospores may be formed on each prothallus but usually only one develops further.

Development of the Zygote into the Sporophyte Generation

Soon after its formation, the oospore commences development without being shed from the venter of the archegonium. By successive divisions,

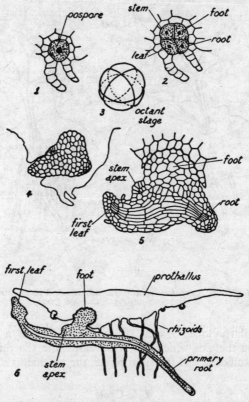

Fig. 13.25. Diagram of the stages in development of *Dryopteris* embryo.

it first forms a group of eight cells (octants) four of which are directed towards the apex of the parent prothallus and four away from it (*see* Fig. 13.25). From the former group, by division, are produced the *main axis* and *first leaf* of the young plant, and from the latter group the *primary root* and an absorptive *foot* are developed. This last structure remains embedded in the prothallial tissues, absorbing nourishment and water for the other parts. The primary root grows downwards into the soil, but is short-lived. It has the normal diarch root structure of the sporophyte. It is soon replaced by numerous adventitious roots which develop on the small main axis. Before this is very large, the first leaf appears with its petiole typically curving upwards between the lobes of the prothallus at the apical notch. The first leaf is not like the mature structure, but is composed of a broad two-lobed blade.

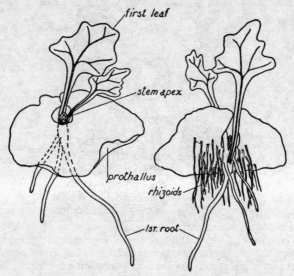

Fig. 13.26. Young *Dryopteris* sporophyte still attached to gametophyte (two views).

Several similarly lobed leaves are produced before a normal leaf originates on the axis which slowly develops into the rhizome. With greater self-sufficiency of the sporophyte, the prothallus slowly withers and dies.

Life Cycle

The life cycle can be diagrammatically represented as shown on p. 277.

Adaptation to Environment

The fern sporophyte is structurally, physiologically and in its reproductive processes well adapted to terrestrial conditions. The reverse is the case with the gametophyte generation. Its delicate structure and the zoidogamous fertilization process demand constant moisture.

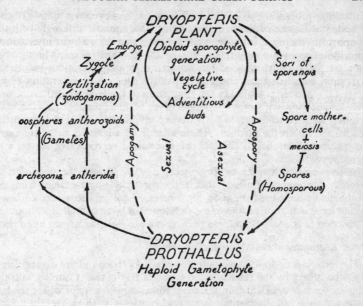

DRYOPTERIS
PLANT
Diploid sporophyte
generation
Vegetative
cycle
Adventitious
buds

Embryo

Zygote

fertilization
(zoidogamous)

oospheres antherozoids

(Gametes)

archegonia antheridia

Apogamy

Sexual

Asexual

Apospory

Sori of
sporangia

Spore mother-
cells
±
meiosis

Spores
(Homosporous)

DRYOPTERIS
PROTHALLUS
Haploid Gametophyte
Generation

Special Features of Biological Importance

As a representative of land plants alongside the bryophytes and the spermato-phytes, the male fern is a curious mixture of advanced and primitive charac-teristics. Vegetatively, the sporophyte shows as complete a morphological and histological division of labour as it is possible to find in any plant. There are distinct root, stem and leaf systems and the plant perennates. There are clearly defined photosynthetic and storage parenchyma, mechanical, vascular and protective tissues. No comparable condition can be seen in the bryophyte sporophyte. It must not be thought, however, that the fern sporophyte is the culmination of vegetative adaptability for a land existence. By comparison with the flowering plant, it shows several primitive characters. For example, the vascular elements are wholly of tracheids and sieve cells. (Note that the xylem elements in the root have been described by some authors as vessels since the end walls may show a certain degree of perforation.) The more efficient vessels and sieve tubes do not occur. Growth is made from a single apical cell; lateral meristems are not formed and there is no secondary growth of the body. By contrast with the high degree of specialization of parts shown by the sporophyte, the gametophyte mode of existence is even less well-adapted to land conditions than that of many mosses. In its reproductive processes, the same wide variance of adaptation to terrestrial conditions is exhibited. The asexual process in the sporophyte clearly shows full adaptation to dry conditions in the manner of the formation and dispersal of the spores. The sexual process on the other hand is completely dependent on wet con-ditions. Neither the structure of the sex organs nor the zoidogamous fertilization process shows any real advance on the bryophyte state. The independent existence of the two generations does contrast strikingly with the bryophytes. We might suppose that it indicates that the pathway of evolution from the bryophyte condition to that of the flowering plant, was through primitive plants which showed this separation of the generations before the ferns came into existence, and that it was the sporophyte generation which showed the greater potentiality for adaptation to the land conditions.

By comparison with other representatives of the Pteridophyta, the male fern may be used to illustrate particular conditions of several characteristics which vary within the phylum. These include an advanced stelar anatomy, the macrophyllous habit, the lack of specialized reproductive leaves, and homospory.

Lastly, in some species of *Dryopteris*, e.g. *D. borreri*, the condition of *apogamy* has been recognized; that is, the sporophyte may develop from the prothallus without the formation of gametes. Another occurrence common among ferns is that of *apospory*, the development of a prothallus without the production of spores. Both these phenomena are worth enlarging upon here.

Stelar Anatomy and the Macrophyllous Habit

The ferns belong to the macrophyllous pteridophytes and are distinguished from the others by the relatively large size of the leaves. Coupled with the large leaves is a stele which in the adult shows large leaf gaps where the leaf traces are given off. In the male fern, these gaps overlap to convert the hollow siphonostele into a dictyostele. In microphyllous pteridophytes, the stele is solid and no leaf gaps occur. The distinction between the macro- and microphyllous conditions is so clear in the Pteridophyta that it has been regarded as a character of taxonomic importance.

Lack of Specialized Reproductive Leaves

Within the pteridophytes, we see an increasing tendency for the localization of sporangia on special leaves or sporophylls aggregated into compact structures known as *strobili* or *cones*. Their absence in the ferns indicate a primitive condition.

Homospory

This describes the condition in which the asexual spores are all identical in structure and development. The opposite condition of *heterospory*, in which there are two spore forms giving rise to distinctly different gametophyte generations, also occurs in the pteridophytes. The heterosporous condition must have been derived from the homosporous and also must have been one of the earliest steps in the evolution of the seed habit in plants. This is discussed in a later chapter.

Apospory and Apogamy

Apospory is the name used to describe the development of a gametophyte from a sporophyte without any spore production. Apogamy describes the phenomenon by which a gametophyte gives rise to a sporophyte without the union of gametes. Both conditions are very widespread among ferns and a single plant may show both conditions.

Gametophytes produced by apospory arise on the leaves in one of three positions. They may develop in place of spores in the sporangia, on the placenta in place of whole sporangia or along the margins or the tips of leaves. The aposporous gametophytes frequently resemble those normally produced by spores, both in form and function. They are thalloid, with rhizoids, and develop antheridia and archegonia. However, they differ cytologically. The nuclei are diploid like those of the sporophyte. In most cases such gametophytes give rise to a new sporophyte apogamously, but cases have been known in which union of diploid gametes from aposporous gametophytes have resulted in tetraploid sporophytes, and these in their turn have produced tetraploid aposporous gametophytes. Occasionally aposporous gametophytes may show sporophytic characteristics. They have been recorded as developing tracheids just behind the growing point and sometimes stomata. They have even been observed to develop sporangia.

Apogamy can occur in aposporous gametophytes as mentioned above or in those normally produced by spores. In a number of cases, the gametophytes which give rise to apogamous sporophytes have been shown to be derived from spores which were diploid, i.e. were formed without a previous meiosis. The sporophytes developed from these, are of course normal diploid sporophytes. Sometimes, however, the gametophytes which give rise to apogamous sporophytes are normally haploid. In such cases, the resultant sporophyte is haploid, but can give rise to normal spores by duplicating the nuclear material in sporogenous tissue.

An apogamously-produced sporophyte may arise in one of several ways from the gametophyte. Any vegetative cell may produce it, or a component cell of the archegonium may be involved. This can be a cell of the venter or neck or the unfertilized oosphere itself. When the last is the case, the phenomenon is one of *parthenogenesis* (*see* Vol. II. Chap. 17).

These conditions of apospory and apogamy tend to abbreviate the normal life cycle replacing spore-production or gametic union by vegetative reproduction.

LYCOPODIUM

This genus includes about 100 species of which five are British. They are *L. clavatum* (wolf's claw), *L. selago* (fir club-moss), *L. alpinum* (savin-leaved club-moss), *L. annotinum* (interrupted club-moss) and *L. innundatum* (marsh club-moss). There are many other tropical species of which *L. phlegmaria* is a notable epiphytic representative. The first two British species mentioned, are commonest, and most of what follows applies to one or other of them.

Habitat

They occur on the wetter heaths and moorlands of upland districts, particularly in North Wales.

Vegetative Structure of the Sporophyte Generation

External Morphology

L. clavatum and *L. selago* both possess a naked underground stem axis, and aerial creeping branches, thickly clustered with small spirally arranged leaves. The plants are described as *microphyllous* (cf. fern). Branching of the axis occurs, but is *monopodial* (*see* p. 383) and not dichotomous as is normal for such primitive plants. The leaves are sessile and lanceolate with a distinct midrib not quite reaching the apex, which is drawn out into a sharp point. The leaf margin is serrate in *L. clavatum*, but not in *L. selago*. Dichotomously-branched adventitious roots arise along the rhizome and along the undersides of the aerial creeping stems. The two species can be clearly distinguished when fertile. *L. clavatum* develops erect aerial branches, called *podia*, lightly clothed with small scale-like appendages and at the tips of these branches, which may be forked, are borne usually two *cones* or *strobili* in which the reproductive parts are developed on the internal faces of specialized leaves or *sporophylls*. These are very much smaller and more

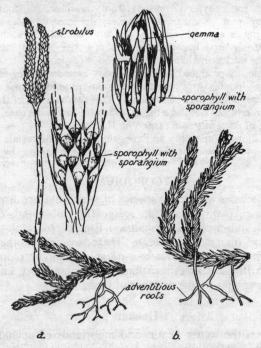

Fig. 13.27. Habit drawings of *Lycopodium* spp. (*a*) *L. clavatum*. (*b*) *L. selago*.

closely crowded in a spiral than the vegetative leaves. In *L. selago* the fertile parts are not so clearly distinguishable from the rest of the plant. The sporophylls are almost exactly like normal leaves and although produced in strobilus formation at the apices of young shoots, they are followed in succession by ordinary leaves developed on the same axis. Thus along a stem there may be found alternating regions bearing sterile and fertile leaves. Further, in *L. selago*, just behind the apices of young vegetative shoots, there frequently occur detachable *gemmae* or *bulbils* which serve for vegetative propagation (*see* Fig. 13.27).

Anatomy

The Stem. Transverse sections through the creeping and erect portions of the stem of *L. clavatum* may show slightly differing structures. The creeping stem is usually markedly dorsi-ventral in that the stele

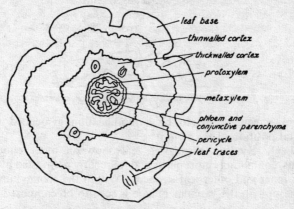

Fig. 13.28. Tissue layout of *Lycopodium* stem. L.P. plan of T.S.

is a banded protostele in which the horizontal bands of xylem alternate with bands of phloem. The arrangement forms a *plectostele*. Protoxylem groups occur at both ends of each of the xylem strips, i.e. in the exarch position. The xylem is all tracheidal. The phloem is composed of sieve cells and parenchyma. The alternating strips of xylem and phloem are separated by pitted parenchyma cells. The conducting elements are surrounded by a pericycle, several cells thick, but there is no recognizable endodermis. The cortex has three zones. The inner and outer layers are thick-walled and sclerenchymatous; the middle layer is composed of larger thin-walled parenchyma cells which may contain a few chloroplasts. In the cortex may be seen small leaf traces but they leave no gaps in the stele. The erect stem is cylindrical and the stele is a ribbed protostele or *actinostele*, usually with four or five ribs of metaxylem, each having a small protoxylem group at its outer edge. Phloem groups alternate with the protoxylem groups. The plectostele seems to be a derivative of the actinostele and at points along a stem, intermediate conditions of the stele may be encountered. The banded

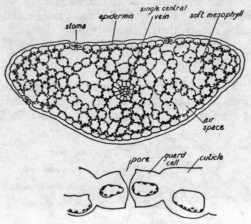

Fig. 13.29. V.S. of *L. clavatum* leaf. H.P. drawing.

stele arrangement seems to be a modification associated with the horizontal position of the stem.

The Leaf. Sections through a leaf show an outer cuticularized epidermis, containing chloroplasts and frequently perforated by stomata on both inner and outer leaf surfaces. Within the spongy, undifferentiated mesophyll, the vascular bundle is seen to be composed of a few

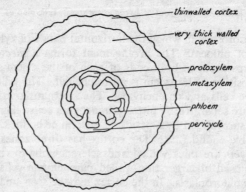

Fig. 13.30. Tissue layout in *L. clavatum* root. L.P. plan of T.S.

thick-walled spirally-thickened tracheids, surrounded by phloem elements lower down in the leaf only. There is no endodermis but sclerenchyma cells may enclose the whole bundle.

The Root. The root stele does not differ markedly from that of the stem but has the actinostele structure with five to seven protoxylem groups. Very small roots may be diarch. There is a pericycle but no endodermis. Young roots show a well-defined cortex of thin-walled cells, but in older roots this becomes very heavily sclerified right out to the outer regions. No lateral roots are formed. At the apex of a root is a root cap and behind it, is a root-hair region, in which the hairs characteristically arise in pairs.

Physiology of the Sporophyte

Normal nutritional processes occur and the product of photosynthesis is starch. Growth of the axis differs from that of most pteridophytes in being the result of the activity of a small group of apical cells instead of a single cell. Root growth is also made from an apical meristem. There is no secondary growth of the sporophyte body.

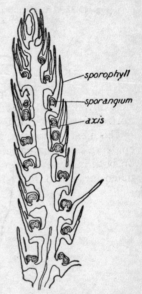

Fig. 13.31. L.S. *L. clavatum* cone. L.P. plan.

Reproductive Structures of the Sporophyte

The two kinds of reproductive structures which may occur in the genus have been mentioned. These are the *sporangia* found in all the species and the *gemmae* of *L. selago*. The sporangia of *L. clavatum* are borne in the clearly-defined terminal strobili whilst those of *L. selago* are scattered along the axis.

Each strobilus of *L. clavatum* is composed of tightly-spiralled sporophylls on a central axis. On the inner face (adaxial side) of each of these are borne singly the kidney-shaped sporangia (*see* Fig. 13.32). The sporophylls are unlike vegetative leaves in having broad bases which overlap to protect the sporangia inside. They have little chlorophyll and are anatomically of great interest in possessing a small basal area of disintegrated cells known as a *parichnos*. This structure seems to parallel that of a similar condition known to have existed in the leaves of fossil relatives of the Carboniferous period (*see* Vol. II, Chap. 20).

Each short-stalked sporangium is covered by a wall initially three

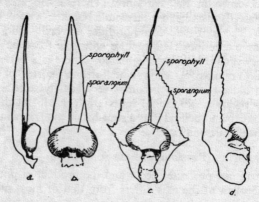

Fig. 13.32. Lateral and adaxial views of sporophylls of *Lycopodium spp.* (a) and (b) *L. selago.* (c) and (d) *L. clavatum.*

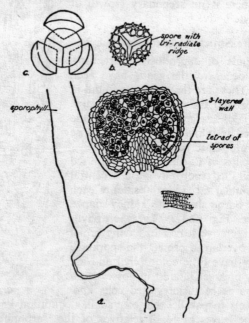

Fig. 13.33. Structure of the sporangium and spores of *L. clavatum.* (a) L.S. sporangium. (b) Single spore. (c) Diagram of spore tetrad to show tri-radiate ridge formation.

cells thick, of which the inner forms a nutritive *tapetum*. Within this is
the *archesporial tissue* which by division develops the *spore mother-
cells*. Each spore mother-cell undergoes meiotic division to form a
tetrad of *spores*. When mature they are very tiny and each is protected
by a sculptured wall showing a tri-radiate ridge system characteristic
of most spores when formed from
a closely-packed tetrad (*see* Fig.
13.33).

The only major differences between
the spore-producing structures of *L.
clavatum* and *L. selago* are their
positions on the axis and the shapes
of the sporophylls, but *L. selago* is
very distinctive in producing gemmae
(*see* Fig. 13.34). These are borne
on small outgrowths of the stem
which are difficult to interpret morphologically. Each gemma is a
resting bud on a short stalk. It is
developed at the apex of a short
branch-like growth from the main
stem. Surrounding the base of the
gemma and protecting it during its
early development, is a *cupule* composed of six leaf-like growths. Five
of these are small and spine-like
whilst the remaining one, occurring
in the outside position, is larger and
hollowed at its base to cup the young
gemma. When mature the gemma is
composed of about six fleshy leaf-like
growths on a shortened axis. Three

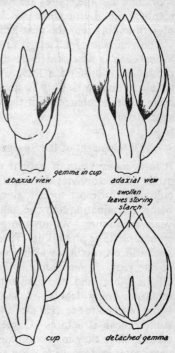

Fig. 13.34. Gemma of *L. selago*.

of these are large, wing-like and conspicuous whilst the others are very
tiny. The fleshy leaves are heavily packed with stored starch and
appear pale in colour by contrast with the dark green of normal leaves.
When the gemma is abscissed it leaves a small scar in the centre of the
base of the cupule which remains on the parent plant. Many such empty
cupules can be found among the leaves of older parts.

Reproduction by the Sporophyte

The development of spores as described above, constitutes an asexual
reproductive process. Each strobilus produces many spores and these
constitute the "lycopodium powder" useful to physicists in sound

experiments. When the spores are maturing, the tapetal layer becomes disorganized and the spores separate from one another, to lie freely in the sporangium. With drying, the sporangium wall shrinks and splits open along a line parallel to the face of the sporophyll on which it grows. The sporophylls bend away from the axis to expose the open sporangia and the spores are scattered by the wind. All the spores are identical, i.e. *Lycopodium spp.* are *homosporous*, and each is capable of germinating into the next generation.

The gemmae of *L. selago* are structures of vegetative propagation. When each is abscissed it develops directly into a new sporophyte by producing roots and a leafy axis at the expense of the stored food which it contains. This is an effective means of shortening the life cycle when compared with the other species which do not reproduce vegetatively.

Development of the Spores into the Gametophyte Generation

It took many years of patient work to find this next stage in the life cycle. Gametophytes develop from the spores, but cannot readily be cultivated for most species, since the spores may rest for several years before germinating and the gametophyte may then take several more years to mature. Within the genus may be recognized two types of gametophyte or prothallus. These are, of the one kind, quickly-developing surface structures which produce chlorophyll and come to maturity in one year. *L. inundatum* is the only British species so characterized. Of the other kind, the gametophytes are slow to develop, spore germination being delayed from three to eight years and maturity not being reached for several more years. Furthermore, they are colourless subterranean structures. Gametophytes of fifteen years of age are on record, since they may continue to nourish the sporophyte for several years after its formation. Both *L. clavatum* and *L. selago* produce this latter kind of prothallus.

Structure, Physiology and Reproduction of the Prothallus

When mature, the subterranean gametophyte of *L. clavatum* is a solid structure shaped roughly like a stumpy cone with its point downwards and with a much convoluted broad base (1–2 cm diameter) uppermost. Nowhere is it green. A vertical section shows that it is covered by an epidermis from the lower region of which many unicellular rhizoids are produced. Internal to this, in the pointed end, is a zone of soft cortical cells which ends abruptly at a plate of single elongated cells which forms a palisade-like layer. Soft cortex containing food reserves fills the central portion, but in the outer zone of this, the cells contain numerous filaments of a *mycorrhizal fungus* (*see* Chap. 34). This fungus enters the developing gametophyte at an early stage, and unless it does so, the gametophyte dies. This is obviously a condition comparable with that known to occur in some higher plants, e.g. *Neottia*, and there is undoubtedly some symbiotic relationship between the gametophyte

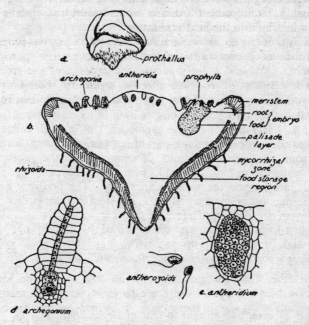

Fig. 13.35. Diagram of the structure of the prothallus of *Lycopodium sp.* (*after Bruchmann*).

and the fungal mycelium. The uppermost surface of the prothallus bears the reproductive organs which are male *antheridia* and female *archegonia*.

Nutritionally, the gametophyte is very distinctive. It undoubtedly depends for its nourishment on its symbiotic relationship with the fungus, since it lacks chlorophyll. The exact relationship is unknown. In *L. selago* the gametophyte may not always be entirely subterranean; its upper surface may be at soil level, in which case a little chlorophyll may be formed and the structure may produce lobed branches over the soil surface.

Growth of the gametophyte is at first from a single apical cell which later develops as a group of meristematic cells.

The antheridia are walled structures originating from a single cell and are deeply embedded in pits towards the central regions of the upper surface (*see* Fig. 13.35). Internally, *antherozoid mother-cells* change form to become biflagellate *antherozoids* similar to those of the bryophytes. These are released when the parent wall ruptures.

Archegonia are produced towards the periphery of the surface and each, originating from a single superficial cell, develops a long straight *neck*, again reminiscent of the bryophytes, protruding above the *venter*, which is embedded in the gametophyte tissue (*see* Fig. 13.35 (*d*)). In the venter is the *oosphere*. A motile antherozoid swims to the neck and fertilization is effected in the normal way.

Development of the Zygote into the Sporophyte Generation

The zygote develops very slowly and for a long time is dependent on the gametophyte into which it pushes itself in its early stages (*see* Fig. 13.35 (*b*)). Early divisions of the zygote mark off a single cell which is known as the *suspensor* and a group of eight cells in octant formation. From some of these, developing downwards into the prothallus, a tuberous absorptive *foot* is formed. From others, expanding obliquely upwards, are formed the *stem* and *first leaf*. The *first root* develops from the side just below the first leaf. The stem increases in length and more leaves are developed along it together with adventitious roots. These first-formed leaves are distinguished by having no vascular supply and are referred to as *prophylls*. It is interesting to note that in a related species, *Phylloglossum drummondi*, all leaves are in this condition.

Life Cycle

This is in all essentials similar to that in *Dryopteris*.

Adaptation to Environment

The sporophyte possesses all the characteristics of a successful land plant, but the slow and uncertain development of the gametophyte is undoubtedly a disadvantage in the struggle for existence with other plants. Consequently most species of *Lycopodium* are best able to thrive where competition is not too keen. As epiphytes, the many tropical species are comparatively more successful than the British species, relying to a greater extent on vegetative propagation of the sporophyte by gemmae, tubers and bulbils.

Special Features of Biological Importance

The species of *Lycopodium* are homosporous and are similar to the ferns in this respect. Their life cycles are essentially similar also. But, by contrast with the ferns, the club-mosses show well the microphyllous habit, coupled with a simple stelar anatomy. They illustrate the localization of specialized fertile sporophylls into strobili The genus also affords an illustration of how modern plants may show indications of relationship with ancient forms. Morphologically the modern lycopod is very similar to a fossil genus *Lycopodites* which flourished among many tree forms of lycopods in the Carboniferous period. In possessing a parichnos in the sporophylls, it is also anatomically similar to many of the fossil genera of those times which exhibited the same type of structure in every leaf. The extraordinary anatomy and physiology of the gametophyte in some species, appears to be an evolutionary step not paralleled by any other pteridophyte group. The importance and significance of mycorrhizal associations is discussed in Chap. 34.

SELAGINELLA

This genus of about six hundred species, mostly tropical, has but one native British species, namely *Selaginella selaginoides* [*Lycopodium selaginoides*]. This is a native of moist mountain pastures in northern and western parts of the country. A native of Africa, *S. kraussiana*, has become a very common greenhouse plant, almost a weed in this country, and since its general characteristics are typical of the genus, it will be described here.

Vegetative Structure of the Sporophyte Generation

External Morphology

The sporophyte body is composed of a creeping stem bearing branches more or less regularly spaced. Because the stem branches develop at much the same rate as the main axis, dichotomy appears to be the case, but in reality the branches are lateral in development and the branching system is monopodial. The creeping habit keeps all the stems more or less in a horizontal plane and the leaves also expand in this plane to form a markedly dorsi-ventral arrangement. The leaves are produced in four rows and are placed in opposite pairs, each pair having one large and one small leaf. The larger leaves originate from the lower lateral surface of a stem and the smaller ones from the upper surface (*see* Fig. 13.36). Each leaf bears a small membranous outgrowth called a *ligule* which is recognizable in young leaves but which withers and disappears on ageing. A similar structure is borne on many of the fossil representatives of the order Lycopodiales, indicating a relationship.

Slightly behind each fork in the stem, sooner or later a structure resembling a root develops and grows downwards. It lacks a root cap and upon reaching a length of a few millimetres but not necessarily sufficient to reach the underlying soil, it proceeds to develop two or more roots from endogenously-placed cortical cells at its apex. The structure is a *rhizophore* and in the whole of the living plant kingdom there is no morphological parallel. It is sometimes described as an organ "sui generis," to indicate that it lacks any ancestral form from which it could have been derived. After root development, it may elongate by intercalary growth to carry the roots down to the soil

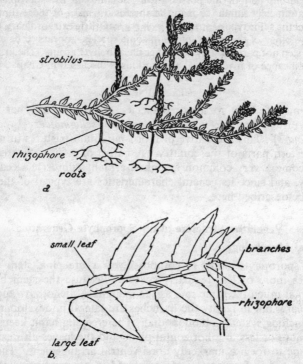

Fig. 13.36. (*a*) Habit drawing of *Selaginella sp.* (*b*) Portion of same, enlarged.

below, where they penetrate rapidly. In some species, a large tuft of roots may be developed at the tip of the rhizophore.

A mature fertile plant bears vertical branches which differ from the rest of the stem structure. They are the strobili, bearing sporophylls all of equal size in four vertical rows. In the axils of the sporophylls, the sporangia are developed.

Anatomy

The Stem. The stem section shows a flattened upper and a rounded lower outline which has two laterally-placed grooves (*see* Fig. 13.37).

In *S. kraussiana* the condition of *distely* occurs. There are two separate steles laterally communicating with one another only where branches arise. In some species, the stem is *monostelic* and in others it may be *polystelic*, having as many as sixteen steles.

Each stele is of protostelic construction and is made up of a central mass of tracheidal xylem cells with one or two exarch protoxylem groups. It is noteworthy that in the species *S. rupicola*, a form of xylem vessel occurs. The phloem forms a ring around the xylem but is separated from it by a layer of parenchyma cells. Exterior to this is a single-layered pericycle which communicates with the cortical region by a few

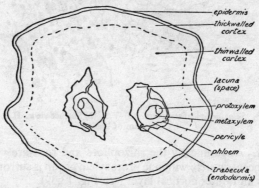

Fig. 13.37. Tissue layout in *Selaginella kraussiana* stem. L.P. plan of T.S.

widely-spaced filaments or trabeculae only. Thus each stele appears to be suspended in a space in the cortex. The trabeculae are at first unicellular and each shows a cutinized band around its radial walls. The structure is therefore regarded as equivalent to an endodermis. With age the trabeculae become multicellular by transverse divisions.

The cortex is made up of closely-packed thin-walled parenchyma cells containing chloroplasts in chains. The epidermis consists of elongated cuticularized cells not perforated by stomata.

The Leaf. Each leaf is enclosed by an epidermis perforated only on the lower side by stomata. Within, the mesophyll is spongy and undifferentiated and each cell usually contains a single, large, cup-shaped chloroplast. Occasionally more than one may arise; each contains at least one pyrenoid-like body at which starch appears to be produced. Through the centre of each leaf, passes an unbranched midrib which originates as a leaf trace on the stele. It leaves no leaf gap. The ligule has a complex structure and is diagrammatically represented in Fig. 13.38.

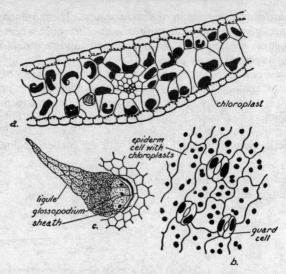

Fig. 13.38. *Selaginella* leaf structure. (*a*) V.S. (*b*) Surface view. H.P. drawings. (*c*) Diagram of ligule.

The Root. Anatomically the rhizophore and root are very similar. A single concentric stele with one protoxylem group is surrounded by an endodermis and outer cortical layer (*see* Fig. 13.39).

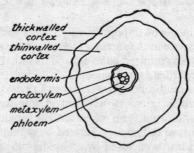

Fig. 13.39. Tissue layout of *Selaginella sp.* rhizophore. L.P. plan of T.S.

Physiology of the Sporophyte

Nutritive processes are normal for the green plant. The main food reserve is starch.

Growth of the main stem is by means of two tetrahedral apical cells, whilst growth of a branch is from one cell of similar shape, formed from a segment of one of the main stem apical cells. The rhizophore has a single apical cell during its early elongation, but this loses its activity when the roots are developed.

The function of the ligule is uncertain but it may serve some purpose of water conservation in young growing-points and around developing sporangia.

Reproductive Structures of the Sporophyte

In the axils of the sporophylls of each strobilus are borne two distinctly different kinds of sporangia. They are distinguishable chiefly by their contents when fully developed. Some sporangia produce a large number of small spores or *microspores* and are called *microsporangia*. The others produce usually four large spores or *megaspores* and are called *megasporangia*. Both kinds occur in the same strobilus, the microsporangia mostly in the upper region, but there is no definite

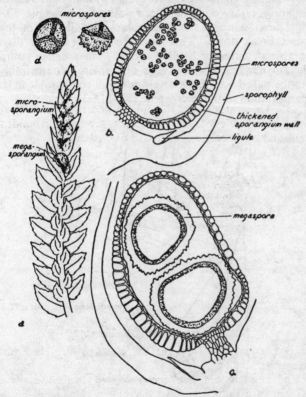

Fig. 13.40. Reproductive structures of *Selaginella*. (*a*) Strobilus. (*b*) L.S. microsporangium. (*c*) L.S. megasporangium. (*d*) Microspore.

rule. Because the *Selaginella* species produce two types of spore they are described as *heterosporous* (cf. the ferns and *Lycopodium spp.* which are homosporous).

Each sporophyll closely resembles a vegetative leaf and bears a ligule. The sporangia arise from groups of cells on the main axis of the strobilus and not on the sporophyll as in *Lycopodium*. Development of both micro- and megasporangia is similar and quite comparable with sporangium development of *Lycopodium*. The wall is a double thickness of cells and during the development, a tapetum internal to this is formed. Centrally placed, are spore mother-cells in large numbers. In the final development of the microsporangia, most of the spore mother-cells undergo meiotic division to produce each a tetrad of haploid spores. When mature, each of these is a tiny tetrahedral two-walled spore showing the characteristic tri-radiate ridging and various other ornamentations on the outer hardened wall surface (*see* Fig. 13.40 (*d*)). In the final development of the megasporangium, all spore mother-cells, except one, break down. This alone undergoes meiotic division to produce a single tetrad of haploid spores. These derive nourishment from the surrounding abortive cells and enlarge considerably, until visible to the naked eye. Each develops a wall comparable in structure and ornamentation to the microspore (*see* Fig. 13.41).

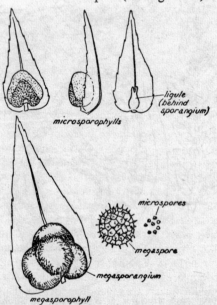

Fig. 13.41. Sporophylls, sporangia and spores of *Selaginella*.

When ripe, the sporangia dehisce by slit-like openings and the spores may be quite violently discharged. This may facilitate cross-fertilization by intermingling spores from neighbouring plants.

Reproduction by the Sporophyte

S. kraussiana sporophytes reproduce only by the formation of asexual spores as described above.

Development of the Spores into the Gametophyte Generation

The two distinctly different kinds of spore develop into distinctly different types of gametophyte. The microspores develop into *male gametophytes* producing male gametes only, whilst the megaspores develop into *female gametophytes* producing female gametes only.

Structure, Physiology and Reproductive Structures of the Male Gametophyte

The development of the male gametophyte from a microspore of several species of *Selaginella* has been carefully recorded on a number of occasions. The precise details need not concern us, but there are

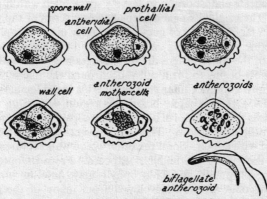

Fig. 13.42. Diagram of the stages in development of the male gametophyte and antherozoids of *Selaginella*.

important features to comprehend. First, *the development is completed entirely within the spore wall* and secondly, *the vegetative part of the gametophyte is reduced to a single cell.*

Development usually commences before the spores are shed. The first division of the spore contents cuts off a small segment to one side. This represents the only vegetative part of the gametophyte and is called the *prothallial cell*. It plays no part in the later events. The other larger cell, known as the *antheridial cell*, continues to divide. From the cells thus formed, a structure equivalent to a single antheridium is produced. This has an outer wall of eight cells enclosing at first four central cells which divide by mitosis into 128 very small antherozoid mother-cells (*see* Fig. 13.42). The antheridium wall disintegrates and the mother-cells lie freely inside the spore wall. From each a tiny, elongated, biflagellate antherozoid develops. By this time, the outer hardened wall of the spore has ruptured along the tri-radiate ridge and the antherozoids are enclosed only by the more delicate inner spore wall. The whole of this development depends upon food stored in the spore by the parent sporophyte.

Structure, Physiology and Reproductive Structures of the Female Gametophyte

The female gametophyte development also commences before the spores are shed and is within the spore wall. By contrast with the male, however, the female gametophyte is large, although no bigger than the spore itself. Development commences when the megaspore protoplast contracts from the wall, the outer layer of which expands away from the more delicate endosporium to leave a space filled with a gelatinous substance. The original single nucleus begins a series of rapid mitoses, to produce a large number of nuclei lying freely in the cytoplasm. The whole structure now expands once more to fill the whole spore space. At the end of the spore, where the three ridges meet, the multinucleate protoplast now begins to form cell walls around the nuclei, converting this region into a multicellular structure. This is the female prothallus (*see* Fig. 13.43). Immediately below this region, extending across the spore, the cells thicken to form a diaphragm separating off the undifferentiated protoplasm below. This latter eventually becomes cellular and charged with starch. Soon the outer spore wall ruptures along the ridges and the female prothallus is exposed. From its outer surface, rhizoids are produced and chlorophyll may develop in the cells. Simple archegonia are now developed from many of the superficial cells. Each has a short protruding neck and a venter embedded in the underlying tissues. This contains the female gamete, the oosphere.

The fact that the female gametophyte may produce chlorophyll and develop rhizoids is of no great nutritional significance. The food material necessary for development of the gametophyte and subsequent development of the embryo is enclosed within the megaspore when it is formed, hence its considerable size in proportion to the microspore. Nutritionally, both gametophytes are dependent on the sporophyte which synthesized the food. This is in sharp contrast to the bryophytes in which the sporophyte is dependent on the gametophyte and to the ferns and lycopods where the gametophytes are nutritionally self-sustaining.

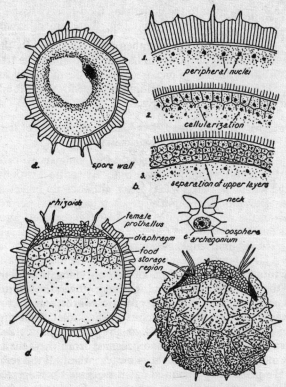

Fig. 13.43. Diagram of the structure of the female gametophyte and archegonia of *Selaginella* and stages in their development.

(a) V.S. megaspore (b) (1, 2, 3) Stages in formation of prothallus tissue. (c) Whole prothallus inside megaspore wall. (d) V.S. of (c). (e) Archegonium.

Reproduction by the Gametophyte Generation

Reproduction by the gametophyte generation is purely sexual and there are no methods by which they can duplicate their own structures. The union of the gametes is effected in the normal way by the motility of the antherozoids. The resulting zygote invests itself with a wall and becomes an oospore seated in the venter of an archegonium. It is the first cell of the diploid sporophyte.

Development of the Zygote into the Sporophyte Generation

After a short rest, the oospore first divides transversely into an upper and a lower cell. This upper cell, nearer the neck of the archegonium, is the *suspensor* and it elongates to push the lower *embryonal cell* through the diaphragm into the underlying food-reserve tissue. Resulting from division of the embryonal cell, there are differentiated, a *stem* whose apex is flanked by *two first leaves*, a *primary root* and an absorbing *foot*. The axis of this embryo is roughly parallel to the

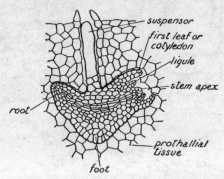

Fig. 13.44. Diagram of the embryo of *Selaginella*.

surface of the prothallus (*see* Fig. 13.44). By elongation of the whole structure, the root emerges to one side and grows downwards, whilst the shoot emerges vertically and grows upwards, carrying the first leaves with it. These first leaves are always somewhat larger than succeeding leaves and are referred to as "cotyledons." The characteristic sporophyte structure is soon formed from the activity of the stem apex and the primary root dies away. When all the reserve substance of the gametophyte is used up, it dies and disintegrates.

Life Cycle

This can be summarized diagrammatically as shown on p. 299.

Adaptation to Environment

The wild *Selaginella* of Great Britain appears to be no more successful than the large club-mosses, when in competition with higher plants. But in the tropics and other temperate regions, the genus has been much more successful and shows a very wide distribution. Some of the species show great xeromorphic modification of the sporophyte. They can grow in the driest of situations and can withstand desiccation for months on end and still regain full activity when wetted once more.

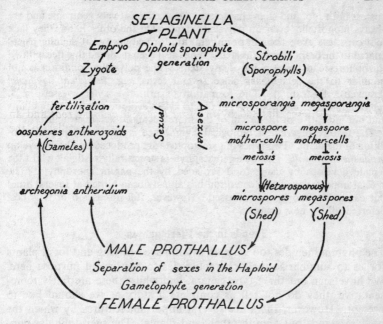

All species show one very great adaptation to the terrestrial existence not shared by any other type genus so far described. The selaginellas are heterosporous and the megaspores are shed from the parent already charged with a large quantity of reserve food, so that their chances of survival and further development are greatly increased. They are not immediately thrown upon their own resources. We shall see that this condition is an early step in the evolution of a much more successful method of sexual reproduction on land, involving the elimination of independent female gametophytes and swimming male gametes.

Special Features of Biological Importance

The selaginellas exhibit several structural similarities to the lycopods, e.g. by being microphyllous, having simple steles with no leaf gaps and in having localized reproductive cones. But there are several important distinctions. In all species, the leaves bear a ligule. We may use this condition once more to indicate relationships with ancient forms. The fossil genus *Selaginellites* is morphologically very similar to the present genus, but many of the larger fossil lycopods also show clear indication of a ligulate condition of the leaves. In such forms, the ligule probably had some biological significance, but it is difficult to understand what it was. The development of rhizophores on the sporophyte is unique among plants. There are no fossil indications as to their origin and morphologically they are difficult to interpret. They possess both root and stem characters. They are positively geotropic and are always monostelic, even on polystelic stems. On the other hand, they lack root caps, are exogenous in origin and are formed always at definite places related to the branching of the stem. It has also been recorded that decapitated rhizophores can develop into leafy stems. The polystelic condition is not peculiar to the selaginellas since several ferns, e.g. *Pteridium aquilinum* (bracken), illustrate it. The formation of primitive xylem vessels in *S. rupicola* must be regarded as a parallel to xylem evolution in flowering plants and not indicative of the origin of the more advanced xylem structure.

The feature of greatest biological significance is the heterosporous condition of the plant. Two types of gametophyte are produced and both develop *inside the spore wall*. The male gametophyte is structurally vestigial, whilst the female develops by using food provided by the parent sporophyte. The special importance of this condition has already been hinted at several times but cannot be too heavily stressed. However, full discussion of it is best deferred till the next chapter.

Trends in the Pteridophyta

The phylum includes too wide an assemblage of living and fossil plants for us to summarize their characteristics to any useful purpose here. We have seen but three type genera, and whilst these are fairly representative, they do not tell as complete a story as we should like to present. However, there are several important features by which the phylum stands out among other land plants. The pteridophytes contrast sharply with the bryophytes in possessing independent sporophyte and gametophyte generations, with the former showing the greater adaptation to the land habit and consequently showing the greater structural complexity. If we seek the origin of the pteridophytes in the bryophytes, we must assume a bryophyte ancestor in which the sporophyte became an independent plant able to adapt itself to terrestrial conditions. No such bryophyte exists today but could have done in an earlier age. By contrast with the spermatophytes, as we shall see, no pteridophyte produces seeds. It was this potentiality, by some pteridophyte ancestor presumably, which gave rise to the dominant vegetation of the world today.

CHAPTER 14

THE SEED HABIT: SPERMATOPHYTA

In the sporophyte generation, the pteridophytes are well adapted to land conditions. Most of them persist satisfactorily with their roots in the soil and their aerial parts in a comparatively dry atmosphere. Their spore dispersal depends on dry conditions. During the gametophyte stages of the life cycle however, they are less able to survive the rigours of such an environment and to reproduce. Many of the gametophytes are unprotected delicate structures which are killed when subjected to drying. The male gametes can only reach the female gametes by swimming through water. Thus the continuity of the pteridophyte life cycle is dependent upon aquatic conditions at one point. The dominant vegetation of the earth at the present time is made up of the plants which, although not greatly more vegetatively advanced in the sporophyte generation, have been able to adapt themselves to the dry conditions in their sexual reproductive stages, by eliminating the independent and vulnerable gametophyte stage and evolving a fertilization mechanism not dependent on swimming male gametes. These are the seed-bearing plants and their origin is presumably in a primitive pteridophyte form. The evolution of the seed habit by these plants undoubtedly accounts for their dominance.

The seed is a reproductive structure composed fundamentally of a protected embryo plant. This embryo develops from a fertilized oosphere of a gametophyte which is at all times, up to full development of the embryo, structurally attached to and physiologically dependent upon a sporophyte. It corresponds to the structure which would have developed in the megaspore of *Selaginella* had the megaspore been embedded in and dependent on the tissues of the sporophyte throughout the whole of the fertilization and embryonic period.

TYPES OF SEED-BEARING PLANTS

There have been three main classes of seed-bearing plants or spermatophytes in the history of the earth's vegetation. These are—

1. The Pteridospermae, or seed-bearing ferns, which had all the vegetative characteristics of pteridophytes but which bore seed-like reproductive structures. All are extinct, but many fossilized remains give us a good picture of their structure (*see* Vol. II, Chap. 20). They form a link between the true ferns and the flowering plants.

301

2. The Gymnospermae, some of which still inhabit the earth. Most are of the tree habit.

3. The Angiospermae, which have achieved the dominant position in the present era.

POSSIBLE STAGES IN THE EVOLUTION OF THE SEED HABIT

To trace the probable lines along which the seed habit has evolved, we must go back to the life cycles exhibited by the thallophytes, bryophytes and pteridophytes. In all these, the most important reproductive and dispersal structure is the haploid spore whose germination gives rise to the gametophyte generation. In these groups, the gametophyte is almost always an independent plant, and particularly in the bryophytes, is more highly specialized than the sporophyte and indeed supports it. In the pteridophytes, this condition is reversed and through them we can trace a gradual reduction in size, specialization and independence of the gametophyte. In the species of *Selaginella*, we see the culmination of this trend. Further, practically all these types were homosporous and the spores gave rise to bisexual gametophytes.

The first steps in the evolution of the seed habit must therefore have been through heterospory, and with this, the change from complete independence of the gametophytes. In such cases, the success of the gametophyte generation must have been due largely to the food received from the sporophyte which, being a more robust plant, less inclined to be killed through desiccation, could give the gametophyte a better chance of survival. Obviously the separation of the gamete-producing organs on different gametophytes must have reduced the chances of successful fertilization so that the step cannot be said to have been an entirely beneficial adaptation. Undoubtedly the swampy conditions under which these early forms were known to have existed, offset this potential handicap to a great extent, so that they were able to survive.

To proceed from this condition, in which food-charged spores were liberated to germinate freely, towards the seed-bearing condition, must next have involved the retention of the megaspore within the megasporangium and the fertilization of its gametes on the parent sporophyte. This was an obvious advantage, since the male gametophytes, if they were small enough, could be wind-borne to the female gametophytes, which were exposed by the opening of the megasporangium wall. Germination of both within the megasporangium would then obviate the difficulties of fertilization when both were shed separately. In conjunction with this, the plant could profit greatly by developing only one megaspore in each megasporangium and so conserve food material. Such a condition is closely paralleled in the modern species *Selaginella apoda* in which the young sporophytes are often formed within the megasporangium on the parent sporophyte.

Thus far, no such plant could be said to be seed-bearing. There is always the development of separate female structures, namely, the

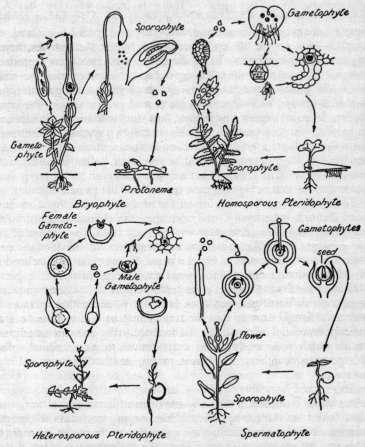

Fig. 14.1. Diagrams of the life cycles of a bryophyte, a homosporous pterido-phyte, a heterosporous pteridophyte and an angiosperm (seed plant).

sporophylls, the megasporangia, the megaspores and the female pro-thallus. The true seed is a structure in which these last three have become compounded into a single reproductive unit, being ultimately detached and dispersed in this state after fertilization and embryo development have been completed. The next steps towards the seed habit, must have been those in which the megasporangium wall gave rise to protective coverings or integuments over the whole structure and became modified for nutritional purposes internally to form a new tissue, the nucellus, within which the megaspore was embedded. The megasporangium did not open to expose the female gametophyte. All these elements, the integuments, the nucellus and the female gameto-phyte form the ovule unit, which when fertilized, becomes the seed. Coupled with such a female reproductive structure, the form and function of the male structure must have undergone equally drastic changes. Transfer of microspores to the vicinity of the enclosed megaspore, and eventual fertilization, necessitated some specialization both of ovule and microspore. Hence there has been the development of the micropyle through which the microspores could be taken into the ovule, a microspore (pollen) chamber in which they could germinate and special adaptation of the microspores to wind-transport by their reduction in size. Having gained access to a pollen chamber and germinated in it, the nutriment necessary for further development could then be drawn by the microspore from the female nucellus by gradually digesting it. This digestion of the nucellus by a special haustorial tube developed by the microspore, then made it possible for swimming gametes to find their way into an archegonial chamber of the megaspore and then to effect fertilization. All these conditions seem to have been evident in the early seed-bearing plants, the pterido-sperms, and the condition in the genus *Cycas*, a primitive gymnosperm to be described in the next chapter, may be said to link modern seed-bearing plants with their ancestors. It must be noted that there have been no changes in the structural relationships of microspore and microsporangium corresponding to those occurring between megaspore and megasporangium. The male structures of even the most advanced of seed-bearing plants, the angiosperms, are clearly seen as the pollen sacs of the stamens, which dehisce to liberate the pollen grains.

The last major change seems to have been that in which the nutri-tional tube developed by the microspore on germination became primarily a means of conveying the male gametes from the microspore chamber to the female gamete, so that the male gametes lost the power of free motility and migrated passively along a fertilization tube which established contact with the oosphere. This might have been due to a change of chemotropic response on the part of the tube which originally functioned as a nutritional organ. This fertilization method is known as siphonogamous as distinct from zoidogamous in which free-swim-ming gametes are involved. This final condition is clearly seen in most gymnosperms and all the angiosperms.

Whilst the angiosperms are true seed-bearing plants, they exhibit striking differences from the more primitive types. These include complete reduction of the female gametophyte to a single mass containing only eight nuclei and the formation of a special nutritive tissue, the endosperm, from the fusion of one male gamete and two female nuclei. Also, whereas in all seed-bearing plants up to and including the gymnosperms, the ovules were attached directly, without protection, to the sporophylls, in the angiosperms, the ovules are further enclosed in a protective case, the ovary, which forms part of an organ called a carpel. Transfer of microspores (pollination) can therefore be only to the outside of this and the fertilization tube must penetrate the carpel before making contact with the ovule inside.

The more obvious advantages of the seed habit are the safe development of the embryo, nourished by the sporophyte under a protective covering which may also be modified to serve in dispersal of the mature seed, and the potentiality of the seed to carry stored food which may last the embryo over the critical period of germination after dispersal.

DISTINCTION BETWEEN GYMNOSPERMS AND ANGIOSPERMS

The names of these two groups of plants stress the chief difference between them. "Gymno-" means "naked" or "exposed," whereas "angio-" means "covered in." The major distinction between them lies therefore in the fact that in the Gymnospermae, the seeds are borne exposed on surfaces of special parts, the megasporophylls, whereas in the Angiospermae, the seeds are borne enclosed within special structures, the carpels. There is no direct fossil evidence to show how this latter condition evolved, but it may be assumed that the angiosperm condition arose somewhere early in the history of the gymnosperms and that the two types of plant have diverged from that point.

There are differences in morphological, anatomical and histological detail between the two groups. Most gymnosperms are of the tree or shrub habit, whereas the angiosperms show every possible variation in this respect. In the gymnosperms, the reproductive parts are concentrated on specialized sporophylls which form the cones or strobili. The characteristic reproductive structure of the angiosperms is the flower.

In the following chapters some detail of structure and function of representatives of both classes will be given.

CHAPTER 15

SPERMATOPHYTES WITH NAKED SEEDS:
THE GYMNOSPERMS; PINUS, TAXUS, CYCAS

EXISTING gymnosperms are represented by five orders and there are two fossil orders of great interest. Of the extant forms, the order Coniferales is by far the most widely represented and species may be found all over the world. They appear in greatest numbers as evergreen trees and shrubs in the northern hemisphere and reach the northernmost limits and highest altitudes at which trees grow. They often show xerophytic characters. They range in size from the giant redwood trees of California to the shrubby juniper. It would appear that the angiosperms have, as it were, pushed the conifers further and further towards the edges of the least favourable land habitats. Among the commoner conifers are the pines, firs, larches, cypresses, cedars, spruces and junipers. *Araucaria*, the monkey-puzzle tree, occurs only in cultivation in this country. The second order, Taxales, is a small one. Most genera are natives of warmer climates but one at least thrives in Europe and North America. The order Cycadales is another small group of gymnosperms now inhabiting localized tropical regions. Their fossilized remains indicate that they were once very widespread. The Ginkgoales are almost extinct, there being but one species remaining in existence, namely *Ginkgo biloba*, the maiden-hair tree. The order Gnetales is another almost extinct tropical group but the representatives show closer relationships with the angiosperms than any of the other living gymnosperms. The fossil orders are the Cordaitales and the Bennettitales.

In this chapter, the genera *Pinus*, *Taxus* and *Cycas* will be described, as representing the first three orders mentioned. The sequence in which they are described has no bearing on their evolutionary history. *Cycas* is undoubtedly the most primitive.

PINUS

The genus includes about seventy-five species. The Scots pine, *Pinus sylvestris*, seems to be the only native British species. Several others have been introduced into this country for forestry and decorative purposes.

Habitat

P. sylvestris is a native of Scotland, where large numbers form open forests in the highlands, but many artificial woods have been formed all over England and Wales as a result of planting by foresters. Isolated specimens are common anywhere in the British Isles. Whilst the pine is a light-loving tree and cannot succeed in partial shade, it will thrive in any well-drained soil, from the dunes on a seashore to inland loams and gravels.

Vegetative Structure of the Sporophyte Generation

External Morphology

When full-grown, the plant, of tree habit, may reach a height of 30 m or more. The main stem or *trunk* is covered with rugged brown-red *bark* and is monopodially branched, having continuous indefinite growth of the main axis (*see* Chap. 17). The secondary branches, produced successively year by year, tend to arise more or less in whorls. This arrangement of branches in young trees is very pronounced and results in the typical conical outline of most conifers. With age, many lower branches may die and some grow irregularly, so that the outline of the tree lacks any symmetry and most of the growth is at higher levels.

If a young shoot is examined, it will be seen to be composed of two kinds of branches and to bear two kinds of leaves. On the *main stem*, which shows unlimited growth, are borne small brown *scale-leaves* in spiral arrangement, and in the axils of these, developed from small buds, are very much shortened branches or *dwarf shoots* (foliar spurs) of limited growth. Around the base of each dwarf shoot are more scale leaves which protect it, and from its apex arise two *foliage leaves* (*see* Fig. 15.1). In other species of *Pinus*, the number of foliage leaves on each dwarf shoot varies between one and five. *Pinus strobus* (Weymouth pine) has leaves in fives. This morphology can best be made out in young shoot apices during their early elongation in the spring of each year. Soon after elongation, the scale leaves bearing the dwarf shoots in their axils, having served their protective function in the bud stage, fall away and leave only a small scar at the base of each dwarf shoot (*see* Fig. 15.1 (*b*)). Around the base of a *terminal bud* there may be one or several *lateral buds* which develop into normal branches instead of foliar spurs. If these develop vegetatively, they become lateral branches.

Each foliage leaf is a dark green "needle," with a distinctly pointed end (acicular). Each has the shiny look associated with a thick cuticle and is grooved along its length. In section, it is roughly semi-circular, with the flattened faces of the two leaves on each spur being pressed together in the bud. The leaves function for several years. When eventually shed, the whole dwarf shoot is abscissed with them and the scars may be seen persisting for some years on older naked parts.

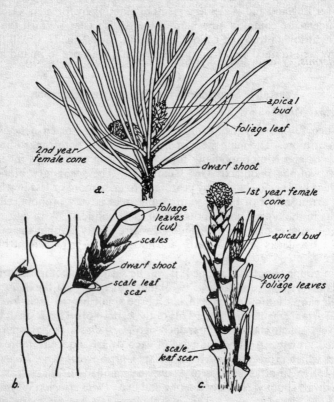

Fig. 15.1. Vegetative morphology of *Pinus*. (*a*) Tip of twig bearing a young female cone. (*b*) Details of dwarf shoot insertion. (*c*) Expanding apical bud.

The root system is usually very extensive but originally is a *tap root* system with many laterals. Not infrequently, the tap root may fail to penetrate very deeply and the laterals spread widely instead.

A fertile tree bears reproductive male and female *cones*, both very distinctive when mature.

Anatomy

The Stem. Anatomically, the vegetative body is comparable in every way with that of an angiosperm and shows *secondary growth* from an

early age in stem and root. Details of how such secondary growth is
made from lateral cambia can be found in Chap. 17 and will not be
anticipated in detail here.

The arrangement of the tissues as seen in a transverse section of the
primary stem is as shown in Fig. 15.2. The irregularity in outline is due
to the cutting through of closely-crowded dwarf shoots. Externally,
the stem is covered by a thickened *epidermis* beneath which is a lignified
hypodermis. Within these layers, is a band of softer parenchyma cells

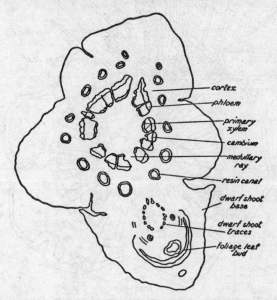

Fig. 15.2. Tissue layout in young *Pinus* stem. L.P. plan of T.S.

constituting the *cortex*. Forming a single ring inside the cortex are
about sixteen *vascular bundles* separated from one another by rays of
parenchyma, the *primary medullary rays*. These connect the outer
cortex with the central pith or *medulla* which is also parenchymatous
and may contain stored starch. There is no endodermis or pericycle
to mark the outer limit of the central cylinder, but within the cortex are
a number of *resin canals*. Each vascular bundle is *collaterally* formed,
that is, with primary xylem, cambium and primary phloem radially
disposed in that order with the xylem innermost.

The xylem is composed of small groups of spirally thickened tracheids
forming the protoxylem in the innermost position, and reticulately
thickened tracheids forming the primary metaxylem outside. Bordered

pits occur on the xylem elements but are larger and more closely crowded in the later-formed xylem cells. External to the xylem lies the *vascular cambium*, a meristematic layer which becomes active to produce secondary vascular tissues. The phloem consists of short sieve elements with sieve areas on longitudinal and end walls. There are no companion cells, but phloem parenchyma cells are present. Unless the stem is very young, the outer protophloem cannot be distinguished

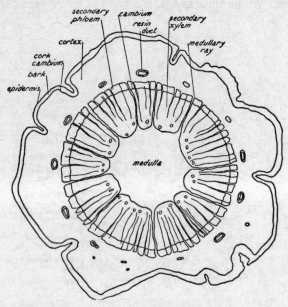

Fig. 15.3. Tissue layout in secondarily thickened stem of *Pinus*. L.P. plan of T.S.

from the inner metaphloem, the distinction having been obliterated by expansion of the tissues. Each resin canal is a duct of sclerified cells lined by secretory cells whose activity fills the duct with the sweet-smelling turpentine substance characteristic of the pines. In some sections, leaf traces to the scale leaves and branch bundles to the dwarf shoots can be seen.

Sections of older stems exhibit the structure after secondary growth has commenced. A composite diagram showing views in the transverse, radial longitudinal and tangential longitudinal planes is shown in Fig. 15.6. Details of the various tissues appear in the other Figures.

The epidermis is replaced by a thick layer of corky cells to form a *phellem* or bark. This is formed from the underlying *phellogen* or *cork cambium* which cuts off the corky cells on its outer side and a few radial rows of soft parenchyma cells on its inner side. This last zone of tissue is the *phelloderm*. Within these tissues lies the more solid-looking vascular cylinder, constituted largely of secondarily produced tissues resulting from the activity of the vascular cambium of each of the original primary bundles. Briefly, the secondary vascular tissues are differentiated from cells produced on the tangential faces of the cambial cells which are in active division. The cells inner to the cambium become *secondary xylem* and those outer become *secondary phloem*. This cambial activity commences first within the region of each bundle but gradually extends circumferentially from each bundle until a complete cambial ring is formed. This continues to cut off cells which differentiate as stated so that the once discrete bundles are now connected laterally to form a complete ring of vascular elements. The tissues of the original vascular bundles continue to exist to the interior and exterior of this ring until eventually they are obliterated. Not all the cambial cells produce potential tracheid or sieve elements. At many points, a few cambial cells in vertical series may continuously produce

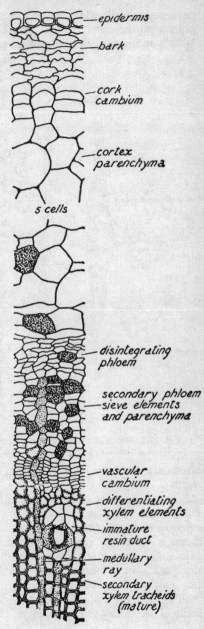

Fig. 15.4. Old *Pinus* stem. H.P. drawing of T.S.

parenchyma cells which extend as radial rays through the xylem and phloem to the outer tissues. These are the *secondary medullary rays*. Within all the secondary tissues more resin canals are developed so that

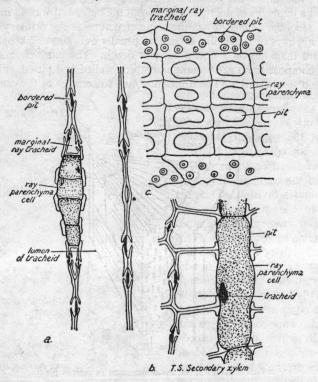

Fig. 15.5. Detail of tracheid and ray parenchyma of *Pinus*. H.P. drawings. (*a*) T.L.S. secondary xylem (*b*) T.S. secondary xylem (*c*) R.L.S. medullary ray.

ultimately the whole stem is permeated by vertical and horizontal resin ducts.

Secondary xylem is composed entirely of tracheids with bordered pits on the radial walls. There are no vessels. Their characteristic square or oblong shape in radial rows as seen in the cross-section, forms a close-knit tissue broken only by medullary rays and resin canals. The xylem elements are not all of the same size or equally thickened. In a stem several years old, alternating wide bands of tracheids with large cavities and narrow bands of thick-walled tracheids with small cavities occur. These mark the termination and commencement of secondary growth each year and are called *growth rings*. The age of the stem may be ascertained by counting them   The trunk of the Californian bigtree in the British Natural History Museum indicates that it lived during the period 557 to 1892 A.D., that is 1335 years. It reached a diameter of 4·9 m at 5·4 m from the base, and was 83 m high.

The secondary phloem has the same structure as the primary. The medullary rays of secondary origin are usually only one cell broad and no more than ten or a dozen cells in depth. The parenchyma cells which compose them are rectangular, thick-walled and pitted. Each is alive and stores starch. The uppermost and lowermost of the cells in a

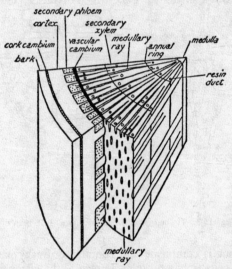

Fig. 15.6. Diagram of old *Pinus* stem seen in various planes.

series through the xylem elements are different from the central ones and resemble short xylem tracheids with their axes horizontal. They are known as *marginal ray-tracheids*. Where the ray traverses cambium and phloem these cells differ again and are larger, thin-walled parenchyma cells containing protein substance. Apparently, they serve a storage purpose and are known as *albuminous cells*.

The Leaf. A transverse section through a leaf shows that it is bounded by a thick-walled epidermis, heavily cuticularized. This is perforated by stomata sunk deeply in the longitudinal furrows of the leaf surface. A hypodermis, one or two layers of sclerenchyma, toughens the outer region. In a transverse section, the mesophyll shows no differentiation but is composed of tightly-packed parenchyma cells containing abundant chloroplasts. Resin canals permeate the mesophyll. Under each stoma is a characteristically U-shaped mesophyll cell outlining the sub-stomatal air space. The mesophyll cells have curiously infolded walls whereby the internal surface area of the cells is increased considerably. In longitudinal section, the compactness of the tissue is seen to be broken by air spaces and in fact the chlorophyll-bearing cells are arranged roughly in transverse plates so that air can circulate readily throughout the leaf. In the centre is the vascular tissue, marked off by an endodermis and a pericycle of several layers. Within this, are two vascular bundles which are parallel through the length of the leaf. They arise from a single leaf trace which divides at the leaf base. The

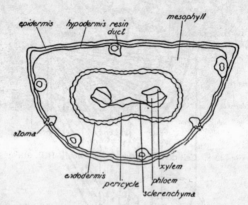

Fig. 15.7. Tissue layout in leaf of *Pinus*. L.P. plan of T.S.

pericycle tissue is composite and contains ordinary parenchyma cells, parenchyma cells rich in proteins, known as the *albuminous cells*, which abut on the phloem groups of the vascular bundles, and empty *tracheidal cells* with thickened walls showing bordered pits, adjacent to the xylem groups. The tissue collectively is termed *transfusion tissue* and may function in a vascular capacity. Each vascular bundle is made up of a group of xylem tracheids nearer the flattened surface of the leaf and a group of phloem elements nearer the rounded face. The two bundles are usually linked by a band of sclerenchyma. The whole leaf structure indicates xerophytism (*see* Chap. 17).

The Root. A transverse section of the young root appears as in Fig. 15.9 (*a*). It is similar in structure to the generalized dicotyledonous angiosperm root as described in Chap. 17, except that it is permeated by resin canals. It may be diarch or triarch, and older roots show secondary growth. At the root tip is a normal root cap and behind the meristematic apex, root hairs develop. It is not infrequently found that

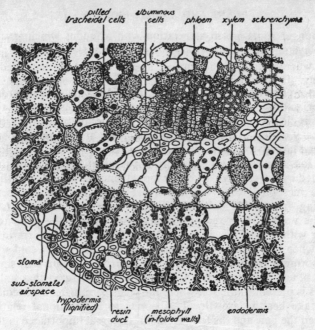

Fig. 15.8. Cell detail in part of *Pinus* leaf. H.P. drawing

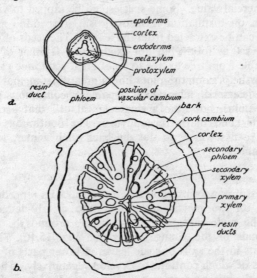

Fig. 15.9. Tissue layout n (*a*) young and (*b*) old root of *Pinus*. L.P. plans of T.S.

the younger roots are in association with a fungus which invests the outer layers, forming an *ectotrophic mycorrhiza* (*see* Chap. 34).

Physiology of the Sporophyte

The general physiological characteristics of the pine are similar in most respects to those of the higher flowering plants. It must be noted though, that it is clearly a xerophyte. The great reduction in leaf surface area, the heavy cuticularization of the leaf surface and the sunken stomata confined largely to grooves in the leaf surface, all point to restriction of water loss from the leaf. Loss of photosynthetic tissue is partly compensated by the closely packed mesophyll and the ingrowth of the walls of the mesophyll cells which increases their internal surfaces, thus allowing greater efficiency of the very numerous chloroplasts which line the walls. Their xerophytic character enables the pines to over-winter without leaf abscission and without coming to harm in conditions when water may be difficult to absorb from a very cold soil.

In forming an association with a mycorrhizal fungus it is similar to many other forest trees and it has been demonstrated that unless the fungus is present in the soil where the seeds germinate, the seedling will not make healthy growth. This points to a nutritional relationship between the pine and the fungus which is of great importance to the tree.

Various products of metabolism of the pines are of interest because of their commercial value. Some species can be tapped to yield an oleo-resin which on distillation furnishes rosin, turpentine and pine oil. Useful oils can be extracted from the leaves. The seeds of some species have been used as foods, but not extensively. Timber of *P. sylvestris* is too variable from tree to tree to be of great economic value.

The growth form of the pine differs greatly from that of any type previously described. The pine is capable of continuous growth from apical meristems, not from a single apical cell that occurs in most pteridophytes and in the bryophytes. The continuous addition of secondary tissues which do not die back each winter, results in the arboreal habit.

Reproductive Structures of the Sporophyte

P. sylvestris is monoecious and heterosporous. Its reproductive *spores* are borne on *sporophylls* aggregated into clearly-defined *cones* or *strobili*. The male cones appear in clusters around the bases of the terminal buds of the young shoots (*see* Fig. 15.10). They replace dwarf shoots in the axils of scale leaves in lower parts of the bud, the upper parts of which continue to develop vegetatively. They mature in spring and the *microspores*, or *pollen grains* as they are called, are shed in vast numbers. The female cones are initially developed each year

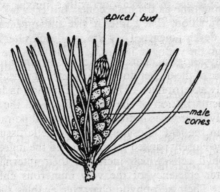

Fig. 15.10. Group of male cones of *Pinus*.

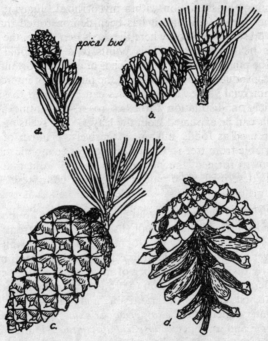

Fig. 15.11. Female cones of *Pinus*. (*a*) Very young cone. (*b*) Cone at end of first year, commencement of second. (*c*) Cone at end of second year, commencement of third. (*d*) Cone at end of third year.

at about the same time as the male cones. but they take three years to complete their function. They differ in size and appearance at different stages of their development. They are produced laterally in the axils of scale leaves on the young branches, separate from the male cones and usually only one or two develop on a branch. When the female reproductive structures are fully formed, they are *megaspores* in *megasporangia* on the *sporophylls*.

The Male Cone

Each male cone consists of a short axis carrying around its base a few scale leaves and above these, in spiral succession, as many as one hundred microsporophylls. When dissected out, each of these appears

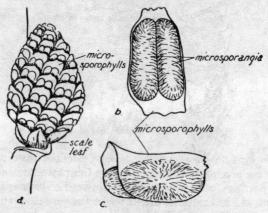

Fig. 15.12. Male cone of *Pinus*. (*a*) Whole cone. (*b*) and *c*) Lower and side views of sporophyll.

as in Fig. 15.12. The microsporangia or *pollen sacs* are borne in pairs on the undersides of the sporophylls. Each arises from a group of initial cells and during early development has an outer wall enclosing a tapetal layer and central archesporial tissue. This central mass of cells gives rise by division to a number of microspore mother-cells each of which undergoes meiotic division to produce four microspores or pollen grains. At first, each pollen grain is a single cell with a three-layered wall, an outer cuticularized *exosporium* or *exine*, a middle *mesosporium* or *exo-intine* and an inner *endosporium* or *intine*. During maturation, the mesosporium becomes distended away from the endosporium to form two large air-filled sacs, and externally the whole structure appears as in Fig. 15.18. The air-sacs aid in wind-dispersal, by making the whole grain very buoyant. A certain degree of development into the male gametophyte generation occurs inside the pollen grain before it is shed. Liberation of the pollen grains is achieved by the longitudinal splitting of the microsporangia. When ripe, the male cones are yellow in colour. The male cone can be interpreted as corresponding

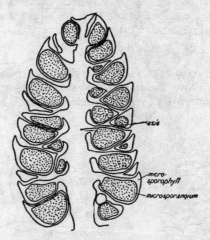

Fig. 15.13. L.S. *Pinus* male cone. L.P. plan.

to an angiosperm flower in which only the essential male organs are present. These are not differentiated into the characteristic filament and anther portions, only two pollen-sacs instead of four arise and the receptacle on which the organs are developed is very elongated.

The Female Cone

A female cone is similarly composed of spirally arranged outgrowths on a central axis. When young, it is quite small and green tinged with brown in colour. Each outgrowth is composite in nature, being made up of two types of scales; a leathery *bract scale* growing from the axis and a larger, woody *ovuliferous scale* growing from its upper surface (*see* Fig. 15.14). The ovuliferous scale is narrow at the base and wider and thicker towards its extremity. As it enlarges, the bract scale becomes hidden. This is not so in some conifers where the bract scales can be seen protruding out of the fully developed cones, e.g. larch (*Larix*), and fir (*Abies*). The morphological nature of this double structure is not easy to elucidate but has been explained as being equivalent to the two leaves on a dwarf shoot. Borne on the upper surface of the ovuliferous scale are two *ovules* lying side by side. An ovule originates from a few superficial cells of the scale which are rapidly

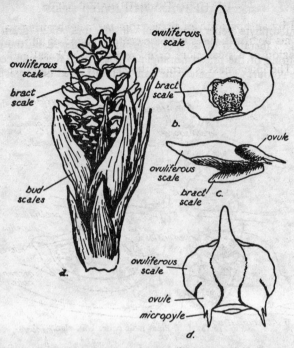

Fig. 15.14. (*a*) Young female cone of *Pinus*. (*b*), (*c*), and (*d*) Underside, lateral and upperside views of scales.

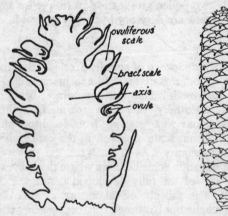

Fig. 15.15. L.S. very young female cone of *Pinus*. L.P. plan.

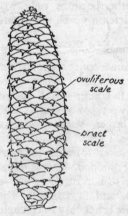

Fig. 15.16. Mature cone of *Abies*.

enclosed by an upgrowth of tissue from the neighbouring part of the scale. This upgrowth fuses with the central mound at all points except in the region of a small pore or *micropyle* at the basal end (*see* Fig. 15.17). The inner mass is termed the *nucellus* and the outer covering

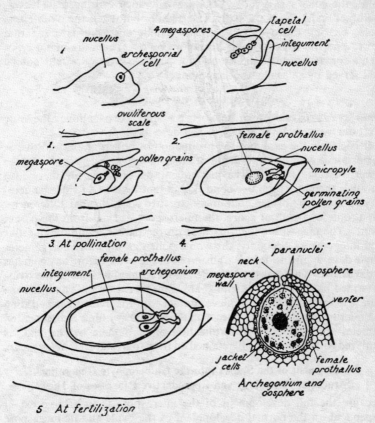

Fig. 15.17. Diagram of the stages in development of an ovule of *Pinus*.

the *integument*. Lying near the micropylar end of the nucellus is a single large *archesporial cell*. By its first division, this cuts off a single *tapetal cell* and a *megaspore mother-cell*. The latter divides meiotically to produce a row or linear tetrad of four potential *megaspores*. One of these develops as the megaspore, complete with wall. The nucellus and integument correspond to a megasporangium wall so that an ovule can be regarded as a modified megasporangium and its contents.

The female cone can be interpreted either as a single flower or as a whole inflorescence. If the cone axis is looked upon as a receptacle and the bract scales as open carpels bearing the ovules on ligular outgrowths, the ovuliferous scales, then the whole cone is a flower. If, on the other hand, the cone axis is looked upon as a branch bearing scale-leaves, the bract scales, in whose axils arise smaller branches, the ovuliferous scales bearing the ovules, then each ovuliferous scale is a separate flower and the whole cone is an inflorescence. There are many arguments for and against these opposing views but space would not be well served by enlarging on them here.

Reproduction by the Sporophyte

Pinus sylvestris has no means of vegetative propagation; the only reproductive structures are those just described.

It is clearly the case that the production of pollen grains and ovules corresponds with the production of microspores and megaspores by the lower vascular plants. The subsequent development of these also parallels the more primitive condition in that male and female gametophytes are also formed, but there are two very distinct differences. First, only one kind of spore, the microspore, is shed from the parent plant. The megaspore is firmly held on the parent inside the nucellus and integument. Secondly, the whole pollen grain, with male gametophyte developing inside it, is transferred to the ovule before any gametes are released. This transfer of pollen grain from pollen sac to the ovule is termed *pollination*. The grains are transported by the wind, i.e. the pine is *anemophilous*, and achieve contact with the ovule by penetrating the micropyle and coming to rest on the nucellus within. Subsequently, gametes are produced and fertilization of the female by the male is achieved with the former still retained on the parent plant (cf. *Selaginella*).

Development of the Spores into the Gametophyte Generations: Structure, Physiology and Reproductive Processes of These

Because the full development of the microspore is to a large extent dependent on the normal development of the ovule and its megaspore and vice versa, and because the whole sequence of the reproductive process can best be visualized when both spore developments are taken in conjunction, there is no attempt here to treat them independently. It is convenient to describe first the events in the microspore before and immediately after pollination, then follow with the stages of development of the megaspore until the female gametes are ready for fertilization, and conclude with final development of the microspore which effects this act.

The microspore commences development before it is shed, during

May of the year of its formation. Inside the wall, the protoplast divides into a small *prothallial cell* and a larger *tube cell*. At this stage, development ceases until after pollination, but once the microspore has gained entry through the micropyle of the ovule, the tube cell divides

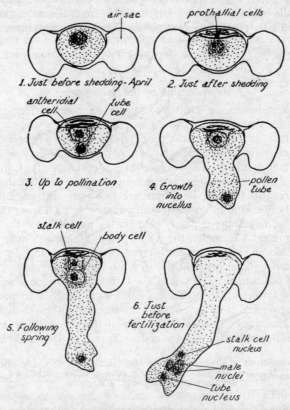

1. Just before shedding - April
2. Just after shedding
3. Up to pollination
4. Growth into nucellus
5. Following spring
6. Just before fertilization

air sac
prothallial cells
antheridial cell
tube cell
pollen tube
stalk cell
body cell
stalk cell nucleus
male nuclei
tube nucleus

Fig. 15.18. Diagram of the stages in development of a pollen grain of *Pinus*.

again to produce one more small prothallial cell. The prothallial cells are of no significance functionally but are vestigial structures representing the vegetative part of a male gametophyte (cf. *Selaginella*). They soon disappear, whilst the tube cell divides yet again to cut off an *antheridial cell* which does not develop further until the following spring. The tube cell, however, grows out to form a tube-like structure penetrating into the tissue of the nucellus on which the microspore is resting.

During the pollination period and subsequent to it, the megaspore inside the ovule continues its development. It enlarges considerably within its membrane to form a bulky vacuolated cell, which is termed an *embryo sac* by reason of its similarity to the corresponding angiosperm structure. Its nucleus divides repeatedly to form more than two thousand nuclei which lie evenly spaced in the peripheral cytoplasm. Soon walls begin to appear; first inwards from the megaspore membrane and later parallel to its surface. They delimit separate cells. The

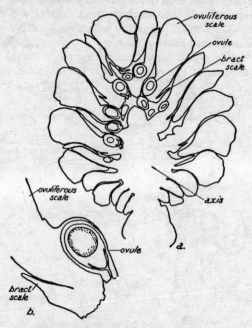

Fig. 15.19. (a) L.S. Second year female cone of *Pinus* (slightly off centre). (b) Section of *Pinus* ovule. L.P. plans.

cells in this single layer now divide repeatedly so that more and more are formed to encroach on the empty central portion of the embryo sac and eventually they fill it. These cells form the tissue of the female gametophyte (*see* Fig. 15.17). From cells towards the micropylar end, three or four *archegonia* are produced. They are very simple, being composed of an embedded *venter* and a short *neck* without neck canal cells. In the venter are the *oosphere* and *ventral canal cell*. During the development of the gametophyte, the nucellar tissue surrounding it acts in a nutritive capacity and becomes spongy except at the micropylar end, where a conical mass of starch-storing cells forms a beak-like projection into the micropylar aperture. It is on this tissue that the microspores are resting. Their entry through the micropyle is aided by activity of the female cone and the ovules. Prior to pollination, the female cone scales are closely adherent around the cone axis, but during the time when the microspores are being released, the edges of the scales roll inwards, so forcing gaps between the scales. Thus microspores can settle between them. Later they enlarge and close up again, but whilst they are open, each ovule secretes a minute drop of mucilage through its micropyle. In this mucilage, some microspores are trapped. As the mucilage dries up, it draws the pollen grains down through the micropyle on to the nucellus.

All the foregoing events have been taking place during the spring, summer and autumn of the year in which the male and female cones

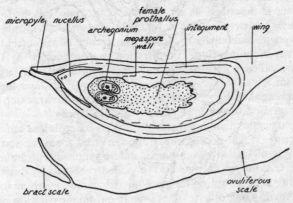

Fig 15.20. L.S. ovule of *Pinus* at the fertilization stage. L.P. plan.

were first formed. Having shed their microspores, the male cones wither and drop off, but the female cones remain on the tree and in the condition described above, they overwinter without further development. In the following April, activity recommences. In the microspore, a further division of the antheridial cell produces a structure which may be regarded as an *antheridium* on a short *stalk cell* (*see* Fig. 15.18). The latter develops no further but the nucleus of the antheridium divides mitotically yet again and the cytoplasm cleaves to form two unequal cells. These correspond to antherozoid mother-cells of more fully organized male structures, but without further change they function as *male gametes*. Meanwhile, the short tube which had grown into the nucellus of the ovule the previous year, also recommences growth and continues its penetration towards the female gametophyte. Into this tube pass the two male cells and the stalk cell nucleus so that with the tube nucleus already there, four nuclei are contained in the advancing tip of the tube. The tube continues to lengthen, often branching, until its tip reaches the neck of an archegonium. It penetrates this as far as the venter. Here it ruptures and all the contents disintegrate, except one of the male cells. The nucleus of the remaining male cell now passes to the oosphere and the male and female nuclei unite to complete the act of fertilization and form the diploid zygote. Although more than one oosphere may be fertilized in this way by other microspores, only one zygote develops further. Fertilization is usually completed by the end of June in the year following pollination.

Special note must be taken of the fertilization mechanism. All types described previous to this have been dependent on free-swimming male gametes to find and fuse with the female nucleus. Such a fertilization mechanism is described as *zoidogamous*. In *Pinus* species free-swimming male gametes are not developed. They are first brought into proximity with the female organs by the agency of air currents during the process of pollination. Fertilization is then effected by the tube, sometimes called a pollen-tube, and by reason of this, the fertilization mechanism is called *siphonogamous*. The need for water-films is no longer apparent and the whole mechanism is an obvious step towards fuller adaptation to the conditions of the dry land.

Physiologically, neither gametophyte is an independent self-supporting structure. Each microspore, although freed from the sporophyte, is incapable of further development unless supplied with nourishment from the nucellus of an ovule. The pollen tube acts in this capacity, penetrating and disrupting the nucellar tissue and absorbing food from it. The female gametophyte is not even free from the parent sporophyte. For the whole period of its development, it is nourished by, and attached to, the sporophyte. By comparison with the Bryophyta, it can be seen that the relative positions of the sporophyte and gametophyte have become reversed.

Development of the Zygote into the Sporophyte Generation

Immediately after its formation, the zygote becomes an oospore and commences its development into the embryo. This occurs inside the ovule which is still on the parent plant. It is a complicated process and full details will not be given here. Reference may be made to the diagrams in Fig. 15.21. The zygotic nucleus divides mitotically three times, to produce eight nuclei. These lie in the oospore away from the micropylar end, arranged in two tiers of four. The lower four become delimited by intervening cell walls: the upper four lie freely and take no further part in embryo development. The four lower cells each divide twice to delimit above themselves two more tiers of four cells. Of these three tiers, the lowermost are termed the *embryonal cells*, those above are the *suspensor cells*, and the highest the *rosette cells*. By considerable elongation of the suspensor cells, the embryonal cells are

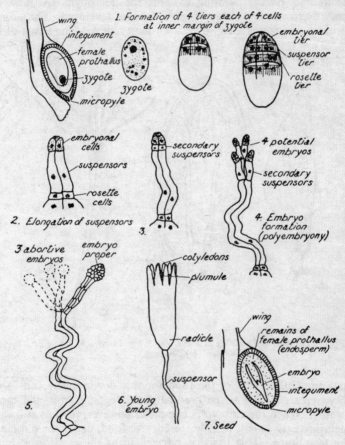

Fig. 15.21. Diagram of stages in embryo and seed development of *Pinus*.

thrust deeply into the tissue of the female gametophyte. Here, each embryonal cell elongates separately and cuts off at its base a long cell termed a *secondary suspensor*. At the tip of each secondary suspensor, the other cell commences rapid division to build up an embryonic structure, so that initially, four embryos commence development. This is the condition of *polyembryony*, which is characteristic of the conifers.

Normally, there is only sufficient nourishment for one of them to mature, so that three abort at an early stage.

The successful embryo differentiates from a cell mass into a straight axis, with its *shoot apex* or *plumule* away from the micropylar end of the ovule and its *radicle* pointing towards the micropyle. Around the plumule five to ten first leaves or *cotyledons* are developed. The suspensor withers and forms a cap over the young radicle. The tissue of the

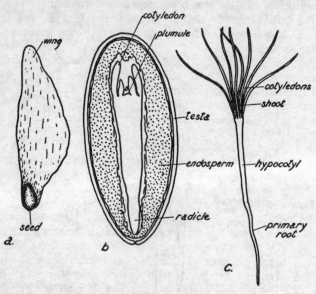

Fig. 15.22. Seed and seedling of *Pinus*. (*a*) Winged seed. (*b*) L.S. seed., L.P. plan. (*c*) Seedling.

female prothallus supplies the food for this development and as the embryo enlarges, this tissue gradually disintegrates from the centre outwards. When the embryo is complete, however, there is still some gametophyte tissue left, heavily stored with food, under the old megaspore membrane. This tissue is referred to as the *endosperm*, but it must be noted that it is not homologous with the true endosperm of an angiosperm, since it originates in the female gametophyte.

Whilst the embryo has been developing, the integument of the ovule has begun to differentiate into hard stony cells, so that by the time the embryo is complete, it is protected externally by a hard coat or *testa*. The whole structure is now a true *seed*. During the later stages, the female cone has altered its nature also and the ovuliferous scales have changed from fairly soft, green tissue to a hard, dry, woody condition. Each scale bears two ripening seeds on its upper surface and to each seed is attached a thin papery wing derived from the outer layer of the ovuliferous scale (*see* Fig. 15.22). As the whole cone dries out, the scales bend outwards away from the axis to expose the winged seeds. These now break contact with the scale and are free to be shaken out. The wing aids in their dispersal by the wind.

The maturation of the seed occupies a period extending over another year after fertilization, so that all the processes leading up to mature seed formation have lasted through three growing periods in the following sequence—

1. Male and female cone formation with production of microspores and megaspores; pollination; gametophyte development.

2. Fertilization; commencement of embryo formation.

3. Maturation of the seed; seed dispersal.

Year by year, the female cone enlarges and changes form and can be clearly recognized as a first, second or third year cone.

If conditions of moisture and temperature are correct, pine seeds germinate quickly after dispersal. Growth of the radicle ruptures the testa at the micropylar end and the radicle emerges to penetrate the soil. Elongation of the axis follows, to bring the plumule and enlarging cotyledons above soil level, carrying with them the remains of the disrupted testa and endosperm. The cotyledons become green and commence food synthesis. The germination is described as *epigeal* (*see* Chap. 17). When properly established, the plumule develops into the shoot, bearing at first delicate, single, spirally-arranged, needle-like leaves. The first dwarf shoots, with their pairs of needles, do not appear until the axis is about 7 to 8 cm long, when the adult form is achieved and maintained throughout life. Within the seed, growth of the plumule is at first from a single apical cell, but this soon gives way to an apical meristem from which all primary growth is derived. These two conditions of single initial apical cell in the shoot and the development of single leaves at first, may be regarded as primitive characteristics recapitulating the ancestral condition.

Life Cycle

The diagram on p. 330 summarizes the life cycle.

Adaptation to Environment

The pine tree is structurally, physiologically, in its reproductive processes and life cycle, well adapted to land conditions. It is much more so adapted than any plant so far described in this text. The principal adaptations to the land environment to be looked for in any plant are

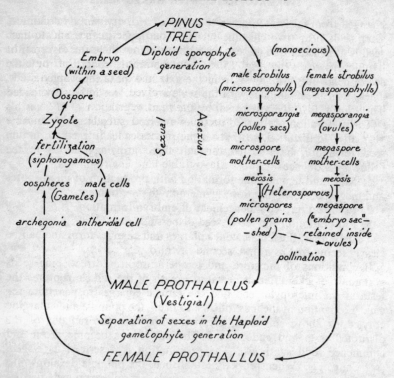

in relation to its physical contact with the surroundings, its means of body support and internal translocating mechanism, its powers of water conservation and whether the fertilization process is dependent on liquid water films. The pine shows the normal root, stem and leaf organization consistent with good contact with the soil and the atmosphere. It has evolved as a plant of considerable stature; it is a tree. It develops the mechanical and vascular tissues necessary for support and translocation of materials. The pine continuously adds secondary tissues which differentiate in the correct proportions to maintain the whole as an evenly-regulated structure, well able to withstand buffeting. In its powers of water conservation, it excels many other plants. It can develop successfully as an evergreen plant in relatively poor, dry soils. It shows special modifications which enable it to reduce the effects of these poor water conditions and is described as a xerophyte. The leaves, from which the largest proportion of water could be expected to be lost, are reduced in surface area to "needle" form and protected externally by a heavy layer of cutin. The trunk is protected by a suberized bark. The reproductive processes of the pine do not demand the presence of water films through which one gamete can reach another. The necessity is eliminated by the liberation and air-borne dispersal of the microspores followed by the siphonogamous delivery of the male gamete to the female gamete, which is retained on the sporophyte.

As such well-adapted spermatophytes evolved, they gradually tended to oust the pteridophytes as the dominant vegetation of the earth's land surface. But the gymnosperms were later subjected to the same kind of competition from the angiosperms and it is these which have assumed the dominant position today and have gradually forced the gymnosperms into the less favourable land environments.

Special Features of Biological Importance

The pines illustrate many features of biological importance but two only will be stressed here. These are the primitive nature of the seed habit when compared with the angiosperms, and the tree habit.

The Primitive Seed Habit

Whilst in essentials the seed habit is fully displayed by the pines, there are several features which indicate a closer link with the earliest of seed-bearing plants than is shown by the angiosperms. In the pines, the reproductive parts are aggregated into strobili. Although these may be taken as representing flowers, they do not show the special features associated with the highly characteristic angiosperm flowers. They are unisexual and have not evolved in association with insects. Pollination is by wind agency and there is great wastage of microspores. Reduction of the gametophyte is not fully complete and archegonia are developed in the ovule. The ovule is naked. It must not be thought that the pines represent a direct step on the evolutionary path to the angiosperm condition. Both may have possessed a common ancestor, but the conifer condition undoubtedly represents an evolutionary divergence from the main line which eventually gave rise to the angiosperms.

The Tree Habit

Among the earth's vegetation at the present time, the tree habit is confined chiefly to the dicotyledonous angiosperms and the conifers among the gymnosperms, although a few other types may exhibit it. There are a few tree ferns still in existence, e.g. *Dicksonia; Ginkgo*, a gymnosperm, is a stately tree and monocotyledonous angiosperms are represented by the palms. The fossil record shows that the tree form was well represented among the pteridophytes. The giant horsetails and lycopods grew in abundance in the Carboniferous period (*see* Vol. II, Chap. 20).

The trees which exist today are woody perennials distinguished from the herbs by possessing parts which overwinter above ground, and from the shrubs by a much greater stature and a single main trunk. The tree form is the most complex state of plant organization ever evolved and the successful trees may be regarded as the dominant vegetation in areas which support their growth, in the sense that they have a greater effect on other vegetation of the vicinity than any other plant form.

A plant of tree habit has several advantages over other forms. By reason of its stature, it is better able to compete for light and air. Its reproductive parts are more elevated and can be dispersed over wide areas. A tree normally has a long life and can reproduce over a period of many years, thus tending to further its continuance as a species. On the other hand, there are disadvantages when compared with the herbaceous plant. By perennating with parts above ground, those parts are subjected to the dangers of exposure during the worst periods of the year. Protection must be afforded if the tree is not to suffer. The deciduous condition and the formation of well-protected winter buds both serve this protective purpose. The pine can only exist as an evergreen by reason of the fact that its leaves are highly frost-resistant and are specially modified to curtail water loss when water may be in short supply in a cold soil. Another disadvantage of the tree is that it is usually slow to come to fruit. Several or many years may pass before a tree is mature and in that period it must survive all the hazards of nature which tend to extinguish it before it has had a chance to reproduce its kind.

TAXUS

This is a genus of only one species, *T. baccata*, the yew. There are a number of slightly differing forms of the species which may be regarded as sub-species. Some authorities would seek to elevate seven of the sub-species to species chiefly on distribution grounds. The yews are evergreen trees or shrubs widely distributed in Europe, Asia and North America. It is not necessary to give such a detailed treatment as has been given for *Pinus sylvestris* since they have certain similarities of life history and only the more obvious differences between the yews and the pines need be stressed.

Yew trees are most often found singly in nature and yew forests are rare. In cultivation, they are common evergreens in ornamental gardens and are frequently associated with churchyards. The reason for this has never been quite clear but we would offer the suggestion that yews were planted in cemeteries to ensure that farmers would keep their cattle out since the foliage is poisonous, or alternatively that it could only thrive there naturally because farmers would destroy all specimens in the fields and hedges. Very large yew trees with ages estimated at well over one thousand years have been recorded.

The chief morphological difference between *Taxus* and *Pinus* is in the leaf form and arrangement. In *T. baccata*, the leaves are borne singly in spiral arrangement, not on foliar spurs. Each is narrow-bladed, obtuse and only about one-third the length of pine needles. Leaves often appear to be in two rows in a single plane on the stem but this is only so on horizontally-growing branches where twisting of the leaf bases causes the apparent change in leaf arrangement. On vertically-growing twigs, the spiral arrangement can be seen clearly.

Anatomically, *T. baccata* does not differ greatly from the species of *Pinus* except in detail. There are no resin canals in the tissues of the

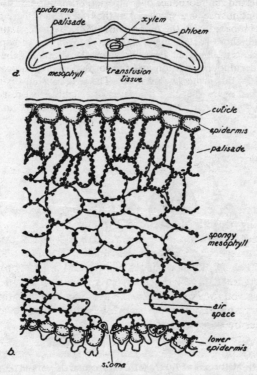

Fig. 15.23. *Taxus* leaf. (*a*) Tissue layout. L.P. plan of T.S. (*b*) H.P. drawing of portion of leaf.

yew. The leaf section, flattened dorsi-ventrally, shows only a single vascular strand flanked by transfusion tissue and loose spongy mesophyll cells.

The yew is dioecious but there are no distinctions vegetatively between the two forms. The male cones appear early in the year, February to March, in the axils of leaves on the previous year's growth. Each consists of a short axis bearing sterile scales at its base and fertile sporophylls above (*see* Fig. 15.24). The sporophylls are so closely crowded as to appear to arise from a common point of origin at the tip of the axis. Each consists of a short stalk ending in an umbrella-shaped (peltate) head and on the underside of this are formed six to eight microsporangia or pollen sacs all laterally united to one another and to the stalk (*see* Fig. 15.24 (*d*)). When mature, they dry and dehisce, to

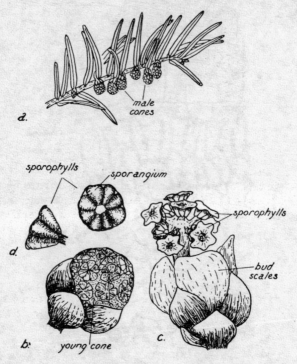

Fig. 15.24. Male cones of *Taxus*. (*a*) Cones on branch. (*b*) and (*c*) Young and mature cones. (*d*) Side and lower surface views of sporophylls.

release the microspores in yellow clouds. These spores are produced by meiotic division of spore mother-cells in much the same manner as in *P. sylvestris*. The microspores are smooth and have no wing-like outgrowths. There are no female strobili comparable with the female cones of the pines. Ovules are borne singly in the axils of vegetative leaves, each on a short axis clothed with scales. The morphology of the ovule axis is complicated in that the axis subtending the ovule itself is really a secondary growth formed in the axil of the uppermost of the scale leaves clothing the lower or primary axis (*see* Fig. 15.27 (*c*)).

A primary axis may thus continue vegetative growth after ovule formation or may produce another ovule in the succeeding year. The ovules commence development at the same time as the male cones and at

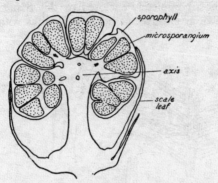

Fig. 15.25. L.S. male cone of *Taxus*. L.P. plan.

first are very tiny. They are enclosed in small scales growing from the secondary axis and all that can be seen of them externally at this stage is a tube-like protuberance from between the tips of the scales. This is

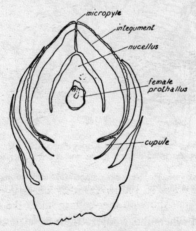

Fig. 15.26. L.S. ovule of *Taxus*. L.P. plan.

the elongated micropyle and may be seen to carry a drop of fluid in which microspores are caught, when shed from the microsporangia on neighbouring trees. Inside the scale leaves, the young ovule can be dissected out as an ovoid body with its micropylar tube formed from an upgrowth of the integument which encloses the developing female gametophyte. Below the integument is a collar of tissue, very tiny at first. It proceeds to grow upwards around the ovule. In the later stages, the ovule is almost completely enclosed by this tissue. It is a *cupule* (sometimes known as an *aril* but not homologous with that organ in

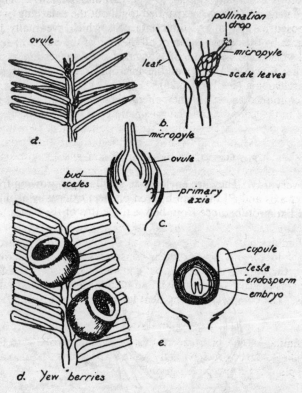

d. Yew berries

Fig. 15.27. Taxus ovules. (*a*) Very early stage. (*b*) Single young ovule (enlarged). (*c*) Same in L.S. (*d*) Mature ovules ("berries"). (*e*) L.S. seed.

angiosperms) and when the whole structure is mature, it forms the bright scarlet cup of the yew "berry" in which sits the seed.

Internal to the integument and within a nucellus, an archesporium develops. It produces several megaspore mother-cells. Each of these divides meiotically to produce a linear tetrad of four megaspores. Usually only one megaspore continues to develop into the female gametophyte.

When pollination has been effected and microspores have penetrated the micropyle to come to rest on the nucellar tissue, each develops a short tube and then rests until the female gametophyte is mature. No prothallial cells are formed in the microspore but only an antheridial cell and a tube cell. The growth of the female gametophyte from the megaspore is essentially similar to that of *Pinus sylvestris*. The fully-formed female prothallus is expanded to fill out the enlarging ovule and is composed at first of multinucleate cells which eventually become uninucleate by the degeneration of all but one of the nuclei in each cell. Centrally placed is a strand of elongated cells suggesting a possible conducting function. Borne at the micropylar end are five to eight simple archegonia (*see* Fig. 15.26).

With continued growth of the pollen tubes, several oospheres may be fertilized in the same siphonogamous manner as in *Pinus* species. Four nuclei pass into an archegonium from a pollen tube, two unequally sized male gametes derived from the body cell of the antheridium, one nucleus from the stalk cell of the antheridium and the tube nucleus. Only the larger of the male gametes enters into the fusion with the oosphere. The other three abort. Only one oospore develops into an embryo, however, and once more this process is comparable with that occurring in the pines. The embryo is short and straight, made up of an axis with the root towards the micropyle and bearing two cotyledons at the plumule end. When the seed is shed, the embryo is embedded in a mass of loose, oily tissue which constitutes an "endosperm." At maturity, the cupule is fully grown and the bright scarlet colour no doubt serves to attract birds which find it edible and so help to disperse the seeds. The complete development lasts only one season (cf. *Pinus*).

Life Cycle

This is similar to the pine except that no female strobili are formed, each ovule being borne separately at the apex of a shoot and on a separate plant from the pollen grains.

CYCAS

The genus is representative of the more ancient gymnosperms and shows accordingly several more primitive characteristics than the conifers. At the same time, it establishes an undoubted connexion with the still more primitive seed-bearing plants, the pteridosperms. For these reasons, the cycads are sometimes called "living fossils." There are altogether about twenty species, of which *Cycas revoluta*, one of the sago palms, is best known. All are tropical plants and widely scattered in parts of Africa, Eastern Asia and Australia. Such geographical distribution again points to a long evolutionary history.

Habitat

Cycas revoluta is a native of China and Japan. It grows naturally in sunny open positions but to some extent is cultivated in the tropics for its food value.

Vegetative Structure of the Sporophyte Generation

External Morphology

The stem is usually unbranched, forming a short stumpy axis bearing at its apex a cluster of closely-crowded leaves of two kinds. The larger leaves are up to three or four feet long with a central rachis bearing many pinnae. These form a handsome palm-like crown at the apex. The smaller leaves are dry and scaly, bearing a felt-like mass of brown hairs. The two kinds of leaves alternate with each other in successive zones on the stem, the scale leaves protecting the developing foliage leaves. The older parts of the stem are covered by the woody remains

Fig. 15.28. *Cycas* plant.

From Strasburger's "Textbook of Botany" (*Macmillan & Co. Ltd.*)

of old leaf bases and a good deal of its thickness is due to this covering. The young leaves are circinnately folded, reminiscent of the ferns. The root system is made up of a short tuberous primary tap root as thick as the stem, bearing many lateral roots of which some, just at soil surface, develop the typical "coralloid" structure associated with some infection of the tissues by other organisms. In this case, the root tissues are enclosing blue-green algal cells of the species *Anabaena cycadacearum*. Bacteria and fungi have also been recorded as present in *Cycas* root nodules.

Anatomy

The Stem. In section, the stem shows primarily a single ring of narrow vascular bundles within a wide cortex of parenchyma cells which are heavily charged with starch and traversed by mucilage

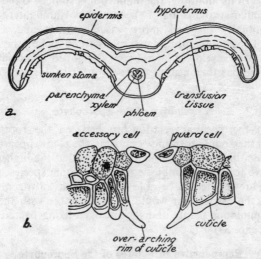

Fig. 15.29. *Cycas* pinnule. (*a*) Tissue layout in T.S. L.P. plan. (*b*) Detail of stoma.

canals. Externally, the old leaf bases form a protective covering. As the stem ages, secondary growth occurs, but very slowly. External to the ring of primary bundles, successive rings of secondary bundles are formed. They arise from cambial layers developed in the cortex. This is known as a condition of *polyxyly*. One very noticeable feature of the stem structure is the direction of the passage of leaf traces through the cortex A leaf is supplied by two vascular traces which arise in the primary vascular cylinder as a single trace diametrically opposite the leaf position on the stem. As the single trace splits into two, the branches diverge from one another and then pass one to each side external to the vascular cylinder, right around the cortex to girdle the whole stem, and finally converge to pass into the leaf base. In the outer regions of the stem and at the leaf bases, a periderm is formed.

The Leaf. A transverse section of a leaf pinna shows the arrangement as in Fig. 15.29. The epidermis is very heavily cuticularized and thickened and beneath is an equally pronounced hypodermis. Stomata occur on the lower surface; they are very deeply sunk in pits with over-arching rims. The mesophyll shows an upper closely-packed layer of elongated cells constituting a palisade, below which is a spongy layer. Between upper and lower mesophyll layers is a band of transversely elongated colourless cells forming the transfusion tissue and possibly aiding in water conduction. The leaf is xerophytic in character.

The Root. In its anatomy, the main root is similar to the stem. The primary vascular strand is diarch, becoming polyarch later. Secondary growth eventually provides more vascular rings and a periderm. Branching of the roots appears externally to be dichotomous but each branch of a fork is really a lateral root developed immediately behind an apex which has then ceased to develop further. Each root apex is protected by a root cap.

Physiology of the Sporophyte

Apart from the peculiar relationship between the roots of *Cycas revoluta* and the nodule-forming organisms, the plant appears to have no special physiological distinction. It could be that the higher plant and the alga have formed a symbiotic alliance. Some species of the blue-green algae are reputed to be able to fix gaseous nitrogen, and if this is the case, the association would be comparable with the symbiosis between leguminous plants and the nitrogen-fixing bacterium, *Rhizobium* (*see* Chap. 34).

Reproductive Structures of the Sporophyte

The two kinds of reproductive structures are borne on separate plants. They are strobili of sporophylls bearing in the one case male microsporangia, and female ovules in the other.

The Male Cone

This may be up to 45 cm in length and is composed of several hundreds of woody wedge-shaped microsporophylls arranged in tight spiral succession. The lower surface of each is covered with densely-crowded groups or sori of microsporangia each of which has a thick outer wall enclosing a tapetum and archesporial tissue (*see* Fig. 15.30).

This gives rise to numerous spore mother-cells; each of these divides meiotically to produce four microspores or pollen grains. Each microspore has a double wall, the exine and the intine. Since each microsporophyll may bear hundreds of microsporangia and each of

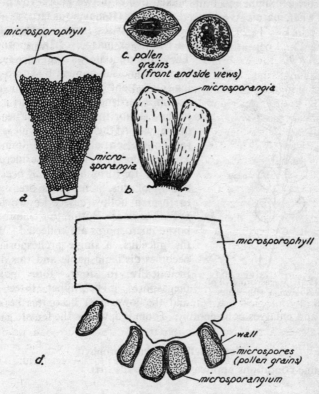

Fig. 15.30. Microsporophyll, sporangia and microspores of *Cycas*. (*a*) Microsporophyll (lower surface). (*b*) Microsporangia. (*c*) Pollen grain. (*d*) V.S. microsporophyll.

these develops thousands of spores, the spore output is enormous. Each is very tiny and easily wind-borne. The male gametophyte has already commenced development before spore liberation.

The Female Cone

This is formed of megasporophylls arranged spirally in a group at the stem apex in direct succession with the vegetative leaves. When they have matured, the vegetative apex continues to produce more leaves and sporophylls in alternation year by year. Each megasporophyll appears as in Fig. 15.31. It is about 15 to 30 cm long and resembles a leaf. The distal end is flattened and pinnately broken up, whilst the proximal end bears naked ovules in two lateral rows. Each ovule, when mature, is a massive structure. It may be as large as a hen's egg. Each arises from a group of cells on the lower margin of the sporophyll.

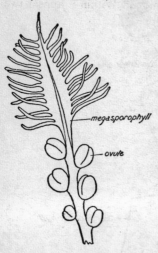

F.. 15.31. Megasporophyll of *Cycas revoluta* with ovules.

These differentiate as the nucellus and later become surrounded by an up-growing integument of soft tissue which later becomes hardened. The nucellus is open to the exterior through a small beak-like micropyle. At this stage, the ovule is ready for pollination although so immature. The nucellus grows up into the micropylar aperture to form a *nucellar beak*. At the tip of this, a few cells break down to form a hollow cavity known as the *pollen chamber*. Within this chamber airborne microspores are collected. Within the nucellus, a single archesporial cell becomes distinguishable and this divides meiotically to form four potential megaspores. The upper three abort and the lowermost becomes the megaspore and enlarges considerably. From it develops the female gametophyte.

Reproduction by the Sporophyte

The same conditions apply as in *Pinus sylvestris*.

Development of the Spores into the Gametophyte Generations; Structure, Physiology and Reproductive Processes of These

The male gametophyte commences development before the liberation of the microspores. It is once more a vestigial structure. A single small *prothallial cell* is cut off inside the pollen grain and this represents the entire vegetative structure. The remaining cell of the pollen grain forms an *antheridial cell* and a *tube cell* with a prominent nucleus. The microspore is liberated at this stage and pollination is effected. The ovule exudes a "pollination drop" from the micropyle to assist in catching the microspores and delivering them to the pollen chamber. In a short while, the microspore continues to develop. The antheridial cell forms a *stalk* and a *body* cell, which are equivalent to an *antheridium*. The microspore wall is ruptured and the tube cell grows out as a pollen tube to penetrate the nucellus and to break down and digest its tissues. The tube acts as a food absorber for several months, whilst the ovule is reaching full development. When this is completed, however, the microspore again commences further development and the body cell of the antheridium becomes very enlarged. Within it appear two

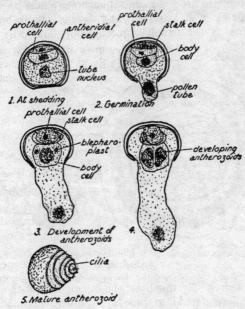

Fig. 15.32. Diagram of stages in development of pollen grains of *Cycas*.

large granular structures or *blepharoplasts*, one on either side of the nucleus. The body cell now divides in a plane between the blepharoplasts and each new cell with one blepharoplast becomes an *antherozoid* in a very remarkable way. The nucleus changes shape and a short beak-like outgrowth develops from it. The blepharoplast breaks up into smaller granules and these take up spaced positions on the nuclear outgrowth. The whole nucleus now rotates, and the outgrowth with its granules is drawn out into a long spirally coiled band. From each granule, cilia are produced until there are thousands of them. Meanwhile, the whole nucleus has enlarged so that it almost fills the cell. The walls of the cells now break down *and the antherozoids, now fully motile, are released into the body of the microspore*. These antherozoids are the largest of all male gametes known, reaching a diameter of about 300μm. They are visible to the naked eye. Fertilization can now soon be effected, for by this time the female gametophyte is well formed.

The megaspore, from which the female gametophyte is produced, enlarges considerably at the expense of the nucellus and develops a thickened outer membrane of two layers, the outer being suberized. Free nuclear division occurs within the megaspore and the nuclei lie in peripheral cytoplasm around a central vacuole. Walls begin to appear, to delimit cells as in *P. sylvestris*, and the megaspore becomes filled with the tissue of the female gametophyte. The cells are heavily

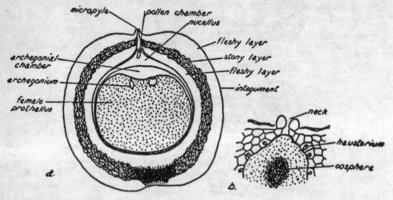

Fig. 15.33. Ovule of *Cycas* at fertilization stage. (*a*) L.S. L.P. plan. (*b*) Archegonium.

charged with starch. By this time, the integument of the whole ovule has become differentiated into three layers, inner and outer fleshy layers and a middle stony layer.

On the female prothallus at the micropylar end, several *archegonial initial cells* arise and by division and differentiation of the cells, *archegonia* are formed. Each of these is very simple, having only a two-celled neck and a neck canal cell surmounting the oosphere cell in the venter. Around the oosphere cell, the female prothallial cells become specially nutritive in function and form a *jacket layer*. The oosphere cell is nourished by these cells for some months and its cytoplasm gradually becomes thick with stored oil, protein and starch food reserves. Eventually, the oosphere cell divides to form an upper transitory ventral canal cell and a lower oosphere, the nucleus of which enlarges up to 500μm in diameter; it is easily visible. At this stage, it is ready for fertilization, and the female prothallial tissue around the group of archegonia grows upwards to form a ridge, so that the protruding necks lie in a shallow depression known as the *archegonial chamber*. Above this chamber, the megaspore membrane ruptures, and the nucellar tissue, already eaten into by the pollen tubes, becomes disorganized, so that a clear passage exists between the pollen chamber and the archegonia. When this passage is clear, one or more pollen tubes now enlarge to hang down into the archegonial chamber. A pollen tube bursts and the motile antherozoids are quickly released together with fluid substances. It is thought that the rupture of the tube is brought about by a very high internal osmotic pressure. It is known that antherozoids can live only in cane sugar concentrations of 30 per cent and upwards and this indicates what the pressure in the pollen tube must be. When an antherozoid contacts the neck of an archegonium, it appears to be sucked violently down to the oosphere. There, its ciliated band is shed, and the nucleus fuses with the oosphere nucleus to form the zygote. *This fertilization mechanism is of great interest and significance to the botanist.*

Development of the Zygote into the Sporophyte Generation

The zygotic nucleus divides rapidly to produce several hundred free nuclei within the oospore, but later these become delimited by cell walls. Near the base of the oospore, some of the cells elongate considerably, to push a still lower group right down into the prothallial tissue. From this lowest group, the embryo develops very slowly into a straight axis, with a root towards the micropyle and with two cotyledons at the plumule end. The embryo is embedded in the food-storing remains of the female prothallus, otherwise known incorrectly as the endosperm (cf. *Pinus*). The suspensors show peculiar development in that they may elongate to several centimetres in length, coiling and twisting and eventually forming a protective pad over the tip of the radicle. The seed coat or testa is formed of the two outer layers of the integument. When ripe, the seeds are shed; they have no dormant period. Germination is *hypogeal*, i.e. the cotyledons remain below ground to absorb food from the endosperm.

Life Cycle

This may be summarized by the diagram on p. 346.

Adaptation to Environment

The cycads are representative of the tropical gymnosperms. They have not the hardiness of the conifers and have not been able to compete successfully for space in the less favoured parts of the earth. They are adapted morphologically and physiologically for life in the hotter and wetter climates.

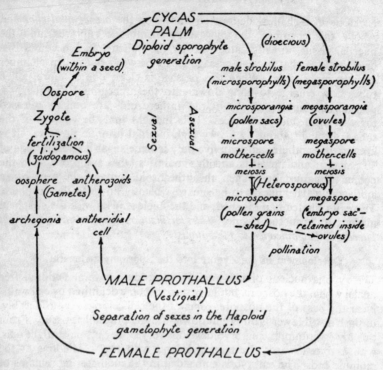

Special Features of Biological Importance

The cycads are of great interest because they are the remnants of a group of plants which were once widespread; they have a long fossil history. Their special characteristics indicate an intermediate position between the most primitive of all seed-bearing plants, the pteridosperms, and the most advanced, the angiosperms. One of these features is the manner in which the fertilization process is effected. The pollination mechanism, the subsequent development of a pollen tube and at the same time the production of motile male gametes, give us a clue as to the origin of the more advanced siphonogamous mechanism. It can be supposed that this mechanism, as we have seen it in the pines, arose from the zoidogamous condition in two stages. The first of these was the evolution of some pollination mechanism, that is, the means whereby the microspores were transported to the megaspore and retained there during germination. The second was the growth of the microspore into the pollen tube, but not primarily as a conveyor of male gametes. Its gradual assumption of the role of gamete conveyor has been accompanied by the loss of motility of the gametes. The cycads stand at the half-way mark. The pollination mechanism is well developed, but fertilization is still effected by motile male gametes, the pollen tube functioning primarily as a nutritive haustorial growth. It merely serves to bring the male gametes into proximity with the oospheres by digesting away the nucellar tissues above the archegonial chamber.

The cycads have been well named "living fossils," but it must not be assumed that the present cycads can be regarded as direct ancestors of the angiosperms. There is some possibility though, that this latter group may have sprung from some cycadean plant now long extinct.

TRENDS IN THE GYMNOSPERMS

They are the simpler of the two kinds of existing seed-bearing plants. A seed can be defined as a fertilized ovule, and an ovule as an integumented megasporangium. In the gymnosperms the megasporangium consists of a nucellus covering the megaspore, and the whole structure is invested by an outer integument, broken only at the micropyle. It is retained on the parent sporophyte until pollination, fertilization and embryo development are completed. This is the fundamental difference between the gymnosperms and the pteridophytes. Other differences such as the great reduction in size of the female gametophyte and its complete dependence on the sporophyte, go with this condition.

Ovules can vary in their position on the plant. In the conifers, ovules are borne on scales aggregated into cones. In the yew, the ovule terminates an axis, whilst in *Cycas*, ovules are borne on the margins of leaf-like sporophylls. But, unlike the angiosperms, in all cases, *the ovules are naked*.

The microspores, although unable to develop unless nourished by the female nucellus, in their manner of production, dispersal and in their ultimate function, are all much alike and they are not so essentially different from those of the heterosporous pteridophytes as are the megaspores. There is a tendency for reduction in size, so that they are more easily air-borne, and complete reduction of the male gametophyte occurs in some cases.

The fertilization mechanism in *Cycas* is still dependent on motile antherozoids, although the microspore develops a pollen tube. This is indicative of the primitiveness of the cycads by comparison with the conifers.

In vegetative form there are two fairly clear-cut structural types. The conifers and most other gymnosperms are much branched and bear small leaves, whilst the cycads are little branched and bear large leaves, somewhat resembling those of the ferns. Stem anatomy is likewise of two kinds. The tree conifers possess large quantities of dense wood, whilst the cycads show only small quantities of loose, soft xylem, more like the pteridosperms.

CHAPTER 16

SPERMATOPHYTES WITH ENCLOSED SEEDS: ANGIOSPERMS

In its earliest usage, when coined in 1690, the term *angiosperm* had not its correct modern taxonomic significance. In 1827, Robert Brown gave it its present taxonomic distinction of meaning from *gymnosperm*, when he established the truly naked character of the seeds of cycads and conifers. Even then, there was no plant classification which separated the gymnosperms from the angiosperms on this characteristic. This was because the life cycles of neither the cryptogams nor seed-bearing plants had been elucidated, and no one really appreciated the nature of a seed. When Hofmeister correctly interpreted the life history of a fern, and in 1851 discovered the nature of the occurrences in seed formation, he was able to see that the two series of events paralleled one another and to establish the significance of the origin and form of the seed as a criterion in classification. From that time, gymnosperms were clearly separated from angiosperms, whereas they had previously been grouped together as *dicotyledonous* plants to distinguish them from the *monocotyledonous* plants. The term angiosperm now includes all the flowering plants other than gymnosperms and comprises therefore all the monocotyledonous as well as the dicotyledonous higher flowering plants.

The angiosperms represent the furthest extent to which plants have so far evolved in the establishment of fixed vegetation adapted to life on land. They dominate in practically every land area where plant life is possible. They occur also in fresh water in considerable numbers, less so in salty conditions, showing that from the land they have been able to reconquer the watery environment. It is little wonder that they form so large a part of the botanist's study.

If habitat is varied, the form and manner of their growth is equally so. We may see every conceivable gradation in form between the lowly buttercup and the stately forest tree. But everywhere the vegetative form is based on a single pattern. The aquatic and terrestrial herbs which may creep, climb or stand erect, and the woody shrubs and trees, have all a common body plan adapted to an almost unlimited number of varying conditions. The internal anatomy is no less varied in detail but again conforms to a pattern. The most characteristic of all the angiosperm features is the *flower*. Once again, the closeness of the

348

relationship of the members of the group is established by the common plan on which all flowers are built. Although flowers may show an enormous range in form and be used by taxonomists almost solely to establish distinctions between smaller groups of angiosperms, their basic similarity cannot be denied.

In view of the great variation in the details of structure of the vegetative and reproductive parts of the angiosperms, it is of no great advantage to select a single genus for detailed study. Instead, three chapters will be devoted to this work. In this chapter will be given a generalized account of the reproductive parts, reproductive processes

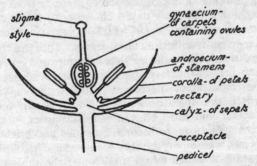

Fig. 16.1. Diagram of angiosperm flower structure. Generalized.

and the life cycle. In the two following chapters, the vegetative morphology and anatomy and the floral morphology and anatomy respectively, are described. The general physiology of plants is based largely on knowledge of flowering plants and is treated fully in Vol. II.

THE GENERALIZED ANGIOSPERM FLOWER

Fig. 16.1 represents diagrammatically the composition of an angiosperm flower seen in vertical section. We may discern the following distinct parts: the *receptacle*, on which the remaining parts are inserted; the *calyx*, composed of a number of *sepals*; the *corolla*, composed of a number of *petals*; the *androecium*, composed of a number of *stamens*; the *gynaecium* or *pistil*, composed of one or more *carpels* within which are the *ovules*. In addition, the flower may include specialized secretory structures, the *nectaries*, which may develop on the receptacle or sometimes on other parts.

The Receptacle

This is the tip of the axis on which the floral parts are borne. It corresponds to an apical meristem of a vegetative shoot, since it is upon this apex that the other parts are initiated during flower development in a way comparable with leaf development on a vegetative meristem (*see* Chap. 17). There is one distinction between the receptacle and a vegetative apex; the receptacle is of limited growth, so that when the last floral parts have been formed, it ceases further activity, whereas a vegetative meristem may continue to produce leaves indefinitely. Further, only in rare instances are buds initiated in the axils of floral parts, whereas they appear almost invariably in the axils of foliage leaves. In different species, the receptacle may be of greatly differing shape and size and may undergo considerable changes with development of the flower.

The Calyx

The sepals may be described as floral leaves. They are the outermost parts and are usually green and leaf-like in texture and general structure. They serve to protect the developing inner parts whilst the flower is a bud. As development of the flower proceeds, the expansion of the internal parts pushes them outwards and they usually fold back and may even wither and drop off. In some instances, the sepals may undergo a change in form to become expanded and brightly coloured, more like petals, whose purpose they often serve, e.g. tulip. The sepals may be separate or united into a single outer sheath or there may be groups of united sepals.

The Corolla

The petals are also floral leaves possessing very distinctive characters. They are seldom green but more often brightly coloured and expanded to form collectively the most conspicuous part of the flower. They serve thus to attract the pollinating insects which are often essential for completion of the reproductive processes. The petals may be separate or united in a single tube, or united in several groups. Differences in the shape and colouring between petals of the same flower often lead to very characteristic types which are again generally associated with the special characteristics of the insects which visit them.

The Androecium

Each stamen is a compound structure consisting of two distinct parts (*see* Fig. 16.2). The lower stalk-like portion is the *filament* and this is surmounted by a swollen head, the *anther*. The anther is usually a bright orange or yellow colour and in cross-section it can be seen that it contains two or four compartments or pollen sacs. *The whole stamen can be regarded as a microsporophyll bearing microsporangia.* The sterile part of the sporophyll is represented by the filament and is reduced to no more than a strand of vascular tissue surrounded by a few rows of cells. The fertile microsporangia are then borne as *pollen sacs* in a group at the distal end of the filament. When mature, the pollen sacs rupture to release the *pollen grains* or *microspores*. Within these, the *male gametes* are developed.

The Gynaecium

In different angiosperm species there is a great deal of variation in the gynaecium. There may be a single carpel, a number of separate carpels or a number of carpels united in a variety of ways. But each carpel, whether a structure separate from the rest or united with them, is effectively a closed, hollow container housing one or more ovules. The ovule-containing portion is called the *ovary*. Its distal end often bears a prolongation, the *style*, which terminates in a sticky surface, the *stigma*. *Each carpel may be considered*

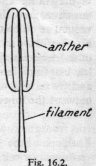

Fig. 16.2.
Generalized stamen.

as being derived from a flattened megasporophyll which has become a hollow container by the folding together and fusion of its free edges (see Fig. 18.8). Within the ovules, the *megaspores* are thus completely enclosed by sterile tissue. It is this characteristic of the angiosperms, that the ovules develop within closed carpels, which distinguishes them from the gymnosperms, since fundamentally both types of microsporangia and both types of ovules are the same. When the reproductive processes have been completed, the fertilized ovules become the *seeds* and the gynaecium as a whole becomes the *fruit*.

The flower so described represents the standard floral construction of the angiosperms. In developing both male and female parts, it is *hermaphrodite*. As has been stressed previously, there are endless variations. These will be discussed in Chap. 18, together with the manner in which the variations are used in the systematic study of angiosperms.

THE REPRODUCTIVE PROCESS

For convenience of study we may isolate comparatively distinct occurrences and describe them separately, but it must be remembered that each is a part of one process. If one fails, the whole process fails. We may distinguish the sequence of events in this series—

1. Development of pollen grains and male gametes.
2. Development of ovules and female gametes.
3. Pollination.
4. Fertilization.
5. Seed development.
6. Fruit development and fruit and seed dispersal.

Development of Pollen Grains

The series of diagrams in Fig. 16.3 represents the stages of development of the anther from the young to the fully mature condition. The very young anther shows as a mass of undifferentiated parenchymatous tissue surrounded by a developing epidermis. It may already possess a two- or four-lobed condition in the transverse plane. Within each lobe, immediately below the epidermis, a vertical row of cells extending the length of the lobe becomes prominent by enlargement of the cells and by their denser cytoplasmic contents. The tissue centrally placed between the lobes is called *connective tissue*, and in it, vascular elements which are continuous with others in the filament will be differentiated. It is from the rows of *hypodermal cells* that the pollen sacs are initiated. Each cell of the vertical row divides periclinally to form an inner large sporogenous cell, the *archesporium*, and an outer smaller *parietal cell*. The parietal cell proceeds to divide radially and tangentially to develop a layer, usually three cells thick, around the sporogenous cell inside. The innermost layer of cells derived from the parietal cell becomes the *tapetum* or nutritive layer; the outer layers are referred to as parietal cells. Meanwhile, the sporogenous cell has been undergoing repeated divisions to form a central mass of *microspore mother-cells*, the outer layers dividing rapidly to keep pace with the internal expansion. It is owing to this expansion in four separate regions that the mature anther has a grooved external appearance. All divisions of the sporogenous tissue have so far been mitotic, but when the production of spore mother-cells is completed, each undergoes a meiotic division to produce a tetrad of four cells. Each of these now undergoes change into a *pollen grain*. It secretes a thick outer exine and thin inner intine. The exine may be smooth, spiny, pitted or variously sculptured according to species. Likewise, mature grains may have a characteristic specific shape and size, but in general, they are always very minute. Their development is always accompanied by very active nutritive functioning of the tapetum and other parietal cells which are densely crowded with starch grains during the stages of pollen-grain development.

Gradually, as the pollen grains mature, other changes in the anther are noticeable. The tapetal cells slowly become shrunken and disorganized to form a broken-up layer at the inner edge of the pollen sac. The cells of the parietal layers external to this, particularly the layer immediately under the epidermis, undergo thickening with strips of lignified material on the radial walls and a meshwork of similar thickening on the inner tangential walls. This forms the so-called *fibrous layer* which is concerned with dehiscence of the anther to release the pollen grains. When the pollen is ripe, these outer cells begin to dry out and

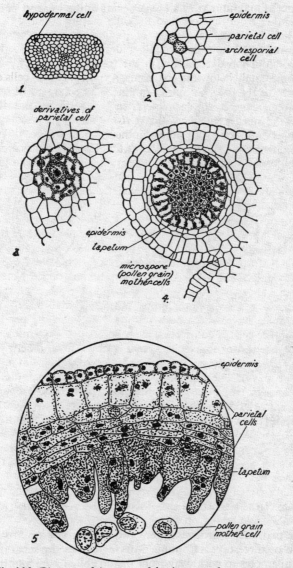

Fig. 16.3. Diagrams of the stages of development of an anther (1–5).

thus contract in a direction around the circumference of the anther lobe. The shortening in this circumferential direction imposes a strain on adjacent cells and ultimately a break occurs at the weakest point. This

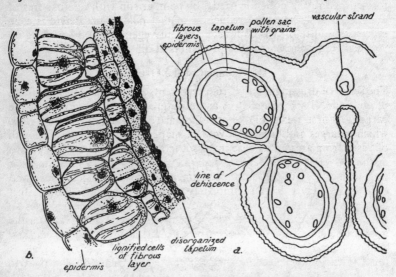

Fig. 16.4. Structure of ripe anther of tulip. (*a*) Part of anther. L.P. plan. (*b*) Pollen sac wall. H.P. drawing.

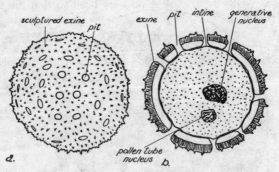

Fig. 16.5. (*a*) Surface and (*b*) sectional views of pollen grain of Marvel of Peru.

is at the two lateral grooves where two pollen sacs are separated by only two or three cells. Continued drying causes the separated edges of the pollen sacs to curl away from the line of rupture and the pollen grains are thus freely exposed to the outside.

When shed, each pollen grain usually contains two nuclei, the *generative nucleus* from which two male gametes will be derived and the *pollen tube nucleus*. In some cases the male gametes may already be formed before the pollen is shed. By comparison with microspores of *Selaginella* and *Pinus*, the reduction of the male gametophyte is even more pronounced. It is completely absent vegetatively, there being no vestigial cells representing the prothallus at all.

Development of the Ovule

The series of drawings in Fig. 16.6 represents the stages of development of an ovule. Each commences as an outgrowth of the *placenta* of the carpel. At first, it is a minute protuberance of tissue called the *nucellus*, which enlarges and becomes ovoid in shape. As it enlarges, upgrowth of tissue from around its base invests it in a sheath or *integument* of two distinct layers. These develop separately and the inner integument is well formed before the second commences growth. These inner and outer integuments do not completely enclose the nucellar tissue. Just before they reach the apex of the ovule, their development ceases so that a small pore, the *micropyle*, is open to the nucellus. This is the micropylar end of the ovule, the opposite end being called the *chalaza*. When this early stage of development is complete, the tiny ovule is raised clear of the placenta on a short stalk or *funicle*. The relative positions of the micropyle, funicle and the chalaza are variable with species, and there are three cases. If the ovule is erect, that is with micropyle, chalaza and funicle in one straight line, it is said to be *orthotropous*. If the ovule is bent back on itself so that the micropyle is situated near the junction of funicle and chalaza, it is said to be *anatropous*. If the funicle joins the main body of the ovule more or less mid-way between the micropyle and the chalaza, it is said to be *campylotropous*. The commonest condition is the anatropous ovule, but for simplicity, the orthotropous condition is shown in the drawings.

Whilst the ovule has been attaining this state, there have been changes inside the nucellar tissue. These again, vary slightly for different species but the minor differences have no great significance. At the nucellar apex, immediately inside the micropyle, a single *hypodermal cell* becomes enlarged and conspicuous. It undergoes division into an outer smaller *parietal cell* and an inner larger *spore mother-cell*. One variation here is that the parietal cell may not be formed and the hypodermal cell becomes the spore mother-cell directly. All cell divisions so far completed to form the ovule, have been mitotic. The spore mother-cell now undergoes meiotic division to produce four haploid *potential megaspore cells* in a linear series. Of these four, in nearly all cases, only the inner develops further, whilst the outer three abort. This inner cell is therefore the single *megaspore*; it proceeds to develop further, nourished by the nucellus. It enlarges and undergoes three consecutive mitotic nuclear divisions to become a large vacuolate sac containing eight haploid nuclei. It is now called the *embryo sac* and

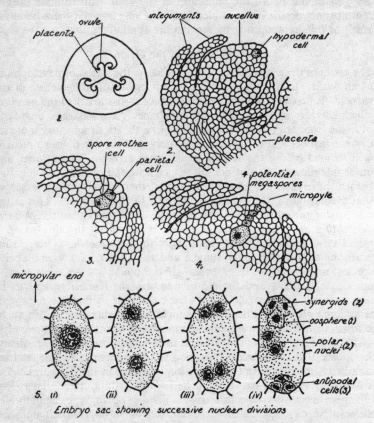

Fig. 16.6. Diagram to show the origin and stages in development of angiosperm ovule and mature embryo sac.

1 Position of ovules on placentae in tulip. 2–4. Development of integuments and megaspore 5 (i–iv). Nuclear divisions in embryo sac.

is in all respects homologous with a female gametophyte of lower groups. It is however very much reduced, a condition similar to the reduction of the male gametophyte.

The eight nuclei formed in the embryo sac are disposed in a manner almost constant throughout the angiosperms. Three are situated at the end of the embryo sac near the micropyle, constituting the *egg apparatus*. The central one of these is the *female gametic* (ovum or oosphere) *nucleus*, whilst the two flanking it on either side are called the *synergidae*. At the extreme opposite end of the embryo sac are grouped three more of the nuclei with cytoplasm surrounding them and sometimes delimited by very delicate cellulose walls. These are called the *antipodal cells*. Mid-way along the sac are the two remaining unenclosed nuclei

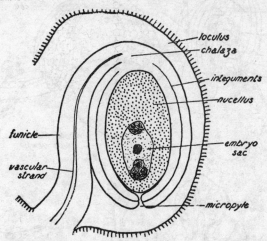

loculus
chalaza
integuments
nucellus
funicle
embryo sac
vascular strand
micropyle

Fig. 16.7. Diagram of anatropous ovule ready for fertilization.

called the *polar nuclei*. In some instances, they may fuse at this stage to form a single diploid nucleus known as the *definitive nucleus*.

When the embryo sac is complete, the ovule is ready for the fertilization process to take place. This involves the union of a male nucleus from a pollen grain with the female nucleus of the embryo sac. Thus it is necessary for the two nuclei to be brought into contact. There are two processes involved, namely, *pollination* in which the pollen grain is transported by some agency to the outside of the carpel, and the *further development of the pollen grain* to effect the transfer of the male nucleus from the pollen grain to the female nucleus in the embryo sac.

Pollination

This is the transfer of pollen grains from the anther of a stamen to the receptive part of a carpel, the stigma. In most cases, the agency by which the pollen is transferred, is one of two kinds, by insects, or by the wind. Flowers are said to be *entomophilous* if the former is the case and *anemophilous* if the latter. It is comparatively easy to distinguish between the two types of flower if their structure is studied. Entomo-philous flowers generally have the following characteristics—

1. They are large, brightly coloured and often scented. If small, they are aggregated in numbers, to form a broad expanse of colour

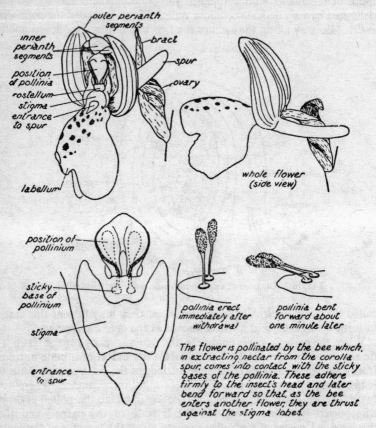

Fig. 16.8. Pollination mechanism in early purple orchis.

against the background. Insects are thus attracted visually and some-times through the olfactory sense over some distance.

2. The flowers provide a source of food for insects which imbibe sugary nectar from the nectaries or collect the pollen, or both.

3. Nectaries, anthers and stigmas are situated in a special relation-ship to one another, so that anthers and stigmas must be disturbed if the nectar or pollen is to be reached by the insect, i.e. there may be

highly specialized pollination mechanisms in the flower, e.g. early purple orchis.

4. The pollen grains are usually thick-walled, sticky and spiny, the better to adhere to insect bodies.

Anemophilous flowers, by comparison, may be described thus—

1. They are often small and inconspicuous and are usually developed well before the foliage, so that this does not interfere with the free circulation of air around the flowers.

2. They do not develop nectaries nor are they scented.

3. The male parts tend to produce very large quantities of pollen by comparison with entomophilous flowers. This compensates for the indirect and somewhat risky means of transport. The greater the quantity of pollen, the greater are the chances of pollination. The aggregation of many male flowers into flexible catkins is common among trees, and clouds of pollen can be seen as it is shed from the hazel, oak and other trees.

4. The stigmas are often large, feathery and very sticky, and extend well outside the flower. Thus the pollen is more likely to reach them.

5. To remain air-borne as long as possible, the pollen grains are usually very tiny, smooth-walled, dry and light; sometimes they have air-bladders.

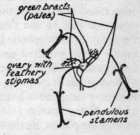

Fig. 16.9. Wind-pollinated flower of a grass.

6. Plants with anemophilous flowers are either trees or herbaceous plants with flowers high above the foliage. Thus there is less interference with pollen dispersal or pollen capture by the stigmas.

In addition to insects and wind, a few plants rely on other agencies for pollination. Some aquatics are pollinated by water currents, e.g. the grass wrack, *Zostera marina*, in which the long thread-like pollen grains, whose specific gravity is the same as that of sea water, are able to move freely at any depth until caught on the submerged feathery stigmas of the female flowers. Some land plants rely on animals other than insects. Humming birds feeding on nectar are said to pollinate many tropical flowers. Creeping animals, such as slugs and snails, must pick up pollen in their slime when moving over plants and may conceivably deposit it on a stigma. There is little doubt that many animals may disperse pollen in one way or another, but flowering plants generally have evolved so that they are well adapted to insect or wind pollination.

It might be noted here that some flowering plants never fully open their flowers and are habitually self-pollinated, e.g. wood sorrel. They are said to be *cleistogamic*. Others have evolved very highly specialized pollination mechanisms such as in the "explosive" properties of the flowers of some leguminous plants and the development of hinged anthers as in the sage. There are too many such mechanisms to enumerate here, but reference is made to some of them in Chap. 18.

By whatever agency pollen may be transported, there are two distinct possibilities with reference to its eventual destination. First, the pollen may be transferred from an anther to a stigma in the same flower or in another flower on the same plant. Secondly, the pollen may be transferred from an anther in a flower on one plant to a stigma in a flower on another plant of the same species. The former case constitutes *self-pollination* and the latter *cross-pollination*. Now, it is well known and is discussed in Vol. II, Chap. 19, that the characters inherited by a new individual are represented in the gametes of its parents by the genes located on the chromosomes. It is also well known that any tendency to mix genetic constitutions in the offspring, by causing the zygote from which it develops to be produced by the union of two distinct sets of chromosomes, leads to differences between the characters of parents and offspring. It is also believed that the introduction of variation between individuals of a species, may lead to the increased fitness of the species as a whole to survive the rigours of competition with other plants, by the weeding out of the weaker and the selection of the stronger.

It will be realized that if gametic union is effected between male and female gametes produced by the same plant, the mixture is less likely to lead to variation than if the gametes of different plants unite. In other words, cross-pollination is a more effective method of producing new variants than self-pollination. Hybridization by plant breeders is effected by controlled cross-pollination, in which pollen is actually transferred from one plant to another by a brush. In nature, there are numerous mechanisms which tend to further the possibility of cross-pollination and obstruct self-pollination. A detailed study of floral development, structure and physiology brings these to light. They are summarized below.

Protandry and Protogyny

In many genera, e.g. *Taraxacum* (dandelion), *Bellis* (daisy), the anthers have matured and the pollen is distributed long before the stigmas of the same flower are receptive. Such flowers are *protandrous*. In fewer genera, e.g. *Scrophularia* (figwort), *Luzula* (woodrush), the stigmas are receptive long before the anthers are mature in the same flower. Such flowers are *protogynous*. The condition in which anther maturity and stigma receptiveness do not coincide is known as *dichogamy*.

Special Floral Structure

In most flowers, details of structure favour the possibility of cross-pollination in one or more of several different ways. Stigmas and anthers may be so located that it is unlikely that pollen can reach the stigma of the same flower unless carried there, e.g. pin-eyed primrose. When the flower is insect-pollinated, the nectaries are usually located where they can be reached by particular types of insect only, e.g. long-tongued or short-tongued. Likewise, the anthers and stigmas are so placed that the visiting insect will come into contact with them while reaching the nectaries. If such flowers are protandrous or protogynous, then the insect, having previously visited flowers of different ages, can readily cross-pollinate them. To achieve this, a flower may be very markedly irregular in structure and develop long corolla tubes or spurs in which to locate the nectaries. More detail of structural devices which appear to favour cross-pollination will be given in Chap. 18

Separation of the Sexes

If individuals of a species produce gametes of one kind only, then cross-pollination is the only possibility. Nearly all animals and a few plants have achieved this condition and are said to be unisexual. It is to be noted that unisexual flowers on the same plant, i.e. the monoecious condition, does not automatically imply cross-pollination.

Self-sterility or Incompatibility

It is very often the case that even though pollen may reach the stigma of the same flower, it is unable to develop, or if it does, then development is slow. This is due to inhibition of its growth by the stigma. Whilst this is not really a case of prevention of self-pollination, it has the same effect ultimately, since it prevents, or at least retards self-fertilization.

Production of Two Types of Flower

Some angiosperms produce two distinctly different types of flower, both hermaphrodite. Often the two types produce different kinds of pollen and they are self-incompatible. Such is the case in many members of the Primulaceae, e.g. primrose, polyanthus.

Fertilization

The act of pollination is purely a step towards the ultimate union of two gametes; the act of uniting the two gametes is the fertilization process.

When pollination has been effected, the pollen grain, containing the male gametes or the generative nucleus from which they are derived, is still separated from the ovule containing the female gamete by the length of the style and the carpel wall. In order for a male gamete to reach the female ovum it must be conveyed by some means through the intervening tissues. This is achieved by the further growth of the pollen grain to form a *pollen tube* which penetrates the tissues of the stigma, style, carpellary wall and nucellus of an ovule to make contact with the embryo sac (*see* Fig. 16.10). Through this tube, the male gametes pass. They are non-motile and are conveyed in the cytoplasm at the tip of the

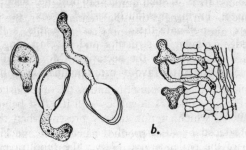

b.

Fig. 16.10. (*a*) Pollen grains of tulip germinating in a hanging drop culture (10 per cent cane sugar). (*b*) Pollen grains of evening primrose germinating on the stigma.

advancing tube. Such a *siphonogamous* mechanism contrasts with the *zoidogamous* fertilization method found in the lower plants, in which motile male gametes make their own way to the female gamete through external water. The angiosperms and most gymnosperms have become sufficiently well adapted to land conditions to be able to dispense with the need for water for this purpose.

The development of a pollen grain on a stigma may show slight variation for different species, but most would follow the pattern to be described. First, unless a pollen grain is upon the stigma of its own species, it does not develop at all, or soon ceases growth after initial germination. There are exceptions to this in a few cases; for example, in the formation of rare hybrids such as the cabbage–radish cross. For full development, certain conditions must be fulfilled. There must be the presence of a sugary solution, with a concentration inside certain limits. There must be physiological compatibility with tissue of the style. The sugary solution is provided by the sticky stigma, and generally speaking, the strength of this solution is constant for a particular species. Most pollen grains will not germinate in solutions with a concentration much outside the value for their species. It may lie between 5 per cent and 30 per cent cane sugar. Physiological compatibility is bound up with the genetics of the species. Some plants are self-incompatible or self-sterile and pollen will not develop on stigmas of plants with the same genetical constitution as the plant which produced the pollen. Hence the need for "pollinators" for some fruit trees, e.g. Cox's orange pippin apple.

If the conditions for germination are correct, the pollen grain proceeds to push out a delicate germ tube or pollen tube which penetrates the tissues of the stigma. This is an outgrowth of the intine, or delicate inner wall, through a pit in the exine. Material for its formation is initially provided by the pollen grain itself, which is rich in protein and fatty substances. On penetrating the stigma tissues, the tube proceeds intercellularly and some of the nutriment required is produced by digestion of surrounding cells. The tube secretes enzymes into the stigmatic and stylar tissues to bring about this digestion. Growth activity of the pollen tube is apparently bound up with the presence of the tube nucleus at its advancing tip, and as the tube pushes further into the tissues, the tube nucleus advances with it. Just behind the tip are two male nuclei, which, if not already present when the pollen was shed, are produced by division of the generative nucleus soon after germination of the pollen grain. Slowly the tube traverses the tissue of the style, and eventually it enters the cavity (loculus) of the carpel in which the ovules lie. The tube crosses this cavity and reaches an ovule. In the general case, it penetrates the ovule tissues through the micropyle, the *porogamous* case, but it is not a rarity to find penetration through the chalaza, i.e. the *chalazogamous* case. Gradually, it grows towards the embryo sac and eventually reaches and penetrates it roughly between the two synergidae. These may play some part in guiding the pollen tube to its destination, but what it may be, is unknown. When the embryo sac has been penetrated, the tip of the pollen tube opens. The tube nucleus disintegrates, if it has not done so already, and the way is clear for the gametes to enter the embryo sac. The first to enter passes between the synergidae and fuses with the oosphere to form the *zygotic nucleus*. The second passes by this diploid fusion nucleus and migrates further into the embryo sac until it reaches the polar nuclei (or definitive nucleus if these have already fused) and all three nuclei fuse to form one triploid nucleus, sometimes known as the *triple fusion nucleus*. The antipodal cells take no part in nuclear fusions and in some cases disappear quickly. These acts of nuclear fusion are the culmination of the fertilization process. From the zygote, the *embryo* develops and from the triple fusion nucleus, the *endosperm* is formed. The embryo becomes embedded in this endosperm.

From this description of the events occurring during fertilization, it should be perfectly clear that one pollen grain can fertilize only one ovule. Normally, there are many pollen grains germinating on a stigma and thus many ovules in one ovary can be fertilized.

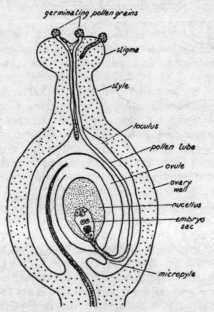

Fig. 16.11 Diagram of the fertilization process in an angiosperm.

Further Development of the Ovule; Seed Formation

When fertilization is completed, an ovule immediately commences development into a *seed*. In brief, we may say *the zygote becomes the embryo*, consisting of radicle, plumule and one or two cotyledons; *the triple fusion nucleus gives rise to endosperm tissue* which replaces the nucellus; *the integuments become the seed coat or testa*. All these transformations may be occurring together or may overlap one another in time sequence.

Details of embryo development vary with species and there are clear differences between the formation of dicotyledonous and monocotyledonous embryos. There is insufficient knowledge of angiosperm embryology as a whole for a generalized case to be given, but a great amount of detail has been recorded for the case of the shepherd's purse, *Capsella bursa-pastoris*, and this will be considered as the general case for the dicotyledonous plants. Monocotyledonous plants vary more

widely among themselves. The main differences between the monocotyledons and the dicotyledons, will be mentioned later, but no monocotyledon case will be described in detail here.

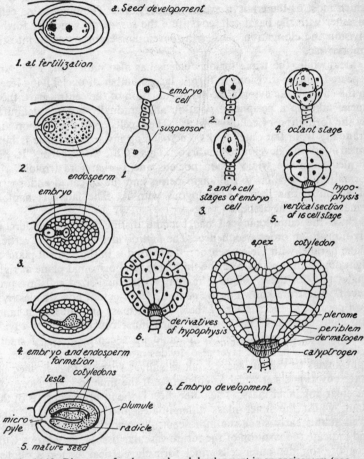

Fig. 16.12. Diagrams of embryo and seed development in an angiosperm (non-
endospermic seed). (a) (1–5) Seed development. (b) (1–7) Embryo development.

Very soon after its formation, the zygote becomes delimited within
the embryo sac by a thin wall and commences mitotic cell division in
planes at right angles to the long axis of the ovule, thus forming a short
filament of cells extending away from the micropyle (see Fig. 16.12).
This filament is known as the *pro-embryo*. The cell at the micropylar

end of the filament is somewhat larger and more rounded than the others, but appears to serve no other purpose than to anchor the pro-embryo. The cell at the end of the filament furthest from the micropyle also enlarges and becomes spherical. This is the *embryonic cell* from which most of the embryo eventually develops. The intervening cells, together with the basal cell, constitute the *suspensor*, which by further division and elongation, pushes the developing embryo deeper into the embryo sac.

Meanwhile, the triple fusion nucleus has also undergone rapid and repeated mitotic divisions to form a large number of nuclei lying freely in the embryo sac cytoplasm. By vacuolation of the central part, these nuclei take up a peripheral position and gradually become delimited by the formation of cellulose walls. These cells continue division and gradually from the outer limits, encroaching inwards, a tissue is built up around the developing embryo. This is the endosperm. It was formed from the triple fusion nucleus and is therefore triploid. Its formation is peculiar to the angiosperms and the so-called endosperm of gymnosperms is not homologous with it. The latter is haploid female prothallial tissue.

Once the embryonic cell has become distinguished, it undergoes divisions in an orderly sequence. The first divides the cell in a vertical plane parallel with the suspensor; the second is in the vertical plane at right angles to the first, and the third is in the horizontal plane at right angles to both these. Thus ultimately eight equal-sized cells are produced. These are known as the *octants*. Each octant now divides by a wall parallel to the surface of the spherical mass and thus eight inner and eight outer cells are formed. Each inner cell proceeds to divide continuously in various planes to build up a central mass of small-celled tissue. The outer layer also divides rapidly, but only in planes at right angles to the surface, i.e. anticlinally. There is thus formed an outer covering sheet which is enlarging all the time to keep pace with the enlarging inner mass. The outer sheet is the future epidermis of the plant, whilst the inner mass differentiates into the internal tissues. Even at this early stage the more centrally-placed cells are elongated and indicate the position of the future vascular tissues, in contrast with the more rounded outer cells which form the cortical tissues. Coupled with this internal cell differentiation, parts of the embryo also become recognizable. The tissue derived from the four octants nearest the suspensor becomes the *radicle* and *hypocotyl* region. To this is added some tissue from the nearest cell of the suspensor, the *hypophysis*, which contributes a root cap over the tip of the radicle. The tissue derived from the remaining four octants develops into a bilobed form. The two lobes represent the very young *cotyledons* and in the groove between them is the apex of the young shoot or *plumule*. Whilst this development is further proceeding, the endosperm, which originally filled the remainder of the embryo sac, is gradually disorganized as more and more of its nutritive content is passed into the embryo. Ultimately, it disappears completely, as the embryo, particularly the cotyledons, enlarges considerably. This is the case in *Capsella*, in which the seed contains no endosperm when ripe, but is not so in many others, e.g. castor oil. In such cases, the endosperm tissue is not disorganized but remains as a permanent part of the seed, the cotyledons

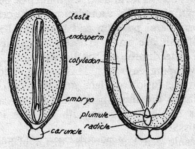

Fig. 16.13. Castor oil seed. Dicotyledonous endospermic seed.

remaining thin and delicate (*see* Fig. 16.13). Such a seed is said to be *endospermic* or *albuminous*, whilst that of *Capsella* is said to be *non-endospermic* or *ex-albuminous*. In the former case, the food storage tissue of the seed is endosperm; in the latter, chiefly the cotyledons. Members of the family Caryophyllaceae differ from both of these and the food is stored in the nucellar tissue which does not disorganize when the embryo sac enlarges. Such tissue is called *perisperm* in the ripe seed.

At maturity, the embryo of *Capsella* appears as in Fig. 16.12. The cotyledons are considerably enlarged and folded back parallel to the main axis, the radicle end of which points towards the micropyle. The remains of the suspensor can sometimes be seen at the radicle tip, if the cells have not become disorganized.

During the later stages of maturation of the embryo, changes are occurring also in the integuments. These have already fused as one layer, but now the cells become thickened with lignin and other substances and the cell contents die, so that over the embryo is produced the *testa*, which is tough and resistant enough to protect the delicate young plant for some long period. The testa is continuous everywhere except at the microscopic micropyle, and the young radicle rests with its tip just inside this. During development of the testa, the whole seed undergoes drying-out, so that its water content may drop to a value as low as 10 per cent by weight of the seed. In this desiccated condition, the seed is dormant or resting and is well able to withstand the rigorous conditions which it may encounter later. The dormancy is broken only when certain conditions are fulfilled. Dormancy and the conditions which may affect it are described in Vol. II, Chap. 13.

In monocotyledonous plants, the general trend of events is comparable with that described above, but there are certain distinct differences, and within the monocotyledons as a whole, there are certain

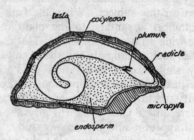

Fig. 16.14. Onion seed. Monocotyledonous endospermic seed.

specific variations, so that there is less uniformity. One major distinction between the two classes is that the monocotyledons develop only one cotyledon in the embryo. In this case, the young plumule is in a position lateral to the cotyledon on the axis and not terminally placed as in dicotyledons. Fig. 16.14 represents the embryo of the onion, *Allium*. Another distinction seen in the case of the water plantain, *Alisma*, is that the suspensor contributes more than the root cap to the radicle.

Development of the Fruit and Dispersal of Fruits and Seeds

The act of fertilization does more than initiate seed development from the ovules. It sets in motion a train of events which affects the nature of the whole gynaecium and sometimes other flower parts as well. The carpel walls, which enclose the seeds, also undergo radical changes and the whole structure when mature is termed a *fruit*. A fruit, strictly defined, is the whole mature gynaecial structure resulting from the fertilization of the ovules within it. The term is often loosely applied to include structures with modified floral parts other than the gynaecium. Not infrequently, the receptacle or even the calyx may develop as well as the gynaecium. The result is a composite structure which is more accurately described as a *pseudocarp* or "false" fruit, e.g. strawberry, mulberry. It is well to note that the greengrocer's distinction between "fruits" and "vegetables" has no botanical significance whatsoever since many of the vegetables are indeed true fruits.

There are numerous different kinds of fruits and their forms are very much dictated by the structure of the gynaecium; whether many or few carpels, whether these are joined or free and whether they contain one, few, or many ovules. The final form is also governed to a great extent by the changes which occur in the ovary walls, whether they remain hard and dry or become fleshy and succulent. Fruit structure and classification can only be understood when sufficient knowledge of floral morphology has been gained. In Chap. 18 will be found much more information on this subject. When the fruit has matured, it is obviously of biological advantage to the plant for the seeds to be dispersed over as wide an area as possible. This is generally achieved by outside agencies such as animals and the wind. Consequently, fruit structure usually shows some adaptation to a particular dispersal mechanism. The nature of these adaptations cannot be fully comprehended until fruit structure is understood, so further enlargement of this subject is deferred until Chap. 18. The physiology of fruit development is also an important and interesting study. It is undoubtedly bound up with the hormones produced by the plant. The subject is treated in Vol. II, Chap. 13.

ALTERNATION OF GENERATIONS IN THE ANGIOSPERMS

We have seen that an alternation of diploid sporophyte with haploid gametophyte is a feature of the life cycles of all plants from the bryophytes upwards. In the bryophytes, the gametophyte is the more persistent vegetative structure and the sporophyte is almost entirely a spore-producing body dependent upon it. In the pteridophytes this condition is reversed, to the extent that the sporophyte is the persistent vegetative plant with the gametophyte a transitory phase, but nevertheless independent. In some pteridophytes we see also a complication in the production of distinct male and female gametophytes, i.e. heterospory. This condition is retained in the gymnosperms and the whole series of events further complicated by the retention of the female gametophyte as a dependent structure on the sporophyte, with subsequent seed formation. The angiosperms do not differ fundamentally from the gymnosperms in the sequence of events. The chief difference lies in the extreme reduction of the gametophyte stages. The male gametophyte exists vegetatively only as a single cell, the pollen grain, which germinates into a tube-like structure to effect fertilization. It is never nutritionally independent of the sporophyte although it is shed. It corresponds to the microspore of the heterosporous pteridophytes, whose sole function is to produce male gametes (and this without the usual sex organs) and to deliver them to the female ovum. The female gametophyte is also an extremely reduced structure compared with those previously described for lower plants. It is represented by the embryo sac with its eight nuclei and once more the female gamete is produced without the usual sex organ. This embryo sac is fully dependent upon the sporophyte for nourishment and protection. The fertilization of its oosphere is dependent upon a mechanism showing full adaptation to the dry land conditions. The development of endosperm from a triple fusion nucleus, of which a male gamete forms a part, is peculiar to the angiosperms and there is no evidence as to its origin in evolution.

A diagram representing the angiosperm life cycle is given below—

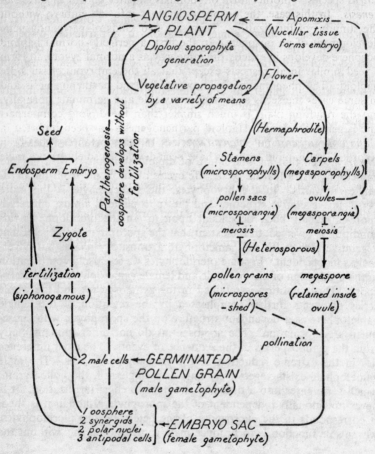

SEED FORMATION WITHOUT FERTILIZATION

Whilst the processes just described are the normal preliminaries to seed production in angiosperms, there are cases where seeds may be produced without the fertilization process taking place at all. The phenomenon is called *apomixis*, several types of which are known. One condition occurs when the oosphere takes no part in the proceedings. Instead, ingrowth of cells of the nucellus into the embryo sac gives rise to the new embryo. Such a seed is diploid and develops normally, but it has a genetic constitution exactly like that of the parent from whose cells it was wholly formed, since no gametic fusion is involved. This form of apomixis is known to occur sometimes in *Rosa*, *Rubus* and *Citrus* species. Another form of apomixis is better known as *parthenogenesis*. In this case, the oosphere develops into the embryo without the stimulus of fertilization. There are two kinds of parthenogenetic development of an oosphere. In the first, a perfectly normal haploid oosphere develops in exactly the same way as a normal zygote, to form a seed similar in all respects except that all the embryonic tissues are haploid. The phenomenon is known as haploid parthenogenesis and in some cases the seeds so formed are viable and germinate normally, but the resulting plant is much smaller than the diploid counterpart and is generally sterile. Haploid parthenogenesis has been reported in *Datura*, *Oenothera* and *Solanum* species. In rarer instances it has been recorded that haploid embryos have been developed solely from a male gamete after reaching the embryo sac. The second form of parthenogenesis is the diploid form in which the megaspore mother-cell directly produces the embryo sac without meiotic division, or if it divides, then it does so mitotically. The oosphere then formed is already diploid and very readily develops into the embryo. The result is a normal diploid seed, but again it lacks a mixture of genetical constitutions. Diploid parthenogenesis is reported as occurring very frequently in *Taraxacum* and sometimes in *Hieracium* and *Artemisia* species. The different forms of apomixis in flowering plants parallel the conditions of apospory and apogamy which occur so frequently in the pteridophytes.

VIVIPARY

This term describes the condition arising in a few grasses and the onion, in which the whole flower is replaced by a bud-like structure which, when detached, develops into a new plant. There are no sexual processes involved and the mode of propagation is an asexual vegetative one.

FRUIT FORMATION WITHOUT FERTILIZATION

Parthenocarpy is the term used to describe this occurrence. The ovary wall, and possibly other parts according to the nature of the fruit, develop just as in the usual case to form apparently normal fruits. But no pollination or fertilization has ever been carried out and no seeds are set. Typical examples are the cultivated bananas, seedless oranges and seedless raisins. The condition can be induced in some plants by spraying with suitable hormone solutions. Fruits produced commercially by this method include tomatoes, cucumbers, apples, pears and pine-apples.

CHAPTER 17

VEGETATIVE MORPHOLOGY AND ANATOMY OF ANGIOSPERMS

In this and the following chapter, a broad description is given of the morphology and anatomy of the vegetative and floral parts of an angiosperm plant in terms of the common plan upon which all are built. Variation is very wide, however, and special attention is paid to the many modifications of parts for special purposes. Owing to the vast extent of the subject, much of the material presented can only be in outline. This applies particularly to morphology. The student is advised to gain a more intimate knowledge from handling as many fresh specimens as possible, rather than from reading. The summary should assist in focusing attention on the more important features to be observed and interpreted.

It must be pointed out here, that in the earlier part of this chapter, attention will be confined almost entirely to angiosperms found in situations where the water supply is sufficient, not too wet, nor too dry. Such plants are termed *mesophytes*. But representatives of the angiosperms may be found in every possible range of water availability, from the most arid desert regions to permanent submersion in ponds, lakes and rivers. Those found in the drier habitats are termed *xerophytes* and the aquatics are termed *hydrophytes*. Not all those plants which exhibit certain anatomical features usually associated with reduction of water loss from aerial surfaces are true xerophytes, since they do not necessarily grow in dry situations, and often are not particularly well able to withstand long periods of drought any better than the typical mesophyte. Such plants may be said to possess *xeromorphic characters*, but are not xerophytic. Such are the *halophytes*, inhabitants of places of high salt content such as salt marshes, e.g. *Salicornia* and *Sueda*, and many of the plants found growing on very wet moorland, e.g. *Molinia* and *Empetrum*. These plants are sometimes described as *xeromorphs*.

GENERAL VEGETATIVE ORGANIZATION

Fig. 17.1 illustrates in diagrammatic form the organization of the generalized flowering plant. It is the sporophyte generation of the life cycle. We may read this common plan into all spermatophyte bodies, although sometimes this is not easy, since the reduction of some parts and the over-development of others may cloud the picture. In some cases, certain parts may not even persist at all beyond the early developmental stages.

The plant is organized from a single *main axis* which we may conveniently divide into the *root system*, generally below ground, and the *shoot system*, generally above. The root system is specially adapted for anchorage and for close contact with the soil, from which water and mineral salts are absorbed. The shoot system is specially adapted for

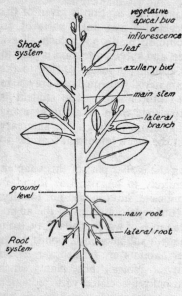

relationship with the atmosphere, to allow rapid gaseous exchange between the cells and their external environment and to capture as much light energy as possible. On the shoot system are borne, sooner or later, the sexual reproductive parts, an insurance that the processes can be carried out successfully, and the resulting reproductive bodies, the seeds, disseminated as widely as possible.

Such a body form at maturity may be described as being of one of three habits, namely, *herb*, *shrub* or *tree*. Herbs are plants which produce no permanent shoot systems above ground. They die back to ground level during some period of the year, usually in the winter months. Such a shoot system is generally of a soft green nature characteristically unlike the hard, woody permanent

Fig. 17.1. Diagram to show the morphology of a generalized angiosperm plant.

shoot systems of shrubs or trees. The distinction between these two is not always easy to draw. Both exhibit a permanent shoot system of woody nature and often size is the only distinction. In general, the tree is greater in size and possesses a single main trunk. Even in shrubs and trees, not all the aerial parts may persist during the winter; annual leaf-shedding is a characteristic of the *deciduous* forms such as oak, beech and ash, whereas *evergreens* such as holly, ivy and the conifers retain their leaves for an indefinite period.

The life span of the plant may be reckoned in terms of the number of growing seasons through which it may persist. The *annual* plant completes its life cycle from seed germination to seed production and subsequent death in a single season, e.g. maize. Some plants are even more rapid than this and may produce several generations in a year, e.g. groundsel. These are called *ephemeral* plants. The *biennial* plant requires two seasons to complete its life cycle. The carrot and parsnip are typical and make only vegetative growth the first season, store food, and then develop more vegetative and reproductive parts before death in the second season. The *perennial* plant continues its growth indefinitely, storing food for the winter and making new growth in the spring. The perennial may produce reproductive parts in successive seasons for a great number of years. It seems that the perennial habit is the more primitive and the other conditions have been derived from it.

Whatever the habit or eventual form of the angiosperm, it is originally developed from an embryo in a seed and possesses a primary body conforming to the general structure shown in Fig. 17.1. In understanding the form of more complicated and modified types, it is well to study seed structure and manner of germination first.

SEED STRUCTURE AND GERMINATION

Any angiosperm seed consists of the following essential parts—

1. The *embryo*, consisting of an axis differentiated into *plumule* or shoot at one end and *radicle* or root at the other, and bearing one (monocotyledonous) or two (dicotyledonous) *cotyledons* which may or may not contain stored food.

2. The *testa*, or seed coat, enclosing the embryo but perforated at one point by a pore or *micropyle* and carrying a scar or *hilum* where it was attached to the ovary wall. The testa may carry a specialized fleshy outgrowth or *aril*, formed from placenta, micropyle or funicle. The term *caruncle* is also used to describe such a structure.

In addition, within the testa, there may be a mass of food-storing tissue, the *endosperm*.

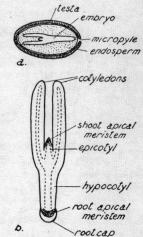

Fig. 17.2. The essential parts of a seed. (*a*) L.S. Seed. (*b*) L.S. embryo.

Seeds may be described, according to the details of their structure, as—

    (*a*) dicotyledonous, non-endospermic, e.g. broad bean, pea;

    (*b*) dicotyledonous, endospermic, e.g. castor oil;

    (*c*) monocotyledonous, non-endospermic, e.g. water plantain;

    (*d*) monocotyledonous, endospermic, e.g. maize, onion, date.

Details of the examples named above are shown in Figs. 17.3 to 17.9.

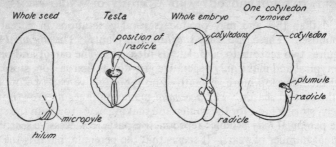

Fig. 17.3. Dicotyledonous non-endospermic seed. Broad bean.

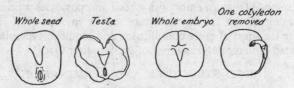

Fig. 17.4. Dicotyledonous non-endospermic seed. Garden pea.

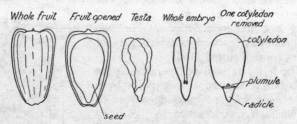

Fig. 17.5. Dicotyledonous non-endospermic seed. Sunflower.

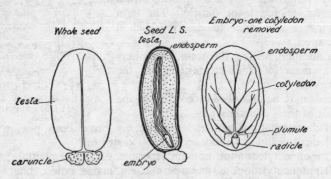

Fig. 17.6 Dicotyledonous endospermic seed. Castor oil.

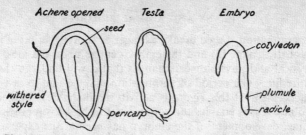

Fig. 17.7. Monocotyledonous non-endospermic seed. Water plantain.

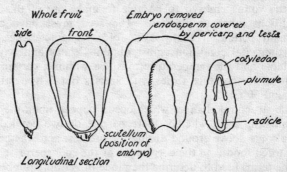

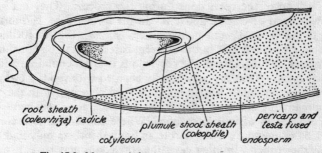

Fig. 17.8. Monocotyledonous endospermic seed. Maize.

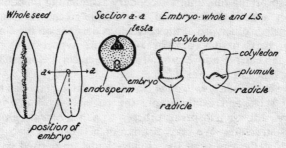

Fig. 17.9. Monocotyledonous endospermic seed. Date.

At germination, a seed breaks a longer or shorter period of inactivity (*see* Vol. II, Chap. 13) and the embryo enters upon the most rigorous of physical and physiological changes that it will undergo throughout its entire life. The period of germination may be said to last from the commencement of this rigorous activity until the development of the first foliage leaves enables the young plant to be self-supporting. Until this time, development of the embryo has been at the expense of food stored by the parent plant in the cotyledons or endosperm. In order for the young embryo to be able to make use of this food, certain conditions must be fulfilled. The seed must have completed its dormant period, if that is one of its characteristics, and certain environmental conditions must obtain. Water and oxygen must be available and the temperature must be within a certain range. This range of temperature varies with species but in general lies between 5°C and 30°C.

The structural changes which occur, depend upon the nature of the germinating seed, whether there be one or two cotyledons, whether these come above ground during the process, and whether the bulk of the stored food is in the cotyledons or the endosperm.

The terms used to describe the mode of germination bear relation to the position of the cotyledons during the process. They may remain below ground or emerge above it. In the former case, germination is said to be *hypogeal*, and in the latter, *epigeal*. Fig. 17.10 illustrates the changing conditions in the different cases. It is to be noted that the emergence or otherwise of the cotyledons is often bound up with their special roles. When they are heavily charged with food, they may not come above ground. If they do, they form chlorophyll in the cells (if not already present as in a few cases. e.g. sycamore, shepherd's purse) and proceed to assimilate carbon. Where endosperm is present, the cotyledons may have a single role as food absorbers only and remain below the ground. In other cases the cotyledons may have, in addition to this absorbing function, a secondary assimilating function. in which case they appear above ground and become green. Anatomically, the emergence or otherwise of the cotyledons depends on the elongation of different parts of the embryo axis. If the hypocotyl elongates, the cotyledons emerge above ground. If the epicotyl elongates, only the plumule emerges (*see* Fig. 17.2).

At the end of the *germination period*, the young plant has reached the *seedling* stage and exhibits only the beginnings of a *primary body structure*. Most angiosperms proceed to add *secondary growth* to this primary structure. We may distinguish between the two growths by saying that the tissues of the primary body are derived entirely from the meristems existing in the embryo, and in general, the derivatives of

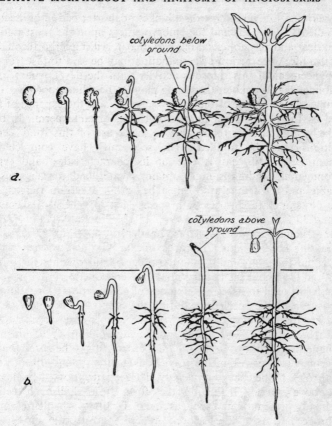

Fig. 17.10. Germination. (*a*) Hypogeal (runner bean). (*b*) Epigeal (sunflower).

these add to the extension in length of the parts. The secondary growth added to this is derived from secondary meristems, which arise during the development of the primary body and in general add to the thickness of parts. The usual relationship between primary and secondary growth in a dicotyledonous angiosperm is shown in Fig. 17.11.

THE SHOOT SYSTEM; THE STEM AND ITS APPENDAGES

The shoot system is that part of the plant which develops from the plumule of the embryo, normally appears above ground (at least at some stage in development) and bears the leaves, buds, flowers and possibly other appendages. There seems to be no other way to distinguish morphologically between a root system and a shoot system

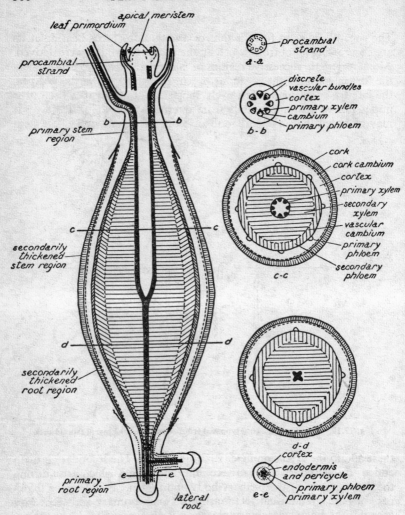

Fig. 17.11. Diagram to show the relationship between primary and secondary growth in a dicotyledonous angiosperm.

except by reference to appendages such as leaves and flowers, which are never borne by roots. The shoot system is composed of a branched or unbranched stem bearing the appendages as outgrowths from it. The stem functions primarily to elevate and expand the assimilating tissues and to act in a conducting capacity between root and leaf systems.

The Stem

The generalized stem form is that of a longitudinal axis bearing at its apex a growing point from which all the tissues basal to it were derived. Along its length, successive regions of *nodes* and *internodes* can be seen, the former marking the positions of leaf insertion. Towards the apex, the internodes become successively shorter until in the apex itself, it is impossible to distinguish node from internode with the naked eye. It may be noted that in some monocotyledonous plants, the whole stem

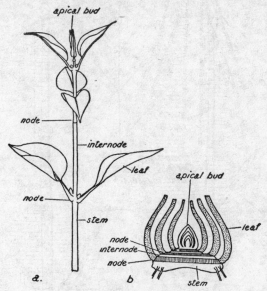

Fig. 17.12. Stem forms. (*a*) Elongated erect axis. (*b*) Shortened axis as in a bulb.

axis is so shortened that it makes the bud condition a permanency, e.g. bulbs.

For a full morphological description of a stem, account should be taken of the following features—

    (*a*) erect, decumbent, procumbent, prostrate or creeping;

    (*b*) smooth or hairy;

    (*c*) round, angular, hollow, ridged or flattened in section;

    (*d*) bearing roots or not;

    (*e*) mode of branching;

    (*f*) any special features of functional or adaptive significance.

Of these only the last two need be considered here.

Branching of the Stem

A branched stem is the more common condition in angiosperms. It allows for greater spread of the system as a whole and for the separation of functions between the branches, some being vegetative and others reproductive. In the lower plants, branching of an axis is by separation of the apex into two equally-active portions to form a *dichotomy*. This

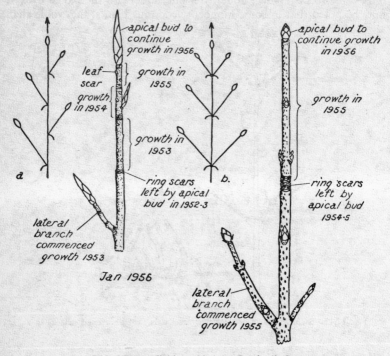

Fig. 17.13. Monopodial branching. (*a*) Beech. (*b*) Sycamore.

condition is rare in angiosperms and the usual method of branching is termed *axillary* since the branches arise from buds in the leaf axils. Axillary buds have all the structural characteristics of the terminal bud but vary according to species as to when and to what extent they may form a branch by further growth. In most species, the presence of an apical bud on a stem inhibits or at least slows down the development of axillary buds behind it. In cases where an actively growing apical bud is a permanency, the branching of the stem behind it is of secondary significance, the main axis always assuming the dominant position.

Such branching is termed *monopodial* (*see* Fig. 17.13). In other cases however, the apical bud, for one reason or another may lose its dominance, possibly by developing as a flower or inflorescence. When this happens, any new growth of the stem must come from axillary buds. Branching resulting from assumed dominance by axillary buds is known as *sympodial* (*see* Fig. 17.14). The resulting outline of sympodially branching twigs depends upon the relative positions of the

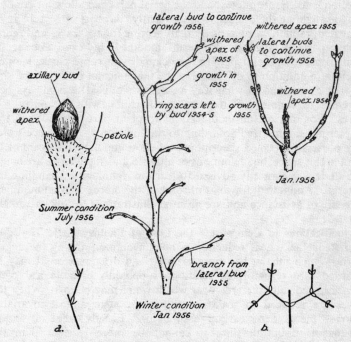

Fig. 17.14. Sympodial branching. (*a*) Elm. (*b*) *Philadelphus*.

developing axillary buds and the directions of their growth as lateral branches (compare sympodial branching in *Philadelphus* and *Ulmus*).

Cases of completely unbranched stems in angiosperms are rare, but trees of the palm habit show this condition where it may be regarded as a primitive characteristic. In other cases, the single axis condition may be due to an excessively preponderant apical meristem which exerts a completely inhibiting influence on the growth of the axillary buds behind it. Removal of an apical bud invariably causes the nearest axillary bud behind it to commence growth.

Modifications of Stems

Structure and function are always linked together in living things and where an organ, common to a particular group of plants or animals has a common fundamental function and no other, it is generally the case that with only minor variations, the organ has a common structure throughout the group. In the case of the angiosperm stem, the primary function is to elevate and expand the aerial parts and allow for conduction throughout the system. Consequently, the basic structure is an elongated, radially-symmetrical organ bearing foliage leaves and reproductive parts at intervals. The term "modified" indicates a change in form from this general pattern, associated with some particular new function in addition to or replacing the fundamental one. In assessing to what degree and in what way a stem is modified, it is always best therefore to couple the structural modification with the purpose it serves. For that reason modifications to plant parts described in this chapter are summarized according to the functional significance which they possess. Detailed descriptions of these modifications cannot be given in this space, but definitions of hitherto undefined terms are made. The student is earnestly advised to learn morphology by handling the material. Annotated drawings of some of the more common modifications are of assistance and are given as illustrations to this part of the text.

Modifications to Compensate for Loss of Photosynthetic Tissue by Leaf Reduction. Leaf reduction is not uncommon among the angiosperms which inhabit the more exposed and drier places. It may be regarded as a xeromorphic condition supposedly of biological significance in reducing the area over which water may be lost. When the leaves are reduced to scales or spines the stem almost invariably assumes the role of carbon assimilator. Exactly what advantage this has is doubtful, since it cannot be more efficient than the leaves for photosynthesis and there are other ways of restricting water loss.

Stems possessing a large measure of photosynthetic activity may be classified thus—

1. *Cladodes:* branches of the stem of one internode length, flattened and of leaf-like appearance, e.g. butcher's broom (*Ruscus aculeatus*), *Asparagus.*

2. *Phylloclades:* whole flattened or globose shoots as in the cacti and some euphorbias, e.g. prickly pear (*Opuntia*).

3. *Winged or ridged stems*: stems bearing expanded cortical tissue, varying in form from lateral plates to superficial corrugations, e.g. broom (*Sarothamnus scoparius*), everlasting pea (*Lathyrus sylvestris*).

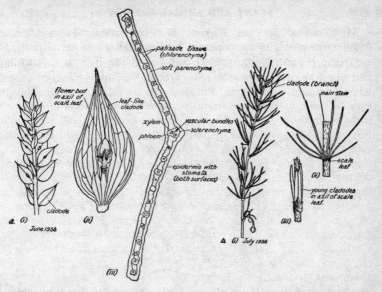

Fig. 17.15. (a) Cladodes of butcher's broom: (i) Branch bearing cladodes; (ii) Single cladode (enlarged); (iii) T.S. cladode L.P. plan (b) Cladodes of asparagus: (i) branch bearing cladodes; (ii) cladodes (enlarged); (iii) young cladodes in axil of scale leaf.

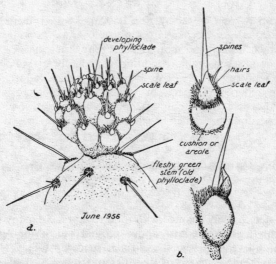

Fig. 17.16 Phylloclade of prickly pear (*Opuntia*). (a) Young phylloclade bearing areoles or cushions and spines in the axils of scale leaves. (b) Enlarged areoles.

Modifications for the Purpose of Perennation. Perennation by herbaceous plants is accompanied by the die-back of aerial parts, the surviving portion being located below ground. This is frequently a

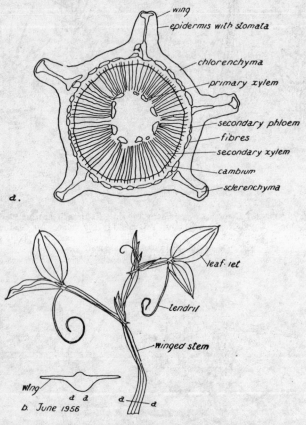

Fig. 17.17. (a) Tissue layout in ridged stem of broom. L.P. plan of T.S. (b) Winged stem of everlasting pea.

modified stem heavily charged with food reserves. In many species, no part of this axis ever comes above ground except for reproductive purposes, and year by year the old axis sends up foliage leaves only. In such cases, the stem is greatly different from a normal aerial stem both morphologically and anatomically.

1. *Rhizomes:* underground horizontally-growing stems of wide

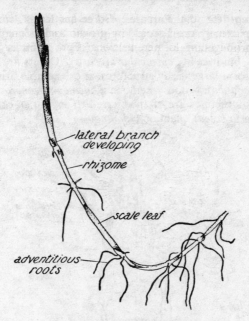

Fig. 17.18. Rhizome of couchgrass.

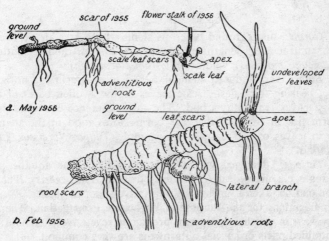

Fig. 17.19. Rhizomes. (*a*) Wood anemone. (*b*) Iris.

variation according to the species. Some are tough, wiry structures capable of extremely rapid spreading growth and as much adapted to vegetative propagation as perennation. For example, couch grass (*Agropyron*), bindweed (*Convolvulus arvensis*). Others are less rapid in spread and form large fleshy structures. For example, iris, Solomon's seal (*Polygonatum*), wood anemone (*Anemone nemorosa*). Vertical rhizomatous structures are often referred to as *root stocks*, e.g. strawberry (*Fragaria vesca*), plantain (*Plantago*).

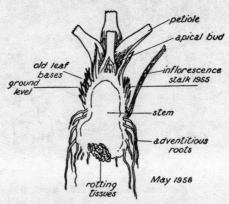

Fig. 17.20. L.S. root stock of plantain.

2. *Corms:* underground tuberous stems whose axes are vertical but much contracted in length, e.g. *Crocus, Gladiolus*, bulbous buttercup (*Ranunculus bulbosus*), wild arum (*Arum maculatum*).

3. *Bulbs:* very reduced stem, flattened to a disc in the horizontal plane, bearing thick fleshy scale leaves or the swollen bases of aerial foliage leaves. In reality a bud. The chief difference between this and a corm lies in the fact that the corm stores food in the stem, the bulb in leaves or leaf bases. For example, *Tulipa, Narcissus, Lilium, Galanthus*.

4. *Turions:* detached winter buds by which some aquatic plants perennate, e.g. arrowhead (*Sagittaria*), frogbit (*Hydrocharis*). The term turion can be taken to mean any vegetative shoot or sucker.

Modifications for the Purpose of Vegetative Propagation. There are many ways in which angiosperms propagate vegetatively. Whole stems or modified parts or special outgrowths are very common.

1. *Runners or Stolons:* stems growing horizontally on the surface of the soil away from the parent. They bear normal buds and readily

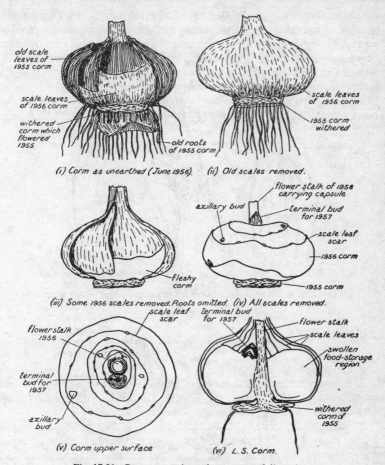

old scale leaves of 1955 corm

scale leaves of 1956 corm

withered corm which flowered 1955

old roots of 1955 corm

(i) Corm as unearthed (June 1956).

scale leaves of 1956 corm

1955 corm withered

(ii) Old scales removed.

fleshy corm

(iii) Some 1956 scales removed. Roots omitted.

flower stalk of 1956 carrying capsule

axillary bud

terminal bud for 1957

scale leaf scar

1956 corm

1955 corm

(iv) All scales removed.

scale leaf scar

flower stalk 1956

terminal bud for 1957

axillary bud

(v) Corm upper surface

terminal bud for 1957

flower stalk

scale leaves

swollen food-storage region

withered corm of 1955

(vi) L. S. Corm.

Fig. 17.21. Crocus corm in various stages of dissection.

produce adventitious roots at the nodes, where they touch the ground. At each point of root development, a bud (or buds) develops a new aerial structure to establish a new plant when the runner dies off. For example, strawberry, bramble (*Rubus fruticosus*), ground ivy (*Nepeta*).

2. *Sucker:* an equivalent structure to the runner but developed below ground from stem or root and acting in the same way, e.g. mint (*Mentha*), raspberry (*Rubus*).

3. *Offset:* merely a shortened runner, e.g. house-leek (*Sempervivum*).

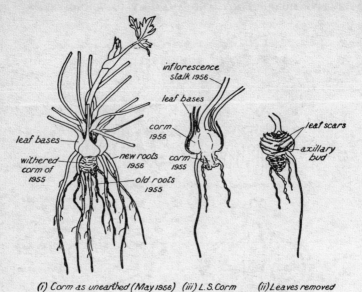

(i) Corm as unearthed (May 1956)   (iii) L.S.Corm   (ii) Leaves removed

Fig. 17.22. Corm of bulbous buttercup in various stages of dissection.

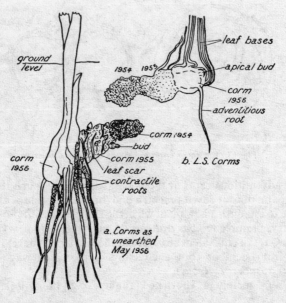

Fig. 17.23. Corms of wild arum in series. (*a*) Whole corms. (*b*) L.S. corms.

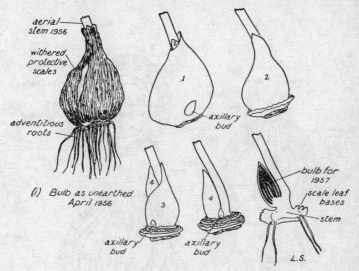

(i) Bulb as unearthed
April 1956

(ii) Scale leaves removed in succession from outside
Numbers indicate the order of removal

Fig. 17.24. Tulip bulb in various stages of dissection.

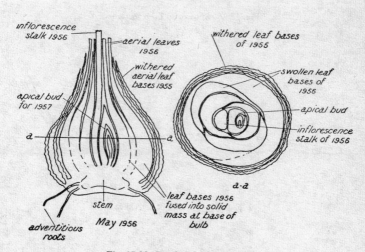

Fig. 17.25. Bluebell bulb sectioned.

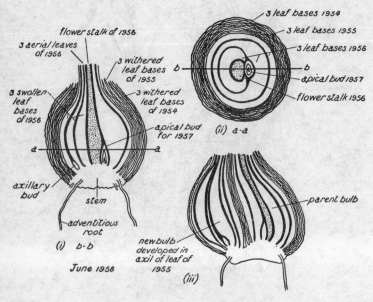

Fig. 17.26. Snowdrop bulb sectioned.

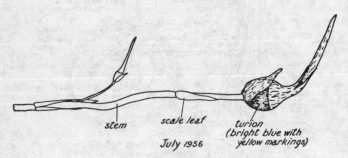

Fig. 17.27. Turions of arrowhead.

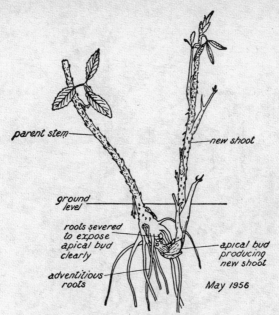

Fig. 17.28. Stolon of bramble.

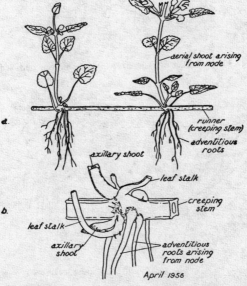

Fig. 17.29. (a) Creeping stem of ground ivy. From specimen 102 cm long with twenty-one nodes. (b) Node (enlarged).

393

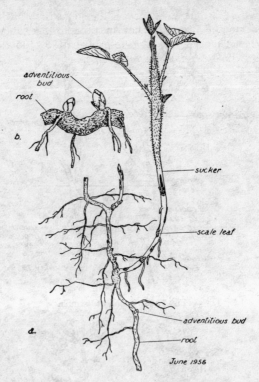

Fig. 17.30. (a) Sucker of raspberry. (b) Adventitious buds (enlarged).

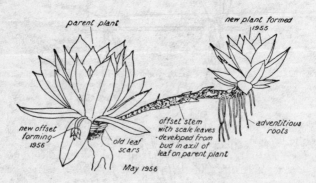

Fig. 17.31. Offset of house leek.

4. *Stem tubers:* solid, thickened whole stems or branches functioning as food storage organs. They may be formed above or below ground. When detached, they serve to propagate, e.g. potato (*Solanum*), Jerusalem artichoke (*Helianthus tuberosus*).

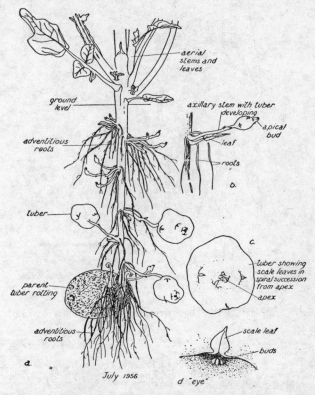

Fig. 17.32. Stem tubers of potato. (*a*) Underground portion of stem. (*b*) Young tuber. (*c*) Apex of tuber showing buds in spiral succession. (*d*) Bud or "eye" (enlarged).

5. *Droppers:* specialized branches developed on some bulbs; at the apex of the branch, a new bulb develops, e.g. tulip.

6. *Bulbils:* axillary buds on aerial shoots transformed into miniature bulbs. The term is often used to include any small bulbous-looking outgrowth formed on leaves, stems, flowers, etc., which serve to propagate vegetatively. For example, *Lilium bulbiferum*, onion and garlic (*Allium*).

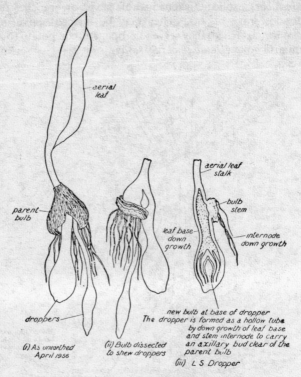

Fig. 17.33. Droppers of tulip.

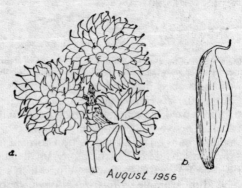

Fig. 17.34. Bulbils of garlic. (a) Head of bulbils in place of inflorescence.
(b) Single bulbil (enlarged).

396

Modifications Associated with Particular Habits.

1. *Climbing stems:* a plant may gain support and elevate itself above surrounding vegetation by—

(*a*) Coiling its stem around a neighbouring plant. i.e. stem twiner. For example, runner bean (*Phaseolus*), honeysuckle (*Lonicera*).

Fig. 17.35. Honeysuckle twining stem.

(*b*) Developing specialized outgrowths in the form of prickles by which it may scramble on overhead vegetation, e.g. wild rose (*Rosa canina*).

(*c*) Some branches may become modified as *tendrils*, e.g. white bryony (*Brvonia dioica*), a vegetative branch, virginia creeper (*Parthenocissus*) [*Ampelopsis*], an inflorescence, and vine (*Vitis*), an inflorescence.

2. *Rosette habit:* a plant may gain advantage over others in open spaces by spreading its leaves in a horizontal plane at ground level, from a considerably shortened axis, e.g. dandelion (*Taraxacum*), daisy (*Bellis*). plantain.

Miscellaneous Modifications of no Obvious Purpose.

Thorns: short modified branches terminating in hard sharp points. They may serve a protective function. For example, hawthorn (*Crataegus*), sloe (*Prunus*).

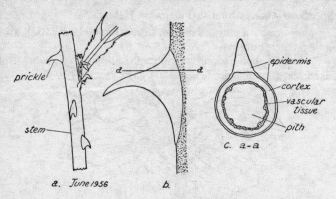

labels: prickle, stem, d, d, epidermis, cortex, vascular tissue, pith, c. a-a

a. June 1956   b.

Fig. 17.36. (a) Prickles of the rose. (b) Single prickle (enlarged). (c) Section of stem and prickle at a—a showing prickle to be of epidermal origin.

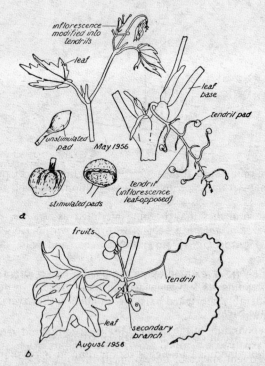

labels: inflorescence modified into tendrils, leaf, leaf base, tendril pad, unstimulated pad, May 1956, tendril (inflorescence leaf-opposed), stimulated pads, a, fruits, tendril, leaf, secondary branch, August 1956, b

Fig. 17.37. (a) Tendrils of virginia creeper. (b) Tendril of white bryony.

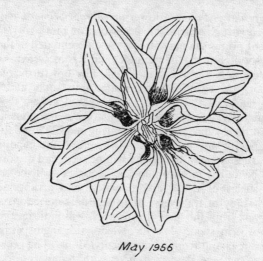

May 1956

Fig. 17.38. Rosette of plantain.

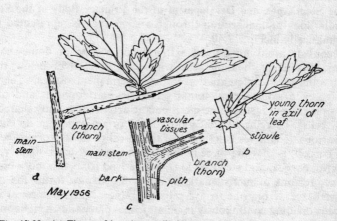

Fig. 17.39. (a) Thorn of hawthorn. (b) Young thorn (branch) in axil of leaf.
(c) L.S. junctions of thorn and main stem.

Anatomy of the Stem

A full understanding of the internal tissue structure and arrangement of any plant part can be gained only by studying its origin (ontogeny) and the subsequent stages of development through which it passes to reach maturity. The student is reminded that the whole angiosperm sporophyte develops from the embryo which consists of an upper *apical shoot primordium* and a lower *apical root primordium*, separated by the *hypocotyl-root axis* which bears one or more *cotyledons*. The shoot and root primordia may already be differentiated in the seed into a miniature shoot system, the plumule, and a root system, the radicle. During germination, the shoot meristem develops further to produce the first shoot, formed of stem segmented into nodes and internodes and bearing leaves at the nodes. As the shoot system develops, the apical meristem is carried upwards by its own continuous addition of new cells and their subsequent enlargement and differentiation behind it. At the apex of any growing stem therefore, the condition of the stem at its earliest state of formation will be seen, and at points further and further behind it in chronological sequence, will be seen all the intervening stages of tissue differentiation and arrangement up to maturity. A study of transverse and longitudinal sections at suitably spaced intervals from the apex downwards, will indicate the structure of any angiosperm stem. The dicotyledonous angiosperms differ in their stem tissue layout from the monocotyledons. The general dicotyledonous case will be described here with references to points of difference from the monocotyledonous case where necessary.

The Stem Apex and Development of the Primary Body of the Stem. A radial longitudinal section through a stem apex is represented diagrammatically in Fig. 17.40.

It consists at its uppermost extremity of a cone or dome-shaped group of actively dividing cells with their derivatives below them undergoing rapid differentiation into the permanent tissues. There is no sign of a single apical initial cell as in pteridophytes and other lower plants, but instead, the meristematic activity is equally shared by many cells. The current conception of the origin and ultimate end of the various derivatives is in terms of the so-called *tunica-corpus theory*. This concept is that the three mature plant tissue systems, namely, the epiderm, cortical and stelar regions, are derived from two more-or-less distinct regions of meristematic activity. The *tunica* forms the most external layer, from one to five cells thick (according to species) with the cells dividing continuously in an anticlinal plane (i.e. at right angles to the surface) to form a sheet-like covering of cells over the inner *corpus*. The outer layer of cells of this tunica ultimately differentiates into the epidermal layers only, whilst the derivatives of the corpus form the three-dimensional cortex and stele by continuous anticlinal and periclinal (i.e. parallel to the surface) divisions. This conception of the stem apex has replaced the older *histogen theory* of Hanstein, who considered the apex to consist of three distinct zones or *histogens*, the *dermatogen*, *periblem* and *plerome*, giving rise to the epidermis, cortex and stele respectively.

Just behind the extreme apex and at the sides, initiating leaves may be seen as lateral prominences and both tunica and corpus contribute to them. The prominences are referred to as *leaf buttresses* and from these the leaves develop outwardly. A little while after leaves are started, *axillary buds* originate. Although these buds eventually come to lie in the leaf axils, they do not always originate there precisely.

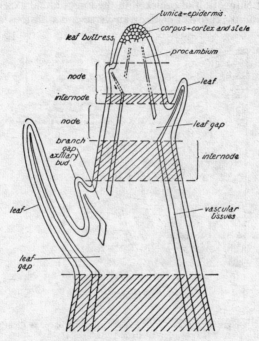

Fig. 17.40. Diagram of radial L.S. through a stem apex.

Most commonly, they originate on the stem just below the leaf above, and it is only by the rapid elongation of the space between the bud and the leaf above into an internode, and by some downward displacement of the bud into the leaf axil below, that they gain their final position.

Buds are initiated from cells in both tunica and corpus but not from an interior zone (cf. lateral root development). Their origin is described as *exogenous* (i.e. outside), because of their superficial source. If the bud eventually becomes a foliage shoot, its apex duplicates the pattern of the parent apex from which it arose, forming leaves and more bud initials. It remains dormant for some period, often being protected by hardened scales in the later stages of development.

Below the meristematic cells at the apex, the epidermal, cortical and stelar tissues differentiate. The general characteristics of epidermal cells have already been described (*see* Chap. 12). The cortex is composed chiefly of parenchyma with usually some collenchyma and later some sclerenchyma. These tissues have also been described. Differentiation of cells into collenchyma and sclerenchyma is accompanied by very marked elongation of each cell in the longitudinal axis of the stem and the sliding overgrowth of the transverse end walls.

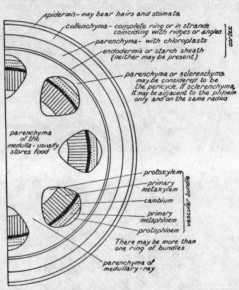

Fig. 17.41. Diagram of tissue arrangement in an herbaceous dicotyledonous stem.

The origin of the primary vascular system needs to be more elaborately described but can best be followed with reference to the completed structure. A transverse section through an internode at some small distance behind the apex of a herbaceous dicotyledonous stem, shows the tissue arrangements as in the annotated Fig. 17.41. Within the cortical region, but not necessarily clearly demarcated from it by a discrete layer, is the stele (cf. root). The original concept of the stele was one of a unit system of vascular tissue throughout the whole plant axis, together with the immediate ground tissue of inner pith (or a space if the stem is hollow) and at least one outer layer of pericycle. Some types of stele have already been described in Chap. 13, from the simple protostele to the complex dictyostele. In dicotyledonous angiosperm stems, the stele is described as a *eustele* in which the vascular system consists of separated strands, with leaf gaps and spaces between the strands not clearly delimited from one another. Nowadays, it is recognized that there is much difficulty in distinguishing the relationships between the stem vascular system and that of the leaves, particularly when it becomes apparent that in many angiosperms the stem vascular system is so profoundly influenced by the development of leaves.

Each strand of vascular tissue is called a *vascular bundle* or *fascicle*. It consists basically of groups of phloem and xylem tissues. The

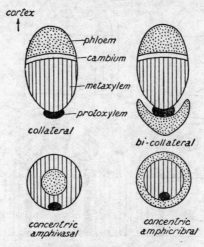

Fig. 17.42. Forms of vascular bundles.

arrangement of these in relation to one another is varied. The commonest arrangement is termed *collateral*, where the phloem occurs on one side of the xylem only, usually externally and on the same radius (*see* Fig. 17.42). If there are phloem groups internal and external to the xylem, the bundle is *bicollateral*. Another arrangement is called *concentric*, and either *amphivasal* if the xylem surrounds the phloem or *amphicribral* if vice versa. There may be a certain amount of transition between the types of bundle mentioned. Between the xylem and phloem groups, the vascular bundle may include a region of potentially meristematic cells forming the *intra-fascicular cambium*. It eventually gives rise to secondary vascular tissues when these occur, but is generally absent in monocotyledons and a few dicotyledons which lack secondary growth. e.g. *Ranunculus*.

The formation of such a system of vascular strands in the stem can be traced backwards from the apex, since sections at different levels represent the chronological sequence of tissue differentiation. The precise details are extremely complicated and difficult to comprehend, so a somewhat simplified concept will be given here.

Each vascular bundle is first represented in the apex as a group of meristematic cells known as the *procambial cells* (*see* Fig. 17.43).

The groups of procambial cells, corresponding to the number of vascular bundles, are symmetrically placed in a complete circular zone

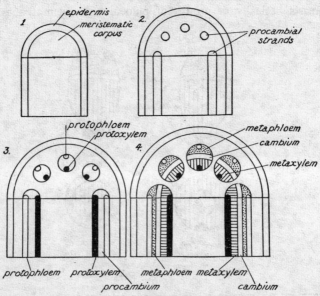

Fig. 17.43. Diagram to show sequence of differentiation of procambial cells in stem apex.

of cells which may all be potentially meristematic. If the whole zone were to differentiate in the manner to be described, there would be formed, from the commencement, a complete circular zone of vascular tissue instead of the isolated strands more often seen. As will be described later, often the vascular tissues eventually do become continuous laterally to form complete rings. This is the result of secondary growth, and the *cambium* which produces the secondary xylem and phloem cells is continuous, as undifferentiated parenchyma, with the procambial cells through the region of primary growth. Here we shall consider only the case of a collateral bundle with cambium and the sequence of differentiation of the procambial cells is shown in Fig. 17.43.

The first recognizable vascular elements to be differentiated are the *protophloem* and the *protoxylem*. The former appears first at the outer extremity of a radius through the procambial strand and the latter a little later at the inner extremity on the same radius. The protoxylem is thus described as arising in the *endarch* position. Further back along the stem, some procambial cells external to the fully-formed protoxylem, differentiate into primary *metaxylem* elements, i.e. in a direction centrifugally with relation to the centre of the stem, whilst procambial cells internal to the protophloem become primary *metaphloem* elements. Sections cut further and further back show increasing numbers of procambial cells changing into metaxylem or metaphloem until only a narrow band of procambial cells separates the two groups of vascular elements. If traced further back, these procambial cells are seen to be continuous with the intra-fascicular cambium of the bundle, or in other words, the intra-fascicular cambium is directly derived from otherwise undifferentiated cells of the procambium. In cases where the fully-formed bundle contains no intra-fascicular cambium, between the metaxylem and metaphloem groups may be seen a few parenchyma cells representing its position. These are

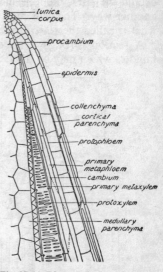

Fig. 17.44. Diagram to show sequence of differentiation of stem tissues in a radial longitudinal plane through a vascular bundle. Only one of each type of cell is shown in each tissue

the remains of the procambial strand from which the vascular elements were differentiated but which lack the property of becoming meristematic as in a cambium.

A longitudinal section taken exactly through a radius on which a developing vascular bundle lies, shows the same developmental picture and serves also to illustrate the rapid cell elongation which occurs during the differentiation of the procambial cells into phloem and xylem (*see* Fig. 17.44).

The differentiation of the layers marking the boundary between stele and cortex is often very vague. According to the concept of the stele, there should be two well-defined layers, the outermost of the stele, the *pericycle* and the innermost of the cortex, the *endodermis*. As will be seen, in roots of angiosperms these are almost always clearly defined, but in the stems this is not always so. There is no clearly-defined layer of stelar tissue external to the phloem, or in other words, there is no distinct pericycle. In some herbaceous stems, particularly in rhizomes, however, the endodermis is as clearly defined as in a root, showing Casparian strips on the radial walls, but in woody dicotyledonous stems it is typically absent. In some stems, when very young, i.e. just behind the apex, the innermost layer of cortex is sometimes defined in another way. The cells may contain abundant starch grains and form what is called the *starch sheath*.

A section through a node will show, in addition to the vascular bundles which may be fused as a complete ring, the *leaf trace* or traces

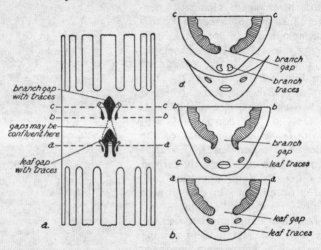

Fig. 17.45. (a) Diagram of branch and leaf gaps at a node. (b, c and d) Transverse sections of node at planes indicated.

which interconnect between the stem vascular system and that of the leaf (*see* Fig. 17.45). Associated with the origin of the trace is a *leaf gap*. Also at the node will be seen the vascular tissue of the axillary bud or branch connecting with that of the main stem. In most dicotyledons, there are two branch traces but one only or more than two may occur. Branch gaps in the stem stele may or may not occur in addition to the gaps caused by the leaves in whose axils the branches occur, i.e. the two gaps may be confluent to appear as one. Leaf and branch gaps are not easily distinguished from the spaces between bundles when the stele is greatly broken up, as in the angiosperms. Leaf gaps may more easily be recognized in those pteridophytes which possess large leaves inserted on a hollow cylinder of vascular tissue, e.g. *Dryopteris*.

Elongation of an internode is largely due to the rapid growth of the differentiating cells in the direction parallel to the stem axis. In monocotyledons, however, particularly the grasses, elongation is due to the activity of intercalary meristems (*see* below).

A transverse section through the typical monocotyledonous primary stem shows a considerable difference from that just described (*see* Fig. 17.46). Instead of a ring of vascular bundles, there are often several hundreds, as in maize, scattered throughout the whole of the ground tissue with no semblance of demarcation into cortical and

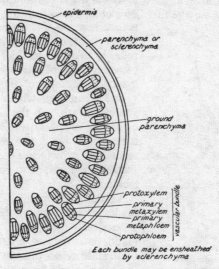

Fig. 17.46. Diagram of tissue arrangement in monocotyledonous stem.

stelar regions. The stele is described as an *atactostele* and represents the most complex of stelar structures. The bundles are usually collateral, lack cambium and are sheathed by sclerenchyma cells. In solid stems, they may be much more frequent towards the periphery than in the centre and the outer layers of the cortex are frequently sclerenchymatous. Origin and differentiation of tissues is generally as in the dicotyledonous case, there being very numerous procambial groups in the apex. The nodal distribution of vascular tissues is very complicated and will not be described here. In many grasses it is not possible to distinguish node from internode at the very young apex. The internodes develop as a result of cell division at the base of each leaf insertion, and thus these points of leaf insertion or nodes gradually become separated from one another by intercalary growth, the intercalated portions being the internodes (*see* Fig. 17.47). At first all cells of the internode are meristematic, but gradually the upper ones differentiate, leaving only the lowermost in active division. These eventually cease activity but remain potentially active for some time at the so-called joints. They may regain activity at a joint to re-elevate a horizontally displaced stem. This is a geotropic growth response.

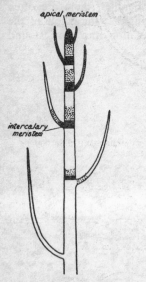

black - *zones of rapid cell division*
stippled - *zones of differentiating tissue*
clear - *zones of matured tissue*

Fig. 17.47. Diagram to show position of intercalary meristems in a grass stem.

Secondary Growth of the Stem. Tissues added to the primary body by the activities of lateral meristems (as opposed to apical meristems) constitute *secondary growth*. Because the growth is manifested as an increase in diameter of a part rather than in length, it is sometimes referred to as *secondary thickening*. It is of very frequent occurrence in dicotyledons as a result of the activity of the vascular cambium which produces more vascular tissue, and the activity of a cork cambium or phellogen which produces a periderm. In a few monocotyledons, secondary growth may occur by other special methods, but in general it is lacking.

As has been pointed out, the intrafascicular cambium is derived from the procambial cells which retain meristematic potentialities instead of differentiating into xylem, phloem or parenchyma. If all the procambium differentiates, then there is no vascular cambium and hence no secondary growth within the vascular system. When there is a cambium, its activity usually commences very soon after the primary tissues have been formed. In some cases, e.g. *Cucurbita* and *Clematis* (*see* Figs. 17.63, 17.64), cambial activity is restricted to the regions of the primary vascular bundles, with the result that they remain as discrete bundles separated by clearly-defined medullary rays. In most cases, however, soon after commencement of thickening of the bundles, there arises in the rays between them, from parenchyma cells, a layer of meristematic cells constituting an *inter-fascicular cambium* uniting the groups of bundle cambial cells into a complete ring (*see* Fig. 17.48). When the whole of this ring becomes active, a lateral union of the primary bundles is achieved, so that a complete vascular cylinder is

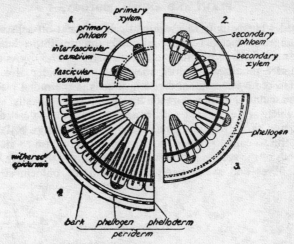

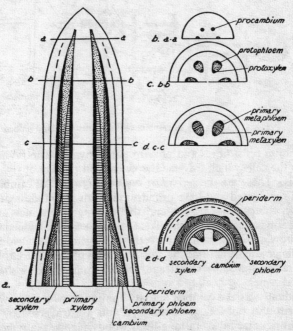

Fig. 17.48. Diagrams to show sequence of tissue development in secondary growth of a stem. Transverse plane.

Fig. 17.49. (a) Diagram to show sequence of tissue development in secondary growth of a stem. Longitudinal plane. (b, c, d and e) Transverse sections at planes indicated.

produced. The activity of a cambial cell is to cut off cells alternately on its tangential faces, the inner cells differentiating into xylem elements and the outer cells into phloem elements (*see* Fig. 17.50). As the vascular cylinder increases in girth, the cambium cylinder also grows in circumference by occasional division of cells in the radial plane.

The vascular cambium is made up of two types of cells. There are those which are elongated with tapering ends, the so-called *fusiform initials*, and those which are relatively small and more or less isodiametric, the so-called *ray initials*. The former give rise to all the elongated cells of the secondary vascular tissue, namely the xylem tracheids, vessels, fibres and xylem parenchyma, and the phloem sieve tubes,

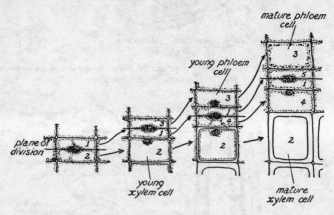

Fig. 17.50. Activity of cambial cell to form xylem and phloem.

companion cells, fibres and phloem parenchyma. The ray initials give rise to the cells which traverse the xylem and phloem at right angles to the axis. These are the *secondary medullary rays*. All cambial cells are highly vacuolated and have primary pits with plasmodesmata. During activity, the cambial initials and their youngest products of division, form a zone of cells all much alike, to make a cambial zone in which the cells show a perfect radial and serial arrangement. Outside this zone, the cells gradually assume the characteristics of the adjacent tissues and often retain the same radial and serial arrangement as shown in the cambial zone.

Gradually, as the cambial activity continues, wider and wider zones of xylem and phloem are developed and are traversed by more and more horizontal rays. In long-lived woody plants, the typical trunk is developed. In temperate and colder climates, seasonal activity in such woody perennials is marked by the occurrence of growth rings in the wood. This has already been described for *Pinus* (*see* p. 312). With each succeeding year, some of the central xylem becomes non-functional as a result of death of the parenchymatous cells and infiltration of oils, gums, resins, tannins and various coloured materials into the walls and lumina of the conducting elements. Thus a constantly widening core of darker-coloured *heart-wood* is built up, surrounded by a narrower band of still functional *sap-wood*. Year by year also, the more external phloem elements become non-functional to form an outer zone of

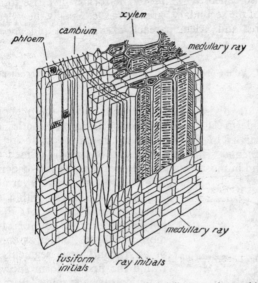

Fig. 17.51. Diagram to show formation of medullary rays by cambial cells.

inactive tissue; this usually becomes compacted into a dense layer almost non-cellular in appearance, by the crushing forces exerted during the expansion of internally and externally placed cells.

In conjunction with secondary growth of the vascular tissues, a similar process usually appears in the outer cortical region of the stem. This new growth is the *periderm*; it is due to the activity of another lateral meristem, the *phellogen* or *cork cambium*. Characteristically, periderm appears on plant parts which show continuous increase in thickness. The woody roots and stems of dicotyledonous plants are typical examples. Periderm may occur in herbaceous dicotyledons but only on the older parts of stems and roots, where the epidermis fails to keep pace with the internal expansion. Monocotyledons very rarely develop any such protective tissue. The tissues of the periderm, namely the *phellem* or *cork*, the *phellogen* and the *phelloderm* have been described in Chap. 12. The phellogen which gives rise to the other tissues, is simple as compared with vascular cambium. It is composed of a single cell type, a vacuolated radially-flattened oblong cell in the transverse section and elongate-rectangular in the longitudinal section (*see*

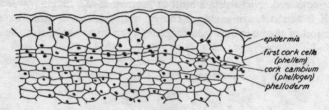

Fig. 17.52. Young phellogen of the elder. H.P. drawing. Cell contents omitted except nuclei.

Fig. 17.52). By division in the tangential plane, the phellogen cuts off inner phelloderm cells and outer cork cells in radial series, comparable with the activity of the vascular cambium in producing xylem and phloem elements. The first phellogen to arise is termed the *primary phellogen* and in most instances it appears in the sub-epidermal tissues.

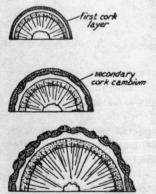

Fig. 17.53. Diagram to show successive phellogen formation.

The exact position is very variable however and may be actually within the phloem tissues in some species. As the stem ages, but in some cases not for several years, more phellogens, either as complete rings or as discontinuous segments, may arise within the first to form successive layers of periderm as the outer layers are cracked or sloughed off by internal pressure (*see* Fig. 17.53). By comparison, the cork cells greatly outnumber the phelloderm elements and some plants may show none of the latter at all. The cork of *Quercus suber* (the cork oak), is a well-known commercial product.

In most cases where periderm formation occurs, an aerating system through the otherwise air-tight covering is developed. This takes the form of *lenticels*, so-named because of their commonly biconvex outline in the external view. They are structurally differentiated parts of the periderm and stand out by reason of the very loose cell arrangement and lack of suberization. They vary greatly in size according to species, but can be seen frequently as protrusions of loose substance through cracks in the periderm (*see* Fig. 17.54).

In a secondarily thickening stem, the first lenticels usually arise beneath stomata in the epidermis and may be in evidence before the periderm itself is initiated. The cells below the stomate lose their chlorophyll and divide repeatedly to form a loose mass. Gradually the region of division penetrates deeper into the cortex, and the plane of division of the cells becomes regularly parallel to the surface so that a *lenticel phellogen* is built up. This proceeds to cut off more and more loose cells towards the exterior to form the so-called *complementary cells* (they complement the periderm), and eventually the epidermis is

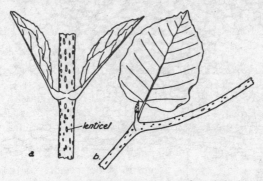

Fig. 17.54. Lenticels on (*a*), young *Hydrangea* twig and (*b*), beech twig.

ruptured. The outer cells die and fall away, but are replaced by more from the inner region by the activity of the lenticel meristem. As the cork phellogen is formed, it becomes continuous with the lenticel phellogens throughout the whole periderm (*see* Fig. 17.55).

Occasionally, lenticels may be formed early in periderm development by activity of cork phellogen, in which isolated patches of cells cut off masses of complementary cells to rupture the cork outside. In later peridermal layers, the lenticels always arise in this way. In some lenticels with very loose complementary cells, occasional more compact layers are developed from time to time. These are called the *closing layers* and are ruptured as the next layer of complementary cells is developed. When the distribution of lenticels is examined, it is found that they are often exactly opposite medullary rays.

The manner of secondary growth in stems, as outlined above, is common to most dicotyledonous plants, but there is a wide variety of anomalous conditions to be found.

Most monocotyledons do not exhibit secondary growth at all, but due to very vigorous and prolonged primary growth they may develop into quite large plants, e.g. the palms. This is chiefly due to activity by a *primary thickening meristem* which originates beneath the leaf primordia and behind the extreme apex (*see* Fig. 17.56). Cells are produced by this meristem in radial rows at right angles to the surface and thicken the stem behind the apex before elongation of internodes commences. Some of the cells differentiate into ground parenchyma and

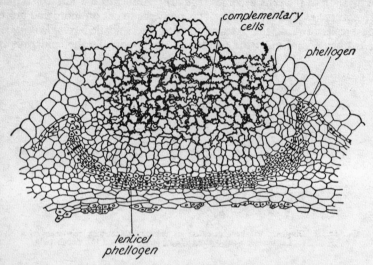

Fig. 17.55. T.S. through lenticel of elder. H.P. drawing. Cell contents omitted except nuclei.

others into procambial strands from which mature vascular bundles are developed.

In some monocotyledons, e.g. *Dracaena*, *Yucca*, *Aloe*, secondary growth does occur and the meristem concerned is usually referred to as a cambium. It is a prolongation of the primary thickening meristem mentioned above, but adds to the girth of the stem after elongation of the internodes has ceased, hence the secondary nature of the thickening. This cambium arises in the parenchyma outside the vascular bundles and proceeds to cut off cells inwards and outwards. Those produced inwards differentiate into radial series of vascular strands, in contrast to the scattered primary bundles, and ground parenchyma. The outer cells become parenchyma (*see* Fig. 17.73).

Stem Abscission. Many plants lose parts by the abscission of stems. Flowers and young fruits may frequently be cut off before much sclerenchyma or hard vascular tissue has been formed, but hard woody stems may be abscissed also. Examples are the foliage-bearing branches of oak, poplar and elm, and the mature pedicels of many fruits. When the tissues concerned are soft, no distinct abscission zone may be seen

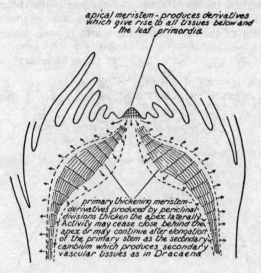

Fig. 17.56. Diagram to show position of primary thickening meristem in a monocotyledonous stem.

until immediately before the break, when a separation layer quickly appears (*see* leaf abscission). In the cases of the hard woody stems mentioned above, a definite abscission zone is formed in the twig from an early age. In this zone, the hard tissues are greatly modified and

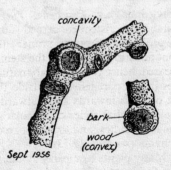

Fig. 17.57. Scars left at twig abscission in oak.

reduced in quantity. A distinct separation layer passes across the twig through them. In some cases, such as poplar and elm, the branches abscissed may still be living and have leaves attached. The age of abscissed branches is variable according to species, but branches up to twenty years old have been known to fall from poplar trees. Usually, branches are abscissed much younger than this. When a twig or branch has been cut off, the scar left is clearly noticeable, often as a protuberance on the main axis. This scar is quickly covered by a protective periderm continuous with that of the main branch.

The following series of drawings of named examples may serve to illustrate more clearly many of the points referred to in this section.

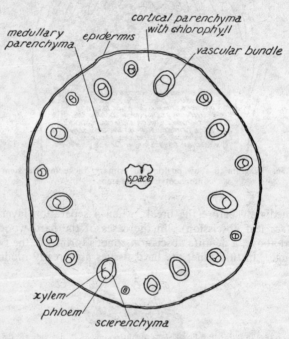

Fig. 17.58. Tissue layout in stem of buttercup. L.P. plan of T.S.

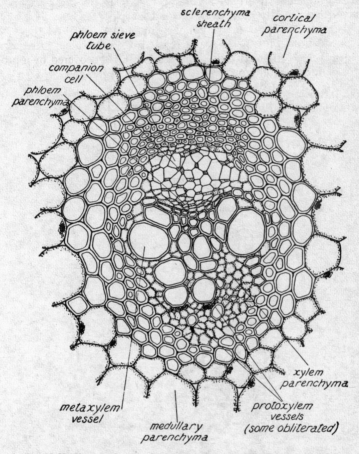

phloem sieve tube

companion cell

phloem parenchyma

sclerenchyma sheath

cortical parenchyma

metaxylem vessel

medullary parenchyma

protoxylem vessels (some obliterated)

xylem parenchyma

Fig. 17.59. Vascular bundle of stem of buttercup. H.P. drawing of T.S.

417

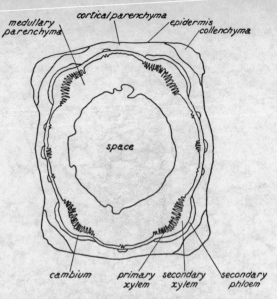

Fig. 17.60. Tissue layout in stem of dead nettle. L.P. plan of T.S.

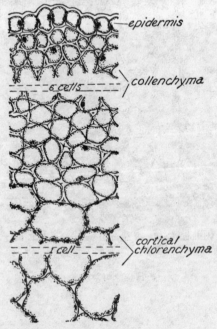

Fig. 17.61. Tissues extending from epidermis to pith through angle of dead-nettle stem. H.P. drawing of T.S.

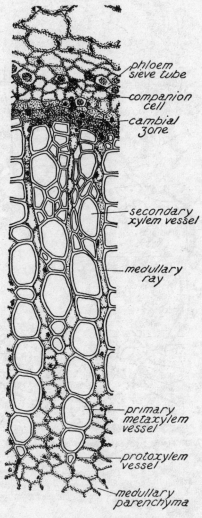

phloem
sieve tube

companion
cell

cambial
zone

secondary
xylem vessel

medullary
ray

primary
metaxylem
vessel

protoxylem
vessel

medullary
parenchyma

Fig. 17.61.—(contd.).

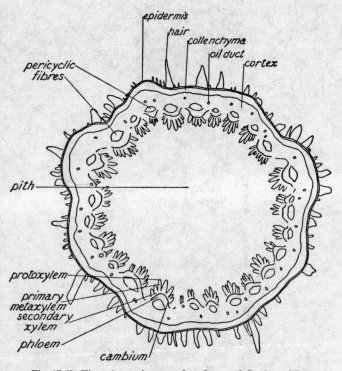

Fig. 17.62. Tissue layout in stem of sunflower. L.P. plan of T.S.

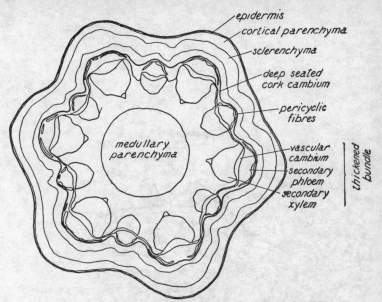

Fig. 17.63. Tissue layout in stem of clematis. L.P. plan of T.S.

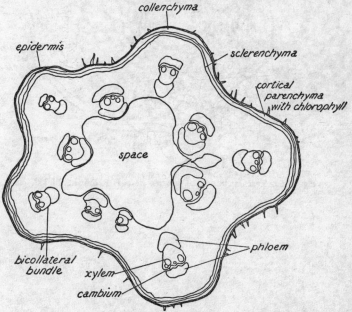

Fig. 17.64. Tissue layout in stem of marrow. L.P. plan of T.S.

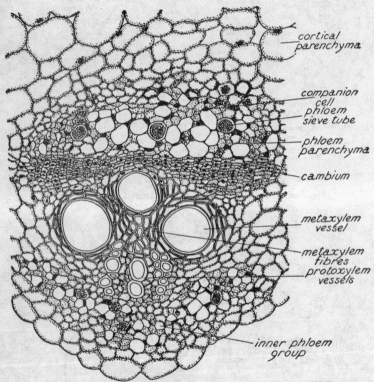

Labels on the figure:
- cortical parenchyma
- companion cell
- phloem sieve tube
- phloem parenchyma
- cambium
- metaxylem vessel
- metaxylem fibres
- protoxylem vessels
- inner phloem group

Fig. 17.65. Vascular bundle of marrow stem. H.P. drawing of T.S.

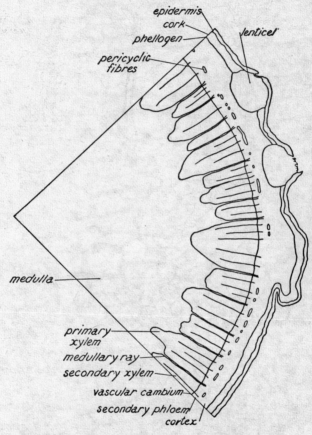

Fig. 17.66. Tissue layout in young elder stem. L.P. plan of T.S.

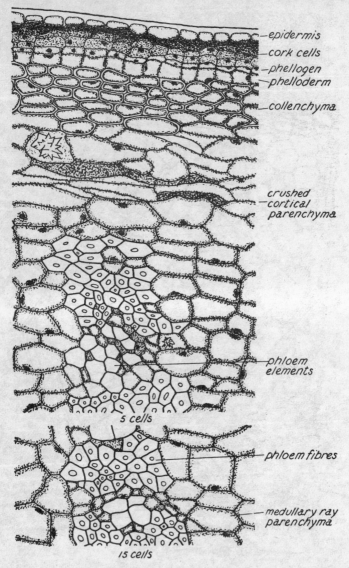

epidermis
cork cells
phellogen
phelloderm
collenchyma

crushed
cortical
parenchyma

phloem
elements

5 cells

phloem fibres

medullary ray
parenchyma

15 cells

Fig. 17.67. Tissues extending from epidermis to pith through young lime stem.
H.P. drawing of T.S.

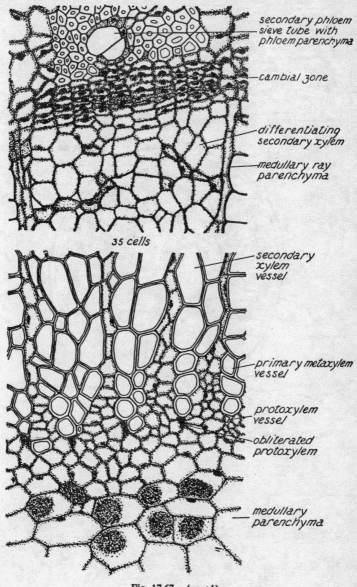

secondary phloem
sieve tube with
phloem parenchyma

cambial zone

differentiating
secondary xylem

medullary ray
parenchyma

35 cells

secondary
xylem
vessel

primary metaxylem
vessel

protoxylem
vessel

obliterated
protoxylem

medullary
parenchyma

Fig 17.67.—(contd.).

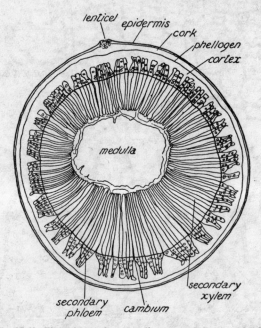

Fig. 17.68. Tissue layout in young lime stem. L.P. plan of T.S.

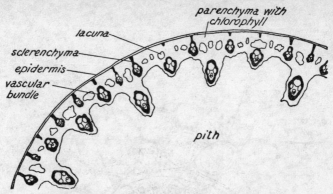

Fig. 17.69. Tissue layout in stem of rush. L.P. plan of T.S.

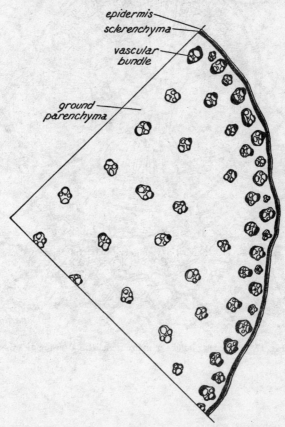

Fig. 17.70. Tissue layout in stem of maize. L.P. plan of T.S.

427

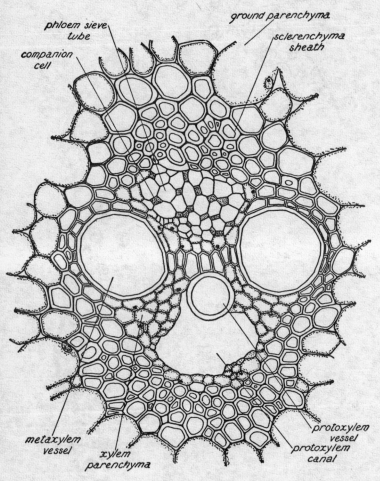

Fig. 17.71. Vascular bundle of maize stem. H.P. drawing of T.S.

428

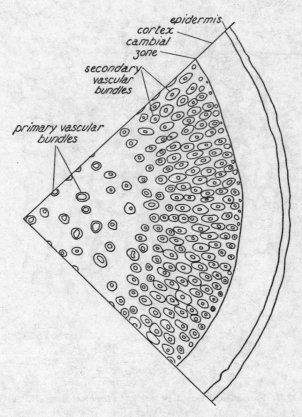

Fig. 17.72. Tissue layout in stem of *Dracaena* (secondarily thickened) L.P. plan of T.S.

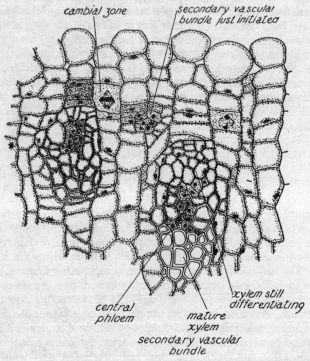

Fig. 17.73. Formation of secondary bundles in *Dracaena* stem **H.P.** drawing of **T.S.**

430

The Leaf

The angiosperm leaf is even more difficult to define morphologically than the stem. Its range of variation is even greater and no clear definition can be made to fit all the organs which may be designated leaves or their modified derivatives. The most familiar leaf structure is the green foliage leaf which has in the past been assumed to be the basic form from which all other leaf-like structures, as appendages of the stem, have been derived. Whether this is truly the case is a matter of speculation, but to assume the opposite and to treat every kind of stem appendage as a separate entity in its own right is much too complicated a procedure. It is intended therefore to assume the older conception for convenience, and thus under the term leaves are included any stem appendages which arise as superficial outgrowths, independent of other outgrowths, arranged in some definite pattern and normally subtending buds in their axils. They generally show bilateral symmetry, reach a fixed maximum size (i.e. show limited growth) and never bear other appendages except sometimes buds.

Leaf Form

The generalized foliage leaf exposes as great a surface area to the atmosphere as possible so that it is efficient as a photosynthesizing organ. At the same time, it must be rigid enough to withstand buffeting, and be protected sufficiently to withstand excessive drying-out. In form, the foliage leaf is a broad flat *lamina* with or without a *stalk* or *petiole*. The variations in size, shape, texture and other features, are so great as to baffle any simple descriptive method, but the older systematists who considered that leaf form was important in establishing relationships, classified leaves according to their external characteristics, bearing in mind certain chief points. Whilst such detailed knowledge of leaf form may not figure so importantly in taxonomic problems as was once thought, such morphological knowledge may be of great help in other spheres. Below is given a summary, by definitions, of the main characteristics of a foliage leaf which may need to be described, together with the commoner variations.

1. *Insertion on the stem*

Petiolate: possessing a stalk or petiole which carries the blade.

Sessile: lacking a petiole, the lamina inserted directly on the stem.

Amplexicaul: a sessile leaf surrounding the stem at the node.

Perfoliate: an amplexicaul leaf extending beyond the stem on the distal side of the node from the centre of leaf insertion.

Decurrent: a sessile leaf prolonged downwards from its point of insertion into a flattened sheet.

Connate: two sessile leaves at the same node having their bases fused around the stem.

2. Composition of the lamina

Simple: a leaf with all parts of the lamina continuous and nowhere separated from each other or the midrib. Such a leaf may be *divided* but all the divisions and subdivisions conform to the above.

Compound: a leaf composed of separate leaflets each having a separate base on the common leaf stalk.

Pinnate: a simple or compound leaf in which the divisions or leaflets are arranged in two series on either side of a common main axis. Bipinnate, tripinnate, etc., are degrees to which this is effected.

Palmate: a simple or compound leaf of which the divisions or leaflets are arranged in a radiating series from a common point.

3. Form of the blade margin

Entire: smooth and without indentations.

Indented: leaf margin broken in outline by indentations of numerous possible kinds so that it may be described as sinuate, dentate, serrate, bi-serrate, spiny, crenate, incised, ciliate, etc.

4. Relative length and breadth of the blade of leaf or leaflet and other points concerning shape

The general shape of the blade may be—

Linear: at least four or five times as long as broad.

Lanceolate: about three times as long as broad, broadest at the base tapering to a pointed apex.

Ovate: about twice as long as broad, broadest at the base and tapering slightly to a rounded apex.

Obovate: about the same size as above but narrowest at the base and broadening towards the apex.

Orbicular, oval, oblong, etc: comparable in shape to the corresponding geometrical figures.

Spatulate: short broad apex above a longer narrow base.

Cuneate: wedge-shaped with the point at the base of the leaf.

Many intermediate forms between these can occur.

Cordate: a leaf whose base is notched on either side of the midrib and prolonged backwards into two lobes or auricles.

Peltate: a leaf in which the lamina develops outwards on all sides of a centrally-placed petiole. Really a cordate leaf with the two lobes united.

Reniform: kidney-shaped.

Sagittate: shaped like an arrowhead, i.e. with backwardly-pointing basal auricles.

Hastate: with horizontally-pointing basal auricles.

Acute: a pointed leaf apex.

Obtuse: gently rounded apex.

Acuminate: apex narrowed and prolonged into a point.

Truncate: apex squarely ended.

Emarginate: apex definitely indented at the end of the midrib.

Mucronate: apex at which the midrib is prolonged into a small point.

5. *Texture*

Fleshy: thick and soft.

Coriaceous: firm and dry, leathery.

Membranous: thin and supple.

Scarious: very thin, colourless and more or less transparent but fairly stiff.

6. *Disposition of vascular strands or veins, otherwise known as venation*

Reticulate: veins forming a meshwork throughout the lamina.

Parallel-veined: veins parallel through the lamina with few, if any, cross-connexions.

Pinnate: single midrib with main branches given off in pinnate order.

Palmate: several main veins arising from the end of the petiole and spreading fan-wise.

7. *Mode of leaf folding in the bud: ptyxis or vernation*

Rolled: margins inrolled towards the midrib.

Folded or pleated: blade folded longitudinally into pleats.

Circinnate: coiled like a spiral spring.

8. *Heterophylly*

This condition is said to arise when the foliage leaves on the same plant are of distinctly different types. Sometimes it is due to particular environmental factors. For example, many aquatics show great differences between the aerial and submerged leaves, e.g. arrowhead (*Sagittaria*), water buttercup (*Ranunculus aquatilis*). Sometimes the same species grown under wet and dry conditions may exhibit two distinct leaf forms; small and scale-like under dry conditions and expanded and broad when conditions are wet. Sometimes in the same plant there may be a distinct difference between the leaves borne on the seedling and those produced by the mature plant, e.g. gorse (*Ulex*). In a few species, heterophylly may not appear to be connected with conditions or stages of development but just appear at random all over the plant.

Phyllotaxis. This is the spacing and sequence of arrangement of the leaves on the shoot. It follows the same arrangement as the leaf

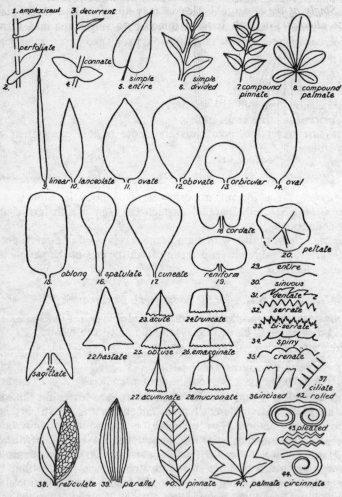

Fig. 17.74. Leaf form. 1–4 leaf insertion; 5–8 composition of lamina 9–28 shape; 29–37 form of margin; 38–41 venation; 42–44 vernation.

primordia at the meristematic apex but can be seen in the expanded form on the older stem. There are three main types of leaf arrangement—

1. *Whorls or circles at the nodes.* The leaves in each whorl may or may not alternate with those above and below them.

2. *Opposite pairs at the nodes.* Pairs may arise in the same plane all the way along the stem, i.e. be *distichous*, or pairs may arise alternating in planes at right angles to one another, i.e. be *decussate*.

3. *Singly at the nodes.* The leaves may alternate in a single plane, i.e. be *alternate*, or their bases if joined by a single line may form a

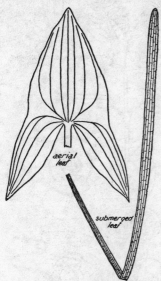

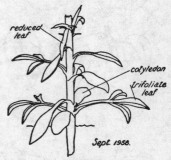

Fig. 17.75. Heterophylly in arrowhead.

Fig. 17.76. Trifoliate leaves of the gorse seedling.

helix around the stem. If cases of this latter arrangement are examined, it can be seen that a geometrical pattern is still followed. Every leaf is separated from the next around the circumference by a fixed quantity known as the *leaf divergence*. The precise arrangement can be expressed in terms of this divergence. If a lower leaf is marked and the helix through the leaf bases of those above is traced out until a leaf vertically above the starting point is reached, data from that helix can be used to fix the geometrical pattern of the leaf arrangement. The expression normally used is a fraction in which the numerator represents the number of times the helix has completed the circumference, and the denominator the number of leaf bases passed through in reaching a leaf vertically above the starting point (but not counting the starting leaf).

Thus $\frac{1}{2}$ represents the single opposite condition (*see* Fig. 17.77). That fraction of 360° is the leaf divergence, i.e. 180°. Thus $\frac{2}{5}$ means passing five leaves in circling twice. Such leaf divergences frequently follow the arithmetical series $\frac{1}{2}, \frac{1}{3}, \frac{2}{5}, \frac{3}{8}, \frac{5}{13}, \frac{8}{21}$, etc., in which each value of the numerator and denominator is the sum of the two values which precede it. The reason for this has baffled physiologists for a long time. Phyllotaxis is not always hard and fast for a species. It may vary during development and sometimes varies on branches of the same plant.

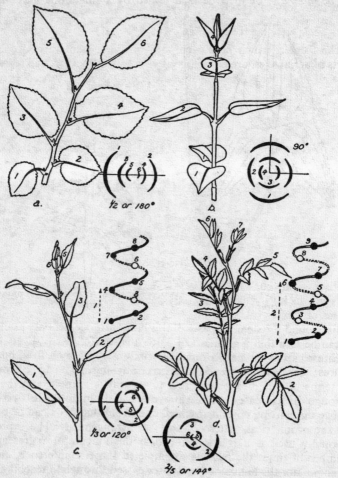

Fig. 17.77. Leaf arrangement. (*a* Elm. (*b*) Lilac. (*c*) Greengage. (*d*) Rose.

Leaf Mosaic. It is often the case in climbing or creeping plants where every advantage must be taken of the available light, that over-shadowing of leaves is reduced to a minimum by the correct placing of leaf blades. This is achieved usually by the twisting growth of petioles to bring the laminae into positions of minimum overlap. The fitting together of the blades to form such a pattern is termed the leaf mosaic.

Structures formed from Reduced or Modified Foliage Leaves

1. *Scale leaves and bud scales*

The former, which may occur on rhizomes, stem tubers or lower parts of aerial axes, are homologous with foliage leaves. Bud scales are specially modified leaves or leaf bases serving to protect the inner apical

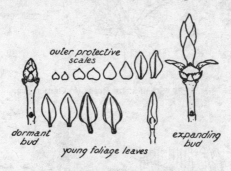

Fig. 17.78. Bud of lilac, dissected.

meristem and young leaves. Such scales often show complete transitions between the fully-reduced and fully-developed foliage structure, e.g. bud scales of lilac or blackcurrant.

2. *Bracts and bracteoles*

Bracts are small leaf-like organs subtending such parts as inflores-cences; bracteoles subtend individual flowers.

3. *Stipules*

These are foliar appendages attached to the petiole or leaf base, e.g. pea, rose.

4. *Ligules and intra-vaginal scales*

These are scale-like appendages of certain leaves, e.g. grasses, *Potamogeton*.

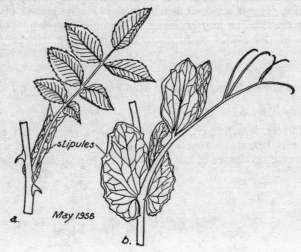

Fig. 17.79. Stipules. (*a*) Rose. (*b*) Garden pea.

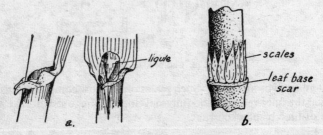

Fig. 17.80. (*a*) Ligule of perennial rye grass. (*b*) Intravaginal scales of *Potamogeton*.

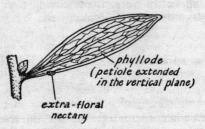

Fig. 17.81. Phyllodes of *Acacia*.

5. Phyllodes

These are broadened leaf bases and petioles performing the photosynthetic function when the lamina is undeveloped, e.g. *Acacia*.

6. Spines

Leaves and/or stipules may be reduced to non-chlorophyllous, sharply-pointed spines, e.g. barberry, gooseberry. Note that the spines of gorse are branches and themselves bear leaves.

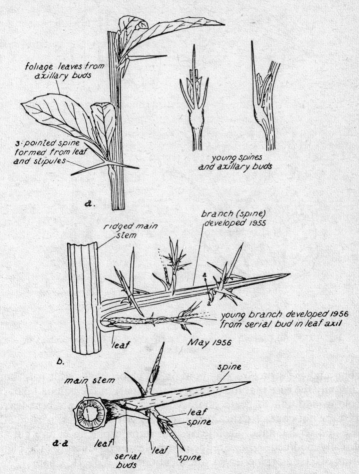

Fig. 17.82. (*a*) Leaf spines of barberry. (*b*) Branch spines of gorse.

Persistence of the Leaves. A plant is deciduous if it sheds its leaves regularly in rhythm with the growing and non-growing seasons. It is evergreen if the leaves are retained for an indefinite period extending over several successive growing and non-growing periods.

Leaf Modifications for Purposes other than Photosynthesis. Such modifications are often accompanied by loss of the power to assimilate

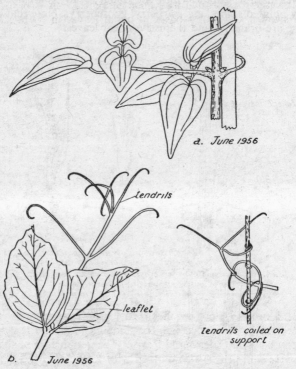

Fig. 17.83. (*a*) *Clematis* climbing by sensitive petiole. (*b*) Pea climbing by tendrils.

carbon and the structure may contain no chlorophyll. But it is more commonly the case that the petiole or some part of the lamina takes on a role in addition to being photosynthetic. Many plants bear leaves which are not characteristically broad, flat, soft structures, particularly those in drier habitats. Such leaves are xeromorphic in nature but are not really modified. They are the normal leaves produced by the plant. Forms of xeromorphic leaves are mentioned in Vol. II, Chap. 7, and some information on their anatomy is given later in this chapter.

Modifications Associated with the Climbing Habit. A few plants make use of *petioles* which are sensitive to touch, in order to climb on or through other vegetation, e.g. *Clematis*. There are many cases of *tendril* climbers in which the sensitive tendril is a prolongation of the laminal midrib or the midrib of an entire leaf or leaflet of which the lamina never develops, e.g. pea (*Pisum sativum*), vetches.

Modifications Associated with Food Storage. This is best illustrated by the swollen scales and bases of aerial leaves in bulbs such as the

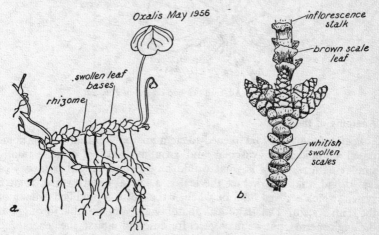

Fig. 17.84. (*a*) Rhizome of wood sorrel with swollen leaf bases. (*b*) Swollen scale leaves of toothwort.

tulip and onion. Food-swollen leaf bases may also be found on rhizomes, e.g. *Oxalis*, in which the underground stem is clothed with the fleshy bases of older aerial leaves. The aerial stem of the parasitic toothwort (*Lathraea*) is also clothed with colourless food-packed scale leaves. Several aquatics form winter resting buds in which the scales are fleshy and packed with stored food, e.g. *Hydrocharis*. Many succulent plants owe their appearance to the deep layers of water storage tissue underlying the epidermis.

Modifications Associated with Vegetative Propagation. Vegetative propagation by leaves can be brought about in some cases by the formation of buds on the leaves, e.g. *Cardamine, Tolmiea, Nymphaea*. Sometimes such buds develop only on injury or detachment of the whole leaf, e.g. *Begonia, Ficus elastica*.

Modifications Associated with the Insectivorous Habit. The sundew (*Drosera*), with its tentacled leaves, the Venus fly-trap (*Dionaea*), with its spiny-margined leaves and the pitcher plants (*Sarracenia* and *Nepenthes*), with laterally-joined leaf edges, are all examples of these modifications (*see* Chap. 35).

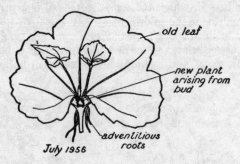

Fig. 17.85. Adventitious bud on leaf of *Tolmiea*.

Anatomy of the Leaf

Leaf anatomy may be likened to stem anatomy in that each is composed of epidermal, vascular and ground tissues of fundamentally similar natures. This is what would be expected on either theory of leaf origin, that is, whether the leaf is a lateral outgrowth of a stem system which evolved first, or whether the leaf is a modified branch of the stem system. Details of leaf anatomy are very variable throughout the angiosperms, but we may select for description first, the generalized dorsi-ventral leaf of the mesophytic dicotyledon (i.e. inhabiting reasonably moist conditions, cf. hydrophytic and xerophytic) and the iso-lateral leaf of the monocotyledon. The former has distinctions in appearance and structure between upper and lower surfaces and the characteristic reticulate venation of the dicotyledon. The latter shows most frequently no distinction between its two lateral faces and its venation is characteristically parallel.

The dorsi-ventral leaf is bounded externally by an *epidermis*, the characteristics of which have been described in Chap. 12. In a leaf, this is almost always *cuticularized*, but more so on the upper than the lower surface. *Stomata* perforate the epidermis either on the upper, lower or both surfaces according to species, but most frequently only the lower (abaxial) side is so perforated. Except for the guard cells of the stomata, the epidermal cells do not generally contain chlorophyll, but certain leaves may produce sap pigments in the epidermal cell vacuoles. The cells are tightly pressed to one another so that there are no spaces between them. This is in accordance with the main function of the tissue, to protect and prevent desiccation of the underlying cells.

Numerous epidermal outgrowths may occur. *Hairs* (trichomes) or *secretory glands* may be present on both surfaces. The mesomorphic leaf rarely shows a composite epidermis.

The ground tissue of the leaf within the epidermis is the *mesophyll* tissue and this is composed of specialized parenchyma cells whose primary function is photosynthesis. The cells contain numerous discoid chloroplasts and much of the tissue is described as *spongy* because of the large *intercellular spaces*. In mesomorphic dorsi-ventral leaves, the sponginess is often confined to the lower region, since the mesophyll is usually differentiated into distinct layers. There is an upper (adaxial) tissue of cells elongated in a direction at right angles to the surface of the leaf and containing very large numbers of chloroplasts. This is the *palisade mesophyll*, so-called from the shape of the cells. Below this, is the more loosely-packed *spongy mesophyll* with fewer chloroplasts. It is largely owing to these differences in the mesophyll layers that the leaf has different appearances on its upper and lower sides. In a few mesomorphic dicotyledons, there may be both an upper and lower palisade mesophyll. It is often the case that leaves of the same species, when grown under different light and moisture conditions, show differences in mesophyll construction. Leaves developing in light, dry positions tend to exhibit an upper palisade layer whilst those grown in damp, shady positions do not. The sponginess of at least some part of the mesophyll is bound up with the efficient aeration of the leaf, and the spaces between mesophyll cells are continuous with the *substomatal air spaces* which are usually very much pronounced. Because of the air spaces, the internal surface area exposed to the atmosphere is enormous.

The vascular system usually gives the leaf a characteristic appearance externally. The closed reticulate venation of the dicotyledonous leaf is due to an anastomosing network of vascular strands, which are branches of finer and finer dimensions originating from one or more main bundles, and which form a continuous system without ending freely in the mesophyll. An open system may occur in which the smaller veins do end freely in the mesophyll.

A vertical section through a leaf blade, including a main vein and some of the tissue on either side (*see* Fig. 17.87), shows the vascular tissue of the main vein to be enclosed by parenchyma and some supporting collenchyma or sclerenchyma in most cases. It is thus fairly clearly marked off from the mesophyll. The minor veins pass through the mesophyll just below the palisade in all directions so that transverse, oblique and longitudinal views of them may be seen in one leaf section. The quantity of xylem and phloem in a vein depends upon the size and position of the vein. Where main veins diverge from the petiole, they usually show a collateral structure with adaxial xylem and abaxial phloem. In some cases, a bicollateral structure with upper and lower phloem may occur. Many dicotyledonous angiosperms show secondary growth in the main vascular bundles, but the minor branches never do. The main veins may also show vessels in the xylem as well as tracheids, but the smaller veins show tracheids only, these being annularly or

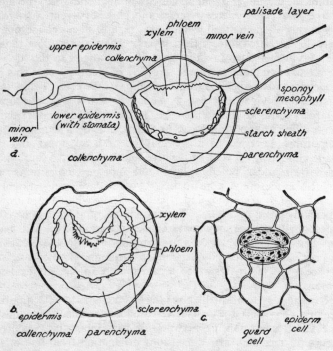

Fig. 17.86. Leaf of pear. (*a*) Tissue layout in T.S. of midrib. (*b*) Same through petiole. (*c*) Stoma in surface view.

helically thickened. The phloem contains sieve tubes, but as a vein and its branches get smaller and smaller, phloem elements become progressively fewer, so that the end of the vein is composed of one or two tracheids only. These may be irregularly shaped, with pitted walls, and are called *water storage tracheids*. Where the small veins traverse the mesophyll, they are nowhere in contact with the intercellular air spaces. Each is enclosed by a compact layer of parenchyma cells, the *bundle sheath*, which follows the course of the bundle and completely encloses the terminal tracheids. The sheath cells are elongated parallel with the course of the vein and may or may not contain a few chloroplasts. Extended outgrowths of these bundle sheaths may pass out from the upper and lower sides into the mesophyll and may be concerned with water distribution.

Mechanical tissues in the leaf are very variable. Typically, the dicotyledonous leaf develops collenchyma beneath the epidermis in the region of the larger veins and sometimes along the edge of the lamina.

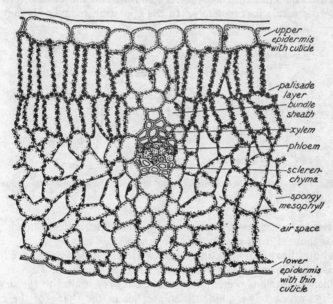

Fig. 17.87. Section through lamina of pear leaf. H.P. drawing of V.S.

Sclereids may occur in the mesophyll in some species. Much of the support for the softer leaf tissues comes from their own turgidity and from the vascular elements which permeate them.

The typical monocotyledonous leaf is parallel-veined and isolateral. A transverse section of such a leaf is shown diagrammatically in Fig. 17.88. Externally, the leaf shows distinct parallel ribs on both surfaces, corresponding to the positions of the main veins. The epidermis is of the usual structure but the stomata are often arranged in parallel rows in the regions between the ribs. The mesophyll may or may not show palisade and spongy layers, but is confined generally to the regions coinciding with the grooves of the leaf. The vascular bundles, according to species, may all be of the same size, or smaller ones may alternate with the larger ones. Sometimes, the central vein may be larger than all the others. The tissues of the vascular strands are in general similar to those of the dicotyledons, but never show secondary growth. Bundle sheaths of various types often occur. Supporting tissue is almost always present in large amounts and most frequently is of sclerenchyma fibres in association with the vascular strands. The bundles of fibres are usually on both outermost edges of the vein connecting the bundle sheath to the epidermis and may extend around the bundle on either flank to encircle it completely. In the epidermis, some cells may also

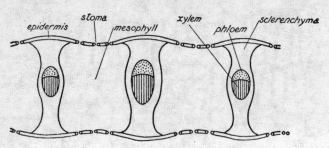

Fig. 17.88. Diagram to show tissue layout in parallel veined monocotyledonous leaf.

be sclerenchymatous so that a solid girder construction extends right across the leaf from one face to the other.

In both dicotyledonous and monocotyledonous leaves may be found specialized *water pores* or *hydathodes* (*see* Vol. II, Chap. 7).

When a petiole is present, its structure is very similar to the stem on which it arises. The major difference lies in the shape of the cross-section and the disposition of vascular bundles and strengthening tissues. Some characteristic petioles in cross-section are shown in Fig 17.89. The structure is obviously adapted to bear the weight of the lamina.

A leaf possessing xeromorphic characters is usually clearly distinguishable from the typical mesomorphic leaf. Among the more outstanding anatomical differences are very heavy cuticularization, localized and deeply-sunk stomata on the abaxial side of the leaf, often in grooves and covered by hairy epidermal outgrowths. There is usually a very well-defined upper palisade mesophyll. The leaf margin may be down-rolled, further to protect the perforated lower epidermis. In some monocotyledons, the whole leaf may be capable of rolling up parallel to the longitudinal axis to enclose the softer tissues. In such cases, the epidermis, as in *Ammophila* [*Psamma*], is equipped with special hinge-cells which effect the rolling movement. Most of these features can be linked with a lessening of the evaporation of water from leaf surfaces under drying conditions. Other modifications associated with dry conditions may be seen in the succulence of various parts,

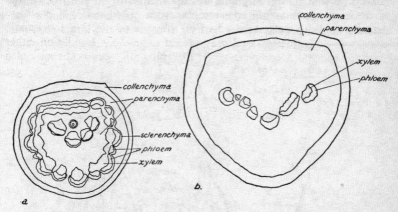

Fig. 17.89. Tissue layout in petioles. (*a*) Sycamore. (*b*) *Aucuba*. L.P. plans of T.S.

whereby stems and leaves may be composed in large proportion of water-storing parenchyma cells (*see* Vol. II, Chap. 7).

More detail of the special anatomy of xerophytes is given later in this chapter.

Leaf Development

As has been stated earlier, leaves arise as *leaf buttresses* at the meristematic apex of the stem from groups of superficial cells (*see* Fig. 17.40), and the points of origin of these buttresses in relation to one another is reflected in the later phyllotaxy. The further development of a simple dicotyledonous leaf is given below.

Once the buttress has been formed, the leaf development may proceed continuously to its conclusion as in herbaceous and some woody plants, or may reach a miniature developmental stage during one growing season inside a bud, winter in the bud and expand fully in the following season, as in other woody plants. In either event, there are two main developmental stages to be considered namely, the formation of the leaf axis and the formation of the lamina. The young axis arises as a peg-like protuberance on the buttress and consists of the petiole and midrib portion bearing along its edge the meristematic initial cells of the lamina. It is, in effect, the complete leaf, but not differentiated into distinct regions of petiole, midrib and lamina (*see* Fig. 17.90). For a short while, the axis may elongate from the apex only, but this is soon followed by intercalary growth. Once the axis begins to appear as a peg, a procambium differentiates in its central region to form continuity with the procambium already formed in the buttress below it. From the procambium, the vascular tissue differentiates, and as the axis continues to enlarge, the pattern of some of the larger vascular

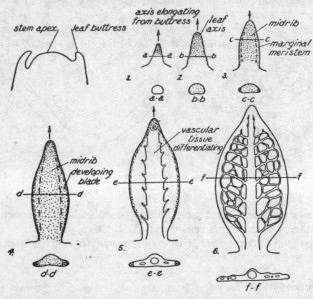

Fig. 17.90. Diagrams to show development of a simple dicotyledonous leaf from a leaf buttress.

bundles of the leaf may be traced out in the procambial form. After the initial enlargement of the axis, the lamina initials at its margins commence activity. They are known as the *marginal meristems* and by repeated divisions they build up the mesophyll and epidermal tissues of the blade. Within the young mesophyll tissues, more procambial strands are differentiated as prolongations of the centrally-formed procambium. From these strands, the minor veins are derived.

Final shape and size of the leaf is determined partly by the shape of the axis during its development and partly by the number and planes of cell division and the extent to which the cells enlarge after their formation. When the meristems have formed the leaf they lose their activity, so that the leaf is of fixed or limited growth.

The formation of a compound leaf is a little more complicated in that the leaf axis, representing the petiole-midrib portion of the leaf, bears lamina initials only at separated points representing the positions of the leaflets. Each leaflet develops in a manner similar to the simple leaf.

Leaf Abscission

When plant parts are cut off from the body of the parent by a definite process, it is known as *abscission*. This distinguishes the occurrence from the gradual decay and wearing away of parts which may also occur. The lost parts vary in nature according to type, and in herbs,

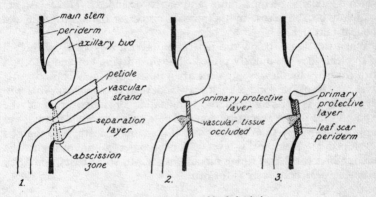

Fig. 17.91. Diagrams of leaf abscission.

only the floral parts may ever be abscinded. In perennial woody angiosperms which pass through successive seasons of good and bad growth conditions, there is nearly always a regular abscission of parts coinciding with the onset of the bad season. This applies particularly to the leaves, and examination of leaf bases shows that the structural modifications made in such plants, ultimately lead to the break. The precise details vary for different species, but the general condition may be described as follows, with reference to Fig. 17.91.

At the base of the leaf may be seen the *abscission zone* which is a narrow transverse band of tissue differing slightly from the regions on either side. For example, the vascular bundles are reduced in cross-sectional area, supporting sclerenchyma and collenchyma may be very weak or entirely absent, and the surrounding parenchyma may be filled with dense cytoplasm. The zone is present as soon as the leaf is mature and its position can often be seen externally as a furrow around the base of a petiole.

Sometimes, many weeks before the leaf eventually falls, the actual layers at which the leaf and stem separate, are developed within the abscission zone. There are several layers of cells of smaller size and different shape from those above and below. They often contain much starch and dense cytoplasm. Their cell walls have a different constitution from the normal. In this region, the *separation layer*, and below it, the conducting elements may gradually become blocked by tyloses and gummy substances. Just prior to leaf fall, the middle lamellae and the walls of the separation cells become gelatinous and finally break down and disappear. This frees the cells from one another all across the abscission zone, so that the leaf is held on only by the vascular strands, which gradually become more and more occluded. These last are gradually broken across by the physical forces of the atmosphere and the leaf falls free.

When the tissues below the separation layer are exposed by the fall of the leaf, they are quickly protected against drying-out and infection with parasites by the development of an outer covering. This covering layer may be of two kinds. First may be developed a *primary protective layer* which is formed from the lignification or suberization of the exposed cells of the abscission zone. These cells may divide rapidly to form a reasonably thick outer coat. Later, underneath this, there is developed a typical corky layer which becomes continuous with the surrounding periderm, which already exists. In some cases, only this *secondary protective layer* is formed.

Buds

Much has already been said about the position and structure of foliage buds, since they are no more than immature portions of a stem axis or its branches. Reference will be made to flower buds in the next chapter.

Buds are formed by normal development of the shoot axis, both in the terminal and axillary positions, but they also arise adventitiously on various parts of the plant, including roots and leaves. In the latter cases, they sometimes arise as a result of injury, but may also be developed under normal conditions as an effective means of vegetative propagation. The "suckers" seen breaking through the soil near the bases of some shrubs and trees are the result of root bud development.

Perhaps the most noticeable of aerial buds are the winter buds of deciduous trees. These are often so characteristic of a species that a reasonably proficient botanist can recognize the tree flora in winter by the buds alone. A few are illustrated in Fig. 17.92.

A dissected winter bud will show the following main parts. There is an outer protective covering of hardened *scales*, often resinous, within which is the young *axis* composed of an *apical meristem* in a dormant condition, and *leaf initials* in various stages of development, from leaf buttresses above, to fully-formed but rolled or folded miniature leaves below. A dissected lilac bud is shown in Fig. 17.78 with the parts in

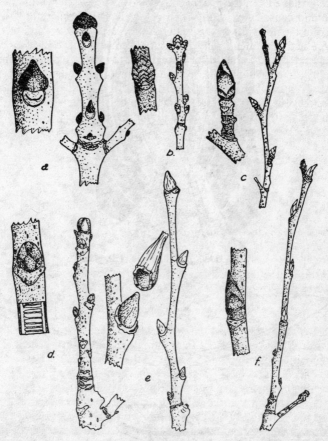

Fig. 17.92. Winter buds of (*a*) ash; (*b*) oak; (*c*) birch; (*d*) walnut; (*e*) plane; (*f*) poplar.

order of their removal from the outside inwards. Fig. 17.93 shows the bud in longitudinal section.

A whole cabbage or brussels' sprout, cut in longitudinal section, will show a comparable structure, but they lack the outer protective scales.

Figs. 17.94 to 17.98 may serve to illustrate more clearly some of the anatomical features of leaves.

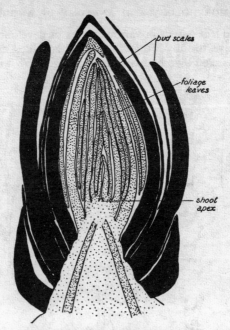

Fig. 17.93. L.S. lilac bud. L.P. plan.

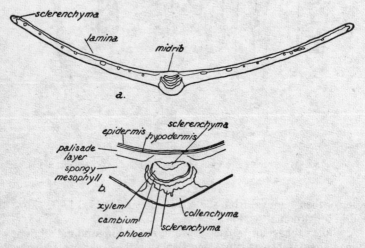

Fig. 17.94. Leaf of holly. (*a*) Tissue layout in V.S. of lamina. (*b*) V.S. through midrib (enlarged).

452

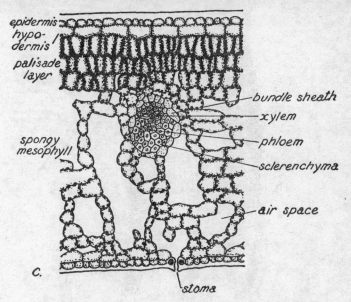

Fig. 17.94.—(*contd.*). (*c*) V.S. of part of lamina. H.P. drawing.

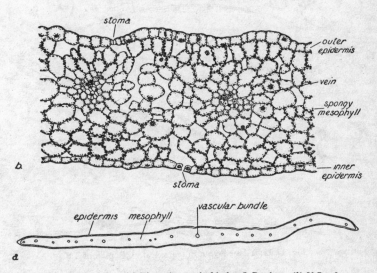

Fig. 17.95. Leaf of lily. (*a*) Tissue layout in blade. L.P. plan. (*b*) V.S. of part of lamina. H.P. drawing.

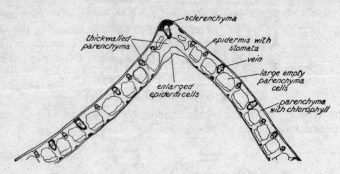

Fig. 17.96. Tissue layout in sedge leaf. L.P. plan of T.S.

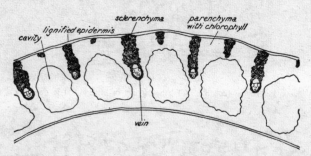

Fig. 17.97. Tissue layout in common reed leaf. L.P. plan of T.S.

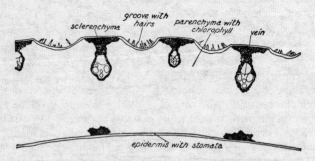

Fig. 17.98. Tissue layout in maize leaf. L.P. plan of T.S.

454

The Root System

The root system is that part of the plant which develops at least originally from the radicle of the embryo, normally stays below ground, and because it never bears leaves or flowers is not divisible into nodes and internodes. It functions primarily to anchor the plant in permanent contact with the soil and to absorb water and mineral salts therefrom, but it may be modified in a variety of ways for other purposes. As a complete system, it is made up of individual roots which may form a

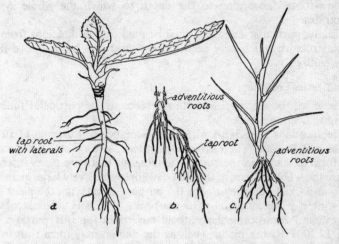

Fig. 17.99. Forms of root systems. (a) Tap-root system of dandelion. (b) Fibrous root system of groundsel. (c) Fibrous root system of grass.

system of one of two kinds. After emergence from the seed, if the primary radicle establishes itself to become a permanent and clearly-defined organ, then together with its lateral branches it forms a *tap root system*, as in the dandelion (*see* Fig. 17.99 (*a*)), and the primary radicle becomes the tap root. If after emergence, the primary radicle branches profusely but fails to develop and persist as the major structure and its branches develop more or less equally, a *fibrous root system* results, as in the groundsel (*see* Fig. 17.99 (*b*)). Similarly, if after emergence, the primary radicle dies and is replaced by roots which develop adventitiously from the base of the stem, the system is also a fibrous system, e.g. the grasses (*see* Fig. 17.99 (*c*)). There are intermediate conditions between the tap root and fibrous root systems, whilst a few plants, notably aquatics, never develop a permanent root system at all, e.g. bladderwort (*Utricularia*). By contrast, a few angiosperms such as *Monotropa* and *Neottia*, live almost entirely as underground root systems, sending up only reproductive aerial stems at intervals.

A morphological description of any root system should state whether it is a tap root system or a fibrous system, and in the latter case, whether of primary or adventitious origin. The system in the soil can be described as *intensive* or *extensive* according to the density of the roots and their branches in a given volume of soil, and the total volume of soil through which the whole system extends. A plant may be deep- or shallow-rooted according to the depth to which the whole system penetrates.

Finally, particular attention must be paid to modifications from the basic structure which may occur. Only these will be described more fully here.

Modifications of Roots

These will be summarized with reference to the particular function the modification serves.

Modifications Associated with Food Storage for Purposes of Perennation and Possibly Vegetative Propagation. Most roots store food in the form of starch in the cortical tissues, but there are many instances where the whole or part of the root develops excessively large quantities of food-packed parenchyma for the purpose of carrying the plant over the winter, when all aerial parts die back. Biennials such as parsnip, carrot, and beetroot, enlarge their tap roots for this purpose (*see* Fig. 17.100). Other plants, such as the dahlia, may form root tubers from the swollen root-bases (*see* Fig. 17.101), or tubers may be formed as branches on the main root system as in *Asparagus*. The perennating organs of some orchids are swollen roots. Whenever root tubers are formed, they may easily serve to propagate the species vegetatively. A well-known example is the lesser celandine, *Ranunculus ficaria* (*see* Fig. 17.102), in which swollen fibrous roots break away from the main root system and develop new independent plants.

Modifications Associated with Additional Stem Support. There are many modifications to roots by which they may serve to strengthen and support stems and branches at their junctions with the soil. Such supporting structures are variously described as *buttress roots*, *prop roots* and *stilt roots* according to their appearance. Prop roots of the maize are illustrated in Fig. 17.103.

Modifications Associated with Water Absorption and Storage in Epiphytic Plants. In the densely-crowded vegetation of tropical forests, it is a very usual occurrence for some plants to grow epiphytically upon others. Their bodies are physically attached to and supported by other

Fig. 17.100. Swollen
taproot of beet.

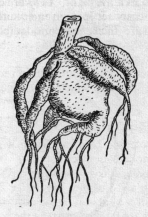

Fig. 17.101. Root tubers of
the dahlia.

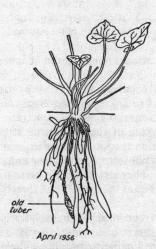

old
tuber

April 1956

Fig. 17.102. Root tubers of the
lesser celandine.

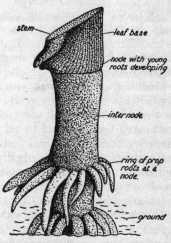

stem

leaf base

node with young
roots developing

internode

ring of prop
roots at a
node.

ground

Fig. 17.103. Prop roots of the
maize.

plants. The epiphytes gain advantage only in being lifted up into sunnier positions and are not parasitic upon the plants which bear them (*see* Chap. 35). In being so elevated, many epiphytes have no contact with the soil and consequently must have provision for water absorption from other sources. The epiphytic orchids characteristically develop clusters of aerial roots which hang down into the air around the base of the plant. They are capable of absorbing and storing water which may settle upon their surfaces from rain or condensation. The roots are thickened considerably by external layers of dead, empty

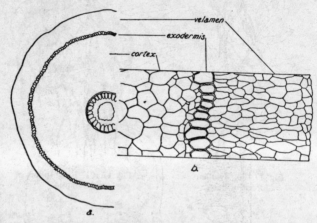

Fig. 17.104. Aerial root of epiphytic orchid, *Vanda*. (*a*) Tissue layout, L.P. plan of T.S. (*b*) H.P. drawing of cell outlines of part of the velamen.

cells which form a whitish spongy tissue known as the *velamen* (*see* Fig. 17.104).

Modifications Associated with the Climbing Habit. Many tropical climbers and the well-known ivy, *Hedera helix*, are able to gain support by the development of short clasping roots which penetrate small cracks and firmly adhere to the surface of the supporting structure. In the ivy, these are groups of adventitious roots on the stem which are not geotropic but strongly negatively phototropic and grow away from lighter regions into darkened crevices. They attach themselves to the surface by a mucilaginous substance formed at the root tip and then become tough and wiry (*see* Fig. 17.105).

Modifications Associated with Mycorrhizal Partnerships. A few British angiosperms such as *Monotropa* and *Neottia* exist without photosynthetic activity since they are unable to produce chlorophyll. They are nourished on the organic matter absorbed from the soil by fungi which form close *mycorrhizal associations* with them. Many forest trees and heath plants in peaty soils show similar fungal relationships. The roots show indications of the presence of the fungus, sometimes externally, when the fungus grows *ectophytically*, and sometimes internally, when the fungus develops *endophytically*. In some instances,

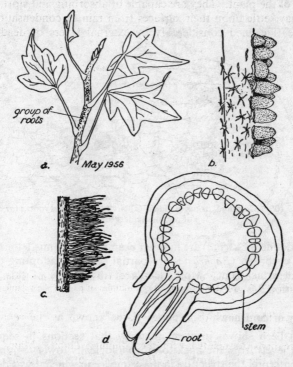

Fig. 17.105. Adventitious roots of ivy. (*a*) Young roots appearing on the stem. (*b*) Same (enlarged). (*c*) Mature roots loosened from crack in wall. (*d*) Tissue layout of stem, through the roots. L.P. plan of T.S.

the presence of the fungal (or bacterial) partner causes considerable variation from normal in the root structure and very typical "coralloid" root formation results, e.g. alder (*Alnus*) (*see* Fig. 17.106). In any event, the physiology of the root must be different from normal, since it lacks root hairs. It is also able to confine the penetration of the fungus into the root tissues to certain localized areas. Mycorrhizal associations are described more fully in Chap. 34.

Symbiotic relationships between bacteria and leguminous plants are well known. On infection, the root rapidly becomes modified by *nodule* formation to localize the bacterial partners (*see* Chap. 34).

Modifications Associated with the Parasitic Mode of Life. The British parasitic flowering plants establish tissue contact with the host plant by the development of highly specialized roots described as *haustoria* (*see* Fig. 31.9). The broomrape (*Orobanche*), the toothwort (*Lathraea*)

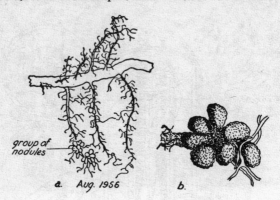

group of nodules

a.   Aug. 1956   *b.*

Fig. 17.106. "Coralloid" roots of alder. (*a*) Nodules on lateral roots. (*b*) Group of nodules (enlarged).

and the dodder (*Cuscuta*) are familiar examples. The mistletoe (*Viscum*) and the eyebright (*Euphrasia*) are partial parasites adopting the same means of attachment. More details of the nature of this form of modification are given in Chap. 31.

Anatomy of the Root

It has been shown in stem anatomy that sections in sequence at different levels from the apex to morphologically lower regions can be used to interpret the structure in the sequence in which it was developed from the apical meristem. The same method of study can be applied to the root, since it develops continuously from an apical meristem in a comparable way. Angiosperm root systems generally conform anatomically to a much more standardized pattern than stems, possibly because the root environment is much more constant. The dicotyledonous angiosperm root anatomy will be described first.

Development of the Primary Body of the Root. A radial longitudinal section through the root apex and transverse sections at different levels are diagrammatically represented in Fig. 17.107. Certain clearly-defined parts can be recognized readily. The *root cap* is a covering of somewhat loose cells which ensheathe the pointed apex and extend

for some distance back along the root. At the extreme apex and within
the sheath is a region of active meristematic cells which by their constant division add more cells, and these, by differentiation involving
elongation, push the cap-protected apex through the soil. Behind this
region of growth and differentiation, the very early beginnings of the
vascular system can be seen. It differentiates from the centrally-placed

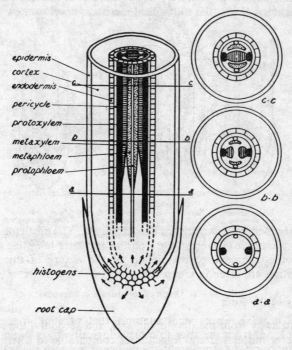

epidermis
cortex
exodermis
pericycle
protoxylem
metaxylem
metaphloem
protophloem
histogens
root cap

Fig. 17.107. Diagram of primary root structure in longitudinal and transverse
planes.

cells, surrounded by a wide *cortex*. The whole structure is covered by a
single layer of *epidermal cells*. A little behind this region, where the
vascular tissues are more fully developed, many of the epidermal cells
develop root-hair outgrowths and constitute the *piliferous layer*. In a
slightly older region, the vascular tissue is fully developed in the primary state and the root hairs may be dead and withered or lacking.
The epidermis here may be dead also and replaced by a layer derived
from the outermost cortical cells which form a suberized *exodermis*.
The epidermis is not thus replaced in all roots; it may persist into older

parts of the root for a long period. Surrounding the *stele*, and arising from the innermost cortical layer of cells, is a clearly-defined *endodermis*, and underlying this is the outer stelar layer, the *pericycle*. Both can be seen developing in conjunction with the vascular tissues.

Within the extreme apical zone, as in stems, no single apical initial is present but many cells participate equally in producing new ones. There are, however, two differences between root and stem in meristematic activity. First, the root apical meristem develops new cells both

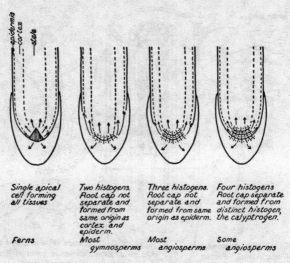

Fig. 17.108. Origin of root tissues in the apex.

Into and away from the developing axis, and secondly, the root meristem never initiates lateral appendages comparable to leaves, nor any branches. The root therefore never shows node and internode segmentation. The tunica-corpus interpretation of the meristem is not often applied to the root. It is generally easier to distinguish the precise origin of the epidermal, cortical and vascular tissues in the root than in the stem. They can be seen to originate from the so-called *histogens* which themselves are derived from distinct groups of initials. But there is no constancy about the numbers and activity of the initials which produce the histogens. Usually there are three groups of initials and in most dicotyledons the outermost of these produces the root cap histogen, the *calyptrogen*, and the epidermal histogen, the *dermatogen*; the middle group produces the cortical histogen, the *periblem*, and the inner group the vascular histogen, the *plerome* (*see* Fig. 17.108). In monocotyledons, there are also three groups of initials which produce four histogens. In this case, however, the outer initial group produces only the calyptrogen cells from which the root cap develops. The epidermis and cortex arise from the middle group and the vascular tissues from the inner group.

The root cap, peculiar to the root, is regarded as a protective structure which assures root penetration without damage to the meristem behind. Its shape is variable according to species, but generally in soil,

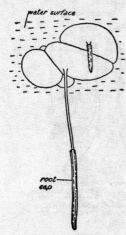

Fig. 17.109. Root cap of duckweed, *Lemna minor.*

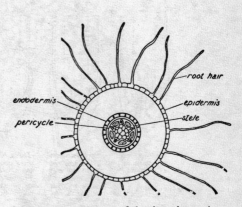

Fig. 17.110. Diagram of the tissue layout in a T.S. of a dicotyledonous root in the region of the root hairs.

the mature cells are loose and parenchymatous, sometimes containing starch, with mucilaginous walls, and are easily sloughed off.

Behind the meristematic region, the primary epidermal, cortical and stelar tissues differentiate and this can best be understood with reference to the completed structure. A transverse section through the root hair region appears as in Fig. 17.110.

Externally, there is an epidermis which is one cell thick. It is composed of closely-packed, elongated cells, with thin uncuticularized walls. In older regions of a root, when it persists, the epidermis may show cuticularization on the outer walls or may even be lignified, but this is not common. The peculiarity of the root epidermis lies in its development of root hairs which increase the surface area over which water and mineral absorption can occur. It is a modified epidermis which forms the velamen in some aerial roots. In this case, the epidermis is many cells in thickness and composed of compact non-living cells with thickened walls which easily absorb water.

The cortex generally consists of homogeneous parenchyma cells forming a wide zone around the comparatively small central stele. There are numerous intercellular spaces and the cells frequently show the presence of starch, but only in a few roots of aquatic plants and occasionally some aerial roots, do chloroplasts occur. The innermost

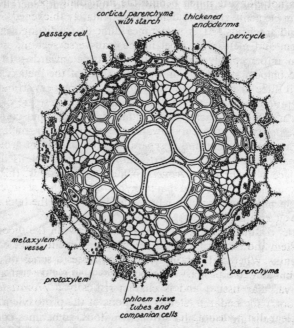

Fig. 17.111. T.S. through vascular cylinder of buttercup root. H.P. drawing.

layer of the cortex is always clearly differentiated as the endodermis, complete with Casparian bands, as described in Chap. 12.

The stele, shown in Fig. 17.111, externally bounded by the pericycle adjacent to the endodermis, is composed of the usual xylem and phloem elements together with some associated parenchyma. The typical tissue arrangement has the xylem centrally placed with the protoxylem groups in the outside (*exarch*) position (cf. stems). Most frequently, the metaxylem occupies the centre and radiating from it are arms at the extremities of which are protoxylem groups. In dicotyledons, according to species, the number of such protoxylem groups varies between two and eight, rarely higher, and the root is described according to this number, i.e. *diarch, triarch, tetrarch*, etc. *Polyarch* describes the condition when the number is higher than eight. Sometimes the metaxylem may form a broken ring of xylem groups, in which case the centre is filled with parenchyma to form a pith. The outer, smaller protoxylem elements usually consist of no more than one or two helically or annularly thickened tracheids or vessels and one or two more heavily thickened. The absence of more of these extensible cells is due to the fact that the root does not elongate much behind the immediate apex. The larger metaxylem elements are more definitely reticulately thickened or pitted vessels and tracheids. It is sometimes difficult to distinguish where protoxylem and metaxylem meet in the transverse section, since cell size often imperceptibly increases from outside inwards. In diarch roots, the phloem strands lie on opposite sides of the metaxylem. In roots with three or more protoxylem groups, the phloem strands lie in the indentations between the protoxylem groups. These are of typical angiosperm phloem elements and contain sieve tubes and companion cells. The protophloem occurs towards the outside of the metaphloem in the strand and each strand is separated from the xylem group by a zone of parenchyma cells. The external layer of the stele is the pericycle, adjacent to the endodermis. In most dicotyledons, this is one cell thick and of thin-walled parenchyma cells. The pericycle cells retain their meristematic potentialities and from them the lateral roots arise as well as other tissues.

The chief distinction in stelar construction between the dicotyledon primary stem and root lies in the different arrangement of the conducting elements. Whereas the primary stem possesses a series of discrete vascular bundles, the primary root possesses a single central arrangement of vascular tissues and is characteristically a *protostele*. The exarch (roots) and endarch (stems) positions of the protoxylem groups are also clear distinguishing features.

The origin of the mature primary root tissues can be traced backwards from the apical zone and Fig. 17.107 represents this pattern of differentiation in the longitudinal and transverse directions. In the region just behind the apex, the very young epidermal layer surrounds the developing cortex which in turn encloses the procambium from which the vascular core differentiates. If the primary vascular tissue forms a solid central mass, then the procambium is distinguishable in a similar form. Where the primary stele contains a central pith, then the procambium is discernible as a hollow cylinder. This procambial region is usually clearly marked off from the cortical zone by the differentiating pericycle, the formation of which commences close behind the apex. The first mature conducting elements to be distinguished in the mass of procambial cells are the protophloem elements, although the cells which eventually become metaxylem and protoxylem may vacuolate and commence to undergo their changes in size and shape before those which form the protophloem. The protophloem strands therefore appear first in their relative positions in the stele, followed by the protoxylem strands. At a little later stage, the cells interior and adjacent to the protoxylem become metaxylem and the cells interior to the protophloem become metaphloem. The strands of phloem and the core of xylem thus gradually become fully differentiated to form the primary vascular structure.

At about the same time as the appearance of the protoxylem elements, the endodermis becomes clearly defined and the Casparian dots in the

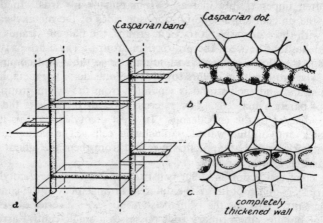

Fig. 17.112. Structure of root endodermis. (*a*) Diagram of endodermal cells. (*b* and *c*) Young and old endodermal cells in T.S.

radial walls are in evidence except in the so-called passage cells. As the endodermal cells age, the radial thickenings may spread around the tangential faces of the cells to appear as in Fig. 17.112 (*c*).

When the primary vascular system of the root is once formed, secondary thickening, in those dicotyledonous species in which it occurs, follows quite rapidly. It rarely happens in monocotyledonous species and this accounts for some of the characteristic differences between old dicotyledonous and monocotyledonous roots.

In the monocotyledonous root, the location of the three major primary tissue groups is the same as that of the dicotyledonous root, but even in the young stages, there are points of distinction worthy of mention (*see* Fig. 17.113). The most noticeable difference lies in the number of protoxylem groups. In the monocotyledons, this is nearly always a large number, commonly as many as thirty, and over a hundred may be found in some palms. This is perhaps more characteristic of the adventitious roots of the monocotyledons rather than the seedling primary roots which may develop only small numbers. Associated with the polyarch condition is an equally large number of phloem groups alternating with the protoxylem groups, and a central pith of parenchyma within the ring of metaxylem vessels. This latter condition

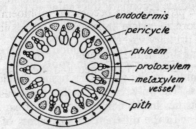

Fig. 17.113. Diagram of tissue layout in a T.S. of the vascular cylinder of a monocotyledonous root.

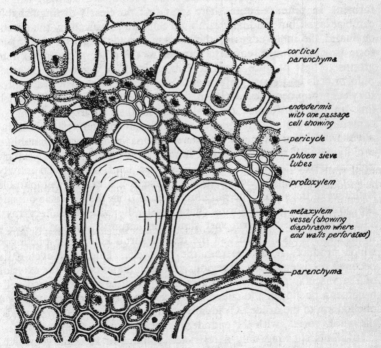

Fig. 17.114. T.S. of part of vascular cylinder of iris root. H.P. drawing.

is not always found however, and the metaxylem elements may be scattered through the parenchyma of the pith. Generally, the innermost metaxylem elements are vessels of considerably larger diameter than any other stelar cells and consequently they stand out very distinctly in the transverse section.

Secondary Growth in Roots. Only a few herbaceous dicotyledons entirely fail to produce secondary thickening in the roots or show only small signs of it. The roots of most monocotyledons, on the other hand, are entirely primary in origin and never show secondary growth. *Dracaena*, as with its stem, is one exception and there are a few others.

The secondary tissues developed in roots of the dicotyledons are fundamentally similar to the secondary tissues developed in the stems of the same plants. The only real distinction between secondary growth in stems and roots lies in the commencement of cambial activity, and this is associated with the different arrangements of the vascular elements in the two parts. In primary stems, the cambium which is first active is recognizable in the intrafascicular position and by extending activity into the interfascicular regions, a complete cambial ring is formed. In primary roots, there is at first no clearly-distinguishable cambial layer, but gradually cambium cells are produced by the parenchyma at the inner edges of the phloem strands (*see* Fig. 17.115) to form isolated groups, equal in number to the phloem or protoxylem groups. These at once begin to cut off internal xylem and external phloem cells and shortly afterwards, the pericycle opposite each protoxylem group becomes meristematic and cuts off cells internally which link up the first-formed cambial cells, so that an irregular ring of cambium is eventually formed to separate phloem and xylem. Gradually this cambium assumes a circular outline as the first formed cambium rapidly cuts off secondary xylem immediately internal to the primary phloem to smooth out the shape. From this point, the cambial activity and the resulting secondary vascular system are exactly comparable with that of the stem. The cambium formed from the pericycle outside the protoxylem groups forms characteristically wide medullary rays. The growth of a periderm very similar in nature to that of a woody stem, also occurs in plants of the tree or shrub kind. The phellogen which produces it, arises from the pericycle. This layer eventually becomes meristematic in all regions and proliferates cells to the exterior of the vascular strand. The outer layer of these newly-formed cells becomes a phellogen and cuts off cork cells to the outside and usually a phelloderm to the inside. Gradually, as the whole inner system expands, the whole cortex, with the endodermis, cracks and is sloughed off.

In plants showing only a restricted amount of secondary growth, there may be no periderm formation and the cortex may remain intact.

There is usually in these cases replacement of the epidermis by the formation of an exodermis in the outer cortical layers.

In the few dicotyledons and the many monocotyledons not showing secondary growth, certain changes do occur in the parts of the primary system. Frequently the parenchyma associated with the vascular elements may become sclerenchymatous and although the cortex is retained, sclerenchyma cells may be differentiated from many of the

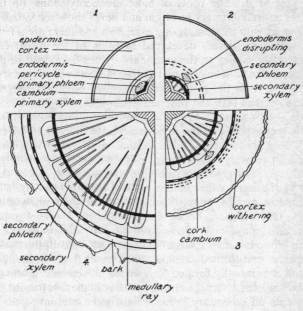

Fig. 17.115. Diagrams to show sequence of tissue development in secondary growth of a root. Transverse plane.

cortical parenchyma cells also. The endodermis develops heavily-thickened secondary walls except in the passage cells. The outer protective layer may still be the original epidermis but this becomes suberized or even lignified in some cases. If the epidermis is sloughed off, then an exodermis arises in the outer cortex.

Development of Lateral Roots. There is a very clear distinction between the development of lateral stem branches and the development of lateral roots. The former arise from superficial meristems, i.e. are *exogenous*, and very near the stem apex. The latter arise in the deeper tissues of the root, i.e. are *endogenous*, and at some distance behind the apex. The site of origin of secondary roots is almost always the pericycle and as they develop they grow through and rupture the cortex (*see* Fig. 17.116). The first sign of development is meristematic activity of the pericycle, usually in the vicinity of a protoxylem group. This may occur opposite all the protoxylem groups at the same time in the same transverse plane of the root so that the lateral roots eventually emerging, do so at the same level and are equal in number to the protoxylem groups in the vascular cylinder.

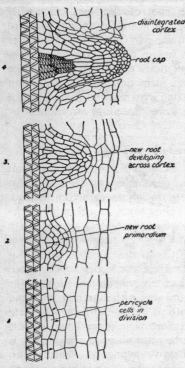

Fig. 17.116. Endogenous development of a lateral root.

Sometimes a new root may arise on either side of each protoxylem group so that there may be double this number of vertical rows of lateral roots. In diarch roots, the laterals more often arise opposite the phloem groups or at least to one side of the protoxylem groups.

As the young lateral begins to be differentiated from the increasing number of cells developed by the pericycle, it begins to protrude outwards as a bulge into the cortex. If the endodermis of the parent root at this region is not itself fully differentiated then it also may contribute cells to the developing lateral, but does not do so otherwise. The enlarging primordium proceeds to differentiate into a root apex in every way comparable with that of the parent and the cells it produces behind its advancing tip proceed to develop in exactly the same way. The innermost region differentiates into vascular tissue and at all points between the young tip and the parent vascular system, there is a link of xylem and phloem cells connecting the new root to the appropriate vascular elements of the parent. In a similar way, the old endodermis and the new are continuous. There is, however, no continuity between the cortex or epidermis of the lateral and the parent. As the young root forces its way across the old cortex, it does so partly by digesting it and partly by physically rupturing the tissues.

Adventitious Root Development. These may be developed in many different plant parts. As stated earlier, in many cases, particularly monocotyledons and dicotyledons which perennate by rhizomes or propagate by runners, etc., they constitute the bulk of a fibrous root system. They may be found most often at the lower parts of stems and at the nodes but also occur in some instances in the hypocotyl regions of seedlings, in stem internodes and in association with buds. The rooting of cuttings is by adventitious root development. Generally they arise endogenously and their origin is near the vascular tissue of the organ giving rise to them. In young parts, cells near the outer region of the stele may initiate them, but in older parts, cells of the vascular cambium or of a parenchymatous medullary ray may be responsible. In any case, the root-apex formation, the differentiation of tissues to link the old and new vascular systems, and the emergence of the root to the exterior, follow the same procedure as outlined for lateral root development.

The Transition between Root Anatomy and Stem Anatomy

As has been explained earlier in this chapter, the primary root and the primary shoot, with cotyledons, of an angiosperm plant, arise at opposite ends of an axis which is formed during the embryonic period. The subsequent development of the mature root and stem is due to the activity of apical meristems, which produce more and more cells to elongate the axis in both directions. The region between these embryonic apical parts is the hypocotyl and it is in this zone that the axial connexion between root and stem lies. Therefore, a developing hypocotyl will show tissue arrangements which are transitional between the characteristic primary root with its central stele with exarch protoxylem, and the characteristic primary stem with its peripheral ring of discrete vascular bundles with endarch protoxylem. The tissue arrangements transitional between these two extremes follow a pattern which is preformed as procambium in the embryo's hypocotyl. There is no *movement* of tissues from inner to outer positions or vice versa as is so often described. The tissues which are eventually recognizable as xylem and phloem, are from the first present as procambium continuous through the axis from apex to base, forming the framework of the whole axial vascular system of the plant. Differentiation of the same longitudinal series of procambial cells into different tissues at different transverse planes in the axis, accounts for the apparent movement of tissues relative to one another.

The precise anatomy of the hypocotylary connecting region is variable in the angiosperms and is nearly always complicated. From an examination of serial transverse sections taken along the axis, from the root through the hypocotyl and into the epicotyl (i.e. region between

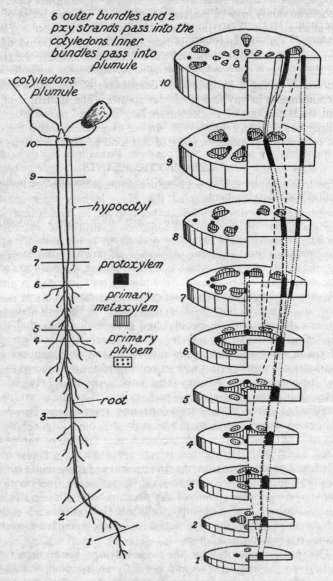

6 outer bundles and 2
pxy strands pass into the
cotyledons. Inner
bundles pass into
plumule

cotyledons
plumule

hypocotyl

protoxylem

primary
metaxylem

primary
phloem

root

Fig. 17.117. Diagram to show transitional tissue arrangements in the hypocotyl
of a sunflower seedling.

cotyledons and first foliage leaves), a three-dimensional picture of the whole anatomy may be built up. Fig. 17.117 shows a series of sections numbered from 1–10 taken at the levels marked on a *Helianthus* seedling. Careful study of this diagram will show the transitional tissue arrangements in this plant and the dotted lines indicate the continuity of the system from one level to the next. No useful purpose would be served in giving a long detailed description of the transitional tissue arrangements in any one particular species. The student is advised to cut serial sections of a selected seedling axis and to compose a three-dimensional picture for himself. In our experience, this is the best way of coming to an understanding of this kind of plant anatomy.

XEROPHYTIC PLANTS

The true xerophyte is able to endure drought by one or two methods, which are frequently coupled together. It may offer considerable resistance to drying conditions because of its specialized structure and/or it may be able to store sufficient quantities of water internally to carry it over excessively dry periods. Typical xerophytes are the woody desert shrubs and the succulent cacti. In addition, the xerophyte is able to recover from degrees of desiccation which would be fatal to any mesophyte. Xerophytes, therefore, may be expected to differ from mesophytes physiologically as well as structurally. One of the important physiological differences is the ability of the xerophyte cells to remain flaccid for long periods without coming to harm, and later to regain turgidity and full activity.

Structural modifications are numerous and frequently so complex as to involve most of the plant parts. The following may be considered as characters primarily associated with restriction of water loss by transpiration under drying conditions.

1. *Reduction of Surface Exposed to the Atmosphere.* This must tend to reduce transpiration for obvious reasons and is generally accomplished by reduction in leaf surface area. Leaves of xerophytes are often small as in heather (*Erica*), or needle-like as in *Pinus*; they may even be completely reduced to the condition of mere scales or spines as in the cacti and some euphorbias. Since leaf area reduction necessarily interferes with photosynthetic activity, this role is generally assumed by the stems, as for example in gorse and broom. In such cases, rapid luxuriant growth is never made and the plants are comparatively small, becoming hard woody shrubs at maturity. The cacti are succulents, storing water in their internal tissues. Having no normal leaf expanses they must carry out all photosynthesis in the stems. These are usually fat and rounded or globose in form, a shape in which there is a comparatively small surface-area/volume ratio.

2. *Protection of Exposed Surfaces.* The formation of a very thick cuticle and the lignification or cutinization of the walls of the epidermal cells are features of all xerophytes. Waterproofing of the outer layers in one or other of these ways may extend well inside the epidermis in some cases. In some plants, as in *Ceroxylon* and *Copernicia*, wax is deposited in sufficient quantity as to be worth collecting as *carnaüba wax*. In others, gums and tannins are secreted by the outer layers of cells. In one or more ways, cuticular transpiration is reduced to an exceedingly small quantity. Coupled with this heavy external protection, in leaves, a hypo-dermis of lignified sclereids or fibrous cells is formed, and in general, the xerophyte leaf possesses much greater amounts of mechanical tissue than the mesophyte. The leaf margins, particularly, are strengthened with strands of sclerenchyma, and in some cases, sheets of the same tissue may extend over the whole leaf between the outer layers and the mesophyll, e.g. *Banksia*.

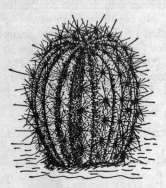

Fig. 17.118. *Echinocactus.* Globose stem with spines.

3. *Protection of Stomatal Apertures.* Since cuticular transpiration is reduced to a minimum, the only water leaving a leaf is through the

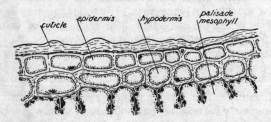

Fig. 17.119. V.S. of cuticle, epidermis and hypodermis of holly.

open stomata, but, in nearly all cases, this is considerably restricted in one or more ways. The guard and accessory cells of the stoma are sunk beneath the surface layer, so that a pit is formed where the surface is broken, e.g. *Hakea*. The effect is to lessen the diffusion gradient of water vapour between the inside and outside of the pore, as it tends to collect undisturbed in the hollow formed by the pit. The pit may be further protected by high over-arching outgrowths of the epidermal cells as in *Cycas*. In some cases, e.g. *Nerium*, stomata are confined to small depressed areas of the leaf surface, which are heavily blanketed with hairy outgrowths. Such trichomes are of frequent occurrence on

xerophyte surfaces and when thickly matted, they serve to reduce water-vapour diffusion by causing the occurrence of pockets of still air, across which movement of water vapour is very slow once the pockets have become saturated. They protect against drying winds and the effects of excessive insolation. The restriction of stomata to lower protected surfaces only, serves a similar purpose. Such protection is often afforded by hairs alone but is further achieved by the down-rolling of leaf margins, so that the

Fig. 17.120. Peltate hairs of sea buckthorn.

stomata occur only in deep grooves on the under side of the leaf, e.g. lavender, heather. In a few cases, e.g. *Ammophila*, under drying conditions, the leaf may undergo a complete inward rolling to protect the surface on which the stomata occur. On this surface, the stomata

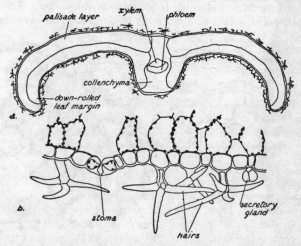

Fig. 17.121. V.S. leaf of lavender. (*a*) Tissue layout of whole leaf. L.P. plan. (*b*) Details of lower epidermis and hairs. H.P. drawing.

are confined to deep hair-protected grooves, and at the base of each groove, large specialized "hinge cells" occur. When turgid, they tend to open the grooves widely, the cumulative effect being to expand the leaf until flat, but when losing turgidity, to allow the groove sides to

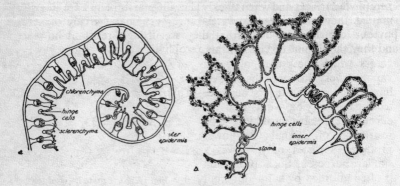

Fig. 17.122. Rolling of *Ammophila* (*Psamma*) leaf. (*a*) Part of rolled leaf. L.P. plan of T.S. (*b*) Hinge cells. H.P. drawing.

come together, thus allowing the leaf to roll up, with the adaxial surface inwards.

4. *Development of Water Storage Tissue.* Many desert plants, such as the cacti and euphorbias, possess thick fleshy stems composed largely of parenchyma cells containing mucilaginous substances. This tissue, when water-filled, serves as a reservoir to tide the plant over the driest

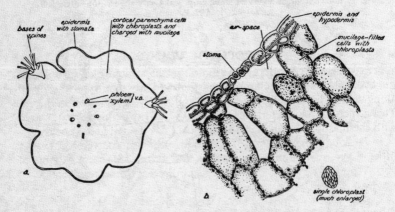

Fig. 17.123. (*a*) Tissue layout in cactus stem. L.P. plan of T.S. (*b*) Cortical cells and epidermis. H.P. drawing.

periods. Such plants usually possess a large extensive root system by which water is absorbed very readily when available in the soil. Thus the most is made of the infrequent periods of rainfall in desert regions. Similar fleshy structures are developed by other plants, and the stone-crop (*Sedum*) is a typical example. The salt-marsh plants are likewise succulent and many have an appearance very characteristic of xerophytes. It is not considered that they are drought-resistant however and they should not be classified as xerophytic.

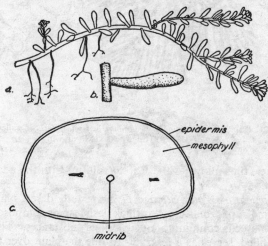

Fig. 17.124. Succulent leaves of stone-crop. (*a*) Leafy shoot. (*b*) Single leaf. (*c*) T.S. leaf. L.P. plan.

HYDROPHYTIC PLANTS

Whereas there is considerable variation in the structure of xerophytes, the hydrophytes are much more constant and all seem to have evolved along similar lines, well suited to the uniformity of aquatic conditions. The structural characteristics of aquatic angiosperms as compared with the mesophytes and xerophytes, may be summarized as below.

1. *Lack of External Protective Tissues.* Epidermal layers show very little, if any, sign of cuticle formation and all the cells seem capable of absorbing nutrients and dissolved gases directly from the surrounding water.

2. *Specialized Leaf Structure.* In many cases, the leaves are finely dissected, e.g. *Myriophyllum*; in others long and ribbon-shaped, e.g. submerged leaves of *Sagittaria*. In most cases, they are thin and delicate

and offer a large surface area to the water. The epidermal cells frequently contain chloroplasts and show no stomatal openings, e.g. *Elodea*. Where the leaves are floating, as in the water lily, they are much sturdier in construction and possess chloroplasts in the upper

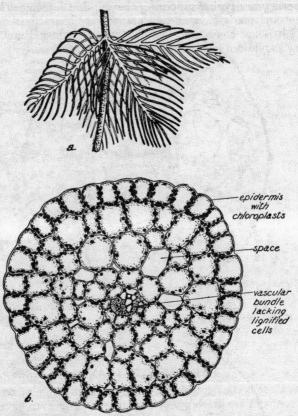

Fig. 17.125. Leaves of *Myriophyllum*. (*a*) Finely dissected leaves. (*b*) T.S. leaf. H.P. drawing.

cells only. Some aquatics develop both submerged and aerial leaves, and in those cases, heterophylly is very marked, e.g. *Sagittaria* and *Ranunculus aquatilis*. In these cases, the aerial leaves are comparable with those of mesophytes.

3. *Presence of Air Cavities*. In all parts of the plant, large intercellular spaces form air-filled cavities extending through the tissues and providing an internal atmosphere as it were. Bubbling of gas from these

cavities is readily noticeable when the plants are photosynthesizing rapidly, and under these circumstances, the gas can be demonstrated to contain a high proportion of oxygen.

4. *Absence of Mechanical Tissue.* Few if any aquatics develop sclerenchyma or other supporting tissues. The submerged leaves are in

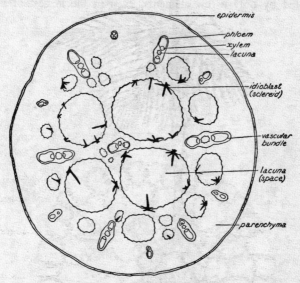

Fig. 17.126. Tissue layout in water lily petiole. L.P. plan of T.S.

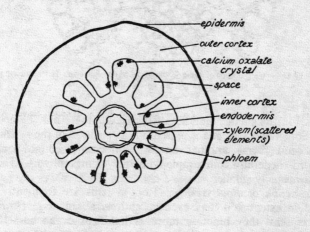

Fig. 17.127. Tissue layout in *Myriophyllum* stem. L.P. plan of T.S.

little need of support or protection since the water adequately serves both purposes. Lack of rigidity in the leaves is a safeguard against the action of currents, the leaves tending to trail with the current and thus suffer no damage.

5. *Reduction of Vascular Tissues.* In nearly all cases, the xylem is represented by only a few elements, even in the largest of vascular

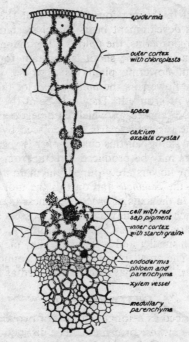

Fig. 17.128. Cell detail of tissues of *Myriophyllum* stem. H.P. drawing of strip extending from epidermis to medulla.

bundles. In the smaller bundles of the leaves, there may be no xylem at all. Sometimes a lacuna is present in the position of the xylem in the bundle, and forms another cavity. Phloem, although somewhat reduced, is generally comparable with that of mesophytes. The sieve tubes are usually smaller.

6. *Reduction of Root System.* Root-systems are frequently much reduced in extent and may even be entirely absent, e.g. *Utricularia*. When present, they function more as holdfasts or anchors than as absorbing organs, and root-hairs are usually lacking.

CHAPTER 18

FLORAL MORPHOLOGY AND ANATOMY OF ANGIOSPERMS

It was pointed out in the previous chapter that the shoot system at some period of its development bears the characteristic reproductive structures of the angiosperms, the *flowers*. The manner of their occurrence and arrangement on the shoot is constant for a species but is variable throughout flowering plants as a whole. We refer to the arrangement of the flowers as the *inflorescence* of the plant. Flowers may develop singly or grouped. They may be at the apex of the main shoot or one of its branches, in which case vegetative activity at the apex ceases and the vegetative parts are replaced by the reproductive structures. The physiology of this change-over is very obscure. Alternatively, the flowers may be produced directly from buds in the axils of leaves. When the flowers are grouped, the main axis on which they are borne is called the *peduncle* and on this the individual flowers are developed, usually in the axils of *bracts*, but these may be very reduced or even absent. Each flower may or may not possess a stalk or *pedicel*. Bracts are very variable. They may be ordinary foliage leaves but frequently are much smaller and scale-like. They may be coloured like petals (petaloid). The small outgrowths often found on the pedicels are called *bracteoles*. These may also be regarded as reduced leaves.

INFLORESCENCES

These may be described as belonging to one of two kinds, the *racemose* or *indefinite* and the *cymose* or *definite*. The distinction lies in whether or not the growing apex of the inflorescence axis is able to produce flower buds in continuous succession, without coming to a halt by producing one in the terminal position. In indefinite inflorescences, flower buds are initiated at the apex which never loses the power to do so. In definite inflorescences, the apex sooner or later forms a terminal flower and then loses its ability to produce more. In each of these forms of inflorescence, there are several possible flower arrangements. These are summarized below and illustrated in Fig. 18.1.

Indefinite Inflorescences

1. *The Spike:* individual, unstalked (sessile) flowers, arranged along a single undivided peduncle, e.g. plantain, *Orchis*. Special forms

include the *spadix* as in *Arum*, in which the axis is massive and fleshy and protected by a large enveloping bract. the *spathe*, and the *catkin*, a pendulous structure found in many trees such as walnut, poplar, oak, hazel, birch.

2. *The Raceme:* individual stalked flowers arranged along a single undivided peduncle, e.g. wallflower, foxglove, hyacinth, lupin. This may be compounded.

3. *The Corymb:* as in the raceme but with the pedicels all of different lengths, the lowermost longest, so that the flowers are all brought to the same level, e.g. candytuft and many other crucifers.

4. *The Umbel:* stalked flowers with the stalks of about the same length arising apparently from the same term inal point of the axis, e.g. cow parsnip, carrot and others of the Umbelliferae The ring of bracts, each associated with one of the flower stalks, is called the *involucre*. The inflorescence may be compounded.

5. *The Capitulum:* sessile flowers arranged in the same plane at the expanded apex of the axis, e.g. dandelion, daisy, thistle and others of the Compositae. The head of flowers is surrounded by a number of sterile bracts collectively termed the *involucre*. The individual flowers may or may not be in the axils of bracts on the disc-like head.

Definite Inflorescences

These can all be called *cymes* but there are several distinguishable forms.

1. *The Monochasial Cyme:* flower production in the terminal position on an axis is followed by the development of another axis from the axil of a bract behind it. There are two main forms of this inflorescence. In the *helicoid monochasium* all the succeeding axes are developed from bracts on the same side of the preceding axes, so that each successive axis tends to coil the whole further and further towards the first axis, e.g. buttercup. In the *scorpioid monochasium* the succeeding axes are developed from bracts alternately on opposite sides of the preceding axes, e.g. *Myosotis* (forget-me-not).

2. *The Dichasial Cyme:* flower production in the terminal position on an axis is followed by the development of two more from the axils of oppositely-placed bracts behind it, e.g. bladder campion, stitchwort and others of the Caryophyllaceae. Such a dichasium can be complex if the paired branching is not confined to a single plane, e.g. *Gypsophila*.

In addition to the more easily recognizable forms described above, there are numerous apparently special forms. On careful analysis, these all conform to one or other of the general patterns but the condition is confused due to shortening of the axes or crowding of the flowers. For example, the somewhat globular heads of *Hydrangea, Viburnum* and hawthorn are really cymes arranged corymbose fashion. The heads of flowers of *Pelargonium* and some narcissi are similarly cymes arranged in an umbellate form. The apparent whorls of flowers in the dead

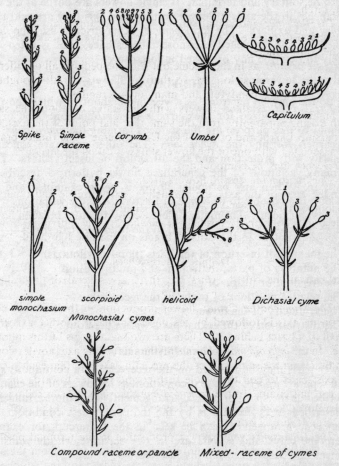

Fig. 18.1. Diagrams of the types of inflorescences. The numbers indicate the sequence of development of the flowers.

nettles are really two oppositely placed cymes. The whole arrangement is known as a *verticillaster*. It is not unusual to find a mixed inflorescence, that is, partly indefinite and partly definite. Such a case arises in the figwort in which the main axis of indefinite growth produces lateral branches bearing flowers of definite arrangement. Another case may arise in which a plant may produce a single flower at the end of the main vegetative axis, e.g. wood anemone, tulip. Such a flower is said to be solitary and terminal. If single flowers are borne at the ends of branches in the axils of leaves on the main axis they are said to be solitary and axillary. The term *panicle*, in its strictest use, should be applied only to branched racemose inflorescences, but is often used loosely to describe any branched inflorescence.

THE FLOWER

The flower may be regarded as a vegetative shoot in which the parts are highly specialized for the purpose of reproduction. The organs essential to this purpose are the stamens forming the *androecium*, and the carpels forming the *gynaecium*. The other parts are concerned primarily with protection and the attraction of insect visitors. There are many variations of the generalized flower pattern as described in Chap. 16. When any particular flower is being examined and described, it is advisable to be aware of the nature of the variations which may possibly occur. The major differences in structure between flowers of different species are summarized in the following categories—

The manner of insertion of the parts (floral phyllotaxis)
The numbers of parts; reduction and multiplication
The freedom or fusion of parts
The relative positions of parts on the receptacle
The symmetry of the flower
The distribution of the sexual parts within the flower

Floral Phyllotaxis

Flower parts may be inserted on the receptacle in a continuous *spiral* or in separate *whorls*. The first condition, as in flowers of the cactus, is described as the spiral or *acyclic* arrangement. The whorl arrangement is described as *cyclic* and is by far the commonest condition. The *hemi-cyclic* arrangement can be seen in the buttercup, for example, where the calyx and corolla are in two separate whorls whilst the stamens and carpels are spirally inserted.

Numbers of Parts; Reduction and Multiplication

In most cases flowers have their parts in definite constant numbers. A few cases occur, as in Ranunculaceae, where particularly the stamens and carpels may vary from flower to flower, but are usually present in large numbers. Such parts are referred to as occurring in *indefinite numbers*. Where the numbers are more constant, they are found most commonly in twos, fours, fives, or multiples of these in the dicotyledons, and in threes or multiples in the monocotyledons. Accordingly, the flowers can be described as *dimerous, trimerous, tetramerous* or *pentamerous*. The number of whorls of parts in a cyclic flower is also variable with the most common number five, that is calyx–1, corolla–1, androecium–2 and gynaecium–1. Complete reduction of some of these is very common, the most common lack being one of the staminal whorls. Others may show the complete absence of a calyx or a corolla or both, whilst absence of one of the sexual whorls shows the *unisexual* condition. Reduction of parts is regarded as an advanced evolutionary character.

Multiplication of parts, particularly those of the perianth, is a very characteristic condition of many cultivated flowers. Whilst such a condition increases their attractiveness, they cannot be said to represent truly the floral structure in any family. In any case, many of them are sterile.

Freedom or Fusion of Parts

The primitive floral condition seems to be that in which all parts are separate and freely inserted on the receptacle. Such a condition is seen in the Ranunculaceae. More advanced families show lesser or greater tendency for parts to fuse laterally or even to be inserted on the next outer whorl instead of on the receptacle. Particularly is this so in the case of stamens. When the members of the whorls are separately inserted, they are described as *polysepalous, polypetalous, polyandrous* and *apocarpous* respectively. When the whorl members are united laterally, they are described as *gamosepalous* and *gamopetalous* in the case of the perianth segments, *adelphous* if fused by their filaments and *syngenesious* if fused by their anthers, in the case of stamens. In the case of the gynaecium, if the carpels are fused laterally the condition is said to be *syncarpous*. When stamens are in groups, fused by their filaments, they are said to be *monadelphous, diadelphous* or *polyadelphous*, according to the number of such groups. When stamens are inserted on the corolla segments, they are said to be *epipetalous*. This is common in such families as Compositae, Labiatae and Scrophulariaceae. If the stamens are adherent to the gynaecium, they are said to be *gynandrous*. This occurs in some orchids.

Relative Positions of Parts on the Receptacle

This is governed by the way in which the receptacle itself develops. There are three distinctive patterns. When the receptacle develops as a conical or domed end to the pedicel and the flower parts are inserted in the order calyx, corolla, androecium, gynaecium from base to apex of the receptacle, the flower is said to be *hypogynous*. In this case, the carpels have the most distal level of insertion and all the other parts are below them; hence the name to describe the structure (*see* Fig. 18.2). In such a case, the gynaecium is said to be *superior*, from its position above the other flower parts. Typical examples of hypogyny are to be seen in the Ranunculaceae and Scrophulariaceae. The second form is the *perigynous* condition. Here the receptacle grows with a

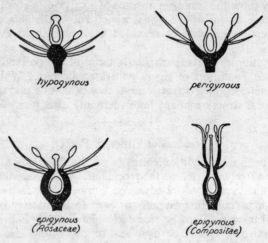

hypogynous

perigynous

epigynous
(Rosaceae)

epigynous
(Compositae)

Fig. 18.2. Positions of floral parts on the receptacle.

dish- or saucer-shaped expanded head and the very young initials of the calyx, corolla and androecium are formed on the outer rim with the gynaecium centrally placed. Thus the gynaecium appears to be at the same level as the other floral parts, or in other words, the outer floral parts appear to encircle the gynaecium at about the same level of insertion, hence the name, perigynous. In reality, the gynaecium still occupies the apical position and is still described as superior. The condition is exemplified by members of the Rosaceae and different degrees of perigyny are clearly to be seen in this family. The receptacle can vary from slightly indented to deeply flask-shaped. Where perigyny is very slight, it is not always possible to distinguish it from hypogyny unless the ontogeny of all the floral parts is carefully worked out. The third condition is known as *epigyny*. A flower is epigynous when the calyx, corolla and androecium are inserted at a level above the gynaecium. The condition appears to arise as an advanced form of perigyny in some cases, as in the Rosaceae, in which the flask-like receptacle is completely closed over the gynaecium. carrying the outer floral parts to a level above it. In other cases, as in the Compositae, the epigynous condition arises in a more complicated manner involving the closure of the receptacular flask by stylar tissue of the carpels. When the gynaecium is below the level of insertion of the other parts it is said to be *inferior*.

The Symmetry of the Flower

The type of symmetry or balanced arrangement of flower parts is dependent upon the disposition of the floral whorls and upon the

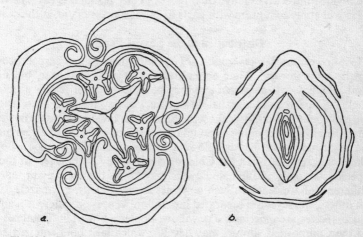

Fig. 18.3. Floral symmetry. (*a*) Radial symmetry of lily. (*b*) Bilateral symmetry of garden pea. Plan views of parts in the bud stage.

number, shape and size of each member of a whorl in relation to the others. A carefully-made diagram representing the relative positions, numbers, and sizes of the separate parts, will always indicate the nature of the symmetry (*see* Fig. 18.3).

There are two general conditions. If a flower can be vertically split through the centre in any one of several planes to produce identical parts in every case, it is said to be *actinomorphic* and to possess *radial symmetry*. This will occur when each part of a whorl is identical with all the others and all are evenly disposed in the whorl. Such a flower is said to be *regular*, a term sometimes used synonymously with actinomorphic. In the other main case, as a result of fusion of parts, the disparity of size of some parts in a whorl as compared with the others in the same whorl, or the absence of one or more parts of a whorl, the flower can be split into two identical halves in one plane only. It is said to be *zygomorphic* and to possess *bilateral symmetry*. Zygomorphy is often due to differences in size and shape of petals and/or sepals as in the pea or snap-dragon. Such a flower is said to be *irregular* and again this term is often used synonymously with zygomorphic. Another condition, as in members of the Cruciferae, is that in which a flower can be divided equally in only two planes at right angles, and the half-flowers produced by cutting in one such plane are different from those produced by cutting in the other. Such a flower possesses *iso-bilateral* symmetry but is still considered to be actinomorphic. If a flower cannot be divided into two exactly equal halves in any plane, it is *asymmetric*. This will apply to flowers with parts in spiral succession, as in the cacti.

Distribution of the Sexual Parts

Most flowers are *hermaphrodite* or *bisexual*; stamens and carpels occur in the same flower. When either stamens or carpels appear, but not both, the flower is *unisexual* and may be called *male* or *female* accordingly. Bisexual and unisexual flowers may be developed in association with one another in different ways. Sometimes male and female flowers may occur together in the same inflorescence, or unisexual flowers may be associated with bisexual flowers in the same inflorescence. Both these conditions arise in the Compositae and the Gramineae. In some species, the male and female flowers may be on the same plant but in different inflorescences. Such a species is *monoecious*, e.g. hazel, oak. In others, the sexes are separated into inflorescences on different plants. Such species are *dioecious*, e.g. willow, poplar. In certain instances as in the Compositae, flowers may develop which lack both stamens and carpels. Such flowers are said to be *neuter*.

THE MORPHOLOGY AND ANATOMY OF FLORAL PARTS

The most widely-accepted concept of the flower is that it is a short axis or branch of definite growth bearing appendages which may be regarded as modified leaves. The arguments against this concept have certain justification but need not concern us.

Origin and Development of the Flower

A flower arises from an apical meristem of a main or lateral shoot when that ceases its vegetative activity and becomes reproductive. The conditions which effect this change-over may be numerous and complicated. Some external conditions affecting it have been the centre of much study and it is known that both day-length and temperature conditions may influence the onset of flowering in some plants through hormone activity (*see* Vol. II, Chap. 13).

The details of the ontogeny of the parts in different flowers are obviously different, but reference to Fig. 18.4 will indicate the condition of the very immature floral apex of the onion (*Allium cepa*). When very young, the floral parts are closely similar to leaves at the same stage of development. They all develop laterally on the somewhat broadened apical meristem and are initiated by periclinal divisions of the cells just under the surface. The sequence in which the whorls develop is variable but is most often *acropetal*, that is from base towards apex, or in other words, calyx first and carpels last. Each organ, when once initiated, possesses its own apical meristem at least for a time, and if it is finally

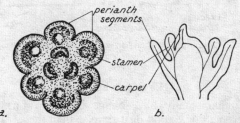

Fig. 18.4. Floral apex of the onion. (*a*) Upper surface view. (*b*) L.S.

laterally expanded as are sepals and petals, it may also possess marginal initial cells which produce the lateral growth. This is comparable with leaf development (*see* Chap. 17). Procambium is differentiated and gives rise to the vascular system as in leaves. Of the parts, the gynaecium is always last to complete development, since fruit formation, the final stage, is dependent on fertilization. The carpels therefore retain meristematic properties long after the other parts have ceased to grow. When the flower parts are fused, the fusion may be present right from the time of initiation of the parts. This is known as *congenital* fusion. In other cases. the fusion may result from lateral blending of the tissues of originally separate parts. This is known as *ontogenetic* fusion.

The Pedicel and Receptacle

These show an internal structure exactly comparable with a primary stem of the plant which bears them. From the stele, consisting of a ring of vascular bundles, within the broadened receptacular tip arise vascular traces to the floral parts, either spirally or in whorls according to the flower structure. In those cases where the receptacle may develop considerably after fertilization to play a part in "fruit" formation, the cortical region may become enlarged and succulent, e.g. strawberry (*see* Fig. 18.5).

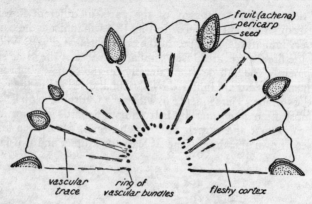

Fig. 18.5. T.S. unripe strawberry to show receptacle structure. L.P. plan.

The Sepals and Petals

Although fundamentally like foliage leaves in form, the internal structure is generally a good deal simpler than these. There is central loose parenchyma tissue permeated by vascular strands and protected externally on both faces by an epidermis. The parenchyma of sepals commonly contains chloroplasts and they are therefore green, but distinction into palisade and spongy mesophyll is rare. The epidermis is perforated by stomata and cuticularized. It may bear hairs. The vascular system is rarely so complicated a meshwork as in the leaves of the same plant.

Petal parenchyma rarely contains chloroplasts but numerous other chromoplasts containing pigments such as carotins (yellow to orange) occur regularly, whilst the sap-soluble pigments called anthocyanins (red, blue, purple) and the anthoxanthins (pale ivory to deep yellow) are also frequently found. The epidermal cells often show special peculiarities, particularly in the ways in which they are fitted together. The anticlinal walls are often wavy in outline and ridged, giving the petal surface a beautiful mosaic pattern. Stomata are normally differentiated in most cases. The cuticle over the epidermis is often striated and very distinct patterns of lines may be formed to give the surface a roughened appearance. Hairs are of common occurrence as epidermal outgrowths, and in many cases, these and the epidermal cells may elaborate volatile oils which give a flower its scent. The vascular system is generally simple, composed of one, or at most a few large veins with some smaller vascular strands. Dichotomous branching of the veins is quite common.

The Stamen

The type of stamen which occurs in the majority of angiosperms has been described in Chap. 16. It is the four-lobed anther on a filament with a single vascular bundle traversing its length. Variations may be encountered however, and among these are the more primitive forms which are more leaf-like, having a broader distal portion through which three veins pass, the pollen sacs lying between these on the abaxial side.

Histologically, the stamen is parenchymatous throughout, except in the vascular regions, and covered by a normal cuticularized epidermis which may bear hairs. Many of the cells may contain sap pigments so that the anther can be of a colour different from the normal yellow. The anthers of the tulip are often purple. Surrounding each group of sporogenous tissue from which the pollen grains develop is a distinct *tapetum* of radially elongated cells. These are most prominent during pollen grain development and usually disintegrate before the pollen ripens. The layers of the pollen-sac wall are formed outside this. Where the pollen sac is beneath the epidermis, its wall is derived from divisions of the parietal cells, but if it is more internal, the ground tissue of the anther may form a part. This wall varies in thickness and final form according to species. Generally, a distinct layer immediately under the

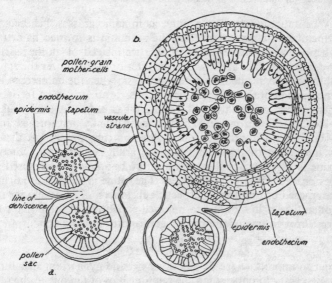

Fig. 18.6. Structure of stamen. (*a*) Tissue layout. L.P. plan. (*b*) Single loculus. H.P. drawing of T.S.

epidermis, known as the *endothecium*, becomes thickened with bars of lignin lying in a direction at right angles to the plane of the epidermis. This layer at least, is concerned with anther dehiscence, but more internally-placed cells may thicken in a similar manner for the same purpose, or may later disintegrate with the tapetum to leave the pollen sac enclosed only by an endothecium and epidermis. At the lateral grooves between two pollen sacs, the line along which dehiscence occurs in most cases, the epidermal cells are very tiny and are easily broken apart to form the slit-like opening, the *stomium*, as the stamen dries

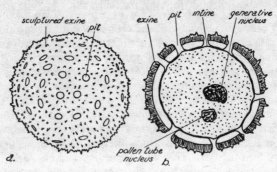

Fig. 18.7 (*a*) Surface, and (*b*) sectional views of pollen grain of Marvel of Peru.

out. When dehiscence is by a pore, as in some grasses, heathers and some members of the Solanaceae, the stomium is formed as a transverse groove along the apex of the anther instead of along its sides. When dehiscence lines are towards the interior of the flower the stamen is said to be *introrse* and conversely, *extrorse*, when the dehiscence lines face the outside of the flower.

When pollen grains are mature, each has a two-layered wall, an outer *exine* and inner *intine*. The former is usually first formed and is rarely complete all over the grain. Pits and furrows are left through which the pollen tube breaks when the grain germinates. Otherwise the exine is heavily cuticularized and may be spiny or sculptured in a manner characteristic of the species. The intine is much more delicate and composed of cellulose and pectic substances. The development of the pollen tube is in fact due to renewed expansion of the intine which emerges through one of the pits or germ-pores in the exine.

The Carpel and the Gynaecium

In order to appreciate the details of carpel and gynaecium structure, it is first necessary to understand the relationships of the one to the other. The gynaecium may consist of one or more carpels inserted either singly (*apocarpous*) or fused together (*syncarpous*) on the receptacle. Each carpel may be considered as being fundamentally a folded leaf-like structure (*see* Fig. 18.8), and is differentiated into lower ovule-containing *ovary*, with an upper outgrowth of *style*, and the *stigmatic surface*. The more primitive apocarpous gynaecium is composed of such individual structures each forming a simple *pistil*, e.g. buttercup. The more advanced and specialized gynaecia consist of comparable carpels but these are fused laterally in one of three possible ways, to form a compound pistil which may have one or many internal cavities or *loculi*. These three conditions are shown in Fig. 18.8, and the gynaecia

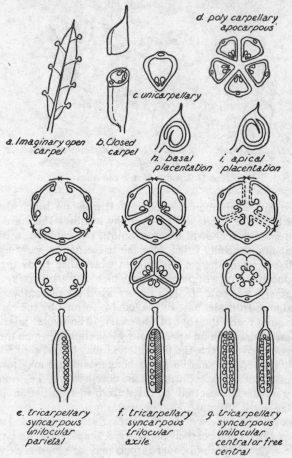

Fig. 18.8. Diagrams of forms of the gynaecium.

concerned may be described in the terms indicated. When the carpel is considered as an inwardly folded leaf bearing ovules on the inner faces of the joined margins, it can be seen that the *ovule placentation* will be variable according to the manner in which the carpels become fused. The two most common but easily distinguishable conditions are *marginal* or *parietal* placentation and *axile* placentation. The former condition results from carpel fusion in which the joint between adjacent carpels does not reach the centre, so that only one loculus is enclosed by all the carpels and the ovules are situated on the outer margin. The latter condition arises when the joint tissue reaches

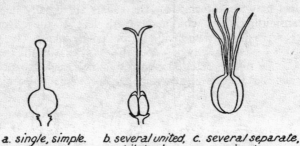

a. single, simple.   b. several united,   c. several separate,
                         bilobed.   simple.

Fig. 18.9. Types of style and stigma.

the centre and forms there a solid central mass on which the ovules arise. In this case, there will be as many loculi as there are carpels. The third condition shown, namely, *central* placentation, arises when carpels, at first centrally fused, lose the tissue of the walls separating the loculi but retain the central column which then bears the ovules. There is one other form of placentation which may arise in a syncarpous ovary, namely, *free-central*. This occurs when the placenta arises as a central column from the base of the loculus formed by the carpels but does not quite reach the roof of the ovary. The ovules arise all over this central column. In an apocarpous gynaecium in which the carpels carry only one ovule each, the placentation may be *apical* or *basal* as in Fig. 18.8. The formation of a syncarpous gynaecium may result from lateral fusion of carpels during their development, i.e. ontogenetic fusion, or all the carpels may be fused from their initiation and grow together as a unit structure, i.e. congenital fusion.

In most gynaecia, the style forms an apical sterile portion. In apocarpous cases, the separate carpels each carry a simple style. In syncarpous cases, the styles of the individual carpels may be separate or variously united to one another (*see* Fig. 18.9). The distal end of each style or branch of a style is structurally and functionally different from the remainder and forms the *stigma*. On this, the epidermis is glandular and secretory, serving to hold pollen and provide the necessary conditions for its germination in the secretions. Through the length of the solid style, from stigma to ovary, is often a centrally-placed tract of tissue similar in nature to that of the glandular stigma. This is looked upon as tissue which facilitates growth of the pollen tube by nourishing it and the tissue may be referred to as pollen-transmitting. It often extends right through the style to the ovule placentae. In a few cases, styles may each have a central empty canal and are said to be open, or where the style is a composite one formed from the fusion of several, a single canal may serve them all. The canals are usually lined with pollen-transmitting tissue continuous with that of the stigma and apparently serve the purpose of conducting pollen tubes.

The ovules have been fully described in Chap. 16 with the exception of their vascular supply. This is connected to the vascular supply of the placenta and consists of a single strand passing through the funicle and

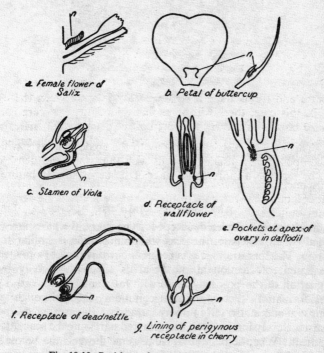

a. Female flower of Salix

b. Petal of buttercup

c. Stamen of Viola

d. Receptacle of wallflower

e. Pockets at apex of ovary in daffodil

f. Receptacle of deadnettle

g. Lining of perigynous receptacle in cherry

Fig. 18.10. Positions of nectaries in various flowers.

into the chalaza, where it may or may not continue into the integumentary tissue, according to species.

With the exception of the vascular strands which form the midribs and their branches in each carpel wall, and the vascular supply to the placentae and ovules, the young gynaecium is entirely parenchymatous. It is covered by a normal epidermis everywhere except at the stigmatic surface. However, as fruit development proceeds, much tissue differentiation may occur which ultimately transforms the whole structure.

The Nectaries

These are specialized glandular regions or fully-differentiated glandular outgrowths of either the receptacle itself or one or more of the floral parts. Some positions for nectaries to be found are shown in Fig. 18.10. The distinguishable histological feature of the nectary is its secretory

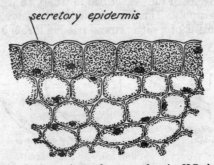

Fig. 18.11. Secretory tissue of nectary of apple. H.P. drawing.

tissue. This may be restricted entirely to the epidermal layer which is often composed of palisade-like cells with thin walls and dense cytoplasm, or may be a more solid mass of tissue of similar nature (*see* Fig. 18.11).

Abscission of Floral Parts

When flowering is completed, except for the ovary, the parts are generally shed by an abscission process which in outline is similar to leaf abscission. A separation layer is formed, but this may be only weakly differentiated. Protection at the break is effected generally by the impregnation of the exposed tissues with fatty substances, rather than by cork formation. Petals are most commonly shed, although sepals, stamens and styles also fall in many instances. In cases where there is no clear-cut abscission process, the withered parts may be seen attached to the fruit. When a plant bears unisexual flowers, the whole male flower may be cut off at the base of the pedicel, or whole male catkins may be shed at the inflorescence axis. Hermaphrodite and female flowers normally only fall when unfertilized, but there are notable exceptions to this in many seedless fruits such as the banana.

FRUITS

A fruit is the fully ripened gynaecium of a single flower, and in most cases, forms only when fertilization has been effected. Sometimes, other floral parts may enter into the formation of a composite structure, in which case we may distinguish these as *false fruits* or *pseudocarps* by contrast with the simpler *true fruits*.

True Fruits

Any true fruit will show the following main parts—

The *pericarp*, i.e. the ovary wall
The *seed* or *seeds*, i.e. the fertilized and ripened ovules
The remains of *style and stigma* or a *scar* where these have been detached

The form of any true fruit is decided mainly by two factors, one, the structure of the young ovary from which it has developed, and two, the manner in which the pericarp tissues are differentiated during ripening. Both these vary with species and there are many forms of true fruits. We may classify them conveniently in terms of their structure, the primary consideration being given to whether the pericarp becomes hard and *dry* or whether it becomes soft and fleshy, i.e. *succulent*. In the former case we can further subdivide according to whether a mature dry fruit opens to disperse its seeds, i.e. is *dehiscent* or *indehiscent*, or in a third instance whether only unopened carpels separate from one another, i.e. is *schizocarpic*. In succulent fruits, we may distinguish different forms in accordance with the manner in which the ovary wall differentiates. It may or may not contribute extra coverings to the dispersed seeds. The main types of true fruits are listed and described below with special cases within each group where they occur. Details of fruit structure can often be more easily understood from young specimens, particularly in cases where the mature fruit contains hardened parts or becomes very soft and pulpy.

Dry Fruits

1. *The Achene:* an indehiscent dry fruit resulting from a single carpel enclosing a single seed. In some cases a receptacle may bear a collection of achenes resulting from an apocarpous gynaecium. Such a collection may be regarded as a compound fruit and is described as an *etaerio* or head of achenes, e.g. buttercup, avens, *Clematis*, *Anemone*.

Special cases of achenes are:

(*a*) *The Nut:* pericarp distinctly hard and woody, e.g. hazel, oak, dock, rhubarb, buckwheat, sweet chestnut, beech.

(*Note:* the acorn is derived from a trilocular ovary with two ovules in each loculus, but almost invariably only one seed in one of the carpels reaches maturity.)

(*b*) *The Caryopsis:* pericarp inseparably fused to the seed coat, e.g. grains of cereals and grasses.

(*c*) *The Samara:* pericarp produced into a wing, e.g. ash, elm.

(*d*) *The Cypsela:* ultimately a one-seeded indehiscent dry fruit but

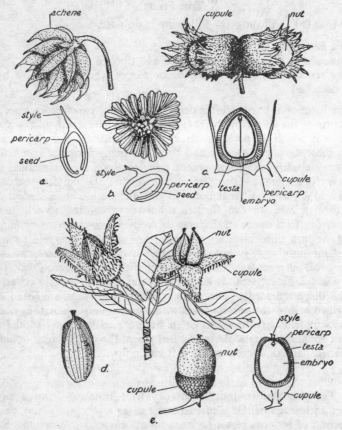

Fig. 18.12. Achenial fruits. (*a*) Wood anemone (*Anemone*). (*b*) Water plantain (*Alisma*). (*c*) Nut of hazel (*Corylus*). (*d*) Nuts of beech (*Fagus*). (*e*) Nut of oak (*Quercus*).

originating in a bicarpellary ovary. Part of the wall is receptacular tissue, although this is not differentiated from the true pericarp and the wall appears as a single layer. It could be regarded as a false fruit and is characteristic of the family Compositae, e.g. sunflower.

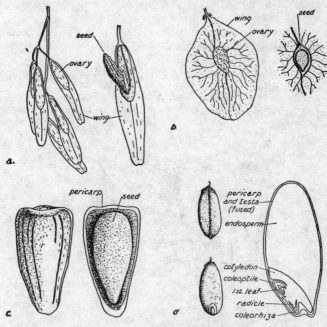

Fig. 18.13. Achenial fruits. (*a*) Samara of ash (*Fraxinus*), (*b*) Samara of elm (*Ulmus*). (*c*) Cypsela of sunflower (*Helianthus*). (*d*) Caryopsis of wheat (*Triticum*).

2. *The Follicle:* a dehiscent dry fruit formed from a single carpel bearing one or more seeds and splitting along one suture (ventral) only.

In many cases a head of follicles is formed from an apocarpous pistil, e.g. *Delphinium*, *Aquilegia*, monkshood, marsh marigold, paeony, *Magnolia*, hellebore.

3. *The Legume:* a dehiscent dry fruit formed from a single carpel bearing one or more seeds and splitting along both dorsal and ventral sutures, e.g. gorse, broom, pea, bean, laburnum, lucerne, lupin, vetch, clover and others of the family Papilionaceae.

Special case—

The Lomentum: a pod or legume transversely divided by false septa into separate compartments each bearing one seed, e.g. *Cassia*,

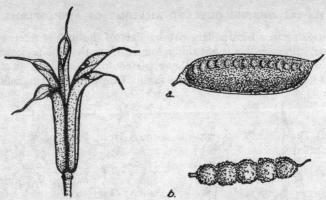

Fig. 18.14. Follicles of *Aquilegia*.

Fig. 18.15. (*a*) Legume of broom (*Sarothamnus*). (*b*) Lomentum of *Hedysarum*.

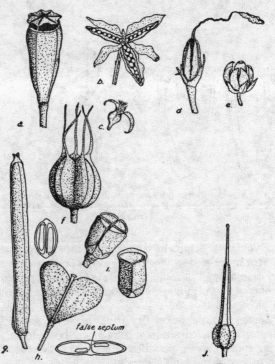

false septum

Fig. 18.16. Capsular fruits. (*a*) Poppy (*Papaver*). (*b*) Pansy (*Viola*). (*c*) Willow (*Salix*). (*d*) Crocus. (*e*) Stitchwort (*Stellaria*). (*f*) Nigella. (*g*) Siliqua of wallflower (*Cheiranthus*). (*h*) Silicula of shepherd's purse (*Capsella*). (*i*) Carcerulus and nutlet of dead nettle (*Lamium*). (*j*) Regma of *Geranium*.

Acacia. Note that siliquas may be classed as loments when transversely divided into one-seeded parts.

4. *The Capsule:* a dehiscent dry fruit formed from a syncarpous gynaecium, the carpels of which open by slits, pores or teeth, e.g. horse chestnut, *Antirrhinum*, poppy, *Lychnis*, *Dianthus*, foxglove, pimpernel, violet, iris.

Special cases—

(*a*) *The Silicula:* a capsule formed from a bicarpellary ovary separated into two loculi by a false septum: broader than long, e.g. shepherd's purse, honesty.

(*b*) *The Siliqua:* as above but longer than broad, e.g. wallflower, cabbage. Both these types (*a*) and (*b*) are peculiar to the family Cruciferae.

(*c*) *The Carcerulus:* a capsule modified by constriction or branching of carpels to form a number of one-seeded segments or nutlets into which the fruit finally splits, e.g. dead nettle and other labiates.

(*d*) *The Regma:* similar to the carcerulus but the separation into segments is explosive and the segments themselves may dehisce, e.g. *Geranium*.

5. *The Schizocarp:* a dry fruit formed from a syncarpous gynaecium

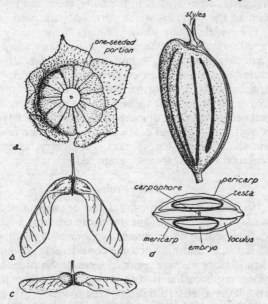

Fig. 18.17. Schizocarpic fruits. (*a*) Mallow (*Malva*). (*b* and *c*) Double samaras of sycamore (*Acer*) and maple (*Acer*). (*d*) Cremocarp of hogweed (*Heracleum*).

in which the carpels separate from one another as one-seeded *mericarps*, e.g. hollyhock, mallow.

Special cases—

(*a*) *The Double Samara:* composed of two or more winged indehiscent carpels which separate before or after wind dispersal, e.g. sycamore, maple.

(*b*) *The Cremocarp:* bicarpellary, bilocular fruit in which the two carpels separate into one-seeded indehiscent mericarps which remain attached for a time to a central supporting strand, the carpophore, before dispersal, e.g. hogweed, parsnip, caraway and others of the family Umbelliferae.

(*Note:* the carcerulus and regma are sometimes considered as schizocarpic fruits.)

Succulent Fruits

1. *The Drupe:* a fleshy fruit formed from a monocarpellary or syncarpous gynaecium, containing one or more seeds each of which is enclosed by a hard, stony portion of the pericarp at dispersal. The dispersal structure may be a single one-seeded "stone" as in the plum, or in several distinct portions as in the holly, elder and ivy. The inner hard portion of the pericarp which surrounds the seed is called the *endocarp*. The middle region of the pericarp, the *mesocarp*, is soft and succulent and this is covered externally by a skin-like *epicarp*. Examples of drupes are cherry, almond, walnut, coconut, elder. In many cases the receptacle bears a collection of small drupes, *drupels* or *drupelets* resulting from an apocarpous gynaecium, e.g. blackberry, raspberry.

2. *The Berry:* a fleshy fruit formed from a monocarpellary or syncarpous ovary containing one or more seeds each of which is surrounded only by its own hardened seed coat at dispersal. There is no hardened endocarp in the pericarp, e.g. currant, gooseberry, marrow, orange, lemon, cucumber, banana, tomato, grape, date.

False Fruits

These are "fruits" in which some floral part or parts in addition to the gynaecium may become part of the unit structure from which the seeds are finally dispersed. The receptacle is commonly incorporated into the "fruit" structure and may become considerably modified from its original form. Hence we may speak of *receptacular* pseudocarps. The most common modification is that in which the receptacle becomes enlarged and fleshy after fertilization of the ovules. A typical example is the strawberry in which the true fruits are separate achenes borne on a succulent receptacle. This structure is derived from a hypogynous or

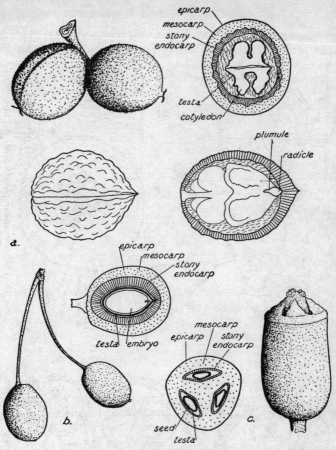

Fig. 18.18. Drupes. (*a*) Walnut (young) (*Juglans*). (*b*) Cherry (*Prunus*)
(*c*) elder (young) (*Sambucus*).

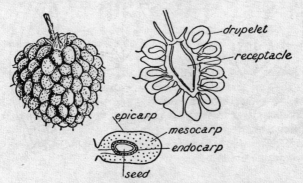

Fig. 18.19. Head of drupelets of raspberry (*Rubus*)

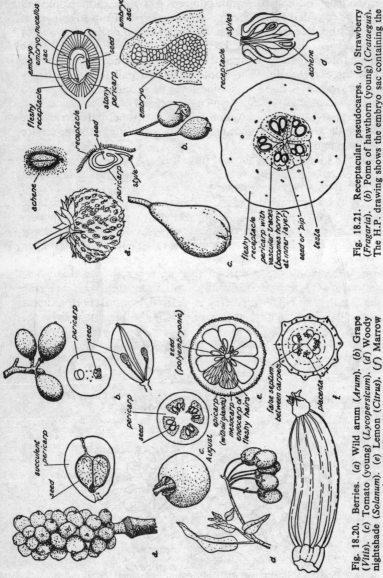

Fig. 18.20. Berries. (a) Wild arum (Arum). (b) Grape (Vitis). (c) Tomato (young) (Lycopersicum). (d) Woody nightshade (Solanum). (e) Lemon (Citrus). (f) Marrow (young) (Cucurbita).

Fig. 18.21. Receptacular pseudocarps. (a) Strawberry (Fragaria). (b) Pome of hawthorn (young) (Crataegus). The H.P. drawing shows the embryo sac containing the embryo. (c) Pome of pear (young) (Pyrus). (d) Hip of dog-rose (Rosa).

only slightly perigynous flower. In the rose *hip*, the fleshy receptacle forms a flask-shaped container for the achenes within it. Such a "fruit" is derived from a deeply perigynous flower. The *pome* of the apple and pear can be considered as a receptacular fruit derived from an epigynous flower. In this case the gynaecium is syncarpous and the inner wall of each carpel, i.e. the endocarp, becomes tough and fibrous whilst the loculi are forced apart by wedges of fleshy tissue formed from the outer layer of the carpel walls. The whole of this partially tough, partially fleshy, gynaecium is fused to a wide layer of succulent tissue derived from the receptacle, which completely encloses it. The pome thus shows certain features in common with both drupe and berry. The "pips" inside are seeds. Pomes may also be seen in hawthorn, service tree, quince and medlar.

There are still more complicated false fruits in which a whole inflorescence, not just a single flower, may form a single but complicated structure. These may be referred to as *infructescences* or *inflorescent* fruits. A typical example is the *syconus* of the fig. In this case the large number of very tiny flowers are formed on the inside of a hollow inflorescence axis. Each female flower produces a single small drupe when fertilized, and the axis develops as a succulent container to form the fig. Each tiny fig "pip" therefore corresponds to a plum "stone." Another example is the *sorosis* of the pineapple in which a whole inflorescence on a fleshy axis becomes a fused succulent mass including all the floral parts. The mulberry is derived from a short spike of flowers and is comparable in structure with the pineapple since the

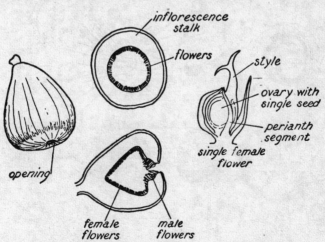

Fig. 18.22. Inflorescent fruit. Syconus of fig (young) (*Ficus*).

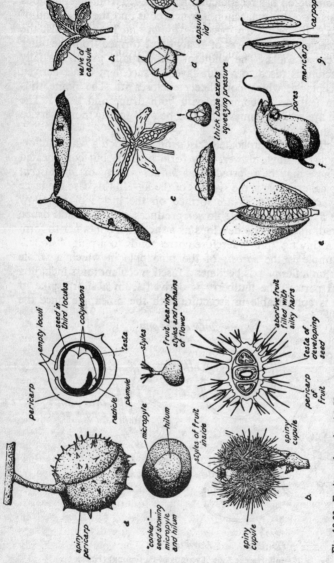

Fig. 18.24. Self dispersal mechanisms. (a) Splitting pod of broom. (b) Loculicidal opening of crocus capsule (c) Loculicidal opening of pansy capsule and expulsion of seeds. (d) Transverse opening of scarlet pimpernel capsule (*Anagallis*). (e) Separation of valves of the silicula of shepherd's purse. (f) Capsule of *Antirrhinum* opening by pores. (g) Separation of merocarps in hogweed cremocarp.

Fig. 18.23. Fruits and seeds. (a) Horse chestnut (*Aesculus*). (b) Sweet chestnut (*Castanea*).

perianth of each flower becomes fleshy as well as the ovary. The final "fruit" is not unlike a head of drupelets in appearance.

Distinction between Fruits and Seeds

Students sometimes experience difficulty in deciding whether a particular specimen is a fruit or a seed. Recollection of the definition of a fruit should help to solve any such problem. A fruit is a fully-ripened gynaecium and is therefore a seed-container. The two will differ clearly in their external characters. The fruit is usually stalked, the stalk being the flower pedicel, whereas the seed shows a scar, the hilum, where the funicle attached it to the placenta. The fruit nearly always carries the withered remains of one or more styles; the seed never does. On the seed, a micropyle or pore can sometimes be seen; there is no such structure on a fruit. If the specimen is dissected, then the differences become more obvious. If the fruit is many-seeded, there is usually clear distinction between the individual seeds and the pericarp of the fruit which encloses them. Each seed will have its own protective covering, the testa, within the pericarp and quite clearly separate from it. A one-seeded fruit, such as an achene or nut, especially a small one, may be more easily confused with a seed. A clear indication that the specimen is a fruit will be obtained during dissection, if not from external characters, since there will be two distinct layers to remove, the pericarp and testa, before the embryo is disclosed. The exception to this is the caryopsis, in which pericarp and testa become fused as a single layer. The occurrence of a cupule, which may entirely enclose the fruit until mature, can also cause indecision. Dissection of such a structure will clearly show three protective layers outside an embryo, the outermost being the cupule. Fig. 18.23 shows the structure of the fruits and seeds of the horse chestnut (*Aesculum*) and the sweet chestnut (*Castanea*); a study of the drawings will show that the "conker" is a seed whilst the sweet chestnut is a fruit.

FRUIT AND SEED DISPERSAL

For success, it is obviously an advantage for any species to be prolific and at the same time disperse its reproductive parts as widely as possible. This gives each a chance of development in conditions less crowded by plants of its own kind. Flowering plants usually produce a large number of seeds and this is an insurance against failure to reproduce, in that a few seeds at least may find suitable conditions provided that all are scattered over a wide area. To effect this wide dispersal we see many adaptations in fruit and seed structure. They may be designed either to propel the fruit or seed to a distance from the plant or to take

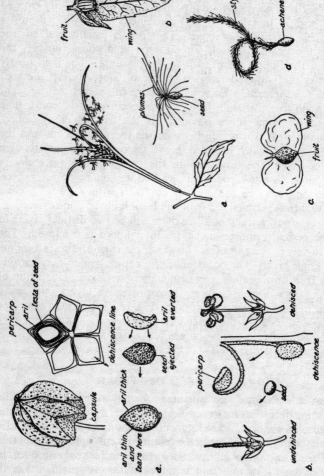

Fig. 18.26. Wind dispersal mechanisms. (a) Plumed seeds of willow-herb (*Epilobium*). (b) Winged nut of hornbeam (*Carpinus*). (c) Winged fruit of birch (*Betula*). (d) Plumed achene of *Clematis*.

Fig. 18.25. Self-dispersal mechanisms. (a) Explosive mechanism of wood sorrel (*Oxalis*). (b) Sling mechanism of cranesbill (*Geranium*).

advantage of one of several external dispersal agents. These latter include the wind, animals and, less commonly, water.

Self Dispersal Mechanisms

These are dependent on some rapid movement of the fruit wall or a seed attachment which causes the sudden jerking outwards of the seeds. The movements are mainly of two kinds. There are those dependent on tensions set up in the drying fruit wall and those dependent on the extreme turgidity of cells in some part of the fruit. The former case is exemplified by the legumes and some capsules. The pods of pea, broom, gorse, etc., are constructed of layers of fibrous tissue set obliquely to one another, so that drying out tends to cause the two halves to twist away from one another. When this twisting tension is strong enough, the weakened sutures are broken suddenly and the seeds thrown outwards to some distance (see Fig. 18.24). Similar tensions in the walls of capsules may cause their violent disruption. In the violet, the capsule first splits longitudinally into three boat-shaped valves, each of which on further lateral shrinkage, squeezes the smooth seeds outwards between the edges of the boat quite violently. A similar adaptation is seen in the box. The wood sorrel is a special case in which each seed possesses a highly elastic aril. When the capsule opens, each aril suddenly inverts itself so forcibly as to jerk the seed away. In the cranesbill, the lower parts of the fused styles suddenly separate and curl up. At the same time, each carpel dehisces, so that the seeds are propelled outwards as from a sling. There is a sling mechanism in the balsam but in this case it is due to the release of tensions set up by turgid tissues. Other examples of plants which possess turgid structures associated with seed dispersal are the squirting cucumber (*Ecballium*) and the flat fig (*Dorstenia*). In the former, the seeds are freely floating in disorganized watery tissue within the fruit. This pulpy mass renders the whole structure very turgid and when it eventually drops off, the contents are violently squirted out through the hole left by the stalk, as a result of the high internal pressure. In *Dorstenia*, each drupelet on the flattened disc is embedded in turgid tissue which exerts an outward pressure so that eventually each fruit is forcibly projected.

Wind Dispersal

There are numerous modifications of seeds and fruits which aid in their dispersal by the wind. A few plants, such as the orchids and wintergreen, produce such small and light seeds that they may be air-borne as easily as spores. Many seeds or fruits are contained in cups formed by capsules, involucres or cupules, in such a manner that as the cup rocks in a strong wind, the contents are shaken out. Such a mechanism is described as a *censer mechanism* and can be seen in the poppy, campion or primrose and many other capsules opening by pores or teeth. Follicles of monkshood, etc., may shed seed by a similar censer mechanism. There are numerous cases in which the seed or fruit wall is expanded into a wing-like structure. This may act as a sail or propeller to catch the wind. The conifers and the yellow rattle have winged seeds. Winged fruits occur in the ash, elm, sycamore and maple. The wings of the hornbeam and hop fruits are bracts. In species of *Salvia*, the calyx may form a sail, and in the dock the fruit is covered by the calyx which bears three wings. Various parachute mechanisms occur in which the seed or fruit has a plume or feathery attachment. The willowherb and willow produce plumed seeds. In *Clematis*, the fruit is plumed by modification of the style. In some members of the Compositae such as the dandelion, groundsel and thistle the very efficient parachute is composed of pappus hairs (*see* Fig. 18.51).

Animal Dispersal

Animals may be agents of dispersal of fruits and seeds in one of two ways. Many animals, particularly birds, use the soft portions of succulent fruits as a source of food. In feeding, they either discard the strongly protected seeds of berries, the stony endocarps of drupes and the achenes of such receptacular fruits as the strawberry or they may swallow them. In the latter case many of the hardened parts are so resistant that they can pass through the animal's body without harm, and when later dropped, can germinate successfully. The succulent portions of a fruit are usually specially modified for attracting the attention of animals visually. Often, a bright red colour makes them conspicuous. The succulent mass may develop from a variety of parts of the flower such as the ovary wall in drupes and berries, the receptacle in the strawberry, hip and pome and the perianth in the mulberry.

Alternatively, fruits or seeds may be carried externally on an animal's body by reason of the fact that they develop special hooks or spines which catch in the fur or wool. It is generally the case that the fruit wall becomes so modified, and there are numerous examples of hooked fruits, the hooks developing from various parts of the ripe structure. In avens it is the modified style which is hooked; in goose-grass, enchanter's nightshade, woodruff, chervil, carrot and sanicle it is the ovary wall; in agrimony, the hooks develop on the receptacle, which encloses the achenes; in burdock it is the involucral bracts of the capitulum which are hooked; in the bur-marigold (*Bidens*) the fruit, a cypsela, possesses barbed pappus outgrowths.

By comparison with the plants whose fruits and seeds are wind-dispersed, those relying on animal dispersal tend to develop fewer dispersal structures. There is a saving in reproductive material and yet success is not jeopardized, because fewer of them are likely to be dispersed into barren areas since animals tend to frequent only the more fertile regions.

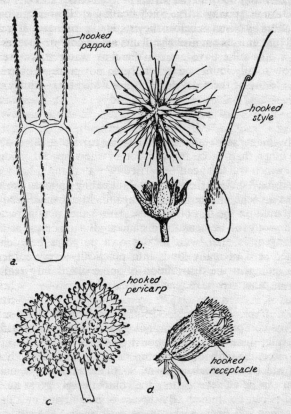

Fig. 18.27. Animal dispersal mechanisms—hooked parts. (a) Hooked pappus of bur-marigold (*Bidens*). (b) Hooked achenes of *Geum*. (c) Hooked ovary walls of goose grass (*Galium*). (d) Hooked receptacle of agrimony (*Agrimonia*).

Water Dispersal

Comparatively few plants have their seeds or fruits specially modified for dispersal by water currents. Many seeds or fruits will float but do not remain viable for long when so treated. Plants which do produce resistant buoyant seeds are the natural inhabitants of river, lake and seaside. Many of them have close relatives which inhabit woods and hedgerows, and in these cases the fruits and seeds are certainly not modified for floating. Examples of plants with specially buoyant dispersal structures are marsh woundwort, marsh bedstraw, marsh cinquefoil, water mint, water lily and alder. The air cavities which give the buoyancy may occur in the pericarp, seed coat or special outgrowths of the nature of spongy arils. Such floating structures can be carried long distances by currents before they settle to germinate. It is generally conceded that at least some of the plants which colonize oceanic islands or coral reefs, must have arrived there by water transport. Plants which grow totally immersed generally do not produce buoyant seeds or fruits. Many of them develop achenes which sink quickly on being shed.

Dispersal by Chance

Obviously, many seeds and fruits may be carried great distances by agencies other than those for which they show special modification. Any seed which will float can be carried by water, and if not wetted for too long it may survive the journey. Nut-eating animals like squirrels may make a cache and never find it again. Many small seeds can be carried in mud on the feet of animals. Hurricanes may blow any kind of fruit or seed for tremendous distances. But not least as a chance dispersal agent is man, who for his own purposes has deliberately transported seed of many kinds into practically every corner of the earth, so aiding in the distribution of some plants into regions they could never otherwise have reached.

PRACTICAL FLOWER STUDIES

To describe completely the morphology and anatomy of a flower, it must be fully dissected. Dissection is the process of separating out, piece by piece, the individual structures of a complicated body down to a level at which the eye can see them. With the unaided eye, only coarse dissection can be achieved; only the comparatively gross anatomy of large bodies can be studied. By the use of magnifying aids of varying strength, finer and finer work can be performed. The student is not debarred from using any aid he may find available. The lowest level of achievement generally acceptable in flower dissection is that made possible by use of a good quality hand-lens ($\times$ 10). No flower is so big that a hand lens becomes totally unnecessary and many have some parts at least which are too small to be otherwise clearly distinguishable. A good hand-lens, then, is a necessity and sometimes a microscope (binocular, for preference) can be used with advantage at this higher level of dissection. The student may often find it necessary when confronted with a small, immature gynaecium, to section it and examine it

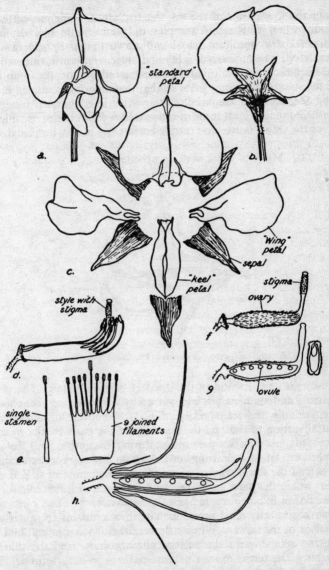

Fig. 18.28. Parts of the sweet pea flower (*Lathyrus*). (*a* and *b*) Anterior and posterior views of whole flower. (*c*) Sepals and petals displayed in whorls. (*d*) Androecium and gynaecium after removal of perianth segments. (*e*) Stamens. (*f*) Gynaecium after removal of stamens. (*g*) L.S. and T.S. gynaecium. (*h*) L.S. of flower.

under the low power of the microscope. In conjunction with aids to vision, other instruments are essential and should include fine and coarse forceps, needles, scissors and a sharp razor or scalpel whereby parts may be held, severed, sectioned or generally dismembered.

Complete dissection involves the removal and display in an orderly sequence of all the floral parts so that they may be examined individually. Sectioning of the whole flower in various planes is necessary to establish the relationships of position and form of the parts. Fig. 18.28 shows the whole flower and the dissected parts of a sweet pea, displayed

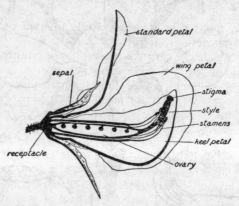

Fig. 18.29. Half of sweet pea flower. Blackened lines indicate cut surfaces.

to show its construction in the greatest possible detail. The perianth segments and stamens are laid out and the gynaecium sectioned both longitudinally and transversely. Fig. 18.29 shows the same flower in sagittal section to indicate the insertion of the parts on the receptacle.

Records of observations made during dissection will be chiefly graphic, i.e. labelled drawings of the whole flower, representative parts of each of the floral whorls where these are separate or of a complete whorl where the parts are joined, and a sagittal or longitudinal section of the flower in one or more planes as necessary. The plane of a section which is generally most useful is that which contains the anterior and posterior of the flower. When a flower develops as a lateral bud on an axis, the side towards the axis is called *posterior* and the side away, *anterior*. The terms cannot be applied to a solitary terminal flower. Note carefully that a longitudinal section should include only those faces of structures cut by a razor in slicing a flower in half; only the sagittal section includes the uncut parts seen in the background. Compare Figs. 18.28 (*h*) and 18.29 to understand the meaning of this.

From the information gained by dissection and illustration the following form of written description may be compiled—

Flower structure and symmetry: pedicellate or sessile; bract present or absent; unisexual or hermaphrodite; regular or irregular; actino-morphic, zygomorphic or asymmetric; spiral, cyclic or hemi-cyclic; hypogynous, perigynous or epigynous.

Calyx: number of parts; free or joined; any special characters such as hairiness, reflexed or otherwise, colour, bearing nectaries or otherwise; variation in form if not all alike.

Corolla: number of parts; free or joined; any special characters as above.

Androecium: number of stamens; freely inserted or epipetalous, adelphous or syngenesious; introrse or extrorse.

Gynaecium: number of carpels; apocarpous or syncarpous; number of loculi; ovule placentation; inferior or superior.

Fruit: type of fruit and possible dispersal mechanism.

Pollination mechanism: special remarks about pollination mechanism from observations in the field or by deduction from flower construction, presence or absence of nectaries, etc.

Further, the flower structure should be represented both diagrammatically and by symbols. The former is the *floral diagram* and the latter the *floral formula.*

The floral diagram is constructed on a series of concentric circles, one for each whorl of floral parts. The axis of the inflorescence is represented at the top of the diagram which is then regarded as the posterior position in the flower and the bract or bracts, if any, inserted at the bottom representing the anterior position. On each circle are drawn the various floral segments in their correct relative positions and showing fusions of parts where these occur. One hint may be found useful. The circle representing the gynaecium must be made large enough. It is not easy to draw clearly the detail of a complex ovary in a small space. The floral diagram of the sweet pea is shown in Fig. 18.30.

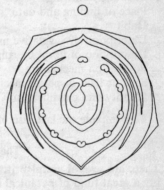

Fig. 18.30. Floral diagram of sweet pea.

The floral formula symbolizes the floral structure by making use of conventional signs for the floral symmetry, parts and fusion of parts. The following symbols are in general use—

$\oplus$ = actinomorphic

$\cdot|\cdot$ = zygomorphic

K = calyx

C = corolla

P = perianth (where K and C are not clearly distinguishable)

A = androecium

G = gynaecium

A number following the whorl abbreviation = the number of parts in the whorl—

∞ = an indefinite number of parts (usually if exceeding twelve)

The same number in brackets = parts joined, e.g. C(5) or G(3)

A link between two whorl symbols = one inserted on the other, e.g.

$\widehat{C(5)}$ A5 = epipetalous stamens

A line over the gynaecium symbol = inferior ovary, e.g. $\overline{G}$

A line under the gynaecium symbol = superior ovary, e.g. $\underline{G}$

Completed floral formulae would appear as the examples below—

Sweet pea: $\cdot|\cdot$ K(5) C5 A(9) + 1 $\underline{G1}$ Buttercup: $\oplus$ K5 C5 A∞ $\underline{G\infty}$

Foxglove: $\cdot|\cdot$ K(5) $\widehat{C(5)}$ A4 $\underline{G(2)}$ Iris: $\oplus$ P(3 + 3) A3 $\overline{G(3)}$

Many other examples of floral diagrams and formulae are given later in this chapter.

A full description of a flowering plant collected in the field should include the following—

Place of finding and date

Habit

Description of vegetative morphology with illustrations

Description of floral morphology with illustrations

Pollination mechanism

Seed or fruit dispersal mechanism

Identity and classification

To complete the last, use of a flora is nearly always essential.

The Use of a Flora

There are several useful British floras in publication. Besides containing a great fund of botanical information, each possesses an analytical key for the purposes of identification. The principle involved in constructing such a key is to find contrasting characters by which a group of plants may be split into smaller and smaller groups by a process of elimination. Finally, one arrives at the name of a plant whose description fits the particular specimen under consideration and no other. By using such a key, the student establishes its identity from its own vegetative and floral characteristics and as an exercise in observation alone, the "running down" of flowering plant species by means of a key is to be thoroughly recommended. It was once a very fashionable parlour game.

Several different types of key may be encountered. We may distinguish the purely arbitrary or artificial system whereby flower colour, habitat, habit and so on may form the basis for criteria on which to separate groups of plants, or we may distinguish the key based on some more natural criteria which tend to weld together the groups which show natural affinities. The former may make an excellent field pocket book but only the latter is to be recommended to the student of botany. In either case, the key is prepared most often in one of two ways and these are reflected in the manner of printing. There are the *indented key* and the *bracket key*. They are better illustrated than described.

Indented key to the species of the genus *Medicago* (Papilionaceae) from the *Handbook of the British Flora* by Bentham and Hooker, p. 110.

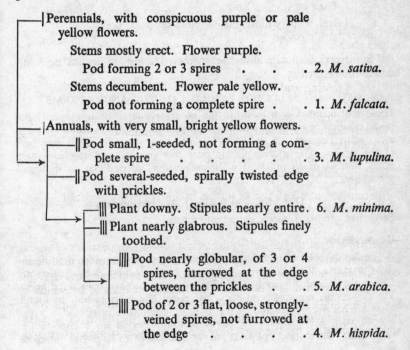

Perennials, with conspicuous purple or pale yellow flowers.

    Stems mostly erect. Flower purple.

        Pod forming 2 or 3 spires   .   .   . 2. *M. sativa.*

    Stems decumbent. Flower pale yellow.

        Pod not forming a complete spire .   . 1. *M. falcata.*

Annuals, with very small, bright yellow flowers.

    Pod small, 1-seeded, not forming a complete spire   .   .   .   .   . 3. *M. lupulina.*

    Pod several-seeded, spirally twisted edge with prickles.

        Plant downy. Stipules nearly entire. 6. *M. minima.*

        Plant nearly glabrous. Stipules finely toothed.

            Pod nearly globular, of 3 or 4 spires, furrowed at the edge between the prickles   .   . 5. *M. arabica.*

            Pod of 2 or 3 flat, loose, strongly-veined spires, not furrowed at the edge   .   .   .   . 4. *M. hispida.*

Bracket key to the species of the genus *Medicago* from *Flora of the British Isles* by Clapham, Tutin and Warburg, p. 418.

1. Fls. 7–9 mm, yellow or purple . . . 2
   Fls. 2–5 mm, yellow 3

2. Fl. yellow; pedicel longer than the calyx-tube;
      pod falcate or nearly straight . . . 1. *falcata*.
   Fl. purple; pedicel shorter than the calyx-tube;
      pod a spiral of 2–3 turns . . . 2. *sativa*.

3. Racemes many-fld; pod unarmed, 1-seeded,
      black when ripe . . . . . 3. *lupulina*.
   Racemes 1–5 fld; pod spiny or tuberculate,
      several-seeded brown when ripe . . 4

4. Plant downy; stipules nearly entire . . 4. *minima*.
   Plant glabrous or nearly so; stipules distinctly
      toothed or laciniate. 5

5. Lflets. not blotched; stipules laciniate; pod
      flat . . . . 5. *hispida*.
   Lflets. usually blotched; stipules toothed; pod
      sub-globose . . . . . . 6. *arabica*.

The arrows indicate how the species *M. hispida* would be "run down" in each case.

NOTES ON SELECTED FAMILIES OF THE ANGIOSPERMS

These are intended as a guide to the observer and to bring out only the broad outlines of the floral characteristics of each family. A real knowledge of a family can only be gained by detailed observation of many members of the family. The student should bear this in mind and augment these notes with as much practical work as possible, carried out as indicated previously.

Dicotyledonous families: Archichlamydeae

Petals free or absent, rarely united into a tube.

Ranunculaceae

The family belongs to the order Ranales, generally considered to be the most primitive of the angiosperm orders. In the Ranunculaceae, there are forty-eight genera, fifteen British. The species are mostly perennial herbs. The flowers are commonly solitary, but cymes and racemes may be found. They are hermaphrodite and each is built on a primitive plan, that is, hypogynous with parts spirally or partly spirally inserted on a cone-shaped receptacle. The numbers of parts are variable and often large and indefinite.

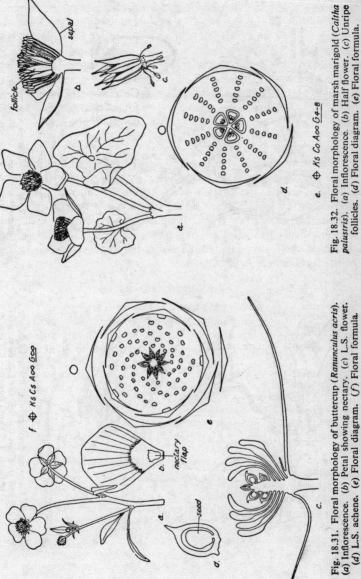

Fig. 18.32. Floral morphology of marsh marigold (*Caltha palustris*). (*a*) Inflorescence. (*b*) Half flower. (*c*) Unripe follicles. (*d*) Floral diagram. (*e*) Floral formula.

e. ⊕ K5 C0 A∞ G 4-8

Fig. 18.31. Floral morphology of buttercup (*Ranunculus acris*). (*a*) Inflorescence. (*b*) Petal showing nectary. (*c*) L.S. flower. (*d*) L.S. achene. (*e*) Floral diagram. (*f*) Floral formula.

f ⊕ K5 C5 A∞ G∞

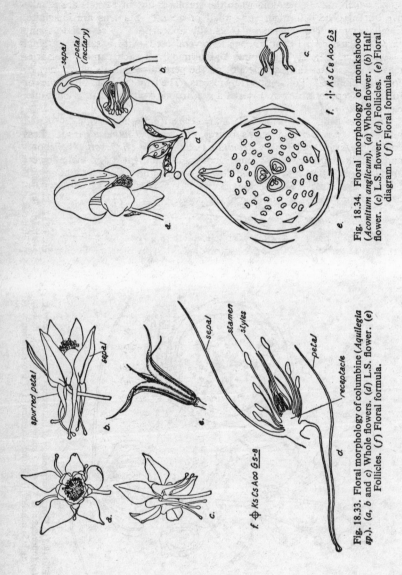

sepal
petal (nectary)

f. ⊹ K5 C8 A∞ G̲3̲

Fig. 18.34. Floral morphology of monkshood (*Aconitum anglicum*). (a) Whole flower. (b) Half flower. (c) L.S. flower. (d) Follicles. (e) Floral diagram. (f) Floral formula.

spurred petal
sepal
sepal
stamen
styles
petal
receptacle

f. ⊕ K5 C5 A∞ G̲5-8̲

Fig. 18.33. Floral morphology of columbine (*Aquilegia sp.*). (a, b and c) Whole flowers. (d) L.S. flower. (e) Follicles. (f) Floral formula.

This is particularly so of the stamens and carpels. There are usually five sepals which may be petaloid when the corolla is absent. Petals are usually five but may be deformed, very small or absent. Stamens are indefinite, usually many. The gynaecium is usually apocarpous of several to many carpels. Each carpel contains one to several seeds with basal or marginal placentation. The style is simple and terminal on each carpel. Nectaries may be present on the receptacle or on the perianth segments which may be specially modified. Pollination is by insects. The fruit is a head of achenes or follicles except in those rare cases of a syncarpous ovary, when it is a capsule, e.g. *Nigella*.

Common wild genera include *Ranunculus* (buttercup), *Caltha* (marsh marigold), *Clematis* (old man's beard), *Anemone*, *Thalictrum* (rue). Less common are the wild genera *Aconitum* (monkshood), *Helleborus* (hellebore) and *Actaea* (baneberry). Members commonly cultivated for their flowers are *Delphinium* (larkspur), *Nigella* (love-in-a-mist) and *Aquilegia* (columbine). None are of great economic importance but some species yield poisonous drugs such as aconitine from the monkshood.

Cruciferae

This family belongs to the order Rhoeadales. It is a large family of 220 genera and fifty-two of these are represented in Great Britain. The members

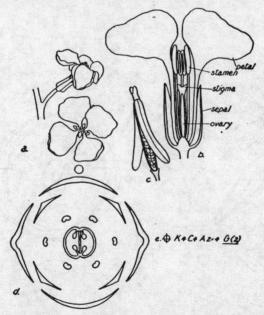

Fig. 18.35. Floral morphology of wallflower (*Cheiranthus cheiri*). (*a*) Whole flowers. (*b*) Half flower. (*c*) Siliqua. (*d*) Floral diagram. (*e*) Floral formula.

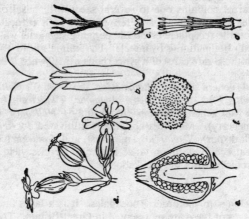

Fig. 18.37. Floral morphology of red campion (*Melandrium rubrum*). (a) Female inflorescence. (b) Petal of female flower. (c) Gynaecium (♀ flower only). (d) Stamens (♂ flower only). (e) L.S. fruit. (f) Campylotropous ovule. (g) Floral formulae.

♂ ⊕ K(5) Cs A5+5 G 0 ♂

♀ ⊕ K(5) Cs A0 G(5) ♀

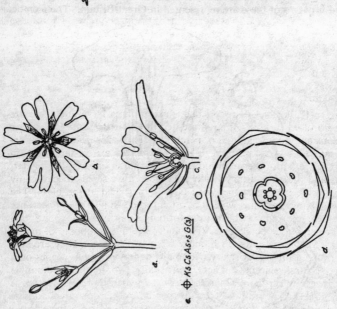

Fig. 18.36. Floral morphology of stitchwort (*Stellaria holostea*). (a) Inflorescence. (b) Single flower. (c) Half flower. (d) Floral diagram. (e) Floral formula.

⊕ K5 Cs A5+5 G(3)

are chiefly herbaceous annuals or biennials with a few perennials. The inflorescence is characteristically a raceme or corymb. The flowers are hermaphrodite and built on a uniform plan throughout the family. Each flower is hypogynous, regular, and the parts cyclically inserted on the receptacle. The calyx is of four free sepals in two opposite and decussate pairs. The inner pair may be sacculate at the base and bear nectaries in the sacs. The corolla is of four free petals alternating with the sepals. The androecium is of six introrse stamens arranged with each of an outer pair standing opposite one another and each flanking two inner pairs standing opposite one another. The inner four stamens have longer filaments than the outer two and the androecium is described as *didynamous*. Rarely, the outer two stamens may be suppressed. The gynaecium is syncarpous of two carpels and the ovules are marginally placed. The single loculus is divided into two by united ingrowths of the placentae to form a false septum across the ovary. The style is single and terminal but often two-lobed or flattened at the head. Pollination is by insects but many species are self-fertile. The fruit is a variety of capsule known as a silicula or a siliqua according to dimensions. It opens from the base by two valves, leaving the seeds attached to the placentae at either edge of the false septum.

Common wild genera include *Capsella* (shepherd's purse) *Cardamine* (cuckoo flower), *Cochlearia* (scurvy grass), *Barbarea* (yellow rocket), *Sisymbrium* (hedge mustard). Cultivated genera of great economic importance for their foliage or roots include *Brassica* (cabbage, swede. turnip), *Raphanus* (radish), *Nasturtium* (water cress). Those cultivated for their flowers include *Cheiranthus* (wallflower), *Lunaria* (honesty), *Aubretia*, *Matthiola* (stock), and *Iberis* (candytuft).

Caryophyllaceae

Belonging to the order Centrospermae, this family is large and there are seventy genera of which thirty are represented in Great Britain. The species are herbaceous and may be annual or perennial. The inflorescence is characteristically cymose, rarely solitary. Floral characters are variable, but in general the flowers are hermaphrodite (occasionally unisexual), regular, hypogynous and the parts are cyclically arranged. Five sepals (occasionally four) make up the calyx and they may be free or joined at the base. The corolla is usually of five petals which are often forked to give the appearance of ten. They are free and may bear scales forming a corona at the mouth of a long tube formed by the petal bases. The androecium is composed of five or ten stamens. The carpels vary in number from two to five. They are syncarpous, forming a unilocular ovary with many campylotropous ovules on a basal or free-central placenta. There are usually two to five free simple styles. Nectaries are on the receptacle below the gynaecium. Pollination is normally by insects. The fruit is a capsule opening by teeth or valves and the seeds possess a *perisperm* (food storage tissue not derived from the embryo sac, i.e. from the nucellus or integuments).

Common wild British genera include *Melandrium* (campions), *Lychnis* (ragged robin), *Cerastium* (chickweeds) and *Stellaria* (stitchworts). Among

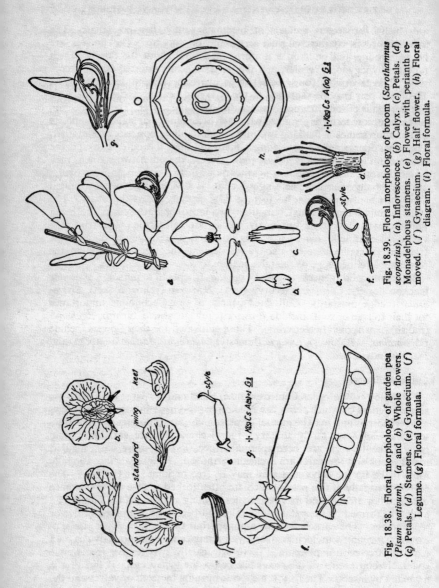

Fig. 18.39. Floral morphology of broom (*Sarothamnus scoparius*). (*a*) Inflorescence. (*b*) Calyx. (*c*) Petals. (*d*) Monadelphous stamens. (*e*) Flower with perianth removed. (*f*) Gynaecium. (*g*) Half flower. (*h*) Floral diagram. (*i*) Floral formula.

Fig. 18.38. Floral morphology of garden pea (*Pisum sativum*). (*a* and *b*) Whole flowers. (*c*) Petals. (*d*) Stamens. (*e*) Gynaecium. (*f*) Legume. (*g*) Floral formula.

cultivated flowers are the pinks, carnations, sweet william and *Gypsophila*. None of the species are of great economic importance.

Papilionaceae [Leguminosae]

This is the only British representative of the order Leguminosae. The family is very large, of 300 or more genera of which twenty-four can be found in the British Isles. The species are chiefly perennial herbs but shrubs and trees are not uncommon. Many are climbers by tendrils or twining stems. The inflorescence is characteristically racemose. The floral characters of the British species, particularly those of the corolla and gynaecium, are very constant and have given rise to the names by which the family is known. The flowers are hermaphrodite, hypogynous to slightly perigynous, very markedly zygomorphic and the parts cyclically arranged. The calyx consists of usually five sepals, sometimes two, and these are joined at the base. The corolla is unmistakable in being made up of five petals always arranged in the same way. There is one large adaxial petal, erect and spreading (the standard) and two lateral petals (the wings), one on either side of two lower petals which are more or less joined by their lower margins (to form the keel). Ten stamens make up the androecium and these may be either all joined by their filaments (monadelphous) or nine joined and one free (diadelphous), or more rarely, all free. The gynaecium is unicarpellary with several ovules on a marginal placenta. The style is terminal and simple. Not unusually it is long and coiled within the keel affording a particular type of insect pollination mechanism. Many species are self-pollinated and no nectaries are developed. The fruit is a legume (dehiscing along two sutures of the carpel, cf. follicle). The seeds are generally large with food-packed cotyledons.

Among the commoner wild British genera are *Ulex* (gorse), *Sarothamnus* (broom), *Trifolium* (clovers and trefoils) and several of the vetches. Garden flowers and shrubs include *Lupin*, *Lathyrus* (sweet pea) and *Laburnum*. Cultivated for cattle fodder are *Medicago* (lucernes) and the clovers. For human consumption *Pisum* (pea), *Vicia* (beans) and *Phaseolus* (runner beans) are common crops.

The family is of great economic importance and members play a part not only as food crops but also in affecting the fertility of the soil. Symbiotic bacteria of the nitrogen-fixing kind inhabit nodules on the roots. Many tropical species exist, and form some of the massive climbing lianas of the jungle.

Rosaceae

This is one of seven British families in the order Rosales. There are a total of ninety genera of which twenty-four are represented in Great Britain. The species are nearly all perennial herbs, shrubs or trees. The inflorescence is variable and both racemose and cymose forms occur. The family may be divided into sub-families on differing floral characteristics which result from variation in the growth and shape of the receptacle. There may be very slightly perigynous flowers as in strawberry, markedly perigynous flowers as in cherry, or epigynous flowers as in apple. The flowers are usually hermaphrodite, regular and with the parts cyclically arranged. The calyx is usually of five

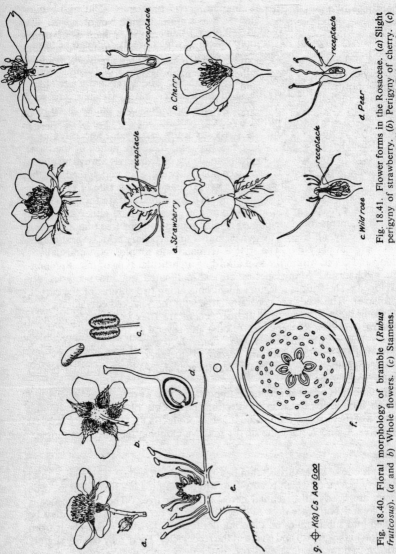

Fig. 18.40. Floral morphology of bramble (*Rubus fruticosus*). (*a* and *b*) Whole flowers. (*c*) Stamens. (*d*) L.S. drupelet. (*e*) L.S. flower. (*f*) Floral diagram. (*g*) Floral formula.

g. ⊕ K(5) C5 A∞ G∞

Fig. 18.41. Flower forms in the Rosaceae. (*a*) Slight perigyny of strawberry. (*b*) Perigyny of cherry. (*c*) Advanced perigyny of wild rose. (*d*) Epigyny of pear.

a. Strawberry

b. Cherry

c. Wild rose

d. Pear

receptacle

free, but imbricate or overlapping sepals, sometimes with an epicalyx (an extra ring of bracts outside the calyx). The corolla is most often of five petals (occasionally none), the petals alternating with the sepals. The androecium is variable, being composed of 1, 2, 3 or 4 times the number of sepals. The gynaecium is also variable, sometimes of a single carpel or many apocarpous carpels or five syncarpous carpels. The anatropous ovules usually occur one in each of the carpels when separate or two in each of the carpels when united. The styles are usually free and there are as many as there are carpels. Pollination is normally by insects and nectaries may be found on the receptacle. The fruit varies from a single achene or a head of achenes, to a drupe or head of druplets or a pome. It is rarely a capsule. Members of the family may be confused with members of the Ranunculaceae but in addition to the perigynous or epigynous condition of the flower, the presence of stipules in members of the Rosaceae is nearly always a point of distinction.

Among the common wild genera are *Rosa* (wild rose), *Filipendula* (meadow sweet), *Rubus* (bramble), *Potentilla* (cinquefoils and tormentils), *Fragaria* (wild strawberry), *Geum* (avens), *Agrimonia* (agrimony), *Prunus* (blackthorn, cherry), *Crataegus* (hawthorn), *Sorbus* (mountain ash). Garden flowers include the cultivated roses, *Spiraea*, *Geum* and *Cotoneaster*. Many of the fruits are of great economic importance and include those of *Malus* (apple), *Pyrus* (pear), *Prunus* (plum, cherry, almond, peach), *Rubus* (raspberry and blackberry), *Fragaria* (strawberry) and *Mespilus* (medlar).

Salicaceae

This is a family of deciduous trees and shrubs belonging to the order Salicales. There are two British genera only, *Salix* (willows) and *Populus* (poplars). There has been controversy over the relationships of the order to the other angiosperm orders because of the arrangement and structure of the flowers. These are arranged in inflorescences called catkins and each flower can be regarded as showing either the simplest possible construction or alternatively a very advanced structure resulting from the reduction of parts of a much more complicated flower. Some have argued that the simplicity represents a primitive condition in the evolution of the flower, whilst others have argued the case for an advanced evolutionary condition by the reduction of parts. The latter view seems to be more widely held.

The species are dioecious, i.e. unisexual flowers are borne on separate plants. Within the catkins, each flower is borne in the axil of a bract or scale.

In the male flower, the perianth is entirely absent, unless the view is taken that the cup-like disc which bears the stamens in *Populus* or the nectary or nectaries in *Salix* which are borne on or in the axil of the bract, are parts of a very reduced perianth. The androecium is of two to many stamens according to genus and species. In *Salix* there are five stamens or less, in *Populus* from four to a large number. The gynaecium is entirely absent. The nectary is composed of one or two small protuberances on the bract near the base of the stamens in *Salix* but absent in *Populus*.

In the female flower, the perianth and androecium are absent. The gynaecium is of two syncarpous carpels, unilocular and with anatropous

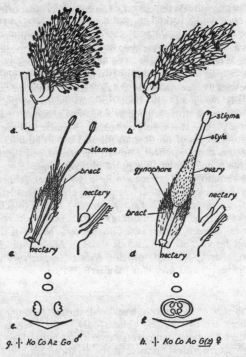

Fig. 18.42. Floral morphology of willow (*Salix caprea*). (*a*) Male catkin. (*b*) Female catkin. (*c*) Single male flower and L.S. of insertion on axis. (*d*) Single female flower and L.S. insertion on axis. (*e*) Floral diagram of male flower. (*f*) Floral diagram of female flower. (*g* and *h*) Floral formulae.

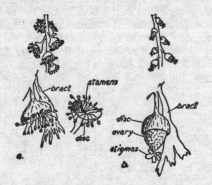

Fig. 18.43. (*a*) Male and (*b*) female flowers of poplar (*Populus*).

ovules on marginal (parietal) placentae. It is borne on or in the axil of a bract in *Salix* or within a cup-like disc around its base in *Populus*. There is usually one style with a forked stigmatic surface. Nectaries occur in *Salix* as for the male flower but are absent in *Populus*. Pollination in *Populus* must be considered as anemophilous, since nectaries are absent. In *Salix* however, the presence of nectaries in both male and female flowers indicates the entomophilous condition. Bees undoubtedly visit both male and female catkins in *Salix* but there is little doubt that a good deal of pollen is also shed from the male catkins under the influence of the wind and thus could be air-borne to the stigmas. The fruit is a capsule opening by two valves. The seeds may be enveloped in long silky hairs. Common British species include *S. pentandra* (bay willow), *S. alba* (white or cricket bat willow), *S. viminalis* (osier), *S. caprea* (goat willow), *P. alba* (white poplar), *P. nigra* (black poplar), *P. tremula* (aspen), and *P. italica* (Lombardy poplar). There are many natural hybrids within each genus and identification is often difficult.

Dicotyledonous Families: Metachlamydeae

Petals united into a tube, very rarely free or absent.

Scrophulariaceae

This is a large family of over 200 genera of the order Tubiflorae. Twenty genera are represented in Britain. Nearly all the species are annual or perennial herbs. Some may be partial parasites. *Euphrasia* (eyebright), *Rhinanthus* (yellow rattle) and *Pedicularis* (lousewort) may parasitize grasses through the roots. The inflorescence is commonly a raceme and the flowers are very typically zygomorphic, with the parts cyclically arranged and hypogynous. The flower parts are commonly in fives except in the gynaecium which always has two carpels. In some genera, reduction from fives is the rule so that parts may be present only as vestiges or absent entirely. The calyx is of five, occasionally four, sepals joined at the base at least. The corolla is of five petals joined to form a tube which may be evenly five-toothed or lobed or very markedly two-lipped. A four-lobed condition can arise when two of five lobes unite to form one. The androecium is basically of five epipetalous stamens alternating with the corolla lobes, e.g. *Verbascum* (mullein). Most frequently there are only four stamens with the upper one absent as in *Digitalis* (foxglove), or represented only by a non-functional staminode as in *Scrophularia* (figwort). In the genus *Veronica* (speedwells), there are two lateral stamens only and the very short corolla tube shows four lobes. The gynaecium is of two syncarpous carpels, bilocular and with many anatropous ovules on enlarged axile placentae. The style is terminal on the ovary and may be simple or with two stigmatic lobes. Nectaries occur around the base of the ovary. Pollination is by large insects such as bees, wasps and hoverflies. The fruit is a capsule dehiscing by two valves. Common British genera include *Digitalis* (foxglove), *Scrophularia* (figwort), *Linaria* (toadflax), *Veronica* (speedwells), and *Verbascum* (mullein). Cultivated garden flowers include *Antirrhinum, Pentstemon, Calceolaria, Mimulus*. Some representatives yield poisonous drugs, the most notable of which is digitalin from the foxglove.

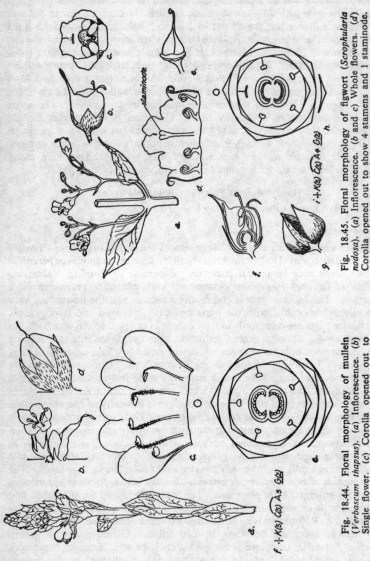

Fig. 18.44. Floral morphology of mullein (*Verbascum thapsus*). (a) Inflorescence. (b) Single flower. (c) Corolla opened out to show 5 stamens. (d) Capsule. (e) Floral diagram. (f) Floral formula.

f. ⊕ K(5) C(5) A5 G(2)

Fig. 18.45. Floral morphology of figwort (*Scrophularia nodosa*). (a) Inflorescence. (b and c) Whole flowers. (d) Corolla opened out to show 4 stamens and 1 staminode. (e) Young capsule. (f) Half flower. (g) Ripe capsule dehiscing. (h) Floral diagram. (i) Floral formula.

i. ⊕ K(5) C(5) A4 G(2)

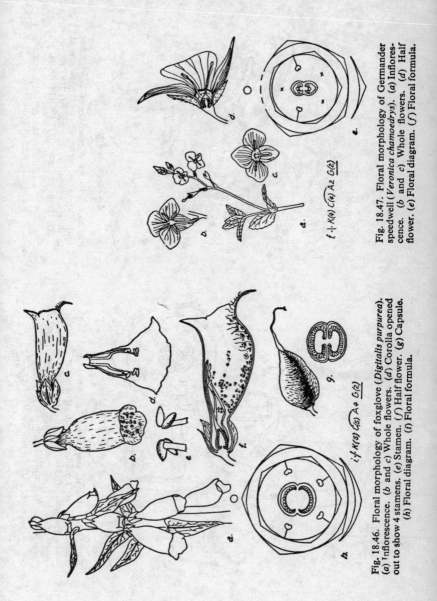

Fig. 18.46. Floral morphology of foxglove (*Digitalis purpurea*). (*a*) Inflorescence. (*b* and *c*) Whole flowers. (*d*) Corolla opened out to show 4 stamens. (*e*) Stamen. (*f*) Half flower. (*g*) Capsule. (*h*) Floral diagram. (*i*) Floral formula.

Fig. 18.47. Floral morphology of Germander speedwell (*Veronica chamoedrys*). (*a*) Inflorescence. (*b* and *c*) Whole flowers. (*d*) Half flower. (*e*) Floral diagram. (*f*) Floral formula.

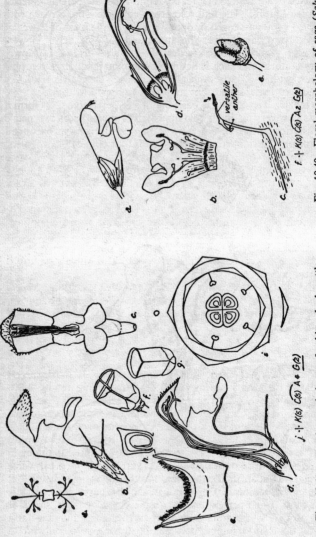

$f \cdot + K(5) \ \widehat{C(5)} \ A_2 \ \underline{\widehat{G(2)}}$

Fig. 18.49. Floral morphology of sage (*Salvia officinalis*). (a) Whole flower. (b) Corolla opened to show stamens. (c) Stamen. (d) Half flower. (e) Group of nutlets. (f) Floral formula.

versatile anther

$j \cdot + K(5) \ \widehat{C(5)} \ A + \underline{\widehat{G(2)}}$

Fig. 18.48. Floral morphology of white dead nettle (*Lamium album*). (a) Diagram of verticillaster. (b and c) Whole flowers. (d) Half flower. (e) Corolla pouch and hairs. (f) Group of nutlets. (g) Single nutlet. (h) L.S. nutlet. (i) Floral diagram. (j) Floral formula.

Labiatae

This is another family of the Tubiflorae. There are about 170 genera of which twenty-five are represented in Great Britain. Most are perennial herbs, but there are a few shrubs. The inflorescence is characteristic, cymose with the very shortened cymes arranged in opposite pairs in the axils of leaves or bracts. Such an arrangement gives the appearance of a whorl of flowers at each node. Each group of flowers is described as a *verticillaster*. Flower structure is very uniform and each is hermaphrodite, markedly zygomorphic and hypogynous, with the parts cyclically arranged. The calyx is of five joined sepals, clearly five-toothed, but may be two-lipped with upper three and lower two sepals. The corolla is basically of five petals joined to form a tube which distally is very distinctly two-lipped. The upper lip of two petals frequently forms a hood whilst the lower lip of three petals forms an expanded three-lobed platform. The androecium consists of four epipetalous stamens, didynamous, alternating with the corolla segments. The anthers may be *versatile*. The gynaecium is made up of two syncarpous carpels with initially two loculi, each with two anatropous ovules on axile placentae. The ovary later appears four-lobed since each carpel becomes subdivided by a wall separating the ovules in each case. The style is simple below, arising centrally from the four ovary segments but forked into two stigmatic surfaces above. Nectaries occur at the base of the ovary and pollination is effected by long-tongued insects. The fruit is a collection of four nutlets formed by the separation of half carpels each containing one seed. The whole structure is known as a carcerulus.

Common wild British genera include *Lamium* (dead nettles), *Nepeta* (catmint), *Prunella* (selfheal), *Stachys* (wound-wort), *Glechoma* (ground ivy) and *Ajuga* (bugle). Cultivated pot herbs include *Mentha* (mint), *Thymus* (thyme) and *Salvia* (sage).

Compositae

This is the only British family of the order Asterales. It is the largest family of all flowering plants having over 900 genera and about 14,000 species. There are fifty-five genera represented in Great Britain. Practically every morphological type is represented and species can be found in almost every kind of habitat. Most of the success of the species must be attributed to successful pollination mechanisms, methods of fruit dispersal and vegetative propagation. The inflorescence is very characteristic. It is the capitulum, in which numerous florets arise on a flattened axis surrounded by a calyx-like involucre of bracts. Fundamentally the floret has the following structure. It is hermaphrodite, actinomorphic, epigynous and the parts are cyclically arranged. The calyx, when present at all, is represented by hairs, scales or teeth to form a *pappus*. The corolla is made up of five petals united to form a tube, at least at the base. Its upper part may be drawn out laterally into a flattened ligule or strap-shaped form. The androecium is of five epipetalous, syngenesious stamens, dehiscing inwardly within the corolla tube. The filaments are contractile, responding to touch in some cases. The gynaecium

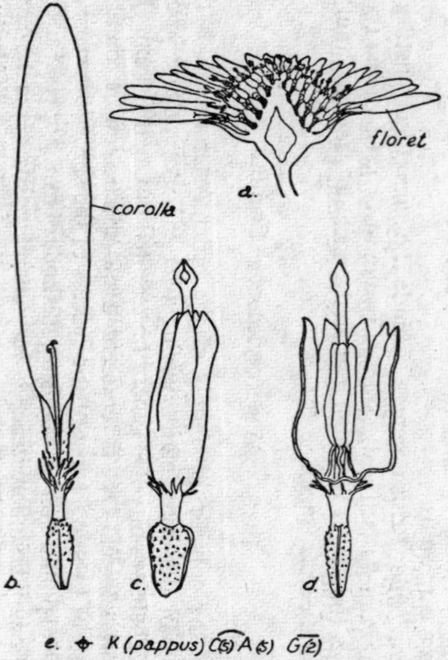

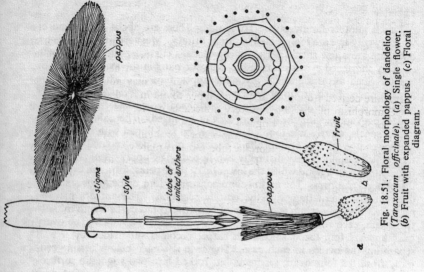

Fig. 18.51. Floral morphology of dandelion (*Taraxacum officinale*). (a) Single flower. (b) Fruit with expanded pappus. (c) Floral diagram.

Fig. 18.50. Floral morphology of daisy (*Bellis perennis*). (a) Inflorescence (capitulum) in V.S. (b) Whole ligulate flower (ray floret). (c) Whole tubular flower (disc floret). (d) Disc floret opened. (e) Floral formula.

$e.$ $\oplus$ $K(pappus)$ $C(5)$ $A(5)$ $\overline{G(2)}$

initially consists of two syncarpous carpels in the inferior position. With development, only one carpel persists and this contains a single basal ana-tropous ovule. The style is single at the base, passing upwards through the corolla tube and forking into two stigmatic surfaces at the distal end. Nectaries occur around the base of the style at the lower end of the corolla tube. Pollina-tion is by insects of great variety but cleistogamy and parthenogenesis some-times occur. The fruit is an achene which may or may not bear an upper structure derived from growth of the pappus to aid in its dispersal.

Dimorphism of the florets is very noticeable particularly in the form of the corolla and we may distinguish two types, the *ligulate* floret in which the corolla tube is extended as a strap-shaped or ligulate expanse, and the *tubular* floret in which the corolla tube remains more-or-less symmetrically tubular with five equal teeth. These two types of floret may appear separately in capitula or both together. When together, the centrally placed tubular florets are referred to as the *disc florets* and the outer ligulate florets as the *ray florets*. In addition to differences in corolla structure, within the same capitulum may be found mixtures of hermaphrodite, unisexual and neuter flowers. By the arrangement of the florets and other characters we can dis-tinguish two sub-families.

1. Tubuliflorae: the florets of one kind only, tubular, or if of both kinds, the disc florets are always tubular. No latex is formed in the tissues.

2. Liguliflorae: the florets are always of the ligulate form only. Latex is formed.

Common British genera include *Bellis* (daisy), *Taraxacum* (dandelion), *Senecio* (groundsel), *Tussilago* (coltsfoot), *Arctium* (burdock), *Carduus* (thistles), *Centaurea* (knapweed), and *Hieracium* (hawkweed). Many genera are cultivated as garden flowers such as *Chrysanthemum*, *Dahlia*, *Helianthus*. Some are cultivated for their value as food such as artichokes, lettuce, etc.

Monocotyledonous Families

Liliaceae

A family of the order Liliiflorae. There are about two hundred genera of which nineteen are represented in Great Britain. The members are mostly herbs perennating by rhizomes, corms or bulbs. The inflorescence may be solitary or racemose. Floral structure is very uniform and flowers are hermaphrodite, actinomorphic, hypogynous and with the parts cyclically arranged in threes or multiples. There is often no clear calyx and corolla but the perianth segments are usually petaloid. There are most often inner and outer whorls of three segments, which may be free, or joined at the base. The androecium is usually of two whorls of stamens, inserted freely opposite the perianth segments, or inserted on them. The gynaecium is of three syncarpous carpels with three loculi containing many anatropous ovules in two rows on axile placentae in each loculus. The ovary is superior (cf. Iridaceae below). The style may be absent and the apex of the ovary expanded into three stigmatic surfaces or a single style may be present, tri-lobed at its distal end. Nectaries may be present at the top of the ovary. Pollination is

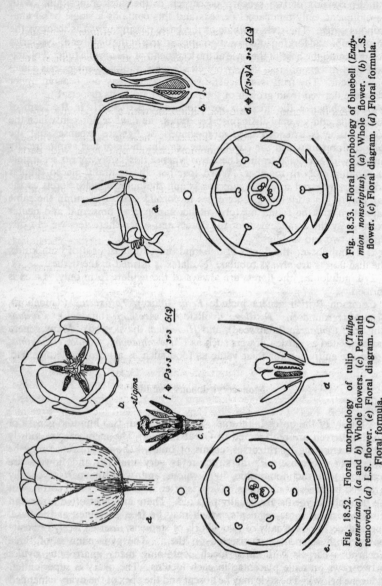

Fig. 18.53. Floral morphology of bluebell (*Endymion nonscriptus*). (a) Whole flower. (b) L.S. flower. (c) Floral diagram. (d) Floral formula.

Fig. 18.52. Floral morphology of tulip (*Tulipa gesneriana*). (a and b) Whole flowers. (c) L.S. flower. (d) Floral diagram. (e) Floral formula.

by insects or self-pollination may occur. The fruit may be a capsule or a berry.

Wild British genera include *Endymion* (bluebell), *Allium* (ramsons), *Ornithogalum* (star of Bethlehem), *Fritillaria* (fritillary) and *Polygonatum* (Solomon's seal). Cultivated for floral decoration are *Lilium* (lilies) and *Tulipa* (tulip). *Allium* (leek, onion) and *Asparagus* are grown for food value.

Iridaceae

This is another family of the order Liliiflorae, with about seventy genera of which seven are represented in Great Britain. The members have similar vegetative characters to those of the Liliaceae. The inflorescence is cymose. The flowers are hermaphrodite, actinomorphic, and epigynous, with parts in threes or multiples, arranged cyclically. Enclosing each flower when young is a spathe formed from one or two large bracts. The calyx and corolla are not distinct, the perianth segments all usually petaloid in an inner and outer series of three, united at the base to form a tube. The androecium is composed of three epiphyllous stamens. The gynaecium is of three syncarpous carpels, with either three loculi containing many ovules on axile placentae, or less commonly with a single loculus and ovules on parietal placentae. The ovary is inferior (cf. Liliaceae). The style sometimes has three petaloid lobes. Nectaries occur on the perianth segments at the base and pollination is by large insects. The fruit is a capsule dehiscing by three valves.

Wild genera in Britain include *Iris* (flags) and *Crocus*; others such as *Freesia*, *Crocosinia* [*Montbretia*] and *Gladiolus* are cultivated for floral decoration.

Gramineae

This is a family of the order Glumiflorae. It is a very large collection of some 620 genera, fifty-nine of them represented in Great Britain. Most are annual or perennial herbs with occasional woody forms. They are probably the most numerous of all higher plants and are distributed throughout almost every possible kind of environment. They compare with the Compositae in this respect. Owing to their extreme economic importance, the grasses have been studied in very great detail and special terms are used to describe vegetative and floral parts. The structure of the main parts of a grass in a generalized form is given in Fig. 18.55 and the specialized terminology is used in the labelling. It is necessary to be familiar with this terminology if success in identifying species is to be achieved.

Each inflorescence is composed of one or more units called *spikelets* which may be arranged on the central axis or *rachis* in various ways. Some collections of spikelets form compound spikes, e.g. wheat (*Triticum*), others are in racemes, e.g. fescue grass (*Festuca*), others in panicles, e.g. oat (*Avena*). It must be remembered that these terms used here are not comparable with the same terms used previously to describe inflorescences, since in grasses the unit is not often the single flower as in other plants, but the spikelet which is a collection of flowers. Each spikelet may consist of one to several flowers or *florets* attached to a central axis, the *rachilla*. Within the spikelet, the flowers

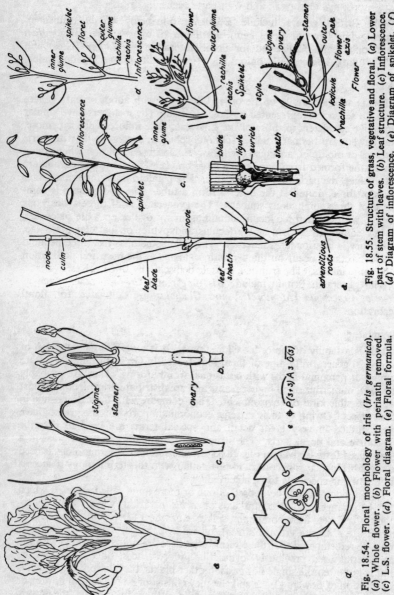

Fig. 18.55. Structure of grass, vegetative and floral. (a) Lower part of stem with leaves. (b) Leaf structure. (c) Inflorescence. (d) Diagram of inflorescence. (e) Diagram of spikelet. (f) Diagram of single flower.

Fig. 18.54. Floral morphology of iris (Iris germanica). (a) Whole flower. (b) Flower with perianth removed. (c) L.S. flower. (d) Floral diagram. (e) Floral formula.

$\oplus \; P_{(3+3)} \; A_3 \; \overline{G}_{(3)}$

are usually hermaphrodite but may be unisexual in the upper parts. They are hypogynous, actinomorphic and with parts cyclically arranged.

At the base of the rachilla is a pair of bract-like structures known as the *glumes*. From their positions they are called *outer* and *inner* or alternatively first glume (lower, outer) and second glume (upper, inner). These partly or

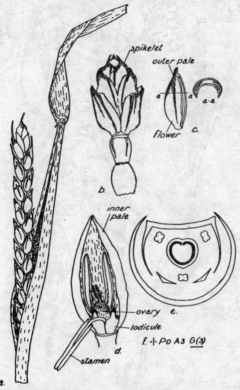

Fig. 18.56. Floral morphology of wheat (*Triticum aestivum*). (*a*) Inflorescence. (*b*) Spikelet. (*c*) Flower. (*d*) Flower partly dissected. (*e*) Floral diagram. (*f*) Floral formula.

wholly enclose the series of florets on the rachilla above them. Each floret has at its base also, a pair of small green bracts known by various names by different authorities. The lower bract may be known as the *lemma*, the *lower pale*, the *flowering glume* or the *valve*. The upper bract may be known as the *palea*, the *upper pale* or the *valvule*. It is simplest to describe them as the lower and upper pales. One or both pales may have the midrib prolonged into a slender *awn* from the tip of the pale or from half-way along its outer surface. Within the outer pale, stand the floral parts. These consist of a pair of delicate scales known as *lodicules* possibly representing a very reduced corolla (they may be absent entirely), three stamens (more rarely six, two or one) with long delicate filaments and often versatile anthers, and a tri-carpellary ovary with a single loculus enclosing a single anatropous ovule. Two of the carpels are never functional. The ovary is superior and from its apex are borne two

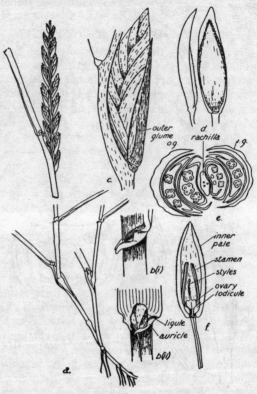

Fig. 18.57. Floral morphology of perennial rye grass (*Lolium perenne*). (*a*) Lower stem and inflorescence. (*b*) (i) and (ii) views of auricles and ligule. (*c*) Spikelet. (*d*) Single flower. (*e*) T.S. terminal spikelet. (*f*) Single flower partly dissected (young).

(rarely three) feathery stigmas on short styles. The structure of both stamens and stigmas indicates a wind pollination mechanism. Each rachilla usually bears several florets formed in the same pattern, but in some cases the extreme upper or lower florets may be sterile. The fruit is one-seeded, indehiscent and dry and therefore within the definition of achene. It has one peculiarity in that the ovary wall (pericarp) becomes fused to the testa of the seed within. Such a fruit is known as a caryopsis or grain. In economic importance to man, members of the Gramineae undoubtedly hold pride of place. Their products form the staple diet of most populations, and the genera *Triticum* (wheat), *Avena* (oats), *Hordeum* (barley), *Secale* (rye), *Zea* (maize) and *Oryza* (rice) have been cultivated for thousands of years. Among the more easily recognized British wild grasses are *Lolium* (rye grasses), *Dactylis* (cock's foot grasses), *Festuca* (fescues), *Agropyron* (couch-grasses) and *Bromus* (brome grasses).

SUMMARY OF THE ANGIOSPERMS

The angiosperms dominate the world's vegetation at the present time and have probably done so for as much as a hundred million years. They are represented in every conceivable habitat and exist in a wide variety of growth forms. Vegetatively each is built on a common body plan but the numerous modifications in response to the wide range of habitats tends to confuse this considerably. Their internal structure also shows the widest range of tissue formation in the plant kingdom. The most characteristic of all angiosperm features is the development of flowers, which again exhibit an enormous variety of form but give the most reliable information on which to classify, and afford the only helpful means of establishing the relationships of the angiosperms with other plant groups. But this is no simple task, since all existing angiosperms possess flowers of a very advanced form and there are no fossils known to exist which point conclusively to the ancestral type.

Most botanists accept the view that the flower is a modified branch (the receptacle) bearing sporophylls (stamens and carpels), the lowermost of which remain sterile to form the calyx and corolla. The difficulty arises in deciding which existing flower form is nearest to the primitive flower from which they all might have arisen. There are two distinct possibilities. One is that the earliest flower form corresponded fairly closely with that of the present day catkin-bearing trees such as the beech, birch and hazel. In this order, the Fagales, the flowers are very simple, unisexual and arranged in compound inflorescences. The other possibility is that the primitive flower was more nearly like those of the magnolias, the tulip-tree (*Liriodendron*) and members of the Ranales. Here the flowers are hermaphrodite and the parts are freely inserted in a spiral on a long conical receptacle. Evidence as to which of these views is the correct one is conflicting. If we seek evidence from the group most nearly related to the angiosperms, the gymnosperms, neither view is substantiated more easily than the other. The majority of gymnosperms existing today possess unisexual strobili and certainly the earliest known gymnosperm fossils, the Cordaitales, did so also. However, the present day gymnosperm order, the Gnetales, has members which develop structures comparable with flowers in which both stamens and ovules appear (*Ephedra*, *Welwitschia* and

Gnetum). There are also fossil remains of gymnosperms, the Bennettitales, some of which possessed strobili most remarkably like the hermaphrodite angiosperm flower. The "flower" of *Cycadeoidea* had many "perianth segments" of leaf-like form surrounding about twenty pinnately branched "stamens" or microsporophylls, and above these on the long receptacle was a "gynaecium" of stalked ovules protected by hooded scales (*see* Fig. 18.58). Other fossil remains from the same plant showed seeds with dicotyledonous embryos, no endosperm and a single integument. There are no other fossils yet found which indicate

Fig. 18.58. Bennettitalean flower.

the origin of such characters in a gymnosperm, but it is possible that the condition found in the modern Gnetales may have been derived from it. Here the hermaphroditism is not really complete, since in both *Welwitschia* and *Gnetum*, the ovules occurring in the male flowers are abortive and no stamens are formed in the female flowers. This condition in the Gnetales might indicate therefore that unisexuality is a derived characteristic in a flower and not the primitive condition. To link the angiosperm flower to the Bennettitalean flower via the Gnetales seems the most straightforward way of arriving at a conclusion, but in order to do this it is necessary to be sure that the perianth segments, stamens and ovules of all three are truly homologous structures, and this is by no means as certain as it seems at first sight. The classical view is that all are modified leaves. The stamen is regarded as homologous with a microsporophyll bearing microsporangia. Such may be adduced from the nature of the male structures in the Bennettitales, the cycads and the conifers, but the earliest gymnosperm group known, the Cordaitales, possessed "stamens" which were more in keeping with branch morphology rather than leaf. Each was a stalk, borne in the axil of a bract, and ending in several microsporangia. This is similar to the condition in the Gnetales, where in the male "flowers" the stalk of each stamen of *Ephedra* bears a pair of scales (perianth) and is subtended in the axil of a bract. In such a case, the "stamen" corresponds to the conception of a whole flower, that is, it is a branch not a leaf. The carpel is also interpreted as a megasporophyll bearing megasporangia (ovules) on its margin, but folded to enclose them. But once more there are many examples of corresponding female structures which may be interpreted as branches and not leaves. In the Cordaitales, ovules were borne on stalks bearing small scales and subtended in the axil of a bract. The ovules of the Bennettitales were borne somewhat similarly and it has already been pointed out in Chap. 15 that the ovuliferous scale of a pine cone may be considered as a branch in the axil of the bract scale. In such case, the strobilus corresponds to an inflorescence and not a flower.

Fossil angiosperms help very little in elucidating the problem of their origin. The earliest known of them appear in the lower Cretaceous rocks and they show characters which indicate that they were then well-established and very much like present types. The flowers of these fossils indicate clearly that they were of the Fagalean form and not Magnolialean or Ranalean.

The position is unlikely to be clarified further until new evidence is forthcoming, and systematists no longer spend a great deal of their time arguing one case against the other. But the issue is important to them nevertheless, since upon it depends the classification of the angiosperms on a phylogenetic basis.

With regard to the relative antiquity of the monocotyledons and the dicotyledons, there are three possibilities; the former could have given rise to the latter, or vice-versa, or each could have arisen independently. Either of the first two possibilities indicates *monophylogeny*, whilst the last indicates *polyphylogeny* of the angiosperms.

Of the many attempts to classify the angiosperms two stand out. The Englerian system, after Engler, published between 1887–1909, corrected misconceptions held previously by taxonomists such as Bentham and Hooker about the relative positions of the gymnosperms and the mono- and dicotyledonous angiosperms. In Engler's classification, the primitive dicotyledon was taken to be the woody plant with apetalous flowers arranged in catkins (aments). Such plants as the oaks, birches, willows, walnut, hazel, beech, etc., were collectively referred to as the Amentiferae and placed first in the group. The monocotyledons were considered as having a separate origin and placed before the dicotyledons.

The other system of note was developed by Bessey in 1894 and further by Hutchinson in 1926–34. The main difference from Engler's classification was in the conception of the primitive flower which was held to be hermaphrodite, with perianth and essential parts freely inserted in a spiral on a long conical axis. The Ranalean type of flower was thus placed in the lowest position and the apetalous flower was considered a very advanced form in which the perianth had been lost by reduction. The monocotyledons were held to have been derived from the more primitive dicotyledons.

It was pointed out earlier (p. 541) that the main difficulty in classifying the angiosperms in a way which meets the approval of every botanist, is the fact that the modern forms are all very advanced and there are very few fossils which give any real indication of their evolutionary history. The perfect natural classification can only be based on a complete knowledge of unbroken lines of descent. The angiosperms represent only a few scattered branch endings of the genealogical tree and there is by no means sufficient fossil material to enable us to build the main trunks and larger branches. In order to classify such a group of living things as naturally as possible, it is necessary to make most use of what material is available and to choose criteria based upon characters which appear to occur most regularly and uniformly over the maximum number of species. We may do this, since it can be reasoned that forms possessing the same characters can be considered as having possessed a common ancestor, providing due allowance is made for possible convergence of evolutionary paths from widely separated starting-points towards the same end. By so choosing suitable major criteria, then the large angiosperm group may be divided into a number of smaller groups and each of these further divided by criteria based on characters of smaller significance, until finally the species are distinguished. The important major characters which have been used to indicate relationships are as follows—

1. Embryonic characters: the most clear cut of these is the number of cotyledons. There are two conditions only, namely one or two cotyledons. The angiosperms are thus immediately divisible into two sub-classes, the Monocotyledones and the Dicotyledones. With this major distinguishing character can be placed others relating to the generalized floral and vegetative morphology of the two sub-classes. These will be mentioned later.

2. Floral morphology: since the flower is the universal characteristic organ of the angiosperms, it is most convenient to use floral variations and similarities as indications of the main guide to relationships within

the two sub-classes, and hence to subdivide them further. Floral characters of significance are included in the following—

(a) Arrangement and numbers of parts. If the development of comparatively large numbers of parts, freely inserted in spiral succession on a long conical receptacle with the carpels in the superior position, is looked upon as being the ancestral condition, then other arrangements, reductions and fusions, taken in conjunction with one another, can be used to indicate degrees of evolutionary advance. Cyclic arrangement of parts may be considered a more highly evolved condition, as may be the reduction of numbers of parts, either of whole whorls or parts within a whorl, and their lateral fusion within the whorls. The dicotyledons are separated into the Archichlamydeae (perianth segments free) and Metachlamydeae (perianth segments fused) on this last character. Such reduction and fusion of parts is not really a degradation but leads to greater efficiency in the flower both economically and in pollination processes. The numbers and arrangement of floral parts are, in general, characters sufficiently clear-cut to warrant the division of the major groups into orders, families, genera and often species.

(b) Actinomorphy and zygomorphy. The latter may be considered the derived character since it is usually associated with reduction in the number of stamens and their positions with respect to the corolla. It is undoubtedly associated with the evolution of specialized insects which could act as pollinators.

(c) The type of inflorescence. The solitary flower and simple raceme are probably the most primitive conditions, with the other indefinite inflorescences such as the umbel and capitulum very advanced modifications, and the cymose inflorescences, derivatives. Massing of small flowers is undoubtedly associated with insect pollination and accompanying it may be special forms of zygomorphy and unisexuality. Members of the Compositae seem to culminate this trend.

(d) Type of fruit. The apocarpous gynaecium giving rise to dry, dehiscent many-seeded follicles seems to be the ancestral condition. Reduction in numbers and fusion of carpels have given rise to the other forms. The development of a fleshy pericarp is an advanced character associated with special methods of fruit and seed dispersal.

3. Characters of vegetative morphology: every flowering plant has a common vegetative body plan but the numerous modifications in response to the wide variety of habitats tend to obscure this. Because of the constancy of the general pattern, no very significant use can be made of vegetative characters in classification except to distinguish

between members which have already been found to be closely related by other criteria. Vegetative characters may sometimes be used to define one species of a genus from another. It is generally conceded that the wide variety of angiosperms have arisen from an erect woody land plant, perennating above ground, with mesomorphic leaves arranged spirally and not shed seasonally. From such have been derived the herbaceous plants, those of creeping or climbing habit, plants perennating below ground, the annual and biennial plants, those showing xerophytic modifications and the aquatics, the comparatively few insectivorous and parasitic forms, the whorled leaf arrangement and the deciduous condition. (Note that evergreen angiosperms are probably recent derivatives of deciduous forms.)

4. Characters of vegetative anatomy: as with morphological characters, these may be important in separating the angiosperms from other groups of plants but much use cannot be made of them in classifying within the group itself except in certain circumstances. For example, xylem anatomy can sometimes be used to define one species from another. The ancestral stem structure was probably that showing collateral bundles arranged in one or more rings. Xylem tracheids are certainly more primitive than vessels, and of the latter, the vessel with round pits seems to have been derived from the vessel with scalariform pits.

These criteria, particularly those of floral morphology, are the ones used by most taxonomists and classifications of the angiosperms have been based almost entirely upon them in the past. More recently attempts have been made to take into account physiological characters, including serum diagnosis, cytological characters, especially chromosome numbers, and evidence from inheritance data, but it is doubtful if any completely new ideas have emerged. The new methods have all tended to confirm rather than destroy the older knowledge.

CHAPTER 19

TRIPLOBLASTIC ANIMALS: PLATYHELMINTHES

It will be recalled that after cleavage of the zygote in coelenterates, a hollow blastula is formed, bounded by a single layer of cells. By delamination from this layer, or by proliferation from one pole, an inner filling of cells is formed. These embryos are thus said to develop two *germ layers*, the *ectoderm* outside and the *endoderm* within it. They are called germ layers because they contain the germs, or beginnings of all the future systems and organs of the mature animal. This *diploblastic condition*, the development of only two germ layers in the embryo, is primitive. All higher animals are *triploblastic*, and in their embryos, a third germ layer is formed between ectoderm and endoderm. This third layer is the *mesoderm*.

Triploblastic animals can be further subdivided into two broad groups, the *coelomates* and the *acoelomates*. The coelomates develop a body cavity called the *coelom* which separates the mesoderm into an outer somatic layer applied to the body wall, and an inner splanchnic layer applied to the gut (*see* Fig. 19.1). The acoelomates do not develop this

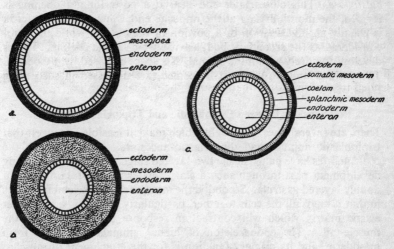

Fig. 19.1. Diagrams representing different body forms in T.S. (*a*) Diploblastic animal, e.g. *Hydra*. (*b*) Triploblastic acoelomate, e.g. *Planaria*. (*c*) Triploblastic coelomate, e.g. *Lumbricus*.

cavity. The principal phyla of acoelomate animals are the Platyhelminthes, the Nemertea, the Rotifera and the Nematoda.

Body Cavities

The primary body cavity of metazoan animals is the *blastocoel*; it is the first cavity developed in the embryo. During gastrulation, the blastocoel becomes more or less constricted. In coelenterates, it is totally obliterated by the secretion of the mesogloea between ectoderm and endoderm. In the acoelomates, it is invaded by mesoderm cells and may become almost completely filled by them, as in the Platyhelminthes, or almost devoid of them, as in the Rotifera (*see* Vol. II, Fig. 9.9). The nematodes have a small number of enormous vacuolated cells occupying this primary cavity, while in the Nemertea a few longitudinal channels remain to constitute a blood vascular system. The coelomates have reduced the blastocoel to a series of blood-filled spaces bounded by walls derived from the mesoderm. In the Arthropoda, the biggest of the coelomate phyla, large portions of this primary body cavity remain. They become filled with blood and constitute the *haemocoel*.

The second body cavity to arise in the embryo is the *archenteron*, which develops into the gut cavity of the adult. It may arise by a split in the endoderm, as in *Hydra* and *Obelia*, or by invagination of the blastula wall. In the latter case, its original opening is known as the *blastopore*. This closes later and near it a posterior gut opening is formed, the mouth arising at the opposite end. Since the archenteron is usually an invagination of a portion of the outside world, it is not considered as the secondary body cavity, which is the coelom. This is developed entirely within the animal, as a space enclosed by mesoderm. The various ways in which it is formed, are discussed in succeeding types.

Relationships between Diploblastic and Triploblastic Animals

There are several lines of thought which make it feasible to suggest that triploblastic animals had diploblastic ancestors. First, although the coelenterates have halted at the two-layered stage, all triploblasts during development pass through such a stage. After the blastula, there is a double-layered gastrula. Secondly, the mesogloea has skeletal functions in that it binds all the cells together, particularly providing a somewhat elastic matrix which will contract in response to the action of the muscle-tails. The endoskeleton of higher animals is formed from mesoderm, and its primary function is for the attachment of muscles. In addition, the development of mesoderm may be foreshadowed in coelenterates by cells which invade the mesogloea. Indeed, in some of the higher coelenterates several types of cells are present. They include wandering amoeboid cells, skeleton-forming and muscle-fibre cells. Some authorities refer to these and to similar cells in sponges as *mesenchyme*, implying that here we have the foundation of mesoderm. But it must be observed that in higher forms, the mesoderm assumes considerable proportions and normally forms the greater part of the bulk of an animal. The largest coelenterates owe their size almost entirely to the extreme thickness of mesogloea. Also, from the mesoderm are developed large and important systems, organs and organ-systems. Such are the reproductive system, the muscular system, the endoskeleton and the all-pervading and important connective tissue. Finally, in coelenterates, the mesogloea forms the only channel for diffusion of food materials from the endoderm to the ectoderm. In higher animals, mesodermal derivatives form the paths for such communication between ectoderm and endoderm. Thus, although there is no definite proof, there seems to be sufficient evidence to make it probable that triploblasts evolved from diploblasts. Study of the Ctenophora would add further weight to this probability.

Implications of the Third Germ Layer

The mesoderm has, in general, given triploblasts a greater bulk of cellular material compared with their volume, than is found in any diploblastic form. This very bulk has caused the wide separation of the digestive tube from the body wall, and thus problems of transport arise. Oxygen from the environment must reach all the cells at a fairly constant rate; food from the gut must be carried to the cells of the body wall; the excretory products from the mass of mesoderm have to be expelled from the body. In acoelomate triploblasts, the problem of oxygen supply is solved by restriction of the body to small volume and flattened or elongated shape. Hence the surface area remains large in relation to the contained volume. Blastocoelic fluid, or mesenchyme cells, or both, serve for transport of food. For excretion, a flame-cell system with ducts opening on the surface, is developed in the mesoderm.

The new mass of mesoderm is partly utilized in the production of new tissues and organs. Mesodermal muscular tissue, excretory systems and reproductive systems are developed. The location of the latter two in the mesoderm involves the need for ducts to discharge the products to the exterior. Thus excretory ducts, oviducts and vasa deferentia make their appearance. In the flatworms much of the mesoderm remains undifferentiated and forms a packing tissue known as *parenchyma* (cf. plant tissues).

The increasing differentiation involves a more elaborate system for control and co-ordination and a central nervous system arises. Though nerve nets still persist, as indeed they do up to the mammals, longer nerves are needed to transport impulses from ectodermal sensory cells and organs, through the mesoderm to the central nervous system, and for outgoing impulses to effector organs.

The majority of these advances in differentiation are seen in the Platyhelminthes. The phylum contains three classes of which the Turbellaria are almost entirely free-living, while the Trematoda and Cestoda are entirely parasitic. Typical platyhelminth organization is found in free-living forms and here we describe, in general terms, the common planarians.

PLANARIA

The small animals of this genus are to be found in practically every pond, stream and canal. They do not normally betray their presence but spend most of the daylight hours concealed under stones or among weeds, emerging at night to search for food. They can frequently be caught in large numbers by placing in the water a jam-jar baited with a freshly-killed earthworm or a piece of raw meat. When the jar is drawn up later, it usually contains a large number of worms attached to the food material.

External Features

The species caught in the British Isles is most likely to be *Planaria lugubris*. It is black in colour and up to 15 mm long. The body is broader in front than at the back, where it is roundly tapered, and is extremely flattened. There is a definite front end, which is always

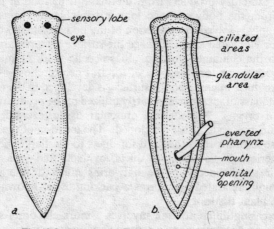

Fig. 19.2. *Planaria*. (*a*) Dorsal view. (*b*) Ventral view.

directed forward during locomotion, an upper or *dorsal* surface and a lower or *ventral* surface which is applied to the substratum. The *eyes* are paired structures near the anterior end and are plainly visible as rounded spots. The *mouth* lies on the ventral surface about a quarter of the distance from the posterior end; it is the only opening of the gut. When the animal is feeding, the *pharynx* may be seen protruding through the mouth as a white tube.

The Body Wall

The epidermis consists of columnar cells which are ciliated at the sides of the body and on the ventral surface except for a long oval glandular tract of cells which secrete slime. Most of the cells of the epidermis, especially those on the ventral surface, possess a few short hyaline rods known as *rhabdites*. When the animal is in contact with prey, they are liberated from the surface, and in water they form a sticky slime which entangles prey. The slime may also be a protective substance; it is produced when a planarian is placed in an irritating fluid. Beneath the epidermis is a strong basement membrane and within this is a thin layer of circularly disposed muscle fibres followed by a thin layer of longitudinal fibres. There are also thin strands of dorso-ventral muscle fibres passing vertically through the thickness of the body. The fibres are long and transparent with no apparent striation or fibrillation; they are secreted by special cells called *myoblasts* which may be seen alongside the fibres. Within the mesenchyme are many glandular cells,

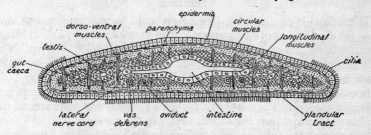

Fig. 19.3. *Planaria.* T.S. body in the region of the forward branch of the intestine (*see* Fig. 19.5).

especially near the ventral surface; they secrete the slime which enables the cilia to work and also helps to entrap the prey. Planarians kept in glass containers leave trails of this slime on the glass.

Thus the body wall consists of ectodermal and mesodermal derivatives. The epidermis is derived from ectoderm; the muscle layers from mesoderm. The body wall subserves the functions of protection, and locomotion, both ciliary and muscular; it assists in the capture of prey;

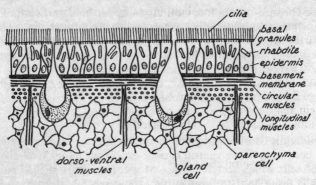

Fig. 19.4. *Planaria*. V.S. body wall.

in the anterior region especially, it possesses sensory cells which enable the animal to perceive light, chemicals, touch, and the flow of the water.

Skeleton and Supporting Structures

No hard skeletal structures are produced. The firm basement membrane provides attachment for both the epidermis and the muscle layers. The shape of the body is maintained mainly by turgidity, all the spaces between the parenchyma cells being fluid-filled.

Nutrition

The animal is carnivorous, feeding on small worms, crustaceans, and on the dead bodies of larger animals. The *mouth* leads into a short *buccal cavity*, then comes a large, muscular, and thick-walled *pharynx*. The lumen of the pharynx leads forward into the *intestine* which begins in the middle region of the body. The intestine divides into three main branches, one of which proceeds forward to the head and ends just behind the eyes. The other two branches lead left and right around the pharynx sac and then backwards nearly to the posterior end. All three branches of the intestine give off numerous blind *caeca*. There is no anus, the mouth being the only opening of the gut.

When feeding on small prey, the planarian creeps over it, entangles it in slime and engulfs it in the everted pharynx. If the food material is larger, the pharynx exudes a digestive fluid on it, and by continued pumping action, it is broken up into small pieces which are then swallowed.

The lining of the gut consists of a single layer of endoderm cells exactly corresponding to the endoderm of coelenterates. Digestion is partly extracellular by the exudation of enzymes into the enteron, and partly intracellular after amoeboid ingestion of small particles. Transport of digested food to other parts of the body takes place via the parenchyma cells, and there are said to be wandering amoeboid cells present which actively transport food. Owing to the numerous gut caeca, no part of the body is far from the source of digested food. Faecal material is egested from the mouth. There is storage of protein and fat in parenchyma cells, and in addition, some of the endoderm cells store protein in the form of small spheres.

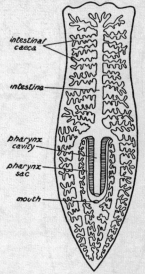

Respiration

Oxygen is absorbed from the water. The area of the animal is large in relation to its thickness and hence diffusion suffices to supply all the cells. The animals cannot survive in foul water where there is much organic material in solution.

Locomotion

A planarian moves with a gliding action, due partly to the beating of the cilia from front to rear, and partly to rippling muscular waves which traverse the body from anterior to posterior. Occasionally, when there is excessive stimulation, more vigorous muscular action may be observed.

Fig. 19.5. Ventral view of the alimentary canal of *Planaria*.

The slime secreted by the gland cells affords a grip for the cilia while protecting them from injury by the substratum. As the animal moves forward, due to the fact that the longitudinal muscles contract alternately in the right and left halves of the body, the head end wavers left and right continuously.

Growth

All the cells of the body, except those of the nervous system, can divide. There are special amoeboid cells of the parenchyma which remain undifferentiated. They migrate to the site of any damage and are able to organize regeneration.

Excretion

There are two longitudinal *excretory canals* which open on the dorsal surface by a number of minute pores. The main canals give off numerous branches which ramify among the parenchyma cells. The ultimate branches end in *flame cells*, each of which has an intracellular cavity and duct, with numerous cytoplasmic branches penetrating between the parenchyma cells. Projecting into the cavity of the cell is a bundle of long cilia which arise from basal granules in the cytoplasm. These

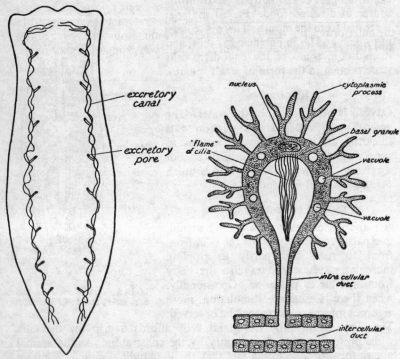

Fig. 19.6. Excretory canals and pores of *Planaria*.

Fig. 19.7. Diagram of a single flame cell leading into an excretory duct.

cilia are characterized by their flickering movement, which gives rise to the name "flame cells." The lumen continues as a narrow intracellular duct which enters one of the main intercellular ducts.

Excretory substances are secreted into the cavity by the surrounding cells. The flickering cilia maintain an outward current and possibly produce a slight negative hydrostatic pressure causing excess water to flow in from the spaces in the surrounding parenchyma. The fact that freshwater turbellarians possess more flame cells than their marine relatives, may indicate that the system is principally important for osmoregulation. Further, the urine excreted is hypotonic to the body fluid.

Sensitivity and Co-ordination

Besides a *nerve net* beneath the epidermis, there is a deeper network situated in the parenchyma within the longitudinal muscle layer. In parts, this network is concentrated enough to merit the name *central nervous system*. It consists of *nerve cells* and *nerve fibres*. The chief concentrations of nerve cells are the paired *cerebral ganglia* situated in the anterior region. They are connected by numerous transverse fibres, and from each ganglion, a *lateral nerve cord* consisting of several fibres,

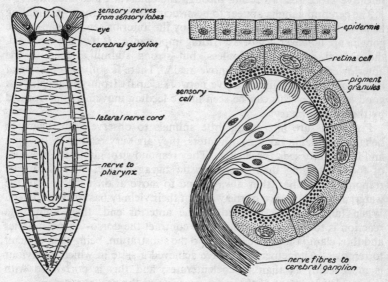

Fig. 19.8. Nervous system of *Planaria*.   Fig. 19.9. *Planaria*. V.S. through an eye.

runs almost to the posterior end. The anterior sense organs send many fibres into the ganglia. Numerous branches of the lateral cords penetrate between the parenchyma cells, supplying chiefly the muscle layers. There is a good supply of nerves to the muscular pharynx (*see* Fig. 19.8).

The *eyes* are situated beneath the upper epidermis just in front of the cerebral ganglia. They consist of a few cup-shaped, heavily-pigmented cells which form the *retina*, while the cavity is filled with sense cells which make contact with the retinal cells. These sense cells send out bunches of fibres which pass forward from the cup, then curve backward to the cerebral ganglia. Thus the eye is in one respect similar to that of vertebrates; the light has to pass through the nervous layers before reaching the retina (*see* Fig. 19.9). The epidermis above the eye is not pigmented, and the optic cups are set almost horizontally. Hence, the only rays of light which can enter the eye must come from the region in front of the animal.

The latero-frontal lobes of the head are rich in sensory cells aggregated into special areas. There are several distinct types of these sensory cells, some perceiving tactile stimuli, some chemical and some are rheotactic, i.e. specially sensitive to the flow of the water. All these sensory cells are essentially similar to those of *Hydra* in that they bear sensitive processes projecting through the epidermis into the water.

The cerebral ganglia appear to be principally organs for co-ordinating behaviour with the stimuli perceived by the anterior sense organs. The ganglia are however not of overriding importance; if they are removed, the animal becomes motionless, but strong stimuli applied to the anterior end, will cause it to move again. There is still some power of basic co-ordination in the nerve networks, apart from the ganglia. A good example of this can be seen in the feeding movements performed by the excised pharynx.

Planarians are interesting little animals to observe with regard to behaviour. Being nocturnal hunters, they are very restless in daylight and incessantly seek for shelter. They respond strongly to the presence of food, pursuing their characteristic zigzag course. The rheotactic response is peculiar, they always tend to move against the flow of the water, and disturbance of the water in their vicinity has the same effect. When fairly heavily touched at the anterior end, their immediate reaction is to secrete more slime, to contract the dorso-ventral muscles and thus clamp themselves rigidly to the substratum, being then difficult to remove. Altogether, they have achieved a state in which behaviour is more complex than in coelenterates, and this is correlated with greater development of the sense organs and the nervous system.

Reproduction, Dispersal and Survival

Many species of *Planaria* can multiply asexually. The posterior region fixes itself to the substratum by discharge of slime and contraction of the dorso-ventral muscles. For some hours, the anterior portion struggles to pull away from it. Eventually it succeeds (*see* Fig. 19.10) and both portions can regenerate all the missing parts. The region of fission is located a little way posterior to the mouth. In some turbellarians, chains of such sub-individuals may be formed before separation.

Planarians are hermaphrodite and the reproductive systems are extremely complex. There is considerable variation even between closely-related species. The system described here is fairly typical for triclad turbellarians (*see* Fig. 19.11). There are numerous small rounded *testes*, laterally placed among the parenchyma. Each consists of a germinal epithelium from which *sperm* are proliferated into the lumen. From the testes, fine *vasa efferentia* lead inwards and unite forming two *vasa deferentia*; these are distended at their ends to form *vesiculae seminales* in which ripe sperm are stored. They lead into a muscular sac containing a protrusible *penis*. This opens into a shallow *genital*

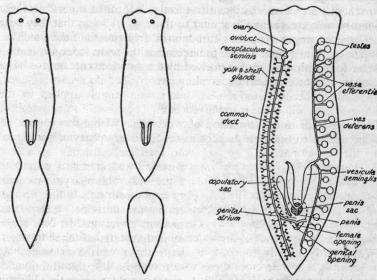

Fig. 19.10. Asexual reproduction in *Planaria*.

Fig. 19.11. Reproductive system of *Planaria*. Male organs only shown on the right, female organs only on the left.

atrium which leads out of the body by a small *genital pore* a short distance behind the mouth.

The paired *ovaries* are situated laterally in the parenchyma just behind the head region; they are rounded bodies, larger than the testes. *Ova* are proliferated inwards by the germinal epithelium and pass by a short *oviduct* into a dilated portion where they await fertilization. Numerous lateral combined *yolk* and *shell glands* send short ducts inward to join the oviduct which continues backward as a combined duct. The two combined ducts meet and discharge into the genital atrium by a short straight tube. Leading from the genital atrium is a third opening into a *copulatory sac*. After copulation this contains sperm from another worm.

Cross-fertilization occurs. Two worms adhere together by their

ventral surfaces and the penis of each deposits sperm into the copulatory sac of the other. Following separation, the sperm swim out of the
copulatory sac into the genital atrium and then up the oviducts. The
eggs are fertilized, and as they pass down the ducts they receive yolk
cells and shell substance which hardens later. The capsules passed out
of the body contain a few eggs and many yolk cells; they are covered
by a sticky secretion which causes them to adhere to the substratum.
Small worms emerge in a few weeks.

Dispersal presents no problems in such freely-motile animals. The
adults can survive the winter, provided that the water does not freeze.
Some forms produce special thick-shelled eggs which can survive both
drought and cold conditions.

Development

Cleavage leads to the formation of a blastula. Within it, a cluster of
cells migrate to one pole and form a rudimentary pharynx leading to
an intestine consisting of a few
flattened and stretched cells (*see*
Fig. 19.12). This pharynx proceeds
to ingest yolk cells, filling up the
embryonic intestine. Later, the
pharynx closes, and its cells form
an undifferentiated clump together
with those of the intestine. A
cavity appears in this clump, and
around it the permanent pharynx
develops, leading into a permanent
intestine. The mesoderm is formed
from a special group of cells which

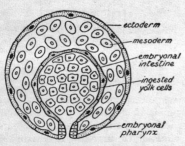

Fig. 19.12. *Planaria*. V.S. of an early
developmental stage.

pass inward into the blastula. In two to three weeks, minute planarians
emerge; there is no free larval stage.

Adaptation

The planarians show all those adaptations connected with the evolution of bilateral symmetry and dorsal and ventral surfaces. Thus there
is dominance of the head end with its associated development of the
principal sense organs and correlated concentration of the nervous
system in this region. The primitive ciliary type of movement is
augmented by muscular movement, since in most circumstances,
ciliary action on a solid substratum, would be insufficient. The feeding
mechanism is adapted for dealing with small or large pieces of food,
and in the absence of a fluid transport system the caeca of the gut
penetrate deeply into all regions of the body. Respiration, again in the

absence of special organs, is facilitated by the flattened shape and small dorso-ventral thickness. The numerous flame cells provide an efficient osmoregulatory mechanism in the freshwater forms. The complexity of the reproductive organs is associated with the problem of ensuring cross-fertilization. For development of the embryos, the capsules are supplied with adequate food. Their colour and nocturnal habits are protective adaptations aided by their dislike of light and an enhanced power of perceiving it. Careful consideration of this animal will reveal many other adaptive features.

Classification

Phylum: Platyhelminthes   Family: Paludicula
Class: Turbellaria   Genus: *Planaria*
Order: Tricladida   Species: *P. lugubris*
           (common in British Isles)

The triclads are characterized by the three-fold division of the intestine. Members of the genus *Planaria* are small forms and deeply pigmented. The various species are separated on grounds of size, colour and shape.

Special Features of Biological Importance

Some of the special features of Platyhelminthes, in common with other acoelomates, were discussed at the beginning of this chapter. In addition, there are a number of important topics worthy of notice here. The organ-system level of organization has been achieved; an amazing degree of the power of regeneration has been retained; bilateral symmetry has replaced radial; there is still dependence on an aquatic environment; apart from the Turbellaria, all the Platyhelminthes are parasitic.

The Organ-system Level

In the Protozoa, we found only the protoplasmic level of organization, with an approach to the cellular level in some of the colonial members. The sponges show an advance to the cellular level, but no tissues are developed. The coelenterates have evolved tissues and the beginnings of organs. Now, in the Platyhelminthes, organs are co-ordinated and combined to form systems. Thus, the mouth, pharynx and trifid intestine form the digestive or alimentary system; the flame cells, excretory ducts and pores form the excretory system; the eyes and other sense organs together with the cerebral ganglia and nerve fibres form the nervous system; the gonads, yolk glands, the various ducts and other genitalia, together form the reproductive system. In fact, only two principal systems are added by higher animals; they are the blood vascular system and the respiratory system. It is to be noted that the protoplasmic level is maintained necessarily by all cells, the tissue level by some tissues and parts of organs, and the organ level in parts of organ-systems.

Regeneration

Planarians are ideally suited for experiments on regeneration. Some of the work which has been done on them is described in Vol. II, Chap. 13. In addition, interesting data have been obtained by starving the animals. First, the reproductive system is entirely absorbed, then, in succession, the parenchyma cells, the gut and the body wall muscles. The epidermis and the nervous system remain intact. The animals become very much smaller, but if fed again, they quickly regenerate all the lost parts. This indicates that few of the types of cells are so specialized that they cannot be regenerated from undifferentiated cells.

In these planarians we see the gradual emergence of the phenomenon of apical dominance in which the head exerts a physiological influence on the rest of the body, diminishing along a linear gradient from the anterior to posterior ends. Thus, a small piece cut from the centre of a planarian will regenerate a head at the correct anterior end.

Symmetry

Few animals show no symmetry; such are the common amoebae and some of the sponges. *Spherical symmetry* is associated with many of the drifting protozoa. They have no particular axis of locomotion; they can feed, detect stimuli and respond to them equally well in any direction. Such a body shape is admirably suited to all the minute drifting creatures like radiolarians and heliozoans, which project stiff, radiating pseudopodia into the water.

Radial symmetry is found in some protozoans and many sponges, but is most characteristic of coelenterates, and here it is associated with either a sessile or drifting life. Hence there is the typical cylindrical or circular shape, with a central mouth and digestive system, and radiating tentacles.

Bilateral symmetry is associated with locomotion in a particular direction with one end normally directed forward. This end is the first to encounter new territory and therefore the sense organs and nervous system are most concentrated there. The location of these entails definite dorsal and ventral surfaces which become further specialized in connexion with locomotion and with camouflage. Thus many of the organs become paired with respect to a single plane which divides the animal into equal right and left halves. Bilateral symmetry occurs in one class of coelenterates, the Ctenophora, in all the Platyhelminthes and, apart from the echinoderms where radial symmetry may be secondary, it exists in all the principal phyla of higher animals.

Dependence on an Aquatic Environment

Of the Turbellaria, only a few animals in the order Tricladida are terrestrial. They all belong to a group known as the Terricola, and the largest triclads are among them. *Bipalium kewense* is plentiful in the humid tropical forests and, as its name implies, is sometimes to be found in heated greenhouses. It may reach a length of some 30 cm. Many small triclads live in the soil and in decaying wood. All these terrestrial forms are very dependent upon high humidity of the air, if not on a wet substratum. The great majority of turbellarians are marine or freshwater. The classes Trematoda and Cestoda contain only parasites, the majority being endoparasitic in the fluids of a host.

Their flat thin bodies, the absence of special respiratory organs and of an impervious protecting layer render the Platyhelminthes very dependent upon the constant presence of external water. In drying conditions on land, none of them can survive.

CHAPTER 20

HISTOLOGY OF ANIMALS

WE are now approaching the study of animals in which very distinct tissues are differentiated, and shall have to refer frequently to different tissues by name. Therefore the four main types of tissues are described here. It must be pointed out that there is an infinite variety of slight differences between the tissues in various phyla. Where there is a very obvious difference, it will be pointed out in the type descriptions. The detailed accounts given here apply specifically to the mammal, but in their general application they will serve for all the triploblastic animals.

Histology deals with the minute structure of the tissues and organs of the body; it may be termed microscopic anatomy. A tissue is defined as an aggregate of similar cells, together with any intercellular substance secreted by them, co-ordinated to perform one or more functions. Such are muscle, blood and bone. An organ consists of various types of tissue aggregated together for the performance of one or more special functions. Examples of organs are the eye, the kidney and the heart.

Four main types of tissues have been evolved in the animal kingdom. They are epithelial, connective, muscular, and nervous tissues. *Epithelial tissues* line all internal cavities and the external surface. They are primarily protective and often secretory. *Connective tissues* join and pack firmly together all the parts of an organism, and also connect the organs together. This is true for blood, as well as skeletal tissues and connective tissues proper. *Muscular tissues* are contractile and enable the animal or parts of it to move. *Nervous tissue* possesses the controlling and co-ordinating mechanism by which stimuli are perceived, impulses transmitted and effectors excited to respond.

EPITHELIAL TISSUES

The cells of an epithelial tissue form a sheet covering a free surface, internally or externally. The internal linings of cavities and tubes are sometimes termed *endothelia*; the term "endothelium" is equivalent to "internal epithelium." In an epithelium, there is always a very small amount of intercellular substance and hence the cells are close together. When the epithelium is one cell thick, each cell is attached to a *basement membrane* of cementing substance which is secreted by the underlying connective tissue. When the epithelium is more than one cell thick, only the lowest layer of cells rests on the basement membrane. The types of epithelia are shown in the table below.

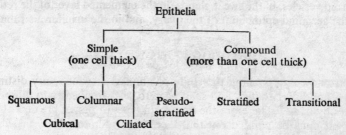

Simple Epithelia

These are always one cell thick. Five types are usually recognized; *squamous*, *cubical*, *columnar*, *ciliated* and *pseudo-stratified*.

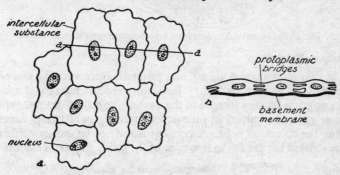

Fig. 20.1. Squamous epithelium from the peritoneum. (*a*) Surface view. (*b*) V.S. across line *a–a*.

Squamous Epithelium

This is sometimes known as pavement epithelium because the cells are very thin and flat. They are very close together and sometimes in transverse section the nucleus produces a bulging effect in the centre (*see* Fig. 20.1 (*b*)). In surface view, squamous epithelium presents a mosaic appearance (*see* Fig. 20.1 (*a*)). Very careful examination of a transverse section will reveal the presence of fine protoplasmic bridges which connect the cells. Good examples for study of squamous epithelium can be found in Bowman's capsules of the kidney, the peritoneum and the endothelium of blood-vessels.

Cubical Epithelium

The cells of cubical epithelium are prismatic and the height dimension is not much greater than the width. In surface view, the cells present a mosaic appearance, with each individual cell hexagonal or pentagonal in outline. Good examples of cubical epithelium are to be found in the thyroid vesicles, in the sweat glands, in the pigmented layer of the retina, in the germinal epithelium of the ovary, and in the uriniferous tubules.

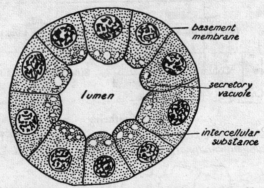

Fig. 20.2. Cubical epithelium from a section through a thyroid vesicle.

Columnar Epithelium

The cells of this tissue are tall and prismatic often with the inner ends tapering. In surface view they form an irregular hexagonal mosaic. The nucleus is usually located at the base of the cell. Columnar epithelium is generally bathed in mucus produced by goblet cells which lie among the columnar cells. A peculiar feature of columnar epithelium is the striated border at the free edge of the cells. Excellent examples of

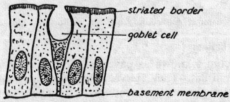

Fig. 20.3. Columnar epithelium from a T.S. small intestine of the cat.

columnar epithelium can be seen in transverse sections of the intestine and in sections of the gall-bladder. The tissue lines the greater part of the gut, and is practically continuous from stomach to anus.

Ciliated Epithelium

The free surfaces of the cells bear fine vibratile cilia each arising from a basal granule. At intervals between the ciliated cells are mucus-secreting cells which taper towards the free surface. This type of tissue is sometimes classed as columnar from the shape of the tall prismatic cells. Ciliated epithelium is present throughout the air passages, in the oviducts, in the ventricles of the brain and in the spinal canal.

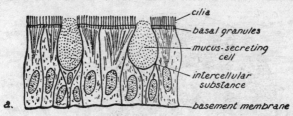

Fig. 20.4. Ciliated epithelium. (*a*) From T.S. trachea of rabbit. (*b*) Single ciliated epithelial cell from mouth of frog.

Pseudo-stratified Epithelium

This type is always one cell thick, but not all the cells reach the free surface. Examples are found in the olfactory mucosa and in the trachea. It is usually columnar and/or ciliated.

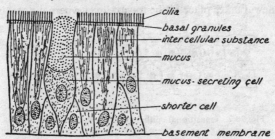

Fig. 20.5. Pseudostratified epithelium from olfactory mucosa.

Compound Epithelia

Stratified Epithelium

This is a compound epithelium consisting of a number of layers of cells. All the cells arise from the germinative layer which lies on the basement membrane. The germinative layer consists of cubical cells which constantly undergo mitosis; thus the cells lost from the outer surface are continually replaced. As cells are pushed towards the free surface, they become progressively flattened and, in some tissues, these squames may form a dead horny layer. Numerous protoplasmic

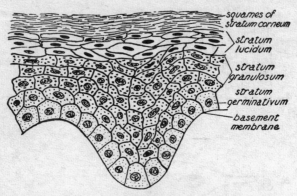

Fig. 20.6. Stratified epithelium in V.S. from the human foot.

fibrils pass from cell to cell, giving greater coherence. Stratified epithelium is present in the epidermis of the skin, in the lining of the buccal cavity, in part of the oesophagus, and in the vagina.

Transitional Epithelium

This is a compound epithelial tissue with only three or four layers of cells. Renewal takes place in the lowest layer where mitosis is frequent;

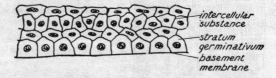

Fig. 20.7. Transitional epithelium from the bladder of rabbit.

the cells are small and polyhedral. There may be another layer of small cells and then a layer of cells which are almost columnar. The cells at the free surface are somewhat flattened, and have indentations on their inner surfaces into which the tops of the columnar cells fit. Transitional epithelium is found in cavities where there may be considerable distension; such are the urinary bladder, the pelvis of the kidney and the ureter.

Functional Aspects of Epithelial Tissues

Functionally, epithelia may be divided into three types Squamous epithelia provide thin membranes for rapid diffusion, smooth surfaces for the passage of fluids, and form lubricating membranes between two surfaces which have to slide on each other. Hence they are found lining cavities where fluids have to pass from one tissue to another, as in blood-vessels, lymphatic vessels and peritoneum; also in tubes where fluids flow, and on the outer surfaces of stomach and intestines, which during peristaltic movements have to rub on each other, and on the peritoneum of the body wall.

Cubical and columnar epithelia are secretory and provide the linings for ducts and glands. The cells are comparatively large and are never far removed from the blood supply. In the columnar epithelium of the gut, the mucus from the goblet cells provides the lubrication which prevents abrasion by hard particles in the food. The mucus also provides protection against the digestive enzymes. The cells of ciliated epithelium in the cerebro-spinal cavities ensure that the fluid is kept in motion; those of the air passages trap foreign particles in the mucus, which is then wafted to the pharynx and swallowed; those of the oviduct ease the passage of eggs and their early developmental stages along the duct.

Stratified epithelia provide protection from abrasion on surfaces which are exposed to considerable wear and tear. Such are the skin and the lining of the buccal cavity where the mastication of food may cause considerable friction against the cheeks. Transitional epithelia allow of considerable alteration in surface area. When fully extended most of the cells will stretch into a flattened condition, and many will be broken off by this stretching. Both stratified and transitional epithelia have a mechanism for replacing losses from the free surfaces.

Blood-vessels do not normally enter epithelial tissues. Their nutriment and oxygen are supplied by the lymph channels which run in the intercellular spaces. In thick stratified epithelia the outer cells become too far removed from the blood supply and hence die, forming keratinized squames which constitute a type of exoskeleton. Nerve fibres often penetrate epithelia, and beneath stratified epithelia there is usually a nerve plexus.

CONNECTIVE TISSUES

All connective tissues have two common characteristics; they are all developed from embryonic mesoderm, and have a large amount of intercellular substance. The types of connective tissue are tabulated overleaf.

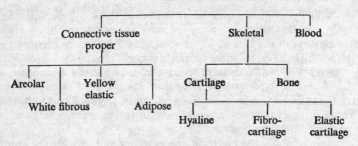

Connective Tissues Proper

These are characterized by the possession of considerable numbers of fibres in the intercellular substance which, in life, is of a fluid or semi-fluid nature. *Areolar tissue* is the characteristic type, the others being specialized forms; in many parts of the body various transitional types may be found.

Areolar Connective Tissue

This contains a great proportion of transparent semi-fluid matrix which contains abundant mucin. Scattered throughout the matrix are numerous bundles of wavy white fibres cemented together by mucin. The fibres largely consist of the protein *collagen* which can be dissolved in the stomach by peptic digestion. Interspersed among these wavy bundles is an anastomosing network of single fine fibres made of the protein *elastin*, which can be dissolved by tryptic digestion. Careful examination of the tissue will reveal a number of types of cells. *Fibroblasts* often lie alongside the fibres which they secrete. They are flattened cells, often branched, with oval nuclei. Wandering phagocytic cells known as *histiocytes* are often found. They may be rounded or amoeboid and have small spherical nuclei. Many small oval *mast cells* with granular cytoplasm may be seen; these produce the matrix. Small *plasma cells* derived by division of migratory lymphocytes from the blood, are common; in inflammatory conditions they may be plentiful. In the areolar tissue of some regions, pigment cells are present. They are much-branched, contain numerous melanin granules, and are especially plentiful in the skin, the eye, and the pia mater enveloping the brain and spinal cord.

Areolar tissue is almost ubiquitous in the body, packing in all organs, connecting the skin to the under-lying structures, surrounding blood-vessels and nerves wherever they penetrate into organs, fastening together the two sheets of squamous epithelium which form the mesenteries, and securing the peritoneum firmly to the body-wall muscle and the muscle of the gut. While being essentially connective,

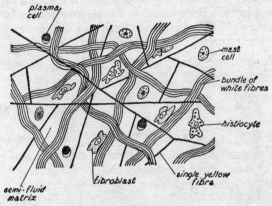

Fig. 20.8. Diagram of areolar connective tissue.

it allows of considerable stretching and recovery. The limit of stretch of the skin, for example, is reached when the white fibre bundles are straightened out, and recovery to the normal position is due to the elasticity of the yellow fibres.

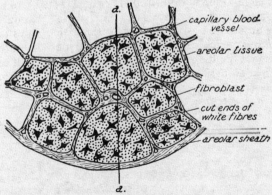

Fig. 20.9. White fibrous connective tissue from T.S. tendon.

White Fibrous Tissue

This consists almost entirely of closely-packed white collagen fibres, occasionally interspersed with continuous rows of fibroblasts. The bundles of white fibres are bound together by areolar tissue. It is found in locations where great strength with limited flexibility are desirable. Such are the tendons of muscles, the dura mater of the brain and other sheets covering organs such as the sclerotic and cornea of the eye, and the kidney capsule. The *perichondrium* of cartilage and the *periosteum* of bone also consist mainly of this tissue.

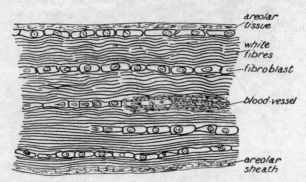

Fig. 20.10. White fibrous connective tissue seen in the plane *a–a* of Fig. 20.9.

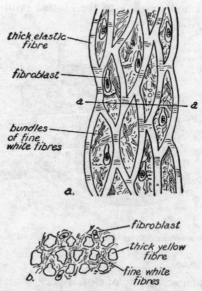

Fig. 20.11. Elastic tissue. (*a*) From L.S. of ligamentum nuchae. (*b*) T.S. of same seen in the plane *a–a*.

Elastic Tissue

This consists mainly of parallel, yellow elastic fibres, with interspersed fibroblasts and intervening bundles of very fine white fibres. It combines considerable strength with great elasticity and is found in the cords of the neck, in many ligaments joining the bones, in the walls of arteries and in the bronchioles. There is a great deal of elastic tissue in the lung; it is largely responsible for recovery of the lung after distension. Elastic tissue reaches its greatest development in the *ligamentum nuchae*, extending from the rear of the skull to the neural spines of the cervical vertebrae.

Adipose Tissue

In several regions of the body, areolar tissue is found with the matrix largely filled up with fat cells. These are large spherical cells with a central globule of fat which has squeezed the cytoplasm and nucleus to the periphery. This adipose tissue is arranged in lobules encased in areolar connective tissue. In mammals, it is mainly located in the dermis of the skin, above the kidneys and sometimes, in older animals around the heart.

All the connective tissues proper are derived from a soft jelly with

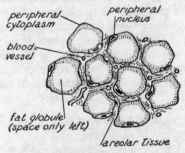

Fig. 20.12. Adipose tissue from V.S. dermis of rabbit.

few fibres in the embryo animal. The only remnant of this embryonic jelly is found in the vitreous humour of the eye.

Skeletal Tissues

Cartilage and *bone* provide firm areas for attachment of the tendons of the muscles. They give a large measure of support to the body, forming a framework to which soft parts can be fastened. Further, they provide a system of levers with fulcra at the joints, and in conjunction with the muscles, enable locomotion.

Hyaline Cartilage

The matrix of this tissue consists of a translucent material called *chondrin*, which is mainly a mucopolysaccharide with combined sulphate groups. It is a firm, bluish-white, and somewhat elastic material;

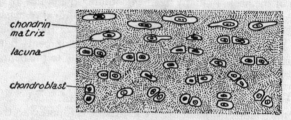

Fig. 20.13. Section through hyaline cartilage.

sometimes fine fibres may be present. The skeleton of the embryo mammal at one stage consists entirely of cartilage. Gradually, most of it is replaced by bone, cartilage remaining in the following locations: the xiphisternal cartilage, the sternal ribs, the suprascapular cartilage, the thin plates between diaphysis and epiphysis of bones, and the articular cartilages at the ends of bones. In the elasmobranch fishes, the skeleton remains cartilaginous throughout life, e.g. dogfish.

Each plate of hyaline cartilage is covered by a tough fibrous sheath, the perichondrium. The cells which secrete the chondrin, *chondroblasts*, lie in small spaces called *lacunae*. In life, they completely fill these lacunae, lying singly, or in twos, fours or eights. The fibres of cartilage are very difficult to demonstrate, and in some cases there do not appear to be any.

Fig. 20.14. Fibro-cartilage from T.S. intervertebral disc.

Fibro-cartilage

In addition to the chondroblasts in their lacunae, the matrix is well packed with bundles of white fibres. Thus the flexibility of the cartilage is combined with the firmness of the fibres. Fibro-cartilage is found in the intervertebral discs, where its cushioning effect between the vertebrae is important, and in the pubic symphysis. Here it allows of parturition without complete breakage.

Elastic Cartilage

This is another variety of cartilage in which yellow fibres form an anastomosing network. The flexibility of the cartilage is enhanced by

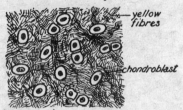

Fig. 20.15. Elastic cartilage from section of ear pinna.

the presence of these elastic fibres, and the tissue readily recovers shape after distortion. Elastic cartilage is present in the epiglottis, the external ear, and supporting the Eustachian tube and the external auditory meatus.

Bone

Bone is a connective tissue with a large amount of intercellular substance consisting of mineral salts; two-thirds of the weight of a bone is

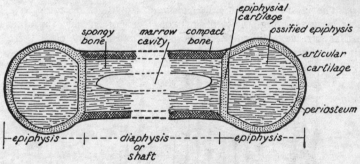

Fig. 20.16. Diagram of long bone. L.S.

mineral. The mixture of salts consists of 85 per cent calcium phosphate, 10 per cent calcium carbonate, about 4 per cent of magnesium chloride and 1 per cent of calcium fluoride. It is a very strong and rigid tissue, providing efficient levers and adequate protection for delicate organs such as the brain and spinal cord. About 15 per cent of the body weight of an adult mammal is bone.

Each bone is enclosed in a tough sheath of fibrous connective tissue, the periosteum. A diagrammatic representation of the structure of a

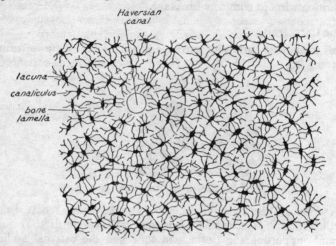

Fig. 20.17. Hard section of compact bone cut transversely to Haversian canals.

long bone is given on p. 573. Underneath the periosteum is a very dense layer of *compact bone* (*see* Fig. 20.16), beneath which is a thicker zone of *cancellated* or *spongy bone*. In the long bones, a *marrow cavity* is

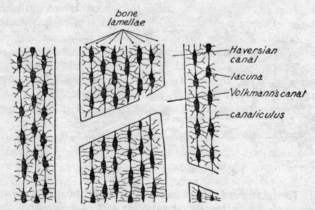

Fig. 20.18. Hard section of compact bone cut parallel to Haversian canals.

present; this is the site of formation of most of the blood corpuscles. Compact bone (*see* Fig. 20.17) consists of longitudinal *Haversian systems*. Each system comprises a central Haversian canal surrounded by successive lamellae of salts. In life, the canal contains an artery, a vein, a lymphatic vessel, a nerve and some bone cells or *osteocytes*. All are packed in with areolar connective tissue. At intervals among the lamellae are osteocytes lying in lacunae. From the osteocytes, fine protoplasmic connexions ramify throughout the matrix in minute canaliculi. In longitudinal section (*see* Fig. 20.18), it can be seen that

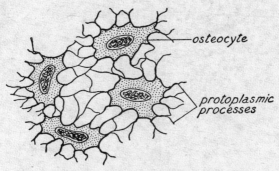

Fig. 20.19. Osteocytes from section of decalcified bone.

the Haversian canals are connected by the transverse *Volkmann's canals*.

The Process of Ossification

Ossification is defined as the making of bone. In the adult mammal, two types of bones are distinguished, by reason of two different modes of ossification. *Cartilage bones* are formed by replacement of cartilage; *membrane bones* are developed directly from the embryonic connective tissue. In the first category we have the bones of the limbs, vertebral column and girdles (except the clavicle); in the second category are most of the bones of the skull, and the clavicles. The two types are formed respectively by *endochondral* and *intra-membranous ossification*.

Endochondral Ossification

Before the process begins, we have a cartilage surrounded by a perichondrium. A primary ossification centre appears in the middle of the shaft. The chondroblasts are arranged in rows; they become hypertrophied and lay down calcium salts in the matrix. The process spreads from the centre outwards. At this stage we have *calcified cartilage*. The perichondrium is now called the periosteum.

Another region of ossification arises in the shaft, just beneath the periosteum. Cells called *osteoblasts*, derived from fibroblasts of the periosteum, proceed to lay down fibres upon the surface of the cartilage.

This region also becomes calcified and will gradually form compact bone.

Now cells called *osteoclasts* eat their way through the sub-periosteal bone into the cartilage. They are followed by vascular tissue. Thus

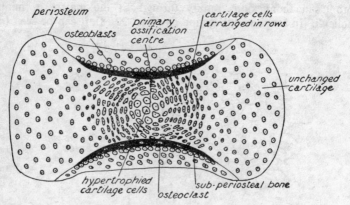

Fig. 20.20. Ossification centres in a long bone.

there are formed a series of mainly longitudinal spaces filled with connective tissue, blood-vessels and osteoblasts. On the walls of the spaces, osteoblasts deposit bone salts. Some of the osteoblasts become enveloped by the bone salts and so are trapped in lacunae, maintaining

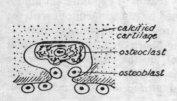

Fig. 20.21. Erosion of calcified cartilage and deposition of bone.

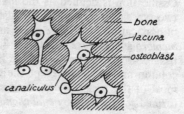

Fig. 20.22. Diagram to show trapping of osteoblasts in bone lacunae.

connexion with other osteoblasts by fine protoplasmic fibrils in bone canaliculi.

From the primary ossification centre, the process proceeds longitudinally towards both ends in this sequence: arrangement in rows; hypertrophy of cartilage cells; deposition of calcium salts forming calcified cartilage; erosion by osteoclasts; deposition of bone by osteoblasts. The sequence is illustrated in Fig. 20.23. Thus the bone in the shaft is deposited in the form of hollow bars called *trabeculae*;

these give it its spongy nature. In long bones the trabeculae are eroded to form the marrow cavity. This spongy bone is surrounded by the

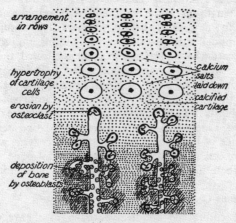

Fig. 20.23. Diagram showing sequence of endochondral ossification.

compact sub-periosteal bone. Later, osteoclasts erode the Haversian canals; they are followed by the vascular and connective tissue.

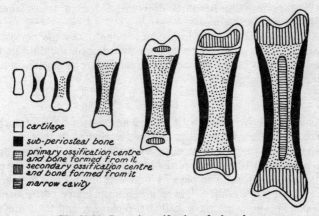

Fig. 20.24. Stages in ossification of a long bone.

This process of ossification has so far affected only the shaft; the two ends of the structure are still cartilaginous. Later, ossification centres appear in each *epiphysis* and eventually epiphyseal bone is formed. It is separated from the bone of the *diaphysis* by the epiphyseal cartilages. When growth is completed, the epiphyseal cartilages are ossified and the bone will grow no longer. Stages in the ossification of a long bone are shown in Fig. 20.24.

Growth in length of bones is due to the epiphyseal ossification centres; growth in girth is due to sub-periosteal ossification. The final shape is modelled in conformity with strains imposed by muscle pull. In every case where alteration in shape is effected, the sequence of processes is the same. The portion concerned is eroded by osteoclasts, then bone is deposited by osteoblasts. In cases of fracture, the repair is due mainly to the activity of the periosteum. Fibroblasts multiply and become osteoblasts. They lay down bony trabeculae and form a swollen callus. Later, this is gradually eroded and replaced, until finally little trace of it remains. A phosphatase enzyme working at an optimum pH of 9 is necessary for the formation of bone. The enzyme catalyses the liberation of phosphoric acid from phosphoric esters.

Intra-membranous Ossification

The dermal embryonic connective tissue in the region of bone formation becomes very vascular. Fine bundles of fibres are laid down in the matrix. Calcium salts are next deposited around the fibre bundles and thus the ossification centre is established. Osteoblasts now form bony trabeculae after erosion of the calcified matrix by osteoclasts. The periosteum becomes differentiated as a tough sheet of white fibrous connective tissue.

The skull grows by deposition of new bone under the periosteum. Simultaneously the inner region of bone abutting on the dura mater is absorbed by osteoclasts. Hence the structure grows in area without much increase in weight.

Blood

Blood is a connective tissue with a large amount of fluid intercellular substance. It differs from other connective tissues in that it has no fibres and the matrix is not secreted by the blood cells. In mammals about 6 per cent to 10 per cent of the body weight is blood; an average man has nearly 6 litres. The pH of blood is about 7·4 and the osmotic pressure about 710 kN m^{-2}. There are four primary constituents in the blood. The fluid matrix is called the *plasma*, and in it are three types of cells, the *erythrocytes* or red corpuscles, the *leucocytes* or white corpuscles, and the *thrombocytes* or blood platelets.

Whole Blood — 79 per cent water
21 per cent dry solids — 12 per cent corpuscles
7 per cent protein
2 per cent other solids

The Plasma

This is the fluid matrix of blood. It is almost colourless, having a faint yellow tinge, and contains essentially seven classes of substances, shown in the table below. Ninety-one per cent of the plasma is water.

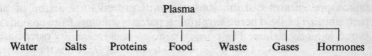

In this water, the other materials are dissolved or suspended. The blood salts are chiefly the chlorides, bicarbonates, sulphates and phosphates of sodium and potassium. Of these, the Na^+, Cl^- and HCO_3^- ions predominate. The blood proteins are in colloidal solution; they are fibrinogen, serum-globulin, serum-albumin, and pro-thrombin. They play an important part in buffering the blood against radical changes in pH, and two of them, fibrinogen and pro-thrombin, are essential for coagulation. Food substances in the blood are glucose, small quantities of amino-acids and minute globules of fat. The excretory substances are urea and traces of uric acid. The gases are carbon dioxide, oxygen and nitrogen. Every 100 cm^3 of blood contains 60 cm^3 of gases of which 40 cm^3 is CO_2, both in solution and held as HCO_3^-, 19 cm^3 is oxygen, mostly combined with haemoglobin in the erythrocytes, and 1 cm^3 is nitrogen, in solution in the plasma. The hormones in the blood are very variable both in type and quantity. They constitute an insignificant fraction, but are of vital importance

Every material transported in the body travels in the blood at some stage; the plasma is essentially a means of transport. It also provides a suitable osmotic medium, as the *lymph*, which directly bathes the tissues. Plasma contains an automatic mechanism for blood clotting in case of damage to the vessels.

Coagulation

There are present in the blood two mutually antagonistic substances. *Anti-thrombin* prevents clotting; *pro-thrombin*, in the presence of calcium ions, forms *thrombin* which promotes clotting. When a blood-vessel is damaged, the blood-platelets and the endothelial cells of the vessel release the enzyme *thrombokinase* into the blood. This substance neutralizes anti-thrombin, and thus pro-thrombin forms thrombin. This then causes precipitation of the fibrinogen from solution, as long fine filaments. The damaged portion of the vessel is soon filled with a meshwork of these threads, and the meshes become blocked by the corpuscles to form a jelly-like clot. This ability to clot the blood is not present in some human beings; the condition is known as haemophilia, and is a sex-linked character inherited in a Mendelian manner. It is a serious disease, for even a small wound may result in fatal haemorrhage. Blood-sucking animals such as leeches, mosquitoes and tsetse flies, produce in their saliva an enzyme which prevents clotting. Drawn blood can be prevented from clotting by the addition of citrate, which precipitates calcium ions and thus prevents the action of pro-thrombin. The fluid remaining after separation of clots from coagulated blood is *blood serum*.

Lymph

Lymph consists of blood plasma with numbers of leucocytes and has a protein content about half that of the plasma. Lymph escapes from the capillaries and circulates among the body tissues carrying food, oxygen, and a scavenging and defensive force in the leucocytes. It also collects excretory materials from the cells. The lymph returns to the blood in lymphatic channels and then vessels.

Blood Groups

In view of the present great use of blood transfusion, and the importance of serology in many fields of study, a brief account of blood groups is given here. Experimental blood transfusions with dogs and other animals were first made in the seventeenth century. Samuel Pepys, in his inimitable manner, described a transfusion from a sheep to a man in 1666. The first human transfusions were performed in London hospitals, Guy's and St. Thomas's, in 1818. The practice became very common and was instrumental in saving many lives. However, there were occasional inexplicable fatalities. Since the discovery of blood groups by Landsteiner in Germany and Shattock in England in 1901, transfusion became almost one hundred per cent successful.

Blood groups are based on the agglutination or clumping of the red cells and their subsequent destruction. The clumping depends on two substances, an *agglutinogen* in the red cells, and an *agglutinin* in the plasma. There are agglutinogens A and B which are Mendelian dominants and agglutinins α and β which are Mendelian recessives. A and α are antagonistic, and so are B and β; both combinations cause self-clumping and thus an individual cannot exist with them. Everyone must possess two of the factors A, B, α, β. Thus we have the following possibilities—

Erythrocytes	A	B	AB	O (neither A nor B)
Plasma	α	β	$\alpha\beta$	o (neither α nor β)

Groups are determined by the following combinations—

	Corpuscles	Plasma
Group A	A	β
Group B	B	α
Group AB	AB	o
Group O	O	$\alpha\beta$

In actual practice, the serum of the donor is ignored; it is soon diluted by the larger bulk of serum of the recipient. It is the effect of the serum of the recipient on the red cells of the donor which is important. The table below shows what transfusions between these various blood groups are possible.

DONOR	RECIPIENT			
	Group A Aβ	Group B Bα	Group AB ABo	Group O O$\alpha\beta$
Group A Aβ	✓	✗	✓	✗
Group B Bα	✗	✓	✓	✗
Group AB ABo	✗	✗	✓	✗
Group O O$\alpha\beta$	✓	✓	✓	✓

It will be seen that Group A (Aβ) can give blood to groups A and AB; Group B (Bα) can give blood to groups B and AB; Group AB (ABo) can give only to group AB; Group O can give to any group. Individuals in Group AB are known as universal recipients, while those in Group O are universal donors. In western Europe, 43 per cent of the population are in Group A and 9 per cent in Group B, 3 per cent are in Group AB, and 45 per cent in Group O.

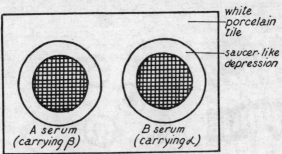

Fig. 20.25. Plate for testing blood groups.

Testing for blood group is a simple process. A drop of A serum and of B serum are placed on a white tile. Then a drop of the blood to be tested is added to both sera.

Group A blood will clot only in 2
Group B blood will clot only in 1
Group AB blood will clot in 1 and 2
Group O blood will not clot in either

Besides the AB system there are numerous other systems of blood grouping, of which the best known are the MN and Rh. The MN system is related to rabbit blood. If a few drops of man's blood are injected into a rabbit, the man's red cells are clumped. The rabbit's serum is then used with man's blood in testing; if it causes clumping, then the man is MN positive; if it does not, he is MN negative. In the Rh system the blood of the rhesus monkey, *Macacus rhesus*, is injected into a rabbit. The rabbit serum is then used for testing human blood. If the human red cells are clumped, the person is Rh positive; if not, he is Rh negative. Eighty-five per cent of human beings are Rh positive.

Many of the blood grouping systems have no medical importance. It has been stated however, that by combination of all the known systems, it might be possible to identify with certainty every single individual in the world. In general, the AB system has led to far less transfusion failures; blood groups are of great value in medico-legal work; they have thrown new light on the study of ethnography, in elucidating human migrations in the remote past; they have been of great assistance in anthropology, and finally the whole field of serology has been of great service in elucidating evolutionary relationships of animals and plants.

Erythrocytes (Red Corpuscles)

These are non-nucleated biconcave discs enclosed in an elastic plasma membrane which contains a solution of haemoglobin and a number of inorganic ions, including Na^+, K^+, Mg^{++}, Ca^{++}, Cl^- and $PO_4^{\equiv}$. They are almost yellow when seen singly, but red in the mass. In blood at

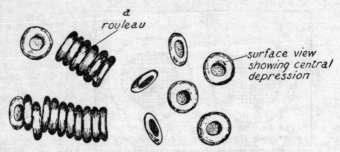

Fig. 20.26. Mammalian erythrocytes (8µm diameter).

rest, or flowing slowly, they form piles known as *rouleaux*. On the average, human blood contains five million corpuscles per cubic millimetre, which gives a figure of at least twenty-five billion for the whole body. In the embryo, they develop first in the blood islands, and later in the liver, and then in the spleen until birth. After birth, they are formed exclusively in the bone marrow. They have an average useful life of four to eight weeks and are then destroyed in the liver sinusoids by Küpfer cells, in the spleen by phagocytes, or in the blood by fragmentation and then phagocytic action. The erythrocytes carry oxygen from the lung capillaries to the tissues and some carbon dioxide in the opposite direction. The haemoglobin molecule combines with one oxygen molecule to form an unstable compound, oxyhaemoglobin.

Leucocytes (White Corpuscles)

The leucocytes are amoeboid nucleated cells, their numbers being approximately one-sixhundredth that of the erythrocytes, about 8,000 per cubic millimetre. Most types are larger than the erythrocytes, ranging from 8μm to 20μm. They are usually classified according to the kind of dye they take up most readily, acidophil, basiphil or neutrophil. *Acidophils* are leucocytes in which the granular cytoplasm stains readily with acid dyes such as eosin; *basiphils* stain readily with haematoxylin or methylene blue; *neutrophils* stain equally well with either. The character of the nucleus is also used as a diagnostic feature A tabular classification is given below.

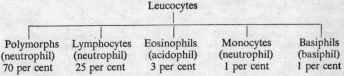

		Leucocytes		
Polymorphs (neutrophil) 70 per cent	Lymphocytes (neutrophil) 25 per cent	Eosinophils (acidophil) 3 per cent	Monocytes (neutrophil) 1 per cent	Basiphils (basiphil) 1 per cent

Polymorphs are up to 12μm in diameter and possess very variably shaped nuclei. They are phagocytic. The lymphocytes are smaller and in a preparation they are roughly the same size as the erythrocytes, about 8μm. They have very large nuclei and pursue a wandering existence, being especially plentiful in the lymph. Their main function appears to be that of producing antitoxins to neutralize bacterial toxins. Eosinophils are fairly large, ranging up to 16μm in diameter. Their nuclei have characteristic bilobed or trilobed shapes. Their main function is detoxification. The monocytes are the largest of the white corpuscles, being up to 20μm in diameter. They have large round or oval nuclei, and are wandering phagocytic cells. Basiphils are from 12μm to 16μm in diameter, with a bilobed nucleus. They are feebly motile; their function is doubtful.

In the embryo, leucocytes are produced in the thymus gland, the liver and spleen. In the adult they are formed in the bone marrow, the **spleen and the lymphatic glands. The dead corpuscles are destroyed** by phagocytic action in the blood, in the liver and in the lymphatic glands. Many are lost in the alimentary canal and pass out with the faeces.

In general, leucocytes form the defensive and scavenging mechanisms of the body. Not only are they present for these purposes in the blood,

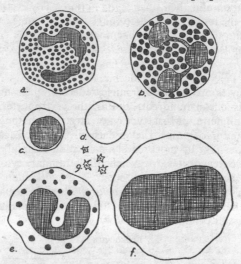

Fig. 20.27. Blood corpuscles (all to same scale). (*a*) Polymorph leucocyte. (*b*) Eosinophil leucocyte. (*c*) Lymphocyte. (*d*) Erythrocyte. (*e*) Basiphil leucocyte. (*f*) Monocyte. (*g*) Thrombocytes.

but they wander freely through the tissues and are especially plentiful at sites of inflammation. When leucocytes escape from capillaries, they squeeze through the mucopolysaccharide intercellular cement of the endothelial cells. They ingest bacteria and remove cell debris and foreign bodies. Some types specialize in the production of anti-toxins.

Fig. 20.28. Thrombocytes as seen in extracted blood.

Thrombocytes (Blood Platelets)

These are the smallest corpuscles in the blood, only about 3 μm in diameter. They are discoid in shape, but rapidly assume a stellate appearance in extracted blood. There is great variation in their numbers, both in different individuals and in the same individual at different times. An average count for a human being, gives a figure of 300,000 to 500,000 per cubic millimetre. They are especially concerned with blood clotting and the tendency to clot depends upon the numbers of thrombocytes present. They are non-nucleated but contain central aggregates of granules. They are made in the marrow of the bones and destroyed by phagocytosis in the blood.

General Functional Aspects of the Connective Tissues

In general, the connective tissues have three functions, mechanical, nutritive and defensive. Their mechanical function lies in supporting and connecting the tissues and organs of the body; it is carried out by connective tissue proper, by cartilage and bone. In a somewhat different sense, all organs and tissues are connected to their sources of supply of materials and to the sites of elimination of waste, by the blood.

The nutritive function is carried out by the fluid matrices of blood and lymph; there is exchange of materials between the cells and the matrix.

The defensive mechanism consists of the leucocytes which engulf bacteria and neutralize their toxins. The cells travel via the matrix of connective tissues. The ability to clot the blood at wounds may be considered another type of defensive mechanism. Protective functions are also characteristic of some bones such as those of the skull, and by connective tissue sheaths such as the sclerotic.

MUSCULAR TISSUES

Muscular tissues consist of elongated cells or coenocytic fibres. These larger units are made up of fine *myofibrils* each consisting of a bundle of *filaments* lying among *sarcoplasm*. The tissues do not secrete inter-cellular substance but are held together by areolar tissue. All muscular tissue is contractile, sometimes to one-half and, in some cases, to one-third of the resting length.

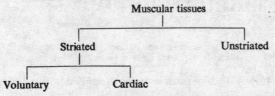

Voluntary Muscle

This is known by the alternative names of skeletal, striped or striated, though the latter two may also be applied to cardiac muscle. All the voluntary muscles, except some of the muscles of the tongue, are attached to the skeleton by tendons. They are innervated by motor nerves from the brain and spinal cord and hence are under voluntary

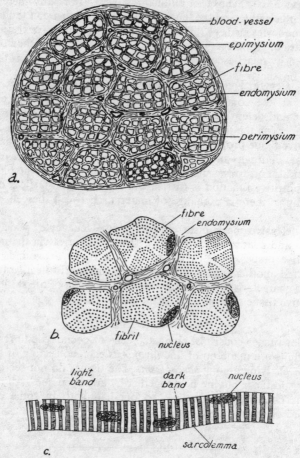

Fig. 20.29. (a) T.S. whole voluntary muscle. (b) Small portion of same (enlarged). (c) Single fibre of voluntary muscle.

control. Formerly, resting muscles were wrongly described as being in a slightly contracted state called *tone* or *tonus;* cutting of the nerve supply was stated to make the muscle lose tone. This however is not the case.

Each muscle is enclosed in a sheath of connective tissue called the *epimysium.* Ingrowths of the epimysium divide it into bundles, the sheath of each bundle being known as the *perimysium.* Further fine ingrowths of the perimysium penetrate among the separate fibres to form the *endomysium* which encases each fibre. These muscle fibres do not extend the whole length of the muscle; normally there are far more in the middle region. At the end of the muscle, the fibres are slightly tapered and here they are fused to the connective tissue which passes directly into the tendon.

Voluntary muscle fibres vary considerably in length and diameter, even in one particular muscle. They may be up to 120 mm long and up to 100μm in diameter. Each fibre is encased by the endomysium,

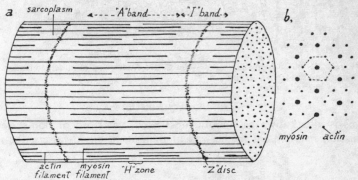

Fig. 20.30. (*a*) Detailed structure of a small portion of a myofibril, × 20,000. (*b*) Arrangement of the filaments in T.S.

within which is an elastic membrane called the *sarcolemma*. Most of the connective tissue is of the yellow elastic type. The muscle fibres are coenocytic with elongated peripheral nuclei. Each fibre is made up of numerous myofibrils grouped in *Cohnheim's areas*; the myofibrils are separated by sarcoplasm. These myofibrils contain thicker, shorter filaments of *myosin*, which give the dark *A* bands; interdigitated with these are the slender filaments of *actin*, giving the lighter *I* bands. Centrally between the ends of the actin filaments is the paler *H* zone. The actin filaments are inserted in the *Z* discs; the myosin filaments lie free in the sarcoplasm. From one *Z* disc to the next, constitutes one *sarcomere*, about 2 to 3μm long. These details (*see* Fig. 20.30) can be seen in fixed, stained specimens, or in fresh muscle by phase contrast.

Muscle fibres have an excellent blood supply with numerous small vessels running longitudinally between them and plentiful semicircular capillary connexions around them. They are well supplied with nerve endings of the end-plate type (*see* Fig. 20.44). Their essential function is to cause movement of the skeleton by contraction of the fibres. This contraction exerts a pull on the tendon and is transmitted to the bone by the tendon insertion. The physiology of muscle is discussed in Vol. II, Chap. 12. Skeletal muscles work in pairs, a *flexor* causing bending at a joint and an *extensor* causing straightening. They are developed from the mesodermal somites of the embryo.

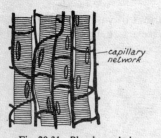

Fig. 20.31. Blood supply in voluntary muscle from a section of injected tongue.

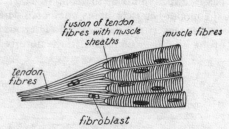

Fig. 20.32. Attachment of muscle to tendon.

Involuntary Muscle

This is also known as smooth, unstriated, unstriped or non-skeletal muscle. It is present in the wall of the gut, in blood-vessels, the iris

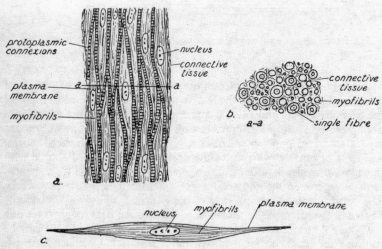

Fig. 20.33. (*a*) Involuntary (unstriated) muscle. L.S. (*b*) Same sectioned in plane *a–a*. (*c*) Single fibre.

and ciliary body of the eye, in ducts, and in the dermis of the skin. It is under involuntary control, being innervated by autonomic fibres.

Involuntary muscle forms sheets with the individual fibres normally passing longitudinally or circularly. Each fibre is a long spindle-shaped cell with an elongated central nucleus. Very fine myofibrils pass along the length, but there are no cross-striations. The fibres have no sarcolemma; each is bounded merely by its plasma membrane. The connective tissue binding the cells together is of the yellow elastic type. The blood supply is scanty compared with that of voluntary muscle.

The general function of involuntary muscle is that of closing and opening cavities or tubes. In the gut, for example, the circular muscle causes narrowing of the cavity, while the longitudinal muscle opens it again. In the iris of the eye, the circular muscle will narrow the pupil, while the radial muscle will dilate it. Involuntary muscle is developed from embryonic connective tissue.

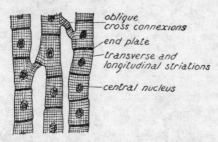

oblique
cross connexions

end plate

transverse and
longitudinal striations

central nucleus

Fig. 20.34. Small piece of section of cardiac muscle.

Cardiac Muscle

This type of muscle is found only in the heart. Each fibre consists of cylindrical short cells arranged in columns. Each cell has a central nucleus, myofibrils and faint transverse striations. Adjacent columns are joined by many oblique cross-connexions. The cells have abundant sarcoplasm.

This is a very specialized type of muscle. In structure it is almost intermediate between voluntary and involuntary. There is a very rich blood supply and innervation is both cranial, by the vagus nerve, and autonomic. All cardiac muscle is developed from splanchnic mesoderm of the embryo.

General Properties of Muscular Tissue

The muscles constitute about 40 per cent of the body weight of a mammal. On the average, they contain 75 per cent water, the remainder consisting of protein, fat, glycogen and traces of NaCl, $K_3 PO_4$, ATP and phosphagen. The myofibrils consist of interdigitated filaments of the proteins actin and myosin.

NERVOUS TISSUES

The cells which constitute nervous tissue always show branching protoplasmic processes, some of which may be very long. There is no intercellular substance, the cells being packed in with a little connective tissue, but mainly with *neuroglia* cells.

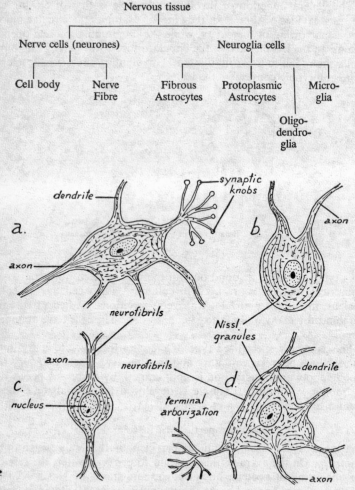

Fig. 20.35. Different types of neurones. (*a*) Motor cell. (*b*) Flask-shaped cell. (*c*) Bipolar cell. (*d*) Pyramidal cell.

Neurones

Each neurone has at least two branched processes. One, called the *axon* carries impulses away from the cell body; in *neurosecretory neurones*, droplets of hormone pass along the outside of the axon to be discharged at its end (*see* p. 1081). Other processes, called *dendrites* carry impulses into the cell body. Both axons and dendrites may be very long, e.g. a dendrite carrying an impulse from a skin receptor on a hand, has its cell body in a dorsal ganglion (*see* p. 833); an axon from a cell body in the brain can extend to a hind limb muscle. Both axons and dendrites end in fine tufts called terminal arborizations, each fibril of which ends in a *synaptic knob* which is very close to another neurone or to an effector cell (*see* Vol. II, Chap. 8.). The slight gaps are the *synapses*. Cell bodies range in size from 2μm to 100μm; the most common shapes are rounded, stellate, pyramidal and flask-shaped. There is always a large nucleus with a pronounced nucleolus, and in stained preparations, rod-like *Nissl* granules can be seen; they are absent from the region where the axon arises. Ramifying through the cytoplasm are minute neurofibrils. The transmission of nervous impulses is discussed in Chap. 8, Vol. II.

Nerve Fibres

Nerve fibres are of two kinds, myelinated or medullated and non-myelinated or non-medullated. The cranial nerves, spinal nerves and white matter of the central nervous system consist chiefly of myelinated nerves. The autonomic nerve fibres are mainly non-myelinated. In both types of fibres the axis cylinder is an essential component.

Myelinated Fibres

These have a central core, *the axis cylinder*, surrounded by a white lipide *myelin sheath*, and enclosed in a delicate membrane, the *neurilemma*, outside which is a fine layer of connective tissue. The axis cylinder is jelly-like and is a continuation of the cytoplasm of the neurone. It contains neurofibrils and many mitochondria and is unbroken from its emergence to its termination. The myelin sheath, continuous within the central nervous system, is interrupted in the peripheral fibres by constrictions, the *nodes of Ranvier*. The sheath is formed by the *cells of Schwann* which grow spirally round the axon forming many turns. When fully grown, the Schwann cells lose their cytoplasm and the sheath then consists of many layers of plasma membrane. The neurilemma consists of thin tubular cells with one large nucleus in each internodal segment. It is continuous over the nodes of Ranvier.

The fibre acquires a myelin sheath shortly after its emergence from the cell body. The sheath continues, except for the nodes of Ranvier, along the length of the fibre and is lost just before the final nerve-ending.

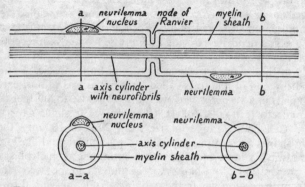

Fig. 20.36. (*a*) Small piece of myelinated nerve fibre. (*b*) Same in sections *a–a* and *b–b*.

Non-myclinated Fbires

There is no myelin sheath but only an axis cylinder enclosed by the neurilemma and by connective tissue. The nuclei of the neurilemma cause characteristic swellings along the fibre.

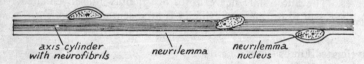

Fig. 20.37. Non-myelinated nerve fibre.

Nerves

A nerve consists of a bundle of fibres bound up with a connective tissue sheath called the *epineurium*. Ingrowths of this divide the fibres into smaller bundles each enclosed by a *perineurium*. Within these smaller bundles, each fibre is separated from the others by further ingrowths of connective tissue, the *endoneuria*. Passing mainly longitudinally in the connective tissue are blood-vessels and lymphatics, and there is always some adipose tissue present.

Nerves are described according to the directions in which impulses are conducted by the fibres. Nerves containing only fibres which carry impulses in to the central nervous system are called *sensory* or *afferent* nerves. Those which contain fibres carrying only outward impulses are called *motor* or *efferent* nerves. Many of the nerves have

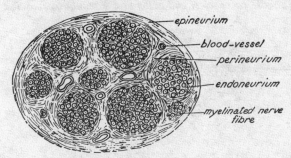

epineurium
blood-vessel
perineurium
endoneurium
myelinated nerve fibre

Fig. 20.38. T.S. whole nerve.

afferent and efferent fibres; they are known as *mixed* nerves. Examples of sensory nerves are the olfactory, optic and auditory; examples of motor nerves are the oculomotor, pathetic and abducens; the trigeminal, facial, glossopharyngeal and vagus are mixed nerves. All the spinal nerves are mixed; at the point of separation just lateral to the spinal cord, the afferent fibres proceed via the dorsal root, and the efferent via the ventral root. The physiology of nervous impulses is discussed in Vol. II, Chap. 8.

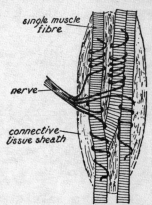

single muscle fibre

nerve

connective tissue sheath

Fig. 20.39. A spindle organ in voluntary muscle.

Nerve Endings

Functionally there are two types of endings. Sensory nerve endings are located in sense organs. They receive the impulses induced in sense organs by stimuli and commence transmission along the sensory nerves. Motor nerve endings convey to effector organs the impulses sent out by the central nervous system along motor nerves.

Seven types of receptor nerve-endings are considered here; for those of the eye, ear, nose and tongue see pp. 1066–1081. In striated muscle there are *spindle-organs*, each consisting of a spindle enclosed in connective tissue and containing several muscle fibres. Nerve fibres enter each spindle and end as spirals round the individual muscle fibres or as arborizations. Epithelial tissues are penetrated by fine non-myelinated

fibres which end as arborizations with varicose endings in the intercellular substance. There are several types of sensory endings in epithelial and connective tissues. Some are simply terminal arborizations,
some are *tactile corpuscles*, *end-bulbs* and *Pacinian corpuscles*. Tactile

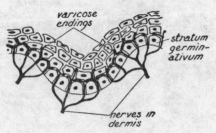

Fig. 20.40. Varicose nerve endings in skin.

corpuscles are common in the dermal papillae. The connective tissue
of the nerve sheath is continuous with that of the corpuscle; the nerve
fibres arborize among the flattened cells of the inner lining. End-bulbs
are small bulbous swellings formed by thickening of the connective
tissue sheath. Within the bulb is soft granular cytoplasm encased by
squamous cells. The axis cylinder may lie in the cytoplasm whole or

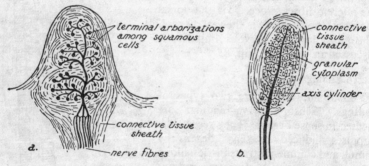

Fig. 20.41. (*a*) A tactile corpuscle in dermis of skin. (*b*) An end bulb from
connective tissue.

form a branching network. End-bulbs are common in the papillae of
the tongue, in the lips, the conjunctiva, in tendons and in the peritoneum. A Pacinian corpuscle may be as large as a pin's head. They
consist of concentric layers of connective tissue bounded on the
inside and outside by squamous epithelium. In the cytoplasmic core a
single nerve fibre proceeds as a straight thread, branching somewhat at
the distal end. These corpuscles are plentiful, occurring most commonly

in the skin of the hands and feet, in tendons and ligaments, and in some animals, they are easily seen in the mesentery.

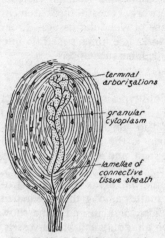

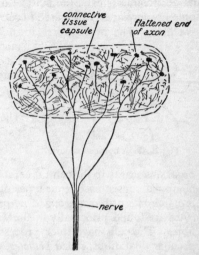

Fig. 20.42. A Pacinian corpuscle from mesentery of cat.

Fig. 20.43. Organ of Ruffini from dermis of skin.

The *organs of Ruffini*, sensitive to warmth, are cylindrical bundles of connective tissue containing flattened expansions of the axis cylinders (*see* Fig. 20.43). The *bulbs of Krause*, sensitive to cold, are similar to

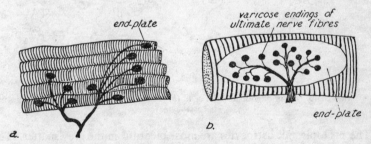

Fig. 20.44. (a) End-plate nerve endings in voluntary muscle. (b) Single end plate (enlarged).

end-bulbs, but smaller. Both types are located in the dermis of the skin.

Motor nerve endings are also of various types. In voluntary muscle, there are characteristic end-plates. The neurilemma sheath with some of its nuclei spreads out over a muscle fibre. The axis cylinder penetrates into the sarcoplasm and splits up into arborizations which end in small varicose expansions. In cardiac and involuntary muscle there are no end-plates; the nerve fibres branch and end in small varicose swellings. The nerve fibres form a network beneath the basement membrane of glandular tissues. From the network, fine fibres penetrate into the intercellular substance.

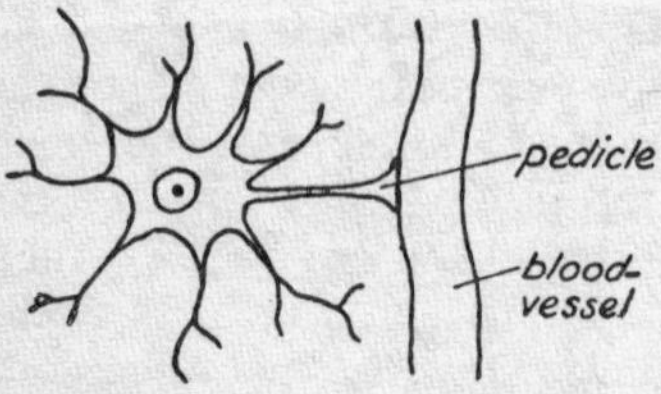

pedicle

blood-
vessel

Fig. 20.45. A fibrous astrocyte.

Neuroglia

The various types of neuroglia form a packing tissue in the brain, spinal cord, and in ganglia. Connective tissue, which is the normal packing in organs, is scanty in the central nervous system, and its place is taken by neuroglia consisting of four types of cells. They are *fibrous astrocytes*, *protoplasmic astrocytes*, *oligodendroglia* and *microglia*. Fibrous astrocytes are found principally in the white matter among the myelinated fibres. The cells have thick processes which branch, and some show peculiar dilatations, called *pedicles*, which abut on small blood-vessels.

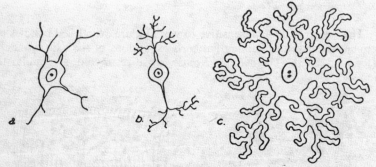

Fig. 20.46.   *a*) An oligodendroglia cell.   (*b*) A microglia cell.   (*c*) A protoplasmic astrocyte.

The protoplasmic astrocytes are most plentiful in the grey matter. The cells have thick branched processes somewhat similar to pseudopodia. Oligodendroglia cells are found in both white and grey matter. They have few very fine processes which show very little branching. Microglia cells are more numerous in grey matter than in white. The cell bodies are small and elongated and from each end arises a thick process which branches freely. All the branches show numerous lateral twigs. These cells are phagocytic and represent the defence mechanism of the central nervous system. They can assume spherical form and exhibit amoeboid motion.

TYPES OF GLANDS

In the protozoa we find that each protoplast is capable of producing various secretions for protection, for digestion, and other purposes. In coelenterates, there are specialized glandular cells. Some secrete an adhesive at the base, some secrete digestive enzymes and yet others, the nematoblasts, secrete a poisonous substance. In higher forms, although special glandular organs are evolved, the secreting cells are still the functional units, and in some cases they are isolated and do not form a glandular tissue. The oxyntic cells of the stomach, and the goblet cells of the gut in general, are still units specialized for particular secretions and do not form tissues. Nevertheless, the glandular cells are for the most part aggregated into tissues which with other tissues, form glands. Here, the main types of glands are outlined, so that only brief reference to them will be necessary in descriptions of animal types.

Glands are organs in which the secretory cells are usually endothelial, arranged around a central cavity. Physiologically, there are numerous types, but anatomically there are only five. Otherwise they may be classified as glands with ducts and those without ducts.

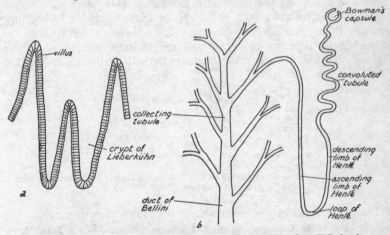

Fig. 20.47. Tubular glands. (a) Simple, crypts of Lieberkühn from T.S. duodenum. (b) Compound, kidney tubule.

Simple Tubular Glands

In their simplest form, these glands have an appearance similar to that of an elongated test tube. Such are the gastric glands of the stomach, often called the gastric pits, and the crypts of Lieberkühn. The secretory epithelium lines the inside of the gland and the substance which it secretes on stimulation, accumulates in the lumen and eventually overflows. The muscular movements of the wall have a considerable

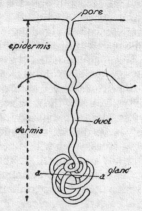

Fig. 20.48. A sudoriparous gland from skin.

effect in squeezing the juices into the gastric and intestinal cavities. Some of the gastric glands and crypts of Lieberkühn are forked into two or three branches near the base and are therefore compound.

A similar type but elongated and folded is the *convoluted tubular gland*; it is still a single tube. Such are the sudoriparous glands of the

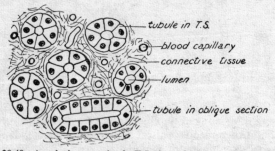

Fig. 20.49. A sudoriparous gland. T.S. through plane *a–a* of Fig. 20.48.

skin. Here secretion is confined to the coiled inner portion, while the straighter part acts as the duct. The glandular part consists of columnar epithelium with fine longitudinal muscle fibres at the bases of the columnar cells. The duct portion consists of a stratified epithelium of very small cells.

Compound Tubular Glands

This type of gland has a richly-branched system of secretory tubules all leading to a non-secretory duct. The kidney of the mammal is a collection of such systems with the ducts opening into the pelvis at the apices of the pyramids. The liver is also primarily a compound tubular gland, though it has assumed other functions as well. Its original function is that of producing bile. It arises in the embryo as an outgrowth of the gut and still maintains its connexion through the bile duct. The final branches of the gland are the so-called "bile twigs," found intracellularly in the liver cells. The testis is similarly a compound tubular gland though it is hardly feasible to call the sperm, secretions. There are however liquid secretions which allow the sperm motility, and supply nutrients and oxygen during its passage to the epididymis. The ducts are the *vasa efferentia.*

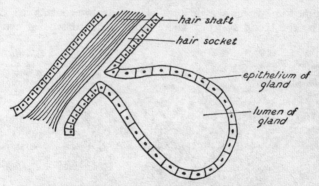

Fig. 20.50. A simple saccular gland. Sebaceous gland from skin.

Simple Saccular Glands

These differ from simple tubular glands in that their distal ends are expanded into spherical or flask-shaped cavities. The straight portion is the duct and the dilated part is secretory. Such glands are common in vertebrate skin, being exemplified in this book by the mucous glands of the dogfish, the mucous, poison and albuminous glands of the frog, and the sebaceous glands of mammalian hair. The latter sometimes approach the compound saccular condition.

Racemose or Compound Saccular Glands

Racemose glands consist of a branching system of tubules with the distal end of each tubule ending in a spherical or ovoid dilatation. Such are the salivary glands, the pancreas and the mammary glands.

Brunner's glands of the duodenum are small racemose glands. The dilatations form the secretory part, while the tubules converge on a single final duct.

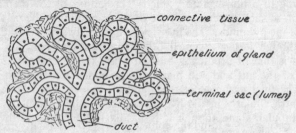

Fig. 20.51. A racemose gland. Portion of salivary gland.

Endocrine Glands

Sometimes known as the ductless glands, their products are carried away by the blood system. There is no standard type of endocrine

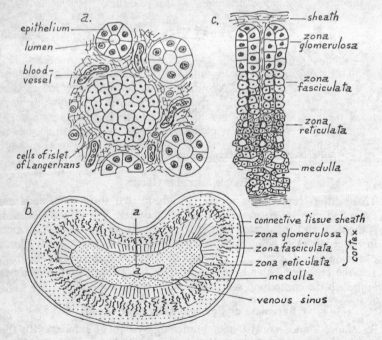

Fig. 20.52. (a) Section of glandular tissue of pancreas. (b) Section of supra-renal. (c) V.S. supra-renal at a–a in (b).

gland. The simplest type consists of small groups of scattered cells dispersed among the tissue of another organ. Such are the islets of Langerhans in the pancreas, and the interstitial tissue of the testis. Others consist of small vesicles bound together by connective tissue, e.g. the thyroid and parts of the pituitary. Some have cortical and medullary zones, e.g. the suprarenals. All, however, are developed from epithelia or nervous tissue, or from both (*see* Fig. 20.52).

ORGANS

It is not possible to give an account of metazoan organs which will be of such wide application as that of tissues and glands. There is enormous variety in organs and the nomenclature is occasionally misleading. The pharynx of the earthworm is a considerably different structure with different functions from the same organ in chordates. The eye of an insect is hardly to be compared with the eye of a rabbit though it may serve the same purpose. Therefore there is no preliminary account of organs here. They will be briefly described in the types, and the major mammalian organs will be treated in the account of the mammal.

INTERDEPENDENCE OF TISSUES

It must be realized that although the tissues have been described separately and although their special functions have been emphasized, no tissue can exist as an independent unit. All are supplied with food and oxygen by the blood and lymph; all are stimulated by the nervous system or by hormones. The presence of cells in the blood depends upon the activity of the bone-marrow and the lymphatic glands. A muscle acts as a unit because of the connective tissue which encases it, binds the fibres together and attaches it to a bone. All the tissues are specialized, yet all are interdependent.

CHAPTER 21

COELOMATE ANIMALS I: ANNELIDA

THIS large and important phylum contains three familiar classes. The Polychaeta or bristle worms are marine and perhaps the best known genera are the rag-worms (*Nereis*) and lug-worms (*Arenicola*), which are found burrowing in the intertidal zone. They are commonly used by fishermen as bait. The class Oligochaeta contains the earthworms and a few freshwater species. The class Hirudinea includes the leeches, which are less well known nowadays than they were when blood-letting was a cure for many ills. In this chapter, we shall deal mainly with the earthworm, with some mention of the marine annelids.

THE EARTHWORM

There are about 1,500 species of earthworms, ranging in size from animals less than 1 mm long to gigantic forms 360 cm in length. The bigger species are found in South America, Africa, Ceylon and Australia; *Megascolides australis* is the largest known. Earthworms are found in every type of soil except very dry or very acid soils. Their geographical range excludes only the Antarctic, Arctic and sub-Arctic. There are 24 British species (*see* Vol. II, Chap. 6); the one described here is *Lumbricus terrestris*.

Habitat and Habits

The worms live in burrows which they excavate in loose earth by pushing the soil aside, or in compacted earth by swallowing the soil. The burrows usually end in small ovoid chambers in which the worms lie coiled. They do not come to the surface in the daytime unless there has been heavy rain, enough to flood the burrows. However, they normally appear on the surface at night, especially after rain. In very cold or dry weather, they burrow deeply, often as much as eight feet, and in these conditions several worms may be found coiled together in a slimy covering.

The worms feed mainly on the surface at night, consuming all kinds of decaying vegetable matter. They also obtain a small proportion of organic material from the soil which they swallow. This soil is egested at the surface and forms the familiar worm-casts. Often they pull leaves and stems into the burrows; these bits of vegetation serve to block the burrow entrance, and if small enough, they are dragged completely below the soil. When feeding at the surface, a worm normally keeps its posterior portion in the burrow, while the exposed part ranges widely in search of food. When alarmed, the chaetae of the posterior segments are protruded; they provide a firm grip on the soil and the rest of the body quickly contracts into the burrow.

All earthworms are hermaphrodite. They pair on the surface on damp warm nights and exchange sperm by a process known as *copulation*. After separation, a cocoon is manufactured by the clitellum and the worm wriggles backward out of it. The small lemon-shaped cocoon contains eggs, sperm and a nutritive fluid. Normally only one worm emerges.

External Features

Full-grown worms average about 15 cm in length, though occasionally specimens as much as 30 cm long may be found. The body is elongated and roughly cylindrical in shape with slight dorso-ventral flattening in the posterior two-thirds. The anterior end is tapered, but there is no well-defined head. The upper surface is a deep red to mauve colour and the outline of the dorsal blood-vessel can be seen distinctly (*see* Fig. 21.1). The lower surface is much lighter, usually pink and sometimes nearly white. Old worms have a brown tint on the dorsal surface due to deposition of excretory granules in the skin. There are very clear external annuli which correspond exactly to the number of internal segments: about 150 in a full-grown worm. The *mouth* is anterior and overhung by the *prostomium* which is not a true segment. The lower border of the mouth is formed by the *peristomium* which is the first true segment. The *anus* is terminal, perforating the last segment. A thickened band, the *clitellum*, extends from segment 32 to 37 inclusive; it is most obvious dorsally and laterally, where it obscures the annuli.

There are four pairs of *chaetae* on every segment except the first and the last; two pairs are lateral and the other two pairs ventro-lateral

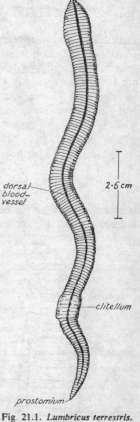

dorsal-blood-vessel

2·5 cm

clitellum

prostomium

Fig. 21.1. *Lumbricus terrestris.*

(*see* Fig. 21.4). The chaetae are slightly curved, pointed rods, embedded in *chaetigerous sacs* which are ingrowths of the epidermis. Each chaeta

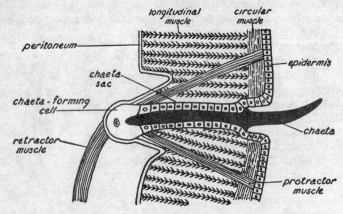

Fig. 21.2. V.S. body wall of earthworm to show insertion of chaeta.

is secreted by a single cell at the base of the sac (*see* Fig. 21.2). In segments 10 to 15, 26, and 32 to 37, the chaetae are longer and more slender; they penetrate the body of the other worm during copulation and thus assist in holding the pair together. The chaetae are made of chitin which becomes impregnated with scleroproteins; these darken and harden it. *Protractor* and *retractor muscles* are used for protruding and withdrawing the chaetae (*see* Figs. 21.2 and 21.4).

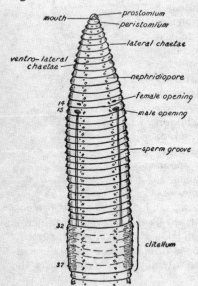

Fig. 21.3. *Lumbricus.* Ventral view, anterior end.

There are a number of external openings. The mouth and anus are both terminal. *Nephridiopores*, which are the openings of the excretory *nephridia*, are found in front of the ventro-lateral chaetae. They are minute pores, present in every segment except the first three and the last. Opening from the coelom to the dorsal surface are *dorsal pores* situated in the extreme anterior region of each segment; they are not present on the first eight or the last segments. In the grooves separating segments 9 and 10, and 10 and 11, are the *openings of the spermothecae*; into these the seminal fluid from the other worm is passed during copulation. Ventrally, on segment 14 are two very small slits which are the *openings of the oviducts*, and on segment 15 are the prominent *openings of the vasa deferentia*.

Structure and Functions of the Body Wall

There is a delicate outer iridescent *cuticle* secreted by the epidermis. It is constructed of fine layers of collagen fibres, each layer lying across

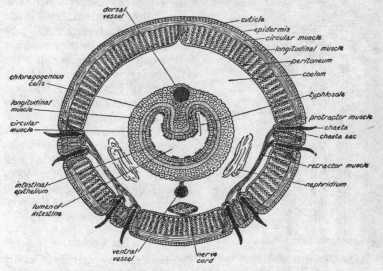

Fig. 21.4. *Lumbricus*. T.S. body in region of intestine.

the last one at an angle of 90°. The *epidermis* consists of columnar epithelium lying on a basement membrane. Interspersed among the columnar cells are mucus-secreting cells which assist in keeping the surface moist, and sensory cells whose protoplasmic projections perforate the cuticle. Beneath the epidermis is a thin layer of connective tissue containing a *sub-epidermal nerve plexus*, similar to the nerve net in *Hydra*. The next layer consists of *circularly-arranged muscle fibres* which are interrupted in the intersegmental positions. Beneath these circular fibres is a thick layer of *longitudinal muscle fibres* which pass the whole length of the worm. Between the two sets of muscle fibres is a *second nerve plexus*. Contraction of the circular muscles makes the body long and thin; contraction of the longitudinal muscles makes the body broad and short. The longitudinal muscle fibres are arranged in a very characteristic pattern (*see* Fig. 21.4), divided into nine blocks; two large dorso-lateral, three pairs of small ventro-lateral blocks and a large ventral block. The fibres are arranged on either side of radial connective tissue partitions containing blood-vessels, thus giving a herring-bone effect. The body wall is separated from the coelom by a squamous epithelium, the *peritoneum*.

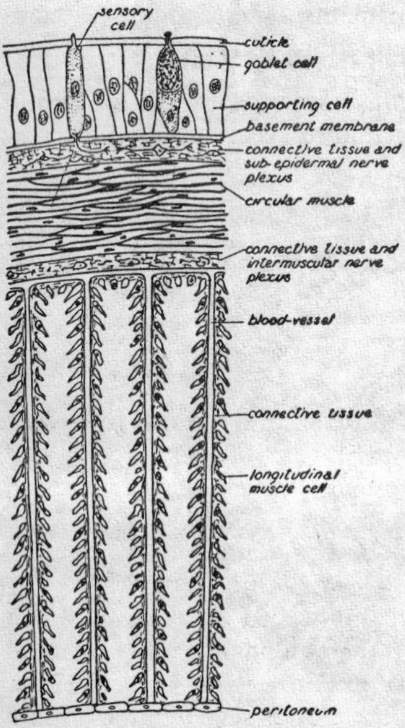

The body wall forms a stout protection for the deeper-seated and more delicate, internal structures. Some measure of mechanical protection is afforded by the strong but flexible cuticle. The epidermis is the main respiratory region and is richly supplied with blood-vessels and kept moist by secretions of the mucous glands and by fluid from the dorsal pores. The exteroceptors for perception of light and touch are situated in the epidermis. The body wall muscles are responsible for locomotion; they have a plentiful blood and nerve supply. Cells of the peritoneum secrete coelomic fluid.

Fig. 21.5. Histology of the body wall of *Lumbricus*. T.S.

The Coelom

This is a spacious perivisceral cavity containing a fluid in which colourless corpuscles are suspended. Each septum bears a small pore just above the nerve cord; through the pores the coelomic cavities of adjacent segments can communicate, but the pores are normally kept closed by a sphincter-like arrangement of muscle fibres. The coelomic fluid can be exuded from the dorsal pores; it assists in moistening the surface, and the corpuscles keep the surface clear of harmful bacteria and other micro-organisms. The incompressibility of the fluid gives it a skeletal function both in locomotion and in maintaining shape. It plays an important part in excretion, and the reproductive ducts open out from it. The gonads are developed from coelomic epithelium. The primary body cavity, the blastocoel, is represented by the spaces occupied by the blood. The septa consist of a double layer of peritoneum enclosing connective tissue and muscle fibres.

Skeletal and Supporting Structures

The cuticle and chaetae are exoskeletal structures, the one for protection from excessive evaporation, the other for affording purchase on the earth during locomotion. The coelomic fluid may also be considered as a skeletal structure, a hydrostatic skeleton. Since it is normally retained in watertight compartments, then each must contain a constant volume of fluid. Thus contractions of the muscles cannot effect change in volume but only change in shape. Its very incompressibility gives effect to muscular action. If, in any particular segment, the circular muscles contract, this pressure inward on the fluid will cause elongation of that particular segment; contraction of the longitudinal muscles will cause shortening and hence radial bulging of the segment, since the volume must remain the same.

Nutrition

The *alimentary canal* leads straight through from mouth to anus; it is to be noticed that here, for the first time in our sequence of types, there is an opening for egestion as well as one for ingestion. The *mouth* leads into a wide thin-walled *buccal cavity* which passes through segments 1, 2 and 3. It leads into a muscular thick-walled *pharynx* in segments 4 and 5. The pharynx bears patches of glandular tissue on its dorsal and lateral walls, and from its outer surface, numerous radial strands of muscle pass across the coelom to the body wall. The pharynx leads into a narrow, tubular, thin-walled *oesophagus*, which extends to segment 13. In segment 10, the oesophagus bears a lateral pair of pouches, the *oesophageal pouches*, and in segments 11 and 12 are two pairs of white *calciferous glands*. The glands secrete a milky fluid containing minute calcium carbonate particles in suspension. This secretion passes into the oesophageal pouches and thence by their slit-like openings into the oesophagus. The next part of the canal is the dilated thin-walled *crop* in segments 14, 15 and 16; it leads to a thick, hard, muscular *gizzard* in segments 17, 18 and 19. From the gizzard, a small aperture leads to the *intestine*, which extends to the *anus*. The intestine is constricted slightly by the intersegmental partitions, and from its dorsal surface a longitudinal fold, the *typhlosole*, hangs downward into the lumen. These two devices serve to increase the area for secretion and absorption. The endothelium of the intestine consists of columnar cells, both secretory and ciliated, interspersed with goblet cells secreting mucus. Outside the basement membrane of the endothelium is a thin layer of circular muscle fibres, then a thin layer of longitudinal muscle fibres. Between these sets of muscles is a nerve plexus. Outside the muscle layers is the peritoneum, composed here of large yellow cells which also fill the trough of the typhlosole. These cells play an important part in excretion.

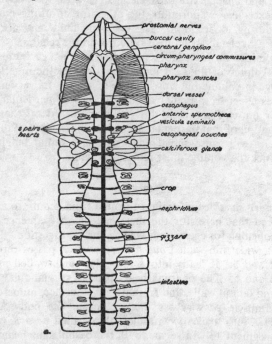

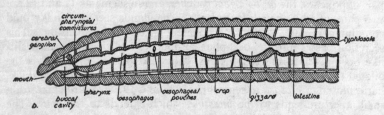

Fig. 21.6. (*a*) General anatomy of the anterior of *Lumbricus*. dorsal body wall removed. (*b*) L.S. body to show the alimentary canal.

The food consists mainly of vegetable matter, though during ingestion of soil, animal remains must also be taken. Food is first softened by exudation of fluid from the pharyngeal glands. This contains mucin and a proteolytic enzyme; these moisten and soften the food before it is sucked in by the pumping action of the pharynx Swallowing occurs by peristalsis and the crop is used for storage and probably some preliminary digestion. In the muscular gizzard, the food is masticated by crushing with small sharp stones. The main digestive processes

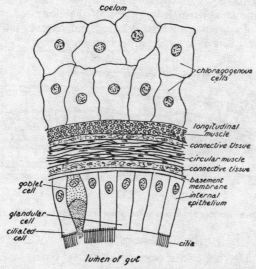

Fig. 21.7. Histology of the gut wall of *Lumbricus*. T.S.

take place extracellularly in the intestine. Gland cells secrete proteolytic, amylolytic and lipolytic enzymes. The intestine also serves for absorption of digested food into the blood capillaries. Thence, via the vascular system, the food is circulated throughout the body.

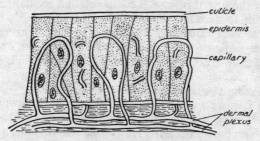

Fig. 21.8. Epidermal capillaries of *Lumbricus*.

Respiration

The worm is aerobic, obtaining oxygen from the air by diffusion through its skin. The cuticle is thin and kept moist by secretions of the epidermal glandular cells and by fluid from the dorsal pores. Looped capillary blood-vessels pass into the epidermis, coming very near the surface. The blood contains the respiratory pigment haemoglobin which greatly increases its capacity for oxygen. The ratio of surface area to volume remains high by reason of the elongated shape. The oxyhaemoglobin circulates with the blood and releases the oxygen to the cells, where there is low oxygen tension.

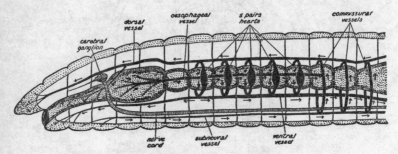

Fig. 21.9 *Lumbricus*. Blood vascular system (side view). Diagram.

The Blood-vascular System

Here, for the first time in our sequence of animal types, we encounter a *blood-vascular system*. In the earthworm it is a *closed system* with the blood circulating in tubes of small diameter, the *blood-vessels*. The cavities of the blood-vessels represent the remains of the blastocoel, while the walls of the vessels and the blood corpuscles are mesodermal in origin.

Blood flows forward along the *dorsal blood-vessel* which lies immediately above the gut; this vessel is contractile and peristaltic waves pass from posterior to anterior. Along its course are small paired valves which prevent backward flow. It is the main collecting vessel of the system. At its anterior end, it narrows over the pharynx and branches repeatedly, finally breaking up into capillaries in the body wall. This dorsal vessel receives blood from a large number of segmentally repeated vessels. The chief ones are—

(*a*) Large *commissural vessels* which pass upward around the gut from the *sub-neural vessel* in every segment from 12 to the posterior end. These commissural vessels receive numerous branches from the body wall and one from each nephridium. Their entrances to the dorsal blood-vessel bear valves (*see* Figs. 21.10 and 21.11).

(*b*) Three branches from the gut in every segment from 12 to the posterior end, *the dorso-intestinal vessels* (*see* Fig. 21.10).

(*c*) Blood from the anterior part of the gut is collected in a pair of *lateral oesophageal vessels*. In these, the blood flows backward to join the commissural vessel in segment 12 and thence it flows into the dorsal vessel (*see* Fig. 21.9).

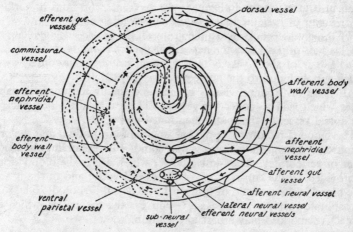

Fig. 21.10. Diagram to show distribution and collection of blood of *Lumbricus* in segments behind the hearts. Distribution, right; collection, left.

(*d*) Blood from the nerve cord flows into the sub-neural vessel and hence by the *dorso-neural commissural vessels* to the dorsal vessel.

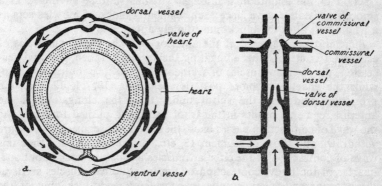

Fig. 21.11. (*a*) Arrangement of valves in hearts of earthworm. (*b*) Valves in the dorsal vessel.

Outflow of blood from the dorsal vessel occurs chiefly in segments 7 to 11, where are the five pairs of large, lateral, contractile vessels often known as *hearts*. Each bears four valves which allow the blood to flow downward only. At their lower ends, the hearts lead into the

large *ventral vessel* which is suspended by a mesentery just beneath the
gut. This ventral vessel is the main distributing channel. In each
segment it gives off the following vessels—

    (*a*) a pair of *parietal vessels* to the body wall;

    (*b*) three vessels dorsally to the gut wall, *the ventro-intestinal vessels*;

    (*c*) a pair of vessels to the nephridia, *the nephridial vessels*;

    (*d*) a pair of short vessels to the *lateral neural* longitudinal vessels
which supply blood to the nerve cord (*see* Fig. 21.10).

All these distributing vessels branch and finally terminate in capillaries which lead to collecting vessels. These take the blood back to
the dorsal vessel by the routes mentioned above.

The blood is red owing to the haemoglobin in solution, and the only
corpuscles present are colourless amoeboid cells resembling the leucocytes of vertebrates. The motive power which drives the blood along,
is provided by the contractions of the dorsal vessel and of the hearts.
The blood is the medium of transport of oxygen, carbon dioxide, food
and soluble excretory materials. It conveys the corpuscles, which are
protective and also play a part in excretion.

Locomotion

Movement is best described by starting with a stationary worm. A
wave of contraction of the circular muscles proceeds from anterior to
posterior and is followed after a short space of time by a wave of contraction of the longitudinal muscles. It must not be envisaged as a
smooth peristaltic wave since each segmental block of muscles acts as
a whole unit after the block immediately anterior to it.

Starting the movement at the anterior end, the circular muscles of
segment 1 contract, thus elongating the segment. Then, in rapid succession, the circular muscles of segments 2, 3, 4, etc., contract. Meanwhile the chaetae of more posterior segments, 10, 11, 12, etc., are
protracted and grip the substratum. Thus the elongation of the
anterior segments results in the front end being pushed forward. As
the wave of contraction passes back, the chaetae of segment 10, etc., are
withdrawn and those of segment 13, etc., protruded. By the time this
wave of contraction of the circular muscles has passed back about one-
quarter of the body, contraction of the longitudinal muscles starts at
the anterior end. This results in shortening and thickening of the
anterior segments. Their chaetae are then protruded and thus succeeding segments are pulled up towards the anterior end. Thus each region
of the body is pulled forward then pushed forward.

Co-ordination of movement is effected in two ways, by mechanical
stretch stimuli and by reflex arcs in the nerve cord (*see* p. 619). Sudden
shock movements of the whole body are due to instantaneous excitation

of all the longitudinal muscles by the medium of the giant fibres (*see* p. 620). A stimulus which excites contraction of the longitudinal muscles, inhibits contraction of the circular muscles and vice versa.

Movement thus involves co-ordinated action of the circular muscles, the longitudinal muscles and the muscles of the chaetae. The muscular contractions exert pressure on the coelomic fluid and thus the shape of a segment is changed.

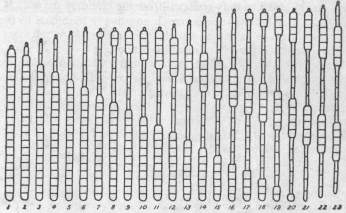

Fig. 21.12. Locomotive movements (from rest) by *Lumbricus*.

Growth

Apart from the neurones, all cells are able to divide and thus growth of every part of the body proceeds harmoniously. In the nervous system, after the initial formation of the neurone equipment of each segment, no new nerve cells are added. The nerve fibres can elongate and there is increase of neuroglia and of connective tissue.

Earthworms have considerable powers of regeneration. If a worm is cut in half, the front half will usually regenerate the posterior portion though the number of segments regenerated is generally less than the number lost. Regeneration of the anterior region, sometimes reported, is not known with any certainty. Worms have been kept under artificial conditions for fifteen years. It is very doubtful whether any survive more than four or five years in natural conditions. They are consumed by birds and by the carnivorous slug, *Testacella*; many die from the depredations of parasitic insect larvae, hatched from eggs laid in the worm by the parent insect. Large numbers are consumed by moles.

Excretion

Carbon dioxide is excreted by diffusion from the epidermal blood capillaries and also in the calcium carbonate excreted into the gut by the oesophageal pouches. The principal excess mineral ion, calcium, is eliminated into the gut in combination with carbon dioxide, as calcium carbonate. There it may play a useful part in neutralizing the acid food. Excess water is expelled from the nephridia, from the dorsal pores and from the mucus glands. This water serves to keep the skin moist for respiratory purposes.

Both urea and guanin are eliminated as the result of nitrogen metabolism. The guanin is mainly collected from the blood by the cells of the

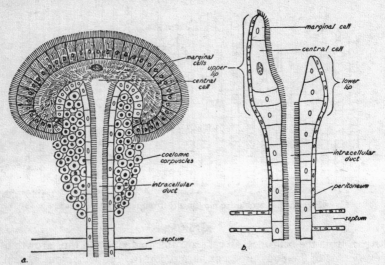

Fig. 21.13. (*a*) Optical section of nephrostome of *Lumbricus* from beneath. (*b*) Nephrostome, V.L.S.

splanchnic peritoneum. They become laden with granules of guanin and appear yellowish-green in colour; they are called *chloragogenous cells*. They disintegrate into the coelomic fluid, where most of the granules are ingested by amoeboid corpuscles. Some of these pass out through the dorsal pores and perish; others migrate into the lumen of the gut and are eventually egested; others still convey the pigment to the epidermal cells where it is deposited, especially on the dorsal surface.

Urea is excreted by the *nephridia* which extract it from the capillary blood-vessels. Each nephridium is a long coiled tube derived by ingrowth of ectoderm, and opens into the coelomic fluid of the segment anterior to the nephridiopore. The first part, the *nephrostome*, is a minute flattened funnel with the upper lip larger than the lower lip. It is attached to the septum and both lips are covered with peritoneum. The upper lip is formed mainly of a large crescentic central cell which

is thickly ciliated on the inner surface of the funnel. Around it is a
border of small columnar marginal cells, ciliated on their inner faces.
The lower lip consists of a thickened cluster of small cells which are not
ciliated. All the cilia beat into the lumen of the tube. The nephrostome
leads into an *intracellular duct* which bears two rows of lateral cilia.
This duct passes through the septum into the *narrow ciliated tube* which
is again intracellular. After making several loops, the narrow tube
leads into the wider *brown ciliated tube* which bears three longitudinal

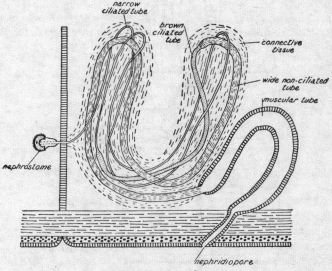

Fig. 21.14. Nephridium of earthworm.

rows of cilia. The brown tube makes only one loop then passes into the
wide non-ciliated tube. This leads into the much wider *muscular tube*,
the exit of which is the *nephridiopore*, regulated by a sphincter. All the
coils of the nephridium are bound up in connective tissue, and numerous
fine capillaries ramify among the coils.

The cilia of the nephrostome drive coelomic fluid, which may contain
excretory substances, into the narrow tube. This, and the brown tube,
extract urea from the blood and there may be some resorption of water
in the wide tube. The urine accumulates in the muscular tube, which
is emptied when the sphincter is opened. Experiment has shown that
earthworms excrete fluid equal to their body weight from the nephridia
in forty to fifty hours. The urine is hypotonic to both the blood and
coelomic fluid; it contains on the average 3 mg of urea, 3 mg Cl⁻, and
30 mg protein per 100 cm³.

Sensitivity, Co-ordination and Behaviour

The *central nervous system* consists of a pair of fused *cerebral ganglia*, two *circumpharyngeal commissures* and a double *ventral nerve cord* lying in the coelom and resting on the ventral body wall. The cerebral ganglia are small white pear-shaped objects lying immediately above

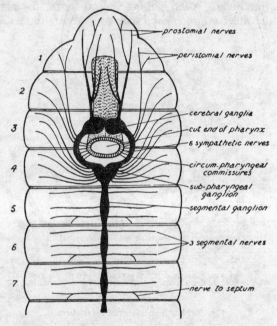

Fig. 21.15. Nervous system of *Lumbricus*. Dorsal dissection.

the buccal cavity in segment 3. The commissures pass around the front of the pharynx obliquely backwards and unite ventrally in segment 4 to form the *sub-pharyngeal ganglion*. The nerve cord then passes down the body, being slightly dilated to form a ganglion in each segment.

A pair of nerves from the cerebral ganglia supply the prostomium; a pair from the commissures supply the peristomium. Segments 2, 3, and 4 receive nerves from the sub-pharyngeal ganglion, whence it is concluded that it represents the fused ganglia of three segments. All the remaining segments receive three pairs of nerves from the ventral nerve cord, one pair in the anterior part and two pairs in the posterior part. From the last pair of nerves in each segment, a minute branch runs to each septum.

The distribution of the main branches in each segment are shown in the transverse section, Fig. 21.16. Each of the *segmental nerves*

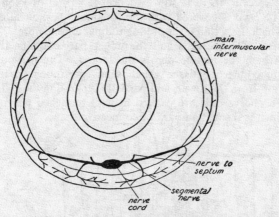

Fig. 21.16. Distribution of the posterior of the three pairs of segmental nerves in *Lumbricus*.

divides into two main branches, one passing downward to the ventral body wall and the other laterally to the lateral body wall. This nerve passes dorsally between the circular and longitudinal muscles to form

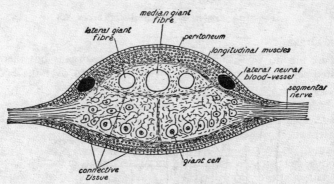

Fig. 21.17. T.S. nerve cord of *Lumbricus*.

almost a complete nerve ring. Branches are given off to the intermuscular plexus and to the sub-epidermal plexus.

From the commissures, a "sympathetic" system consisting of six small nerves on each side starts in the pharynx; this connects with a gut plexus lying between the two muscle layers.

Though the ventral nerve cord does not appear to be a double structure, it arises by the fusion of two separate cords in the embryo, and in transverse section, there is still evidence of partial division (*see* Fig. 21.17). The cord is covered with the squamous peritoneal epithelium beneath which lies a thin layer of longitudinal muscle fibres. The lower part consists of nerve cells and the upper part contains three giant fibres of which the middle one is the largest. The nervous layer is enclosed in connective tissue which sends partitions separating the upper region from the lower, and partially separating the right and left halves. The nerve cells are packed in with branched neuroglia cells, among which is a small amount of connective tissue.

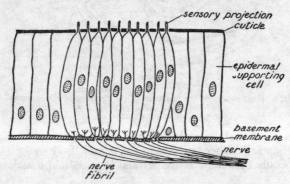

Fig. 21.18. *Lumbricus*. Epidermal sense organ, V.S.

Sense Organs

There are no well-defined macroscopic sense-organs but there are isolated sensory cells and groups of cells scattered over the body in

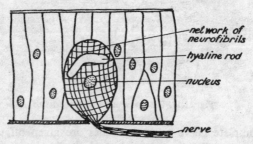

Fig. 21.19. Light cell of Hess from epidermis of the earthworm.

the epidermis. They are especially numerous in the anterior region. The organs consist of clusters of sensory cells which are long and narrow. From each cell a minute protoplasmic process projects through a pore in the cuticle. The cells are sensitive to touch and chemical stimuli. From their bases, nerve fibres pass into the central nervous system (*see* Fig. 21.18).

The whole body is sensitive to light, sensitivity being greatest on the dorsal regions of the anterior and posterior ends and least in the middle of the body. Light sensitivity is due to the *light cells of Hess* which contain refractile rods connected to neurofibrils in the cells (*see* Fig. 21.19).

Situated in the muscles of the body wall are minute proprioceptors which are receptive to mechanical stimuli.

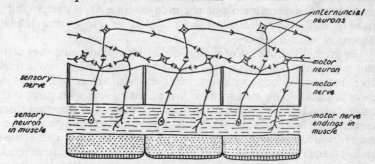

Fig. 21.20. Intra- and inter-segmental nervous connexions for the longitudinal muscles of the earthworm body wall. A similar set supply the circular muscles.

Co-ordination and Behaviour

The principal nervous connexions in the worm are shown in Fig. 21.20. Axons from sensory cells in the epidermis or muscles pass into the central nervous system, where they make synapses with both motor neurones and internuncial neurones. The motor cells convey impulses out to muscles of the same segment. The internuncial neurones convey impulses up and down the cord to motor neurones of adjacent segments.

During locomotion there are two routes of stimulation of the segmental muscles. The contraction of longitudinal muscles in one segment activates the stretch receptors in the muscles of the next segment. The axons of these stretch receptors pass into the central nervous system and make synapses with both motor and internuncial neurones. The axons of the motor neurones pass out to stimulate the muscles of that particular segment; the axons of the internuncial neurones pass down the cord to make synapses with motor neurones of the next segment. Thus stimulation of successive segmental muscles can pass by either of two routes. If a worm is cut in half and then stitched together, movement will continue normally; this shows that mechanical stimulation across the gap is quite effective. On the other hand, if the worm is incompletely severed with only the nerve cord remaining intact, and if then the segments in front of, and behind, the cut are securely pinned down to prevent their movement, the wave of contraction will continue down the segments posterior to the cut. This shows that the local reflex arcs are also sufficient of themselves. During movement both routes are probably used.

The cerebral ganglia, as in the planarians, mainly provide concentrations of internuncial neurones for relaying to effectors, impulses perceived by anterior sensory cells and organs. If the cerebral ganglia are removed, movement continues, even in spite of obstacles which make it ineffective. Hence we infer that these ganglia can inhibit movement when necessary.

The giant fibres consist of many smaller fused fibres, and they contain a peculiar oblique synapse in every segment. The two lateral fibres make connexions with each other and with ventral giant cells in every segment. The median fibre makes connexions with giant cells only. It has been shown that the lateral fibres conduct impulses from anterior to posterior only, while the median fibre conducts impulses only forward. Through the agency of these fibres, rapid and almost instantaneous contraction of all the longitudinal muscles is effected. An obnoxious stimulus at the anterior end will stimulate an action potential wave passing backward in the lateral fibres, and such a stimulus at the posterior region will send the wave passing forward in the median fibre.

Earthworms are very sensitive to light; they are negatively phototactic to strong light and positively phototactic to light of very low intensity. Ultra-violet rays are lethal to them, and that is the principal reason why dead earthworms are seen in puddles after heavy rain. If they are shielded from the light, the worms can live for a long period in water or in moist air. A strong touch stimulus at the front causes immediate protrusion of the chaetae in the posterior region and simultaneous violent contraction of all the longitudinal muscles so that the major part of the worm shrinks backward suddenly. Similarly a strong stimulus at the posterior end will cause the reverse procedure.

They are sensitive to temperature changes, their reaction to very low and very high temperatures being to burrow more deeply. They also react to humidity conditions and do not often come to the surface on dry or windy nights. On warm humid nights, they are to be seen in plenty, by the light of an electric torch, but the watcher must tread warily since they are very sensitive to vibrations. The worms also possess olfactory sense; they consume certain types of decaying leaves in preference to others; they prefer carrot leaves to celery, and celery to cabbage. The sensory cells concerned appear to lie around the mouth or just inside the buccal cavity.

Reproduction

Earthworms are hermaphrodite and show only sexual reproduction. Each individual possesses a complete set of male and female organs.

The female organs consist of a pair of small pear-shaped *ovaries* attached to the posterior surface of the septum dividing segments 12 and 13. They lie ventrally near the mid-line and their narrower ends

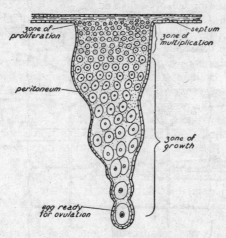

Fig. 21.21. Ovary of *Lumbricus*.

float almost horizontally in the coelomic fluid. They are mesodermal derivatives enclosed in an extension of the peritoneum. At the base is a zone of multiplication where many small cells are present. Then follows a zone of growth, and a single fully grown cell lies at the apex (*see* Fig. 21.21). The eggs are liberated into the coelom and undergo maturation divisions in a small *ovisac* which is a diverticulum of the *oviduct*. The funnel of the oviduct opens into the same segment, 13. The eggs are passed out through the short oviducts which open in segment 14 just outside the ventro-lateral chaetae. The *spermothecae*, which receive sperm from the co-copulant, are small white flask-shaped receptacles lying in segments 9 and 10. Their openings lie in the inter-segmental grooves behind the lateral chaetae.

There are two pairs of very small palmate *testes* lying attached to the posterior sides of the septa separating 9 and 10, and 10 and 11 respectively. Their free ends float in the coelomic fluid of segments 10 and 11, but they are shut off from the main coelom by two flattened compartments formed by outgrowth of the peritoneum. From these two median *testis sacs*, three large lobed diverticula project laterally. They are called *vesiculae seminales*, though besides being storage chambers for mature sperm, the maturation divisions take place there. The *sperm funnels* lie opposite the four testes in segments 10 and 11. They are

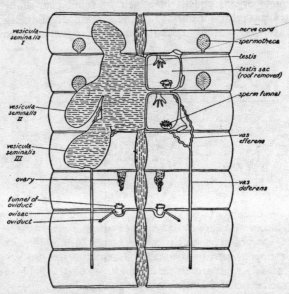

Fig. 21.22. Dorsal view of reproductive organs of *Lumbricus*. Right testis sacs opened.

ciliated, with folded borders, and are quite visible to the naked eye as small fluffy masses. Mature sperm pass back from the vesiculae seminales into the testis sacs, into the funnels, then through fine coiled *vasa efferentia*. The two vasa efferentia on each side unite in segment 12 to form *vasa deferentia* which pass back to open on the ventral side of segment 15 just outside the ventro-lateral chaetae. These male openings have thick lips and are easily discerned. From the male openings a pair of shallow seminal grooves pass back to the clitellum.

Copulation takes place at night on the surface. Sometimes both worms are completely clear of the burrows and sometimes, if their burrow entrances are close together, both worms may retain their posterior portions in the respective burrows. They lie with their ventral surfaces opposed in such a position that segments 9, 10, and 11 of each worm are opposite the clitellum of the other (*see* Fig. 21.24).

The long slender chaetae of segments 10 to 15, 26, and 32 to 37 are thrust by each partner into the body wall of the other and thus assist in maintaining close contact. Each worm secretes a mucus tube surrounding its body from segment 11 to segment 31; these separate tubes

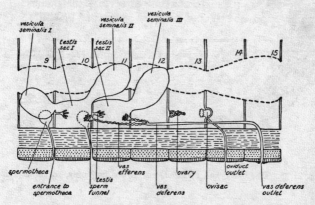

Fig. 21.23. Lateral view of *Lumbricus* reproductive organs.

prevent the mingling of sperm during copulation. Around the clitellar region the copulants are bound by a common mucus tube so tightly as to cause very obvious constriction there. In this position, seminal fluid containing sperm is squeezed along the *seminal grooves* from segment 15 on each worm to the clitellum, where the fluid is forced into the spermothecae of the other worm.

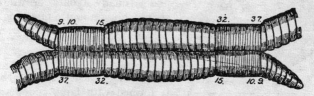

Fig. 21.24. Earthworms in copulation position.

Passage of seminal fluid along the grooves is effected by the contraction of special *arc-shaped muscles* which lie among the longitudinal muscles in the positions shown in Fig. 21.25. They are found only in segments 15 to 32. Their contraction deepens the groove and their relaxation squeezes the fluid along. Successive waves of contraction of these muscles keep the movement continuous.

Exchange of sperm having been effected, the worms separate and cocoon formation will take place at intervals until all the seminal fluid is used. Before a cocoon is formed, the worm secretes a mucus tube from segment 8 to segment 38. Within this tube, the cocoon, with contained albuminous fluid, is secreted by the clitellum. About a dozen eggs are

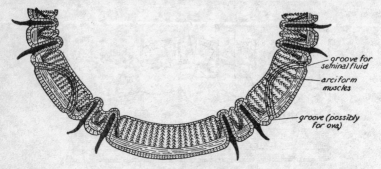

Fig. 21.25. T.S. body wall of *Lumbricus*, lower half only, to show arciform muscles.

passed back from the female openings to the cocoon. Here again the grooves and arciform muscles are probably brought into use. Then the worm forces the cocoon forward by expansion of the segments immediately behind it. This forward movement of the cocoon continues and as it passes the spermothecal openings, seminal fluid passes into it. Eventually, the cocoon is forced free of the body; its elastic ends close, and it lies beneath the surface or under leaves or stones. As it dries, it darkens and is finally a dark brown lemon-shaped body about 5 mm long. Normally, only one worm eventually emerges.

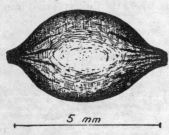

Fig. 21.26. Cocoon of *L. terrestris*.

Development

After cleavage, a hemispherical blastula is formed with large endoderm cells forming the flattened base and much smaller ectoderm cells forming the cap (*see* Fig. 21.27 (*a*)). The endoderm is invaginated and the blastopore forms the mouth. The embryo now swallows the albuminous fluid present in the cocoon (*see* Fig. 21.27 (*b*)). Two posterior mesoblast cells which were already present in the blastula proliferate two ventral bands of mesoderm forward between ectoderm and endoderm. Splits in these bands give the first signs of the coelom which arises as two portions latero-ventrally (*see* Fig. 21.27 (*c*)). The

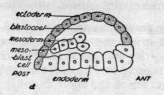

ectoderm
blastocoel
mesoderm
meso-
blast
cell
POST
endoderm
ANT
d

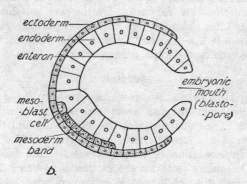

ectoderm
endoderm
enteron

meso-
-blast
cell

mesoderm
band

embryonic
mouth
(blasto-
-pore)

b.

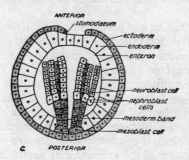

ANTERIOR
stomodaeum
ectoderm
endoderm
enteron

neuroblast cell
nephroblast
cells
mesoderm band

mesoblast cell

C
POSTERIOR

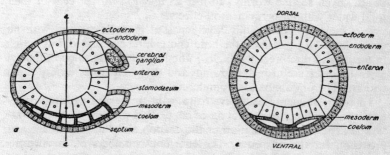

ectoderm
endoderm
cerebral
ganglion
enteron
stomodaeum
mesoderm
coelom
septum
a

DORSAL
ectoderm
endoderm
enteron
mesoderm
coelom
e
VENTRAL

Fig. 21.27. Developmental stages of *Lumbricus*. (*a*) Blastula. (*b*) Gastrula.
(*c*) Horizontal L.S. of embryo. (*d*) Sagittal L.S. of embryo. (*e*) T.S. in plane
a–a in (*d*).

mesoderm gradually grows dorsally between ectoderm and endoderm and becomes divided up into segmental compartments by septa (*see* Fig. 21.27 (*d*)). Two posterior cells called neuroblasts proliferate the nerve cords separately; the nerve cords, as yet mere chains of cells, bifurcate round the anterior gut region and rejoin dorsally. Later the two ventral chains fuse to form the nerve cord. A pair of nephroblast cells on each side proliferate chains forward. During segmentation, these are separated into small clumps which form the nephridia. After hatching, when the worm is less than half an inch long, posterior segmentation continues and the reproductive organs develop.

Adaptation

The most striking adaptations in earthworms are those in connexion with their life below the soil, with feeding at the surface and with reproduction. Their shape is ideal for burrowing and the chaetae of each segment give a strong eight-pointed grip affording considerable leverage. The exudation of mucus serves to bind the walls of the burrows. The ability to thrust the earth aside when it is loose or to consume it when it is tightly packed, ensure efficiency under both types of soil conditions.

Its omnivorous feeding and particular ability to deal with dead vegetation ensure an endless food supply. The lack of an enzyme for digesting cellulose is no handicap; the efficient grinding apparatus in the gizzard is well suited to breaking up plant tissues.

Under natural conditions, it is not a very active animal and thus its oxygen consumption is low. It can obtain sufficient oxygen in moist air or in water; the looped surface vessels ensure efficient absorption over a short diffusion distance and the haemoglobin confers large oxygen capacity. There is a considerable measure of control over loss of water by utilization of the sphincters at nephridiopores and dorsal pores. Even so, the worms can lose as much as 70 per cent of their total water without permanent ill-effects.

In correlation with a life largely passed in darkness and with no particular food necessities, the head end is little elaborated, but is rich in tactile and photoreceptive cells. The locomotion is so co-ordinated as to be most useful in burrowing, and the giant fibres ensure rapid withdrawal from obnoxious stimuli.

There are numerous adaptive features in connexion with reproduction. They include all the details of copulation whereby cross-fertilization is assured, the formation of the cocoon and the general efficient provision for the offspring. The enormous numbers of earthworms and their widespread distribution provide eloquent testimony of their efficiency in adapting themselves to their environment.

Classification

Phylum:	Annelida	Family:	Lumbricidae
Class:	Oligochaeta	Genus:	*Lumbricus*
Order:	Megadrili	Species:	*L. terrestris*

Worms in the order Megadrili are distinguished from those in the Microdrili by many characteristics. The chief of these are: Large number of segments, lack of asexual multiplication, no specialization of anterior chaetae, the position of the clitellum (never in front of segment 12), the lack of eye-spots, and the relatively large size. The order includes all the earthworms. The Lumbricidae are distinguished by the presence of the dorsal pores, and by different chaetae on the clitellum, which is always behind segment 20 and occupies six to nine segments. In the genus *Lumbricus*, the chaetae are always paired, with longer chaetae on the clitellum. Other details concern the positions of the reproductive structures which are as described previously. The species in this genus are separated by the number of segments, the general shape of the body and the form of the prostomium.

The Importance of Earthworms

Charles Darwin's classic study of earthworms, *The formation of vegetable mould through the action of earthworms, with observations on their habits*, was published in 1881, shortly before his death. Since that time the importance of the worms has been increasingly recognized. Indeed, at the present time there are well-known earthworm-breeding farms, both in Great Britain and in the United States, and apparently, demand for these "tillers of the soil" exceeds supply. The following quotation from Darwin's book is worth the careful consideration of all those who have to deal with the soil, in however small a capacity—

It may be doubted whether there are many other animals which have played so important a part in the history of the world as have these lowly organized creatures.

We may here summarize briefly the main benefits which accrue from a thriving population of earthworms.

(*a*) Their burrows provide natural drainage channels.

(*b*) The same burrows improve soil aeration.

(*c*) They increase the depth of topsoil by burrowing into subsoil and bringing it to the surface.

(*d*) The topsoil produced by worms is neutral; they have the general effect of reducing both acidity and alkalinity.

(*e*) They increase the organic content of the surface layers of the soil, thus favouring plant growth.

(*f*) The constant passage of soil through the gut reduces the particles to a fine state of division. The scattering of worm-casts provides an ideal medium for germination of seeds. Darwin estimated that worms add one inch of topsoil every five years.

(*g*) Their urine and faeces have considerable manurial value and encourage particularly those bacteria which attack cellulose.

The numbers of earthworms are truly phenomenal. Darwin estimated that there were between six million and thirteen million per square kilometre. More recent investigations show that he was very conservative in his estimates. Several careful counts give enormous figures varying between one hundred and twenty million and six hundred million per square kilometre, for grassland and fertile farm land.

MARINE ANNELIDS: POLYCHAETA

The earthworms are scarcely to be regarded as typical annelids, being specialized and modified for both the burrowing habit and for terrestrial conditions. The polychaetes are far more representative of the general characteristics of the phylum. They are all marine and may be conveniently divided into three ecological groups; free-swimming, tube-living and burrowing. These divisions are not completely rigid since there are intermediate types in all groups.

The rag-worm genus, *Nereis*, may be regarded as typically annelid. The common rag-worm is to be found easily in the intertidal zone, where at low tide it burrows into the mud. It swims gracefully by

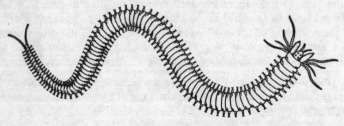

Fig. 21.28. *Nereis*. Dorsal view.

gentle undulation of the body and also crawls upon the substratum (*see* Fig. 21.28).

There is a considerably greater degree of cephalization than in *Lumbricus*, the prostomium bearing tentacles and palps and two pairs of well-developed eyes. The peristomium bears four pairs of joined appendages known as *cirri*. The prostomium and peristomium together constitute the head.

The alimentary canal shows less differentiation than that of the earthworm. The mouth opens into a large muscular eversible pharynx which bears a pair of stout chitinous teeth. Nereids are carnivores, capturing prey by the two pharyngeal jaws; the prey is then swallowed

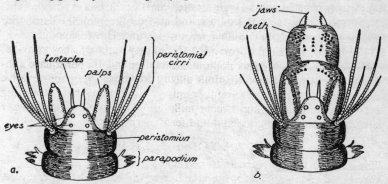

Fig. 21.29. *Nereis* head. (*a*) Pharynx inverted. (*b*) Pharynx everted.

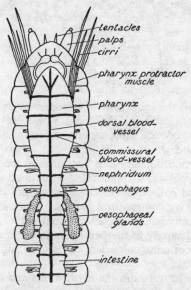

Fig. 21.30. General anatomy of *Nereis*. Dorsal body wall removed.

by inversion of the pharynx. The oesophagus bears a pair of backwardly directed digestive glands, and then the intestine passes as an undifferentiated tube to the anus (*see* Fig. 21.30). There is a pair of ventrally-situated *anal cirri* on the last segment.

Behind the head, every segment bears paired lateral outgrowths of the body wall called *parapodia*. Each parapodium is divided into a dorsal *notopodium* and a ventral *neuropodium*, each bearing a bundle of fine slender chaetae and a single stouter chaeta called an *aciculum*. On the dorsal side of the notopodium and also on the ventral side of the neuropodium is a small jointed *sensory cirrus*. The parapodia serve several functions; they increase the respiratory surface; they provide broad blades for use as paddles in swimming and they are used for obtaining a grip on the substratum during crawling.

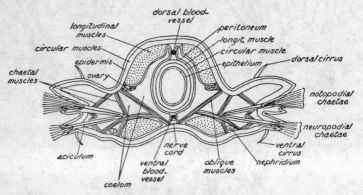

Fig. 21.31. T.S. body of *Nereis*.

The body wall has the same general arrangement as in *Lumbricus* but the longitudinal muscles lie in four blocks, two dorsal and two ventral. There are oblique segmental muscles, one pair to the notopodia and one pair to the neuropodia.

The gut is attached dorsally and ventrally by mesenteries, and the intestine does not possess a typhlosole. The blood system essentially consists of a dorsal collecting vessel and a ventral distributing vessel joined segmentally by commissural vessels. There are no hearts, but both dorsal and commissural vessels are contractile. There is a particularly good blood supply to the parapodia in connexion with respiration. The blood contains colourless corpuscles and haemoglobin in solution.

Excretion is carried out as in the earthworms and there are segmentally arranged nephridia. The nervous system is essentially similar to that in *Lumbricus* but there are more highly developed sense organs evolved in adaptation to the predatory mode of life; they are the tentacles, palps, cirri and eyes. The eyes are well developed and contain a gelatinous lens; the optic nerve leaves the back of the cup as in the vertebrate eye.

The sexes are separate and gonads grow on the lateral regions of somatic mesoderm. There are no ducts conveying gametes to the exterior. Maturation of the sperm or ova takes place in the coelom. At breeding times there are distinct changes especially in the posterior

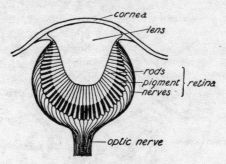

Fig. 21.32. Eye of *Nereis* in V.S.

half of the body. The parapodia become more blunted and the fine chaetae are replaced by stouter oar-like structures spread like a fan; the eyes become very enlarged. Such sexually mature worms are known as *heteronereids*. They swim near the surface and in the presence of

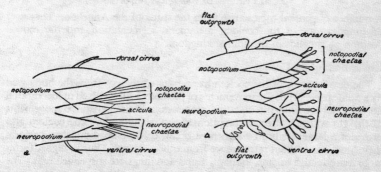

Fig. 21.33. (*a*) Parapodium of *Nereis*. (*b*) Parapodium of *Heteronereis*.

the opposite sex, the sexual segments burst and release the gametes into the water. The adults then die.

The larvae which hatch from the eggs are ciliated and they metamorphose into adults. The typical polychaete larva, not found in *Nereis*, is a *trochophore* (*see* Fig. 21.34). This type of larva is of considerable interest. since it occurs in other groups, particularly in Mollusca, and thus provides one line of evidence relating Annelida and

Mollusca. Another line of evidence indicating this relationship is provided by the similar mode of development of the mesoderm in the two groups.

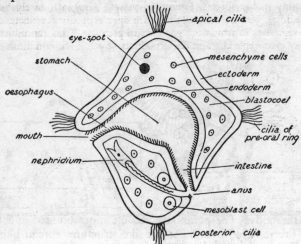

Fig. 21.34. Polychaete trochophore larva.

Special Features of Biological Importance

A number of general topics arise from the study of the Annelida. They are: the implications of the coelom, metameric segmentation and the central position of annelids in the animal kingdom.

Implications of the Coelom

The development of the coelom has separated the gut from the body wall by a fluid space. Thus the movements of the body wall involved in locomotion do not interfere with the digestive processes, and the peristaltic movements of the gut will not affect locomotion of the whole body. The coelom also provides a large cavity in which organs can be developed and can perform their functions without interference from other organs. Thus in higher forms large reproductive organs, kidneys, hearts and lungs are suspended in it. The location of organs in the coelom involves the necessity for ducts to convey their products to the exterior. Thus excretory and reproductive ducts become necessary.

Excretory ducts developed in annelids are of several types. Those derived solely by ingrowth of ectoderm are called nephridia. Some nephridia do not open into the coelom but end blindly in tufts of cells called solenocytes, each bearing a single long flagellum and hence somewhat reminiscent of the flame cells of Platyhelminthes. This type is known as a protonephridium (*see* Fig. 21.35(*a*); it is found in some polychaete families (Glyceridae, Phyllodocidae). Nephridia which open into the coelom by ciliated funnels are called metanephridia; they are present in the majority of Polychaeta and in all Oligochaeta. The other main type of duct is a coelomoduct which is developed from mesoderm by outgrowth of the coelomic epithelium. Coelomoducts may or may not have internal openings. They may, rarely, be used as excretory ducts, but more usually they are open reproductive ducts, confined to those segments in which the gonads are present. Thus reproductive segments may bear nephridia and coelomoducts. Such is the condition found in

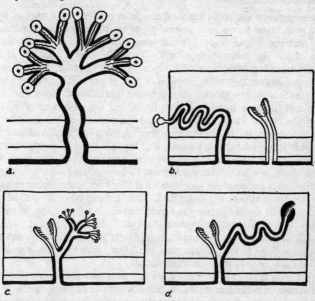

Fig. 21.35. Types of coelomic ducts. (a) Protonephridium with solenocytes. (b) Condition in *Lumbricus*. Sexual segment with metanephridium and coelomoduct. (c) Nephromyxium with protonephridium and coelomoduct. (d) Nephromyxium with metanephridium and coelomoduct.

Lumbricus (see Fig. 21.35(b)). Other conditions exist in some polychaete families. The most important is the development of a nephromyxium, which is a compound duct consisting of a nephridium into which a coelomoduct opens. Such nephromyxia are found in the families Alciopidae (protonephridia) and Capitellidae (metanephridia).

The coelomic fluid gives support, protection, and assistance with locomotion. Its incompressibility allows change of shape but not volume; after muscle contraction has ceased, the body reverts to its normal shape, maintained essentially by turgidity of the segments. Protection from external damage is afforded by the fact that fluids disperse force equally in all directions, hence a blow on the surface of the worm has its effect largely dissipated in the coelomic fluid. The assistance which the coelomic fluid gives in locomotion, has been described for the earthworm.

Development of the coelom, in all but certain very small annelids, has necessitated a blood system. Digested food from the gut must be transported across the new fluid layer to the body wall; oxygen absorbed by the skin must be carried to the deeper tissues. Such a vascular system must have some means of keeping the blood in motion, hence contractile, valved, muscular vessels have evolved.

Metameric Segmentation

This is perhaps the most marked characteristic of the Annelids by comparison with lower forms. No animal exists which shows perfect metamerism throughout the whole body. Polychaetes such as *Nereis* and most Oligochaetes show the nearest approach. Typically every segment is exactly similar, possessing a portion of body wall with chaetae, a portion of the coelom, gut, nerve cord with ganglion, a pair of nephridia and the segmental blood vessels. Although the segments are partitioned from one another, they do not function as independent units, but are co-ordinated as integral parts of the body. There is, for each species, a more or less definite limited number of segments. In the embryo, they develop in definite order of precedence from the head end backwards, and the first signs of segmentation arise in the mesoderm. In the tapeworms, the continuous proliferation of proglottides from one particular zone is not to be confused with true segmentation. Similarity between the proglottides is absolute; the number proliferated is very large and apparently unlimited. They are not co-ordinated to work in harmony; their main function is reproductive. And perhaps, more important still, the most mature segments are at the posterior end, whereas in metameric development, the anterior segments are the first to mature. All important higher phyla, except the Mollusca, preserve this segmentation though it may be very obscure in the adult.

The main advantage of segmentation is that it provides an opportunity for specialization in certain segments without interference with others. Further, the embryonic repetition of segments, ensures basic and co-ordinated equipment for each segment.

The Central Position of Annelida in the Animal Kingdom

The typical annelids such as the free-swimming polychaetes may be said to occupy a central position in the animal kingdom. All the major organsystems have been evolved, the coelomate condition and metameric segmentation have been achieved.

The gut is separated from the body wall; it has an entrance and an exit, and various digestive glands are present. Special respiratory organs in the form of foliaceous or filamentous outgrowths are found, especially in tubicolous forms. A blood-vascular system with valved vessels, contractile portions and thin-walled capillaries is present. The blood contains various oxygen-absorbing pigments; the red haemoglobin is common, though some forms possess the green chlorocruorin. Efficient excretory organs make contact with both blood and coelomic fluid. A central nervous system with a brain has been achieved, and many kinds of sense organs, including well-developed eyes, are present. In many cases, reproductive organs with special ducts are localized in certain segments. A considerable degree of cephalization is present in some groups.

Higher forms show only elaboration of structures already present. Perhaps the least elaboration is in organs of locomotion, though some authorities hold that parapodia may be considered as limbs. The greatest developments we find in higher groups, apart from inevitable specialization, are in cephalization, in organs of locomotion, in the skeleton, and hence musculature connected with locomotion.

Hormones in Annelids

Most of the investigations into hormones in annelids have been carried out on polychaetes, particularly several species of nereids. It has been shown that growth, reproduction, regeneration and metamorphosis are controlled by neurosecretions from the brain (*see* p. 1081).

Normal growth is regulated by a growth hormone, and when the mature form is achieved, either the amount of secretion wanes, or the tissues become less sensitive to it. Maturation of the sex cells is inhibited by a "juvenile" hormone from the brain, but when the level of this is sufficiently reduced, maturation begins. Later, for full development of the oocytes, a very low level of the hormone is necessary. There is some justification for regarding this "juvenile" hormone as being identical with the growth hormone. It has also been suggested that when the oocytes reach a certain stage of maturity, they themselves, or tissue associated with them, may secrete a hormone which stimulates the final development of ripe eggs.

Regeneration of segments cut off, or lost naturally, takes place first by the formation of a growing point or *blastema* at the site of loss. This blastema is particularly sensitive to growth hormone and new segments are formed, at first slowly and then much more rapidly. It has been shown that both the blastema and the hormone are necessary for regeneration to take place.

Metamorphosis from the nereid to the heteronereid condition is also hormonally controlled. Again, this may depend on the concentration of the growth hormone, or, if it exists, of a low level of the "juvenile" hormone. In either case, when the level of hormone is low enough, metamorphosis will proceed. There is some possibility that the developing oocytes may produce a hormone influencing metamorphosis.

The facts of hormone control of certain processes are clearly established, but as yet there is no certainty as to how many hormones are involved. Some workers have suggested that the growth hormone controls all the above processes by its varying concentration. Others suggest that there may be at least three different hormones, two produced by neurosecretion from the brain and one by secretion from the oocytes.

CHAPTER 22

COELOMATE ANIMALS II: ARTHROPODA; CRUSTACEA

THE vast phylum Arthropoda contains three-quarters of all known species of animals. One class alone, the Insecta, includes over half the total number of animal species. Arthropods have conquered all types of environment; they abound in the seas and in fresh water; they live on the earth and in it; many spend considerable periods in the air, and some are parasites. They range in size from tiny water-fleas to the giant crabs which may measure 3·5 m from claw to claw with the limbs outstretched.

The key to an understanding of the arthropods *lies in an appreciation of the implications of the exoskeleton*. It is made of chitin and this is commonly impregnated and hardened to form a protective armour. Mobility has not been sacrificed, for though the major part is usually rigid, there is flexibility by provision of thin chitinous articular membranes at the joints. The exoskeleton has provided firm attachment points for the muscles and thus we have separate muscle bundles used in moving particular joints. The continuous body-wall muscle of the annelids is not found. The success of the terrestrial arthropods, can be attributed partly to the support afforded by the exoskeleton, and to the protection it provides from loss of water from the body surface. Portions of this cuticle have been fashioned into an imposing array of organs used for many purposes. There are biting jaws, piercing stylets, sucking tubes, grinding surfaces, lenses of eyes, walking legs, pincers, paddles for swimming, copulatory appendages, sense organs, food sieves, and wings.

However, the acquisition of a massive exoskeleton has imposed limitation of size, by reason of its weight. It has also made growth difficult and has obliged its possessors to resort to periodic moulting or *ecdysis* when the enveloping armour becomes too tight.

The body still shows very obvious *metameric segmentation* but it is not as complete as in the annelids. *Cephalization* has been carried much further and six segments constitute the head. They cannot be recognized in the adult animal except occasionally by observation of the appendages, but careful study of embryos has shown that these six segments are always incorporated into the head. The next region of the body is not homologous in the various classes. It is called the *thorax*. In the Crustacea, it usually consists of eight segments, and in the

636

Insecta of three. In the Arachnida and Myriapoda, no clearly marked thoracic region is recognizable. The *abdomen*, where distinct, also shows great variation.

The Crustacea

This class includes the largest arthropods, the crabs and lobsters, as well as the smallest, the tiny water-fleas and shrimps. A few members, such as the land crabs and woodlice are terrestrial, but the great majority are aquatic. Crustaceans are so plentiful in the sea that they have been termed "marine insects." In the larger members, the exoskeleton is thick and often strongly impregnated with calcium carbonate. Five of the six head segments bear appendages, which include two pairs of sensory antennae and three pairs of mouth parts. Some of the thoracic appendages are also modified as jaw-feet and assist with feeding.

The crustacean described here is the crayfish, a close relative of the lobster. The account will apply to both, minor differences being mainly in the reproductive process.

THE CRAYFISH

Crayfishes and lobsters belong to the sub-order Astacura of the order Decapoda. They are "long-tailed" forms, and of crawling habit. The crayfish usually studied may be the English species, *Astacus torrentium*, which is dark green in colour and about 8 cm long, or the continental *Astacus fluviatilis*, which is somewhat larger, of the same general colour but with red patches on the walking legs and pincers. Both become red when boiled. *A. torrentium* was very common in England until 1887, when a mysterious disease practically exterminated them. The pollution of rivers has prevented any large-scale revival and nowadays they are comparatively rare. One genus, *Cambarus*, of North America, is known as the marsh crayfish. It can spend long periods out of the water. *Engaeus*, of Australia and Tasmania, is very largely terrestrial. The particular species discussed in this chapter is *Astacus fluviatilis*.

Habitat and Habits

The animals live in burrows below the river banks; they are found especially in rivers originating in chalk or limestone areas, calcium carbonate being an essential constituent of the exoskeleton. They are nocturnal feeders and spend the daylight hours in their burrows, with the long antennae protruding. Their normal movement is slow and stiff, but they can dart quickly backward by rapid flexure of the abdomen. They feed on any type of organic material, dead or alive, the food being seized with the large pincers, which are normally held clear of the substratum. Ecdysis takes place frequently in the young animals, but the adult females moult only once a year and the adult males twice. Mating takes place in the autumn and the young crayfishes emerge in the following spring. There is no larval stage.

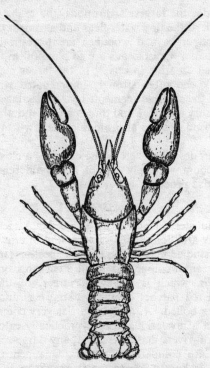

Fig. 22.1. Dorsal view of male crayfish.

External Features

The body is about 10 cm in length and of a dark green colour. It is completely covered with the thick cuticle which is strengthened with calcium carbonate except at the thin articular membranes, where it remains soft and flexible. The head and thorax are fused together to form a *cephalothorax*; the line of demarcation may be indicated by the transverse *cervical groove*. Dorsally, the cephalothorax is covered by a large *carapace* which also covers the gill chambers by means of two downward folds called *branchiostegites*. Two longitudinal *branchio-cardiac grooves* pass from the cervical groove to the posterior edge of the carapace; they indicate the limits of the pericardial cavity beneath.

Anteriorly, the carapace is prolonged into a pointed *rostrum* at the sides of which are the stalked *eyes*. Beneath the eyes are the *antennules*, and behind them the *antennae*. At the base of the rostrum, the front of the head slopes vertically downward, then curves backward to the

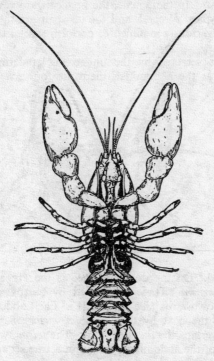

Fig. 22.2. Ventral view of male crayfish.

mouth, which is concealed by other appendages. First come the toothed *mandibles*, then the flattened delicate *maxillules* and *maxillae*. These latter are the last head appendages.

Ventrally, the thorax shows segmentation though the segments are immovable. In succession the appendages of the thorax are: the first, second and third *maxillipeds*, the great pincers or *chelipeds*, and the four pairs of walking legs or *pereiopods*. The thorax consists of eight segments.

The abdomen shows complete segmentation and each of the six segments can move only in the vertical plane. This enables the abdomen to be bent forward and underneath the animal; the movement takes place swiftly with the tail fan spread, and thus the animal is thrust

backward. The abdomen cannot be moved upward beyond the horizontal plane. All the abdominal segments bear appendages. In the
male, the first two pairs are modified as *tubular copulatory organs*, the
next three pairs are typical *biramous pleopods*, while the last pair are
the broad *uropods*. In the female, the first pair are vestigial, the next
four pairs are typical *pleopods* and the last pair are the *uropods*. The
appendages are variously modified to perform special functions; each
is discussed below.

The cuticle is secreted by the underlying epidermis. In typical
segments, such as the abdominal, there are four *sclerites*, thickened

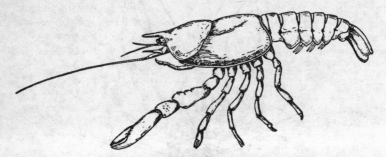

Fig. 22.3. Lateral view of male crayfish.

and impregnated. On the dorsal surface is the arched *tergum*, and
ventrally the *sternum*. These are joined by narrow angular *pleura*
which project downwards (*see* Fig. 22.18). Each abdominal segment
articulates with the next by thin *articular membranes*, and dorsally
each sternum overlaps the one behind it. The *telson*, which forms the
middle portion of the abdominal fan, is not a true segment. Ventrally
it bears the prominent *anus*.

The Appendages

Of the twenty body segments, nineteen have pairs of appendages.
The first segment has no appendages but bears the eyes dorsally. There
is some controversy as to whether the variously modified appendages
are derived from a thin flattened *phyllopodium* or from a biramous
stenopodium. In the study of the crayfish appendages it seems most
essential to understand the structure of a typical complete biramous
limb. These limbs, in a primitive ancestor, can be pictured as being all
similar and all hanging vertically downward. Such a limb, with all
parts complete, is shown below (*see* Fig. 22.4 (*b*)). For comparison, a
figure of a generalized phyllopodium is also shown. Attached to the
body wall is a *protopodite* consisting of the two *podomeres*, a proximal

coxopodite and a distal *basipodite*. Both or either of these may bear flattened outgrowths called *exites* (*epipodites*). This basal protopodite bears distally, two rami, an inner *endopodite* and an outer *exopodite*. Typically, both consist of five podomeres. From base to tip, they are the *ischiopodite*, *meropodite*, *carpopodite*, *propodite* and *dactylopodite*.

The first pair of appendages are the antennules. The protopodite has three podomeres, a basal *precoxa* (not distinct in any of the other appendages), then a coxopodite and a basipodite. The precoxa has a

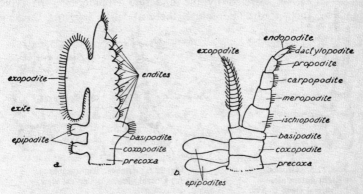

Fig. 22.4. (*a*) A typical phyllopodium. (*b*) A typical stenopodium.

narrow slit on its outer surface; it leads into a *statocyst sac*, housing the organ of balance. The basipodite bears two slender many-jointed lashes, the outer one being somewhat longer than the inner. Both lashes are beset with small bristles, and on the underside of the outer lash are special bristles subserving the olfactory sense. The two lashes are probably not homologous with an endopodite and an exopodite.

The antennae are the second pair of appendages. There is a typical protopodite consisting of a proximal coxopodite and a distal basipodite, the latter bearing a long slender many-jointed endopodite, and a short triangular scale-like exopodite. This scale seems to be used as a plane in diving movements, whilst the long bristly "feeler" is sensitive to tactile stimuli. Beneath the coxopodite is a prominence which bears the opening of the organ of nitrogenous excretion, the *green gland*.

The mandibles, when apposed, cover the anterior part of the mouth. The basal podomere is strong and thick. It bears a toothed margin on the inner side, and probably corresponds to the precoxa. There is no coxopodite but a small basipodite which articulates anteriorly with a slender two-jointed *palp*. The toothed process is not used for chewing or cutting up the food, but it assists in holding the material while it is shredded by other appendages. The palp is sensitive to chemicals and acts as a tasting organ.

The maxillules or first maxillae are delicate and flattened. Both the coxopodite and basipodite bear flattened endites having on their inner

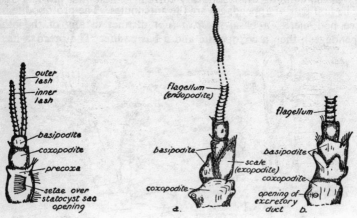

Fig. 22.5. *Astacus.* Right antennule, dorsal view.

Fig. 22.6. *Astacus.* Right antenna. (*a*) Dorsal view. (*b*) Ventral view.

edges, fringes of strong bristles. The basipodite bears a small endopodite. The maxillules play a part in shredding the food and pushing it into the mouth behind and beneath the mandibles.

The maxillae are also flattened but larger than the maxillules. There are two endites, each deeply cleft. The proximal endite is probably an

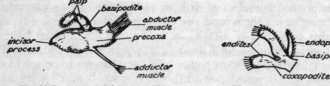

Fig. 22.7. *Astacus.* Right mandible, ventral view.

Fig. 22.8. *Astacus.* Right maxillule, ventral view.

ingrowth of a fused precoxa and coxopodite, and the second an ingrowth of the basipodite. The latter bears a short, slender endopodite and a large flattened exopodite which fits neatly into the gill chamber and by its forward and backward movements maintains a flow of water over the gills. It is known as the *scaphognathite* or *baler*. The flattened endites assist in breaking up the food and pushing it into the mouth.

The first appendages of the thorax are the first maxillipeds. There are flattened basi- and coxopodites with endites similar to those of the maxillae, a small two-jointed endopodite and a large exopodite. The coxopodite bears a flattened epipodite which may assist the scaphognathite in maintaining the respiratory current. These first jaw-feet assist

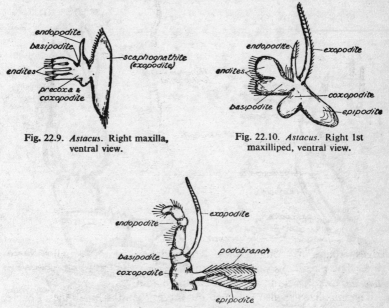

Fig. 22.9. *Astacus*. Right maxilla, ventral view.

Fig. 22.10. *Astacus*. Right 1st maxilliped, ventral view.

Fig. 22.11. *Astacus*. Right 2nd maxilliped, ventral view.

in tearing up the food into fragments and carrying them forward to the mouth.

The second maxillipeds approximate to typical biramous appendages. The endopodite, though small, consists of the five standard podomeres, while the exopodite is larger, with a long basal and many small distal podomeres. The coxopodite bears a flattened epipodite with a *podobranch* or "foot-gill." Thus apart from assistance with feeding, this limb has a respiratory function.

Of all the appendages, the third maxillipeds present the nearest approach to the typical stenopodium. The protopodite consists of coxopodite and basipodite, the former bearing an epipodite with a podobranch. The endopodite is typical with five podomeres, while the exopodite is many-jointed and much reduced. On the ischiopodite are stout median bristles which grip large pieces of food material posteriorly while the mandibles hold them anteriorly. The distal podomeres of the endopodite play a large part in tearing the food.

The remaining thoracic appendages lack an exopodite, but otherwise the typical podomeres are present. All except the last pair of pereiopods bear epipodites with podobranchs. The large and powerful chelipeds

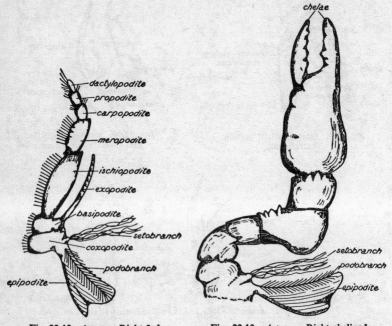

Fig. 22.12. *Astacus*. Right 3rd maxilliped, ventral view.

Fig. 22.13. *Astacus*. Right cheliped, ventral view.

are used for securing food, for offence and defence. The pincer device is effected by the dactylopodite biting against a prolongation of the propodite. The first two pairs of pereiopods or walking legs are also chelate, the small pincers being used in cleaning the feeding appendages, and in passing food forward from the chelipeds. The last two pairs are non-chelate and are used only for walking. On the coxopodite of the second pereiopod in the female is the opening of the oviduct, while the male opening is in a similar position on the fourth pereiopod.

The typical abdominal appendages are pleopods. Each is biramous, consisting of a coxopodite, basipodite, endopodite and exopodite. There are no endites or epipodites. The two rami have many small distal podomeres and a larger proximal podomere and are fringed with

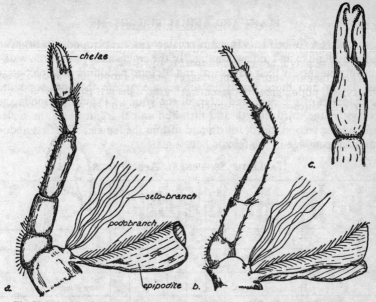

Fig. 22.14. *Astacus.* (*a*) Right 1st pereiopod, ventral view. (*b*) Right 3rd pereiopod, ventral view. (*c*) Chelae of young crayfish.

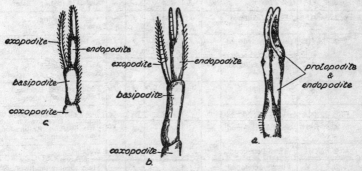

Fig. 22.15. *Astacus.* (*a*) Right 1st male pleopod, ventral view. (*b*) Right 2nd male pleopod, ventral view. (*c*) Right 3rd male pleopod, ventral view.

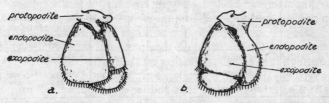

Fig. 22.16. *Astacus.* (*a*) Right uropod, dorsal veiw. *b*) Right uropod, ventral veiw.

opposite rows of bristles. In many crustaceans. the pleopods are broader and paddle-like and aid swimming. In the crayfish they assist the walking movements by their backward and forward paddling. The pleopods are larger and more bristly in the female, where they are used for attachment of the eggs, and later, of the young. Typical pleopods are borne on the third, fourth and fifth abdominal segments of the male, and on the second, third, fourth and fifth in the female. The first abdominal appendage in the female is vestigial.

TABLE OF SEGMENTAL APPENDAGES

Region of Body	Number of Segment	Name of Appendage	Precoxa Present	Coxopodite Distinct	Basipodite Distinct	Endites Present	Epipodite Present	Podobranch Present	Functions
Head 1	I	—	—	—	—	—	—	—	—
2	II	Antennule	√	√	√	—	—	—	Olfactory. Balance.
3	III	Antenna	—	√	√	—	—	—	Tactile. Planing. Green gland opening.
4	IV	Mandible	√	—	—	—	—	—	Holding food. Tasting.
5	V	Maxillule	Fused		√	√	—	—	Assists in feeding.
6	VI	Maxilla	√	√	√	√	—	—	Assists in feeding. Baler.
Thorax 1	VII	First Maxilliped	—	√	√	√	√	—	Assists in feeding. Assists baler.
2	VIII	Second Maxilliped	—	√	√	—	√	√	Assists in feeding. Respiration.
3	IX	Third Maxilliped	—	√	√	—	√	√	Assists in feeding. Respiration.
4	X	Cheliped	—	Fused		—	√	√	Food capture. Offence. Defence Respiration.
5	XI	First Pereiopod	—	√	√	—	√	√	Pass food from chelipeds to mouth. Cleaning mouth parts. Walking. Respiration. Female opening on 2nd.
6	XII	Second Pereiopod	—	√	√	—	√	√	
7	XIII	Third Pereiopod	—	√	√	—	√	√	Walking. Respiration. Male opening on 4th.
8	XIV	Fourth Pereiopod	—	√	√	—	√	—	
Abdomen 1	XV	First Pleopod	—	Male-fused female-vestigial		—	—	—	Copulatory in the male. Vestigial in the female.
2	XVI	Second Pleopod	—	√	√	—	—	—	Copulatory in the male. Paddles in the female and for securing eggs and young.
3	XVII	Third Pleopod	—	√	√	—	—	—	Paddling in both sexes.
4	XVIII	Fourth Pleopod	—	√	√	—	—	—	Fastening the eggs and carrying the young in females.
5	XIX	Fifth Pleopod	—	√	√	—	—	—	
6	XX	Uropod	—	Fused		—	—	—	Tail fan for darting backward

In the male, the first abdominal appendages are tube-like. The protopodite is undivided and with the single-jointed endopodite forms a scroll-like tube used for transferring spermatophores to the female. The second male abdominal limbs show a transition between the first and the third. There are a small coxopodite, a larger basipodite, again scroll-like, a slender many-jointed exopodite and a stout endopodite forked at its end. This limb assists in transfer of spermatophores.

The last appendages are the uropods, each with an undivided protopodite and broad endopodite and exopodite. Together with the telson, they form, when spread out, the wide tail fan.

The Body Wall

There are no continuous muscle layers as in annelids; the muscles are now in separate bundles, each specialized for moving a particular segment of the body or podomere of a limb. Thus the body wall consists only of the *cuticle*, the *epidermis* which secretes it, and a little underlying connective tissue which forms the *dermis*. These layers enter into the formation of all parts of the exoskeleton, including the many types of bristles, the stomodaeum and proctodaeum.

The epidermis is a columnar epithelium which in most parts becomes syncytial. It rests on a basement membrane secreted by the underlying connective tissue which abuts directly on a haemocoel. Embedded in the connective tissue are *tegumental glands* from which many fine canals pass up through the lower layers of the cuticle. The greater part of the cuticle consists of soft, flexible, laminated chitin which is a polyglucosamine (*see* Vol. II, Chap. 4). Starting from the outer surface, five zones are present. First there is a waxy layer of lipoid material which is extremely thin and almost impermeable to water, though gases can pass freely through it. Beneath this, is a layer of protein, which is hardened and pigmented by the combination of an oxidized phenolic compound with the protein. The compound is 3:4-dihydroxyphenyl-acetic acid and it seems to act as a link, binding protein chains together. The oxidized compound gives the dark colouring; it is achieved by the

HO OH → protein side—O O—protein side
chain   chain

CH$_2$COOH   CH$_2$COOH

3:4-dihydroxyphenylacetic acid → oxidized and uniting protein chains

medium of an enzyme, polyphenol oxidase. The waxy and protein layers constitute the *epicuticle*, and both substances are secreted by the tegumental glands, of which there are several different kinds.

Beneath the epicuticle is the much thicker *endocuticle* consisting largely of chitin secreted by the epidermal cells. An outer region of it is pigmented; in the sclerotized areas, the middle zone is impregnated with calcium salts, while the inner zone consists of unchanged chitin. In the articular membranes there are fewer layers of chitin and there is no hardening.

This crustacean body wall subserves the functions of protection, of providing joints and muscle attachment points, and of sensitivity. In

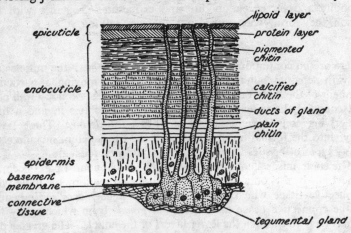

Fig. 22.17. V.S. of body wall of crayfish.

the appendages, it has been fashioned into a wide variety of structures, each peculiarly adapted for its functions. By the thickness of cuticle, it affords protection from mechanical damage; the waxy layer prevents both loss and absorption of water; the chitin gives joint flexibility, and the bristles with their sensory inclusions give the animal the power of perceiving a variety of stimuli.

The Skeleton

The materials of which the exoskeleton is composed have already been described. Except at the articular membranes it is thickened, hardened and darkened to form plates called *sclerites*. At all movable joints, the sclerites are fastened together by thin flexible *articular membranes* made of chitin alone. All the segments of the head and thorax are immovably fused, but in the abdomen there are articular membranes between the segments, allowing movement in the vertical plane. Typically, a segment is made up of four sclerites fused together; they are a dorsal *tergum*, two lateral *pleura* and a ventral *sternum* (*see* Fig. 22.18). The movable joints are hinged together by a peg and socket, restricting the

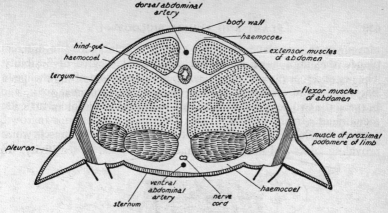

Fig. 22.18. T.S. of abdomen of crayfish.

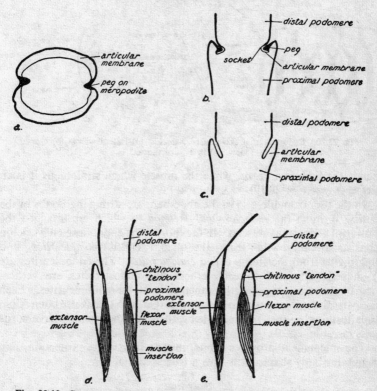

Fig. 22.19. Crustacean joints and muscle attachments. (*a*) Distal joint of meropodite of cheliped separated from carpopodite. (*b*) A joint cut longitudinally in plane of peg and socket. (*c*) A joint cut longitudinally at right angles to plane of peg and socket. (*d*) Muscle attachment in extended condition. (*e*) In flexed condition.

movement to one plane, but since successive joints move in different planes, the limbs have achieved a considerable degree of flexibility. The peg and socket joint is best examined by dissection of the chelipeds. Each podomere fits inside the one immediately proximal to it, and between the two pegs and sockets are the two inwardly-folded articular membranes. In the middle of each membrane, a chitinous ingrowth forms a "tendon" for the attachment of the muscle. The muscle which

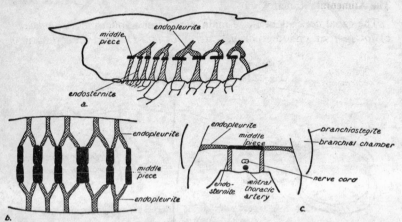

Fig. 22.20. Endophragmal skeleton of *Astacus*. (*a*) Lateral view. (*b*) Dorsal view. (*c*) In T.S. of thorax.

bends the limb is a *flexor*, while the muscle which straightens it is an *extensor* (*see* Fig. 22.19).

In the thorax and less so in the abdomen, are strong ingrowths of the cuticle forming the *endophragmal skeleton* to which are attached the powerful abdominal muscles. In the thorax, the endophragmal skeleton consists of ingrowths from the pleura called *endopleurites*, and upgrowths from the sterna called *endosternites*. The endopleurites are Y-shaped and fused to each other; the endosternites are vertical upgrowths which support the inner ends of the endopleurites. Each endosternite is joined to its opposite member by a transverse connexion, thus forming a series of arches beneath which the ventral nerve cords pass (*see* Fig. 22.20).

The integument provides joints, muscle insertions, protection, and maintains body shape. It is thus a true skeleton.

Nutrition

The animals are omnivorous, eating animal or plant material, dead or alive. The food is seized by the pincers of the chelae and passed

forward by the smaller pincers of the first two pairs of pereiopods. It is
then held by the mandibles anteriorly and between the toothed inner
edges of the ischiopodites of the third maxillipeds posteriorly. The
backward and forward movements of the latter, break the food into
smaller pieces. Then it is shredded by action of the first and second
maxillipeds and maxillae and pushed into the mouth by the maxillules.

The Alimentary Canal

The canal consists of three main parts; an ectodermal *stomodaeum*
or *fore-gut*, an endodermal *mesenteron* or *mid-gut*, and an ectodermal

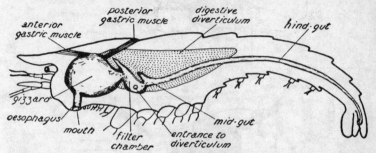

Fig. 22.21, *Astacus.* Left lateral view of alimentary canal, digestive gland
removed.

proctodaeum or *hind-gut*. Both the stomodaeum and proctodaeum are
lined with chitin which is thickened and calcified in the ossicles and
teeth of the gizzard.

The fore-gut consists of an *oesophagus* which passes upwards almost
vertically, a large rounded *gizzard* and a smaller *filter chamber*. The
mid-gut is a short tube only a few millimetres long; at its sides are the
openings leading to the *digestive diverticula* which are also endodermal
derivatives. The hind-gut is a straight tube leading out of the body at
the *anus*, in the middle of the telson (*see* Fig. 22.21).

Food is swallowed by peristaltic action of the muscular walls of the
oesophagus. A valve guards the entrance to the gizzard. In the gizzard
the food is masticated by three "teeth" and also digested by enzymes
from the digestive diverticula. There are powerful lipolytic, amylolytic
and proteolytic enzymes. Indeed, the gizzards of crayfish and lobsters
provide a good source of enzymes for experimental purposes. The
filter chamber prevents the passage of solid particles into the digestive
diverticula and also presses together the indigestible residues which
pass into the hind-gut. Soluble digested products are absorbed in the
diverticula. The hind-gut is mainly a tube for the passage of faeces;
during its progress, water is absorbed.

In the gizzard, the food is ground up by the action of the so-called *gastric mill*. The food is retained by the closure of the valves at the entrance of the oesophagus and passed backward by the action of the

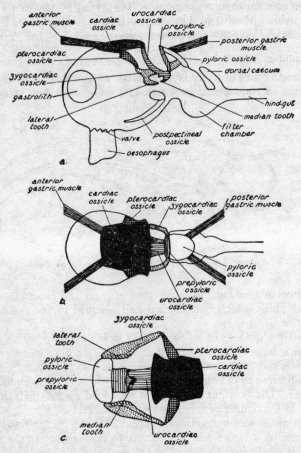

Fig. 22.22. *Astacus*. Ossicles of gizzard. (*a*) Right half, lateral view (after Yonge). (*b*) Dorsal view. (*c*) Plan of ossicles in ventral view.

circular and longitudinal muscles aided by the backwardly-pointing setae which line the gizzard. Thus the food particles are guided to the dorso-posterior part. There they are cut up by the grinding action of three "teeth." Certain areas of the cuticle are thickened and calcified to form the *ossicles* and "teeth." Dorsally the gizzard has a downward fold. In front of the fold there is a large *cardiac ossicle* and behind it a flat *pyloric ossicle*. From the cardiac ossicle, a curved *urocardiac ossicle* follows the fold downward, and bears the pointed *median tooth*. From the urocardiac a *prepyloric ossicle* curves up the posterior fold to join the pyloric ossicle (*see* Fig. 22.22 (*a*)). Laterally, two *pterocardiac ossicles* curve backward from the cardiac ossicle and join two *zygocardiac* ossicles which are somewhat triangular. Their inner dorsal corners join the pyloric ossicles, while their ventral corners bear large serrated teeth (*see* Fig. 22.22 (*a*)). *Anterior gastric muscles* are attached to the front of the cardiac ossicle and proceed forward to be fastened at the other ends near the front of the carapace. *Posterior gastric*

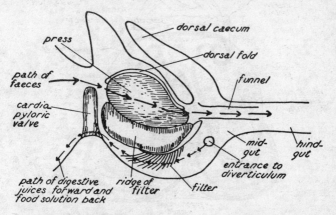

Fig. 22.23. Right half of filter chamber of *Astacus* (*after Yonge*).

muscles are attached to the pyloric ossicles and to the carapace near the cervical groove. The contraction of these muscles brings the three teeth together, the dorsal fold flattens out and the sides of the gizzard move inwards. Separation of the teeth is effected by the elasticity of the chitinous lining and by a pair of *cardio-pyloric muscles* joining those two ossicles.

The masticated particles fall into the gutter formed by the two long *post-pectineal* ossicles. At the base of this gutter is a narrow groove covered with two rows of curved setae, one row from the post-pectineal ossicle of each side. Along this ventral groove, digestive juices flow into the gizzard from the mid-gut diverticula, and soluble digested substances flow back by the same route. Solid particles are prevented from entering the groove by the setae which have a filtering action. The gizzard thus performs the function of digestion as well as mastication. In addition, before each moult, two disc-like calcareous *gastroliths* are secreted in the anterior wall beneath the cuticle. After moulting, they are no longer protected; they dissolve in the digestive juice and are passed out of the body.

The small filter chamber is largely separated from the gizzard by the teeth and by a *cardio-pyloric valve* which projects upward from the floor. A number of small channels allow passage from the gizzard to the filter chamber—

1. A dorsal groove starts behind the median tooth; it divides into right and left channels on entering the filter chamber.

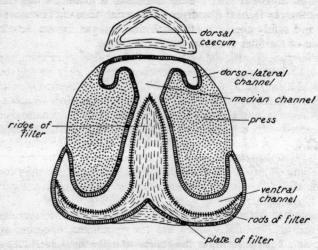

Fig. 22.24. T.S. filter chamber of *Astacus* (*after Yonge*).

2. A route starts below each lateral tooth and curves around the cardio-pyloric valve, after which the two join to form a median channel.

3. The groove between the post-pectineal ossicles, forks ventrally around the cardio-pyloric valve and thus two ventro-lateral channels are formed.

Above the filter chamber is a small dorsal *caecum of the mid-gut,* and at the sides are two thickened muscular areas which form the *press.* Ventrally are two *pouches* which bear the filter (*see* Figs. 22.23, 22.24). The mass of undigested particles passing along the dorso-lateral and median channels is compacted by the press and liquid squeezed out of it. The liquid runs down the sides of a valvular ridge projecting upwards from the filter, while the compacted faecal mass passes into a chitinous funnel through the mid-gut and into the intestine. Thus no solid particles get into the ventral grooves to enter the digestive diverticula.

The filter is on the ventral wall. It consists of two concave plates extending backward. The plates unite in the mid-line to form an upward ridge and a backward process, thus keeping separate the two ventral channels, and ensuring that fluid entering the digestive diverticula must pass over one of the filters. Each filter has numerous radially-arranged chitinous rods, each having plentiful bristles, giving the general effect of a number of fine combs. The food solution runs by the two ventral channels *over* the filters, trickles through, and then passes into the digestive diverticula. The filter chamber thus allows the flow forward of digestive juice; after digestion it channels the digested substances away from the undigested material, then the latter are compacted and safely conducted through the mid-gut by an ectodermal extension of the filter chamber itself, the funnel.

The digestive diverticula are large yellow masses occupying most of the thorax. They consist of countless fine tubules, each having delicate circular and longitudinal muscles. They work rhythmically, a period of secretion being followed by a period of absorption. Each tubule consists of three physiologically-distinct zones. The proximal region is concerned with absorption, the middle zone with secretion of enzymes, and the distal blind end with cell multiplication (during secretion whole cells are discharged into the lumen). The tubules are extremely fine and even very small particles would block their lumina, hence the elaborate filtering mechanism which will remove any particles above 10 μm in size.

Dorsally, the mesenteron carries the funnel-like ectodermal channel for faeces, and ventrally there are the prominent openings of the diverticula. Peristalsis urges the faeces into the hind-gut. The small dorsal caecum has no obvious function.

The hind-gut comprises three-quarters of the total length of the alimentary canal. Circular and longitudinal muscles squeeze the faeces along to the anus. There are six longitudinal folds which wind spirally along its course.

Food solutions absorbed in the tubules, diffuse through them into the haemocoel whence they are distributed by the blood. Apart from some reserve of oil and glycogen in the proximal cells of the digestive diverticula, there is no prominent region of food storage in crayfishes.

Respiration

The crayfish obtains its oxygen from the surrounding water through its *gills*, which are thin vascular outgrowths of the body wall. The blood pigment is haemocyanin which is a protein with a prosthetic group containing copper and sulphur. The pigment is in solution and in the oxidized condition it gives a faint blue colour to the blood. The gills are enclosed in the gill chamber by the branchiostegite, a double lateral downgrowth of the carapace. There are three series of gills, named according to the region from which they grow. Thus *podobranchs* grow from the coxopodites, *arthrobranchs* from the articular membranes and *pleurobranchs* from the lateral thoracic wall. There is evidence that all are originally derived from exites (epipodites), the arthrobranch probably being a division of the podobranch, while the pleurobranch may be derived from an ancestral exite of the precoxa which has now become indistinguishably fused with the body wall. A typical thoracic segment bears a podobranch, two arthrobranchs, anterior and posterior, and a pleurobranch. Such a condition is found in the lobster but not in the crayfish. The thin epipodites also function as gills, and on the coxopodite of some segments are borne tufts of very fine setae, called *setobranchs*, which probably also aid respiration. A table showing the gill equipment of the crayfish is given below.

Seg-ment	Appendage	Epipo-dite	Podo-branch	Anterior Arthro-branch	Posterior Arthro-branch	Pleuro-branch	Seto-branch
7	1st maxilliped	✓	—	—	—	—	—
8	2nd maxilliped	✓	✓	✓	—	—	✓
9	3rd maxilliped	✓	✓	✓	✓	—	✓
10	Cheliped	✓	✓	✓	✓	—	✓
11	1st pereiopod	✓	✓	✓	✓	vestigial	✓
12	2nd pereiopod	✓	✓	✓	✓	vestigial	✓
13	3rd pereiopod	✓	✓	✓	✓	vestigial	✓
14	4th pereiopod	—	—	—	—	✓	✓
Total		7	6	6	5	1	7
				18			

Thus there are eighteen gills plus the accessory epipodites and setobranchs (*see* Fig. 22.25).

The gills are typical of the kind known as *trichobranchs*, with a central axis and filaments radiating outwards and upwards somewhat like a test-tube brush. The wall consists of cuticle, epidermis and connective tissue surrounding a blood channel. On the outer side is an upward afferent blood channel and on the inner side is a downward efferent blood channel. The two blood channels are connected at the top of the axis. Blood passes into the gills from the sternal sinus and

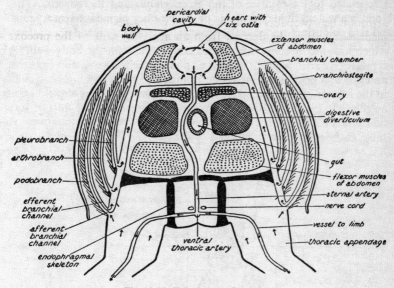

Fig. 22.25. T.S. thorax of *Astacus*.

out of them by intersegmental channels into the pericardium (*see* Fig. 22.25).

Movement of water over the gills is imperative and this is maintained by the baling movements of the scaphognathite of the maxilla. Water is sucked in between the bases of the legs and swept forward and out under the bases of the antennae, where it also sweeps away excretory products from the green glands. The scaphognathite beats once per second; its movements can be observed in the living animal by cutting a small portion out of the branchiostegite just below the cervical groove. Fine setae on the inner wall of the branchiostegite probably help in cleaning the gills as they are brushed to and fro. Occasionally, the beat of the scaphognathite is reversed, to clean the gill filaments of sifted debris.

Each podobranch has its axis fused with the edge of the epipodite. The deep fold of the epipodite probably accommodates the front of the podobranch next behind it.

The Blood Vascular System

The system consists of the *heart*, the *arteries*, and large *blood sinuses* which together constitute the *haemocoel*. *This space is not a coelom*; it represents the blood-filled cavity of the blastocoel. The true coelom is restricted to the cavities of the green glands and the gonads. The blood is a watery fluid containing the respiratory pigment haemocyanin and also colourless amoeboid corpuscles; it clots very readily, a distinct

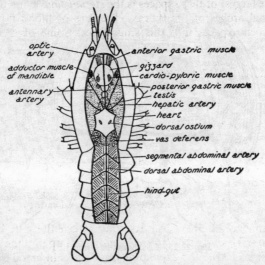

Fig. 22.26. Dorsal dissection of *Astacus* showing heart and arteries.

advantage to a creature possessing such large blood-filled spaces, in the event of injury.

The heart is situated dorsally, above the mesenteron. It lies in a cavity bounded by a thin-walled *pericardium*, not homologous with a true pericardium which encloses a coelomic space. It is suspended from the sides of the pericardium by six bands of fibrous connective tissue, called the *alae cordis*. The extent of the pericardium is outlined externally by the cervical and branchiocardiac grooves. Three pairs of *ostia*, dorsal, lateral and ventral, give entry from the pericardial cavity into the heart. All six ostia bear valves allowing blood to pass inward only. Leaving the heart are the arteries; a *median ophthalmic* passing forward to the eyes; paired *antennary arteries* which supply the gizzard, antennules, antennae, and green glands; paired *hepatic arteries* supplying the filter chamber, mesenteron and digestive diverticula; a backward *dorsal abdominal artery* supplying the hind-gut and abdominal muscles. Bifurcating from the dorsal abdominal artery as soon as it leaves the heart, is the *sternal artery*, which passes vertically downwards between the commissures connecting the fourth and fifth thoracic ganglia. Then it divides into the *forward ventral thoracic artery* and the *backward ventral abdominal artery* (*see* Fig. 22.27).

When the heart contracts, it pumps blood into these arteries. They divide into smaller arteries in the various tissues, but there are no capillaries, the blood passing into haemocoelic spaces surrounding the organs. The largest of these spaces is the *sternal sinus* lying beneath the endophragmal arches of the thorax. Pressure of blood flowing from the haemocoelic spaces into this sinus forces some of the blood by

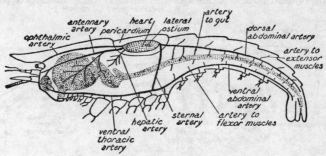

Fig. 22.27. Heart and arteries of *Astacus*, lateral view.

afferent channels into the gills. It returns from the gills by efferent channels and passes by small *intersegmental tubes* up into the *pericardial cavity* (*see* Fig. 22.25). The expanding heart sucks in blood through the ostia. When it is full, it contracts and forces the blood into the arteries; their exits bear valves so that the blood is not sucked back by the expanding heart. Blood from the haemocoel around the gizzard passes into the branchiostegite and returns to the pericardium by a small vessel passing upwards along its posterior border. A diagram showing the sequence in this circulatory system is given below.

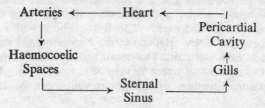

The functions of the blood system are distribution of food and oxygen, transport of excretory products, and by reason of its amoeboid leucocytes, there is protection from small disease organisms. Certain of the leucocytes initiate clotting by their cytolysis at the site of a wound. Because it is not completely enclosed in tubular vessels, it is known as an *open system* in contrast to the closed system already seen in annelids.

Locomotion

All the muscles which cause movement of the sclerites on one another about the axis of the peg-joints, are of the striated type and thus capable of rapid contraction. This is in contrast with the unstriated muscle of the gut which is only capable of slow rhythmic contractions. The system of flexors and extensors has already been described for the

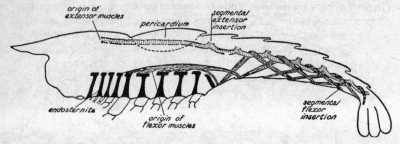

Fig. 22.28. Extensor and flexor muscles of the abdomen of *Astacus* (one side only).

podomeres of the appendages. The mandibles have powerful *abductor* and *adductor muscles* which respectively separate and bring together the biting surfaces. They are inserted in the dorsal surface of the carapace. The muscles operating the proximal podomeres of the limbs at their articulations with the body, are inserted on the endophragmal skeleton. Muscles of the abdomen are large and powerful. Dorsally, slender extensors start from the dorso-lateral regions of the carapace, pass through the pericardium and are inserted into each tergum. Their contraction brings about approximation of the terga and hence straightening of the abdomen. The flexor abdominal muscles are extremely complex. They originate in the endophragmal skeleton and are inserted in each sternum. Their contraction brings about approximation of the sterna and hence flexure of the abdomen. Their great thickness is some measure of the power which can be applied (*see* Fig. 22.28).

The crayfish is capable of two forms of locomotion; gentle forward walking and violent backward darting. In walking, the chelipeds are held up clear of the substratum and the abdomen is extended. Six of the eight pereiopods are always on the substratum. The two moving at any moment are on opposite sides and of different segments. The first three pairs of pereiopods pull the body forward while the last pair push. The forward movement may be aided by paddling with the pleopods.

In the darting movement, the tail fan is extended widely, the antennae are directed backwards over the body, and then the abdomen is violently flexed. The great thrust exerted against the water by the fan and the abdomen causes a sudden dart backwards. It is a rapid escape reaction.

Growth and Ecdysis

Growth occurs by division and consequent enlargement of the cells of all tissues except the nervous tissues. No increase in size is apparent until a moult takes place. The onset of ecdysis is marked by a number of well-defined internal changes. Glycogen accumulates in the digestive diverticula and in the connective tissue beneath the epidermis. It will be remembered that glucose is the main constituent of chitin and that glycogen hydrolyses into glucose units. The gastroliths situated in the gizzard between the old cuticle and the new, become much larger, due to the withdrawal of calcium salts from the calcified layers of the integument. Later, when the fore-gut lining is cast, they fall into the gizzard, become broken up, dissolved, and mainly passed out with the faeces. Amoeboid cells from the connective tissue migrate through the epidermis and dissolve the inner layers of chitin, thus loosening the old cuticle free of the epidermis.

The crayfish retreats into its burrow and violent movements of the limbs and abdomen take place. The carapace splits transversely across the junction of cephalothorax and abdomen. The crayfish now lies on its side and nearly folds its body into two. The exoskeleton of the legs splits longitudinally. The anterior part of the body is now drawn out of the old cuticle and then, by a violent jerk, the posterior part is freed.

Secretion of the new cuticle begins before ecdysis; the chitin secreted by the epidermis and the protein and lipoid layers by tegumental glands, have already formed a thin layer. Nevertheless, there is considerable absorption of water and the animal swells appreciably. After its exertions it is weak, and with its meagre cuticle, it is defenceless. Consequently it hides in the burrow until the cuticle thickens and hardens, the process taking about a week. The swelling produced by water absorption provides space in which new growth of cells can take place. This continues until the confining armour renders it impossible. It is probable that moulting hormones are produced, which initiate the metabolic processes involved. Such hormones are known in insects.

Regeneration and Autotomy

The power of regeneration, though not so extensive as is found in annelids, is still pronounced. It is, however, limited to the regrowth of appendages or portions of them which are broken off or damaged. Sometimes a limb, when caught or held under a stone, or even when stimulated, will be broken off by reflex action of the animal itself. The process is known as *autotomy*. It has been thoroughly studied in the lobster and probably applies also to the pereiopods of *Astacus*. The

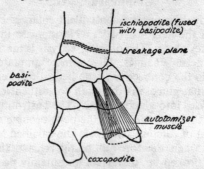

Fig. 22.29. Lobster. 2nd walking leg. showing mechanism for autotomy (*from Yonge, after Wood and Wood*).

ischiopodite of the limb bears a groove near its base (*see* Fig. 22.29). From a point just proximal to the groove two *autotomizer muscles* are inserted. When they contract, the limb is bent over against a process on the coxopodite and snaps. The breakage plane does not damage any muscles, as it lies between the origins of one set and the insertions of the next. Immediately proximal to the break is a connective tissue membrane stretched across the limb. It has a small perforation in the centre through which the artery and nerve passed down the limb. At autotomy they are withdrawn through this hole into the body. The blood forms a clot over it by cytolysis of special leucocytes, and soon the epidermis spreads over the inside. A delicate layer of chitin is formed to protect it. At each moult the stump enlarges until it attains the normal size. The whole process is of distinct survival value; the animal cannot be permanently held by a limb. It is only the more prominent limbs which are likely to be held by a predator and thus autotomy is limited to the chelipeds and pereiopods. Some of the Astacura are known to pull off a damaged or crushed limb; it will regenerate as described above.

Excretion

The excretory products of the crayfish are carbon dioxide, water, excess salts and certain nitrogenous substances. The organs concerned are the green glands and the gills.

Carbon dioxide passes out mainly from the gills though some is undoubtedly used in conjunction with calcium for impregnation of the exoskeleton. Excess salts, nitrogenous substances and water utilize both the green glands and the gills. Examination of the urine from the green glands shows that of the nitrogenous substances present 60 per cent consists of ammonia, 10 per cent of urea and 10 per cent of amino-acids.

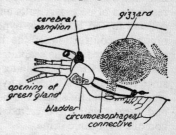

Fig. 22.30. Location of green glands in *Astacus* (one side only shown).

The green glands, or antennary glands, are situated at the anterior end of the haemocoel, one behind the base of each antenna. When distended, they press backward against the gizzard (*see* Fig. 22.30). The whole gland is cushion-shaped with the large bladder lying above all the other parts. When unravelled, it is seen to consist of four distinct parts, a small *end sac*, a green flattened disc called the *labyrinth*, a *white tube* and the *urinary bladder*. All are mesodermal derivatives lined with glandular epithelium.

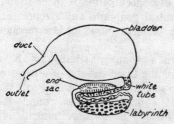

Fig. 22.31. *Astacus*. Green gland.

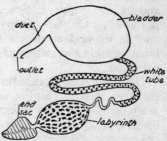

Fig. 22.32. *Astacus*. Green gland unravelled.

The end-sac is a small brown structure enclosing a coelomic cavity. Into the lumen project ingrowths from the walls. It leads, by a small opening guarded by a sphincter, into the green labyrinth, which is a maze of anastomosing canals. The next portion, the white tube, has sponge-like ingrowths from its walls. It leads into the large thin-walled bladder which opens on the coxopodite of the antenna. The actual opening is difficult to find, being but a tiny slit in a membranous diaphragm.

For a small organ, the green gland has a very good blood supply. It receives many small branches from both the antennary and ventral thoracic arteries. By a process of ultra-filtration, water and dissolved salts pass into the end-sacs, while nitrogenous materials mainly pass into the labyrinth. Through the walls of the white tube selective resorption of necessary salts and glucose takes place. The urine which collects in the bladder is hypotonic to the blood; it is expelled by muscular contraction of the bladder walls, and wafted away in the current created by the scaphognathite.

Osmoregulation necessitates the continuous elimination of water, since the crayfish's blood is hypertonic to the surrounding fresh water which continually enters the body through the highly permeable gills, and excess water is excreted by the green gland. Hence there is a copious hypotonic urine.

Sensitivity, Co-ordination and Behaviour

Considered in its entirety of *central nervous system*, *nerves* and *sense organs*, the nervous system shows a considerable advance on that of *Lumbricus*.

The central nervous system consists of the *cerebral ganglia*, a pair of *circum-oesophageal connectives* and a *double ventral cord* with *ganglia* along its course. In primitive crustaceans, such as the fairy shrimps of the class Branchiopoda, there is a pair of ganglia in each thoracic and abdominal segment, and the two ventral cords are widely separated. But in other Crustacea, every degree of concentration is to be found, until in the crab there is a single ventral ganglion which represents fused thoracic and abdominal ganglia. *Astacus* shows an intermediate condition.

The cerebral ganglia are fused to form a prominent white mass above the green glands. This brain represents the fused ganglia of a pre-segmental region, of the first segment, the second and the third. From the cerebral ganglia, circum-oesophageal connectives pass round the oesophagus. They are joined by a *transverse commissure* immediately posterior to the oesophagus. The connectives join two fused *sub-oesophageal ganglia* just under the front end of the endophragmal tunnel. They represent the fused ganglia of the fourth, fifth, sixth, seventh and eighth segments. The first thoracic ganglion is close behind the sub-oesophageal; it supplies segment nine. The remaining thoracic and the abdominal segments have separate ganglia joined by connectives. The double nature is very apparent in the thorax but it is not easily distinguishable in the abdomen. Between the fourth and fifth thoracic ganglia, the connectives curve outward to permit the downward passage of the sternal artery (*see* Fig. 22.33). The following table, showing body segments, appendages and ganglia, indicates the extent to which concentration of the central nervous system has taken place.

Region	Segments	Appendages	Ganglia
Head	Presegmental	—	—
	1	(Eyes)	Cerebral ganglia
	2	Antennules	(presegmental to 3)
	3	Antennae	
	4	Mandibles	
	5	Maxillules	Sub-oesophageal
	6	Maxillae	ganglia
	7	1st maxillipeds	(4 to 8)
	8	2nd maxillipeds	
Thorax	9	3rd maxillipeds	
	10	Chelipeds	Six thoracic ganglia
	11	1st pereiopods	all separate
	12	2nd pereiopods	(9 to 14)
	13	3rd pereiopods	
	14	4th pereiopods	
Abdomen	15	1st pleopods	
	16	2nd pleopods	Six abdominal
	17	3rd pleopods	ganglia, all
	18	4th pleopods	separate
	19	5th pleopods	(15 to 20)
	20	Uropods	

Neurones are limited to the ganglia, the connectives containing only fibres. Nerves supplying the eyes, antennules, antennae and green glands, join the cerebral ganglia. They contain both afferent fibres from receptor cells in these organs and efferent fibres passing out to their muscles. The suboesophageal ganglia supply nerves for the mandibles, maxillules, maxillae, first and second maxillipeds. The fibres are mainly efferent to the musculature, but each nerve has a few afferent fibres. Paired cardiac inhibitors and accelerators pass dorsally through two small holes in the endophragmal tunnel to the heart. Each segmental ganglion supplies three pairs of nerves to its segment; the last abdominal ganglion innervates the telson as well.

Two dorsal giant fibres begin in the cerebral ganglia and pass down the connectives, making synapses with motor cells in each ganglion. They end in the last abdominal ganglion. They are mainly concerned with rapid stimulation of the pereiopods and the abdomen, thus enabling the rapid backward darting reaction to be performed swiftly. There are also two ventro-lateral giant fibres which begin in the last abdominal ganglion. They conduct impulses forward and again make synapses with motor cells in each ganglion. The giant fibre system is thus similar to that in the earthworm with one set conveying impulses backward and the other forward.

There is a *sympathetic system* innervating the alimentary canal. Anteriorly it begins by fusion into a single nerve of a branch from the middle of the brain with two branches from the circum-oesophageal

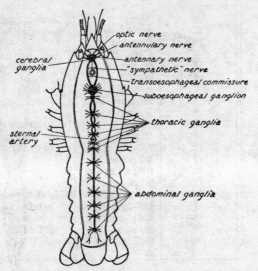

Fig. 22.33. *Astacus.* Nervous system, dorsal view.

commissures. This nerve supplies the fore-gut and mesenteron. Posteriorly a nerve from the last abdominal ganglion branches over the hind-gut.

Sense Organs

The sense organs definitely known in the crayfish are the *eyes*, the *statocysts*, *chemoreceptors* and *tactile receptors*. The last two are located in individual setae, but there are probably others concerned with temperature and pressure sensitivity.

The eyes are movable structures borne on stalks above the bases of the antennules. They are compound eyes, each consisting of more than 10,000 receptor units called *ommatidia*. Each ommatidium is a separate optical unit, represented on the surface by a square *cuticular lens* secreted by a group of four *lenticular cells* of the epidermis. These corneal lenses have little if any refracting power; they are mainly protective and necessarily transparent. Beneath the lenticular cells, four elongated *vitrellae* contribute to the formation of a central *crystalline cone*. This is transparent and refractive, made up of four rod-like portions from the four vitrellae. Beneath the vitrellae is a similar but smaller system consisting of four *retinulae*. They form at their central junctions, a striated spindle-shaped *rhabdom*. This is the sensitive region; it contains the pigment known as visual red. From the bases

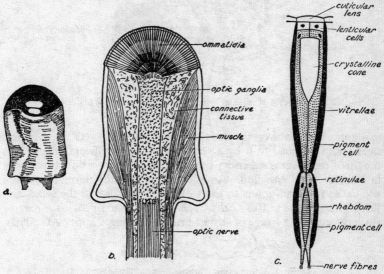

Fig. 22.34. Eye of *Astacus*. (*a*) Entire, ventral view. (*b*) L.S. (*c*) A single ommatidium.

of the retinulae, nerve fibres lead, via the *optic nerve*, into the cerebral ganglia (*see* Fig. 22.34). The crystalline cone focuses the light on the retinulae, affecting the visual pigment and thus setting up nervous impulses. Each ommatidium is surrounded by elongated cells containing black pigment. The pigment can be retracted to the upper and lower ends of the cells or evenly spread out. In bright light, it is spread and thus each ommatidium is an isolated unit. The image formed will be a series of separate points; it is a *mosaic image*. In poor light, the pigment is retracted and light can enter the system from many directions. Hence the image formed will be blurred and is called a *superposition image*. We do not know how either kind of image is interpreted in the brain of the crayfish, but it makes the correct responses to suitable stimuli.

The statocysts are organs of balance; they are very sensitive to change in orientation from the normal position. Each is a sac formed by invagination of the epithelium of the dorsal surface of the precoxa of the antennule. The epithelium secretes a thin chitinous cuticle prolonged also into delicate, feathered, sensory setae. These are arranged

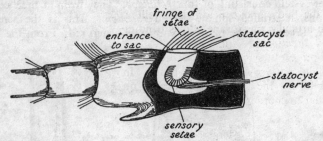

Fig. 22.35. Statocyst of *Astacus* in antennule. The proximal podomere is cut longitudinally.

in a horseshoe shape on the floor of the cavity. Each seta bears several sand-grains fastened to it by a secretion of the tegumental glands. In the tip of each seta is a sensory cell from which a nerve fibre leads back into the cerebral ganglion. Any deviation from the normal position, will cause the sand-grains to exert different pressure on the setae, and this stimulates the sensory cells. The statocyst sac opens by a narrow slit, protected by a fringe of curved bristles (*see* Fig. 22.35). At ecdysis,

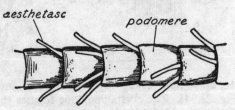

Fig. 22.36. Aesthetascs on antennule of *Astacus*.

the lining of the sac is shed, together with the sand-grains. After the moult, the crayfish shovels sand over its head with the chelipeds and also rubs its antennules in the sand. Grains which are small enough will enter the sac and some of them will be secured by the secretion. Some will remain free on the floor of the sac.

The chemical sense of the crayfish seems to reside mainly in the antennules and mouth parts. The sensory cells on the antennules lie in peculiar blunted setae known as *aesthetascs*. They are grouped in tufts of three or four (*see* Fig. 22.36). On the mouth parts, the aesthetascs

are single. Scattered sparsely over the body, even on the carapace, are
small pores at the bases of which are chemoreceptors. The sense is a
combination of smell and taste of the higher animals.

Tactile setae are present on many parts, especially on the antennae
and on the components of the tail fan. They are small pointed bristles
feathered with setules. Each bears a bulbous swelling at its articulation
with the body, and beneath the swelling,
a thin articular membrane allows bending
in any direction (*see* Fig. 22.37).

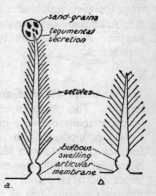

Proprioceptors must also be present to
maintain posture and muscle tonus. In
allied forms, they have been located on
articular membranes of the pereiopods.

Endocrine Glands

There are neurosecretions from the brain
and from the optic ganglia. These are discharged via the *sinus glands* in the eye-stalks
and the *post-commissural organs* just behind
the brain (*see* p. 678). The hormones affect
ecdysis, reproduction, and the state of
chromatophore pigment. There are *pericardial glands* lateral to the heart and

Fig. 22.37. Sensory setae of
Astacus. (*a*) From statocyst sac.
(*b*) From antenna (tactile).

androgenic glands on the course of the vasa deferentia. There is further
discussion of crustacean hormones on p. 678.

Co-ordination and Behaviour

Although the nervous system does not show important anatomical
advance over that of the annelids, there is a much greater degree of
co-ordination and hence more complex behaviour. Each appendage
can work independently, in a reflex manner, but in addition they are
grouped into a number of self-regulating units. Thus the eight pereiopods are co-ordinated in walking, the mouth parts in feeding, and the
pleopods in paddling. The brain is still an organ for reception of
stimuli from the anterior sense organs and re-transmission of impulses
to effector organs, but there is more precise selection of these effector
organs. In *Lumbricus*, each segment responds in turn to stimuli requiring locomotive response, but in *Astacus*, only the pereiopods are thus
stimulated. Very precise co-ordination is necessary in the feeding
process; it involves a complex series of movements from grasping by
the chelipeds to the eventual arrival of food at the mouth. A decere-
brated crayfish can still perform a variety of responses such as walking

and feeding, but it attempts to do them all at once. There is no inhibition. From such experiments, it is apparent that the brain inhibits certain activities while allowing others. It controls the reflex actions of the appendages; in the absence of the brain, the control is removed and each segment works independently.

Another distinct advance is found in the decussation of nerve fibres from the eyes, antennules and antennae, so that stimulus of only one eye, antennule or antenna, transmits an impulse to both cerebral ganglia. A similar condition is found in the optic chiasma of the vertebrates.

Reproduction

The sexes are separate and easily distinguished by external characteristics. The genital opening in males is on the coxopodite of the fourth pereiopod, while in females it is in a similar position on the second pereiopods. On the abdomen, the female has a number of features associated with security of the eggs and young. The abdomen is broader and more downwardly curved at the sides; the pleopods are larger and fringed with longer setae. In the male, the first and second pleopods are modified as tubular copulatory organs.

In both sexes, the *gonads* are three-lobed organs, shaped somewhat like a letter Y extremely thickened. The two anterior lobes project above and beside the gizzard, while the single lobe may reach back as far as the first abdominal segment. They lie immediately beneath the pericardium. The *oviducts* lead laterally from the middle of the sides of the ovary, and then proceed almost vertically downward. The *vasa deferentia* start from a similar region; they are considerably coiled in the first part of their course.

The *testes* are racemose glands and in the minute terminal vesicles, cells of the germinal epithelium are proliferated inward to become sperm. These sperm are very peculiar, each consisting of a flattened disc containing the nucleus, and a number of stiff curved radiating processes. They are non-motile and in the vas deferens, they are surrounded by a gelatinous envelope. Separated elongated *spermatophores* are forced out of the aperture during copulation.

The ova develop from cells of the germinal epithelium and when mature, they pass down the oviduct in a single row. They are centrolecithal with a large amount of yolk situated centrally. When laid they are about 3 mm in diameter and covered with a very thin chitinous membrane secreted by the lower part of the oviduct. Egg-laying takes place several weeks after copulation.

The presence of the haemocoel has necessitated the attachment of the ducts to the gonads in both sexes. The small lumina of testis and ovary

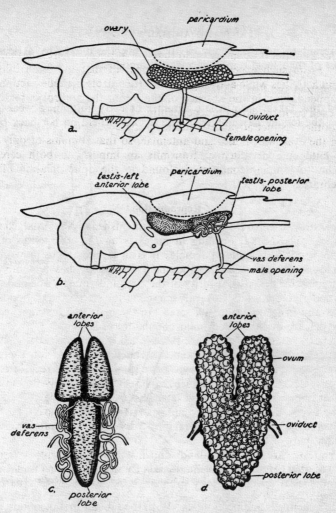

Fig. 22.38. Reproductive organs of *Astacus*. (*a*) Female seen from left side. (*b*) Male seen from left side. (*c*) Male, dorsal view. (*d*) Female, dorsal view.

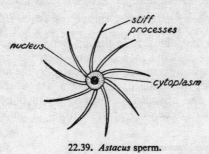

22.39. *Astacus* sperm.

represent reduced coelomic cavities, while the ducts are, at least for most of their length, mesodermal coelomoducts.

Copulation and Fertilization

Mating takes place in late summer or early autumn, a week or so after the female has moulted. The female is held on her back by the

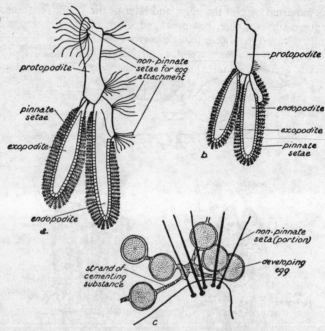

Fig. 22.40. Lobster. (a) Female pleopod. (b) Male pleopod. (c) Portion of endopodite of pleopod showing attachment of eggs to setae (all after Yonge).

male's chelipeds and pereiopods. With the tubular first pleopods, aided by the second, spermatophores emerging from the vas deferens are transferred to the female and plastered over her abdomen particularly in the regions of the oviducal openings. Egg-laying does not take place for several weeks.

During egg-laying, the female lies on her back with the abdomen flexed. The eggs pass out in a continuous stream and their passage backward is effected by water currents created by the anterior pleopods. By some obscure mechanism, the sperm are liberated from their spermatophores and attached to the eggs by their hooked processes. An explosive disruption of a sperm forces its nucleus through the chitinous lining into the egg. The fertilized eggs are attached to special long setae of the proximal regions of the pleopods by a cement secreted by tegumental glands which open to the surface of these setae (*see* Fig. 22.40). The female then rests while the cement hardens, and within a day, resumes normal activity. In this "berry" condition she carries the eggs until they hatch in the following summer.

The maternal care of the eggs, and later of the young, ensures a high percentage survival rate, but great reduction of their numbers occurs when they leave the mother to seek burrows of their own. Cannibalistic tendencies of the adults make for fairly wide dispersal of the young; crayfishes are not social animals. In the winter, they display little activity, but spend most of their time hiding in their burrows. They live for many years in captivity, but the average duration of life under natural conditions is not known.

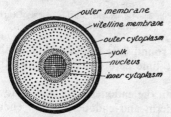

Fig. 22.41. V.S. egg of *Astacus*.

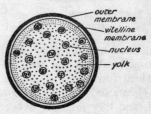

Fig. 22.42. V.S. zygote of *Astacus* in coenocyte stage.

Development

There are a number of peculiar features in the development of the crayfish, even when compared with its close relatives, the lobsters, where there are several larval stages. It does not illustrate any general principles and therefore will not be described very fully here.

The egg is of the centrolecithal type (*see* p. 670) and consists of a central nucleus surrounded by a thin layer of cytoplasm, and then a thick layer of yolk covered by another thin zone of cytoplasm. The egg is surrounded by a thin vitelline membrane, a layer of chitin and finally by the secretion of the tegumental glands of the pleopods.

Cleavage is unusual in that there are many nuclear divisions before there is any partition of the cytoplasm. Eventually all the nuclei pass to the surface zone of cytoplasm which becomes divided among them. Thus there is an outer layer of cells called a blastoderm surrounding a huge mass of undivided yolk.

The embryo forms on the surface with its ventral surface outermost. A number of well-marked thickened areas appear; they are the head lobes, thoracico-abdominal lobes, a mesodermal plate and an endodermal disc. All are surrounded by unmodified ectoderm.

The endoderm is invaginated by sinking in to form the archenteron and for a time the blastopore remains open. Between the head rudiment and the thoracico-abdominal lobes, three further pairs of thickenings appear. They will form respectively the antennules, antennae and mandibles. The stomodaeum appears as a slit between antennules and

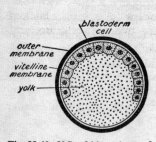

Fig. 22.43. V.S. of blastoderm of Astacus.

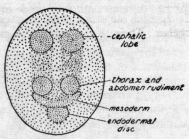

Fig. 22.44. *Astacus*. Surface view of early embryo at gastrula stage.

antennae, and the proctodaeum as a round hole in the middle of the thoracico-abdominal area. It is some time before they open into the archenteron.

The mesoderm cells invaginated with the endoderm become budded off, and they multiply between ectoderm and endoderm. The endoderm cells of the archenteron move radially outwards and gradually

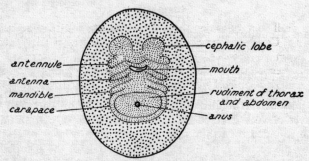

Fig. 22.45. *Astacus*. Surface view of embryo showing rudiments of head appendages.

ingest all the yolk. In the process these endoderm cells become very long columns abutting on ectoderm. The rudiments of thorax and abdomen become elongated, with the abdomen bent over the thorax. Thus mouth and anus are close together.

The carapace develops as two folds lateral to the embryo; they are ectodermal and they represent the ventral edge of the carapace. They extend dorsally to meet in the mid-line above the embryo. The nerve cord is formed of double ectodermal thickenings which sink in, and the heart and arteries of mesenchyme cells delaminated from both ectoderm and endoderm.

The embryo hatches in summer. By comparison with the adult form, it has a disproportionately large cephalothorax and a small abdomen. It clings to the setae of the mother's pleopods with its special hooked chelae. Their first moult takes place within twenty-four hours and

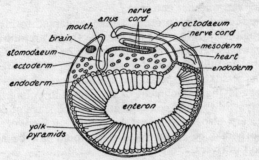

Fig. 22.46. Median L.S. of late embryo of *Astacus*.

they remain with the mother for some time after this. She shows great maternal care.

Adaptation

Here we shall not consider the general adaptations for aquatic life found in the Crustacea generally, but those features of the freshwater crayfish which adapt it for life in flowing rivers and in burrows.

Its dull green colour is ideal camouflage for river water and coupled with its stealthy nocturnal movements, make it a far from conspicuous animal. Its relative density is about 1·1, so that although it stays easily on the river bed, the great majority of its weight is supported by the water.

It is not particular about its food, but will scavenge any debris or attempt to capture smaller creatures swept by in the current. The rivers it inhabits contain relatively pure water, highly oxygenated and include sufficient calcium salts for impregnation of the skeleton. In a large crayfish these salts may amount to 15 per cent of the total weight of the exoskeleton.

The slow forward movement is indicative of the fact that it is not an active predator; that the food supply comes easily to it, while the rapid backward darting enables quick escape from danger. Here, the versatility of the antennae is important.

As it is a freshwater animal, osmoregulation is a serious problem. In this connexion, its blood pressure of 20 cm of water enables it to force fluid into the green gland.

A number of adaptations are to be found in its nervous system. The eyes can be both light and dark adapted. The giant fibres enable practically simultaneous transmission of stimuli to the muscles concerned in backward movement. There is a light detector in the last thoracic ganglion which guards against the danger of backing into a burrow which has another entrance.

The whole reproductive process is highly adapted to life in flowing water. Though fertilization is external, the sperm are not liberated as swimming gametes; indeed they can scarcely be said to be liberated at all. They are carefully deposited in sticky masses on the female abdomen. This necessitates a special fertilization mechanism. The whole process of egg-laying, attachment of the eggs and young, is adaptive. Finally, the type of egg and consequent advanced stage of development at hatching, are also adaptations to secure survival of the young. Small larvae would be swept away and would not be able to find sufficient food in rivers.

Classification

Phylum: Arthropoda	Family: Astacidae [Potamobiidae]
Class: Crustacea	Genus: *Astacus*
Order: Decapoda	Species: *A. fluviatilis*, *A. torrentium*

Crustacea in the order Decapoda have five pairs of legs, each possessing endopodite only. There are usually three series of gills; podobranchs, arthrobranchs and pleurobranchs. The thorax bears three pairs of maxillipeds. Members of the family Astacidae have the podobranchs partly united with the epipodites and there are appendages present on the first abdominal segment of the male and usually also on the female. The genus *Astacus* is distinguished from other genera by details of body proportions and by small details in the appendages. The various species are distinguished on matters of size and colour.

Special Features of Biological Importance

The Arthropoda show a variety of lines of evolution and in each class a graded series can be studied. Nevertheless, there are certain general features which show that this branch of the coelomate animals has achieved definite advances in complexity. Also, it will be convenient at this point for the student to gain some idea of the main lines of coelomate evolution.

Advances in Complexity

The possession of jointed appendages has given the arthropods greater precision and variety of movement. It has also enabled the evolution of a variety of uses to which these appendages can be put. These jointed limbs have necessitated special muscles to move them, and hence the continuous body wall muscle has disappeared and the muscles now are separate bundles. Thus there can be precise movement of a single appendage or of any group of appendages.

There is a greater degree of cephalization than in any group previously described. Six segments are incorporated into the head, together with their sense organs. Correlated with this greater degree of cephalization, there is greater concentration of the nervous system. Here a series can be traced, from a condition very like that of annelids, to the condition achieved by the crab. Concomitant with limb specialization has been the greater degree of co-ordination and control in the brain.

The evolution of a true skeleton is a distinct advance. The skeletons of animals previously described have been purely protective or supporting structures. In the arthropods, however, the skeleton achieves a second important function, that of muscle attachment.

There is traceable a tendency towards gradual loss of individuality of segments, and the merging of a number of segments to form one structure. This is seen in the head, in the nervous system, in the heart and in the reproductive system. In limbs of chordates, this tendency is further extended.

The Main Lines of Coelomate Evolution

Diagrams of "evolutionary trees" have some value in that they attempt to show possible relationships between the phyla. Nevertheless, they should be regarded with great caution; versatile zoologists are capable of deducing a common origin of groups from one fact, and a diverse origin from another. Thus on the sole evidence of the possession of choanocytes, we say that the Porifera probably evolved from choanoflagellates, thus implying that the collared flagellate cell evolved once only. Similarly, we could say that all animals possessing cilia have evolved from Ciliophora. Some cells of all animals, at some stage in life, exhibit amoeboid motion; but we do not assert that all animals evolved from Rhizopoda. There are three main types of eye, the vertebrate, the molluscan and the arthropod. They differ in detail but operate on the same essential principles. We do not infer that thereby, the three groups are closely related. The main evidence for relationship is derived from similarities in mode of development, as it seems fairly conclusive that embryos repeat the embryonic stages of their forbears. At this stage it should be noted that there are two great coelomate stocks; the molluscan—arthropod—annelid, and the chordate—echinoderm. Each stock has produced great and flourishing phyla (*see* table on p. 1268).

Hormones in Crustacea

Experimental work on Decapoda has shown that besides neurosecretion there are definite target endocrine glands stimulated by tropic hormones. There is neurosecretion from cells in the brain and in the optic ganglia (X-organs). The secretions pass, in droplet form, along the axons of the neurons which discharge the droplets in the *sinus glands* and *post-commissural organs*. The former release three hormones and the latter, one (*see* Fig. 22.47).

The sinus glands release into the haemocoel (1) *a moult-inhibiting hormone*, (2) *an androgenic hormone* (oestrogenic in females), and (3) a *chromatophorotropic hormone*. The target glands of the first are the

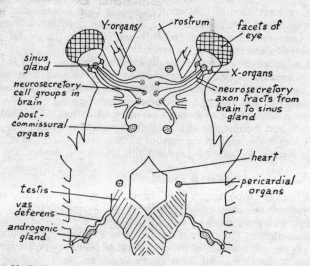

Fig. 22.47. Diagram showing endocrine structures in decapod crustaceans.

Y-organs, and when the amount of the hormone is low enough, the Y-organs secrete a *moulting hormone* which stimulates ecdysis. Thus, ecdysis is under the control of the brain by neurosecretion after correlation of internal and external stimuli. This is similar to vertebrate neurosecretion by the hypothalamus after modulation of stimuli in the brain. The second hormone stimulates the *androgenic glands* to secrete *male sex hormones*; if these glands are transplanted into young females, they suppress development of ovaries, and testes develop. In females, an *oestrogenic hormone* stimulates secretion of *female sex hormones* by the ovaries. The third neurosecretion is a *chromatophorotropic hormone* which affects the pigment in the colour cells.

The post-commissural glands secrete a hormone which is antagonistic to the sinus gland chromatophorotrophin; one causes expansion of the pigment, the other, contraction. *Pericardial glands*, at the sides of the heart, secrete hormones controlling rate and amplitude of heart-beat.

CHAPTER 23

COELOMATE ANIMALS III: ARTHROPODA; INSECTA

INSECTS constitute more than half the known species of animals. About one million species have been named and classified and several thousand more are discovered each year. Their ubiquity, small size, amazing range of adaptation and their fecundity, all make them man's most serious rivals for the possession of the earth. The proper study of insects is a lifetime task; here some introduction to that study is given by description of a typical but somewhat primitive form, the cockroach. This is followed by outline life histories, to give the student some little appreciation of the wide range of variation found in this important group.

It is hardly possible to over-emphasize the importance of insects. Some bring direct benefit to man as pollinators of flowers, as predators on pests, and as objects of beauty; others are directly harmful as pests of crops, as carriers of diseases, as consumers of food stores, as destroyers of clothes, furniture, books and buildings. At these and many other points they impinge upon our daily lives. In spite of tremendous efforts and enormous expense, malaria mosquitoes flourish and plagues of locusts still occur. The story of the insects is one of fantastic evolutionary success, culminating perhaps in the highly organized social Hymenoptera.

THE COCKROACH

Six species of cockroach, belonging to four genera, occur in Great Britain. They are *Periplaneta americana*, *P. australasiae*, *Blatta orientalis* and *Blatella germanica*, and two species of *Ectobius*. The latter are both endemic, but rare. The others have been brought in by trading ships, mainly in the seventeenth and eighteenth centuries; they are typically tropical and sub-tropical animals. In our colder climate, they established themselves in buildings where they found the warmth they required; thus they were formerly very common in warehouses, bakeries, boiler-houses, factories and private dwellings. There has been considerable diminution in their numbers in recent years, probably due to better standards of building, more hygienic food preparation and less scattering of food debris in buildings. *Ectobius* species are found in woods among litter.

Cockroaches are of ancient lineage. Insects very closely resembling them flourished in the Carboniferous period; there has been very little change throughout the vast periods of time that have elapsed since those early insects flourished. The species usually used for dissection is either the brown *P. americana* or the smaller black *B. orientalis*. They differ little, apart from the fact that the female *B. orientalis* has vestigial wings and is incapable of flight. *P. americana* is described here.

Habitat and Habits

The animals live in cracks and crevices of walls especially in the vicinity of fireplaces and boilers. They are nocturnal, emerging to feed only at night, when they devour a wide variety of organic materials. Cockroaches run very swiftly, but very rarely fly. The sexes are separate and there is a complicated copulatory process during which the male deposits a spermatophore near the female spermotheca. The female produces a purse-like ootheca containing sixteen eggs in two rows of eight. The young which emerge are almost small replicas of the adults except that they have no wings; it takes five years to complete development to maturity. Insects which pass through such a slight metamorphosis are described as *heterometabolic*, and those in which the wings develop externally are placed in the division Exopterygota.

External Features

The animal is about 40 mm long and is coloured a rich brown on the dorsal surface, though beneath the wings and on the ventral surface it

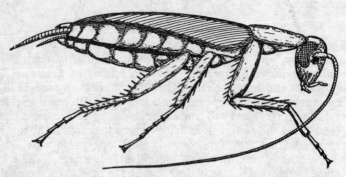

Fig. 23.1. Side view of male *Periplaneta americana*. Only right legs shown.

is almost yellow. The body is clearly divisible into *head*, *thorax* and *abdomen* and is conspicuously flattened.

The head is small and when viewed from the front is almost pear-shaped; from the side it is much narrower. It is placed almost at right angles to the body, so that the mouth parts are ventral and the eyes dorsal. The *sclerites* covering the head are not always clearly separate. On top of the head and extending downward between the

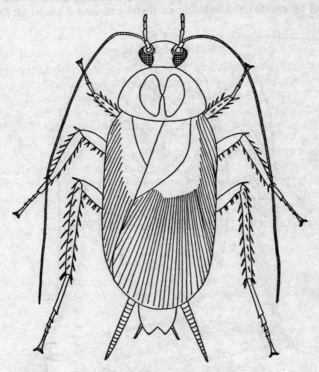

Fig. 23.2. Dorsal view of male *P. americana.*

eyes and antennae are the two *epicranial plates*. Below them in front are successively the *frons, clypeus* and *labrum*. The latter forms the roof of the buccal cavity and is sometimes called the upper lip. At the sides are two cheek sclerites, the *genae*. The back of the head is joined to a flexible short neck region, and the floor of the buccal cavity is formed by the fused proximal portions of a pair of appendages. It is known as the *labium*. The large *compound eyes* are kidney-shaped, black in colour, and are situated dorso-laterally. In front of them lie the long flexible *antennae*. The *mouth parts* are hinged at the sides;

there are three pairs; the *mandibles*, *maxillae* and two *second maxillae*
partially fused to form the labium. The mandibles are strong, hard,
toothed structures, which do not bear palps. Immediately behind the
mandibles are the maxillae, consisting of a protopodite of two podomeres, the *cardo* and *stipes*, a five-jointed endopodite called a *maxillary
palp* and an endite subdivided at its distal end into a claw-like *lacinia*

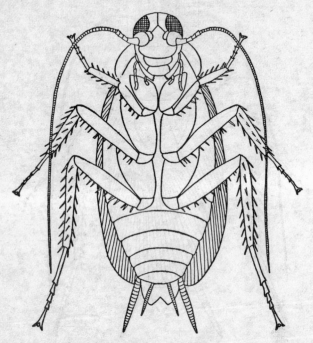

Fig. 23.3. Ventral view of male *P. americana*.

and a hooded *galea*. The lacinia, when not in use, fits into the hood of
the galea. The second maxillae have their three proximal podomeres
fused to form the labium. They are known as the *submentum*, *mentum*
and *prementum*; the latter bears a pair of endopodites known as *labial
palps* and two endites having distally a *glossa* and *paraglossa* similar to
the lacinia and galea of the first maxilla. The mandibles are used for
chewing the food; the lacinia, galea, glossa and paraglossa assist in
holding it and pushing it into the mouth, while the palps are olfactory
in function. There are six segments in the head, and three in the thorax,
and their comparison with the same segments of the crayfish is tabulated on p. 683.

Segment	Crayfish	Cockroach
1	No appendages	No appendages
2	Antennules	Antennae
3	Antennae	No appendages
4	Mandibles	Mandibles
5	Maxillules	Maxillae
6	Maxillae	Labium
7	1st maxillipeds	1st pereiopods
8	2nd maxillipeds	2nd pereiopods
9	3rd maxillipeds	3rd pereiopods

Connecting the head to the thorax is a short slender *neck*. It is not a segmental region but an extended articular membrane supported by a few sclerotized patches known as the *cervical sclerites*.

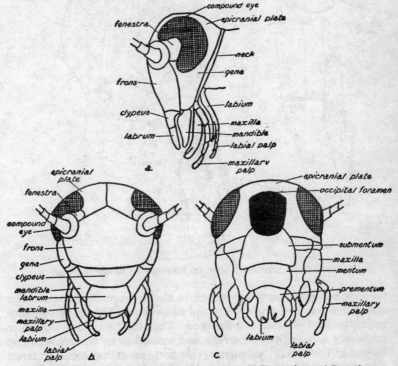

Fig. 23.4. Head of *Periplaneta*. (*a*) Lateral view. (*b*) Front view. (*c*) Posterior view.

The three thoracic segments are the *pro-*, *meso-*, and *metathorax*. Each consists of four sclerites, a dorsal *tergum*, a ventral *sternum* and small lateral *pleura*. The first tergum is the *pronotum*; it covers the neck dorsally. There are three pairs of *thoracic walking legs*, one pair

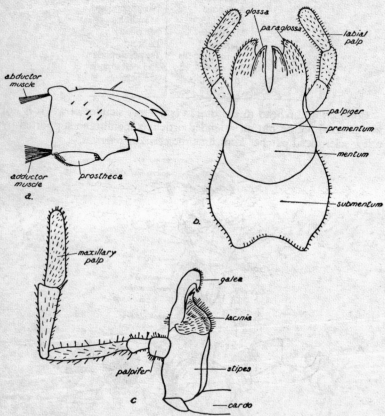

Fig. 23.5. Cockroach mouth parts. (*a*) Mandible. (*b*) Labium. (*c*) Maxilla.

on each segment; they correspond to the pereiopods of the crayfish and each consists of protopodite and endopodite. The proximal podomere, the *coxa*, is wide and flattened. Then follow a small triangular *trochanter*, a large *femur* and *tibia*, and a distal *tarsal* consisting of one large and four small podomeres. On their lower surfaces, the tarsal podomeres bear soft pads called *plantulae* which produce an adhesive substance; this assists the cockroach in gripping a slippery substratum.

At the distal end of the appendage are the sharp *claws*, between which is a soft hairy pad, the *arolium*. Both devices aid in maintaining a grip.

Paired *wings* are borne on the *meso-* and *meta-thorax*. They are cuticular outgrowths from the region between tergum and pleuron in

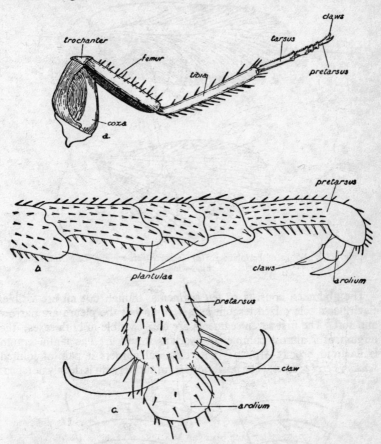

Fig. 23.6. (*a*) Third leg of cockroach. (*b*) Tarsus and claws (enlarged). (*c*) Claws and arolium (enlarged).

the anterior regions of the segments concerned. At first each consists of a double fold of epidermis which secretes the cuticle. Later the epidermis degenerates except in the tubular strengthening veins or nervures which each contain a nerve, a trachea and blood. Later still, when the wings are fully formed, they consist of double sheets of cuticle fused together and supported by the network of nervures. The anterior wings are brown and stiff; they are called *tegmina* and they cover the folded membranous posterior pair.

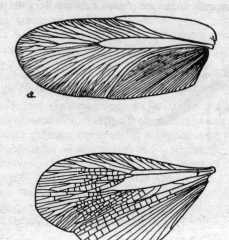

Fig. 23.7. Wings of Periplaneta. (*a*) Tegmen (fore-wing). (*b*) Membranous hind-wing.

The abdomen consists of ten segments, though not all are visible. Each has a sclerotized tergum and sternum but the pleura are narrow and soft. The first seven segments are easily visible in both sexes; the tergum of 7 almost completely overlaps 8 and 9. The tenth tergum is flat and broad; from its antero-lateral corners a pair of jointed *sensory cerci* project. The posterior end of this tergum is deeply notched.

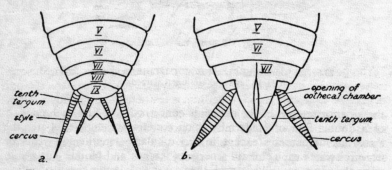

Fig. 23.8. *Periplaneta*. Ventral views of posterior region. (*a*) Male. (*b*) Female.

In the male, the more posterior sterna are modified to form accessory
genital organs; the ninth sternum bears a pair of slender unjointed
bristled *styles*. In the female, the seventh sternum is greatly enlarged
and divided longitudinally to form a blunt keel-shaped projection.
This houses the oothecal chamber. The posterior sterna are also
modified to form *genitalia*. The posterior surface of the abdomen is
covered by two triangular *paraprocts* extending between the anus and
the *cerci*.

Structure and Functions of the Body Wall

The body wall abuts directly on the haemocoel except at those points
where muscles are attached. It consists of a delicate layer of *connective
tissue*, an *epidermis* lying on a basement membrane, and the *cuticle*
secreted by the epidermis. The cuticle can be subdivided into an inner
endocuticle of laminated soft chitin, a thin *exocuticle* which is pigmented
and hardened, and a very thin waxy *epicuticle*. *Tegumental glands*
situated in the connective tissue secrete the protein and tanning materials
for the exocuticle, and the lipoid material for the epicuticle. In thin
areas, and especially in the articular membranes, there is no exocuticle.

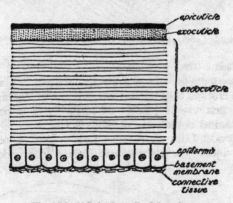

Fig. 23.9. V.S. body wall of *Periplaneta*.

The possession of a cuticle is a major factor in the success of insects
as terrestrial animals in that it is practically impermeable to water though
permeable to gases. Hence water loss is restricted to a minimum. It is
also a protective layer, and an exoskeleton in that it provides joints and
muscle attachments. Outgrowths of the cuticle provide the appendages,
sensory, ambulatory, feeding, sifting and copulatory organs. The
setae provide various kinds of sensory organs and in the gut act as
filters.

Skeleton and Supporting Structures

The *exoskeleton* consists of sclerotized plates jointed together by articular membranes and peg-and-socket joints, as described for the crayfish on p. 650. In general, the muscle attachments are also similar to those of the crayfish. The thorax contains special muscles concerned with flight (*see* p. 697). The *endophragmal skeleton* in the thorax and abdomen consists of very slight ingrowths. There is, however, an important part of this skeleton in the head. Behind the eyes and below

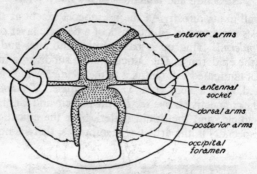

Fig. 23.10. Head of cockroach with dorsal surface removed to show tentorium.

the oesophagus is a transverse bar known as the body of the *tentorium*. From this, three pairs of bars pass out to the exoskeleton. Anteriorly, the front arms join the suture between the frons and clypeus, the dorsal arms join the epicranial plates near the antennal sockets and the posterior arms pass to the back of the epicranial plates. The various bars support the brain and the oesophagus, and are bases for the attachment of the head muscles. The exoskeleton imposes the necessity for ecdysis during development; adult insects do not normally moult.

Nutrition

The *alimentary canal* consists of an ectodermal *fore-gut* or *stomodaeum*, a short endodermal *mid-gut* or *mesenteron*, and an ectodermal *hind-gut* or *proctodaeum*. Histologically the fore-gut consists of connective tissue, circular muscle, longitudinal muscle, basement membrane, epithelium and the cuticle on the inside. The mesenteron lacks the cuticle but has the same layers otherwise; the epithelium consists of tall columnar cells with smaller replacement cells in groups at their bases. The hind-gut consists of the same layers as the fore-gut with the addition of an extra layer of circular muscle. This is probably correlated with some difficulty in eliminating both the faeces and the solid

nitrogenous excreta which leaves the body via the hind-gut (*see* Fig.
23.11).

The fore-gut can be divided into *buccal cavity, pharynx, oesophagus,
crop* and *gizzard*. The buccal cavity is roofed over by the labrum
which has the soft *epipharynx* on its inner surface; it bears gustatory
organs. The floor of the buccal cavity is formed by the prementum,

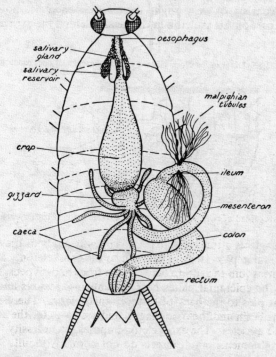

Fig. 23.11. Dorsal view of alimentary canal of cockroach.

mentum and submentum of the labium. On its inner surface is a soft
median tongue-like structure, the *hypopharynx*. The mandibles and
maxillae complete the buccal cavity at the sides (*see* Fig. 23.4(*a*)). The
salivary duct enters beneath the hypopharynx.

The pharynx is short and not well developed in the cockroach. It
leads into the narrow oesophagus which passes almost at a right angle
over the body of the tentorium, and gradually becomes dilated in the
thorax and first two abdominal segments to form the crop. The
oesophagus is folded longitudinally and in its anterior regions it bears
many backwardly-directed setae.

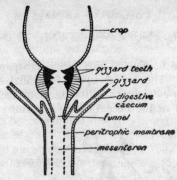

Fig. 23.12. Diagram of crop, gizzard and mesenteron of cockroach in L.S.

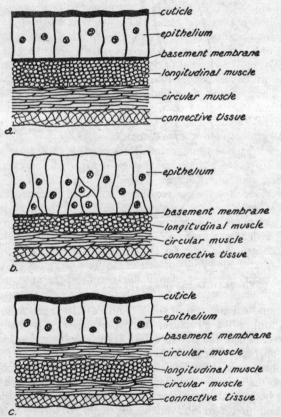

Fig. 23.13. Histology of gut of *Periplaneta*. (a) Fore-gut in T.S. (b) Mid-gut in T.S. (c) Hind-gut in T.S.

The gizzard is a short conical chamber with thick muscular walls. Its lumen is considerably reduced by infolding of the wall: the six principal folds have heavily sclerotized thickenings culminating in pointed teeth. Behind the teeth, the six folds are thickly beset with fine setae. A funnel-shaped invagination of the gizzard projects a short distance into the mid-gut (*see* Fig. 23.12).

This is lined completely by tall columnar endodermal cells. At its anterior end, there are eight delicate endodermal outgrowths, the *mesenteric caeca*. They are devices for increasing the area of absorptive surface. The mid-gut ends just in front of a tuft of very fine outgrowths, the excretory *Malpighian tubules*.

The hind-gut consists of the *ileum, colon* and *rectum*. At the junction of the mid-gut and ileum there is a sphincter-like arrangement, sometimes called the *pyloric valve*. The ileum is short and narrow; it receives the openings of the Malpighian tubules. Internally it is much folded longitudinally and possesses many fine backward-pointing setae. A ring-like internal fold marks the junction of ileum and colon, which is wider and longer than the ileum and comparatively smooth inside. The rectum is short and wide. Internally it has six pronounced longitudinal ridges covered with fine setae. The ridges form the so-called *rectal glands*. The *anus* is a slit-like aperture lying beneath the tenth tergum between the paraprocts.

The cockroach is omnivorous; it is capable of dealing with almost any kind of organic material, though it shows distinct preference for sugary and starchy substances. It can maintain its body weight almost indefinitely on a nitrogen-free diet. The food is seized by the mandibles and held by the laciniae and galeae of the maxillae, and the glossae and paraglossae of the labium. The powerful mandibles chew the food with a lateral action. During chewing it is irrigated with saliva.

The *salivary glands* lie on either side of the crop in the pro- and meso-thorax. Each gland consists of a diffuse secretory portion divided into two main branches. Small ducts unite to form a main duct on each side; the two main ducts join beneath the oesophagus in the neck region. At each side, there is also a dilated *reservoir*; the ducts from the reservoirs unite beneath the oesophagus. The common reservoir duct joins the common gland duct to form the main salivary duct which empties under the hypopharynx (*see* Fig. 23.14). The saliva is a neutral liquid containing an amylase which converts starch to maltose. It also wets the food, thus assisting chewing and later, swallowing.

After chewing, the food is pushed into the buccal cavity by the maxillae and labium and proceeds to the crop by peristalsis. Much of the digestion takes place in the crop by means of enzymes regurgitated from the mesenteron. In the gizzard, there is further trituration by the sharp teeth, and the setae in its posterior region have a filtering action, preventing large particles passing further. They are pushed forward for further reduction in size.

The cells lining the mesenteron secrete three types of enzymes. There are proteases of the trypsin and erepsin types but no enzyme resembling the pepsin of vertebrates; these proteases hydrolyse proteins to amino-acids. Lipases act on fats and various carbohydrate-splitting enzymes produce monosaccharide sugars from the carbohydrate intake. The

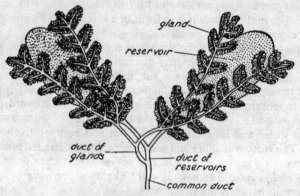

Fig. 23.14. Salivary glands of cockroach.

digested products are absorbed by the cells lining the mesenteron and digestive caeca. Secretion of the mesenteron cells is both by diffusion and by cytolysis, when whole cells are liberated to break up in the lumen.

A peculiar structure in the mesenteron is the *peritrophic membrane*. This is a delicate tube, chitinous in nature, which encloses the food mass as it passes through the mid-gut. It appears to be continuously secreted by the funnel-shaped extension of the gizzard and its function seems to be that of protecting the fragile mesenteron from abrasion by indigestible particles among the food. It is fully permeable to both enzymes and food solutions; both of these must pass through the peritrophic membrane. Traces of the membrane can be seen around the pellets of faeces.

In the hind-gut, and especially in the region of the rectal glands, absorption of water takes place. Conservation of water is very important in insects, and hence the faeces are nearly dry. It will be appreciated that continuous and powerful peristalsis of the hind-gut is essential, not only for egestion of faeces, but also for elimination of the practically solid uric acid. The dilated rectum serves for temporary storage of faeces while water is being absorbed.

Absorbed food is circulated by the blood, and storage substances in the fat body include carbohydrates, proteins and fats. The fat body fills a great part of the haemocoel and is in close contact with the gut. From the fat body, soluble food materials are released for circulation in the blood. It is noteworthy that the blood of insects contains a high concentration of sugar; this accounts, in part at least, for their amazing energy output.

The total time taken for materials to traverse the alimentary canal of the cockroach varies from ten to thirty hours.

Respiration

Oxygen penetrates all parts of the body by an intricate branched network of tubes which form the *tracheal system*. Each trachea consists

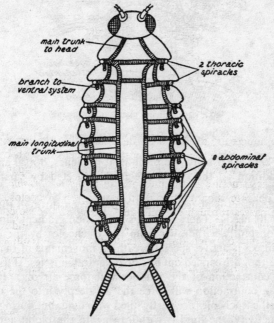

Fig. 23.15. Tracheal system of cockroach, dorsal view

of a squamous epithelium which secretes a chitinous lining. To prevent the tubes collapsing, they are strengthened by a further spiral band of chitin. The tracheae diminish in size as they branch, and they finally end in minute *intracellular tracheoles* which lack the chitinous lining.

These ultimate air vessels penetrate the tissues of the body and ensure that no cell is far removed from its oxygen supply.

Air enters the body by means of ten *spiracles*, which are narrow oval slits in soft rounded patches of cuticle. There are two pairs of thoracic spiracles, one between pro- and meso-thorax, and one between meso- and meta-thorax, situated in the pleura. In the abdomen, each of the first eight segments has a pair located in the soft pleura. The spiracles are controlled by a valvular arrangement operated by special muscles. Internally, they lead into air sacs from which the tracheal trunks

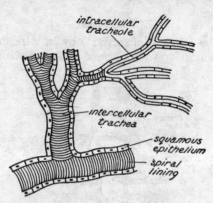

Fig. 23.16. Trachea with tracheoles.

branch. There are usually two prominent branches, dorsal and ventral, and, in addition all the trunks are interconnected by smaller trunks (*see* Fig. 23.15).

When the insect is at rest, diffusion of oxygen through the spiracles suffices for its needs. There is always a diffusion gradient, since oxygen is being constantly withdrawn from the tracheoles by the cells. But when the insect is active, special breathing movements of the abdomen take place; they are carried out by dorso-ventral muscles. If the spiracles are open, contraction of the muscles will force air out. If they are closed, then contraction will force the air deeply into the tracheoles. Normally, the tracheoles are partly filled with fluid, but during increased muscular activity, the fluid is withdrawn into the blood and thus the air comes into still closer contact with the tissues. Withdrawal of the fluid is an osmotic phenomenon due to the increase of soluble substances in the blood. The chief of these is lactic acid.

Of all animals, insects show the greatest increase in rate of metabolism when active. Three of the factors which enable them to perform sustained and rapid muscular activity should now be clear. They are:

the efficient method of supplying oxygen to the tissues, the high concentration of sugar in the blood, and the large stores in the fat body.

The Blood Vascular System

The blood is colourless and contains suspended amoeboid leucocytes. The *heart* and the *aorta* are the only walled vessels, the rest of the system occupying *haemocoels* between other organs. The heart is a

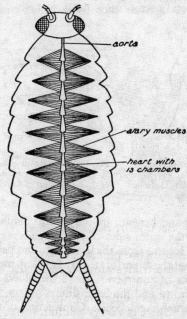

Fig. 23.17. Heart and alary muscles of cockroach, dorsal view.

dorsal tube lying immediately beneath the terga of thorax and abdomen. It can easily be seen and its pulsations watched in a living cockroach, if the wings are removed. There are thirteen *segmental dilations* sometimes called chambers; ten are abdominal and three thoracic. From the most anterior dilation a narrow aorta leads forward over the oesophagus and empties the blood into the sinuses of the head (*see* Fig. 23.17). At the front of each chamber, a pair of valves prevent backward flow. Each chamber, except the last abdominal, has a pair of *ostia* guarded by valves which allow blood to pass in but not out (*see* Fig. 23.18).

The thorax and abdomen are divided by two delicate membranous horizontal diaphragms into three regions: a *pericardial haemocoel*, a *perivisceral haemocoel* and a *sternal haemocoel* (*see* Fig. 23.19). The heart lies in the pericardial haemocoel which is delimited by the dorsal diaphragm or *pericardium*; this is bulged slightly upwards. To its floor are attached intersegmental *alary muscles*. Each is triangular with its broad end near the middle of the pericardium; its pointed outer end is attached somewhat laterally to the terga. Portions of the alary muscles also appear to be attached to the ventral surface of the heart. The perivisceral haemocoel is the largest; it is bounded dorsally

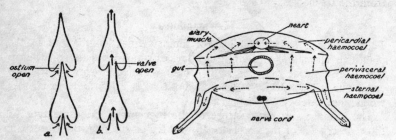

Fig. 23.18. Diagram of portion of *Periplaneta* heart. (*a*) Valves closed, ostia open. (*b*) Ostia closed, valves open.

Fig. 23.19. Diagram of body of cockroach in T.S. showing the main haemocoels and direction of flow of blood.

by the pericardium and beneath by the ventral diaphragm. Laterally, channels lead into the outer sides of the appendages from the sternal haemocoel. Blood returns from the limbs into the perivisceral haemocoel. Both diaphragms are perforated by small apertures.

Rhythmical waves of contraction drive the blood forward through the heart, into the aorta and the head sinuses. Thence it runs into the perivisceral and sternal haemocoels. Contraction of the alary muscles flattens the dorsal diaphragm thus increasing the capacity of the pericardial haemocoel. Thus blood enters from the perivisceral region. Negative pressure in the successive chambers of the heart causes them to suck in blood from the pericardial haemocoel. The general course of the circulation is represented in the diagram below.

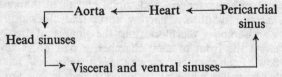

At the base of each antenna is a small contractile vesicle which pumps blood into a perforated vessel leading almost the whole length of the appendage. Escaping from the perforations, the blood runs back into the head sinuses. Similar pulsating mechanisms are found at the bases of the wings. They force blood into the nervures in the anterior part of the wings and it returns by the posterior nervures.

The functions of the blood in the cockroach are chiefly transport of food and excretory substances, and circulation of the defensive leucocytes. It has little to do with transport of oxygen though there must be some in solution. It plays a part in enhancing the rate of absorption of oxygen during periods of rapid metabolism by withdrawing water from the tracheoles.

Locomotion

The cockroach has strong legs of almost equal length, and in the plantulae, claws and arolium it has devices which will enable it to grip any type of surface. It is a swift runner, as anyone who has tried to catch one will appreciate. Though both sexes in *Periplaneta* possess wings, they rarely fly.

The jointing and musculature of the legs are of the same type as those described for the crayfish. In walking or running, the front pair of legs pull the body forward while the other two pairs push it. Three of the legs are on the ground together while the other three are moving forward. The first and third legs of one side respectively pull and push, while the second leg of the other side acts as a prop. Then the other three legs are placed on the ground a little further forward and the process is repeated.

Though cockroaches rarely fly, a brief account of insect flight is given here. The insects are the only animals which have evolved organs specially for flight. In other animals which fly, the wings or planes are modifications of organs primarily evolved for other purposes. In bats and birds, the wings are modifications of pentadactyl limbs, while in flying squirrels, lizards and phalangers there are merely lateral expansions of the body wall which allow of planing.

The movements of the wings provide both forward thrust and lifting power. Furthermore, precise control of the individual wings enables some insects to perform the most fantastic feats with agility and precision. The wings are controlled by two different sets of muscles, known as *direct* and *indirect muscles*. The direct muscles are attached to the wing-bases and they exercise control over the wing setting; the indirect muscles are longitudinal and dorso-ventral bands in the thorax; they are not connected to the wings (*see* Fig. 23.20 (*a*)). The attachment of the wings to the thorax is a simple but highly effective example of a lever. The pleural point of attachment lies a little outside the tergal point (*see* Fig. 23.20 (*b*)). Thus a very small movement at the point of attachment will be multiplied many times at the wing-tips. For some insects the factor is as high as several thousands. Contraction of the dorso-ventral indirect muscles will lower the dorsal wall and thus force the wing up, while contraction of the longitudinal muscles will arch the dorsal wall upwards and so force the wing down. In some insects, these indirect muscles can cause the wings to beat several hundred times per second. However, the flight is not a simple matter of beating up

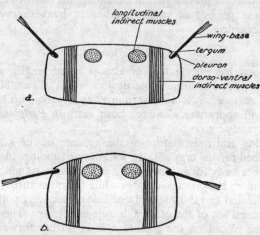

Fig. 23.20. Diagrams of thorax of cockroach in T.S. to show wing movements caused by indirect muscles. (*a*) Dorsal-ventral muscles contracted, wings up. (*b*) Longitudinal muscles contracted, wings down.

and down; the small direct muscles alter the angle of the wing as required. In straight flight, the wings beat diagonally forward and downward, then backward and upward. On the downstroke, the wing is concave beneath; on the upstroke the wing is turned over so that the concave lower surface is now on top. Thus both strokes give lift to the body. Turning is accomplished by altering the angle of one wing so that it has less thrust than the other.

In the cockroach the front pair of wings probably act more as stiff planes, while the hind-wings do the work. More advanced insects have both pairs of wings fastened together by various devices, or have one pair considerably reduced (*see* pp. 718–19).

Growth

As in all multicellular animals, growth occurs by addition of new cells formed by division of existing cells. Apart from nervous tissue, all cells are able to divide and thus the body grows harmoniously in accordance with a predetermined plan, if temperature, food supply and other environmental factors are favourable. As in all poikilothermous (cold-blooded) animals, growth is considerably affected by temperature.

Growth in an insect is not however smooth and regular. The existence of the cuticle imposes arbitrary checks. Thus, immediately after ecdysis, an insect grows quickly, but the rate of growth gradually slows down and ceases altogether until the next moult takes place. In the cockroach there are usually seven ecdyses in the life. It moults three times in the first year, and once each in the second, third, fourth and fifth years. Before moulting, the endocuticle is dissolved by the secretion of special glands activated by moulting hormones (*see* p. 746). The new cuticle is begun before the old is cast. The actual ecdysis begins by a longitudinal split down the thorax, then the abdomen and limbs split. The body is then drawn out of the old cuticle. The new one thickens and slowly hardens. After the seventh moult, the animal grows for a short time, and then, apart from minor fluctuations, there is no more change in weight. The only major changes which occur in the first five years are the gradual development of wings and reproductive organs. With the exception of a few wingless species of the lower orders, no adult insects moult, and hence they cannot grow except for a short period after the last moult. The disparities in size of adult insects are due mainly to nutritional conditions during the growing period; starved larvae produce small adults.

Excretion

The waste products of carbohydrate metabolism are, as usual, carbon dioxide and water. Much of the carbon dioxide is eliminated through the cuticle which is permeable to gases, and the remainder by the tracheal system. Water is carefully conserved since insects with mouth parts like the cockroach cannot drink. The principal nitrogenous waste is uric acid; it is eliminated by way of the *Malpighian tubules*.

The tubules are ectodermal growths extending from the anterior region of the ileum into the haemocoel. They are long and extremely slender and penetrate among the viscera over the greater part of the thorax and abdomen. In *Periplaneta*, they appear to lie in six groups, with about twelve tubules in each group. Functionally, each consists of two distinct regions. The distal half secretes the urates of potassium and sodium which are extracted from the blood. This region is alkaline. In the proximal half, secretion of carbon dioxide renders the contents acid, uric acid is precipitated and the potassium and sodium are resorbed as bicarbonates. The urine passes into the ileum and is mixed with faeces and excreted via the rectum, where more water is absorbed.

Uric acid is also stored in special cells of the fat body. Much of it appears to remain there; it illustrates excretion by storage.

Insects differ from other animals in the small fraction of the osmotic pressure of the blood due to chlorides and the large fraction due to organic substances in solution. Of these, the chief are amino-acids. The osmotic pressure of the blood is very high and the salt fraction is regulated by the Malpighian tubules. The cuticle is practically impermeable to water; loss takes place mainly by evaporation through the

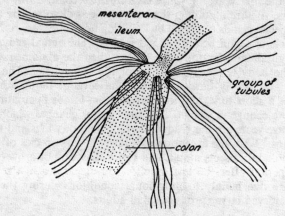

Fig. 23.21. Malpighian tubules of *Periplaneta*.

spirocles. Cockroaches do not drink; the cuticle, the rectal glands and some measure of control of the spiracular apertures, ensure that there is little loss. Deficiency is made up by water from the food and from oxidation of carbohydrate (the complete oxidation of 100 g of glucose yields 60 g of water).

Sensitivity, Co-ordination and Behaviour

The central and peripheral nervous systems are essentially similar to those of the crayfish. There is, however, a greater degree of differentiation in the brain. Also, there is a greater variety of sense organs.

The fused *cerebral ganglia* are two white bilobed structures lying in the head above the tentorium and almost between the bases of the antennae. Two *circum-oesophageal commissures*, short and thick, pass around the oesophagus and join the *sub-oesophageal ganglion* which is situated just inside the occipital ring (*see* Fig. 23.22). The *ventral nerve cord* consists of *segmental ganglia* joined by double *connectives*. Each segment of the thorax has a large ganglion and there are six abdominal ganglia, the last being larger than the others.

A pair of large *optic nerves* pass out laterally to the eyes; below and behind them, the smaller *antennary nerves* can be seen. The sympathetic system consists of three parts; from the brain, nerves pass to the *corpora cardiaca* and *allata* and supply the heart and foregut (*see* Fig. 23.23); a ventral nerve from the sub-oesophageal ganglion passes

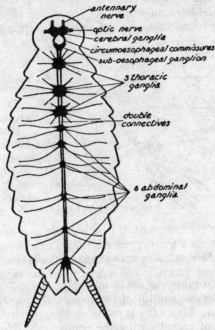

Fig. 23.22. Central nervous system of *Periplaneta*, dorsal view.

between the longitudinal connectives and supplies the spiracles; a nerve from the last ganglion supplies the hind-gut and reproductive system. The sub-oesophageal ganglion supplies nerves to the mandibles, maxillae and labium, and therefore represents three fused pairs of ganglia. Each thoracic ganglion gives out four pairs of nerves and each abdominal ganglion has two pairs, except the last, which has four pairs supplying the posterior five segments. Passing through the nerve cord is a giant fibre system facilitating rapid escape reactions. There is little more concentration of the central nervous system than was seen in the crayfish, but the shortening of the commissures brings the cerebral and sub-oesophageal ganglia very close together.

The compound eyes are the most obvious sense organs. They consist of *ommatidia* as in the crayfish, though it seems probable that the pigment cannot be retracted, and hence only mosaic images can be formed. Sensitivity to touch, chemicals, vibration and pressure, is located in minute sensillae of various types. Each tactile sensilla is situated at the

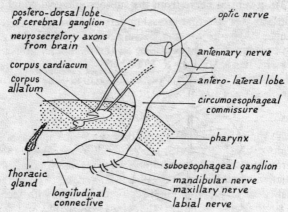

Fig. 23.23. Lateral view of anterior part of nervous system of cockroach, and endocrine structures (*partly after Buch and Keister*).

base of a fine pointed seta. At its base is a thin ring-like area of cuticle to which is attached a sensory cell embedded in a larger epidermal cell which secretes the seta. Any movement of the seta will stimulate the sensory cell, from which a fine nerve fibre passes into the central nervous system. Tactile sensillae are thinly distributed all over the body, but are particularly plentiful on the antennae (*see* Fig. 23.24).

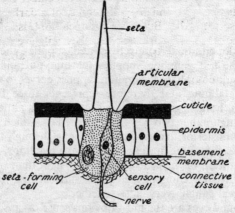

Fig. 23.24. V.S. of tactile sensilla of cockroach.

There is good evidence for the existence of two kinds of olfactory sensillae, respectively subserving smell and taste. Several kinds of these organs occur on the antennae, maxillary and labial palps, and possibly also in the buccal cavity. They are of great value to the insect in finding its food, recognizing its fellow species and the opposite sex.

Some insects, for example grasshoppers and crickets, have complicated tympanal organs for the perception of sound. They are not present in cockroaches, but sensillae on the anal cerci are sensitive to vibrations with frequencies up to 3,000 cycles per second. This enables the insect to detect movements of the air behind it; such stimulation causes the cockroach to run away at full speed.

Behaviour

The brain mainly serves as a reception centre for impulses from the sense-organs of the head, and it relays impulses to effectors which will produce responses to the stimuli. There are a number of regions which function as units controlled by local reflexes. Thus the mouth parts constitute a single functional region concerned with feeding; the legs with running and walking; the wings with flying and the genital armature with copulation. The only concern of the brain with these functional units is the initiation of action and the inhibition of other functional units.

Insects are essentially creatures whose behaviour, to a large extent follows fixed patterns which have reached very complex routines in social insects such as ants, bees, wasps and termites. Nevertheless, in all these fixed-behaviour patterns, there is always some degree of plasticity, and some portion of "learned" behaviour. Very numerous experiments show that insects can learn and remember for a short time. Cockroaches dislike light, and given the choice of a dark or light abode, they will choose the dark. But if we produce unpleasant stimuli such as electric shocks, in the dark habitat, they will eventually learn to choose the light. However, they do not appear to be able to remember for more than an hour or so. It has also been shown that they are capable of learning the right path through a maze. There are glimmerings of intelligence, possibly as much as one would expect from a creature with such a minute brain.

Endocrine Glands

Several endocrine glands have been located in insects and their effects determined by experiment. There are hormones which control moulting, growth, metamorphosis and gamete production. Neurosecretions (*see* p. 1081) from the brain are released via the *corpora cardiaca*, minute blue structures behind the brain. They have nervous connections with the *corpora allata*, more posterior small yellow structures. The only epithelial endocrine glands are the *thoracic* glands in the first segment of the thorax (*see* Fig. 23.23). There is further discussion of insect hormones on p. 746.

Reproduction

The sexes are separate and can be distinguished by several external features in the abdominal region (*see* Fig. 23.25). The female abdomen

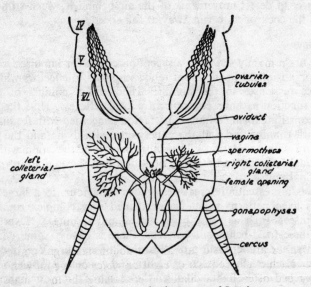

Fig. 23.25. Female reproductive system of *Periplaneta*.

is broader and bears the boat-shaped oothecal chamber with the slit for the emergence of the oothecae. In the male, the ninth sternum bears the anal styles. The reproductive organs of both sexes are embedded in fat and extend backwards from the fourth abdominal segment.

The *testes* are small lobed masses lying latero-dorsally in the fourth and fifth abdominal segments. Slender white *vasa deferentia* are joined to the testes and pass backwards and inwards to join a wider *ejaculatory duct* in the seventh segment. Their entrance is concealed by the numerous white tubules of the *utricular gland* (*mushroom gland*). Among the tubules are shorter thicker diverticula of the ejaculatory duct which constitute the *seminal vesicles*. Dorsal to the ejaculatory duct, and opening separately into the genital chamber is a *phallic (conglobate) gland*. In the genital chamber is a complicated series of chitinous bristles, teeth, hooks and pads known collectively as the *gonapophyses*. They function only during copulation.

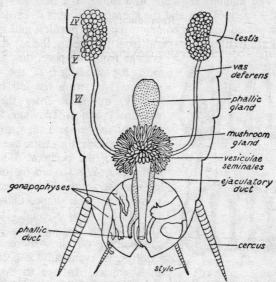

Fig. 23.26. Male reproductive system of *Periplaneta*.

The *ovaries* are situated laterally in abdominal segments four, five and six. Each ovary consists of eight *ovarioles* or *egg tubules*. At the posterior end of each is a dilatation containing the most mature egg, then towards the anterior is a string of developing eggs, gradually diminishing in size. The bases of the eight ovarioles of one side unite to form a wide *oviduct* which meets the other in the mid line. The wide flabby tube formed by their union leads into the genital chamber at a slit-like aperture. Just anterior to this aperture is a small sac with a narrow duct; this is the *spermotheca*. Opening into the genital chamber in front of the oviduct are the large branched *colleterial glands*. The left gland has yellow tubules and is much larger than the right, in which the tubules are white. In the female, the *gonapophyses* are much less elaborate than those of the male and consist essentially of three pairs of chitinous rods concerned with shaping the ootheca and deposition of the eggs in it (*see* Fig. 23.25).

Mating is a complicated process during which the posterior ends of the male and female are locked together by the genital armature; the heads face in opposite directions. The sperm are ejaculated together with fluid from the utricular gland to form a sticky *spermatophore*. After one hour or so, the spermatophore is attached to the spermothecal opening and then fluid from the phallic gland cements it firmly in position. The animals separate, and during the next day the sperm pass into the spermotheca and the spermatophore is discarded.

Eggs are passed into the common oviduct from left and right alternately and are fertilized by sperm from the spermotheca. As the eggs

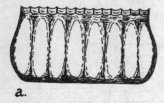

a.

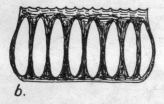

b.

Fig. 23.27. Ootheca of *Periplaneta*.
(a) Closed. (b) One side removed to show eggs.

emerge from the pore, they are coated with the secretions of the colleterial glands. That from the left contains a protein, and that from the right a dihydroxyphenol. Together, in the presence of oxygen and the enzyme polyphenol oxidase, they form the dark hard covering of the ootheca. While this is still plastic, it is shaped by the gonapophyses into a purse-like capsule. It contains sixteen eggs shaped like cigars and lying in two rows of eight. It is carried about by the female for several days, gradually protruding more and more until it is eventually deposited in a dark crevice. In two to three weeks, the ootheca is completely black (*see* Fig. 23.27). It is about 1 cm in length. The young cockroaches hatch out in about six weeks, depending somewhat on temperature. Apart from the absence of wings, they are, in external features, small replicas of the adults.

Development

The development of insects is very complicated and specialized. In all essentials, it is similar to that of the crayfish, but there is one notable exception connected with adaptation to the land habitat. This is the presence of embryonic membranes which enclose a fluid cavity in which the embryo can develop.

The egg is centrolecithal and at first many mitotic divisions produce a coenocyte. The nuclei then migrate to the periphery and form a cellular layer, thus establishing the blastoderm. One half of the blastoderm forms a thickened plate of cells and from this the embryo develops (*see* Fig. 23.28).

Gastrulation proceeds much as in the crayfish and soon the surface of the blastoderm shows thickenings which mark the positions of head and appendages (see Fig. 23.28). The embryonic ectoderm and the extra-embryonic blastoderm grow up round the embryo as a double fold which soon encloses the ventral surface completely. The inner

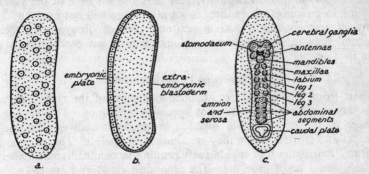

Fig. 23.28. Early stages in development of cockroach. (a) V.S. coenocyte stage. (b) V.S. blastoderm. (c) Surface view of ventral plate.

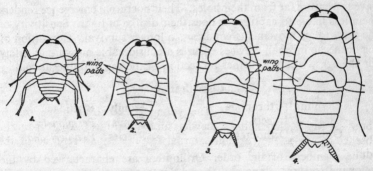

Fig. 23.29. Four stages in the growth of a cockroach showing developing wing pads.

membrane is the *amnion* enclosing a fluid cavity; the outer layer is the *serosa*.

The ventral plate extends round the sides of the embryo and eventually grows over and completely encloses the yolk. Thus is reached the peculiar condition of an embryo well developed ventrally and carrying a large yolk-sac dorsally. The yolk is absorbed and dorsal development completed before hatching.

The young cockroach which emerges is about one centimetre long. It has no wings, but after the first moult they appear as small outgrowths at the sides of the meso- and meta-thorax. They increase in size at each moult, and after the last, they are fully formed. Carnivorous tendencies of older, stronger animals are somewhat conducive to dispersal. Except in very favourable conditions, however, *P. americana* does not produce very large numbers. The long period of development to sexual maturity will be completed by comparatively few under natural conditions. In captivity, they may live for nine or ten years. Living in buildings where there is warmth, there will not normally be any adverse conditions such as extreme cold or drought. In their natural habitat, in the warmer regions, there is less need for special survival adaptations.

Adaptation to Environment

Apart from general features applicable to most of the class Insecta, cockroaches show a number of special adaptations. The flattened shape of the body enables them to insinuate themselves into small cracks and crevices where they are almost inaccessible. The shape and disposition of the legs enable swift running in confined spaces where flight would be of little use. The plantulae, claws and arolia ensure satisfactory grip on any type of surface, so that running is not impeded. They can survive on a wide variety of food materials and hence do not have to venture far from their holes. Their nocturnal emergence renders them less liable to capture, as does their dislike of light. Sensitivity of the cerci to air movements conduces to longer survival. Deposition of the oothecae in small crevices ensures a considerable measure of safety for the eggs, with the further protection of the tough oothecal coat.

Classification

Phylum:	Arthropoda	Family:	Blattidae
Class:	Insecta	Genus:	*Periplaneta*
Order:	Orthoptera	Species:	*P. americana*

The members of the order Orthoptera are characterized by the following features: long and thread-like antennae; the possession of anal cerci; mouth parts of the biting type; the presence of long, narrow, tough tegmina and broad membranous hind-wings. The Blattidae have large flat coxae at the roots of legs of equal size, adapted for running. Cockroaches of the genus *Periplaneta* are distinguished by colour and by the possession of wings in both sexes. Minor differences, such as size, separate the species.

THE VARIETY OF INSECTS

One reason for the outstanding success of insects as terrestrial animals has been their adaptability. They have evolved countless variations on a common theme; these have enabled them to inhabit every type of environment with conspicuous success. It is strange that they have failed so lamentably to colonize the sea; only one species, a midge, lives in the sea throughout all the stages of its life. Even in a single order, there may be an enormous range of diversity; here we can only indicate the main features in which the insects differ among themselves. They are: size, shape and colour; mouth parts and hence food materials; legs, and thus type of locomotion on a solid substratum; wings, and thus the kind of flight, if any; the various types of reproduction; the life history and type of metamorphosis.

Size, Colour and Shape

Two basic features of the insect body plan, the exoskeleton and the tracheate system of respiration, have prevented the achievement of large size. The bulkiest insect known, is the Goliath beetle of Africa; specimens have been measured which were more than 100 mm or so long and about 50 mm wide. Certain stick insects of the tropics are more than 30 cm long, but their bodies are very thin and hence the volume is small. Some moths have a wingspan of nearly 30 cm, while extinct dragonflies of the Carboniferous period had a wing-span of 60 cm. At the other end of the range of size, some beetles which live in fungi, and some tiny flies, may have bodies less than one-quarter of a millimeter long.

The general small size has given insects several advantages in the struggle for existence. They need but little food, and they can conceal themselves effectively in a small space. Hence they tend to occupy situations which are not available to other animals on account of size. The amount of food they consume is insignificant; insects can generally exist perfectly well on unconsidered trifles. Tracheate respiration is very effective for a small body, but it would be impossible in a large body. Any major increase in size would involve corresponding increase in the exoskeleton and flight would be sluggish if not impracticable.

In all animals, colour provides some protection from predators. We find among insects many which are sombre in colour and hence inconspicuous. Others resort to camouflage of various types so that they resemble the background. Yet others imitate the twigs and leaves or bark of the plants which they normally inhabit. Most strange are those which have evolved mimicry, whereby they appear to copy, more or less perfectly, other insects which are generally avoided for their distasteful properties; such inedible or dangerous insects display bold and bright colours and parade themselves ostentatiously in full view of would-be predators. Wasps and ladybirds and many caterpillars provide striking examples of this warning coloration.

The shape of the body is always an expression of the mode of life. As with all their features, in the insects we find great variety of shape. Some groups such as the stick insects, the May-flies and dragonflies have evolved attenuated shapes; some like the sturdy dor beetles and ladybirds have bulbous, almost hemisperical shapes; others like the scale insects are extremely flattened. A flea's body is flattened laterally to allow of easy passage between hair and feathers. Sometimes the shape is adapted for flight; sometimes for concealment in small crevices; sometimes for mimicry; each insect's particular shape suits it for its particular purposes.

Mouth Parts

No musician could compose so many variations on a single theme as the insects have done with their mouth parts. All have the same basic equipment consisting of labrum, mandibles, maxillae and labium. In many adult insects, these parts have become so transformed that we could not possibly recognize them without embryological studies of their development. The primitive pattern, adapted for biting and chewing, was probably somewhat like that described for the cockroach, and it is still present in most orders. They include the Thysanura, Diplura, Collembola, Orthoptera, Plecoptera,

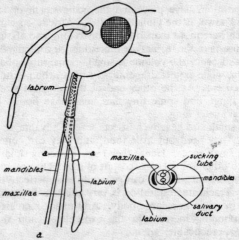

Fig. 23.30. Mouth parts of *Aphis*. (*a*) Lateral view. (*b*) T.S. at plane *a–a* when sheathed.

Dermaptera, Odonata, Psocoptera, some Anoplura, Neuroptera, Mecoptera, Coleoptera, Strepsiptera and some Hymenoptera.

A very large number of insects have mouth parts adapted for piercing plant or animal tissues and for sucking out the juices. Many of them are serious pests of plants and animals and are often carriers of disease. They belong to the orders Thysanoptera (thrips), Hemiptera (aphides), some Anoplura (lice), some Diptera (two-winged flies), and Aphaniptera (fleas). In the Hemiptera, the labrum forms a beak to contain the other mouth parts when the insect is not feeding. The mandibles and maxillae are produced into slender sharp-pointed stylets, while the labium forms a four-jointed sucking tube (*see* Fig. 23.30). The stylets pierce the plant tissues, then the labium enters the wound and sucks up the juices. Great damage is caused to crops, and, perhaps of greater importance, virus diseases are spread by the feeding habits of these insects. The green-fly of roses and the black-fly of broad beans are familiar examples.

Two notorious blood-sucking Diptera with piercing and sucking mouth parts are the mosquitoes (*Anopheles spp.*), and the tsetse flies (*Glossina spp.*). The former carry *Plasmodium* which causes malaria, and the latter carry *Trypanosoma* which causes the dreaded sleeping-sickness (*see* Chap. 32). The mouth parts of both these insects are shown in Fig. 23.31. Other piercing and blood-sucking pests are the lice (Anoplura). The body louse and head louse of man are well-known examples, though practically all mammals are afflicted with other species. The body louse (*Pediculus humanus*) is known to

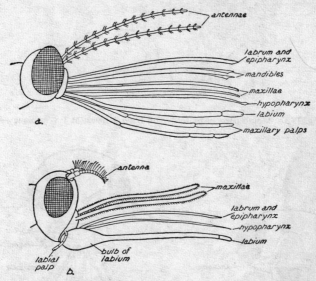

Fig. 23.31. (*a*) Mouth parts of female *Anopheles*. (*b*) Mouth parts of *Glossina*.

be the carrier of the organisms causing typhus fever, relapsing and trench fever and other diseases.

The Lepidoptera and some Diptera have mouth parts only suited for sucking liquid food. In most of the Lepidoptera, the mandibles are absent while the maxillae form a sucking tube made of two halves which are the greatly elongated galeae. The maxillary palps are either absent or poorly developed. The labium is a small plate forming the floor of the mouth. Interlocking spines and hooks fasten together the two galeae; through this tube the insects suck up nectar. When not in use, the proboscis is coiled in a spiral under the thorax (*see* Fig. 23.32).

The sucking Diptera have extremely modified labia which are bent under the head when not in use. There are no mandibles, and the maxillae are represented by small palps only. The labium forms a soft proboscis expanded at the tip into two pads called labella. The mouth is in the centre and the salivary duct opens above it. A number of minute food channels spread laterally over each labellum and lead to the mouth; the size of these channels ensures that only liquid food and particles less than $4\,\mu$m in size can be sucked in (*see* Fig. 23.33).

Some Hymenoptera such as bees and wasps also have mouth parts modified to form a sucking apparatus. The honey-bee has blunted mandibles used

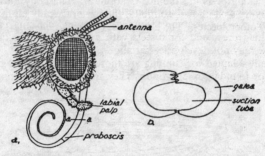

Fig. 23.32. Mouth parts of butterfly. (*a*) Lateral view. (*b*) T.S. at plane *a–a*.

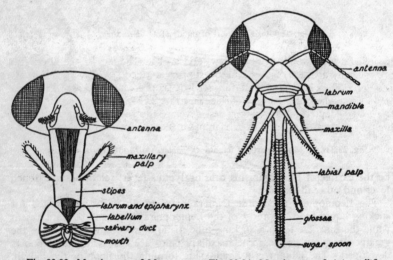

Fig. 23.33. Mouth parts of *Musca domestica*, from the front.

Fig. 23.34. Mouth parts of *Apis mellifica* (worker) from the front.

for moulding wax; the maxillae are blade-like and bristled, their palps being vestigial; the labial palps are prolonged while the paraglossae are vestigial. The greatest modification is in the glossae which are fused to form a long sucking tube with an expanded tip known sometimes as a "sugar spoon" or "bouton." Together, the galeae, glossae and labial palps form the tubular device used for sucking up the nectar of flowers (*see* Fig. 23.34).

In the Ephemeroptera (May-flies), the mouth parts are atrophied. The adults of various species are very short-lived. Some live only a few hours, and the maximum for any species is a few days.

Legs

A study of insect legs reveals many interesting adaptations. Some of the more important are those subserving running, jumping, clasping, swimming, digging, catching prey, and for insects with a short adult life the legs are slender. Some may not develop legs at all.

Legs typically adapted for running are those described for the cockroach, though they are found in other groups. They are slender, but strong, of equal

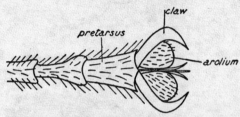

Fig. 23.35. Lower part of tarsus of *M. domestica.*

length and have well-developed claws and arolia. The legs of the house-fly are specially adapted for walking on slippery surfaces, even in an inverted position. The claws and arolia are well developed and the latter exude a sticky fluid when pressed on a surface (*see* Fig. 23.35).

The leg adapted for jumping is best developed in some Orthoptera (grasshoppers and crickets) and in Aphaniptera (fleas). In the grasshopper, the

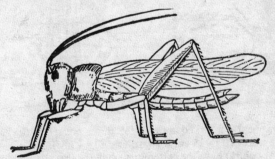

Fig. 23.36. Lateral view of grasshopper to show powerful femur of 3rd leg.

hind-limb is considerably larger than the others. The femur is long and thickened to contain the main jumping muscle; the tibia is also elongated but slender, while the tarsus is small and all of it lies on the ground (*see* Fig. 23.36). A similar condition is found in the fleas, though the disparity between the limbs is not so marked (*see* Fig. 23.37). The jumping powers of fleas are usually much exaggerated; a jump of 15 cm high and twice as much horizontally may be regarded as an expert performance. An interesting adaptation for jumping is found in the *Collembola* (spring-tails). On the fourth

Fig. 23.37. Lateral view of *Pulex irritans*, showing adaptation of 3rd leg for jumping.

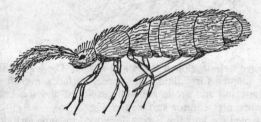

Fig. 23.38. Lateral view of spring-tail showing forked springing appendage.

Fig. 23.39. Claws of body louse. (*a*) Open. (*b*) Closed.

abdominal segment is a forked appendage; this is pressed to the ground and it hurtles the insect 20 to 25 cm forward (*see* Fig. 23.38).

The lice (Anoplura) have the extremities of all the legs adapted for clinging tightly to the hair or feathers of their hosts. The tibia has a claw-like process, the tarsus is a single podomere and very short, so that the claw can be closed against the tibial spur and a firm grip maintained (*see* Fig. 23.39).

Some insects alight very gently; the mosquito settles on the skin almost without the touch being perceptible. The legs are long and very slender and they cannot contain sufficient muscle to enable much walking or running (*see* Fig. 23.72). Crane-flies have similar but even longer legs adapted for alighting.

Many adult insects are adapted for movement in or on the water. The pond-skaters (Hemiptera) have narrow light bodies and widespread, thin, middle- and hind-legs with which they move over the surface. The short fore-legs are used for seizing prey. These insects are covered with a pile of very short fine setae, and their bodies are unwettable. The water-measurers (Hemiptera) have extremely attenuated bodies and all six legs are long and

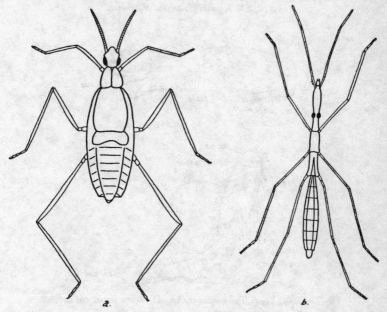

Fig. 23.40. (*a*) A pond skater, *Gerris*. (*b*) The water measurer, *Hydrometra*.

slender; it walks on the water. The water boatmen (Hemiptera) have the hind-limbs elongated and set with fringes of bristles; they act like oars and row the insect along, lying on its back. The water beetles swim by oar-like movements of the hind-limbs which have expanded tibiae and tarsi, fringed with setae.

Adult insects which dig into the earth have the front legs shortened and broadened. Often they are shaped like shallow scoops. In the mole-cricket (Orthoptera) there is, in addition, a pincer-like arrangement of the tibia and tarsus. This operates as a shears for cutting through roots (*see* Fig. 23.42).

The dragonflies (Odonata) have all the legs adapted for catching prey. They are of no use for walking but of some value in climbing. The expert at capturing prey with its fore-legs is the praying mantis, whose ferocious behaviour belies its devout appearance. The coxae are elongated and each

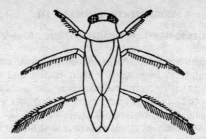

Fig. 23.41. A water boatman, *Notonecta*.

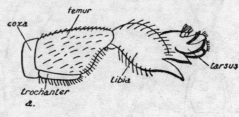

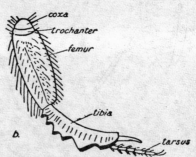

Fig. 23.42. (*a*) Front leg of mole cricket. (*b*) Front leg of dor beetle.

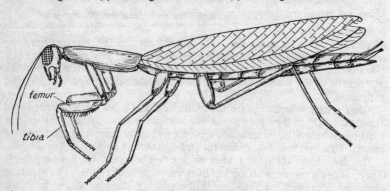

Fig. 23.43. *Mantis religiosa.*

femur is grooved underneath; the edges of the groove bear sharp spines. The tibia closes into this femoral groove like the blade of a pen-knife closes into its slot, and thus the hapless prey is firmly retained (*see* Fig. 23.43).

Wings

Here again we find a vast number of variations and it is not possible to do more than indicate the main evolutionary trends.

Many insects have no wings. They may be divided into two groups; those in which the wingless condition is primitive by derivation from wingless

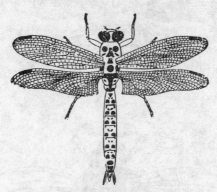

Fig. 23.44. Dragonfly, *Aeshna cyanea.*

ancestors; those in which the wings are secondarily absent, having been derived from winged ancestors. To the former group belong the Apterygota, containing the orders Diplura, Thysanura, Collembola and Protura. To the latter belong the parasitic orders Anoplura and Aphaniptera and the sterile castes of ants (Formicidae) and termites (Isoptera). In many orders, however, there are isolated cases in which one sex is without wings. For example, the females of many species are wingless; such are the common cockroach, the glow-worm, most scale-insects, the winter moth, and the vapourer moths. In the aphides, whole generations of parthenogenetic females are wingless.

Winged insects may be considered in three grades; those with two pairs of wings functioning separately; those having two pairs, with the anterior wing fastened to the posterior, and those which have reduced the wings to one pair with the posterior pair forming the peculiar halteres or balancers.

The ideal example of two pairs functioning separately is found in the dragon-flies (Odonata). Here both pairs of wings are of the same shape and size (*see* Fig. 23.44); this may be considered a primitive condition, since insects very similar to the present dragon-flies existed in the Carboniferous period. A somewhat similar condition is present in the stone-flies, the winged termites, the web-spinners, the scorpion-flies and the book lice.

In the cockroaches and their relatives, and in the ear-wigs, the front-wings are somewhat sclerotized and are called tegmina; the hind-wings are membranous and folded under the tegmina when the insect is not in flight. In both groups there is relatively little flying.

In the beetles, the front-wings are heavily sclerotized and are called elytra. During flight, they are held stiffly and act as planes. The Hemiptera have the front-wings partly sclerotized; they are called *hemi-elytra* (*see* Fig. 23.45).

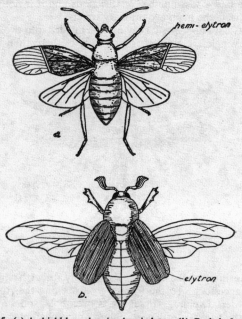

Fig. 23.45. (*a*) A shield bug showing hemi-elytra. (*b*) Cockchafer in flight.

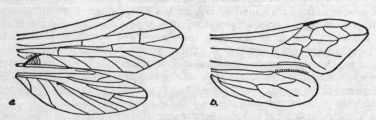

Fig. 23.46. Wing-locking mechanisms. (*a*) A moth. (*b*) A bee.

Some groups have evolved the device of locking fore- and hind-wings together, so that during flight they act as a single unit. Such are the thrips, the alder-flies, many moths, and the Hymenoptera. In the moths, the mechanism consists of a bristle projecting from the base of the hind-wing locked into a catch on the fore-wing (*see* Fig. 23.46(*a*)). The Hymenoptera have a series of hooks on the hind-wing which curve into a groove on the fore-wing (*see* Fig. 23.46(*b*)).

Two orders have reduced one pair of wings to form stalked or knob-like organs known as *halteres*. In the parasitic Strepsiptera, the fore-wings form the halteres (*see* Fig. 23.47(*b*)); in the Diptera, they are formed by the hind-wings (*see* Fig. 23.47(*a*)). The halteres have special muscles, are freely movable

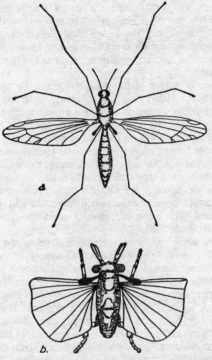

Fig. 23.47.   (*a*) Cranefly, *Tipula oleraceae*, showing posterior halteres. (*b*) A strepsipteran, *Stylops*, showing anterior halteres.

and capable of vibration. In the basal portion there are plentiful sensory cells. Halteres are regarded as organs perceiving stimuli related to balance and by their initial perception, correct nervous reactions and muscular adjustments are made to enable the insect to co-ordinate flight movements.

Types of Reproduction and Numbers of Offspring

Although most insects reproduce in the normal bisexual manner, there is a variety of other methods. Usually, the male produces sperm which are passed into the female and stored in a spermotheca. Then the eggs are fertilized through special pores in the tough egg-shells. Other methods include herma-phroditism, viviparity, parthenogenesis, paedogenesis and polyembryony.

There are a few instances of hermaphroditism where an adult insect, though female in appearance, produces both sorts of gametes and there is self-fertilization. Such are one species of scale insect (Hemiptera), one of the stone-flies (Plecoptera) and a Dipteran fly which inhabits the nests of ter-mites. The phenomenon of hermaphroditism has not become of any major importance in the insect world; where it occurs, it is probably secondary.

Viviparity is fairly common; the eggs are retained in the mother's body after fertilization; they hatch there, and then the young emerge. It is very common in the aphides, though there is oviparity as well, and is found also in several other groups. In certain Diptera such as the flesh-fly and tsetse-fly it is well recognized.

Parthenogenesis, or virgin birth, is reproduction by the female without previous fertilization. Hence, all the offspring must be females. In the aphides, there are many cycles of viviparous parthenogenetic reproduction alternating with one phase of oviparous reproduction. Males are only produced in the generation before oviparous reproduction and the fertilized eggs form the winter resting-stage. In the social Hymenoptera, the queen has the power of withholding, as well as of releasing, the sperm. Thus some of the eggs are not fertilized; they develop into males, while the fertilized eggs develop into females. Some of the Diptera have achieved a condition where males are unknown; there is only parthenogenesis and the entire species consists of females! The same unfortunate condition prevails in some of the gall-wasps (Hymenoptera).

Neoteny occurs when the larvae or pupae develop the power of repro-duction before metamorphosis into the adult form. It occurs in tiny insects. Such are the minute dipterans known as gall-midges and the chalcid wasps which lay their eggs inside the eggs of other insects. In the gall-midges, larvae produce parthenogenetic embryos internally (paedogenesis). Some chalcid wasps have an even more remarkable process. It is known as poly-embryony; the embryonic cells from a single egg, divide into groups and each group will form another embryo. An egg is laid inside a moth egg. As the chalcid embryo develops, it divides up into a chain of minute embryos which develop inside the body of the moth caterpillar. Thus a single egg may produce a large number of chalcid wasps; there are authentic counts of sixty or more, and one of over a thousand.

Type of Life History

The typical life history of insects is divisible into four clear-cut stages. They are: egg–larva–pupa–imago. In the egg, the embryonic development takes place. During the larval stage, growth, coupled with a number of ecdyses, occurs. Then there is a resting-phase, when the insect is called a pupa. During this, there is more or less drastic reorganization, and finally the fully developed imago emerges. Though this four-stage plan is the commonest, there are variations from it. For the purpose of life history, the insects may be divided into three groups, the Ametabola, Hemimetabola and Holometabola.

The Ametabola

This division includes four orders of small wingless insects: the Diplura (two-pronged bristle-tails), the Thysanura (three-pronged bristle-tails), the Collembola (spring-tails), and the Protura (*see* p. 723). The young hatch from the egg with the adult form of body; they differ from the adult only in their size and their sexual immaturity.

The Hemimetabola

Here are included eleven orders: the Orthoptera, Plecoptera (stone-flies), Dermaptera (earwigs), Ephemeroptera (May-flies), Odonata(dragon flies), Embioptera (web-spinners), Isoptera (termites), Psocoptera (book-lice). Anoplura (biting and sucking lice), Thysanoptera (thrips), Hemiptera (bugs). In all these orders, the young hatch in a form closely resembling the adult, but there are no wings. During successive moults, the wings gradually develop and the sex organs mature. The young stages are known as nymphs; in the Plecoptera, Ephemeroptera and Odonata, the nymphs are aquatic. Since there is no pupal stage, the Hemimetabola are said to undergo incomplete metamorphosis.

The Holometabola

Nine orders undergo the four-stage life history. They are: Neuroptera (alder-flies, lace-wings), Mecoptera (scorpion flies), Trichoptera (caddis-flies), Lepidoptera (butterflies and moths), Coleoptera (beetles), Strepsiptera (*see* p. 730), Hymenoptera (bees, wasps, ants), Diptera (two-winged flies), Aphaniptera (fleas). The young emerge from the eggs as larvae which do not resemble the imago, and during the life, there is a pupal stage. Hence metamorphosis is said to be complete. The larvae are variously known as grubs, maggots and caterpillars. The grub is known as a protopod larva; it emerges in a very undeveloped state when the appendages are rudimentary. Grubs are characteristic of protected larvae such as those of bees and wasps. Caterpillars hatch in a more advanced stage; they are known as polypod larvae, and are characteristic of the Lepidoptera. The oligopod larva has reached the highest phase; the transitory abdominal appendages are not even present at hatching. There are many examples in the Coleoptera. Apodous larvae have no trunk appendages; such are the maggots of flies.

THE CLASSIFICATION OF INSECTS

The class Insecta is split into two sub-classes and twenty-four orders. Here, a very brief outline of the main diagnostic features of each order is given, together with some common examples.

Sub-class Apterygota

The orders in this sub-class consist of wingless insects, the condition being primitive. They are the Diplura, Thysanura, Collembola and Protura. None undergo metamorphosis.

Order 1. Diplura

Very small white insects with no eyes. Found in soil and under stones. Long antennae and anal cerci. Almost "living fossils," they are survivors of a very ancient group (e.g. *Campodea*, *see* Fig. 23.48). All the Diplura were

Fig. 23.48. A two-pronged bristle-tail, *Campodea*.

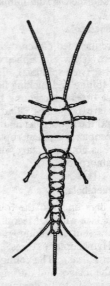

Fig. 23.49. A silver fish, *Lepisma saccharina*.

formerly included in the Thysanura, and were known as the two-pronged bristle-tails.

Order 2. Thysanura

The well-known silver-fish and sugar-brats. The antennae are long and there is a median appendage on the last segment as well as the two long anal cerci. The body is covered with scales (e.g. *Lepisma saccharina*, the silver-fish, *see* Fig. 23.49).

Order 3. Collembola

Very small insects with short antennae and a forked springing organ on the fourth abdominal segment. They have no compound eyes. The abdomen is peculiar in possessing only six segments (*see* Fig. 23.38). They are extremely common in the soil, on pasture land and in decaying organic matter (e.g. the spring-tails).

Order 4. Protura

Minute insects with twelve segments in the abdomen. No antennae or compound eyes or cerci, very small legs. Found under the bark of trees, in turf and in soil. Size about 1 mm or less (*see* Fig. 23.50).

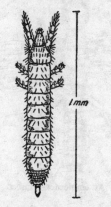

Fig. 23.50. A proturan insect.   Fig. 23.51. A stone-fly, *Perla*.

Sub-class Pterygota

This sub-class contains the remaining twenty orders. All either bear wings or are secondarily wingless. There is a metamorphosis which may be complete or incomplete.

Order 5. Orthoptera

The characteristics of the order have been given on p. 708. It includes cockroaches, crickets, grass-hoppers, locusts, stick insects, praying insects.

Order 6. Plecoptera

Long slender antennae and anal cerci. Mouth parts are reduced and weak. Always found near water; the nymphs are aquatic (e.g. the stone-flies, *see* Fig. 23.51).

Order 7. Dermaptera

Cerci modified to form forceps. Front-wings reduced to small leathery tegmina. Slight metamorphosis (e.g. the earwigs, *see* Fig. 23.52).

Order 8. Embioptera

Mainly tropical and sub-tropical. They spin silken tunnels in which they live. Both pairs of wings alike and often absent in the females. Elongated antennae. Slight metamorphosis in the male; none in the female (e.g. the web-spinners, *see* Fig. 23.53). None are British.

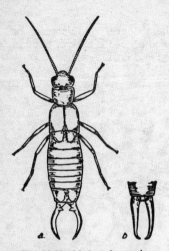

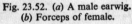

Fig. 23.52. (*a*) A male earwig.
(*b*) Forceps of female.

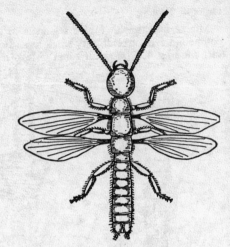

Fig. 23.53. An embiopteran insect.

Order 9. Isoptera

Social insects living in large communities. Reproductive castes and sterile castes; king, queen, soldiers and workers. Fully winged, partly winged and non-winged forms. Wings both similar and can be shed. Mouth parts biting. Metamorphosis slight or incomplete. Mainly tropical and subtropical (e.g. the termites or "white ants," *see* Fig. 23.54).

Order 10. Ephemeroptera

Short-lived imagines; aquatic nymphs. Mouth parts atrophied or almost so. Very long cerci and a median caudal filament. Long antennae. Hindwings much reduced (e.g. the May-flies, *see* Fig. 23.55).

Order 11. Odonata

Long-bodied, brilliant metallic colours. Mouth parts biting. Wings equal. Very large eyes. Aquatic nymphs (e.g. the dragonflies, *see* Fig. 23.44).

Order 12. Psocoptera

Very small insects. Winged with anterior wings larger or wingless. Cerci atrophied or almost so. Antennae fairly long. Biting mouth parts. Metamorphosis little or absent (e.g. book-lice and their allies, *see* Fig. 23.56(*a*)).

Order 13. Anoplura

All ectoparasites of birds and mammals. Wingless. Mouth parts for biting or piercing. Flattened body, short legs with claws adapted for clinging. No cerci. Biting and sucking lice. Notorious carriers of disease (*see* Fig. 23.56(*b*)).

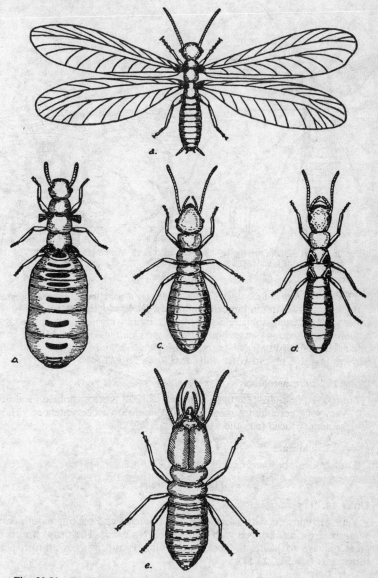

Fig. 23.54. Termites. (*a*) Winged male. (*b*) Queen. (*c*) Wingless worker. (*d*) King. (*e*) Wingless soldier.

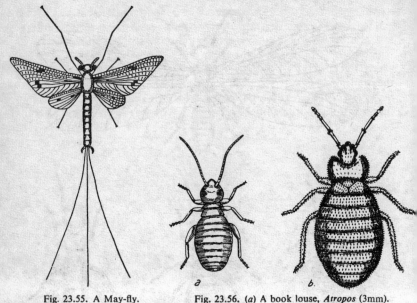

Fig. 23.55. A May-fly.   Fig. 23.56. (a) A book louse, *Atropos* (3mm).
                                        (b) A bed bug, *Cimex*,

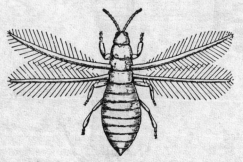

Fig. 23.57. A thrips.

Order 14. Thysanoptera

Very small insects with short antennae. Piercing and sucking mouth parts. Wings narrow and fringed with long setae. No cerci. The thrips insects do great damage to plants by sucking the sap. Pea-thrips, corn-thrips, pear-thrips, etc. (*see* Fig. 23.57).

Order 15. Hemiptera

Small insects with piercing and sucking mouth parts. Often wingless parthenogenetic generations. No cerci. Usually gradual metamorphosis.

The plant bugs. Aphides, scale insects, mealy bugs, leaf-hoppers, the "musical" cicadas, the greenhouse white-fly. Many are carriers of virus diseases (*see* Fig. 23.58).

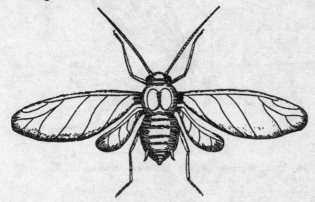

Fig. 23.58. *Aphis fabae*, winged female.

Order 16. Neuroptera

Medium soft-bodied insects with long antennae. Biting mouth parts. No cerci. Many have aquatic larvae. Alder flies, snake flies, lace-wings, ant-lions (*see* Fig. 23.59).

Fig. 23.59. An alder fly, *Sialis*.

Order 17. Mecoptera

Small insects with biting mouth parts. Long antennae. Wings similar. Cerci reduced. Conspicuous bands or spots on the wings. The scorpion flies (*see* Fig. 23.60).

Order 18. Trichoptera

Medium insects of weak flight, often resembling moths. Mouth parts adapted for licking but many imagines do not feed. Antennae and cerci of medium length. Aquatic larvae, the caddis-worms, which make remarkable cases for concealment and protection (*see* Fig. 23.61).

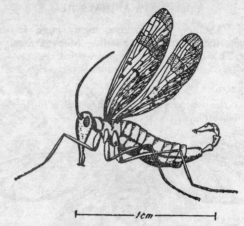

Fig. 23.60. A scorpion fly (legs and wings shown on left side only).

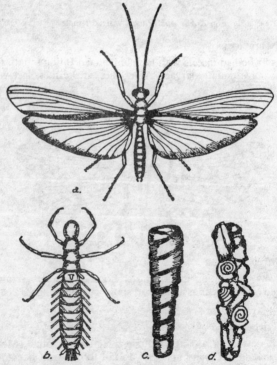

Fig. 23.61. (a) Caddis fly. (b) Caddis worm (larva). (c and d) Two types of larval case.

Order 19. Lepidoptera

Small to large insects with entire covering of powdery scales. Wings fastened together. Sucking proboscis formed by maxillae. No cerci. Metamorphosis is complete. The butterflies and moths (*see* Fig. 23.62).

Order 20. Coleoptera

Size ranges from minute to large. Fore-wings always horny elytra. Mouth parts biting. Metamorphosis complete. The beetles (*see* Fig. 23.63).

Fig. 23.62. (*a*) Swallow tail butterfly. (*b*) Privet hawk moth.

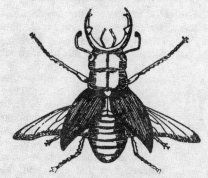

Fig. 23.63. Stag-beetle in flight.

Order 21. Strepsiptera

Small insects; larvae parasites in other insects, especially Hymenoptera. Antennae bifid, mouth parts biting, but often degenerate. Fore-wings are halteres, hind-wings fan-shaped. No cerci. *Stylops*, a British genus, has sixteen endemic species (*see* Fig. 23.47 (*b*)).

Order 22. Hymenoptera

Small to medium insects, many of them social. Metamorphosis complete. Antennae short. Mouth parts very modified for biting or sucking. Often castes present; queens, drones, workers, soldiers. Parthenogenesis is common. The saw-flies, ichneumon flies, chalcids, gall-wasps, ants, wasps, bees, hornets (*see* Fig. 23.74).

Order 23. Diptera

Hind-wings form halteres. Antennae various but usually short. Mouth parts suctorial, often piercing also. Cerci very reduced or absent. Metamorphosis complete. Larvae are apodous. The true two-winged flies. Many are important as vectors of disease; the house-fly, mosquito, tsetse fly; crane-flies, midges, horse-flies, hover-flies, warble-flies (*see* Figs. 23.71, 23.72).

Order 24. Aphaniptera

Small insects, all ectoparasitic. Body laterally flattened. Short antennae. Mouth parts for piercing and sucking. Legs adapted for jumping. No cerci. No wings. The fleas (*see* Fig. 23.37).

LIFE HISTORIES OF INSECTS

Outlined below are the life histories of some well-known insects. These are only a few examples from an enormous variety. They do not therefore represent any trends but merely emphasize the main types mentioned previously.

The Earwig. Forficula auricularia

Earwigs belong to the order Dermaptera. They are nocturnal, hiding by day in cracks and crevices. The front-wings are small, almost rectangular, leathery flaps. The hind-wings are well developed and are folded longitudinally and transversely under the tegmina. Nevertheless, they rarely fly. The sexes can be distinguished easily by the cerci (*see* Fig. 23.52). They are omnivorous and often cause damage to fruits and flowers in gardens by the bites of their strong mandibles. The eggs are white and elliptical and are laid in groups of about twenty in a shallow cavity excavated by the female in the soil. The female watches over the eggs and the newly-hatched young, covering them with her body if danger

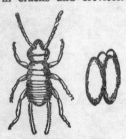

Fig. 23.64. Earwig nymph and eggs.

threatens. The nymphs emerge in a form very like the adult, but there are no wings and the body is relatively shorter and stouter. They undergo several ecdyses and are mature by the late summer. The adults hibernate in crevices and usually die in the following summer. Only one generation of young is produced each year.

The Dragonfly. Aeshna cyanea

This large brilliantly-coloured insect is often seen flying near ponds in the summer. Its predominant colour is brown; it has blue eyes, green spots on the thorax and blue spots on the abdomen. All dragonflies are carnivorous, catching prey with their prehensile legs which are placed far forward and hence are totally unsuited to walking or running. Mating takes place in the

Fig. 23.65. Nymph of dragon fly (*Aeshna cyanea*) with mask extended.

air, during the midsummer. The female lays eggs in slits made in leaves of aquatic plants by her ovipositor. A dingy aquatic nymph without wings emerges in about three weeks. Respiratory exchange is effected by gills produced in the expanded rectum; water is taken into the rectum and forced out again; this helps locomotion. The nymph has a remarkable feeding organ called the *mask*. It consists of the greatly expanded labium modified to form a tube, with toothed processes at its tip. When not in use, it is folded beneath the head but can be shot out with great rapidity. The nymph feeds and grows for more than a year, undergoing many moults. The wings gradually develop and when they are about a centimetre long the nymph climbs up a suitable support, out of the water. It remains stationary for several hours, then the final ecdysis takes place. This takes several hours; the wings have to be dried and the skeleton hardened. The fluid which distended the body during moulting is released from the anus, drop by drop. Eventually, the wings are spread out at right angles to the body and after a few tentative flaps, off it flies. If it survives the attacks of birds and of other dragonflies, it will lead its predatory existence until the late autumn when the falling temperature kills it (*see* Fig. 23.44).

The Common Louse. Pediculus humanus

These are small insects, usually smaller than 3 or 4 mm long. They live on the clothing of human beings, hiding among seams and folds, and migrating to the body surface to suck the blood. Several hundred eggs are laid by the adult female at the rate of ten or so per day. Each egg is attached to a body hair or to clothing by a cementing substance. The young lice hatch in a week. There is no metamorphosis and after three ecdyses they are sexually mature. The length of life is about six months (*see* Fig. 23.66).

Lice are characteristic of unclean communities; they are rare among civilized peoples, where there is regular washing and changing of clothes. More serious than the actual damage caused by them is the fact that they transmit a number of serious diseases among which are typhus or gaol fever, and relapsing fever. During the 1914–18 war and to some extent in the 1939–45 war they carried the pathogens responsible for trench fever.

There are two races of *Pediculus humanus*. They are the body louse, *P. humanus corporis*, and the head louse, *P. humanus capitis*. The latter is by no means uncommon in this country.

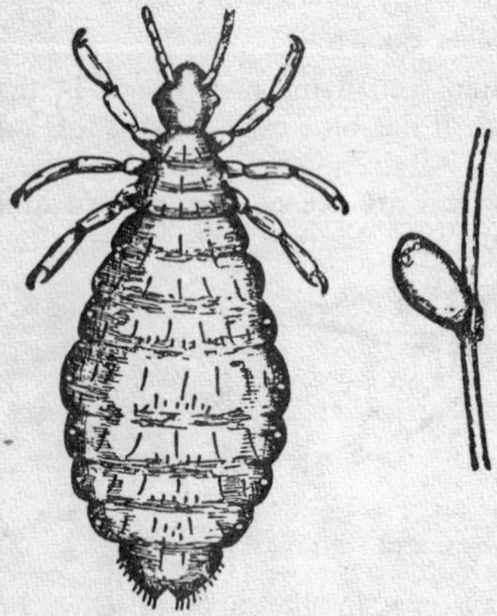

Fig. 23.66. A body louse, *Pediculus humanus*, and egg attached to hair.

The Bean Aphis. Aphis fabae

Aphides are familiar to everyone as the black-fly of beans and the green-fly of roses. In addition to damage caused by aphides to many crop plants, they are known to be the vectors of a number of virus diseases.

The attacks of bean aphis begin in early summer by the migration of winged viviparous females from their winter hosts, the spindle tree (*Euonymus*) or guelder rose (*Viburnum*). These produce parthenogenetic young at the rate of two or three a day. The first generation consists of wingless females. In their turn, they mature in about

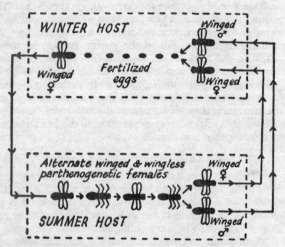

Fig. 23.67. *Aphis fabae*. Life history

three weeks and produce winged females which colonize further plants. Thus the wingless females increase the size of established colonies while the winged females migrate to found fresh colonies.

In the autumn, the last generation of winged females fly to the winter host and there produce oviparous females. At the same time, winged males appear on the summer host, migrate and fertilize the eggs of the oviparous females. These lay small, black, ovoid eggs in cracks and crevices of the winter host. In the spring, the eggs hatch to produce winged females which migrate to the summer hosts.

The variety of summer hosts, including beans, beet, and many weeds, ensures plentiful survivors. The habit of piercing foliage and sucking the sap makes them difficult to eradicate. They are obviously not affected by the so-called stomach poisons used against leaf-eating insects. The only feasible method of attack is by contact spray or powder; nicotine is largely used.

The Cabbage-white Butterfly: Pieris brassicae

This insect and its life history are generally familiar. It is included here because of the ease with which the various stages can be obtained and because it is a fairly typical lepidopteran life history.

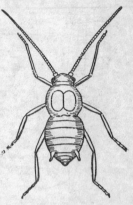

Fig. 23.68. *Aphis fabae*: wingless female.

The adult butterflies appear in May and after aerial fertilization, the females lay eggs in batches of ten to one hundred on the undersides of various brassicas such as cabbages, cauliflower, brussels sprouts; nasturtium leaves are also used. The eggs are small, yellow in colour, and are ribbed vertically and horizontally; they are attached to the leaves by a sticky secretion. The small hairy caterpillars emerge in ten days or so, and proceed to eat the egg-shells. They are yellowish-green in colour, with three prominent longitudinal yellow stripes. There are numerous small rounded tubercles, each of which bears a stiff seta. The body consists of the head, three thoracic segments and ten abdominal. On the head are three small ocelli on each side, and a pair of rudimentary antennae. The mouth parts consist of strong toothed mandibles, minute maxillae with small jointed palps and a labium produced into a small pointed tube from which silk emerges. Each thoracic segment bears a pair of five-jointed legs. On the abdomen, there are four pairs of stout fleshy protuberances known as pro-legs, each having a semicircular row of hooks. On the last abdominal segment is a pair of curved claspers used during pupation. Breathing takes place through minute spiracles situated on the first thoracic and first eight abdominal segments. The larva feeds voraciously on the leaves and grows rapidly. It moults five or six times and when full-grown is about 40 mm long. Then it proceeds to pupate.

The caterpillar climbs to a sheltered spot beneath an overhanging ledge. It accomplishes this by weaving a silken zig-zag ladder to which the pro-legs cling. It spins a small quantity of silk by which it is suspended and then undergoes its last moult. After a short resting period, a chitinous fluid is exuded from the skin. This hardens into the beautiful chrysalis with metallic colours, green and blue, with golden spots. Metamorphosis takes two to three weeks; the adult external features are vaguely visible through the

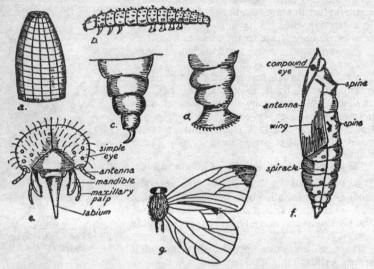

Fig. 23.69. *Pieris brassicae.* (*a*) Egg. (*b*) Caterpillar. (*c*) True leg. (*d*) Pro-leg. (*e*) Head (front view). (*f*) Chrysalis. (*g*) Male wings.

chrysalis skin. Finally it splits along the dorsal surface; the imago emerges and after a short rest to dry and harden its cuticle, it flies away.

The imago has distinct head, thorax and abdomen, the former two thickly beset with setae. On the head are the prominent clubbed antennae and large lateral compound eyes. The mouth parts consist of vestigial mandibles, a long coiled proboscis formed of the galeae of the maxillae and a rudimentary labium with jointed palps. The wings are cream in colour; by brushing off the scales, which are modified setae, the sparse venation can be seen. The sexes are clearly distinguished, the female having two prominent black spots on the fore-wing. They feed on nectar, thrusting the proboscis into flowers.

This second generation produces eggs in August. The caterpillars mature in early autumn and spend the winter as chrysalides, emerging as imagines in the following May.

The larvae cause considerable damage to brassica crops. They are not much favoured by birds, though parasitized extensively by ichneumon flies which lay their eggs in the caterpillars. Some measure of control is effected by squashing eggs, hand-picking larvae, and on a field scale by the use of stomach poisons such as Derris and lead arsenate.

The Cockchafer beetle: Melolontha melolontha

The cockchafer is a large yellowish-brown beetle about 2·5 cm long, the elytra having fine longitudinal ridges. Laterally, there are wedge-shaped patches of short white setae. The antennae are characteristic of lamellicorn beetles in which the distal podites of the antennae are divided into seven club-shaped portions (six in the female). During the daytime, the adults shelter among the foliage of oaks and other forest trees, on which they feed. They are more active at dusk, when they fly in swarms, their wings making a loud humming noise.

Small yellow eggs are laid at the end of May in holes in the soil, often 20 cm deep. Two or three clusters of 10–30 eggs are laid in separate holes. The larvae hatch in 6 weeks and feed on organic matter in the soil; later they eat the roots of plants. They are soft white grubs with black heads, no eyes and six weak black legs. They grow rapidly and assume a curled shape (*see* Fig. 23.70). Feeding and growing, they live for 3 years, burrowing more deeply before winter hibernation.

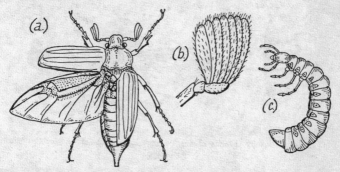

Fig. 23.70. The cockchafer beetle, *Melolontha melolontha*. (*a*) Adult with wing and elytron spread on one side. (*b*) Antenna. (*c*) Larva.

The pupa is covered with the last larval skin in an ovoid chamber deep in the soil. The adults emerge in late summer but remain in the soil until the following summer, emerging in May, hence the common name May-bugs. They live for 5 or 6 weeks.

The grubs cause considerable damage to crops; their natural enemies are moles, badgers, and birds, especially after cultivation, when they may be brought to the surface.

The House-fly: Musca domestica

The common house-fly has long been known as a serious menace to health. The female lays five or six batches of one hundred or more eggs on fresh animal manure or human faeces or other decaying organic material. The eggs are minute, about one millimetre long, and spindle-shaped. Under favourable conditions, tiny white maggots hatch within twenty-four hours, though they may, in adverse circumstances, take as long as five days. The larvae have very small heads bearing hooked mandibles; the head can be retracted into the body. There are no eyes. Behind the head are twelve segments; there are no legs, but slight pads beset with setae serve for locomotion. Two pairs of spiracles are present, on segments two and twelve. The larva feeds continuously, hiding from the light when possible. It moults two or three times and then pupates about five days after hatching.

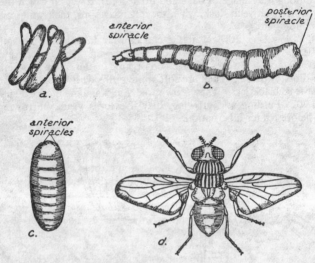

Fig. 23.71. Housefly, *Musca domestica.* (*a*) Eggs. (*b*) Larva. (*c*) Puparium.
(*d*) Imago.

The pupa is much shorter than the larva, brown and barrel-shaped; it is formed of the last larval skin. Metamorphosis is completed in three or four days in summer, but some pupae survive through the whole winter. The imago emerges by dilating a special vesicle on the front of the head, thus pushing off the cap of the pupa case.

The imago is clearly divided into head, thorax and abdomen. The head bears large compound eyes and three ocelli. The short, stumpy antennae are sunk in sockets, and each has a short feathery branch. House-flies feed on any kind of organic material, with their peculiar sucking device (*see* p. 712). The anterior wings are large and membranous with little venation; the hind-wings are modified as halteres, which are concealed by lobes of the front-wings. The flies appear to live a considerable time; often they hibernate, and a warm day in winter may stir them into activity.

Owing to its dirty habits of feeding, and to the variety of materials it can attack, the fly is a dangerous carrier of pathogens. Spores of bacteria, eggs of worm parasites, virus particles and protozoan parasites may all be transferred to the food of man and his animals. Transit takes place on the feet, on the mouth parts, and in the fly's faeces. Diseases known to be thus disseminated are typhoid fever, infant diarrhoea and cholera. There is some evidence that it may spread smallpox, plague and poliomyelitis.

Control of flies is a difficult problem. Rapid and efficient disposal of faeces and organic rubbish, covering of food materials, fly-papers and sprays, are all effective. Nevertheless, where there are young children and domestic animals, there is bound to be some infection. The general improvement of hygienic conditions in food shops is a welcome sign of public awareness of the danger from flies.

The Malaria Mosquito: Anopheles maculipennis

Mosquitoes occur all over the world. They are most plentiful in the tropics, though in the brief Arctic summer, enormous swarms occur in Lapland, Finland, Northern Siberia and North America. There are over 1,500 species known, twenty-eight of which are native to Great Britain.

The female lays up to one hundred eggs singly in water. They are boat-shaped, less than one millimetre long and equipped with two lateral floats. In a few days, the larvae emerge. They are very active creatures, commonly known as "wrigglers." The head is large, the three thoracic segments are fused to form a broad middle region, and the abdomen has nine segments. On the head are short antennae, a pair of plumed brushes at the sides of the mouth, and mandibles and maxillae which comb food particles out of the brushes. These brushes sweep through the water at the rate of 150 strokes per minute; small particles are entangled in them; these constitute the food. The penultimate segment bears two spiracles. When it comes to the surface, the larva lies supported by the surface film with the spiracles just breaking the surface; they secrete an oily substance which prevents the entry of water. The body is supported horizontally by tufts of palmate setae which cling to the surface film. The head is rotated through 180° so that its ventral surface is upward and the larva proceeds to sweep the underside of the film for food. After a period varying from several days to several months, the pupa is formed. Under good conditions of temperature and food, the larva is full-grown in less than a week.

The pupa is very active also. It has a large head and a curved body and is sometimes described as comma-shaped. It does not feed but has to come to the surface to breathe; the spiracles are now borne on the dorsal surface of the head. This stage, during which the metamorphosis takes place, usually lasts less than a week. The pupal skin splits along the dorsal side and the imago emerges in a few minutes.

The sexes can be distinguished by the condition of the antennae. In the male, they are tufted while in the female they are slender and beset with fine setules. The body is very slender and covered with setae and fine scales. On the head are the large compound eyes, but no ocelli. The mouth parts (*see* p. 711), are adapted for piercing and sucking, though it is only the female that sucks blood. The fore-wings are narrow, sparsely veined and fringed with setae. The halteres are well marked and very typical. In adaptation to

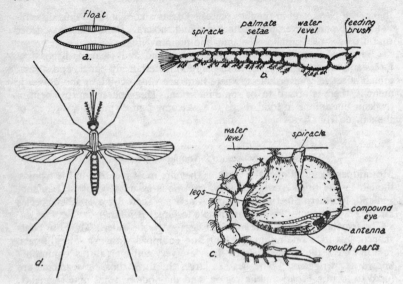

Fig. 23.72. *Anopheles maculipennis.* (*a*) Egg. (*b*) Larva. (*c*) Pupa. (*d*) Imago.

settling gently, it has very long and extremely delicate legs. The adults often hibernate in dark sheltered places.

Mosquitoes are notorious for conveying pathogenic organisms but it must be remembered that relatively few species do this. The most dangerous are *Anopheles maculipennis*, which conveys malaria parasites, *Culex fatigans*, conveying filaria worms, and *Stegomyia fasciata* [*Aedes aegypti*] which transmits the unknown organism causing yellow fever. Malaria was common in south-eastern England until the end of the last century; the disease was known as ague. Some of the principal methods employed in eradicating these dangerous insects are described in Chap. 32.

The Honey Bee: Apis mellifica

Because of its great importance as a pollinator of flowers and as a producer of honey, *Apis mellifica* is described as a representative of the large and varied order Hymenoptera.

The remarkable organization of the community is not nowadays described in terms of "instinct" or "intelligence". There is undoubtedly a large measure of inheritance of fixed behaviour patterns but these always have some degree of plasticity and are not absolutely rigid.

The queen is the supreme being in the hive and all the manifold activities revolve around her. A new community is formed when a queen and thousands of attendant workers fly out and form a swarm. If not placed in a proper hive, they will proceed to colonize a hollow tree or some such place. The first task of the workers is to seal up all holes, except an entrance, with "propolis," a substance prepared by the workers from gummy exudations of twigs and buds. The next activity is the secretion of wax, which is exuded as four pairs of plates between the abdominal segments. This wax is nipped off by the joint between tibia and tarsus of the hind-limb, and then it is moulded into a thread which is suspended from the roof of the hive. Soon a large mass of wax is collected together, then older workers set to work to make the cells, starting at the top and working downwards to form vertical plates with hexagonal cells.

Within a few days, the queen takes her nuptial flight. She soars high into the air, pursued by many males. Eventually one succeeds in the act of fertilization, and dies. The queen returns, carrying enough sperm in her spermotheca to last for several years. Then she proceeds to deposit eggs, one to each cell. They are small, bluish-white spindle-shaped structures fastened to the inner end of the cell by a sticky secretion. Fertilized eggs give rise to queens or workers, the latter being sterile females. The unfertilized eggs give rise to the males. The rate of egg-laying may exceed 3,000 a day. It is not until many cells have fertilized eggs that any unfertilized eggs are laid. Special cells are enlarged to contain the larvae destined to become queens; they are fed on a special mixture regurgitated by the workers; it is known as "royal jelly."

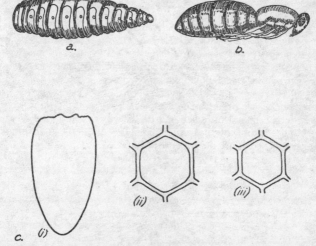

Fig. 23.73. *Apis mellifica. a)* Larva. (*b*) Pupa. (*c*) Relative sizes of cells: (i) queen; (ii) drone; (iii) worker.

The normal larvae hatch in three or four days. They are fed by the workers on pollen and honey, mixed to form a paste. After several moults, they pupate in an imperfect silken cocoon, having become fully-grown larvae in five days. Metamorphosis takes eight to ten days, and then the imago emerges.

The three types of imagines are quite different in external features. The workers are small with well-developed wings and freely movable antennae. There are very interesting modifications of the legs. The first leg has a very open joint between tibia and tarsus; the proximal end of the tarsus is almost semicircular and it bears a comb of short stiff setae. This comb is used for cleaning the antennae, proboscis and head, of pollen. On the tibia of the second leg is a stout seta called the prong; it is used for digging the pollen out of the pollen basket on the third leg. The third leg has the tibia deeply grooved with stout bristles on each side of the groove which serve to retain the pollen; it is known as the pollen basket. The tarsus has rows of setae forming the brush; it is used for sweeping the pollen from the body into the basket of the other side. The ovipositor of the worker is modified to form a

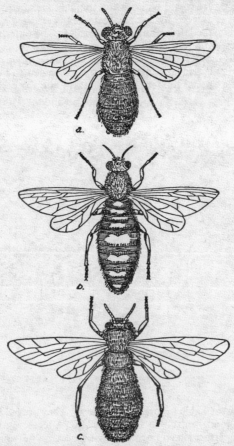

Fig. 23.74. *Apis mellifica*. (*a*) Worker. (*b*) Queen. (*c*) Drone.

barbed sting; it can be used once only, since the barbs cannot be withdrawn from the wound, and as the bee frees herself, the poison sac and often other abdominal organs are torn out of her body and she soon dies. The mouth parts are adapted for sucking nectar and for moulding wax. These busy workers graduate from one job to another. They start as cleaners of the wax cells and attendants of the older larvae; later they are able to secrete the nutritive fluid necessary for the young larvae. After a few days of this task, they keep the hive clean, assist in storing food in the storage cells, and by their wing movements assist ventilation. When they are about three weeks old, they begin to fly outside and are soon occupied as collectors of pollen and nectar. Such a strenuous life does not last long, and in the honey season, they die after four or five weeks. The survivors hibernate by clustering in a dense mass around the queen, feeding themselves on stored honey.

The queen senses the maturing of the young princesses in their large cells, and if not prevented by her attendant workers, she would sting them to death. Soon she leaves the hive with a large number of the workers to form a swarm and begin a new colony. Then, the most mature princess is allowed to emerge. There may be several swarms a year, but as the cold season approaches, the workers allow the queen to kill off any others still awaiting release from the royal cells. The queen is larger and longer-bodied and the wings are relatively

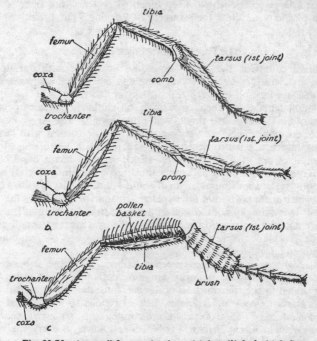

Fig. 23.75. *Apis mellifica*, worker legs. (*a*) 1st. (*b*) 2nd. (*c*) 3rd.

smaller; she flies only two or three times. The sting is not barbed and so can be used repeatedly. The mouth parts are rudimentary; she is fed by the workers all her life. A queen may live for five or six years. The type of food decides whether a larva will become a queen or a worker.

The drones have bulky bodies, feeble mouth parts and no stings. There may be a hundred or more in a hive. Their only use to the community is to fertilize a queen. They are killed by the workers or driven out of the hive when the cold season begins.

Control of the community is maintained by the spread of secretions from the queen. The workers who tend her, lick these and they soon spread throughout the colony by mutual feeding (trophallaxis). They give the bees a common odour, so that intruders, even of their own variety, are readily distinguished. The substances also prevent oogenesis in the workers, and inhibit the building of "queen cells". Bees are not creatures of "blind instinct". They can vary their method of navigation according to conditions; by the sun, by variation in pattern of polarized light, and by recognition of landmarks. They communicate information about food sources, or nesting sites, by touch, taste, and dances. Direction, distance, type and quantity of the food source are indicated by variations in the length and pattern and direction of the dance; this indicates choice. Their behaviour undoubtedly contains a large component of fixed inherited patterns, but there is always enough plasticity to allow for a moiety of learning. The brain weighs less than 2·5 mg!

The Human Flea: Pulex irritans

In civilized countries, the flea is nowadays associated with our domestic animals and with flea-circuses. Not long ago most dwellings were infested with these insects, and they are still present in many.

The adult females lay their eggs singly on clothing, under carpets or in floor-cracks. The eggs are small, white, and ovoid. The larvae emerge in three to ten days. They are very small elongated creatures with head and thirteen segments, but no eyes or legs. Their antennae are single-jointed; the mandibles are of the biting type. Each segment has a band of stout setae. These larvae are not parasitic; they feed on organic debris, and after two moults, reach a maximum length of about 4 mm. The larva spins a cocoon within which metamorphosis takes place. In four or five days, the imago emerges. It is laterally compressed and has no trace of wings. The mouth parts are adapted for piercing and sucking, the eyes are very small and the antennae short and thick. The adaptations of the legs for jumping have already been considered.

Over 2,000 species of fleas have been described. Many are associated with specific hosts, though the majority are more catholic in their tastes. Fleas are implicated in the transmission of disease, since they leave a dead animal when it starts to cool and transfer their attentions to the nearest warm-blooded creature. In the tropics, rats are infested with *Xenopsylla cheopis*; it appears rarely in Great Britain. This flea is known to carry the bacillus causing bubonic plague, a dreaded and fatal disease in tropical countries.

Fig. 23.76. Flea, *Pulex irritans*. (*a*) Egg. (*b*) Larva. (*c*) Pupa.

Sporadic outbreaks often occur in temperate zones. The Black Death of the fourteenth century in England was almost certainly due to the same pathogen, *Pasteurella pestis*, introduced with rat-fleas in the growing volume of shipping of that century.

Special Features of Biological Importance

From our brief study of the insects a number of features worthy of further reflection arise. To what factors may we attribute the amazing success of insects? Their astounding variety, their ubiquity and their enormous numbers have ensured that they have made no small impact on other terrestrial organisms.

The Success of the Insects

As terrestrial animals, their outstanding feature is the impervious exoskeleton. This has allowed the insects to colonize even the driest of habitats, and it has enabled them to overcome the greatest danger to all land animals, that of desiccation. It must be borne in mind that this same cuticle has imposed on its possessors limitation of size and the necessity for ecdysis. The insects have conquered these problems by undergoing their ecdyses during larval stages usually protected against desiccation, and by ceasing growth after metamorphosis. The adult life is usually brief and is concentrated on reproduction.

The evolution of special organs for flight has been a major factor in the success of insects. It has enabled them to establish themselves in fresh territory; it ensures dispersal, and it gives them access to locations not available to the great majority of animals.

Tracheal respiration coupled with the high percentage of blood sugar has given them the means of maintaining the high-energy performance necessary for their swift and often prolonged locomotion.

Finally, their amazing adaptability has enabled the various groups to occupy practically every niche in terrestrial environments, the small size being an important factor.

Flowering Plants and Insects

The first undoubted fossils of the flowering plants (Angiospermae) appear in the middle of the Cretaceous period, about 125 million years ago. Trees such as willow and poplar were common. By the end of the Cretaceous, the angiosperms dominated the flora. Pollinating insects appeared at the same time as the flowering plants, and there is no doubt that the two groups have evolved together, one being complementary to the other. There are some remarkable adaptations of particular flowers to suit the pollinating powers of particular insects. The bee visits flowers for pollen and nectar, but pays for the fare by rendering the flower the service of cross-pollination. Long-tongued moths can sip nectar only from flowers with long corollae; in doing so, they cross-pollinate the flower. If they are night-flying moths, they can feed from nocturnally-opening flowers, which attract them by scent. The economic value of the insect pollinating service is inestimable.

Larvae and Metamorphosis

When a female produces many eggs, they cannot be well-endowed with yolk. Such eggs are necessarily small, and with such little food-supply, the new generation cannot achieve either the organs of the adult form or any reasonable size. Thus they develop larval organs for locomotion, for feeding and for all the other purposes necessary to their existence. Changes, more or less radical, are necessary, so that the adult form might be attained. These changes constitute metamorphosis. In some cases, they are slight; we have a good example in the cockroach, where only size, wings and gonads are necessary to achieve the adult state. In the higher insect orders such as the Coleoptera, Lepidoptera and Hymenoptera, the eggs are numerous and small. The larvae bear not the slightest resemblance to the adults. Therefore the metamorphosis is a striking process. Much of the body of the larva is dis-organized and then re-organization takes place. For protection during this helpless stage, the creature is encased in a silken cocoon or a chitinous chrysalis or pupa. The phenomenon of metamorphosis is found in many other animal groups, notably the Mollusca, the Echinodermata and the Amphibia. It is always associated with the production of large numbers of eggs.

Biological Control

This is an aspect of biology commonly exercised without realization of its full implications. When we keep cats to reduce the mouse population, or spray our fruit-trees, or introduce myxamotosis into rabbits, or put snails and green plants into our aquaria, we are using biological control of populations. The term has, however, a narrower significance to trained biologists. It means the control of a pest by employing natural enemies. Gardeners encourage ladybirds because they destroy aphides; this is true biological control. The necessity only arises when natural populations are unduly disturbed and the greatest disturber is man. He has introduced foreign species and has sometimes found that they succeed beyond his wildest dreams. Therefore, he attempts to restore the balance by introducing a missing biological factor which is usually a predator on the species which has run wild.

A single cactus plant (*Opuntia inermis*) introduced into New South Wales in 1839 was the beginning of one of the major infestations in history. By 1925 over 245 000 km² were covered by this prickly pear. Various attempts at clearing were unsuccessful. An examination into the natural pests of the cactus in America was instituted, and of a number of species discovered, one proved to be outstandingly successful. This was a small moth, *Cactoblastis cactorum*, obtained from the Argentine. Several thousand eggs were dispatched to Australia and from the moths several millions were reared and disseminated among the cactus. The moth lays its eggs in strings containing about seventy-five each. These strings were fastened to the cactus plants. When the larvae emerged, they proceeded immediately to bore into the plant. The tunnellings of the larvae provided access for fungus and bacterial infections. The success was stupendous; the last big tract of prickly pear was destroyed in 1933, and there seems to be little danger of a large scale recurrence.

The adult *Cactoblastis cactorum* is a small grey moth. The female lays her egg-sticks on the *Opuntia*, attaching them by a sticky secretion. There are two generations a year, one laying in October and the other in March. Dull-grey caterpillars, about three millimetres long, emerge after a few days. Immediately they burrow into the plants, devouring them incessantly until full-grown, when they are about 4 cm long. They pupate on the ground, under stones or leaf trash, in silken cream-coloured cocoons. The imago emerges in about a week and usually flies several miles before laying her eggs.

The citrus groves of California were threatened with extermination by a scale insect introduced accidentally from Australia. By 1882, the pest had almost rendered futile the growing of oranges and lemons. Search in Australia for a natural predator, revealed a ladybird, *Vedalia cardinalis*. Introduction of a small number of these, and breeding from them, soon produced millions, which were distributed. In two years the scale insect menace had disappeared.

The introduction of sugar-cane from the Orient into the West Indies was a very successful venture for many years. Eventually in some of the islands, and particularly Puerto Rico, the attacks of the white grubs of certain beetles, began to make cane-growing unprofitable. In 1924, forty large Surinam toads were introduced from Jamaica. By 1934 the plague of white grubs was reduced to insignificant proportions.

There are numerous other examples of the biological control of insects, and of biological control by insects; the three examples given will serve to show the importance of this type of treatment and the promise it shows for the future of agriculture.

Economic Importance of Insects

Man suffers and benefits from the insect legions. On the whole, perhaps the suffering outweighs the benefit.

Insects are of great value to man as pollinators. Apart from wind-pollinated cereals, almost every crop plant is pollinated by insects, mainly bees. Many insects are scavengers, consuming organic rubbish or burying it as food for their larvae. Commercial products derived from insects are honey and wax from bees, silk from *Bombyx mori*, cochineal from some Hemiptera, and shellac from certain scale insects.

On the debit side, insects consume man's possessions—his crops, clothing, books; they suck his blood and parasitize his domestic animals. The diseases they transmit have caused enormous loss of life: malaria, sleeping sickness, plague, cholera, yellow fever, typhoid, food poisoning and many others. We now know that transmission of virus diseases by insects is common.

Hormones in Insects

A great deal of experimental work has been carried out on this subject, particularly on cockroaches, locusts, grasshoppers, and most noteworthy is the work on the Heteropteran bug *Rhodnius*, by V. B. Wigglesworth. As might be expected, there is considerable variation among the insect orders with regard to endocrine structures, but certain general principles have been well established. In all insects, there is neurosecretion from four groups of cells in the brain, two medial and two lateral. The axons of the medial groups pass to the corpora cardiaca, and those of the lateral groups pass through the corpora cardiaca to terminate in the corpora allata. Also there are minute groups of neurosecretory cells in each ganglion; their axons lead to small neurohaemal organs closely associated with the ganglia. The only epithelial endocrine organs yet known are the thoracic glands in the first thoracic segment.

A neurosecretion from the brain, released into the blood via the corpora cardiaca, stimulates the thoracic glands to secrete the steroid *ecdysone*, which stimulates moulting during metamorphosis. An antagonistic hormone *neotenin*, from the corpora allata, prevents metamorphosis during the immature stages. There is progressive differentiation during each instar due to the influence of neotenin. During the last one or two moults, production of neotenin gradually ceases, and ecdysone stimulates metamorphosis.

Another neurosecretion, released from the corpora cardiaca, is a growth hormone which promotes protein synthesis; there are also two hormones which affect the concentration of blood sugar. In several groups of insects, rhythmic behaviour, e.g. in light and in darkness, is concerned with a neurosecretion from the suboesophageal ganglia; this is itself controlled by a tropic hormone released by the corpora cardiaca. A diuretic hormone from the brain, and probably also from the segmental ganglia, promotes the movement of fluid through the Malpighian tubules. From the corpora allata, gonadotropic hormones affect the maturation of the gonads and accessory structures; the gonads themselves secrete hormones which stimulate ripening of the gametes and also control the reproductive process.

Probably many details of the insect endocrine system are not yet known, but the general pattern is strictly comparable with that of vertebrates: a sequence of neurosecretion—tropic hormones—endocrine glands.

CHAPTER 24

COELOMATE ANIMALS IV: CHORDATA

ANIMALS included in the phylum Chordata form a closely-knit group of somewhat doubtful affinities (*see* p. 756). They have strongly-marked common characteristics, though all the chordates do not possess all the features described below.

THE CHARACTERISTICS OF CHORDATE ANIMALS

In common with arthropods and annelids, chordates are *bilaterally symmetrical* and *metamerically segmented*; they possess, however, certain distinctive features not found in any of the other coelomate phyla. These are described below.

The Notochord

This is a stiff but flexible rod situated dorsal to the gut, ventral to the nerve cord, and between the laterally placed somites. It is sometimes known as the *chorda dorsalis* and is the first axial structure laid down

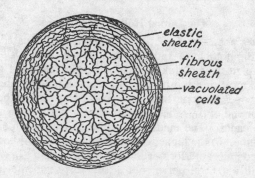

Fig. 24.1. T.S. of a notochord.

in the embryo. The notochord has a skeletal function and was probably associated originally with muscle attachment and axial stiffening correlated with lateral swimming movements of the body, especially of the tail region. In its most characteristic condition, in embryo craniates, or in cephalochordates, it consists mainly of vacuolated cells which give support by reason of their turgidity. The cells multiply and at the periphery they give rise to a thin epithelium. This is enveloped by two covering sheaths. The inner sheath is thick, consisting of fibrous connective tissue; the outer sheath is thin and is composed of elastic connective tissue (*see* Fig. 24.1). The notochord persists in its entirety only in adult cephalochordates; in hemichordates its very existence is doubtful, while in urochordates, it is restricted to the larvae. In the higher chordates it becomes constricted and partly replaced by the vertebral column, though some vestiges of it are always present (*see* pp. 805, 869 and 1014).

Visceral Clefts

These are present in all chordates. They are slits perforating the body wall at the pharynx, thus placing the latter in communication with the outside medium. Primitively, they may have been concerned with sifting food particles from the water which passed in at the mouth and out at the clefts. Such a condition is present in cephalochordates and urochordates, though even there, the water current has an accessory respiratory function. In fishes, the clefts form vascular gills and are primarily respiratory. The visceral clefts of Amphibia are respiratory in the larvae, but in the adults, all disappear except the first, which forms the closed Eustachian tube. The remaining classes of chordates, Reptilia, Aves and Mammalia, form some clefts in their embryos; they are never respiratory, and all save the Eustachian tube disappear.

The Dorsal Hollow Nerve Cord

All chordates possess a dorsal hollow nerve cord situated in the midline above the notochord and beneath the epidermis. It arises from a dorsal flat plate which sinks beneath the surface. The lateral edges fold over to meet one another, thus forming a hollow tube. The front end remains open for some time, the opening being called the neuropore; the posterior end of the tube communicates with the archenteron by the neurenteric canal. The epidermis grows in from each side to cover the neural tube. In the higher chordates the nerve cord becomes highly differentiated in its anterior portion to form the brain. In each segment, a dorsal and a ventral nerve root arise; this segmental arrangement becomes obscured in the head region but can be clearly seen in the spinal cord (*see* pp. 771, 831 and 895). All the craniates (vertebrates) enclose the nerve cord in the cartilage or bone of the cranium and vertebral column.

Direction of Blood Flow in the Main Vessels

The main directions of blood flow in chordates are in sharp contrast with those found in non-chordates. The blood flows forward toward

the heart, or other pumping mechanism, ventrally, below the gut.
Then a number of branches pass dorsally around the pharynx. This
blood is collected and flows backward dorsal to the gut. In *Lumbricus*,
the flow is forward in the dorsal vessel, downward around the gut in

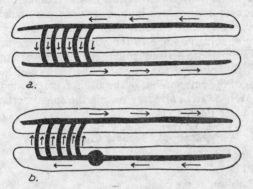

Fig. 24.2. Comparison of main outline of blood systems in (*a*) an annelid
and (*b*) a typical chordate.

the hearts and backward in the ventral vessel. A generalized comparison between the chordate and non-chordate condition is shown
in Fig. 24.2.

Position of the Heart

A heart is merely a pumping station along the course of the blood
system. It develops as a blood-vessel but becomes more highly differentiated, with a larger lumen, thickened muscular walls and valves
which ensure flow in one direction. In the higher chordates it becomes
folded and divided into chambers; it is always situated ventrally,
below the gut, while in non-chordates, it lies dorsally, above the gut.

The Possession of a True Tail

A true tail is a post-anal metamerically segmented structure; it is only
found in the chordates. Structures resembling tails in non-chordates
are either not post-anal or not truly segmented. Originally, the tail was
essentially an organ of locomotion, and in many aquatic animals it
serves that purpose. In higher chordates, it has often been adapted to
other uses. Thus, in some monkeys, it is prehensile; in crocodiles, it is
a formidable weapon; many mammals use it for flicking insects from
the skin; lizards store food in it, while in many chordates, it is vestigial
or absent in the adult.

Limbs formed from more than One Segment

Limbs are outgrowths of the body containing tissue derived from both ectoderm and mesoderm: their primitive purpose was locomotive. We cannot refer to the tentacles in *Hydra* or the chaetae in *Lumbricus* as limbs. In non-chordates, each limb is derived from tissue belonging to one single segment; thus, in some Crustacea, there is a complete series of appendages, corresponding to the number of segments. The limbs of chordate animals are derived from tissue belonging to more than one segment. Early traces of the origin of the limbs can be seen in the development of the embryo, but in the adult, segmentation is obscured. It can, however, be recognized by tracing the spinal nerves which pass into the limb (*see* Fig. 24.11).

Summary of Chordate Characteristics

1. Notochord.
2. Visceral clefts.
3. Dorsal hollow nerve cord.
4. Blood flow forward ventrally, backward dorsally.
5. Ventral heart.
6. Post-anal segmented tail.
7. Limbs formed from more than one segment.

The main features of chordate animals are represented in Fig. 24.3.

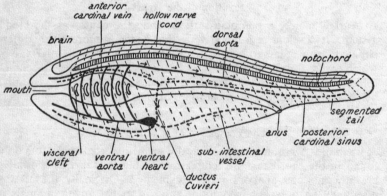

Fig. 24.3. A generalized chordate animal.

THE LOWER CHORDATES

The phylum can be subdivided quite clearly into the sub-phyla Acrania and Craniata. All the animals included in the Acrania are unfamiliar and highly peculiar. They do not possess a highly differentiated brain and there is no skull. They have no heart or kidneys. It is the possession of these structures which characterizes the Craniata.

The classes of the Acrania are the obscure hemichordates, the very plentiful marine urochordates, and the localized cephalochordates.

Hemichordata

This class is subdivided into two orders, the Enteropneusta and the Pterobranchia. The order Enteropneusta contains the acorn-worms *Balanoglossus* and *Dolichoglossus*, which are free-living. They burrow into mud or sand in shallow coastal waters. The order Pterobranchia includes several deep-sea genera of which the best-known are *Rhabdopleura* and *Cephalodiscus*; both are sessile.

Dolichoglossus is fifteen to twenty centimetres long. The body is clearly divisible into proboscis, collar and trunk (*see* Fig. 24.4). The

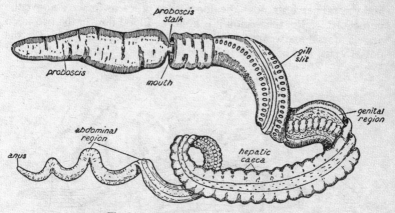

Fig. 24.4. *Dolichoglossus (after Bateson).*

proboscis is pre-oral and can be distended or relaxed by entry or exit of sea-water through one or two pores near its base. This mechanism is used for burrowing. Connecting the proboscis to the collar is a proboscis stalk and ventral to this, within the collar, is the mouth which is permanently open. Mud and sand are swallowed, and the organic matter is digested; the anus is terminal. The collar somewhat overlaps the base of the proboscis in front and the trunk behind. The anterior part of the trunk is known as the branchio-genital region; here numerous paired gill slits open dorso-laterally. Behind this region the body shows lateral sacculations where the hepatic caeca lie. The abdominal region shows no external differentiation.

There is a dorsal diverticulum of the anterior part of the gut into the proboscis: it becomes filled with vacuolated cells, and is said to correspond to the notochord (*see* Fig. 24.5). There are single solid dorsal

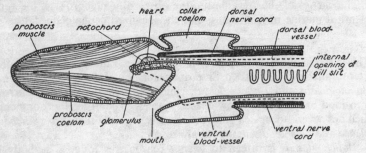

Fig. 24.5. Diagram of median L.S. through the anterior part of *Balanoglossus*.

and ventral nerve strands; the dorsal cord proceeds forward above the notochord, and in this region it is hollow. Blood flow in the two main vessels, dorsal and ventral, is on the non-chordate plan, forward in the dorsal vessel and backward in the ventral vessel. There is a contractile

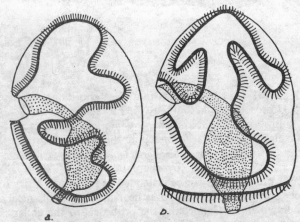

Fig. 24.6. (*a*) Auricularia echinoderm larva. (*b*) Tornaria larva of *Balanoglossus*.
Gut and ciliated bands shown.

structure sometimes known as the heart, at the forward end of the dorsal vessel in the base of the proboscis. By its pulsations, blood is driven through two lateral networks called glomeruli, which are the excretory organs. Then the blood flows into the ventral vessel. There is no tail and there are no limbs. In some hemichordates development is direct, but some, such as *Balanoglossus*, have a free-swimming larva called a *tornaria*. This bears a remarkable resemblance to the free-swimming larvae of echinoderms, especially to the *auricularia* larva of holothurians (*see* Fig. 24.6). This indicates that there is, at least, a remote affinity between these hemichordates and the echinoderms.

The general features of *Dolichoglossus* are common to all the hemichordates, though there is considerable variation in external appearance. In the opinion of some zoologists, the group should constitute a

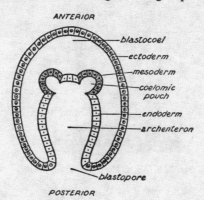

Fig. 24.7. Diagram to show similarity of pattern of early development in echinoderms and lower chordates. The first pair of coelomic pouches are forming. Horizontal L.S. appears same in both cases.

separate phylum, on the grounds that their chordate affinities are too slender. However, the undoubted visceral clefts, the small portion of dorsal hollow nerve cord, and the possible notochord, would seem to be strong enough grounds for including them in the chordates.

Urochordata

This class is subdivided into three orders, the Larvacea, the Ascidiacea and the Thaliacea. Members of the Larvacea are free-swimming and they retain the larval features in the adult stage. The ascidians or sea-squirts are mainly sedentary and often colonial. Most of the Thaliacea are large colonial pelagic forms, commonly known as *salps*.

The ascidians (tunicates) seem to be the most characteristic representatives of the urochordates. The body is enclosed in a tough tunic made of a polysaccharide resembling cellulose. This tunic is perforated by two external openings, one slightly higher than the other. The higher one is the mouth, the lower is the atrial opening, the atrium being a cavity which surrounds the pharynx. Into the atrium open the gill slits,

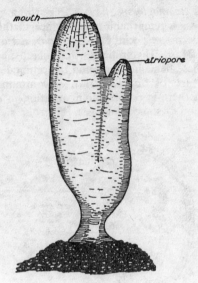

Fig. 24.8. An ascidian, *Ciona intestinalis*.

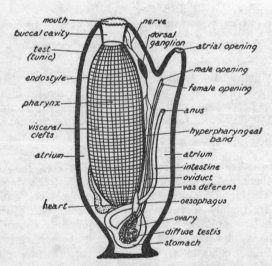

Fig. 24.9. Diagram of *Ciona* to show arrangement of internal organs.

the anus, and the genital openings. The pharynx is perforated by numerous clefts whose main function is food collection (*see* Fig. 24.9). Pharyngeal cilia create an inward current of water through the mouth; this water passes out into the atrium through the pharyngeal clefts and food particles are sifted out. They pass in a stream of mucus to the dorsal band along the pharynx whence they are carried back as a mucous cord to the oesophagus and stomach (cf. *Amphioxus* pp. 766–7).

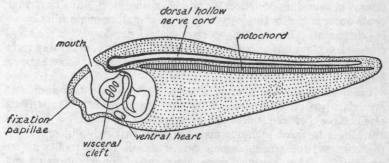

Fig. 24.10. Diagram of ascidian tadpole larva (appendicularia) to show chordate features. Median L.S.

There is no notochord in the adult and the sole remnant of the nerve cord is a dorsal ganglion above the pharynx. There is a ventral heart which pumps blood alternately backward and forward.

The larva is like a tadpole and is known as an *appendicularia* larva. It possesses a true notochord, a dorsal hollow nerve cord, visceral clefts in the pharynx, a ventral heart, and a tail (*see* Fig. 24.10). None of the urochordates have limbs. On balance, it is clear that the urochordates possess the essential characteristics of chordates; their affinities seem to lie with the cephalochordates.

Cephalochordata

The cephalochordate *Amphioxus* is considered to be the basic chordate type. It possesses the notochord in its most complete state; the pharynx is perforated by visceral clefts; there is a dorsal hollow nerve cord; the blood flows forward ventrally and backward dorsally; there is a post-anal segmented tail. There are no limbs and there is no heart, though there are contractile bulbils at the bases of the pharyngeal bars. Its early development illustrates the basic principles of chordate embryology. Nevertheless, it has many primitive and also many specialized features. *Amphioxus* is described in the next chapter.

THE AFFINITIES OF THE CHORDATES

The origins and affinities of chordate animals have long been subjects of interesting speculation. Relationships between creatures are postulated mainly on grounds of comparative anatomy and development. For existing creatures, the methods of comparative physiology and serology are also of great importance. In any comparison also involving fossil forms, it is important to remember that any evolutionary change does not affect the whole existing stock. Such a change could occur in one locality only and the existing stock might still survive in other areas. Thus it is that we have such "living fossils" as the king-crab, the coelacanth, *Cycas* and *Equisetum*. A primitive existing form may be very closely related to the ancestors of more advanced existing forms.

From the available evidence, it seems fairly certain that chordates are related to echinoderms. In the first place, we have the striking resemblance between the tornaria larva of *Balanoglossus* and the auricularia larva of echinoderms. Both are strikingly different from the characteristic trochophore larva of annelids and molluscs (*see* pp. 631–2). Also, during the development of lower chordates and echinoderms, the mesoderm is formed in the same manner, by budding off pouches dorso-laterally from the archenteron. The cavities of these pouches constitute the beginning of the coelom (*see* Fig. 24.7). This is different from the manner in which mesoderm and coelom are formed in annelids, arthropods and molluscs. Both in echinoderms and chordates, the central nervous system develops from a dorsal strip of epiblast. A final point of comparison lies in the type of phosphagen present in the muscle (*see* Vol. II, Chap. 4). In chordates the phosphagen is creatine phosphate; in non-chordates it is arginine phosphate. However, in *Balanoglossus* and in a few echinoderms, both types of phosphagen are found. The chordate and echinoderm stocks must have diverged very early in animal evolution; fossils of both types are found in early Palaeozoic rocks.

It is often suggested that we must look for chordate origins in the coelenterates. There seems to be no evidence in the comparison of existing chordates with existing coelenterates. Recently there has been presented certain evidence that *Rhabdopleura*, a deep-sea hemichordate, shows features in its colony formation which show a strong resemblance to the same process in the fossil graptolites. Unfortunately, *Rhabdopleura* has very slender qualifications for inclusion in the Chordata. It has no visceral clefts or dorsal hollow nerve cord, and its notochord is a structure like that of *Balanoglossus*. Here again we may possibly consider that both the graptolites and the ancestral hemi-

chordates were offshoots which diverged early from the coelenterate
stock (*see* Chap. 20, Vol. II).

Comparison of *Amphioxus* has been made with two Silurian fossils of
Jamoytius kerwoodi. These fossils show a soft-bodied animal with a
distinct notochord and with the same general arrangement of intestine
and myotomes as are found in *Amphioxus*. But *Jamoytius* had
undoubted eyes. It seems that by the Silurian period, the graptolites,

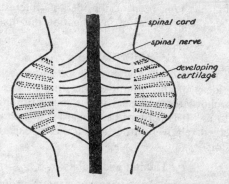

Fig. 24.11. Developing fin of a cartilaginous fish showing nine mesodermal
skeletal elements and nine spinal nerves.

Jamoytius (*see* Vol. II, Fig. 20.24), Ostracoderms related to the present
lampreys, and the bony fishes had already been evolved.

A recent interesting suggestion connects the higher chordates with
the urochordates. The suggestion is that the tadpole larvae of ancestral
ascidians may have migrated into fresh water via estuaries and there
gave rise to the fishes. We know that fishes evolved in fresh water and
that their occupation of the seas is secondary. From the same tadpole
larvae, some type may have returned to the shallow coastal waters and
given rise to the cephalochordates.

We may sum up by saying that the chordate-echinoderm stock
evolved from coelenterates in the early Palaeozoic or the late Archaeo-
zoic era, and that this stock split into the two phyla. The early chordates were probably soft-bodied boneless animals which later diverged
to give hemichordates, urochordates, cephalochordates and craniates.
No common ancestor of the chordates is known; it is perhaps unlikely
that one will ever be found.

CHAPTER 25

A PRIMITIVE CHORDATE: AMPHIOXUS

THIS little animal has long been of considerable interest to zoologists and there has been a great deal of investigation into its structure and development.

AMPHIOXUS

While there is no basic chordate type, *Amphioxus*, the lancelet, is closest to our ideas of the primitive ancestors of the craniates. In addition to its chordate characters it has many primitive and many specialized features. It is perhaps best regarded as a modern chordate which has diverged relatively little from a more generalized common chordate ancestor.

Habitat and Habits

The lancelet is found in shallow coastal waters around the Mediterranean, the North Sea and the English Channel. It is also extremely common on the Chinese coast near Amoy; at certain seasons of the year, it is so plentiful that it becomes a favoured article of food and is sold in the markets. The related genus *Asymmetron* has a tropical and southern distribution, while *Amphioxides* is a pelagic form. The species described here is *Amphioxus lanceolatus* [*Branchiostoma lanceolata*]. It inhabits localities where the sea-floor is sandy and spends most of its time almost buried, in a vertical position, with the head end protruding. Being a ciliary feeder, it subsists on microscopic creatures in the plankton; the method entails almost ceaseless feeding. Occasionally, it swims, especially at night, by rapid and sinuous lateral movements of the whole body. Sometimes it lies passively on its side on the sand. It is able to burrow with great rapidity, proceeding with the pointed end foremost and the exposed part of the body vibrating rapidly from side to side. The sexes are separate and fertilization takes place in the sea. There is a free-swimming larval stage which shows pronounced asymmetry; this feature persists in the adult, but is not so easily recognized.

External Features

A. lanceolatus has a whitish translucent body, compressed laterally and about 40 to 50 mm in length. It is pointed at both ends. There is

758

a shallow median *dorsal fin* along the whole length; at the posterior end it passes into a slightly deeper triangular *caudal fin* around the tail. Ventrally, the caudal fin is continuous with a shallow *ventral fin* which proceeds forward for about a third of the body length to end at a prominent ventral opening, the *atriopore*. In front of the atriopore, the ventral surface is somewhat flattened and at its sides are the two *metapleural folds*. These pass forward to the anterior end where they merge into the borders of the *oral hood*. This lies dorsally and laterally

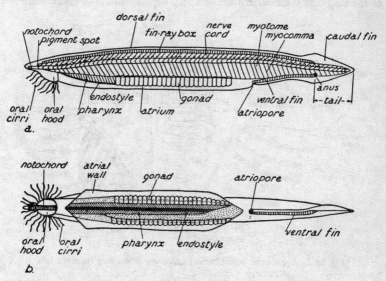

Fig. 25.1. *Amphioxus*. (*a*) Transparency from left side. (*b*) Ventral view with atrium opened.

over the anterior end and its large aperture may be considered to be the *mouth*. From its edge, about twenty stiff *cirri* radiate outwards. The *anus* lies on the left side near the end of the body just above the ventral fin.

Because of the semi-transparent nature, the major internal structures can be seen. The V-shaped *myotomes*, with the apex of the V pointing forward, are prominent; there are about sixty. Small *fin-ray boxes* supporting the dorsal and ventral fins can be seen with a lens. Below these lies the *nerve cord*, easily discernible by reason of black pigment spots along it. Beneath the nerve cord is the *notochord*, characterized by its extreme anterior and posterior extension. In immature specimens, the narrow parallel *gill bars* show that the *pharynx* extends from a position immediately behind the oral hood almost half-way down the body. But in mature animals, most of the pharynx is obscured by the row of twenty-six *gonads* on each side. The whole pharynx is covered laterally and ventrally by downgrowths of the body wall enclosing a cavity called the *atrium*.

The lower surface of the oral hood is wrinkled by a number of finger-like depressions with ridges between them. They constitute the ciliated *wheel-organ*. A deeper pit in the roof of the hood, to the left of the mid-line is called *Hatschek's pit*; its function is to secrete mucus.

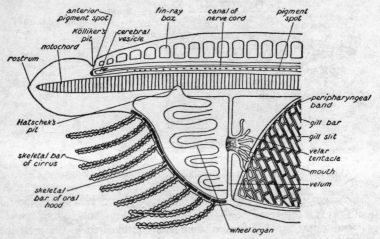

Fig. 25.2. *Amphioxus*. Right half of anterior portion seen from the left.

At the back of the oral hood is a vertical partition, the *velum*. This is pierced by a small aperture sometimes known as the mouth. Since, however, it leads directly into the pharynx it is perhaps preferable to refer to it as the *enterostome*.

Structure and Functions of the Body Wall

The body wall is very thick dorsally and dorso-laterally owing to the myotomes which taper ventrally (*see* Fig. 25.5). There is a thin iridescent *cuticle* made of a substance resembling chitin. Beneath the cuticle is an epithelium of cubical cells. This constitutes the *epidermis* and is noteworthy in being only one cell thick. In all the higher chordates the epidermis is a stratified epithelium. Interspersed among the supporting cells are sensory and glandular cells; above both types, the cuticle is perforated. The basement membrane lies on connective tissue which constitutes the *dermis* and also separates the myotomes.

Between the myotomes, the connective tissue partitions are called *myocommata*. The internal epithelium of the body wall is the meso-dermal *peritoneum* which abuts on the *coelom* (*see* Fig. 25.3). The muscle fibres of the myotomes are all of the striated type; they are mainly longitudinal. In the floor of the atrium beneath the pharynx there are transverse bands.

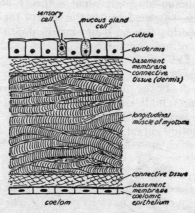

Fig. 25.3. V.S. body wall of *Amphioxus*, through plane *a–a* of Fig. 25.4.

The structure of the body wall as described above, is best seen lateral to the gut in a transverse section of the intestinal region. In the pharyn-geal region, the arrangement is somewhat complicated by the presence of the atrium (*see* Fig. 25.5).

The functions of the body wall are, as is usual, protection, sensitivity, and locomotion. Protection is afforded by the cuticle and the mucus. Sensitivity to touch, temperature changes and possibly other stimuli, is provided by the various types of sensory cells. The myotomes supply the power for locomotion. In addition, there is considerable skeletal value in the various connective tissue sheaths. They serve for muscle attachment and provide relatively resistant material against which the muscles can work.

Skeleton and Supporting Structures

In *Amphioxus* there is no cartilage or bone, the main skeletal structure being the notochord. It is formed from the roof of the archenteron and the cells form a single longitudinal row. This condition persists in the adult though the cells become flattened and squeezed together like a pile of coins. The more typical fibrous and elastic sheaths are not present, but mesodermal connective tissue surrounds the rod. The notochord forms the *axial skeleton* maintaining body shape and providing resistance for the muscles. These it carries out by means of the turgidity of the cells; in this respect it resembles the "coelomic skeleton" mentioned in the annelids. There are no muscles attached to the notochord; connective tissue always intervenes.

Besides the notochord, there are various accessory skeletal structures, all the connective tissue being important in this respect. The gill bars of the pharynx are supported by rods of a firm though pliable gelatinous material (*see* Fig. 25.7). It appears to consist of agglutinated elastic fibres. There are two plates of similar material beneath the *endostyle* (*see* Fig. 25.9) and the oral hood is held in position by a half hoop of the same substance (*see* Fig. 25.2). Short rods strengthen the oral cirri. The fin-ray boxes consist of connective tissue compartments filled with a gelatinous material (*see* Fig. 25.5); the dorsal fin contains about 250 of these boxes. In addition, the fluid-filled coelomic cavities have a skeletal function in that they are protective and aid in giving the firmness without which muscular contraction would be useless.

The Coelom and the Atrium

In its typical state, the coelom is best seen in a transverse section through the body just in front of the anus (*see* Fig. 25.4). There, it appears as a fluid-filled cavity interposed between the gut and the body wall except

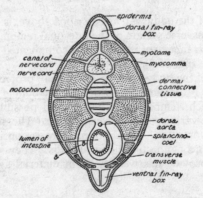

Fig. 25.4. *Amphioxus.* T.S. through intestinal region near anus.

in the dorsal region where the dorsal mesentery suspends the gut. A similar condition prevails for most of the region behind the atriopore except that on the right-hand side there is a backward extension of the atrium which partially obliterates the coelom. In the pharyngeal region, there is some complication due to the numerous gill bars and the development of the atrium. At first, the pharynx is completely surrounded by the coelom (*see* Fig. 25.28). Before the gill slits open, the metapleural folds develop and an ingrowth from each, called an *epipleure* moves inward. The two epipleural growths fuse in the midventral line, thus enclosing a small cavity, the atrium (*see* Fig. 25.28 (*b*)). It is obvious that the lining of the atrium is ectodermal. Gradually, the atrium extends upward on each side of the pharynx (*see* Fig. 25.28 (*c*)),

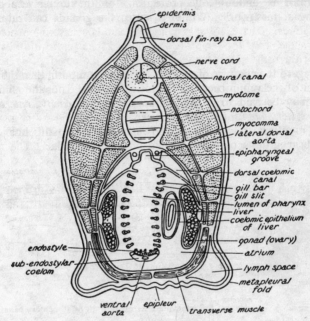

Fig. 25.5. *Amphioxus*. T.S. through pharyngeal region.

and later the gill slits open into it (*see* Fig. 25.28 (*d*)). When they open, the endoderm of the pharynx meets the ectoderm of the inner wall of the atrium and thus a small coelomic cavity is enclosed in each primary bar. The paired coelomic canals are cut off dorsally and the sub-endostylar coelom ventrally (*see* Fig. 25.28 (*d*)). The adult condition is shown in Fig. 25.5. The section shows a number of gill bars because their slight obliquity is considerably increased in fixed specimens.

The atrium is thus a portion of outside space enclosed within the body. Water drawn in through the enterostome passes through the gill slits and makes its exit through the atriopore. Behind the pore on the right side, there is a backward extension of the atrium nearly as far as the anus. Two conical projections extend forward into the dorsal coelomic canals above the posterior end of the pharynx. They are atrial cavities known as the *brown funnels*; their function is unknown, though they may be concerned with excretion.

During development, mesodermal tissue grows down into the atrial folds, and when finally formed there is a strong thick wall lying outside the morphologically external wall of the pharynx. The function of this extra wall is undoubtedly protection for the excessively delicate pharyngeal meshwork. Within it, also, the gonads can develop in safety.

Nutrition

If we regard the aperture of the oral hood as the mouth, then the region in front of the velum becomes the buccal cavity. Thus the alimentary canal may be said to consist of *mouth, buccal cavity, enterostome, pharynx, oesophagus, intestine* and *anus*.

The mouth is fringed by about twenty oral cirri, stiff, but jointed. They bear groups of sensory cells on small papillae. The ciliated

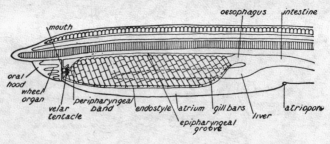

Fig. 25.6. *Amphioxus.* L.S. showing anterior portion of alimentary canal.

wheel-organ and Hatschek's pit occupy the roof of the buccal cavity. This is bounded posteriorly by the thin muscular velum pierced by the enterostome which is controlled by a sphincter. On the posterior wall of the velum, surrounding the enterostome and projecting into the pharynx are twelve *velar tentacles*.

The pharynx is very large, occupying almost half the length of the body. Its lateral walls on each side are perforated by some 180 slits. Between the slits are the gill bars of two sorts. *Primary bars* fork at their ventral ends; *secondary bars* do not. Both types are joined dorsally by arches, and they are also inter-connected along the sides of the pharynx by small cross-pieces called *synapticula*. The secondary bars, with their unforked ends, grow down between the primary bars.

The structure of both types in transverse section is shown in Fig. 25.8. The essential difference between them is that the primary bars contain a coelomic canal. The arrangement of the cilia and the direction of their beat in the various regions, are mainly responsible for the entry and exit of water and the capture of food particles.

Along the ventral floor of the pharynx is a shallow gutter, the *endostyle*. It consists of nine longitudinal tracts of cells, four glandular and five ciliated (*see* Fig. 25.9). The glandular cells produce the mucus in which food particles are entangled; the cilia waft the mucus in the

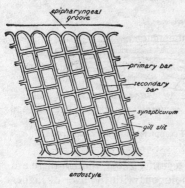

Fig. 25.7. Portion of pharynx wall showing arrangement of gill bars in *Amphioxus*.

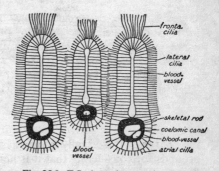

Fig. 25.8. T.S. through two primary and one secondary gill bar.

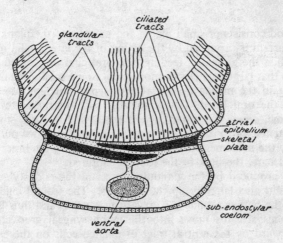

Fig. 25.9. T.S. endostyle.

right directions. The endostyle is supported by two skeletal plates and beneath it is a coelomic canal containing the ventral aorta. The gill bars join the endostyle at the sides of the coelomic canal. From the anterior end of the endostyle, *peripharyngeal bands* fork to left and right, upwards around the front of the pharynx. In the dorsal mid-line is the *epi-pharyngeal groove*. All the mucus streams with their trapped food particles converge here and the material is swept backward toward the oesophagus.

The short oesophagus leads into the intestine. Here there is a large *diverticulum* on the right-hand side; it projects forward at the side of

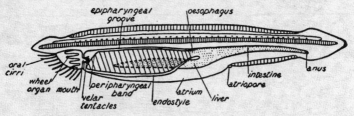

Fig. 25.10. *Amphioxus*. Side view of complete alimentary canal.

the pharynx. It is usually known as a *digestive gland*, though there are grounds for considering that it is homologous with the liver of higher forms. The intestine continues as a straight tube to the anus (*see* Fig. 25.10).

Feeding

The food consists of small plants and animals of the plankton. An inward current is produced by the action of the lateral cilia of the gill bars. While the animal is feeding, the oral cirri are folded over the mouth so that large particles cannot enter. Some small organisms may be caught in the mucus from Hatschek's pit; this spreads over the inside of the oral hood. The cilia waft such particles towards the enterostome, where the water current enters and is again strained by the velar tentacles. From the pharynx, the water is drawn out into the atrium by the movement of the lateral cilia, and on the inner surfaces of the gill bars, the bulk of the food is captured.

Mucus produced by the glandular tracts of the endostyle is swept forward and also laterally up the gill bars. The frontal cilia, on the inside of the bars, continue the upward movement and thus the food-laden mucus streams move into the epipharyngeal groove. Mucus swept forward by the central tract of ciliated cells on the endostyle, moves upwards along the peripharyngeal bands to the beginning of the epipharyngeal groove. Here, the cilia beat backwards, driving the food cord to the oesophagus. There is thus a constant current of water passing in at the mouth and out at the atriopore. Occasionally, by violent contraction of the transverse ventral muscles, the water is expelled through the enterostome and mouth, with the atriopore closed. This tends to free the various sifting mechanisms of large particles which have become entangled.

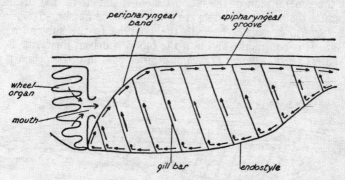

Fig. 25.11. Diagram showing ciliary currents in the pharynx of *Amphioxus*.

The food cord passes along the oesophagus where it is slowly rotated by the arrangement of cilia in special tracts. Enzymes from the liver and from the intestine wall digest the food. Absorption takes place mainly in the hind-gut; there is probably also amoeboid seizure of particles and some intra-cellular digestion. All the blood-vessels from the gut lead into a sub-intestinal plexus; this leads forward to a hepatic portal vein which proceeds to the liver, where there is a further network. It does not, however, appear to deal with the food in the same manner as in the higher forms; its main function is undoubtedly secretion of digestive juice.

The faeces are expelled through the anus where there is a sphincter. The whole length of the gut, including the liver, is ciliated, the region behind the oesophagus containing special tracts of cilia for rotating the food cord and thus producing better contact with the enzymes.

There is never any lack of suitable food in the sea and consequently there is no appreciable food storage except in the eggs.

Respiration

Oxygen is obtained by diffusion from the sea-water. There is no respiratory pigment, but in such a small animal with such large fluid cavities and a constant moving current, diffusion provides ample oxygen. The gill bars, the atrial epithelium and the external epithelium present a very large surface for absorption of oxygen.

The Blood Vascular System

The blood is colourless and it contains amoeboid corpuscles. There is no distinction in structure between arteries, veins, and capillaries, but since the general plan of the blood system is similar to that of higher chordates, the principal vessels are given the same names.

The *ventral aorta* lies beneath the pharynx in the sub-endostylar coelom. It is contractile and in it the blood is driven forward. From the ventral aorta, *afferent branchial arteries* pass into the primary gill

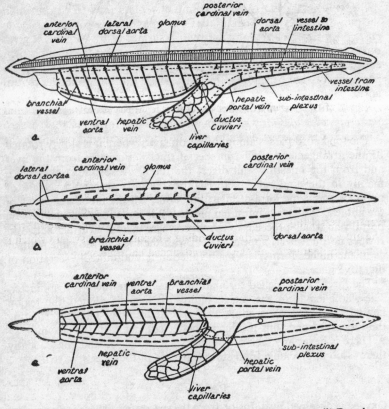

Fig. 25.12. Blood vascular system of *Amphioxus*. (*a*) Lateral view. (*b*) Dorsal view. (*c*) Ventral view (liver displaced).

bars. There are contractile bulbils at the bases of these vessels. From the primary bars, blood passes into the secondary bars through the synapticula. In both primary and secondary bars the blood flows dorsally into two *lateral dorsal aortae*, one on each side above the epipharyngeal groove. The latter portions of the pharyngeal vessels are known as *efferent branchial arteries*. Before they enter the aortae, they branch into small networks, each called a *glomus*, near the excretory organs, nephridia. In front, the dorsal aortae continue forward as the *carotid arteries*. The main flow is, however, backward, and just behind the pharynx, they unite to form a single median *dorsal aorta* (*see* Fig. 25.12). This continues down the body beneath the notochord, supplying *segmental branches* to the myotomes and to the gut, and finally entering the tail as the *caudal artery*.

Blood from the gut is collected into a *sub-intestinal plexus* in which the flow is forward. Behind the liver, this plexus forms a *hepatic portal vein* which runs along the ventral surface of this organ. It gives out many branches to form a network in the liver and the blood is then collected into a *hepatic vein* on its dorsal surface. This hepatic vein proceeds forward beneath the pharynx where it is known as the ventral aorta.

Blood from the myotomes is collected into lateral *anterior* and *posterior cardinal veins* which join on each side to form a *ductus Cuvieri*. The ducti Cuvieri pass down to join the hepatic vein and thus form the ventral aorta.

The general plan of the blood system is thus characteristically chordate. Flow in the main ventral vessel is forward, then the blood is forced up the gill arches to a distributing dorsal vessel where the flow is mainly backward. There is no heart, but it is from such a contractile ventral vessel that the heart develops in higher chordates. Blood from the gut goes to the liver, thus providing a hepatic portal system which is a constant feature of all the more advanced chordates.

Locomotion

The animal swims by lateral movements of the whole body. The myotomes of one side contract in rapid succession from anterior to posterior, and thus the body lashes to one side. Then the myotomes of the other side contract. There is therefore a series of violent lateral flexures which drive the animal forward by the thrust against the water. Burrowing in the sand is effected by the same type of movement, the anterior end, stiffened by the notochord, providing a firm pointed apex. The head enters first, and by rapid flexures of the body, the animal changes direction to push the head upward through the sand to emerge a short distance from the point of entry. Most of the body remains buried. Simultaneous contraction of all the myotomes, enables it to withdraw its anterior region beneath the sand when danger threatens.

Growth

The lancelet grows throughout life, though the rate of growth decreases rapidly with age. Every individual examined shows new posterior gill slits developing. As is true for animals in general, all types of cell except nerve cells increase in number. A peculiar feature is the asymmetry which occurs during development and persists in the adult. This asymmetry can be seen in the gill bars, in the myotomes, in the gonads and in the spinal nerves. The average length of life is unknown but probably does not exceed four or five years under natural conditions.

Excretion

The organs of nitrogenous excretion are *nephridia* of which there are about ninety pairs. They are situated above the pharynx in the

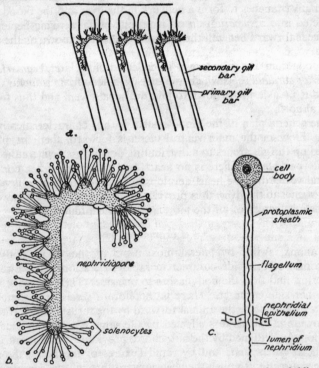

Fig. 25.13. Excretory system of *Amphioxus*. (*a*) Location of nephridia on outer wall of pharynx. (*b*) Single nephridium. (*c*) Single solenocyte.

epithelium between the atrium and the dorsal coelomic canals. They are ectodermal protonephridia, consisting of small tubes bent almost at right angles with bunches of solenocytes projecting from the dorsal and anterior surfaces (*see* Fig. 25.13 (*b*)). The forward arm of a nephridium lies mainly in the coelomic canal of a primary gill bar, while the backward horizontal arm sends solenocytes into the dorsal coelomic canals and opens by a small pore into the atrium opposite a secondary gill bar. Near each nephridium, in the dorsal coelomic canal is a glomus on the course of an efferent branchial artery. Presumably, substances from the blood pass into the coelomic fluid from the glomeruli and are then extracted by the solenocytes and passed out into the atrium. The nephridia probably also serve as organs of osmoregulation. A single nephridium lies dorsal to the oral hood on the left side of the mid-line. It is known as *Hatschek's nephridium*. Its posterior limb opens into the pharynx just behind the mouth. An excretory function has also been ascribed to the brown funnels and to small *"renal" papillae* on the floor of the atrium.

The presence of nephridia is a primitive characteristic. They are ectodermal and therefore cannot be related to the mesodermal coelomoducts, which form the excretory tubules of the higher chordates.

Carbon dioxide passes out of the body at all surfaces in contact with the sea-water, particularly the pharynx and the atrial epithelium.

The Nervous System

The *central nervous system* consists of a dorsal, hollow *nerve cord* lying above the notochord and beneath the fin-ray boxes. Its anterior end is at the level of the first myotome and its posterior portion tapers considerably and terminates some way in front of the end of the notochord. The nerve cord contains a minute *central canal* and there is a *dorsal septum* indicating where the tube closed. In front, the canal is dilated to form the *cerebral vesicle* though the external diameter of the cord is unchanged. There is a small *dorsal diverticulum* of the cerebral vesicle and a median ventral depression called the *infundibular organ* (*see* Fig. 25.15). A transverse section of the nerve cord (*see* Fig. 25.16) shows that the neurones are arranged around the central canal while the rest of its thickness consists of non-medullated nerve fibres; there are giant cells and giant fibres similar to those found in *Lumbricus* and *Astacus*. The whole cord lies in a stout sheath of connective tissue.

The *peripheral nervous system* consists of two pairs of *"cranial" nerves* and a segmental series of *"spinal" nerves*. The first pair of cranial nerves leave the anterior end of the cord; the second pair leave the cord dorsally a little further back. Both are sensory nerves bearing axons which convey sensory impulses from the sense organs of the snout, oral hood and oral cirri. The spinal nerves emerge dorso-laterally. There are, on each side, distinct *dorsal* and *ventral roots*; they do not unite to form a mixed spinal nerve as in craniates. The general asymmetry of the animal is found here also, the dorsal root of one side lying opposite the ventral root of the other side (*see* Fig. 25.14). The ventral root consists of a bunch of nerves, emerging somewhat in front of the single dorsal root. The ventral roots supply the myotomes and are purely motor or efferent. The dorsal roots pass out to the surface in the mycommata; they are mainly sensory or afferent, con-veying impulses from peripheral sense organs, though some fibres are

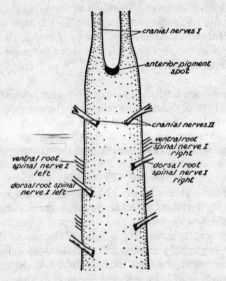

Fig. 25.14. Dorsal view of the anterior part of the nerve cord of *Amphioxus*.

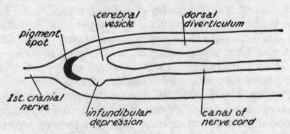

Fig. 25.15. V.S. cerebral vesicle of *Amphioxus*.

said to be motor, supplying the unstriated muscle of the gut and the atrium. The primitive condition of the sensory nerves resembles that found in invertebrates; the cell bodies of these afferent nerves lie peripherally, and the axons pass directly into the central nervous system.

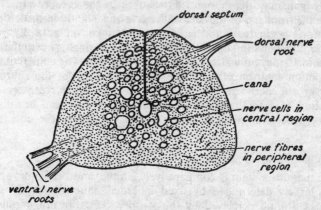

Fig. 25.16. *Amphioxus.* T.S. nerve cord.

In craniates, the impulses from sensory cells are conveyed along fibres whose cell bodies lie in ganglia on the dorsal nerve root. These relay the impulses into the central cord. The *autonomic system* is represented by two networks in the gut wall. They communicate with the central nervous system by means of visceral nerves in the dorsal roots.

Sense Organs

There are no large sense organs but only sensory cells or groups of such cells. On the oral cirri and the velar tentacles are groups of cells

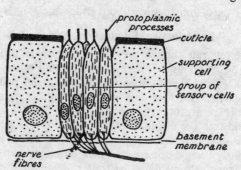

Fig. 25.17. *Amphioxus.* Tactile receptor.

arranged in small papillae; they are probably chemoreceptors. Along the central canal of the nerve cord are two lateral tracts of pigmented eye-spots. A larger pigmented area at the front end of the cerebral vesicle is thought to be a thermal sense organ, and the median infundibular organ may detect pressure changes in the cerebrospinal fluid. Above the front end of the cerebral vesicle and slightly to the left of the mid-line is a ciliated ectodermal depression known as *Kölliker's pit* (*see* Fig. 25.2) or sometimes the *olfactory pit*, by analogy with the single median olfactory pit which occurs in cyclostomes. The epithelium does not contain sensory cells; it is probably a vestige of the neuropore. All over the body are scattered groups of tactile receptors, each consisting of a small group of spindle-shaped cells and bearing stiff sensory processes which protrude through pores in the cuticle (*see* Fig. 25.17).

Co-ordination and Behaviour

The nervous system is comparatively simple, and behaviour appears to be largely determined by fixed inherited patterns, mainly simple reflexes. Stimuli perceived by the sensory cells transmit impulses to the central cord and there evoke motor impulses to the myotomes. These contain proprioceptors which are probably stimulated by contraction of adjacent myotomes. Thus we can picture the movement as a series of localized contractions stimulated by intersegmental reflex arcs, much as in *Lumbricus*. The giant fibres probably act in the same way as those of non-chordates by providing pathways of rapid conduction along the whole body. If a shadow, such as might be caused by a fish, is moved over the animal, it withdraws into the sand at once. It has been shown that such light perception is localized in the eye-spots which are really unicellular eyes of the planarian pattern (*see* Chap. 19).

There is a lack of information about endocrine glands or hormones.

Reproduction, Survival and Dispersal

The sexes are separate though they cannot be distinguished except by examination of the gonads. These are segmental organs, though again asymmetrical. There are twenty-six or twenty-seven pairs, situated in segments twenty-five to fifty-one, where they bulge prominently into the atrium. There are no reproductive ducts, the ripe eggs or sperm being liberated into the atrium by the bursting of the gonads.

The gonads develop from the antero-ventral portions of the somites of the embryo. Such a somite becomes differentiated into an inner *sclerotome*, a central *myotome*, an outer *dermatome* and a ventral *gonotome* (*see* Fig. 25.27). Cell multiplication in the young gonotome causes it to bulge forward into the posterior region of the next mesodermal pouch. Finally it loses all connexion with its own segment and is cut off in a bulge in the posterior portion of the next pouch in front. It develops a coelomic cavity and becomes surrounded by another epithelium derived from the other somite. Thus the gonad comes to lie on the inner side of the postero-ventral corner of the somite in front

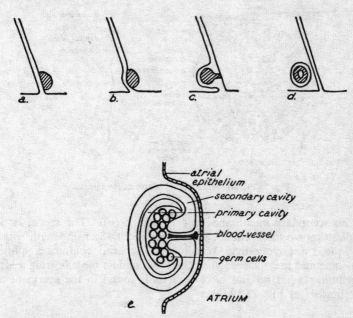

Fig. 25.18. Reproductive organs of *Amphioxus*. (*a*) Gonotome developing. (*b*) Gonotome bulging forward. (*c*) Gonotome held by stalk. (*d*) Gonotome enclosed in next pouch with primary and secondary cavities. (*e*) Older gonad.

of the one from which it originated. They are separated from the atrium by the ectodermal atrial epithelium, the secondary mesodermal epithelium, and the primary or follicular epithelium. The germ cells develop from the inner primary epithelium. Each gonad has a large blood space communicating with the anterior cardinal vein (*see* Fig. 25.18).

Breeding takes place in the late spring and early summer. The animals leave the sand and swim about in the surface waters, shedding eggs and sperm. The egg is spherical and about 0·1 mm in diameter. When it reaches the sea, it is at the secondary oocyte stage (*see* Vol. II,

Chap. 17) and the first polar body is outside the vitelline membrane. There are numerous minute granules of yolk scattered evenly throughout the oocyte except for a peripheral layer crowded with granular mitochondria, and the large germinal vesicle or egg nucleus. It is enclosed in a vitelline membrane secreted by the egg itself, and there

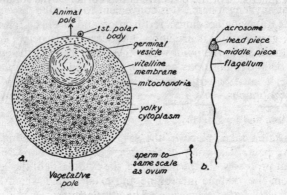

Fig. 25.19. (a) Ovum and (b) sperm of *Amphioxus*.

are no secondary membranes (*see* Fig. 25.19 (a)). The sperm is the smallest known in chordates, being only about $18\mu m$ in length with a head-piece not more than $1\mu m$ long. The head contains a minute acrosome and the nucleus; then there is a middle piece bearing a long flagellum. It has no end piece such as is found in the sperm of all vertebrates (*see* Fig. 25.19 (b)).

Survival and Dispersal

The animal is not likely to encounter adverse physical and chemical conditions in the sea, where the environment remains fairly constant. Its burrowing habit renders it inconspicuous and its transparency makes it almost invisible in the water. In favourable localities, they are abundant.

Dispersal is effected by the drifting eggs and by the motile larvae. It is not really an urgent problem since the method of feeding and the constant movement of the water would allow of a very high density of population. The tunicates, with a similar method of feeding, are very crowded in many regions of the sea-bed. There is necessarily very great mortality of eggs and larvae and also of the adults during the breeding periods. The balance is adjusted by the large numbers of eggs produced.

Development

The early development in *Amphioxus* is considered to be the basic type of chordate embryology, not complicated by such factors as abundance of yolk, embryonic membranes, or retention within the mother's body. Its later development is atypical and specialized and will not be considered at any length here. It is convenient to describe the embryology under the following headings: fertilization and its effects, cleavage, the blastula, gastrulation, neurulation, mesoderm and coelom formation. This will take us to the point where the germ layers of the embryo are in their definitive positions and then tissue and organ formation can proceed. It must be remembered that the whole process of development is continuous.

Fertilization and its Effects

Fertilization takes place in the sea, a sperm penetrating near the vegetative pole. The entry of the sperm sets in motion a number of important processes. In the first place, the cytoplasm of the egg shrinks away from the vitelline membrane and exudes fluid which forms the so-called *fertilization membrane*. This repels further sperm which are no longer attracted to the egg. The egg is stimulated to undergo its second maturation division and the second polar body is extruded; it remains within the vitelline membrane until the hatching of the larva. There is rearrangement of the cytoplasm of the egg so that various presumptive areas can be defined (*see* Fig. 25.20 (*a*)). These areas have been outlined after numerous experiments involving principally the use of harmless dyes. Because a definite pattern of presumptive areas can

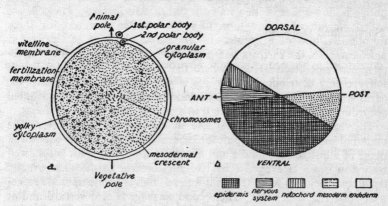

Fig. 25.20. (*a*) Fertilized egg of *Amphioxus* showing rearrangement of cytoplasmic areas. (*b*) Presumptive areas on egg.

be recognized in the egg, it is known as a *mosaic egg*; the eggs of echinoderms and tunicates are also of this type. If the egg is orientated with regard to the antero-posterior axis and the dorsal and ventral surfaces of the future embryo, as shown in Fig. 25.20 (*b*), the positions of the presumptive areas are as follows—

1. The *presumptive ectoderm* occupies almost the whole of the ventral hemisphere with the exception of a small postero-ventral crescent.

2. This crescent is the *presumptive mesoderm.*

3. Diametrically opposite the mesodermal crescent is the *presumptive neural plate*, another crescent-shaped region.

4. Dorsal to the presumptive neural plate is the crescentic area destined to become *notochord.*

5. The remainder of the dorsal hemisphere, containing most of the yolk, will become *endoderm.*

Since these presumptive areas must be equally divided between the right and left halves of the embryo, then the act of fertilization has determined the plane of the first cleavage and hence the plane about which the embryo will be bilaterally symmetrical. The antero-posterior axis and also dorsal and ventral surfaces are likewise determined.

Last, but by no means least, fertilization restores the diploid number of chromosomes, which in *Amphioxus* is twenty-four. The twelve paternal chromosomes entering with the sperm nucleus constitute the male contribution to the inherited characteristics of the embryo.

Cleavage

After fertilization, the egg divides mitotically, by a series of cleavages, until a hollow sphere with a wall one cell thick is formed. The cells are called *blastomeres.* The term cleavage is often reserved for these mitotic divisions of a zygote. In *Amphioxus* the type of cleavage is *holoblastic*, i.e. the furrows pass right through the egg. This is characteristic of microlecithal eggs where the amount of yolk is small and fairly evenly distributed. Cleavage is not a haphazard process; the various potentialities in the cytoplasmic areas are carefully distributed according to an invariable pattern in a normal and undamaged egg.

The first cleavage is vertical and in the plane of symmetry. The maternal and paternal chromosomes are arranged on the equatorial plane of a horizontal spindle and mitosis takes place. This is followed by cytoplasmic cleavage. The two blastomeres formed are exactly equal and they will form the right and left halves of the animal respectively (*see* Fig. 25.21 (*a*)). The second cleavage is also vertical and at right angles to the first, so that four equal blastomeres are formed, two anterior and two posterior (*see* Fig. 25.21 (*b*)). The third cleavage is horizontal; the four upper blastomeres are slightly larger than the four lower (*see* Fig. 25.21 (*c*)). The fourth cleavage is vertical in two planes at right angles to each other. Thus there are now sixteen cells; eight upper *megameres* and eight lower *micromeres* (*see* Fig. 25.21 (*d*)). In the fifth cleavage, division takes place in two horizontal planes, the eight micromeres and the eight megameres dividing to give thirty-two

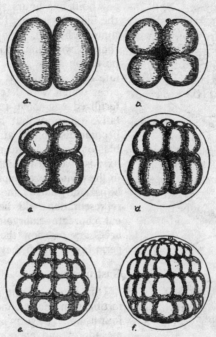

Fig. 25.21. Cleavage stages in *Amphioxus* egg. (*a*) 2-celled. (*b*) 4-celled. (*c*) 8-celled. (*d*) 16-celled. (*e*) 32-celled. (*f*) 64-celled. All lateral as the egg floats except (*b*), from above.

cells (*see* Fig. 25.21 (*e*)). Next, all the cells divide vertically and thus there is a *morula* of sixty-four cells, with the largest in the mid-lower region and the smallest in the mid-upper region and a gradation from large to small between (*see* Fig. 25.21 (*f*)). After this, division becomes more irregular, the smaller blastomeres dividing slightly faster than the larger ones.

After each cleavage, the blastomeres become rounded off, except where they are pressed against each other. From the beginning, they secrete a jelly into the central region; this absorbs water and swells, so that the cells are gradually forced outward around a fluid cavity, the *blastocoel* or *segmentation cavity*. During cleavage, the cells gradually become smaller; no food material can be taken in and there is loss by metabolism. Hence, until the blastocoel assumes reasonable proportions, the embryo is smaller than the original fertilized egg.

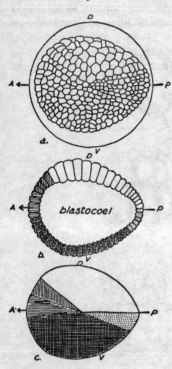

Fig. 25.22. Blastula of *Amphioxus*. (a) Lateral view. (b) V.S. (c) Presumptive areas, side view.

The Blastula

About five hours after fertilization, the blastula is fully formed. It is not quite spherical, being slightly pear-shaped with the more pointed end posterior (*see* Fig. 25.22 (*a*)). A fate map shows that the cytoplasmic areas which were determinable on the fertilized egg, have retained their relative positions but have, of course, become distributed among the various blastomeres. A fate map for *Amphioxus* is given in Fig. 25.22(*c*). **The key to the various presumptive areas should be carefully noted; the same method of representation will be used throughout chordate embryology where it is necessary to show these areas or the germ layers which they form.**

Gastrulation

This begins about six hours after fertilization and is completed in about four hours. The germ layers, ectoderm, mesoderm and endoderm, are all on the outside and have to be moved to their correct positions before tissue differentiation and organ formation can commence. These movements of cells constitute the process of *gastrulation*.

The first sign is the flattening of the dorsal surface to form the *endodermal plate* (*see* Fig. 25.23 (*a*)). Gradually this sinks inward to form a two-layered cup with a large opening known as the *blastopore*. The process is known as *invagination*. At an early stage, the lip or edge of the blastopore consists of presumptive notochord dorsally and presumptive mesoderm laterally and ventrally. While invagination of the endodermal plate is proceeding, cells of the dorsal lip roll over its edge into the interior and proceed forward (*see* Fig. 25.23 (*b*)). This

type of activity spreads to the lateral lips so that presumptive mesoderm is tucked in. Finally the ventral lip takes up the process to turn in
the last of the mesoderm, the thick central region of the crescentic
band we saw in the blastula (*see* Fig. 25.23 (*c*)). Meanwhile the shape
of the embryo alters, owing to the rapid backward growth of the dorsal
lip, followed by the lateral lips. Then the ventral lip grows up to narrow
the diameter of the blastopore which now lies in a posterior position.
The presumptive notochord cells multiply and stream forward to
form a band in the mid-dorsal line of the inner layer. The presumptive

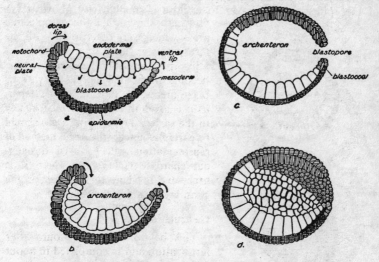

Fig. 25.23. Gastrulation in *Amphioxus*. (*a*) Early. (*b*) Later. (*c*) V.S. of nearly
complete gastrula. (*d*) Vertical half of same.

mesoderm cells also move rapidly forward and somewhat dorsally to
lie on either side of the notochord and form the dorso-lateral portions
of the inner layer. The floor and sides are formed of presumptive
endoderm. On the outer layer of the embryo, there is now a broad
dorsal band of presumptive neural plate while the rest consists of
presumptive epidermis (*see* Fig. 25.23 (*d*)).
The cavity of the blastocoel is practically obliterated by the close
apposition of the two layers. The new cavity enclosed by the inner
layer is the *archenteron* and its opening the blastopore. The dorsal and
lateral lips of the blastopore now consist of presumptive neural plate
cells, while the ventral lip consists of presumptive epidermis.
At this stage, gastrulation may be said to be completed. It takes

place mainly by simple invagination assisted by inflection of presumptive notochord and mesoderm, and by growth of the lips of the blastopore. This type of gastrulation is only possible when there is comparatively little yolk.

The Formation of the Neural Tube, Notochord, Mesoderm and Coelom

The separation of the neural tube, notochord and mesoderm, all begin at the same time, but for convenience, they are described separately.

The neural plate on the dorsal surface sinks down and lateral folds of the epidermis grow over to enclose a small cavity above it (*see*

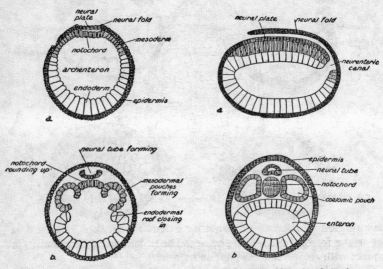

Fig. 25.24. T.S. Neurula of *Amphioxus*. (a) Early. (b) Late.

Fig. 25.25. Neurula of *Amphioxus*. (a) V.S. early neurula to show neurenteric canal. (b) T.S. completed neurula.

Fig. 25.24 (*a*)). The process starts by closure of epidermis over the blastopore and the fusion extends forward until the epidermal folds meet all along the mid-dorsal line to the anterior end of the neural plate. The edges of the plate become folded upward and inward to close off the *neural tube* (*see* Fig. 25.24 (*b*)). In front it is open at the *neuropore*, which becomes Kölliker's pit in the adult, and posteriorly it communicates with the archenteron by the *neurenteric canal*, which is really a portion of the blastopore (*see* Fig. 25.25 (*a*)). Later, this neurenteric canal closes. This stage in the embryo's development, when the neural tube is being formed, is usually referred to as the *neurula*. Neurulation by sinking-in of a flat plate is not typical of chordates generally and is not found in any of the vertebrates.

Meanwhile, the presumptive notochord in the roof of the archenteron, becomes indented from beneath (*see* Fig. 25.24 (*b*)) and the two sides of the groove bend downward and inward to fuse and form a solid rod (*see* Fig. 25.25 (*b*)). At first, this takes place in front and gradually proceeds backward. The cells forming the notochord eventually become rearranged to form a cylindrical rod made of a series of disc-like cells: these become vacuolated and maintain axial support by

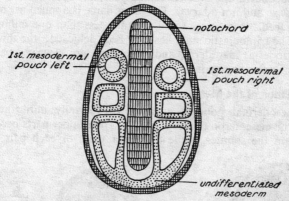

Fig. 25.26. Embryo of *Amphioxus* in horizontal L.S. to show early asymmetry.

their turgidity. The extreme anterior extension develops later and is due to the forward growth of the tip. The posterior region remains in contact with the archenteron for some time.

The bands of presumptive mesoderm develop upward grooves on their inner surfaces (*see* Fig. 25.24 (*b*)). The edges of the grooves bend inward until they meet (*see* Fig. 25.25 (*b*)). Transverse grooves also develop, cutting the mesoderm into a series of closed dorso-lateral pouches, each containing a cavity which was part of the archenteron (*see* Fig. 25.25 (*b*)). The cavities of these pouches together represent the coelom, formed by a method which is not found in vertebrates. Repetition of these paired mesodermal sacs proceeds backward and provides the first sign of metameric segmentation in *Amphioxus*. Soon, they become asymmetrical, the pouches on the left being slightly in advance of those on the right (*see* Fig. 25.26). After four pairs have been formed, the remaining unsegmented mesoderm separates from the archenteron as a tube on each side of the notochord. The tube gradually becomes cut up into further pouches. More mesoderm is proliferated from the region of the blastopore until finally about sixty pouches are formed.

While the mesoderm and coelom are being formed, the sides of the archenteron grow inward to form the true endodermal roof of the mesenteron (*see* Fig. 25.24 (*b*)). Again, this starts in front and proceeds backward at the same rate as mesoderm separation.

When the first mesodermal pouches are formed, the embryo develops cilia, one to each epidermal cell. It rotates within its vitelline membrane and finally escapes to become free-swimming. Until its mouth develops, it is still dependent upon the remaining yolk, and is therefore known as a *free embryo* and not a larva. The latter name is applied as soon as it is able to feed. It is a very small creature, less than one millimetre in length. The triploblastic state has now been achieved; the three germ layers, ectoderm, mesoderm, and endoderm, are clearly separate, at least in the anterior region.

Differentiation of the Mesoderm

The mesodermal pouches grow down ventrally until they meet beneath the mesenteron (*see* Fig. 25.27). Their upper parts become cut off to form the somites, while the lower parts of each pair become

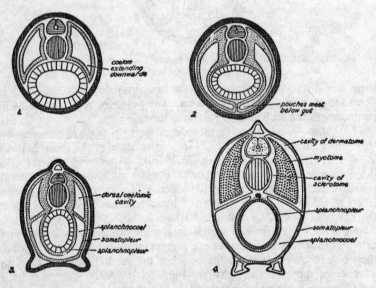

Fig. 25.27. Differentiation of the mesoderm in *Amphioxus*. T.S. 1–4 are successive stages.

confluent by the breaking down of their junction in the mid-ventral line (*see* Fig. 25.27 (3)) The transverse septa between the pouches also break down ventrally and thus there is formed beneath the mesenteron and at its sides a spacious coelomic cavity called the *splanchnocoel* Its inner layer of cells which is applied to the mesenteron is known as the *splanchnic mesoderm*. Later it will form the involuntary muscle of the gut and the peritoneum in this region. The outer layer of cells bordering the splanchnocoel is the *somatic mesoderm*; it is applied to the epidermis and will later form the dermis.

Each somite becomes differentiated into three parts, a *dermatome*, a *myotome* and a *sclerotome*. In segments 25 to 51, a portion of the somite also forms the *gonotome*. The coelomic cavity of each somite is called a *myocoel*. The inner wall thickens to form the myotome which will develop into the voluntary muscle of that particular segment

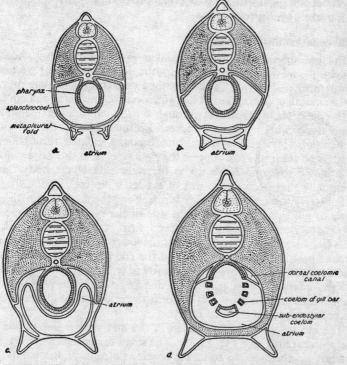

Fig. 25.28. Development of the atrium in *Amphioxus*. (*a*) Pharynx surrounded by splanchnocoel, metapleural folds growing. (*b*) Atrium enclosed by meeting of metapleural folds. (*c*) Atrium growing up around pharynx. (*d*) Gill slits open, splanchnocoel split into three regions.

(see Fig. 25.27). The outer wall remains thin and is applied to the epidermis; later it will form the dermis. From the inner side of the ventral end of the somite, the sclerotome grows upward to form the connective tissue sheaths of the nerve cord, notochord and myotomes. The sclerotome also forms the fin-ray boxes. The gonotome develops from the antero-ventral portion of the somite (see p. 774). The myotomes soon assume their characteristic V shapes and become asymmetrical, the ones on the left being slightly in front of those on the right. Thus each left-hand somite lies opposite a right-hand myocomma and vice versa.

From the anterior portion of the mesenteron, a pair of cavities are pinched off. They are known as the head cavities. The right hand one eventually occupies the region in front of the first pair of myotomes and forms the head cavity. The left cavity remains small and later acquires an outlet confluent with an ectodermal pre-oral pit. This is represented in the adult by *Hatschek's pit*.

Outline of Further Development

Further development in *Amphioxus* is not typical of chordates generally and is of little value in the interpretation of vertebrate development. Therefore, it is described here in brief outline only.

The mouth opens on the left side and soon becomes large and bordered with cilia. The anus breaks through on the left side just behind the neurenteric canal which now closes. Behind the anus, the tail grows. The internal epithelium of the gut becomes ciliated throughout its length and the liver grows out on the right side. Gill slits arise ventrally in a single row and move up to the right side of the body though eventually they become the slits of the left side (see Fig. 25.29). The definitive slits of the right side form above them. Between the two rows of gill slits now on the right side of the pharynx, a rudiment of the endostyle develops as a V-shaped strip of glandular and ciliated cells (see Fig. 25.29). The gill slits of the lower row move round to their correct position on the left side and the endostyle comes to lie in the mid-ventral line. The mouth moves round to the anterior position and the secondary gill bars grow down dividing each primary gill slit into two. Folds of skin grow out to form the oral hood and the anterior end of the notochord grows into it.

The atrium arises by the fusion in the mid-ventral line of the two metapleural folds (see Fig. 25.28). The small cavity thus enclosed, soon extends up the sides to form the spacious atrium of the adult. The nephridia arise as blind ectodermal sacs at the top of each primary gill slit before the secondary bars grow down. Later, their solenocytes grow dorsally into the coelomic canals.

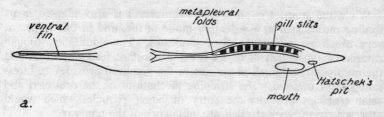

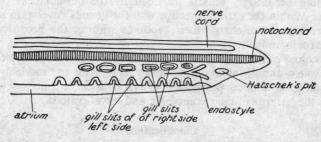

Fig. 25.29. Larva of *Amphioxus*. (*a*) Ventral view of young larva. (*b*) Lateral view of larva from right side.

For about three months, the larva leads a pelagic existence, gradually making its way into deeper water. At the end of this period it is about 3·5 mm long. Eventually, it burrows into the sand and slowly develops the adult characteristics. By the time it is one year old and about 20 mm long, its gonads have been formed and are able to proliferate mature germ cells.

Adaptation

The lancelet shows admirable adaptation to its environment in many ways, but particularly so in three respects, swimming, burrowing and feeding. Its streamlined shape, pointed at both ends and with no lateral projections, offers very little resistance to its passage through the water. The shape of the creature similarly adapts it to burrowing in the sand with the additional strengthening of the front end by the anterior extension of the notochord. The long continuous double row of myotomes is attached to the connective tissue sheath surrounding the notochord. The turgidity of the notochord cells, make it practically incompressible so that when the myotomes contract, it does not crumple but is forced to bend. The backward components of the lateral movements thrust the body forward, the greatest thrust being achieved by the expanded caudal fin.

While the lancelet is an expert swimmer, it is also adapted in its feeding mechanism to a sedentary mode of life, and in this respect it very much resembles the fixed tunicates. The admirable, though complex arrangement of cilia ensures a constant feeding current and the multiplicity of small organisms in the plankton provides an incessant supply of food. The straining mechanism of the oral cirri and velar tentacles prevents the entry of larger particles which would otherwise soon block the delicate meshwork of the pharynx.

The flimsy structure of the pharynx renders additional external protection necessary. This is provided by the development of the atrium. Within the extra protective wall the gonads develop in safety and are able to discharge their products without the necessity for special coelomoducts.

The colour of the animal and its translucence render it inconspicuous in the water, and the ability to withdraw its anterior end suddenly into the sand gives a good prospect of survival to those lancelets which escape the hazards of their embryonic and larval periods.

Classification

Phylum:	Chordata	Family:	Branchiostomidae
Sub-phylum:	Acrania	Genus:	*Amphioxus* [*Branchiostoma*]
Class:	Cephalochordata	Species:	*A. lanceolatus*

The characteristics of the class Cephalochordata have been given in Chap. 4. There are only two families in this class, the Branchiostomidae, and the Amphioxididae. In the Branchiostomidae, the genera are distinguished by comparatively insignificant differences.

Special Features of Biological Importance

In *Amphioxus* we have an outstanding example of a phenomenon to be found in varying degree in all animals. We classify them in phyla and each member of a phylum possesses at least the main basic characteristics of that phylum. There are certain animals whose relationships are doubtful but they are exceptions. In addition to possessing the characteristics of its phylum, an animal possesses primitive and specialized features. By a primitive characteristic we mean some attribute which appeared long ago in evolution and though the highest members of a phylum may have lost such a feature, the lowest members still retain it. Superimposed on its phylar and primitive characteristics are the specialized features which every creature has attained in the progress of its own particular line in evolution.

We see in *Amphioxus*, animals with the principal chordate characteristics present but with many primitive features retained and, in addition, many specialized singularities overlie these basic and primitive attributes. Of all extant animals, the genus is probably nearest to the remote common chordate ancestors.

In the ensuing paragraphs, the primitive and specialized features in *Amphioxus* are summarized, and there is later mention of the importance of the pharynx.

Primitive Features of Amphioxus

The ciliary mode of feeding is undoubtedly primitive and has been lost completely in many metazoan phyla; it persists however in lamellibranch molluscs, in the urochordates and cephalochordates. The endostyle, as an accessory feeding organ is found only in urochordates, cephalochordates and in the larvae of cyclostome craniates. In the *ammocoete* larva of the lamprey, *Petromyzon fluviatilis*, the endostyle is present and functional, but in the adult it becomes the thyroid gland and that is its destiny in all vertebrates.

Amphioxus possesses a complete row of segmental myotomes from front to rear. This persistence of complete segmentation is associated with non-chordates and particularly with annelids. In the vertebrates, though there is always segmentation of the mesoderm, it often disappears in adults, especially in the anterior region. We see in the dogfish a long series of myotomes but the first three pairs become modified to form the eye-muscles.

In the condition of its nervous system, *Amphioxus* is primitive. There is very little differentiation of the brain; there are no paired sense organs. The afferent nerve fibres originate in superficial sensory cells and proceed directly into the central nervous system without the mediation of dorsal ganglia on the afferent roots. This is the condition we find in annelids and arthropods.

The blood has no respiratory pigment and there is no heart. The blood-vessels do not show distinction into arteries and veins.

Even by comparison with the great non-chordate phyla there is a startling lack of cephalization and of paired limbs.

The structure of protonephridia and their primitive nature are described on pp. 632, 770. It is surprising to find them persisting in an animal with such well-marked chordate features. The same remark applies to the occurrence of segmental gonads with no coelomoducts

The persistence of the notochord in an unmodified state throughout life is not found in other chordates. In vertebrates, traces of it are present though it becomes enveloped and in some cases almost obliterated by the vertebral column.

The skin presents a condition with which we are familiar in the annelids. There is an epidermis one cell thick, lying over connective tissue. In all the vertebrate chordates, the epidermis becomes a stratified epithelium.

Specialized Characteristics

The atrium is found in two groups only, the urochordates and cephalo-chordates. It is a very specialized feature and undoubtedly arose in connexion with protection of the delicate pharynx, which is found only in those two groups. The very large number of gill slits with the additional specialized tongue bars is another unusual feature. The peculiar and asymmetrical development of the larva and the extreme anterior extension of the notochord are additional singularities of this little creature. In its development also, we noted a number of specialized features.

The Importance of the Pharynx

In *Amphioxus* we see the pharynx at the height of its evolution. It occupies almost half the total length of the alimentary canal and is much more than half the total volume. The pharynx seems to have been evolved primarily as a device for sifting food particles from the water current and in this condition it is present in urochordates and cephalochordates. In the lower vertebrates it is primarily connected with respiration though still necessarily a passage for food. Its extent becomes less as we ascend to the higher chordates, though in all, visceral clefts are formed, and the respiratory organs whether gills or lungs open out of it. The Eustachian tube of adult amphibians, reptiles, birds and mammals represents the last remaining visceral cleft; its outlet is closed by the tympanic membrane. Like the endostyle, it is an example of an ancient structure retained and converted to another purpose.

CHAPTER 26

AN AQUATIC CRANIATE: SCYLIORHINUS

THE outstanding characteristics of the sub-phylum Craniata [Vertebrata], to which the dogfish belongs, have been summarized in Chap. 4. There are two vertebrate branches, the Agnatha and the Gnathostomata. The former are certainly the more primitive and they show strong relationships with the Palaeozoic Ostracodermi which are the earliest known craniate fossils. In the latter branch are forms ranging from the most primitive fishes to man himself. The cartilaginous fishes were probably the first true fishes to appear, their fossilized remains being found in rocks of the Silurian period. They are all placed in the sub-class Chondrichthyes, the other extant sub-class being the Osteichthyes, the bony fishes (*see* p. 851).

SCYLIORHINUS

The dogfish is usually selected for study as the basic vertebrate type because it shows most of the characteristics of the sub-phylum in their generalized form, and, in addition, the animal is plentiful and of a suitable size for dissection. The species described here is the spotted dogfish, *Scyliorhinus caniculus*.

Habitat and Habits

Dogfish are entirely marine and are plentiful in the waters of the European continental shelf. Similar species are found in most parts of the world. They justify their common name by hunting in packs and by their great reliance on their highly-developed sense of smell.

The fishes normally swim near the sea-floor hunting for the crustaceans, molluscs and worms which form the major part of their diet. There are separate sexes, the males and females being easily distinguishable by external as well as internal characteristics. Mating takes place near the surface and each egg is passed out of the body encased in a horny protective covering of distinctive shape. Egg-laying takes place throughout the year, except in autumn; the female passing out ten or twelve egg-cases per month. There is no larval stage; the embryo develops within its horny case and the young fish emerges in a well-advanced state.

External Features

The body is about 60 cm long, tapering considerably towards the tail. In front, the *head* is blunt, rounded, and flattened dorso-ventrally. The *trunk* region is also flattened ventrally but arched dorsally. Much of the *tail* is almost cylindrical, the posterior region being somewhat flattened laterally (*see* Fig. 26.1). On the dorsal surface, the body is dark in colour, with plentiful brown to black spots. The colour fades and the spots diminish down the flanks and the ventral surface is almost white. Covering the body are small sharp spines which all point backward. Breaking up the smooth outline are the *fins*, of two types. There are four median fins, an *anterior dorsal*,

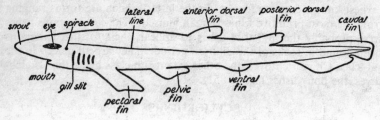

Fig. 26.1. *Scyliorhinus caniculus.* Lateral view to show body form.

posterior dorsal, *caudal* and *ventral*, and two sets of paired fins, *pectoral* and *pelvic*.

The head extends from the *snout* to a point just behind the last gill slit. It is rounded in front and thickens both dorsally and laterally towards its posterior region. The paired *eyes* are narrow and are placed laterally; they are protected by upper and lower lids, the latter being movable. The wide crescentic *mouth* is ventral and some distance behind the snout. From it, the *oronasal grooves* pass forward to the rounded *nostrils* (*see* Fig. 26.2 (*c*)). Behind the eyes are two small round openings called *spiracles*, which are vestigial gill clefts. Posterior to the spiracles, on each side, is a row of five *gill slits*, which open from the pharynx to the exterior and are concerned with breathing. Above the gill slits, from a point just behind the eye, a faint *lateral line* passes down the whole length of the body. It contains sense organs concerned with detection of vibrations in the water; branches of the main lateral line ramify over the head (*see* Fig. 26.2 (*b*)). Scattered in this region are rows of very small pores which lead into *ampullae* containing mucus. At the bases of these canals are sense organs concerned with perception of temperature changes. There is no neck, the trunk and head being confluent.

The trunk extends from the front of the pectoral fin to the *cloaca*, where it merges with the tail region. Dorsally and laterally, it is thick and firm, owing to the presence of the myotomes. Ventrally, the muscle

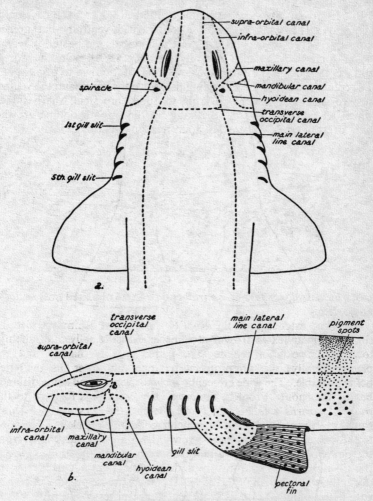

Fig. 26.2. (a) Dorsal and (b) lateral views of anterior of dogfish.

is thinner and the body wall is more yielding to the touch. Both pectoral and pelvic fins are attached to the trunk, and between the left and right members of each pair respectively, lies a firm girdle of cartilage. These paired fins are roughly triangular in shape and lie in the

colour to merge with the bed; respiration. Dorsally and dorso-laterally it is brown and ventrally, with its contrast with the upper side, dorsally an animal

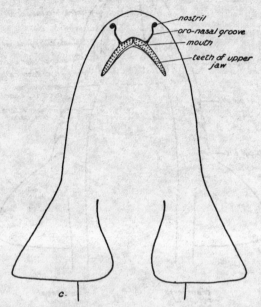

Fig. 26.2—(contd.). (c) Ventral view of anterior of dogfish.

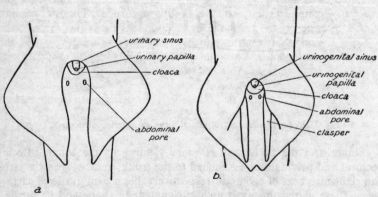

Fig. 26.3. Pelvic fins of (a) female, (b) male dogfish.

horizontal plane. Between the pelvic fins is a shallow depression called the cloaca into which the *anus*, the reproductive ducts and the urinary papilla open. At the sides of the cloaca are the two small *abdominal pores* which lead from the splanchnocoel (*see* Fig. 26.3). In the male, two stout curved rods extend backward, one attached to the inner border of each pelvic fin. These are the *claspers*, which play a part in the mating process; the spines on these point forward.

The tail, which is more than half the length of the body, tapers continuously and is slightly flattened laterally. Apart from the axial

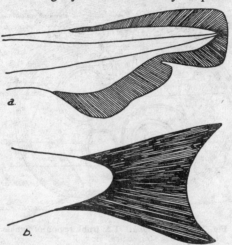

Fig. 26.4. (*a*) Heterocercal tail of *Scyliorhinus*, (*b*) homocercal tail of trout.

skeleton, it is a firm solid mass of muscle and contains none of the viscera. At its posterior end, it is slightly upturned. The four median fins are borne on the tail; the anterior dorsal fin is just beyond the cloacal region, the posterior dorsal is half-way between this and the end of the body, while the extensive caudal fin passes along the dorsal surface around the posterior end and then along the ventral surface. This caudal fin is asymmetrical, bearing an extra lobe on the ventral side. Such a tail is said to be *heterocercal* compared with the symmetrical *homocercal* tail of many bony fishes (*see* Fig. 26.4). Since the dogfish is heavier than sea-water and has no swim-bladder with which to adjust its relative density, this fin with the extra ventral lobe gives it lift in the water when required. The ventral fin lies in a position midway between the dorsal fins but on the lower surface. The tail is postanal and metamerically segmented; in the fishes it reaches its greatest development as an organ of locomotion.

Structure and Functions of the Body Wall

In all the vertebrates, the body wall has the same general arrangement of skin, muscle, and the peritoneum abutting on the coelom. The classes show variation mainly in two particulars, the specialized structures developed in the skin and the arrangement of the myotomes. The body wall of the dogfish is very thick and firm dorsally, gradually

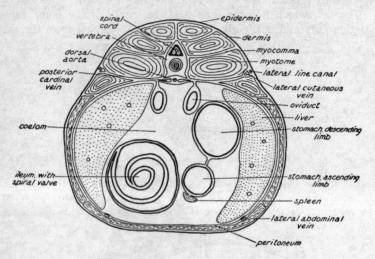

Fig. 26.5. *Scyliorhinus.* T.S. trunk region of female.

becoming thinner and less firm towards the soft ventral region (*see* Fig. 26.5).

The skin consists of a stratified epidermis and a thicker meso-dermal dermis (*see* Fig. 26.6). This condition contrasts sharply with the invertebrate condition of an epidermis one cell thick and a narrow zone of dermis. The generalized condition of stratified epithelium has been described in Chap. 20. In the dogfish, the outer cells are dead, flattened and horny; they are continually lost from the surface and replaced by the activity of the stratum germinativum. Small simple saccular mucus glands are plentiful; their secretion affords some measure of protection against infection.

The dermis consists mainly of connective tissue in which bundles of white fibres predominate. During dissection, it will be noticed that the skin is very firmly attached to the underlying muscle. Blood-vessels ramify among the connective tissue and many fine nerves pass through it from the superficial sense organs. Immediately beneath the stratum germinativum are the branched *chromatophores* containing the pigment melanin. The concentration of these cells determines the colour of the skin. Embedded deeply in the dermis are the *dermal denticles* or

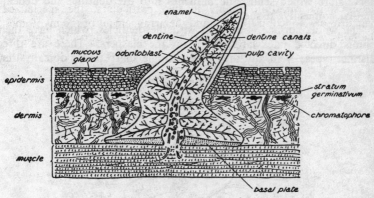

Fig. 26.6. Skin of dogfish. V.S.

placoid scales, with their points projecting into the water through the epidermis. Each denticle consists of a four-lobed basal plate connected by a narrower neck to the crown. The basal plate is composed of loose

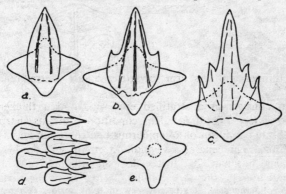

Fig. 26.7. Dermal denticles of dogfish. (*a*) Ventral region. (*b*) Dorsal region. (*c*) Tooth. (*d*) Pattern seen from above. (*e*) Basal plate from below.

calcified trabeculae, somewhat similar in structure to bone but lacking Haversian systems. The main part of the crown consists of spongy dentine perforated by numerous fine canals in which are protoplasmic fibrils from the cells in the central pulp cavity (*see* Fig. 26.6). The dentine is covered with a thin layer of hard enamel, consisting of hydroxy-apatite, which infiltrates into the surface of the dentine. In the pulp cavity are the dentine-forming cells called *odontoblasts*, a small artery and vein with an intervening network of capillaries, a nerve fibre which sends fine branches into the dentine, and delicate areolar connective tissue.

The whole surface is covered with the denticles, which have their points directed backward except on the claspers. There are three distinct types; ventrally they have a single sharp point, dorsally they

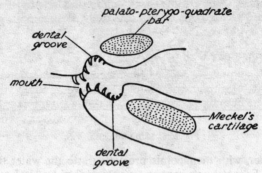

Fig. 26.8. Jaws of dogfish. V.S.

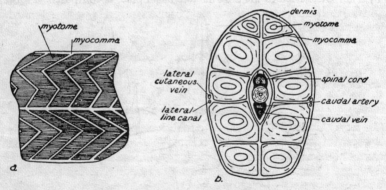

Fig. 26.9. *Scyliorhinus.* (a) Lateral view of trunk region, skin removed. (b) T.S. tail region showing muscle cones.

have three points, while the teeth on the jaws have five points (*see* Fig. 26.7). All are continually replaced, the teeth by the development of new denticles from grooves within the jaws. Comparison with teeth of higher vertebrates will show that the structure is almost identical, but teeth differ from dermal denticles in being attached to the skeleton of the jaws, and in the separate secretion of enamel by the ectoderm.

Beneath the skin lies the muscle of the body wall arranged in myotomes. Viewed from the side with the skin removed, each has a zig-zag shape (*see* Fig. 26.9 (*a*)). Seen in a transverse section, there are a number of separate blocks, each consisting of several concentric rings. It is thus evident that each backward or forward projection of a single myotome is almost a cone, and several closely-fitting cones will be cut in one section. The myotomes are connected by myocommata of very tough white fibrous tissue, and those of the left and right are joined by a similar vertical sheet. In the trunk region, the innermost connective tissue is joined to the peritoneum, consisting of squamous epithelium which abuts on the coelom.

Functions of the Body Wall

The skin has protective and sensory functions. Protection is afforded by the horny stratum corneum, by the mucus and by the dermal denticles. The chromatophores produce the resultant dappled colour pattern which provides some degree of camouflage. The sensory function is located in the various types of sense organs and nerve-endings.

The myotomes, in conjunction with the strong connective tissue sheets and the axial vertebral column, provide for locomotion (*see* p. 819). The vertebral column is developed in the median sheet of connective tissue; it provides axial firmness together with a limited degree of flexibility.

The peritoneum is a serous membrane which allows almost friction-less sliding of the viscera. In addition, it secretes the coelomic fluid.

Fins are outgrowths of skin into which skeletal tissues penetrate (*see* Chap. 24).

Skeleton and Supporting Structures

The term "skeleton" as used in connexion with vertebrates, usually denotes the bulky *endoskeleton*. It must be remembered however that there is always some form of *exoskeleton*, and that sheets of connective tissue and coelomic fluid have a skeletal function. The exoskeleton of the dogfish consists of the stratum corneum and the dermal denticles. The endoskeleton consists of cartilage and may be conveniently divided for description into the *skull*, the *vertebral column*, the *girdles* and *fins*.

The skull is the skeleton of the head which is usually held to include the whole region from the snout to the last gill arch. It consists of the *cranium* or brain-case to which are fused the *sense capsules*, and the *visceral skeleton*, a series of *arches* supporting the tissue between the visceral clefts.

The cranium is a roughly rectangular box which contains the brain.

To the front of it are fused the *olfactory capsules* which house the olfactory organs, and behind are the *auditory capsules* which contain the internal ears (*see* Fig. 26.10 (*a*)). Laterally, between the olfactory and auditory capsules are two large depressions called the *orbits*, bounded dorsally by the *supraorbital ridge* and ventrally by the *infra-orbital ridge*. The *optic capsule* is represented by the sclerotic coat of the eye which fits into the orbit. Dorsally, the roof of the cranium is incomplete, being pierced by a large *anterior fontanelle* in the mid-line

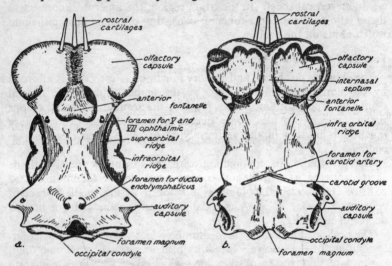

Fig. 26.10. Skull of dogfish. (*a*) Dorsal and (*b*) ventral views of cranium and sense capsules.

behind the olfactory capsules, and by two small *foramina* between the two auditory capsules; through these foramina the *endolymphatic ducts* pass to open on the top of the head (*see* p. 845). In the middle of the supraorbital ridge is a small foramen on each side; through these pass the ophthalmic branches of the fifth and seventh cranial nerves (*see* p. 841). A foramen is an aperture in the cartilage (or bone) through which a nerve or a blood-vessel passes.

Ventrally, the floor of the cranium is complete; it also forms the roof of the mouth or *primary palate*. The olfactory capsules have wide ventral openings by which they communicate with the nostrils. On the posterior ventral region are two grooves forming a flattened V with its apex directed forward. In these grooves are the internal carotid arteries which fuse at the apex and pass into the brain through a small foramen. At the outer edges of the grooves are two small foramina through which orbital arteries pass into the orbital sinus surrounding the eye.

Posteriorly, the large *foramen magnum* is the aperture through which the brain and spinal cord are continuous (*see* Fig. 26.11). At its sides

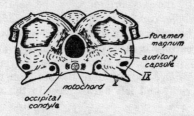

Fig. 26.11. Skull of dogfish, posterior view.

are two rounded knobs, the *occipital condyles*, which make a fixed joint with the first vertebra. Lateral to each condyle is a foramen for the tenth cranial nerve, and further to the side, one for the ninth cranial nerve. A small rounded peg in the cartilage between the occipital

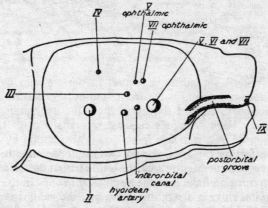

Fig. 26.12. Foramina of the skull of dogfish. Roman numerals refer to the cranial nerves.

condyles indicates where the notochord passes into the cranium for a short distance.

A number of foramina are visible in a lateral view of the orbit. They are indicated in Fig. 26.12. The great majority are utilized for cranial nerves. Through the *orbito-nasal foramen* in the front of the orbit, the olfactory blood sinus is in communication with the orbital sinus. The *interorbital canal* joins the right and left orbital sinuses, which are also in communication with the anterior cardinal sinus along the *post-orbital groove*. On the lower side of each auditory capsule is a depression into which the hyomandibular cartilage fits. By this joint the jaws articulate with the cranium.

The Visceral Skeleton

This consists of a series of skeletal arches, namely, the *mandibular*, *hyoid* and five *branchial arches*. The mandibular arch on each side consists of two stout bars, an upper *palato-pterygo-quadrate* and a lower *Meckel's cartilage*, constituting the skeleton of the upper and lower jaws. The right and left halves meet in the mid-line in front.

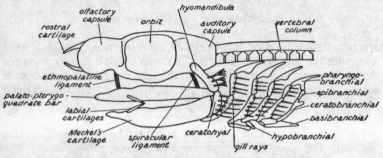

Fig. 26.13. Skull of dogfish. Lateral view of whole skull.

Each palato-pterygo-quadrate is bound to the cranium by two ligaments, an *ethmopalatine* near the front, and a *spiracular* near the rear; it is also bound to part of the hyoid arch, the hyomandibula at the posterior end. Each Meckel's cartilage articulates with the palato-pterygo-quadrate by a movable joint, and is also bound by a ligament to the hyomandibula. Opening and closing of the mouth is effected only by movement of Meckel's cartilages. The paired *labial cartilages* support the corners of the mouth (*see* Fig. 26.13).

The hyoid arch consists of the *hyomandibula*, a broad *ceratohyal* which passes within Meckel's cartilage and a median flat plate, the *basihyal*, which supports the tongue. The hyomandibula is the only skeletal attachment of the jaws to the cranium, such a method of jaw suspension being termed *hyostylic*, in contrast with the *autostylic* method where the jaws themselves articulate with the cranium (*see* p. 866).

The five branchial arches are essentially similar though differing in details, the most typical or complete being the second. It consists of nine jointed cartilages, movable by muscles. Two *pharyngobranchials* lie in the roof of the pharynx with their points directed forward, then two *epibranchials* pass laterally outward to articulate with two *cerato-branchials* which pass round the pharynx obliquely backward. They articulate ventrally with two short *hypobranchials* which pass forward to join a single plate, the *median basibranchial* (*see* Fig. 26.14).

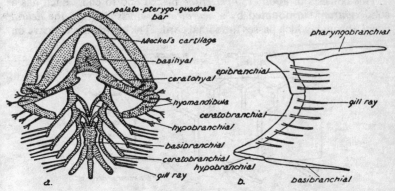

Fig. 26.14. Skull of dogfish. (*a*) Ventral view of visceral skeleton. (*b*) Parts of a visceral arch.

The first branchial arch has the hypobranchials fastened to the basihyal. The second, third and fourth are similar to each other. The fifth has no hypobranchials, the ceratobranchials joining the basi-branchial, and its pharyngobranchials join those of the fourth. Outside

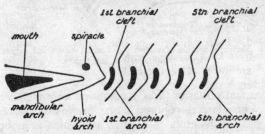

Fig. 26.15. Relationship between visceral clefts and visceral arches in the dogfish.

the ceratobranchials of the second, third and fourth branchial arches are small *extra-branchial* cartilages. The labial cartilages probably represent the extrabranchials of the mandibular arch. Extending outwards to support the gills are fine tapering *branchial rays*. They are present on the hyomandibula and ceratohyal, and on the epibranchials and ceratobranchials of the first four branchial arches.

The relationship between the skeletal arches and the visceral clefts is indicated in Fig. 26.15.

The Vertebral Column

This consists of about 130 *vertebrae* placed end to end. Each has a solid *centrum* surmounted by a *neural arch* which encloses the *neural canal*, through which passes the spinal cord. The centrum is concave on

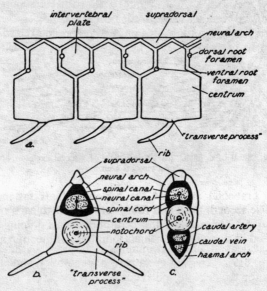

Fig. 26.16. Vertebral column of dogfish. (*a*) Lateral view, trunk region. (*b*) T.S. trunk region. (*c*) T.S. tail region.

both anterior and posterior faces, a condition known as *amphicoelous*. From the ventro-lateral regions, short "*transverse processes*" pass outwards, each terminating in a small rib which is embedded in a myocomma (*see* Fig. 26.16 (*b*)). These transverse processes are not homologous with those of bony vertebrates since they do not arise from the neural arch. In side view, it is seen that each neural arch tapers to a point, the gaps between successive arches being filled with *intervertebral plates*. These also taper dorsally and the roof is completed by small *supra-dorsal plates*. Between the neural arches and the intervertebral plates are small apertures for the passage of the dorsal and ventral roots of the spinal nerves (*see* Fig. 26.16 (*a*)). In the tail region, the transverse processes are vertical and fused at their lower ends to form a succession of *haemal arches* which house the caudal artery and vein.

Between the centra are lens-shaped fibrous discs enclosed in the remnants of the *notochordal sheath* (*see* Chap. 24). Within each fibrous capsule is a gelatinous material which represents the remains of the notochord; small canals filled with the same material perforate the centra and thus the notochord has the structure shown in Fig. 26.17. Anteriorly, the notochord penetrates a short distance into the ventral cartilage of the cranium between the occipital condyles.

The vertebrae are not movable on each other, and the whole column is resistant to pressure. It can, however, be bent and will recover by

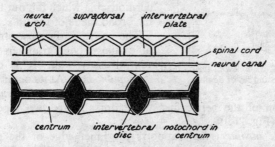

Fig. 26.17. Vertebral column of dogfish. Sagittal section of vertebral column showing notochord in black.

its own elasticity. During swimming, it is bent alternately left and right (*see* p. 819). Thus it plays a part in locomotion and also provides protection for the delicate spinal cord.

The Girdles and Fins

The *pectoral girdle* consists of two half-hoops of cartilage fused in the mid-ventral line and embedded in the body wall muscle. The ventral portion of the girdle forms a stout horizontal bar which is continued up the sides and tapers inwards in the dorsal region. The two tapered ends are not fused, neither do they join the vertebral column. The whole girdle lies almost in the vertical plane. By comparison with the girdles of higher vertebrates, it is customary to name the ventral part the *coracoid region*, and the lateral and dorsal part, the *scapular region*. On the upper side of the coracoid region is a shallow depression in which the pericardium rests (*see* Fig. 26.18). Between the coracoid and scapular regions on the outer faces are two slight protuberances to which the pectoral fins are bound by fibrous tissue. These protuberances are the *glenoid surfaces*.

The skeleton of the pectoral fin consists of an inner series of cartilages and an outer series of horny fin-rays called *dermotrichia*. The latter are skin derivatives and therefore exoskeletal structures. Articulating with the girdle are three inner cartilages, a small anterior *propterygium*, a

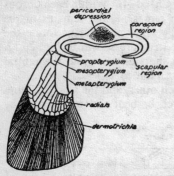

larger *mesopterygium* and a much longer posterior *metapterygium*. Following the pterygia is a row of *radials* with two large flat anterior cartilages and about a dozen rod-like pieces towards the inner border. Then there are two rows of polygonal plates, covered on both upper and lower surfaces by dermotrichia which fan out to support the broad blade of the fin.

The pelvic girdle is a straight rod of cartilage lying transversely in the ventral body wall. It is called the *ischiopubic bar*. At its outer ends ventrally are the *acetabular surfaces* for

Fig. 26.18. Dorsal view of the pectoral girdle and fin of dogfish.

articulation of the pelvic fins, while dorsally are two tapering *iliac processes* (Fig. 26.19).

A single *basipterygium* supports the inner edge of the pelvic fin, while distally there are about sixteen rod-like *radials*. The broader

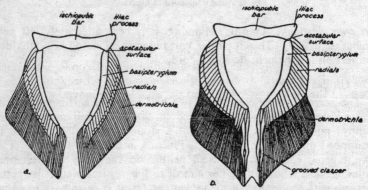

Fig. 26.19. Dorsal views of pelvic girdles of (*a*) female and (*b*) male dogfish.

expanse of the fin is again supported by upper and lower rows of dermotrichia. In the male, the two fins are joined along their inner borders in the posterior region and there are grooved cartilaginous claspers (*see* p. 826), articulating in front with the posterior end of the basipterygium and stretching backward almost to the hinder border of the fin.

The dorsal and ventral median fins are each supported by a row of radials embedded in the muscle and each has a double row of dermotrichia (*see* Fig. 26.20). The radials of the caudal fin are attached dorsally to the supradorsals and ventrally to a row of small *hypural* cartilages.

Functions of the Girdles and Fins. The girdles provide firm bases for attachment of the paired fins and fulcra about which they move. Also, the cartilages of the girdles serve to secure the inner ends of the fin muscles. The muscles which move the visceral arches are attached to the coracoid portion of the pectoral girdle. They overlie each other in

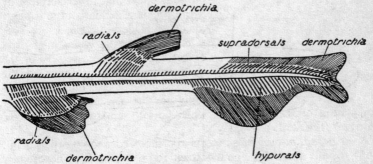

Fig. 26.20. Lateral views of ventral, posterior dorsal and caudal fin skeletons of dogfish.

pairs, the *coraco-mandibular* muscles which lower Meckel's cartilages by their contraction, are the most ventral pair. Then come in dorsal succession the *coraco-hyal* muscles and four sets of *coraco-branchial* muscles. The pectoral girdle also provides ventral protection for the heart. In the male, the claspers and the muscles for moving them are attached to the pelvic girdle.

All the fins play a part in locomotion. The main forward thrust is provided by the broad blade-like caudal fin, while the paired fins can adjust the angle of ascent and descent. The three vertical fins confer stability and prevent rolling laterally.

The Coelom

In the dogfish the coelom consists of two distinct portions, the *splanchnocoel* and the *pericardial cavity* (*see* Fig. 26.21). The splanchnocoel is spacious and in it the viscera are suspended by double sheets of peritoneum called *mesenteries*. It is to be noted that the liver, testis, stomach and other viscera do not lie "in" the splanchnocoel since they are separated from it by the peritoneum which lines all the organs abutting on the coelom.

The pericardial cavity is small and contains the heart, which is covered with peritoneum continuous with that which lines the inside of the cavity. In the heart region, the peritoneum is known as the *pericardium*. The splanchnocoel and the pericardial cavity are placed in communication by a small canal which perforates the *pericardio-peritoneal septum* somewhat dorsally.

These coelomic, fluid-filled cavities, provide protection for the viscera and allow independent movement of the gut and heart, etc., apart from movement of the whole body. Ciliated tracts of peritoneum waft the eggs from the ovary into the oviducal funnels. The serous

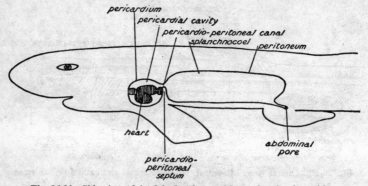

Fig. 26.21. Side view of dogfish showing positions of coelomic cavities.

nature of the peritoneum allows almost frictionless sliding of the viscera on one another during such movements as peristalsis. The fluid is secreted by the squamous peritoneum and any excess passes out through the abdominal pores.

The major viscera are not suspended by mesenteries along their whole length. Dissection will show that the gut is attached only at the anterior end of the stomach and at the rectum, while the liver is attached in front. Other portions of the mesenteries are used to bind organs firmly together; such mesenteries are known as *omenta*.

Nutrition

The alimentary canal consists of the *mouth, buccal cavity, pharynx, oesophagus, duodenum, ileum,* and the *rectum,* which opens into the cloaca at the *anus.*

The ventral mouth is crescentic in shape and has a wide gape so that large pieces of food material can be taken in. Enlarged denticles form the teeth, which are continually produced from furrows parallel to and inside the lips (*see* Fig. 26.8). The buccal cavity is wide and flattened dorso-ventrally; it is confluent with the pharynx, and though there is no distinct line of demarcation, it is usually considered that the buccal cavity ends immediately in front of the spiracle. In the embryo the anterior portion of the alimentary canal is formed by an ectodermal

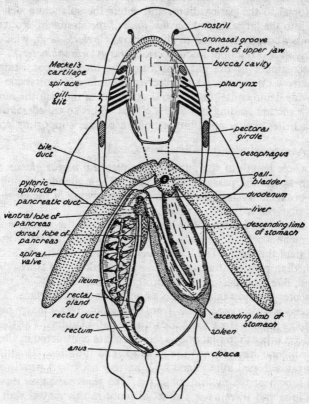

Fig. 26.22. Ventral dissection of dogfish to show alimentary canal.

invagination called the *stomodaeum*. The buccal cavity of the adult is derived from this ectodermal stomodaeum.

The pharynx is a much longer region but is also wide and flattened dorso-ventrally. On its floor in the anterior portion lies the *tongue*, whose free end protrudes into the buccal cavity. The tongue is not freely mobile or extensible; it is a hard muscular pad supported by the basi-hyal cartilage and used to assist swallowing. Behind the tongue, the pharynx is pierced on each side by six *gill clefts* which lead into the rounded *gill chambers*. These chambers also open to the sea water. The first cleft appears as a round hole both on the inside and outside; it is the spiracle, and is a vestigial cleft.

Posteriorly, just in front of the heart, the pharynx narrows considerably and leads into the folded oesophagus, which proceeds backward, dorsal to the pericardium, and enters the splanchnocoel. Here it leads into the large dilated *cardiac limb* of the stomach. Posteriorly, this bends abruptly forward to the narrower *pyloric limb*, which ends anteriorly at a pronounced constriction, the *pyloric sphincter*.

The remainder of the gut constitutes the intestine consisting of a short narrow duodenum which receives the bile and pancreatic ducts, a long wide ileum containing a spiral extension of the endothelium, and a narrow rectum leading out at the cloaca. This so-called *spiral valve* is like a helter-skelter spiralling around a central supporting column.

Glands Associated with the Alimentary Canal

The whole length of the gut contains plentiful *mucus glands*, whose secretion assists the passage of the food. These glands are numerous in the buccal cavity and pharynx so that swallowing of the large pieces of food material is rendered easier.

The *liver* is very large, often extending almost the whole length of the splanchnocoel. It consists of two long lobes, the left somewhat shorter than the right. The left lobe is subdivided anteriorly and in its small median portion, the *gall-bladder* is embedded. It stores the liver secretion, *bile*, and passes it out through the *bile duct*, which traverses the mesentery to open into the duodenum on its dorsal surface. The bile duct receives two *cystic ducts* from the main liver lobes; by these cystic ducts the bile is passed back into the gall-bladder. The functions of the liver, other than that of bile secretion, are considered in Chap. 29.

The *pancreas* lies between the stomach and intestine. It consists of an elongated dorsal lobe joined by a narrow neck to a small rounded ventral lobe near the pyloric sphincter. The *pancreatic duct* leaves this ventral lobe and travels for a short distance in the ventral wall of the duodenum before opening in its posterior region.

Although the *spleen* was derived from the embryonic enteron, it has nothing to do with digestion and has no opening into the gut. It is an elongated gland extending the length of the pyloric limb of the stomach and partly up the cardiac limb. It is essentially a lymphatic gland.

Both stomach and duodenum contain numerous gland cells, secreting respectively, the *gastric juice* and the *succus entericus*.

The small, brown, ovoid, *rectal gland* sends its *rectal duct* into the beginning of the rectum. Its function is the excretion of salts from the blood; in structure it is like kidney medulla.

Food, Digestion, Absorption

The dogfish feeds mainly on the sea floor, consuming crustacea, especially hermit crabs, molluscs, particularly whelks, annelid worms, small cuttle-fish and an occasional fish. The cardiac limb of the stomach will usually contain an assortment of these and other creatures in various stages of decomposition. The prey is grasped by the teeth which prevent escape by their backwardly directed points. Swallowing is assisted by upward pressure of the hard tongue against the roof of the mouth; the passage of the food is lubricated by copious secretion of mucus. The folded oesophagus normally has its lumen closed to prevent continuous swallowing of water, but it is capable of considerable dilatation. In the stomach, the acid phase of digestion takes place mainly in the cardiac limb. Examination of the pyloric limb shows a smooth paste. At intervals, the pyloric sphincter opens and contraction of the stomach ejects small portions into the duodenum, where the alkaline juices complete digestion.

The spiral valve is a device to slow down the passage of the food mass and also to increase the absorptive area. Indigestible material collects in the rectum and is defaecated at intervals.

Diffusible products of digestion are absorbed by capillaries in the wall of the ileum and in the spiral valve. Via the intestinal veins and gastric veins, all the blood from the gut is taken to the liver in the hepatic portal vein. In the liver blood sinuses, the food content of the blood is regulated before the blood leaves by the hepatic veins, which enter the sinus venosus. From the heart, the blood distributes the food materials around the body.

The food supply is practically inexhaustible and in the seas there is no lean season, hence the fish has little need for large reserves. Glycogen and oil are held temporarily in the liver.

Respiration

The visceral clefts are modified for use as respiratory surfaces and are thus known as *branchial clefts*. The respiratory organs are *gills* developed on the septa which separate the clefts. A typical branchial cleft opens from the pharynx into an ovoid chamber or *gill pouch* which leads out into the sea-water. The septa between the clefts are supported on the pharyngeal side by the cartilaginous branchial arches from which gill rays pass obliquely outward and backward to support the septum. On each side of the septum, delicate thin-walled *gill filaments* abut on the branchial chamber. These filaments are attached to the septum except at their outer borders, which are free. Each septum is prolonged into a thin external flap which can close the outer aperture of the cleft behind it.

A horizontal section across a complete branchial arch will show these details of structure and will also indicate the disposition of the afferent and efferent branchial arteries and their connexion by means of small sinusoids (*see* Fig. 26.23).

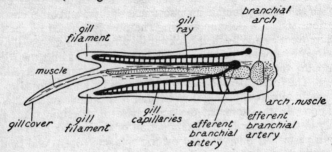

Fig. 26.23. Horizontal section of a complete branchial arch of the dogfish.

A typical branchial arch thus has gill filaments on both anterior and posterior surfaces, and it is called a *holobranch*. Where the gill filaments are present on one surface only, it is called a *hemibranch*. The few filaments on the mandibular arch constitute a *pseudobranch*. Thus the total gill equipment of the dogfish consists of four holobranchs, one hemibranch and one pseudobranch on each side. The hyoid arch

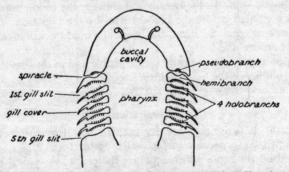

Fig. 26.24. Horizontal L.S. of pharynx of dogfish showing gill equipment.

with gill filaments on its posterior surface only, is the hemibranch (*see* Fig. 26.24).

There are definite breathing movements which proceed rhythmically. Essentially, the fish fills the buccal cavity and pharynx with water and then forces it out through the gill slits. The mouth is opened, and the floor of the pharynx lowered, by simultaneous contraction of the coraco-mandibular, coraco-hyal and coraco-branchial muscles. At the same time, muscles of the septa contract and the gill flaps close the exits. Because of the reduced internal pressure, water rushes in through the mouth and possibly through the spiracle. Then the mouth and spiracle are closed, all the muscles are relaxed, the gill flaps open, and the water passes into the branchial chambers and out through the clefts.

The oxygen-absorbing capacity of the gills is low compared with that of bony fish. Less than half the oxygen content of the respiratory water is absorbed, whereas for many teleosts the figure is as high as four-fifths. Relatively, the dogfish has a small gill surface and a small quantity of water passing over that surface, but it has certain compensating factors. The blood volume is high, the blood pressure low, and it is by no means as active as most teleosts (*see* Vol. II, Chap. 9).

Oxygen is absorbed mainly by the haemoglobin of the red corpuscles, and distributed to the tissues in the vascular system. That the system is efficient for its purposes is shown by the prolonged struggles of the dogfish when brought out of the water; it survives for a much longer period than the majority of teleost fish.

The Blood Vascular System

The circulation is described as *single*, which means that in one circuit of the body the blood passes once through the heart. The *double*

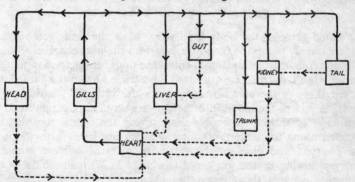

Fig. 26.25. Diagram to represent the general circulation of blood in the dogfish. Unbroken lines show distribution by the arterial system, broken lines show collection by the venous system.

circulation will be described in the chapters on the higher craniates. The general outline of the circulation in a dogfish is illustrated in Fig. 26.25.

The *heart* is a muscular pump providing the main force which drives the blood along, though the *arteries* are contractile. In the *venous sinuses* the pressure is very low and the blood is sucked from them into the heart by the negative pressure set up in the pericardium. Developing as a single tube, the heart becomes bent so that the auricle is dorsal to the ventricle (*see* Fig. 26.26). There are four chambers, the *sinus venosus*, the *auricle*, the *ventricle* and the *conus arteriosus*. One-way flow is assured by valves between the chambers. The sinus venosus and auricle are thin-walled; the ventricle and conus are much thicker-walled. The latter chambers must develop a pressure sufficient to force

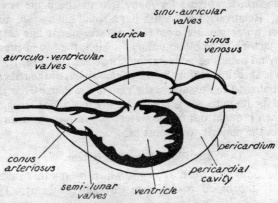

Fig. 26.26. Vertical L.S. of heart of dogfish.

the blood through the body capillaries, while the sinus venosus and auricle merely pump the blood forward into the next chamber.

Blood from the venous sinuses enters the sinus venosus and is pumped through the *sinu-auricular valve* into the auricle. From the auricle it is forced through the *auriculo-ventricular valve* into the ventricle. The ventricle pumps the blood into the conus where reflux is prevented by two rows of three *semi-lunar valves*. From the conus, the blood is directed along the large *ventral aorta* which lies beneath the floor of the pharynx and gives off laterally five pairs of *afferent branchial arteries* flowing in the gill septa (*see* Fig. 26.27). Sinusoids in the filaments connect the afferent branchials to the *efferent branchials* which collect the oxygenated blood (*see* Fig. 26.23).

Round the first four branchial clefts the efferent branchials form complete loops, while the fifth cleft has half a loop on its anterior side. All the loops are connected across the septa by narrow connecting vessels. From the middle of the first efferent loop, a small *spiracular (pseudobranchial) artery* runs forward beneath the spiracle, and from the inner end of the same loop, an *internal carotid artery* passes inward along the roof of the buccal cavity (*see* Fig. 26.28).

From the first four efferent branchial loops, four *epibranchial arteries* pass diagonally backward and inward to join the *dorsal aorta*, the main distributing artery. This passes forward from the point of junction of the first pair of epibranchials and then forks into right and left branches, which join the internal carotid arteries. These pass inward and meet in the middle of the roof of the buccal cavity. The

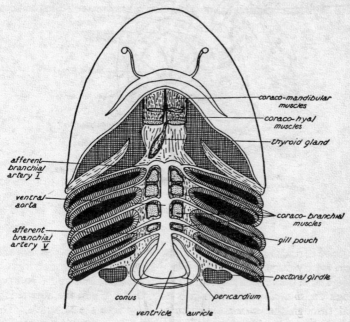

Fig. 26.27. Ventral dissection of the afferent branchial arteries of the dogfish.

single *carotid* now perforates the cartilage and distributes blood to the brain. Blood is carried to the sides of the head by the pseudobranchial artery.

The main flow in the aorta is backward and along its course it distributes blood first into the *subclavian arteries* which leave the aorta just in front of the entry of the last epibranchials. The subclavians supply the pectoral fins (*see* Fig. 26.30 (*a*)). The alimentary canal is supplied by three main arteries, the *coeliac*, forking into *gastric* and *hepatic*, the *anterior mesenteric*, the *lienogastric* and posteriorly the *posterior mesenteric*. There are paired *renal* and *gonadial* arteries and small paired *iliac* arteries. The aorta continues as the *caudal artery* to the end of the tail. Besides these major branches, there are *segmental arteries* to the myotomes.

After passing through networks of capillaries, the blood travels back to the heart in the venous sinuses and veins. The sinuses are wide and

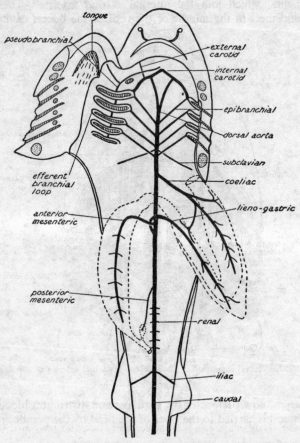

tongue

pseudobranchial

external carotid

internal carotid

epibranchial

dorsal aorta

subclavian

efferent branchial loop

coeliac

anterior mesenteric

lieno-gastric

posterior mesenteric

renal

iliac

caudal

Fig. 26.28. Main arteries of the dogfish as seen from the ventral side.

thin-walled; they have no power of contraction. The veins are much narrower; their walls are muscular and they bear valves. Blood from the tail returns in the *caudal vein* which forks into right and left *renal portals* just inside the body cavity. These portal veins distribute the blood among a second set of capillaries in the kidneys, from which it is collected in the two large *posterior cardinal sinuses*, which originate along the inner sides of the kidneys. The posterior cardinal sinuses lead forward, bending slightly outward, and enter the *ducti Cuvieri*, two large sinuses which pass horizontally inwards in the pericardio-peritoneal septum. Also entering the ductus Cuvieri on each side are

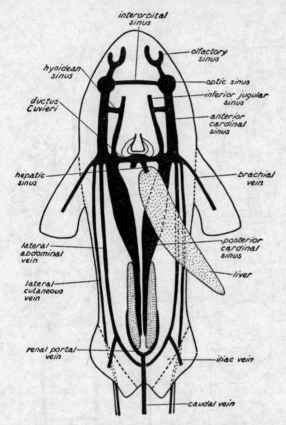

Fig. 26.29. Main sinuses (veins) of the dogfish as seen from the ventral side.

the *lateral abdominal vein* from the flanks and the more superficial *lateral cutaneous vein*.

Entering each ductus Cuvieri are several vessels from the anterior region. They are the *brachial vein*, the large *anterior cardinal sinus* and the *inferior jugular sinus*. An *olfactory sinus* surrounds each olfactory capsule and leads back to an *orbital sinus* surrounding the inner surface of the eyeball. Both lead into the anterior cardinal sinus

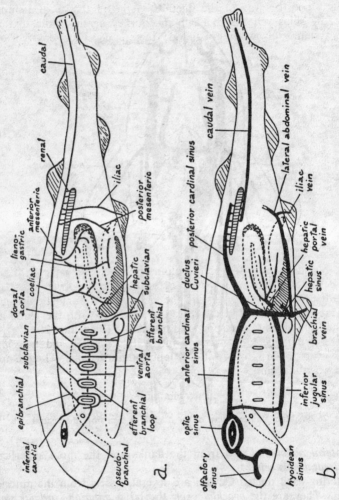

Fig. 26.30. Lateral views of (*a*) arterial system and (*b*) venous system of dogfish.

a.

caudal
renal
iliac
posterior mesenteric
anterior mesenteric
lieno-gastric
coeliac
dorsal aorta
subclavian
epibranchial
internal carotid
pseudo-branchial
efferent branchial loop
ventral aorta
afferent branchial
subclavian
hepatic

b.

caudal vein
posterior cardinal sinus
ductus Cuvieri
anterior cardinal sinus
optic sinus
olfactory sinus
hyoidean sinus
inferior jugular sinus
brachial vein
hepatic sinus
hepatic portal vein
iliac vein
lateral abdominal vein

which is connected to the inferior jugular sinus by a *hyoidean sinus*. The orbital sinuses are joined by an interorbital sinus.

Blood from the gut travels to the liver in the *hepatic portal vein*. This blood is distributed in the liver sinusoids and finally collected in two large *hepatic sinuses* which enter the sinus venosus. Thus all the venous blood, by way of the ducti Cuvieri and the hepatic sinuses enters the sinus venosus to begin its journey again. Note that the whole system is always full of blood; there is never any empty space.

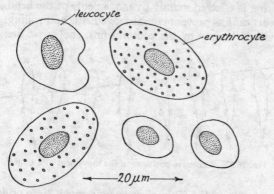

Fig. 26.31. Blood corpuscles of the dogfish.

The blood consists of watery colourless plasma in which are suspended the erythrocytes and leucocytes. The erythrocytes are large ovoid nucleated corpuscles, while the leucocytes are amoeboid; both types are manufactured in the spleen. Associated with the blood are the usual functions of transport and protection (*see* Chap. 20).

There is a *lymphatic system* of intercellular spaces and *lymphatic vessels* which open into two dorsal longitudinal trunks. These empty into the cardinal sinuses.

Locomotion

Swimming is effected by successive contraction of the myotomes first down one side of the body and then down the other. This is most effective in the tail, which lashes laterally from one side to the other. The curve of the axis is greatest in the caudal fin, and this, with its flat expanded surface, exerts the greatest thrust on the water. The force exerted by the tail from its fully bent position can be resolved into two components, one at right angles to the body and one in line with the body, acting posteriorly. It is this backward component which drives the fish forward. The lateral component is resisted by the whole lateral area including that of the expanded vertical fins (*see* Fig. 26.32).

The contraction of successive myotomes is initiated by reflex excitation and there is a series of local reflex arcs, each myotome being activated by a reflex from the one in front of it. The condition is much the same as described for *Lumbricus* (*see* Chap. 21). Severance of the spinal cord from the brain does not cause cessation of swimming; it removes any inhibition to swimming. A dogfish thus treated will swim purposelessly until it dies.

The fish cannot swim backwards; when in flight it has to turn round first. Steering is effected mainly by movements of the head and trunk, while the vertical fins prevent lateral movements and rolling. Elevation is accomplished mainly by the pectoral fins, the pelvic fins being stiff

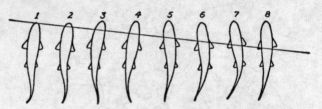

Fig. 26.32. Successive positions in the movement of a dogfish.

and almost immovable. Though it spends much time cruising along the sea floor, the dogfish can swim very rapidly. Speeds of 48 km per hour have been recorded several times.

Growth

Like many other fish, the dogfish appears to grow throughout life though the rate of growth diminishes rapidly with age (*see* Vol. II, Chap. 13). The maximum recorded length approaches 1 m. The average length of captured dogfish is about 60 cm. A fish of this size would be five or six years old and the probable duration of life under natural conditions seems to be ten to fifteen years. All types of cells, except possibly nerve cells, can increase in number.

Small dogfish are very rarely captured and there is some mystery as to where they spend their early life. It has been suggested several times that they probably pass at least the first year or two in deep water beyond the continental shelf.

Urinogenital Systems of Craniates

The urinary and genital systems are so intimately connected in craniates that they must necessarily be discussed together. The organs of nitrogenous excretion consists of aggregates of mesodermal *renal tubules*. Such an embryonic renal tubule is represented in Fig. 26.33. They are originally segmentally arranged, but in adults, there is considerable multiplication and metamerism is lost. A ciliated funnel, the *coelomostome*, which opens into the splanchnocoel, leads by a ciliated tubule into a longitudinal duct formed by the conjoined ends of all the tubules. This duct passes back to open into the cloaca. A small duct grows out from the side of the tubule and ends in a dilated *Malpighian body* consisting of a double-walled funnel, *Bowman's capsule*, enclosing a knot of capillaries, the *glomerulus*. Fluid from the splanchnocoel is wafted into the coelomostome, and excretory substances from the blood pass into Bowman's capsule. In the common urinary tubule, which is often long and coiled, resorption of water and certain solutes takes

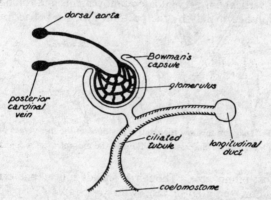

Fig. 26.33. Diagram of an embryonic renal tubule.

place. The coelomostomes rarely remain open in adults, though they are found in cyclostomes and in some cartilaginous fishes. A collection of such tubules enclosed in a connective tissue capsule, is a *kidney*. In development, the first kidney to arise is the *pronephros*, the second, the *mesonephros*, and where applicable, the third is the *metanephros*.

The pronephros arises in all craniate embryos but it functions only in cyclostomes, some fishes and some amphibia. It does not persist in any adult craniate but is replaced by a more posterior mesonephros. This second kidney uses the pronephric duct which now becomes the mesonephric or *Wolffian duct*. Such is the functional kidney of adult cyclostomes, fishes and amphibians. In reptiles, birds, and mammals, the mesonephric kidney is replaced by a still more posterior metanephros, with a new duct, the *ureter*. Fig. 26.34 illustrates the relative positions and ducts of these three kidneys.

The *gonads* are suspended in the splanchnocoel by folds of peritoneum called *mesorchia* in males, and *mesovaria* in females. It is in the ducts utilized for the gametes that the reproductive system is associated with the urinary system. Two different typical conditions are clearly recognizable in the craniates, that of the Anamnia (cyclostomes, fishes and amphibia), and that of the Amniota (reptiles, birds and mammals). The basic distinction between

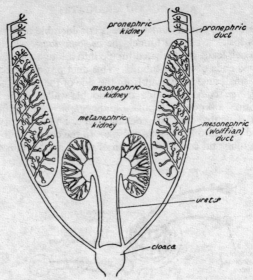

Fig. 26.34. Diagram to show the relative positions of the three types of kidney.

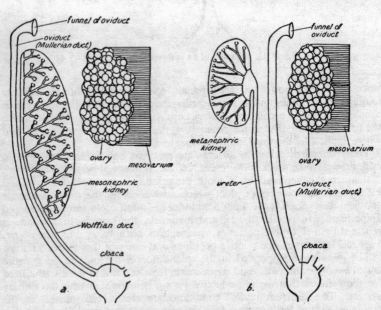

Fig. 26.35. (a) Typical urinogenital condition in a female anamniote. (b) Same in female amniote.

the two divisions lies in the fact that the latter develop an amnion in embryonic life (*see* Chap. 28).

In typical male Anamnia, the sperm are passed by fine *vasa efferentia* supported in the mesorchium, into the anterior part of the mesonephros. There, the anterior mesonephric tubules are utilized for transfer of the sperm into the Wolffian duct, which therefore serves for the passage of both sperm and urine. Near the cloaca, the duct bears a backward dilatation, the

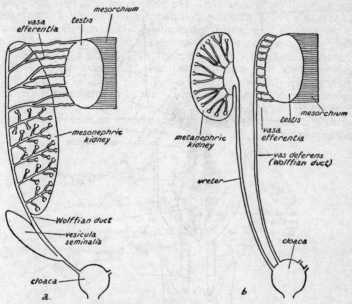

Fig. 26.36. (*a*) Typical urinogenital condition in a male anamniote. (*b*) Same in male amniote.

vesicula seminalis, for the storage of sperm (*see* Fig. 26.36). Males develop also a rudimentary *Mullerian duct* formed in some cases by longitudinal splitting of the Wolffian duct. The Mullerian duct bears a funnel-like anterior entrance, sometimes developed from conjoined pronephric tubules. The duct does not function as an oviduct in males, but is represented in the adult by the anterior funnel and possibly by the vesicula seminalis, the middle portion having disappeared.

In female Anamnia, the Wolffian duct is solely urinary, while the Mullerian duct is the *oviduct* (*see* Fig. 26.35).

Male amniotes retain the Wolffian duct as a vas deferens with its first portion becoming the coiled *epididymis* (*see* Fig. 26.36 (*b*)). Traces of the Mullerian duct are always found. The metanephric kidney acquires a new duct, the ureter. Females lose the Wolffian duct, the Mullerian duct functions as the oviduct, and the metanephric duct is the ureter (*see* Fig. 26.35 (*b*)).

Urinogenital System of the Dogfish

The male is not typical of anamniotes in that the Wolffian duct is not utilized for both sperm and urine. The *kidneys* are mesonephric and lie on each side of the dorsal aorta, covered with the tough peritoneum. They are very long and extend almost the whole length of the body cavity, gradually tapering anteriorly. The front half consists of soft

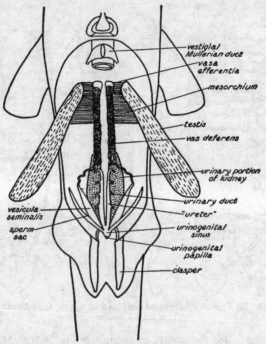

Fig. 26.37. Urinogenital system of male dogfish.

masses of tissue known as *Leydig's gland* and overlying this is the white, much-coiled *vas deferens*. The posterior portion is the urinary part of the kidney and from it five ducts lead into a "ureter." The two "ureters" enter a small *urinogenital sinus* which opens into the cloaca by a protruding *urinogenital papilla* (*see* Fig. 26.37). The *testes* are long cylindrical organs tapering slightly towards their posterior ends; they are suspended along the anterior half by the mesorchium. Each consists of numerous tiny discrete ampullae within which the sperm develop. They pass through a number of fine *vasa efferentia* in the anterior region of the mesorchium to enter the *vas deferens*. Seminal fluid, which nourishes the sperm is added by Leydig's gland. Posteriorly, the vas deferens is dilated to form a *vesicula seminalis* in which the sperm are stored; this enters the *urinogenital sinus*. The vas deferens and vesicula seminalis represent the Wolffian duct with possibly part of the sinus as well. In the front of the body cavity, ventral to the oesophagus, are the vestigial funnels of the Mullerian duct, and extending backward from

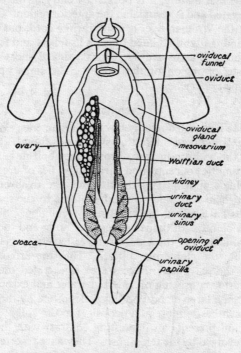

Fig. 26.38. Urinogenital system of female dogfish.

the urinogenital sinus are the blindly ending *sperm sacs*. These may represent posterior vestiges of the Mullerian duct; possibly also sperm stores. Beneath the skin of the ventral surface is a thick-walled muscular sac, the *siphon*. It extends back from the cloaca for about two inches and communicates by small channels with the grooved claspers, which are analogous with the penis in higher craniates.

The female is fairly typical of anamniotes except that only the right ovary is present; the left does not develop. The *ovary* is a large lobulated sac and in it can be seen eggs in all stages of development, the most mature being approximately 13 mm in diameter. Suspending the ovary is the mesovarium. The Mullerian ducts are white, thick-walled and almost straight. Their anterior openings have fused to form a single wide slit, and a short way along each oviduct is a firm swollen *oviducal gland* (*see* Fig. 26.38). The oviducts enter the cloaca separately, on each side of a small *urinary sinus*. In immature females, the opening of each oviduct is closed by a sheet of connective tissue called the *hymen*. At the first mating, it is broken by entry of the claspers. The kidney is elongated and is vestigial in the anterior region. On the ventral surface there, the Wolffian duct is a solid white cord, but posteriorly it has a lumen and is slightly dilated to meet its fellow and form a urinary sinus. Entering this sinus are five or six pairs of short *urinary ducts* from the posterior region of the kidney. The sinus opens into the cloaca by a fine *urinary papilla*.

Excretion

Carbon dioxide is excreted mainly by the gill filaments. With regard to nitrogenous excretion, an interesting situation is found. The dogfish is *ureotelic*, i.e. the end-product of nitrogen metabolism is urea. But to maintain its osmotic concentration, large quantities of urea are retained in all body fluids and most of the tissues. The freshwater origin of fishes has left them with body fluids hypotonic to the sea-water. The elasmobranchs have solved the problem by retaining 2 to 2·5 per cent of urea in the blood. All tissues, except the brain and the blood itself, can synthesize urea, and the kidney tubules have a special loop for its resorption from the glomerular filtrate. Thus the urine is eventually hypotonic to the sea-water. Excess urea is excreted mainly through the gills, the urine consisting of little but water and excess salts. Even the eggs contain a large quantity of urea, deposited by the mother, and the embryos synthesize more and deposit it in the yolk.

The condition presents an interesting contrast with the solution to hypotonicity evolved by the teleost fish. They have resorted to drinking large quantities of the sea-water, and excreting the excess salts through the gills.

Reproduction

Apart from the presence or absence of the claspers, the sexes are distinguishable by other external differences. The male has a narrower head than the female and the rami of the male jaws are wider apart.

Pairing is infrequent and probably takes place in deep water, the male coiled around the middle of the female in a curious back to back position (*see* Fig. 26.39). Seminal fluid containing sperm is squeezed out from the urinogenital papilla as a viscous cord. This probably passes directly into the clasper grooves and then is flushed into the female oviducts by a current of sea-water from the siphon. It is suggested that the claspers penetrate into the oviducts and it is significant that their denticles point in the opposite direction from those on the general body surface, thus obviating any slipping-out during copulation.

Fig. 26.39. The mating position in dogfish.

The sperm pass up the oviducts partly because of the current from the siphon and partly by swimming. The whole mating process is said to last about twenty minutes.

Eggs are laid throughout the year at the rate of about ten per month. Two eggs are ovulated at close intervals and passed forward to the

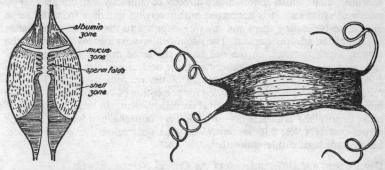

Fig. 26.40. V.S. oviducal gland of dogfish showing various secretory zones.

Fig. 26.41. Egg case of dogfish.

oviducal funnel by cilia on the peritoneum, on the mesovarium and on the inner sides of the liver lobes. The mouth of the funnel is fimbriated and thickly ciliated. The first egg to be ovulated enters the left oviduct and the second the right, the passage through the splanchnocoel taking several hours. The oviduct and oviducal gland are both ciliated and the egg takes about two hours to reach the gland from the funnel. Three distinct zones can be identified in a longitudinal section of the gland (*see* Fig. 26.40). The most anterior region secretes albumin, then there is a narrow mucus-secreting zone, but the major part of the gland secretes the egg-case. This latter region contains deep folds, where sperm are stored and remain viable for a considerable time. The greater part of the egg-case is secreted before the arrival of the egg, and fertilization is coincident with secretion of the last portion of the case. This is a horny container, rectangular in shape, with the four corners prolonged into elastic tendrils (*see* Fig. 26.41). It passes down the remainder of the oviduct by peristaltic action. During laying, the female swims among seaweeds and the tendrils coil around the weeds and the egg-case is thus clear of the sea-bed and hidden from view. Development is slow and the young fish does not hatch until six to twelve months have elapsed. These fingerling dogfish are rarely captured, and it seems probable that they migrate to deeper water and do not return until they are mature.

Nervous System of Craniates

In their nervous systems, the craniates show outstanding advances on any types previously described. These advances are particularly evident in the brain. The nervous system, as in the invertebrates, may be divided into three sections for purposes of description. The *central nervous system* consists of the *brain* and *spinal cord*. It contains the main aggregates of neurones, all of which communicate directly or indirectly with one another by means of synapses. It is concerned with receiving impulses from the sense organs, co-ordinating them and relaying impulses to the muscles and glands which are the effector organs. The *peripheral nervous system* consists of the nerves, which connect, on the one hand, the sense organs with the central nervous system, and on the other hand, the central nervous system with the effector organs. The third component of the nervous system includes all the *sense organs*, which are specialized for perception of various stimuli and the initiation of impulses into the central nervous system. In their equipment of sense organs, the craniates do not show any remarkable advances over the higher invertebrates, but the central nervous system, particularly the brain, has become highly differentiated.

Development and Differentiation of the Central Nervous System

Details of the early formation of the neural plate and the neural tube are described in the accounts of the embryology of various craniates (*see* Chaps. 25, 27 and 28). Owing to the greater width of the neural plate in front, the neural tube in this region is, from the beginning, somewhat dilated as compared with the remainder. This dilated vesicle will form the brain and the narrower tube will form the spinal cord. Owing to different rates of growth, the three *primary cerebral vesicles* are formed, respectively known as the *fore-brain*, *mid-brain* and *hind-brain*. By further differential growth, the fore-brain and hind-brain each become divided into two distinct regions (*see* Fig. 26.42 (*b*)). Thus there are five regions whose further differentiation needs to be considered. They are the *telencephalon, thalamencephalon, mesencephalon, metencephalon* and *myelencephalon*. Various outgrowths and thickenings develop so that the final adult structure presents a picture very different from the three primary vesicles.

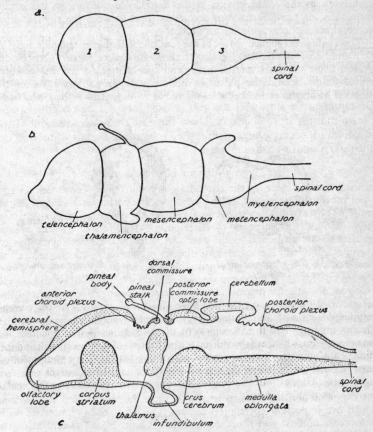

Fig. 26.42. (a) The three primary cerebral vesicles and (b) their differentiation into five regions. (c) Generalized adult vertebrate brain, in sagittal section.

The Telencephalon. The front of the telencephalon is called the *lamina terminalis* and this is the true anterior end of the brain. Antero-laterally grow out the two *olfactory lobes* which become closely applied to the olfactory organs, whose sensory cells send in nerve fibres. The roof of the telencephalon is the *pallium* which produces antero-dorsally the paired *cerebral hemispheres*, which become of enormous size and importance in the higher craniates. Internally, the ventro-lateral walls become thickened to form the *corpora striata* (*see* Fig. 26.43). The various thickenings constrict the central canal but the *first* and *second ventricles* remain as the cavities of the cerebral hemispheres. Usually there are also two narrow *rhinocoels* in the olfactory lobes; these communicate with the lateral ventricles. The only transverse connexion in the telencephalon is the *anterior commissure* in the lamina terminalis. It provides nervous communication between the right and left cerebral hemispheres and olfactory lobes.

The Thalamencephalon. Most of the roof of the thalamencephalon remains thin and becomes vascular, forming the *anterior choroid plexus*; here blood-vessels enter the front of the brain and the membrane secretes cerebro-spinal fluid. Behind the plexus, a hollow stalk grows forward over the cerebral hemispheres and becomes dilated at its end. This is the *pineal body*,

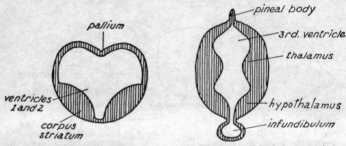

Fig. 26.43. T.S. telencephalon of vertebrate brain.

Fig. 26.44. T.S. thalamencephalon of vertebrate brain.

which in cyclostomes and some reptiles forms a pineal eye. In other verte-brates its function is not certainly known; there are indications that it may be an endocrine gland. Ventrally, the *optic chiasma* indicates where the optic nerves cross, and where the optic stalks grow out to form the optic cups. Behind the chiasma, a downgrowth forms the *infundibulum*, which, together with the *hypophysis* invaginated from the stomodaeum, forms the *pituitary body*, an endocrine gland of great importance. The side walls of the thala-mencephalon are thickened internally to form the *thalami* and *hypothalami* which are important correlation centres, the latter being concerned with autonomic outflow and neurosecretion (*see* Chap. 29). The central cavity forms the *third ventricle*; it communicates with the lateral ventricles by the Y-shaped *foramen of Monro*. The cavities of the pineal and infundibulum open into the third ventricle.

Two important transverse commissures lie in the thalamencephalon. In front of the origin of the pineal stalk is the *dorsal commissure*, and also dor-sally in front of the junction of thalamencephalon and mesencephalon is the *posterior commissure*. The telencephalon and thalamencephalon together form the fore-brain.

The Mesencephalon. The mesencephalon or mid-brain always remains a relatively small region. Dorsally, the two prominent *optic lobes* grow out;

they usually contain *optocoels*. Ventrally and laterally, the wall is thickened by longitudinal tracts of nerve fibres forming the *crura cerebri*. These contain the nervous connexions passing between the fore-brain and hind-brain. The cavity is reduced to a mere slit known as the *aqueduct of Sylvius* or the "iter a tertio ad quartum ventriculum."

The Metencephalon. Dorsally the prominent *cerebellum* extends forward over part of the optic lobes, and backward over the posterior choroid plexus. The floor is thickened to form the anterior part of the *medulla oblongata*.

The Myelencephalon. The roof is thin and non-nervous, forming the *posterior choroid plexus*, which has the same functions as the anterior choroid plexus. Continuous with the aqueduct of Sylvius anteriorly and the spinal canal posteriorly is the large *fourth ventricle*. The floor consists of the *medulla oblongata* which tapers back into the spinal cord.

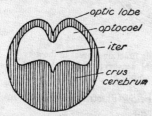

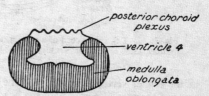

Fig. 26.45. T.S. mesencephalon of vertebrate brain.　　Fig. 26.46. T.S. myelencephalon of vertebrate brain.

Distribution of White and Grey Matter. Both the brain and spinal cord consist of two types of nervous tissue, the cell bodies or *grey matter* and the nerve fibres or *white matter*. These are packed in with neuroglia cells and a little connective tissue, and enclosed in membranes termed *meninges*. In the brain, the grey matter forms the cortex or rind enclosing the white matter which abuts on the central cavity. The order is reversed in the spinal cord where the white matter forms the cortex and the grey matter surrounds the spinal canal.

Membranes of the Brain and Spinal Cord. The whole of the central nervous system is enclosed in two meninges, the outer being the tough *dura mater* and the inner, the delicate *pia mater*. The dura mater consists mainly of white fibrous connective tissue which is fused to the cartilage or bone of the investing skeleton. The pia mater is delicate and vascular, and in the higher vertebrates it is separated from the dura mater by a filmy *arachnoid layer* of areolar tissue containing lymph spaces.

The Cranial and Spinal Nerves. In the spinal cord of all craniates, the nerves are segmental and paired, each segment having *dorsal* and *ventral roots*. The dorsal roots carry only *afferent fibres* whose cell bodies are in the *dorsal root ganglia*, while the ventral roots carry only *efferent fibres* whose cell bodies are in the grey matter of the cord. Both roots are united outside the cord to form *mixed spinal nerves* (see Fig. 26.48).

The nerves connected to the brain are known as *cranial nerves* and owing to considerable re-arrangement, they do not show segmentation in the adult (*see* p. 856). In lower vertebrates, there are ten pairs of cranial nerves, and

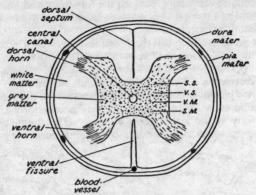

Fig. 26.47. T.S. spinal cord of a vertebrate showing functional areas in the grey matter. *S.S.* = somatic sensory; *V.S.* = visceral sensory; *V.M.* = visceral motor; *S.M.* = somatic motor.

in the higher vertebrates, twelve. The table below illustrates the relationships of the cranial nerves with the head segments.

Cranial nerve number	Cranial nerve name	Body segment	Dorsal or ventral root	Sensory, motor or mixed
I	Olfactory	Presegmental	—	Sensory
II	Optic	Presegmental	—	Sensory
III	Oculomotor	1st	Ventral	Motor
IV	Pathetic or Trochlear	2nd	Ventral	Motor
V	Trigeminal	2nd	Dorsal	Mixed
VI	Abducens	3rd	Ventral	Motor
VII	Facial	3rd	Dorsal	Mixed
VIII	Auditory	3rd	Dorsal	Sensory
IX	Glossopharyngeal	4th	Dorsal	Mixed
X	Vagus	5th to 8th	Dorsal	Mixed

In reptiles, birds and mammals, the process of cephalization is carried further by the addition of two more nerves, the *spinal accessory* and the *hypoglossal*, into the brain.

Functional Components of the Nervous System

The *nerve fibres* may be divided into four sets according to their function. The general plan of this division pertains to segments behind the head, since the arrangement is more complicated there, by the development of the special sense organs, and by the breathing apparatus of the pharynx. In a typical trunk segment, there are sense organs which perceive stimuli from the external environment and transmit impulses along sensory fibres to the dorsal root ganglion; these are *somatic sensory* or *somatic afferent fibres* whose cell bodies lie in the dorsal ganglion. From them post-ganglionic fibres pass inwards to end in the dorsal part of the grey matter. Stimuli in the viscera are perceived by enteroceptors, which set up impulses along *visceral afferent fibres* which pass along a *ramus* to their cell bodies in the dorsal ganglion whence their post-ganglionic fibres proceed to a portion of the spinal cord

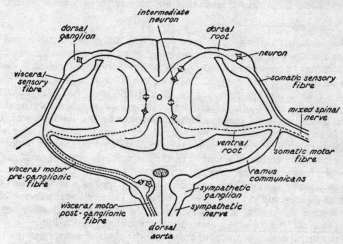

Fig. 26.48. Diagram showing the segmental nervous pathways.

just ventral to the somatic sensory region. *Visceral motor* neurones lie still lower in the grey matter and send out efferent impulses to glands or un-striated muscle. These travel in fibres leaving the cord by the ventral root and make synapses with cell bodies in a sympathetic ganglion. Their axons travel to the visceral effector organs. *Somatic motor* neurones lie in the most ventral region of the grey matter. They send impulses out along motor fibres, via the ventral root and mixed spinal nerve, direct to voluntary muscle. The general arrangement of these four components is illustrated in Fig. 26.48.

Of the cranial nerves, the *olfactory* and *optic* are special sensory nerves. General somatic sensory fibres are present in the *trigeminal, facial, auditory, glossopharyngeal* and *vagus*. All these fibres end in the dorsal part of the medulla oblongata. Visceral afferent fibres from the pharyngeal region pass in the facial, glossopharyngeal and vagus nerves to the medulla oblongata, where their centre is immediately below that of the somatic afferent. Visceral efferent fibres travel to muscles of the jaws and pharynx in the trigeminal, facial, glossopharyngeal and vagus nerves. Somatic motor fibres run from the mid-brain in the *oculo-motor* and *pathetic*, and from the medulla in the *abducens*; all supply the voluntary muscles which move the eye-ball.

Thus there are functionally four types of nerve fibres, corresponding to four areas in the grey matter of the spinal cord and in the medulla oblongata, though this arrangement does not persist in the rest of the brain.

The visceral efferent (motor) fibres leave the central nervous system by the ventral roots and travel via a *ramus communicans* to one of a chain of ganglia lying at the sides of the aorta. There they make synapses with neurones which send exciter fibres to the smooth muscle and glands. The reactions stimulated are entirely involuntary and hence the system of ganglia and visceral efferent fibres is considered separately and termed the *autonomic system*.

The Autonomic Nervous System

This is entirely efferent and consists of the autonomic ganglia and the motor fibres which are pre- and post-ganglionic. The visceral sensory components may be considered almost as somatic sensory since their cell bodies lie only in the dorsal-root ganglia. Most of the autonomic ganglia are joined in two chains, one on each side of the dorsal aorta; such are called the *lateral ganglia* and by the longitudinal connexions impulses may be distributed up and down the chain as well as out to the tissues. Ganglia which are not joined by longitudinal commissures are termed *collateral*; the most important are those which lie near the roots of the coeliac, anterior mesenteric and posterior mesenteric arteries. In the mammal, a group of such ganglia form the important *solar plexus*.

Functionally, the autonomic system may be divided into two portions with mutually antagonistic effects on the tissues. Those visceral efferent fibres which leave the central nervous system in the thoracic and lumbar regions constitute the *sympathetic system*, while those fibres which leave the brain and the sacral region of the cord constitute the *parasympathetic system*. The table below summarizes the principal responses evoked by each of these systems. The effects of parasympathetic stimulation may be caused by

Region affected	Sympathetic	Parasympathetic
Gut smooth muscle	Slackened	Tightened
Gut sphincters	Tightened	Slackened
Heart and arteries	Tightened	Slackened
Skin muscles	Tightened	Slackened
Oviduct muscle	Tightened and slackened	No effect
Iris muscle (radial)	Tightened	Slackened
Iris muscle (circular)	Slackened	Tightened

administration of acetylcholine, and the effects of sympathetic stimulation by adrenalin. Hence the division of nerve endings into *cholinergic* and *adrenergic* (*see* Vol. II, Chap. 8).

Sympathetic visceral fibres travel out from cell bodies in the grey matter of the spinal cord via the ventral root. They leave the mixed nerve in a *ramus communicans* and make synapses with neurones in the lateral ganglia. These send out axons which terminate in the tissues and there cause the exciting effect.

Parasympathetic fibres leave the brain by the oculo-motor, trigeminal, facial, glossopharyngeal and vagus nerves. Those affecting the iris and ciliary body have their synapses in the *ciliary ganglion;* those fibres affecting the lachrymal gland and the glands of the nasal organ are supplied by the facial nerve, the exciter neurones lying in the sphenopalatine ganglion. The salivary glands are similarly supplied by the facial and glossopharyngeal visceral efferent components. These fifth, seventh and ninth cranial nerves have rami to lateral ganglia on the autonomic chain. The visceral efferent components of the vagus nerve run in its visceral branches and travel direct to the exciter neurones on the lungs, heart, stomach and small intestine. In the latter region these exciter neurones form a plexus between the two muscle layers known as *Auerbach's plexus*. It is of particular interest since it maintains reflex control of peristalsis even when all the nerves to the gut are severed, and is thus very reminiscent of the nerve net of *Hydra*. Deeper in the intestine wall, within the muscle coats is *Meissner's plexus*; its function is unknown.

Throughout the vertebrates, increasing complexity of the autonomic system can be traced. In *Amphioxus* there are two networks in the gut wall, and it is very rudimentary in cyclostomes. The cartilaginous fishes have the ganglia present in chains, while the amphibia show almost the typical arrangement. The higher vertebrates have varying degrees of concentration into less ganglia and the whole system reaches its highest development in the mammals with a good deal of fusion of ganglia (see p. 1066).

The Physical Basis of Behaviour

The behaviour of an animal at any particular time may be defined as the total response of its effector organs to internal and external stimuli. Since the environment varies, particularly externally, then the stimuli will vary and hence the behaviour. No living creature acts always in the same way; all must be capable of adjustment, in however slight a degree.

The physical basis of behaviour lies in the nerve cells and their fibres, and since, in the higher animals, the cell bodies are largely concentrated in the central nervous system, it is here that behaviour is determined, or even sometimes pre-determined. The simplest type of behaviour is the *reflex action*, where a certain stimulus invariably elicits a certain response. The mechanism involved is the *reflex arc*, though it is rarely a simple afferent–association–efferent circuit. An afferent impulse entering the central nervous system, along even a single axon, will make synapses with several *association neurones*, and these will certainly communicate with many more nerve cells both up and down the nerve cord. Thus there are many possible paths by which efferent impulses may travel out to effector organs. It is known that in all nerve cells, impulses leave the cell by the route which provides the least resistance. Continued repetition of the same stimulus brings about easier passage of impulses across certain synapses. This easing of particular paths is known as *facilitation* and in the case of reflex actions it is inherent. In other words, we may say that there is innate facilitation at certain synapses.

In the lower animals, most of the behaviour is reflex. Often a very complicated pattern of behaviour has been evolved, whereby each reflex action provides the stimulus for the next. Such a sequence is known as an *instinct*. Good examples are to be found in any insect and especially in the social bees, ants and termites, where almost the whole pattern of life is based on instinct. In the birds we have the complex series of reflexes involved in mating, nest-building and rearing the young.

On a somewhat higher plane we may place *conditioned reflex actions*, which, in aggregate, form *habits*. Here the facilitation is not inherent but is established by continued practice. Thus we learn to walk, run, swim, ride a bicycle or play a musical instrument. Even in *Amoeba* or *Paramecium* conditioned reflexes can be established. Earthworms can learn to traverse a maze,

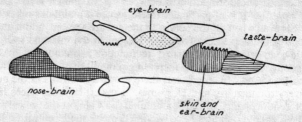

Fig. 26.49. Lateral view of a generalized vertebrate brain showing the main centres.

and fishes to come to a certain spot for food when a bell is rung. Where a nervous system is present, all learning depends on two factors. They are, first the acuteness of the sense organs, and secondly, the ease with which facilitation across the correct synapses is established.

With the development of the organs of special sense in the head, there has been parallel development of large aggregates of nerve cells in the brain. They are grouped in special centres, both sensory and motor. In the vertebrate series, these centres form a chequered pattern in the outer portion of the brain, the grey matter. The concentration of the cell bodies and the intricacy of the pattern show ascending complexity through cyclostomes, fishes, amphibians, reptiles, birds, and reaches its greatest development in the mammals. Corresponding with the sensory centres are ventral motor centres. Thus in the fore-brain are the *olfactory centres* or *nose-brain*, in the mid-brain are the *optic centres* or *eye-brain*, and in the medulla are the centres forming the *skin-brain*, *ear-brain* and *taste-brain*. The generalized locations of these are shown in Fig. 26.49.

An animal could not function with this equipment alone, since impulses from all types of sense-organs are constantly streaming into the central nervous system. There would be hopeless confusion and overlapping of responses by effector organs. Hence, there have been developed *correlation centres* which are connected with all the sensory and motor centres, and also tracts of fibres linking the various centres together. In the correlation centres, the stimuli from various types of sense organ are received and the resultant response determined. The fox may smell the poultry, see the farmer and hear the dog; it can adjust its response to a nicety.

The main correlation centres in fishes are the *corpora striata*, the *thalamus* and *hypothalamus* and the *cerebellum*. The first of these correlates olfactory impulses with others; the thalamus and hypothalamus seem to be the highest centres, while the cerebellum co-ordinates muscular activity especially with regard to balance and orientation. In the higher vertebrates, the greatest addition is the thickening and enlargement of the cerebral cortex to form at first the *archipallium*, and in the mammals, the *neopallium*. In man, the latter is the largest part of the brain and is the supreme correlation centre, concerned with the most advanced nervous functions. Thought, imagination, reasoning, judgement and consciousness, all are the result of activity in the neopallium. Here is the physical basis of mind. Here, a new situation is considered in the light of past experience and the response is chosen. Practically nothing is known about the relationship of these abstractions with the enormous numbers of nerve cells in the neopallium, but these powers have enabled man to triumph over all other animals. They have given him intelligence, the ability to solve new problems by careful consideration of, and selection from, a store of past experiences.

Correlation between the Brain and the Mode of Life

Where a particular sense is very important to the animal, the corresponding centres of the brain are well developed, and similarly correlation centres which mainly concern that particular sense become relatively large. Thus, the fishes, which rely a great deal on the olfactory sense, have large olfactory regions in the brain. In the amphibia, sight is more important and thus the optic region is large and the olfactory small. Many examples of such correspondence will be given in later chapters (*see* Chaps. 27, 28 and 29).

Nervous System of the Dogfish

In the brain, the telencephalon is occupied mainly by the very large olfactory lobes which are attached to the bulbous olfactory organs. Behind these, the cerebral hemispheres (pallium) are indicated by a faint longitudinal groove. The floor of each cerebral hemisphere is thickened to form a corpus striatum. The roof of the thalamencephalon mainly consists of the non-nervous anterior choroid plexus, and behind it the long narrow pineal stalk grows forward between the hemispheres, to end in the pineal body beneath the membrane covering the anterior fontanelle. Ventrally, entering the anterior region of the thalamencephalon, are the optic nerves, forming in the mid-line the optic chiasma. Here the fibres of each nerve cross over to enter the opposite optic lobe. Behind the optic chiasma, the large pituitary grows back to cover the ventral surface of the mesencephalon. The pituitary

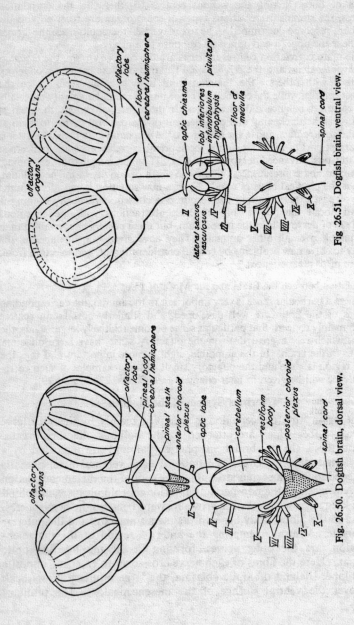

Fig 26.51. Dogfish brain, ventral view.

Fig. 26.50. Dogfish brain, dorsal view.

consists of the infundibulum with its narrow central lobe and two lateral *lobi inferiores*, and the rounded hypophysis posteriorly. At each side of the hypophysis is a vascular downgrowth from the floor of the thalamencephalon. Each is a *lateral saccus vasculosus*, a structure of unknown function, peculiar to fishes. Internally the thalamencephalon contains the lateral thickenings which form the thalami and hypothalami.

The mesencephalon is expanded dorso-laterally to form the optic lobes, while ventro-lateral thickenings form the crura cerebri. These

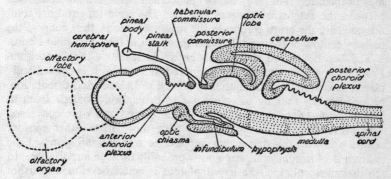

Fig. 26.52. Dogfish brain, median L.S.

are tracts of fibres by means of which the hind-brain is connected to the fore-brain and vice versa.

The metencephalon has a large dorsal outgrowth, the cerebellum, which overhangs the optic lobes in front and the posterior choroid plexus behind. The floor is thickened to form the beginning of the medulla oblongata. At the sides of the cerebellum posteriorly are the *restiform bodies*. In the roof of the myelencephalon is the thin posterior choroid plexus, while the floor and sides are thickened to form the medulla oblongata, which tapers imperceptibly into the spinal cord.

Cavities of the Brain

Two narrow rhinocoels in the olfactory lobes communicate with the lateral ventricles in the cerebral hemispheres. The third ventricle in the thalamencephalon joins the lateral ventricles by the Y-shaped foramen of Monro. There are also cavities in the infundibulum, lobi inferiores, sacci vasculosi and pineal organ. The cavity of the mesencephalon is reduced to a narrow slit by the crura cerebri; there are large optocoels in the optic lobes. Through the metencephalon, the narrow iter opens dorsally into a large space in the cerebellum. The largest cavity of the brain is the fourth ventricle, beneath the posterior choroid plexus. This tapers rapidly into the very narrow spinal canal. All the cavities are filled with cerebrospinal fluid secreted by the pia mater in the region of each choroid plexus.

Commissures and Correlation Centres

The principal transverse commissures are the anterior in the lamina terminalis, the *dorsal* or *habenular* in front of the pineal stalk and the *posterior commissure* at the dorsal junction of thalamencephalon and mesencephalon. All are mainly concerned with lateral connexion between the extensive olfactory centres. The main longitudinal commissures are the crura cerebri in the mesencephalon; they connect the sensory centres of the medulla with those of the fore- and hind-brains.

The best-developed correlation centre in fishes is the cerebellum. From its position near the ear-brain and hind-brain, it is conveniently placed to correlate motor impulses related to balance and orientation, hence impulses making for muscular co-ordination emanate from it. The corpora striata are relatively little developed; they are concerned with correlating olfactory impulses with those from other sensory centres and with relaying motor impulses to muscles and glands. The pallium is of insignificant size and is probably of little importance. In the thalamencephalon, the hypothalamus is better developed in fishes than in any other vertebrates and is probably the region of highest control, receiving connexions from all the sensory centres. The true thalamus is small.

Relationship of Brain to Mode of Life

The large size of the olfactory lobes indicates that smell is a very important sense; the olfactory organs are the most important sense organs in fishes. Sight also plays a large part; the optic lobes are well developed. The huge cerebellum suggests that the dogfish is an active and muscular animal, needing a specially efficient balancing and orientation mechanism; such indeed it is. That the higher mental powers are almost totally absent can be inferred from the very undeveloped pallium. The large medulla indicates the importance of the *acoustico-lateralis system*, the taste organs and the sense organs of the skin.

The Spinal Cord

The spinal cord is long and well developed in the dogfish. Structurally, there is little variation in vertebrates from the general pattern shown in Fig. 26.47. It is perhaps noteworthy that in the fishes, the dorsal and ventral nerve roots emerge from the vertebral column by separate foramina and join outside to form the mixed spinal nerves, which are segmental.

The Cranial Nerves

I. The *olfactory* nerve. This is not a single nerve but consists of many groups of fibres passing into the olfactory lobe from sensory cells in the nasal epithelium. It is purely sensory in function.

II. The *optic* nerve. This is made up of fibres which grow back along the optic stalk. The two sets of fibres, from the right and left eye

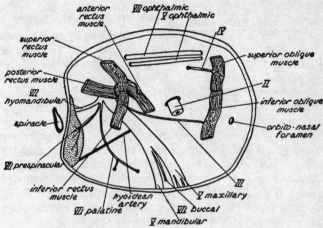

Fig. 26.53. Dissection of the right orbit of a dogfish.

respectively, cross at the optic chiasma and enter the optic lobes on the opposite side from their origin. It is again a sensory nerve.

III. The *oculomotor* nerve. This arises from the floor of the mesencephalon and passes into the orbit to supply four of the six external muscles of the eye. They are, the *anterior, superior* and *inferior rectus* and the *inferior oblique* (*see* Fig. 26.53). The nerve also carries autonomic connexions with the ciliary ganglion in the eye.

IV. The *pathetic* (*trochlear*) nerve. This arises dorso-laterally between the optic lobe and the cerebellum, passes into the orbit and supplies the *superior oblique* eye muscle. Hence it is motor only.

V. The *trigeminal* nerve is related to the mandibular arch and its two main branches, the *maxillary* and *mandibular*, pass to the upper and lower jaws. The former is sensory carrying impulses from sensory organs in the skin, while the latter carries motor fibres to the jaw muscles as well. It arises from the medulla just beneath the restiform body and almost immediately gives off a *superficial ophthalmic* branch which passes into the orbit, along its proximal wall and then passes out and forward to sensory organs in the snout. While still inside the cranium, V bears the autonomic *Gasserian ganglion*.

VI. The *abducens* nerve passes from the ventral surface of the medulla into the orbit and supplies the last eye muscle, the *posterior rectus*. It is a very small motor nerve.

VII. The *facial* nerve derives its name from human anatomy; it is really related to the hyoid arch, but even in the dogfish it has a number

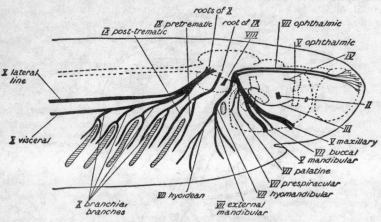

Fig. 26.54. Cranial nerves of the dogfish.

of other branches. The nerve arises in the medulla just below the root of V, and passes into the posterior part of the orbit. A *superficial ophthalmic* branch leads to the sensory organs of the snout in company with the same branch of V. A small *buccal* branch joins V maxillary and mandibular in the floor of the orbit and innervates the infra-orbital lateral line organs. The *palatine* passes forward along the floor of the orbit beneath V maxillary and mandibular, and turns down through the floor to supply taste organs in the roof of the mouth. A small *pretrematic* (*prespiracular*) passes in front of the spiracle to innervate sense organs on the side of the head. The *hyomandibular* passes behind the spiracle and down the hyoid arch; its branches supply the sense organs of the lower jaw and the muscles of the hyoid arch.

VIII. The *auditory* nerve is a specialized branch of VII. Its fibres pass from the ear to join the brain close behind the root of VII.

IX. The *glossopharyngeal* nerve arises in the medulla behind the root of VIII. It bears the same relationship to the first branchial cleft as VII does to the spiracle. Its *pretrematic* branch in front of the cleft is sensory, supplying lateral line organs in the occipital region. The *post-trematic* branch passes down behind the cleft and is a mixed nerve.

X. The *vagus* leaves the back of the medulla by several roots, two of which bear autonomic ganglia. As they pass through the cranial cartilage, all the roots join to form one large thick nerve. This soon splits into three branches, a *lateral line* branch, a *branchial* branch and a *visceral* branch. The lateral line branch supplies the lateral line sense organs and continues down the body almost to the end of the tail. The visceral branch is bound to the branchial which gives off a nerve to each of the last four gill clefts. These *branchial* nerves each have sensory *pretrematic* branches supplying lateral line organs in the pharyngeal region, and mixed *post-trematic* branches. The visceral branch enters the body cavity and supplies the heart and gut; it is part of the parasympathetic system.

Spinal and Autonomic Nerves

The spinal cord is typical; indeed it changes very little throughout the vertebrate series. The dorsal and ventral roots emerge separately and join outside the vertebral column to form mixed spinal nerves. The autonomic system has its ganglia joined by longitudinal chains. *Parasympathetic ganglia* are present; the *ciliary ganglion*, the *Gasserian ganglion* and the two ganglia on the roots of X are the chief of these.

Sense Organs

The olfactory epithelium subserves the sense of smell, which is, in fishes, closely associated with taste. Both senses enable the fish to perceive substances in solution, the olfactory sense from greater distances, the taste sense from food in the mouth. There is, however, a fundamental difference in that olfactory impulses are transmitted to the brain by somatic sensory nerves, while taste impulses pass along visceral sensory fibres. The olfactory epithelium is thrown into folds to increase the surface area (*see* Fig. 26.55). There are columnar supporting cells, mucus-secreting cells and patches of sensory cells with projecting processes. From the sensory patches, nerve fibres pass direct into the olfactory lobe of the brain. The sense is very important in fishes.

The taste organs consist of patches of sensory cells scattered over the buccal cavity and pharynx. Unlike the olfactory sensory cells, the taste cells are sunk in small pits. They are innervated by cranial nerves V and VII.

The eye has the same basic structure in all vertebrates (*see* Chap. 29). There are, however, certain features peculiar to the eyes of fishes. The cornea is flat and does not aid in the formation of images. There are no lachrymal glands in aquatic animals. Normally, the eye is focused for distant vision and accommodation is achieved by moving the lens in relation to the retina. Dogfish are colour-blind, the retina containing rods but no cones. A silvery reflecting layer beneath the light-sensitive

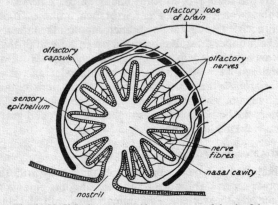

Fig. 26.55. V.S. through an olfactory organ of the dogfish.

cells enables the fish to take maximum advantage of the dim light on the sea bed. It is probable that sight plays an important part in the life of the fish, especially in the actual capture of prey.

The acoustico-lateralis system for the appreciation of vibrations in the water is highly developed. It includes the ear and the *neuromasts*.

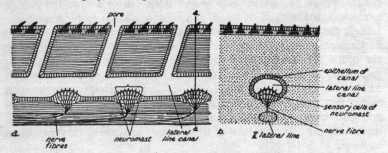

Fig. 26.56. (a) Longitudinal V.S. of lateral line of the dogfish. (b) T.S. plane a–a in (a).

These lie in canals sunk beneath the skin and filled with jelly (*see* Fig. 26.56). The canals open out to the surface at intervals; many of the openings can be seen, especially in the head region. Along the side of the body is the lateral line canal, and there is a network of similar canals on the head (*see* Fig. 26.2 (b)). Inside the canals are small rounded neuromasts, each consisting of a group of sensory cells with fine processes projecting into the jelly. The cells are innervated by the tenth nerve in the case of the main lateral line and by the fifth and seventh nerves in the case of the canals on the head. The hair-like processes are sensitive to low frequency vibrations in the water. Since these neuromasts are scattered over a wide area, impulses from a variety of them will arrive in the medulla at different instants of time. Thus the fish is able to produce a resultant which locates the source of vibrations, and it makes the appropriate response. The sense is of great importance in the detection of obstacles, in maintaining connexion with the pack, and in location of other swimming creatures. There is also awareness of the size and speed of moving objects.

The ear is really a modified portion of the lateral line which has become more deeply sunk beneath the surface. Only the inner ear is present, and, as in all craniates, it consists of a double *labyrinth*. The inner membranous labyrinth contains *endolymph*, and the outer cartilaginous labyrinth contains *perilymph*. There are two chambers, a vertical tubular *utriculus* and a horizontal disc-like *sacculus* (*see* Fig. 26.57). The three *semi-circular canals* lie in three planes at right angles; an anterior vertical canal in line with the horizontal axis; a posterior vertical canal transverse to the main axis, and a horizontal outwardly-bowed canal. All the chambers and canals are confluent and they communicate with the external environment through a *ductus endolymphaticus* which opens by a minute pore on top of the head. Each semi-circular canal is swollen at one end into an *ampulla*. The posterior ventral region of the sacculus is prolonged into a small triangular outgrowth, the *lagena*.

In the utriculus, sacculus and lagena are patches of sensory epithelium called *maculae acusticae*, while similar patches in the ampullae are called *cristae acusticae*. The perilymph gives some measure of protection and also transmits vibrations to the membranous labyrinth. The endolymph contains numerous minute *calcareous otoliths* in suspension; they play an important part in detection of change of position. Changes in acceleration will cause the endolymph to be left behind, as it were. The condition is similar to that which we feel in a rapidly accelerating lift. Thus the sensitive processes of the cristae will sweep through the endolymph and be bent over. Change in position is detected by impingement of the otoliths on the sensitive hairs of the maculae. A special large macula in the lagena is sensitive to sound vibrations, though this sense is poorly developed in fishes. Thus, the ear detects changes in acceleration, changes in position of the body, and to a lesser extent, sound. All these changes set up impulses which are transmitted to the brain by the auditory nerve.

Scattered over the surface, and particularly plentiful on the snout are the fine jelly-filled canals known as the *ampullae of Lorenzini*, each branched into pouches at its base (*see* Fig. 26.58). They are innervated by the superficial ophthalmic branches of V and VII. They are now considered to be *electroreceptors* for perception of weak local discharges. Apart from the special senses, there are plentiful nerve-endings in the skin which are sensitive to touch and temperature; the

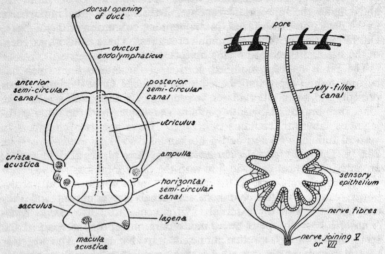

Fig. 26.57. Left membranous labyrinth of the dogfish.

Fig. 26.58. V.S. ampulla of Lorenzini.

fish is very sensitive to temperature changes and can detect a change of 0·5°C in the range 10–15°C. In the viscera, there are *enteroceptors*, and in the muscles and skeleton, there are *proprioceptors*. Both send impulses to the central nervous system by visceral sensory fibres.

Endocrine Glands

The *thyroid* is a well-developed pear-shaped object lying beneath the floor of the pharynx and underlying the anterior end of the ventral aorta. *Parathyroids* are possibly represented by small patches of cells behind the last gill slit. The *thymus* consists of small glandular masses around the dorsal end of each gill slit. The well-developed *pituitary* has been described previously. An interesting condition appears in connexion with the glands known in mammals as *suprarenals*. In the dogfish, there is between the kidneys posteriorly a narrow elongated *inter-renal gland*, and dorsal to the posterior cardinal sinuses near the sympathetic ganglia are small yellowish patches constituting the suprarenal glands. These have the same embryonic origin as the ganglia. In mammals, they have combined to form the suprarenal with its medulla and cortex producing different hormones. The hormones of the testes and ovaries are *steroids* similar to those of mammals (*see* Vol. II, Chap. 4).

Development

Development is very slow, the embryo dogfish taking one day to reach a stage comparable with that reached by the chick embryo in one hour. The rate of development is dependent on temperature and it has been shown that a rise of 5°C in the temperature of the water will double the rate of development.

The egg is of the extreme *telolecithal* type like those of reptiles and birds, the cytoplasm from which the embryo will form, being restricted

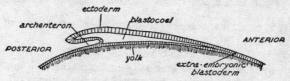

Fig. 26.59. Median V.S. early gastrula of dogfish.

to a germinal disc. It is enclosed in a vitelline membrane secreted in the ovary, and then by albumin and finally by the horny egg-case (*see* Fig. 26.41). Cleavage starts soon after fertilization and is *meroblastic*, the furrows not passing into the yolk. Thus a lens-shaped *blastoderm* is formed, lying on top of the yolk (*see* Fig. 26.59). Soon a *blastocoel* appears in the blastoderm.

Gastrulation begins by the infolding of the posterior edge of the blastoderm, the cavity thus formed being the *archenteron* (*see* Fig. 26.59). This edge corresponds to the dorsal lip of the blastopore and in the mid-line it proliferates forward a central strip of cells to form the notochord. The ingrowth of the archenteron soon obliterates the blastocoel. Gradually, the *neural plate* along the dorsal surface forms the *neural groove*, which sinks in and by the dorsal closure of its sides, the *neural tube* is formed and covered by epidermis. The mesoderm, on each side of the mid-line arises from two separate sources. An inner groove near the notochord proliferates a sheet of cells outwards, and an outer groove near the lateral limit proliferates a sheet of cells inwards (*see* Fig. 26.60). The mesodermal sheet thus formed becomes cleft into an outer lateral plate and an inner somitic portion which becomes segmented into *somites*. Each somite separates into an inner *sclerotome* and an outer *myotome*. In the anterior region just behind the future head, narrow cords of cells connect the somites with the lateral plate. These cords develop pronephric tubules and the pronephric duct. A cleft appears in the lateral plate separating it into a *somatic layer* applied to the epidermis and a *splanchnic layer* applied to the enteron.

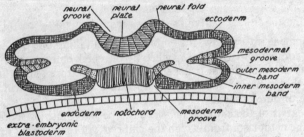

Fig. 26.60. T.S. early embryo of dogfish in front of yolk stalk.

The cavity is the *splanchnocoel* and it soon becomes confluent on each side of the body.

Meanwhile, the edges of the blastoderm, which are *extra-embryonic*, have been spreading out and gradually enclosing the yolk in a *yolk-sac* which becomes very vascular. Ingrowths lift the embryo off the yolk, until it remains connected only by a narrow *stalk* through which blood-vessels pass to and from the yolk (*see* Fig. 26.61). The fins

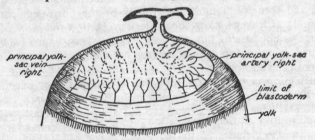

Fig. 26.61. Early embryo of dogfish showing yolk sac circulation.

develop as longitudinal ridges enclosing mesoderm. Later, buds from the somites grow out into the fins to form the musculature.

Essentially, the development of the organs is similar to that of higher vertebrates and will be described in later chapters. The fish emerges from a split end of the egg-case as a replica of the adult. We see here features common to all animals with large yolky eggs; the suppression of a larval stage, the production of fewer eggs, and the advanced stage of the embryo at emergence.

Adaptation

The fishes show remarkable adaptation for aquatic life. Their stream-lined shape, powerful tail and fins, are all ideally suited for swimming, and their gills for breathing under aquatic conditions. The scales provide a protective exoskeleton. They have developed to a high degree the senses which are most useful in water.

Within the fishes, the dogfish shows many individual useful adaptations. Its ventral mouth is admirably suited for capturing its natural prey on the sea-floor. The dappled neutral coloration makes it almost invisible from above, while the lighter ventral colour camouflages it from beneath. Admirable protection from would-be predators is provided by the sharp dermal denticles; their backward points add little resistance to forward motion. The denticles on the claspers are adapted to retain a grip during copulation. Its specific gravity, greater than that of the sea-water, ensures that it can remain at feeding level with no effort, while the heterocercal tail will give lift in the water when required. Since few eggs are produced, adequate provision is made to ensure a high survival rate. There is internal fertilization and the siphon mechanism aids the movement of the sperm. The eggs are large and yolky and with the egg-case, suitably deposited, ensure an advanced stage of development before the young emerge. A simple method of counteracting hypotonicity has been evolved and of particular interest is the special tubule loop for resorption of urea.

Classification

Phylum:	Chordata	Order:	Selachii
Sub-phylum:	Craniata [Vertebrata]	Family:	Scyliorhinidae
Class:	Pisces	Genus:	*Scyliorhinus*
Sub-class:	Chondrichthyes	Species:	*S. caniculus*

The diagnostic characters of these groups up to the order Selachii, have been given in the classification tables (*see* Chap. 4). The family Scyliorhinidae includes all the dogfishes. They are distinct from the Squalidae, which includes some sharks as well as the "spiny dogfishes," by the fact that members of the latter family have a prominent anterior spine on each dorsal fin. All the Scyliorhinidae have elongated bodies and bluntly-pointed heads. The genus *Scyliorhinus* is distinguished by the spotted pattern of the skin and the very long tail. The species are distinguished by small differences of size, pattern and shape of the body.

Special Features of Biological Importance

Among aquatic animals, fishes have achieved outstanding success. Further-more it is believed that the earliest land vertebrates were derived from a group of extinct fishes. Other topics suitable for discussion here are the importance of the tail, the significance of portal systems, the metamerism of the head, and that "living fossil," the coelacanth.

The Evolutionary Importance of Fishes

The earliest known vertebrates were the Ostracodermi, which flourished in the Silurian period, about 350 million years ago. They were fish-like animals less than 30 cm long and heavily armoured with bony plates on the head, and smaller bony scales on the rest of the body (*see* Fig. 26.62 (*b*)). Their mouths

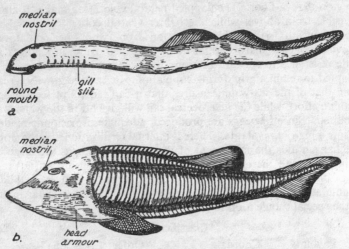

Fig. 26.62. (*a*) The river lamprey, *Petromyzon fluviatilis*. (*b*) A fossil ostracoderm, *Cephalaspis*.

were small, slit-like or round, and they had no jaws. They probably fed by grubbing in the mud on the floor of the freshwater areas of the period. The ostracoderms are undoubtedly related to the modern cyclostomes, though the latter are degenerate forms, having lost all trace of bone or exoskeleton. In common, the two groups have a single nostril on top of the head, no paired fins, and similar ear and brain structure. In neither group can we find a likely ancestor of fishes or of tetrapods.

The origin of fishes lies in unknown ancestral chordates. The first fishes to appear in the fossil record are found in the Devonian rocks laid down about 320 million years ago. They were cartilaginous, belonging to the Chondrichthyes and they evolved in fresh water. The body was streamlined and they had paired fins and biting jaws. The lack of bone is probably a secondary feature; bone appears to have been an ancient acquisition of the vertebrate stock. During the later Devonian period, there was a great migration of Chondrichthyes into the seas, though freshwater representatives are found in the Mesozoic and even in the Tertiary rocks. Many types of cartilaginous

fish became extinct and the present representatives are the well-known
Selachians and the deep-sea chimaeras. The present Chondrichthyes may be
regarded as relatively unspecialized forms, more closely related to a common
vertebrate ancestry than any existing fishes.

The Osteichthyes (bony fish) are a much more important group, having
given rise to the lung-fishes (Dipnoi), the lobe-fins (Crossopterygii) and the
ray-fins (Actinopterygii). Both the lung-fishes and lobe-fins belong to the
group Choanichthyes, which evolved internal nares. When the majority of

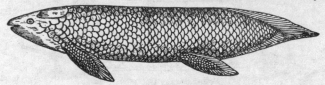

Fig. 26.63. A lung-fish, *Ceratodus*.

bony fishes migrated from fresh water to the sea, these two groups remained
and the opening of the nostrils into the buccal cavity enabled them to breathe
air at the surface. The present occurrence of Dipnoi, in Australia (*Ceratodus*),
Africa (*Protopterus*) and South America (*Lepidosiren*) is evidence of a once
wider distribution.

It is in the lobe-fins (Crossopterygii) that we find the probable ancestors of
land vertebrates. Apart from internal nares and lungs, their fins had fleshy
lobes attached to the body by a narrow base. The skeleton of these paired
fins shows one bone attached to the girdle, then a more distal pair forming
the second joint, then a more branched series of bones. The pattern is almost

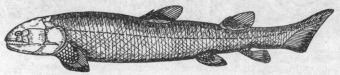

Fig. 26.64. A typical crossopterygian, the fossil *Osteolepis*.

pentadactyl and very like that of the early amphibians. Among the Crossopterygii, the most likely ancestor of terrestrial vertebrates probably belonged
to the Osteolepidoti, all of which became extinct before the end of the
Permian period, 200 million years ago. One order of the Crossopterygii, the
Coelacanthini, has surviving representatives only recently discovered (*see*
p. 856).

The Actinopterygii (ray-fins) evolved along a different line, in which the
supporting skeleton of the fins consisted of dermal fin-rays. They still bear
the relic of a lung in the swim-bladder, which has now lost all connexion
with the gut. It is used as an organ for adjustment of specific gravity, enabling
the fish to remain at a particular level or to rise or fall in the water without
involving muscular effort. This use of the lung was undoubtedly an important

feature in the success of the Teleostei, an order which includes most of the bony fishes of today. Their migration to the sea rendered an accessory breathing organ unnecessary, while the greater depths involved some method of hydrostatic adjustment. They have been a remarkably successful group,

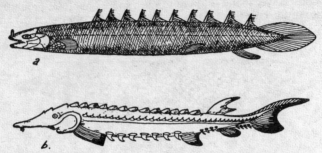

Fig. 26.65. (*a*) *Polypterus.* (*b*) *Acipenser,* the sturgeon.

most ideally adapted for aquatic life. Nevertheless they have become too specialized, and are to be regarded as an end-line in evolution.

A number of other orders of the Actinopterygii have become extinct except for solitary modern representatives. Of the Polypterini, only *Polypterus* of African rivers survives; it has both lungs and ray-fins. The sturgeons,

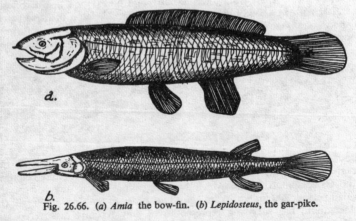

Fig. 26.66. (*a*) *Amia* the bow-fin. (*b*) *Lepidosteus*, the gar-pike.

well-known for caviare, have a few marine and freshwater species left of the order Acipenseroidei. In North American rivers are found the gar-pike, *Lepidosteus*, of the Lepidosteoidei, and the bow-fin, *Amia* of the Amioidea.

The Tail

The post-anal metamerically segmented tail is a characteristic feature of chordates. With the evolution of bilateral symmetry, cephalization came

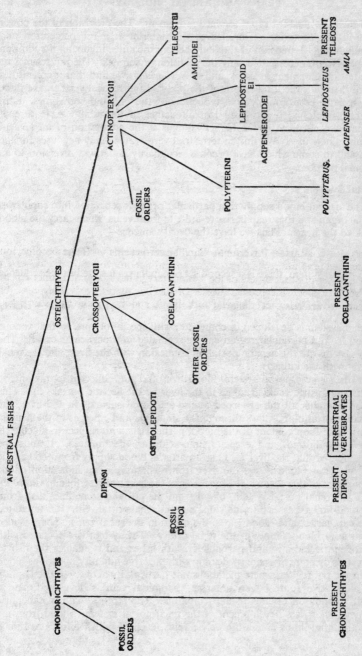

Chart showing the classification of fish and the origin of terrestrial vertebrates.

and then the need for rapid forward movement. The provision of the power unit in the posterior region leaves the anterior free for perception and manoeuvring. Extension of the body behind the anus, involving no addition to the viscera, necessitated only the addition of somites. The tail reaches its greatest development in fishes, and in *Scyliorhinus* we find that it constitutes more than half the total length of the body. In terrestrial vertebrates, there has usually been considerable reduction of the tail and sometimes, as in anuran amphibia, it has been lost altogether in the adult. A feature of common occurrence in the higher animals is the adaptation of an ancient organ to new uses. We find in terrestrial vertebrates many new uses for the tail, and in some which have become secondarily aquatic, a reversion to its original purpose.

Portal Systems

The arterial blood supply to a particular organ is separated into capillaries in the organ and these capillaries re-unite to form veins which carry the blood back to the heart. Thus we have the usual sequence—

$$\text{Heart} \rightarrow \text{Arteries} \rightarrow \text{Capillaries} \rightarrow \text{Veins} \rightarrow \text{Heart}$$

In a portal system, there is a second set of capillaries inserted in the sequence and thus we have—

$$\text{Heart} \rightarrow \text{Arteries} \rightarrow \text{Capillaries} \rightarrow \text{Veins} \rightarrow \text{Capillaries} \rightarrow \text{Veins} \rightarrow \text{Heart}$$

Such a system is developed in connexion with special organs, so that venous blood from a particular region can be regulated in a particular organ. The two systems are the hepatic portal, in connexion with the liver, and the renal portal with the kidneys.

In the hepatic portal system, blood from the gut, collected by mesenteric veins and gastric veins, is taken to the liver by the hepatic portal vein. This blood contains all the absorbed amino-acids and sugars. In the liver, the hepatic portal blood flows through the sinusoids and emerges in the hepatic veins. The food content of the blood, particularly with respect to glucose, is carefully adjusted, and excess amino-acids are deaminated. It must be remembered that the liver also has an arterial blood supply from the hepatic artery. Thus blood enters the liver from two sources, an indication of the importance of this organ. The functions of the liver are described in Chap. 29.

In the renal portal system, blood from the tail and sometimes also from the hind-limbs, passes into the kidney by the renal portal vein. It is separated into capillaries, and blood leaves the organ in the renal veins. There is also an arterial blood supply in the renal artery. The system is associated with mesonephric kidneys and particularly with fishes and it enables the fish to adjust its osmotic pressure by dealing with the large quantity of venous blood from the tail region, where metabolism is particularly active. In the Dipnoi, an alternative route by an anterior abdominal vein is developed, and a similar condition obtains in the Amphibia. The reptiles, with metanephric kidneys, show less development of the renal portal system. Blood from the tail and hind-limbs enters the pelvic veins, each of which bifurcates into a

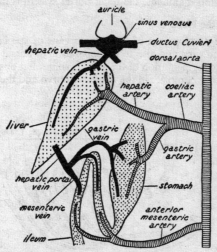

Fig. 26.67. Generalized hepatic portal system of the vertebrates.

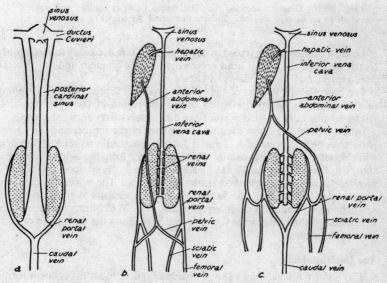

Fig. 26.68. Renal portal systems of (a) dogfish, (b) frog, (c) lizard.

renal portal and a median abdominal. It is noteworthy that both the anterior abdominal of Amphibia, and the median abdominal of Reptilia pass to the liver. In birds and mammals, the renal portal system is not represented.

Metamerism of the Head

Owing to the development of the large organs of special sense, the nasal sacs, the eyes and ears, and also to the separation of dorsal and ventral nerve roots, metameric segmentation of the head is somewhat obscured. Nevertheless, metamerism is complete in the dogfish embryo and the segmental nature

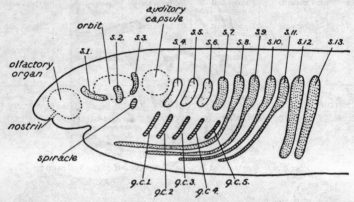

Fig. 26.69. Diagram showing the relationship between somites and visceral clefts in an embryo dogfish. Somites numbered S.1 to S.13; gill clefts, g.c.1 to g.c.5.

of head structures can be traced in development. It is necessary to distinguish clearly between the neural head represented by the cranium and the visceral head represented by the visceral arches.

The morphological front of the head is probably represented by the point of closure of the neuropore which lies in the region of the optic chiasma. All structures in front of this point are due to secondary forward growth.

In the visceral head, there are the derivatives of the somites and the lateral plate mesoderm. Somites 1, 2 and 3 form the extrinsic muscles of the eye, while somites 4 and 5 degenerate. Somites 6 and 7 form hypoglossal muscles, somite 8, the coraco-mandibular muscles, somite 9, the coraco-hyal muscles, somites 10 and 11, the coraco-branchial muscles. The visceral arches are segmental, formed from the lateral plate, with cavities derived from the splanchnocoel; the clefts are intersegmental. Fig. 26.69 illustrates the somites in relation to the clefts, while the table opposite shows the derivatives of each embryonic segment.

The Coelacanthini

The order Coelacanthini of the Crossopterygii includes many fossil forms and the recently-discovered coelacanths. The earliest fossils of this group

SEGMENTS AND THEIR DERIVATIVES IN THE DOGFISH

Segment	Name	Muscle derivatives	Visceral arch	Dorsal nerve-root	Ventral nerve-root
1	Premandibular	4 eye muscles	—	—	Oculomotor
2	Mandibular	Superior oblique	Mandibular	Trigeminal	Pathetic
3	Hyoid	Posterior rectus	Hyoid	Facial and Auditory	Abducens
4	1st metaotic	Disappears	1st branchial arch	Glossopharyngeal	—
5	2nd metaotic	Disappears	2nd branchial arch	Vagus—1st branchial	—
6	3rd metaotic	Hypoglossal muscles and myotome	3rd branchial arch	Vagus—2nd branchial	Hypoglossal
7	4th metaotic	Hypoglossal muscles and myotome	4th branchial arch	Vagus—3rd branchial	Hypoglossal
8	5th metaotic	Coracomandibular muscles and myotome	5th branchial arch	Vagus—4th branchial	Hypoglossal

date from the Devonian period, about 300 million years ago, and there is a succession showing very little change through all the intervening formations

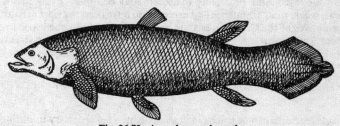

Fig. 26.70. A modern coelacanth.

up to the Cretaceous, about 60 million years ago. The first extant specimen examined by scientists was caught in 1938 off East London in the Cape Province of South Africa. Identified by Dr. J. L. B. Smith of Rhodes University, it caused a major sensation in scientific circles. Being somewhat different from known fossil forms, it was placed in a new genus and called *Latimeria*. As a result of publicity among local fishermen, another coelacanth of a different genus was caught in 1952 off Anjouan island, 200 miles west of Madagascar. This was 1·5 metres, blue in colour and was trapped at a depth of twenty metres; it has been called *Malanii anjouani*. Since then, four others have been obtained and are being investigated at the Natural History Museum in Paris. All caught to date have been males. An expedition, including deep-sea divers, is working from the Comoros Islands, in an attempt to locate the type of habitat, and to capture female fish.

These discoveries are of great importance for a number of reasons—

1. Coelacanths have existed in an unbroken line for over 300 million years. They are, in this respect, the most remarkable of living vertebrates and may

truly be called "living fossils." In external structure, the recent captures are practically identical with those known from their fossilized remains.

2. They are the only known survivors of the Crossopterygii and very closely related to the Osteolepidoti which seem to contain the ancestors of tetrapods. By careful examination of these coelacanths, traces of a pre-fish ancestry may be found. One remarkable fossil seems to indicate that some of the coelacanths were viviparous. If this is so, and if a living female is captured, we might discover from developing embryos, evidence of phylogeny on the basis of the recapitulation theory.

3. The lobed fins with proximal fleshy lobes (see Fig. 26.70) and distal hollow spines (coel-acanth), have a skeletal structure from which the pentadactyl limb might easily have been derived. Coupled with this is the fact that the position and angle of the pectoral fin are both very variable, differing even on the two sides of one fish. Thus in this important feature there is great variability and such is the raw material of evolution.

4. Examination of the coelacanths is confirming the remarkable accuracy of palaeontologists in piecing together structure from fragmentary remains. This engenders confidence in such scientific work.

5. These discoveries of extant species of an order thought to be extinct, present the fascinating possibility that there may be other "living fossils" in the seas, where man's influence and exploration have been the least exhaustive.

The natives of the Comoros Islands speak of the fairly frequent occurrence of these "fish with legs" among their catches. Perhaps it is not entirely fantastic to hope that one day we may see coelacanths swimming in tanks in the major zoological collections.

CHAPTER 27

AN AMPHIBIOUS CRANIATE: RANA

THE frog is usually selected for study because of its relative abundance and convenient size. Also, it illustrates in some measure the changes which took place during the transition from an aquatic to a terrestrial life. It must be clearly understood that the frog is not to be regarded as an unsuccessful or partially successful land animal, but as a true amphibian, equally at home in both media. All modern Amphibia are small animals and are very specialized. The larger and more typical members became extinct during the Triassic period.

RANA

There are several hundred species included in the genus *Rana*, the most striking being the golden and green tree frogs and the gliding frogs of Java and Borneo. The species described is the common British grass frog, *R. temporaria*, which differs only in minor details from *R. esculenta*, the edible green European frog, and from *R. pipiens*, the commonest North American frog.

Habitat and Habits

The frog favours damp situations and is usually to be found in grass near water, in damp ditches, and frequently, swimming in ponds or streams. It is carnivorous, feeding on a variety of small animals, which it swallows whole. During the winter it hibernates in mud-holes, often being completely covered. In spring, the frogs congregate in shallow ponds, the males croaking loudly, and mating takes place. The fertilized eggs develop into the familiar tadpole larvae, which hatch in two weeks. Slowly they metamorphose into frogs, the whole process taking about three months.

External Features

The usual colour of the animal is mottled green with black or dark brown patches and some tints of yellow. It has however some power of changing its colour slowly, to blend more harmoniously with the background. The body is about 10 to 11 cm long when full-grown and is squat, being flattened dorso-ventrally. There is no neck, the *head* passing imperceptibly into the *trunk*, and there is no tail (*see* Fig. 27.1)

The head tapers in front and is bluntly rounded; the wide *mouth* is terminal. Above the mouth are a pair of small holes, the *external nares*, which lead into the *nasal sacs*. The *eyes* are large and protruding; they lie almost dorsally but face laterally. *Eyelids* are poorly developed, the upper being stiff and immovable, while the lower represents a *nictitating membrane*. Special muscles retract the eye into the head and then the nictitating membrane can be moved up to cover it. Behind the eye is a prominent circular patch which is the *tympanic membrane* or eardrum.

The trunk widens laterally and then tapers between the hind-limbs to end at the *cloaca*. About half-way along its length are prominent

Fig. 27.1. *Rana temporaria.*

humps called the *sacral prominences*. Ventrally, the thoracic region is firm while the abdominal region is soft and yielding to the touch.

The *front-limbs* are short and stout, consisting of an upper arm, a fore-arm, a wrist and a hand which ends in four digits. It supports the front of the body clear of the ground, and in the resting position, the elbow is bent outward and the hand has its *palmar* surface downward. The *hind-limbs* are long, muscular, and folded tightly into three regions. The knee points forward and outward, the heel backward and inward, while the ankle and foot form a very long segment which lies on the ground. There are five toes joined by thin webs of skin. Except during jumping, the abdominal region is not supported clear of the substratum.

The skin is soft, moist and slippery to the touch. Distinction between the sexes is not very obvious since there are no external genitalia, but the male usually has a more slender body than the female. At breeding times, the female is considerably bloated with eggs, while the male develops a rough black warty patch on the first (pre-axial) finger.

Structure and Functions of the Body Wall

A transverse section of the trunk (*see* Fig. 27.2) shows the usual vertebrate arrangement of skin, muscle and peritoneum abutting on the coelom. The skin is thin but tough and is attached to the underlying muscle at intervals only, the intervening spaces being occupied by large *lymph sacs*. The *epidermis* is five or six cells thick and is constantly renewed by division of the stratum germinativum. All the cells are

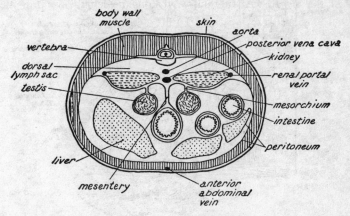

Fig. 27.2. *Rana*. T.S. Trunk region.

living, except the outer stratum corneum, which consists of flat squames. This outer layer is cast periodically and eaten by the frog. Beneath the epidermis are branched chromatophores of several kinds, the majority containing the brown pigment melanin. When the pigment is dispersed into the branches, the skin becomes dark, but when the pigment is collected into the centre of the cell, the skin is lighter in colour. The changes are controlled by a pituitary hormone.

The *dermis* consists mainly of connective tissue in which bands of white fibres predominate. There are very numerous blood-vessels since the skin is an important respiratory organ. Nerve-endings of various types are present, some of them penetrating into the epidermis. Most conspicuous are the simple saccular glands which secrete a watery mucus. This keeps the skin in a moist condition, thus enabling absorption of oxygen and elimination of carbon dioxide. Some of the glands secrete an acrid-tasting substance which renders the animal unpalatable to larger carnivores. All the glands, which lead out to the surface by small pores (*see* Fig. 27.3) are epidermal, being formed by downgrowths of the stratum germinativum.

The skin is almost entirely separated from the underlying muscle by the large *lymph sacs* which are really dilated lymphatic vessels. There are occasional strong attachments by white fibrous tissue. The *body wall muscle* is thin in the ventral region, but thick dorsally where the

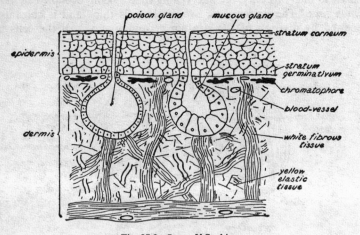

Fig. 27.3. *Rana*. V.S. skin.

vertebral column is embedded. The inner layer is the *peritoneum*, a squamous coelomic epithelium.

Functions of the Body Wall

The skin has protective, sensory, and respiratory functions. Protection is afforded by the stratum corneum, by the secretions of the epidermal glands, and by the colour changes due to the chromatophores. Sensitivity is located in various types of sense organs which are stimulated by touch and by temperature changes. The moist surface with the thin skin and excellent blood supply make the body wall a very important respiratory organ. Segmental myotomes cannot be distinguished except in the ventral abdominal region, and their function in locomotion, so important in the dogfish, does not apply to the frog. Movement is the function of the limbs and certain of the myotomes have grown out to form the limb muscles. The peritoneum allows easy movement of the viscera and it secretes the coelomic fluid.

The Coelom

The coelom shows almost the same condition as in the dogfish except that there is no firm strong pericardio-peritoneal septum and hence no pericardio-peritoneal canal. Also there are no abdominal pores. All the viscera, including the heart and lungs, are suspended in the splanchnocoel by folds of the peritoneum. The heart lies in a separate *pericardial cavity* enclosed by the *pericardium* (*see* Fig. 27.4). The functions

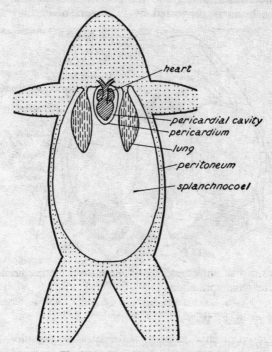

Fig. 27.4. Coelomic cavities of frog.

of the coelomic fluid and coelomic epithelium are the same as those discussed for the dogfish in Chap. 26.

The Skeleton

In the frog, the *exoskeleton* consists of the thin stratum corneum. The *endoskeleton* shows many modifications in adaptation to terrestrial conditions. All vertebrates have at first a cartilaginous endoskeleton; certain of the cartilages become ossified, and in addition, membrane or dermal bones arise by intramembranous ossification in connective tissue. In some cases, these overlie existing cartilages, and sometimes they form entirely new bones. The skeleton of the frog may be conveniently divided into the *skull*, the *vertebral column*, the *girdles* and the *limbs*.

The Skull

As in the dogfish, the skull may be considered to consist of the *cranium*, the *sense capsules* and the *visceral skeleton*. In the young tadpole, the brain is supported by two pairs of cartilages, anterior

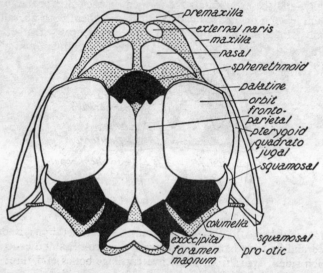

Fig. 27.5. *Rana temporaria.* Dorsal view of skull. Cartilage bones black; membrane bones white; cartilage stippled.

trabeculae and posterior *parachordals*. The sense capsules consist of an anterior pair of *olfactory sacs* supported by connective tissue, the lateral *optic capsules* in which the sclerotic later becomes cartilaginous, and the *auditory capsules*. Beneath the eyes are the rod-like *palato-pterygoids* articulating posteriorly with the auditory capsules (*see* Fig. 27.7). The trabeculae fuse and grow forward between the olfactory sacs to commence the formation of the olfactory capsules. Laterally, the trabeculae grow up around the brain to meet above it and form an incomplete roof. Posteriorly the parachordals grow up to form a complete covering to the hind-brain. The auditory capsules become fused to the parachordals and the palato-pterygoid is extended by a *quadrate cartilage* posteriorly and an anterior *orbital cartilage* in front (*see* Fig. 27.7). Thus the *chondrocranium* is completed and both the manner of its formation and the final product differ little in all terrestrial craniates. It is to be noted that the upper jaw of the dogfish, the palato-pterygo-quadrate bar, is fully represented, but in the frog, it no longer functions as a jaw.

Ossification now begins with the formation of five cartilage-bones, the *sphenethmoid*, the *pro-otics* and the *exoccipitals*. The sphenethmoid is a ring-like bone enclosing the front of the brain; the pro-otics form in front of the auditory capsules, projecting backward dorsally and ventrally, and the exoccipitals are formed on each side of the foramen magnum leaving unchanged cartilage between them both dorsally and ventrally. Intra-membranous ossification commences with the formation of paired *fronto-parietals* above the chondrocranium and a single

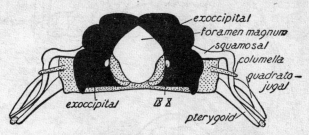

Fig. 27.6. Posterior view of skull of *Rana temporaria*.

parasphenoid beneath it (*see* Fig. 27.8). The latter bone is dagger-shaped and its wide handle lies between the pro-otics and exoccipitals on each side. Apart from these five cartilage-bones and three membrane-bones, the rest of the cranium remains unossified.

The parachordals continue growth forward and finally they enclose the olfactory sacs. Above the olfactory capsules, paired *nasal* bones form, and ventrally, paired *vomers*; both sets are membrane-bones.

The upper jaw is formed entirely of membrane bones and consists of an anterior *pre-maxilla*, a lateral *maxilla* and a posterior *quadrato-jugal* fused to the quadrate cartilage. It is firmly attached to the cranium by a series of bony struts and is not movable. In the front of the orbit, a *palatine* dermal bone is applied to the posterior face of the anterior orbital cartilage. At its inner end, it is fused to the sphenethmoid and at its outer end to the pterygoid. The *squamosal* is a tri-radiate bone with its inner point fused to the auditory capsule, its outer point to the quadrate cartilage and quadrato-jugal, while its forward point is free (*see* Fig. 27.9). Ventrally, the upper jaw is supported by another tri-radiate bone, the *pterygoid*, an intra-membranous ossification applied over the pterygoid cartilage. Its inner point is fused to the auditory capsule, its forward arm passes along the inside of the maxilla to fuse with the outer end of the palatine, while a backward arm fuses with the quadrate cartilage (*see* Fig. 27.8).

The lower jaw is first represented by *Meckel's cartilage*, most of which persists in the frog. The anterior portions become ossified to form the *mentomeckelian* bones. Later, each cartilaginous ramus is

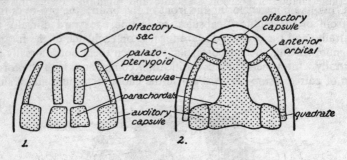

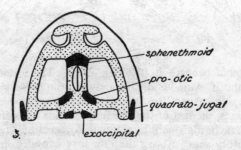

Fig. 27.7. Three stages in the development of the skull of a tadpole.

partially covered by membrane bones, an inner *angulo-splenial* and an outer *dentary* (*see* Fig. 27.10). The posterior articulating portion remains cartilaginous and forms a movable joint with the quadrate. Such a method of jaw suspension, where the lower jaw makes a joint with the upper jaw which is itself fixed to the cranium, is known as *autostylic* (*see* p. 802).

Loss of the gill clefts and reduction of the pharynx have led to considerable modification of the visceral skeletal arches. In considering the condition of these arches, we refer back to their original state as represented in the dogfish. The *mandibular arch* is still present as the palato-pterygoid-quadrate cartilage, though its function as an upper jaw has disappeared and it now supports the new jaw formed of membrane bones. Meckel's cartilage, the lower half of the mandibular arch, persists, though partly ossified. Teeth are borne on the upper jaw, on the premaxilla and maxilla. There are also a few teeth on the vomers, but the lower jaw is toothless. The *hyoid* arch shows considerable change of position, structure and function. Projecting outwards from the auditory capsule is a small rod, the *columella auris*.

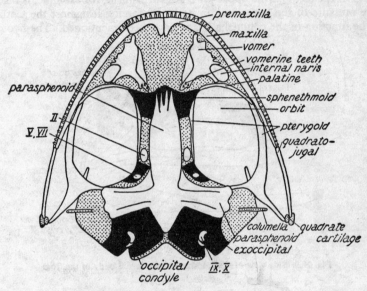

Fig. 27.8. *Rana temporaria*. Ventral view of skull.

At its outer end, it supports the tympanic membrane; its inner end is fused to a small knob of cartilage which covers a *fenestra ovalis*. The columella represents the hyomandibula and its function is far removed from jaw suspension; it transmits sound vibrations across the tympanic chamber to the inner ear. The hyoid cleft (the spiracle) is now closed externally by the *tympanic membrane*, and its cavity forms the *tympanic chamber* with the *Eustachian tube* leading into the pharynx. The cerato-hyals form the *anterior cornua* of the *hyoid body*. They lead from the front of this plate, curve backward and upward to fuse with the auditory capsules just behind the columella. The body of the hyoid lies in the floor of the mouth; it represents the basihyal and possibly the basibranchial. Projecting backward on each side of the **larynx are** the *posterior cornua*. They are cartilage bones and probably represent portions of the first branchial arch. The only traces which remain of the other *branchial arches* are the laryngeal cartilages, consisting of paired flat *arytenoids* and a single *cricoid* ring.

Functions of the Skull Components. The cranium houses and protects the brain and is perforated by foramina through which the nerves and blood-vessels pass. The sense capsules enclose and protect the three pairs of organs of special sense. Escape of prey is prevented by the grip of the teeth on the upper jaw. An earthworm, for example, is held by pressure of the lower jaw on its body, forcing it against the teeth. The function of the columella has already been mentioned. The hyoid

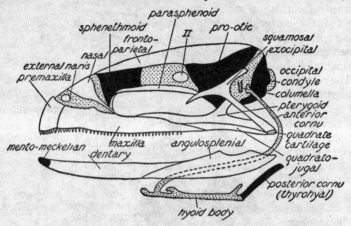

Fig. 27.9. Side view of skull, lower jaw and hyoid body of the frog.

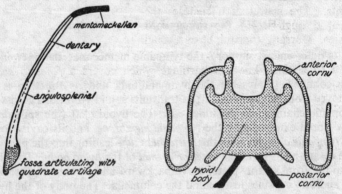

Fig. 27.10. Dorsal view of lower jaw of frog. (Left half shown.)

Fig. 27.11. Dorsal view of hyoid body of frog.

body is utilized for the attachment of muscles which change the position of the floor of the mouth during breathing movements (*see* p. 880), and also for those which move the tongue (*see* p. 878).

The Vertebral Column

In all the Anura, the vertebral column is remarkable for its short length and for the small number of *vertebrae*. There are nine vertebrae in the frog and the column terminates in a slender tapering *urostyle*, which represents several fused vertebrae (*see* Fig. 27.12). The whole column is first formed of cartilages, which have constricted the notochord into a mere vestige in the middle of each centrum. Later the cartilages ossify, though the remnants of notochord still remain.

The vertebrae, from the second to the seventh inclusive, are identical, except for the angle of the transverse processes. Examination shows that each of these vertebrae consists essentially of two parts, a solid bony *centrum* surmounted by a *neural arch*. Each centrum has a flattened oval shape in end-view (*see* Fig. 27.14) and is concave anteriorly and convex posteriorly, a condition known as *procoelous*. Thus the successive centra articulate by ball-and-socket joints. The neural arch encloses the canal through which the spinal cord passes. Dorsally, the arch bears a small *neural spine*, and laterally, the *transverse processes*, to the ends of which

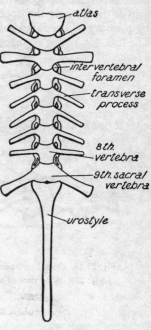

Fig. 27.12. Ventral view of vertebral column of frog.

are fused tiny cartilaginous ribs. Anteriorly and posteriorly, the arch bears paired projections known as *zygapophyses*. The *prezygapophyses* have smooth facets which face upward and inward, while the facets of the *postzygapophyses* face downward and outward. Thus the prezygapophyses of a vertebra fit below the postzygapophyses of the next in front of it. In life, all the articulating surfaces are covered by smooth slippery cartilage. The vertebrae are bound together by strong ligaments but there are no intervertebral discs between the centra. Lateral intervertebral foramina allow for the emergence of the spinal nerves (*see* Fig. 27.13).

The first vertebra, the *atlas*, has no transverse processes, no prezygapophyses and a reduced centrum. On its anterior face are two concave
facets with which the occipital condyles of the skull articulate (*see*
Fig. 27.15). Dorsally, between the atlas and the back of the cranium
is a small gap covered in life by the *atlanto-occipital membrane*. At

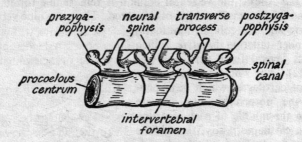

Fig. 27.13. Side view of three vertebrae of the frog.

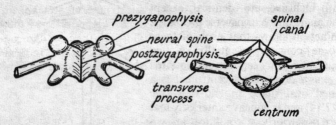

Fig. 27.14. Dorsal and posterior view of a typical vertebra of the frog.

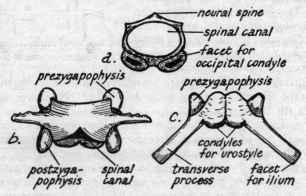

Fig. 27.15. (*a*) Anterior view of atlas. (*b*) Ventral view of 8th and (*c*) of 9th
vertebrae of the frog.

this point a needle can be inserted into the brain during the operation known as pithing.

The eighth vertebra is *amphicoelous*, bearing concavities on both anterior and posterior faces of its centrum. Posteriorly, it articulates with the convex centrum of the *sacral vertebra*, which is characterized by its strong, thick transverse processes, to which the ilia of the pelvic girdle are fused. The posterior face of the centrum of this ninth vertebra bears two rounded convexities which articulate with corresponding concavities on the *urostyle*. The latter bone is a slender tapering rod which extends backward almost to the junction of the two halves of the pelvic girdle.

Functions of the Vertebral Column. It protects the spinal cord and allows for emergence of the spinal nerves. In front, it provides support for the head, which is held clear of the ground. The joint between the atlas and the skull allows slight movement of the head in the vertical plane. During jumping and swimming, the thrust exerted by the hindlimbs is transmitted along the axis of the body through the vertebral column. The transverse processes provide points of attachment for the tendons of muscles which straighten the back and for those muscles which move the suprascapula during landing. In the frog, the column is comparatively rigid, but the aggregate of the slight movements possible between each successive pair of vertebrae gives the animal limited axial flexibility.

The Girdles

These structures are never complete girdles. Each half-girdle arises as a flat plate of cartilage, which, by differential growth, becomes tri-radiate (*see* Fig. 27.16). Thus in the *pectoral girdle* are formed an antero-ventral *pre-coracoid*, a postero-ventral *coracoid*, and a dorsal *scapula*. The dorsal segment becomes partly ossified as the scapula, but the larger portion of it remains as the *suprascapular cartilage*. The coracoid becomes ossified except for a small *epicoracoid cartilage*, which forms a

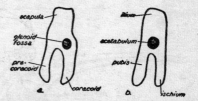

Fig. 27.16. Early stages in girdle development of tadpole. (*a*) Pectoral. (*b*) Pelvic.

symphysis between the right and left halves in the mid-ventral line. Posteriorly, between the coracoid and the scapula is a concavity called the *glenoid fossa* which provides a socket for the articulation of the front-limb. Antero-ventrally, the *clavicle* is deposited as a membrane bone overlying the pre-coracoid cartilage. The clavicle is the only membrane bone in the appendicular skeleton. Between the clavicle and the coracoid is a large gap known as the *coracoid fontanelle* (*see* Fig. 27.17). A chain of bones and cartilages in the mid-line form the so-called *sternum* which is probably not homologous with the sternum of higher forms. Anteriorly to posteriorly, they are the *episternum* (cartilage), the *omosternum* (bone), the *epicoracoid* (cartilage), the *mesosternum* (bone) and finally the flattened *xiphisternum* (cartilage).

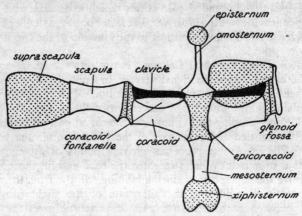

Fig. 27.17. Pectoral girdle of frog, ventral view. The scapula and suprascapula on right side have been flattened out.

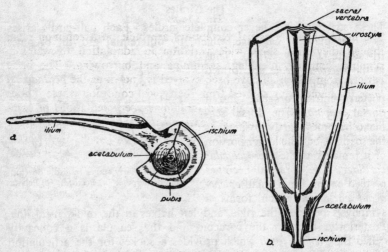

Fig. 27.18. Pelvic girdle of frog. (*a*) Left half from the side. (*b*) Dorsal view of both halves.

The tri-radiate cartilages forming half the embryonic pelvic girdle are the antero-ventral *pubis*, the postero-ventral *ischium* and the dorsal *ilium*; they undergo great changes in shape. Antero-dorsally, the ilium becomes very long and its forward end fuses with a transverse process of the sacral vertebra. The posterior ischium remains small, while the ventral pubis remains cartilaginous. A large almost hemispherical concavity called the *acetabulum* is formed at the junction of the three components; the hind-limb articulates with this socket. The ischia, pubes and the posterior regions of the ilia are fused in the mid-line, forming almost a circular disc-like structure, the *pubic symphysis*.

Functions of the Girdles

Both girdles provide sockets for the articulation of the limbs. The pectoral girdle provides firm attachments for muscles of the limbs, of the back and breast, and of the floor of the mouth. The pelvic girdle provides points of attachment for the muscles of the back and of the hind-limbs. Protection for the heart and lungs is provided by the more extensive pectoral girdle. When the frog is jumping or swimming, the thrust of the hind-limbs is transmitted to the girdle and hence to the axial skeleton via the ilia. Thus there is fusion between the girdle and the vertebral column. The front-limbs break the shock of landing and thus there is no fusion to the spine, the only attachments being by muscles from the suprascapular to the transverse processes. This arrangement makes the girdle springy, the better to absorb shock.

The Limbs

The limbs of all terrestrial vertebrates are built on a common plan, though they now show wide variation in adaptation to walking, running, jumping, climbing, swimming and burrowing. The basic pattern from which all have been evolved is known as the *pentadactyl limb*, the name being derived from the typical condition where it ends in five digits. Fig. 27.19 gives diagrammatic representations of complete front- and hind-limbs; the basic resemblance between the two is noteworthy. Articulating with the girdle is a single bone, the *humerus* in the front-limb, and the *femur* in the hind-limb. Distally this is joined to two parallel bones, a pre-axial *radius* and post-axial *ulna*, and, in the case of the hind-limb a pre-axial *tibia* and a post-axial *fibula*. Forming the skeleton of the wrist and ankle respectively are a number of small bones, the *carpals* and *tarsals*. Each has, proximally to distally, three, one and five bones. The last articulate with five *metacarpals* in the fore-limb and five *metatarsals* in the hind-limb. Each hand and foot consists of five *digits*, each of which has a small number of *phalanges*.

In the frog, there is great disparity in length between front- and hind-limbs. The front-limb has a short thick humerus with a pronounced pre-axial *deltoid ridge*. The radius and ulna are fused to form a *radio-ulna* though a distal groove indicates their separate origin. A

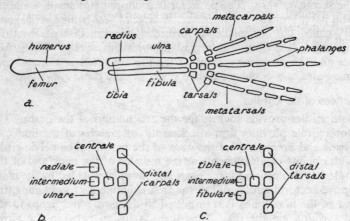

Fig. 27.19. Typical pentadactyl limb. (*a*) Whole limb (fore-limb names above, hind-limb names below). (*b*) Carpals. (*c*) Tarsals.

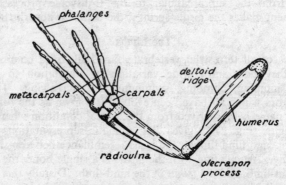

Fig. 27.20. Left front-limb of frog (from left).

slight backward projection at the elbow joint is the *olecranon process* (*see* Fig. 27.20). In the *carpus*, there are six small bones in two rows of three, the first row consisting of pre-axial *radiale*, middle *intermedium* and post-axial *ulnare*. There is no *centrale* and the other row contains the first and second distal carpals and a post-axial bone which probably represents the fusion of the other three distal carpals. In the palm are five metacarpals, the most pre-axial being much reduced. Four digits are present with phalanges numbering 2, 2, 3, 3 from pre-axial to post-axial.

The elongated hind-limb skeleton contains a proximal *femur*, then a *tibio-fibula* corresponding to the radio-ulna. The *tarsus* and foot are much extended, part of the increase in length being due to the proximal tarsals and part to the elongated metatarsals and phalanges. In the tarsus are two rows of two bones each. The proximal row consists of

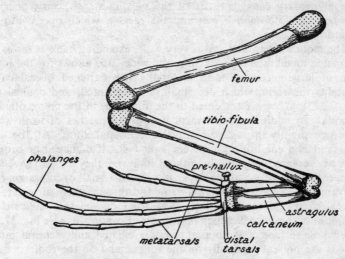

Fig. 27.21. Left hind-limb of frog (from left).

the elongated *astragulus* and *calcaneum*, pre-axial and post-axial respectively. Distally, there are two or sometimes three small bones. The five metatarsals are long and the digits contain respectively 2, 2, 3, 4, 3 phalanges. On the pre-axial side of the distal tarsals is a small sixth digit, the *pre-hallux*; it does not appear through the skin (*see* Fig. 27.21).

Functions of the Limbs

In tetrapods, the paired limbs have functions very different from those of the paired fins of fishes. They are now the organs of locomotion and in addition they have to support the weight of the body in a medium which provides practically no support. The earliest Amphibia of which we have fossil evidence were not capable of lifting the body clear of the substratum and consequently much of the ventral surface trailed along the ground. Even in the frog, the posterior region still does so. We will see, in higher vertebrates, a gradual rotation of the limbs until they lie vertically beneath the trunk, which is held high off the ground.

In addition to their other functions, the long bones have marrow cavities where blood corpuscles are elaborated.

Nutrition

The alimentary canal consists of the *mouth, buccal cavity, pharynx, oesophagus, duodenum, ileum,* and the *rectum,* which opens into the cloaca at the *anus.*

The mouth is terminal and is very wide, extending back as far as the tympanic membrane on each side. Its wide gape allows for the ingestion of large pieces of food material. The flattened buccal cavity contains the *teeth,* which are small, sharp-pointed, and conical (*see* Fig. 27.23). They are cemented to the inner side of the premaxilla and maxilla. In addition, the vomers bear small patches of teeth which protrude slightly through the dorsal buccal epithelium. All the teeth are similar, a condition known as *homodont.* If damaged or broken, they are replaced, apparently without limit, i.e. they are *polyphyodont.* Between the vomers and the upper jaw are two small openings guarded by valves. They are the *internal nares* and through them air enters the buccal cavity. Two large paler oval areas on the roof indicate the positions of the eyeballs which play a part in swallowing (*see* Fig. 27.22). The whole surface of the buccal cavity is ciliated and plentiful mucus glands are present especially on the tongue and on the roof.

The buccal cavity merges with the pharynx, which is very ill-defined, but certainly very small when compared with its extent in fishes. Laterally, almost at the angles of the jaws, are two small openings which lead into the *Eustachian tubes.* Ventrally in the mid-line is the *glottis,* a narrow longitudinal slit which leads into the *larynx* (*see* Fig. 27.22). Posteriorly, the pharynx tapers abruptly into the oesophagus.

The short oesophagus has longitudinal folds which close it to prevent entry of air to the stomach and yet allow of dilatation when food is being swallowed. Cilia of the buccal cavity, pharynx and oesophagus constantly waft the mucus backward into the stomach. This assists swallowing and ensures that small food particles are not retained in the anterior regions.

The stomach is elongated and thick-walled. Internally it is folded longitudinally, both to allow of distension and to increase the area for secretion of gastric juice. Posteriorly, a slight constriction indicates the position of the *pyloric sphincter* and the end of the stomach.

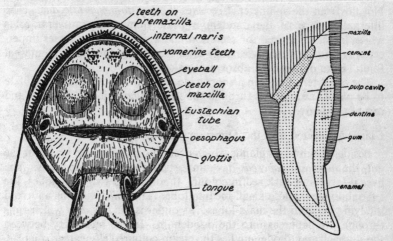

Fig. 27.22. Open mouth of frog, tongue pulled forward.

Fig. 27.23. V.S. tooth of frog.

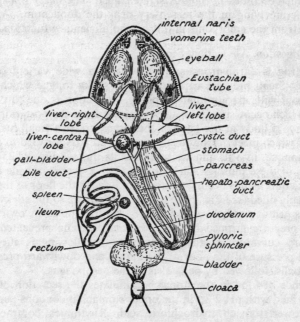

Fig. 27.24. Alimentary canal of frog, ventral view. Floor of mouth removed.

The duodenum turns forward and runs parallel with the stomach. Not far from the sphincter it receives the *hepato-pancreatic duct*. The internal surface of the duodenum bears numerous transverse folds which increase its area for secretion and absorption. It passes imperceptibly into the ileum which has several coils and longitudinal internal folds. Here most of the absorption takes place.

The canal terminates in a short wide rectum where faeces accumulate to be passed at intervals through the *anal sphincter* into the cloaca and out of the body.

Glands associated with the Alimentary Canal

Besides the mucous glands which occur along the whole length of the gut, the *liver* and *pancreas* have important alimentary functions. The liver is large and dark red in colour. It consists of two large lobes, the left subdivided, and a small median lobe. The *gall-bladder* is an ovoid sac lying between the main lobes; its outlet is the *bile duct* which runs through the pancreas into the duodenum. In the mesentery between the stomach and duodenum lies the cream-coloured elongated pancreas. It has no separate duct but its secretions are discharged into the bile duct, which becomes a *hepato-pancreatic duct*. The *spleen* is a spherical red structure lying in the mesentery near the duodenum. Although derived from the embryonic gut, it has no alimentary function.

Food, Digestion, Absorption, Storage

The frog is carnivorous and will ingest a wide variety of small animals. Small prey are captured by the sticky tongue which can be flicked out with extraordinary rapidity. Its action is due to two processes which occur simultaneously. Arising from the posterior cornua of the hyoid body at the level of the larynx are two small hyoglossus muscles which meet in front of the larynx and pass forward to the root of the tongue, into it, and backward to its tip (*see* Fig. 27.25). Contraction of these muscles will flick the tongue over in a wide arc. At the same time as this occurs, a large lymph sac in the floor of the mouth is suddenly filled (*see* Fig. 27.25). The prey adhere to the sticky tongue which is just as suddenly withdrawn by contraction of its own muscle. Larger prey are gripped by the jaws, escape being prevented by the backward curvature of the sharp teeth. Swallowing is effected by upward pressure of the floor of the mouth and downward pressure by the eyeballs, followed by peristalsis in the oesophagus.

Presence of food in the stomach stimulates the secretion of gastric juice, a fluid with pH 2·2; in the upper stomach it contains pepsin and in the lower stomach, hydrochloric acid. Rhythmical contractions of the muscle churn the food and mix it thoroughly with the gastric juice.

Thereby, proteins are partly broken up into peptones by the action of pepsin. Periodically, the pyloric sphincter opens and small portions of food are ejected into the duodenum. Here the bile, the pancreatic juice and the succus entericus, act very much as in mammals, with the result that amino-acids are produced from proteins, hexose sugars from carbohydrates, fatty acids and glycerol from fats. The amino-acids and hexose sugars are absorbed into blood capillaries to be taken to the liver in the hepatic portal vein. Fatty acids and glycerol are absorbed into the lacteals and taken finally into the blood by the lymphatic system.

Reserves of food are stored in the liver and in the fat bodies just anterior to the kidneys. In late summer and autumn, the liver becomes

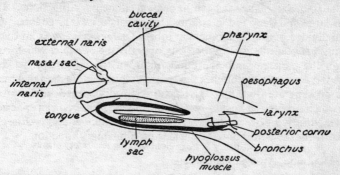

Fig. 27.25. Median V.S. of frog's head showing the mechanism for protruding the tongue.

swollen and light in colour. It is gradually accumulating glycogen and fat for use during the hibernation period. In spring, the reserves are practically exhausted, and the liver is small and darker in colour. The *fat bodies* are lobed structures attached to the anterior borders of the kidneys (*see* Fig. 27.34). The food supplies they accumulate are chiefly utilized by the sex glands, especially in the female.

Respiration

The frog has three different respiratory surfaces, the *skin*, *the epithelium of the buccal cavity* and the internal epithelium of the *lungs*. Thus there are cutaneous, buccal and pulmonary gas exchange, and when the animal is active on land, all three may be in use together.

The skin is thin, moist and well supplied with blood through the cutaneous artery and also by numerous smaller arteries. The erythrocytes contain the respiratory pigment haemoglobin and thus the conditions are almost ideal. It is practically certain that during hibernation, all the oxygen absorbed, enters through the skin, but it must be remembered that during that time, metabolism is at a very low ebb. The oxygen uptake by the skin is constant throughout the year and though it probably accounts for the total during winter, it is only a small fraction of the total in spring, when the frogs become most active. A frog can be submerged in water for several days, relying entirely on cutaneous respiration. Careful measurements have shown that the

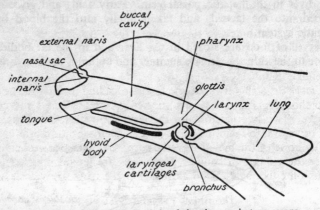

Fig. 27.26. Median V.S. frog's head showing respiratory organs.

amount of carbon dioxide passed out by the skin is four times the amount passed out by the lungs.

Buccal breathing is responsible for the regular palpitation of the floor of the mouth. Here again there is a moist epithelium and a liberal supply of blood, but it becomes necessary to change the air content of the buccal cavity frequently. This is carried out by depressing the floor of the mouth by contraction of the sternohyoid muscles which stretch from the hyoid body to the pectoral girdle. Then, with the nares open, air rushes through the nasal passage into the buccal cavity. Exhalation follows by contraction of the petrohyoid muscles which extend from the hyoid body to the auditory capsule. Some of the air is thus forced out again.

Pulmonary respiration takes place infrequently, often not more than once in every ten or fifteen minutes. First the buccal cavity is filled by the method described above. Then the nares are closed, the glottis opened and the floor of the mouth raised. Thus the air is forced into the lungs, which are ovoid hollow sacs with some folding of the internal epithelium (see Fig. 27.27). In exhalation, the nares are closed, the glottis opened and the floor of the mouth lowered. The air in the lungs is thus partially sucked out and partially forced out by the elasticity of the lungs themselves. Pulmonary respiration cannot be very efficient since it is of infrequent occurrence, the air used has already lost some of its oxygen in the buccal cavity and the lung epithelium does not present a very large surface area. However, during periods of great activity, the pulmonary breathing rate becomes much faster.

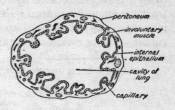

Oxygen is distributed to the tissues by the blood system and to the individual cells by the lymph in the intercellular channels.

Fig. 27.27. T.S. lung of frog.

The *larynx* is a slightly swollen chamber leading directly to the lungs by two short *bronchi*, and it is supported by the arytenoid and cricoid cartilages. Two internal folds of the larynx are stretched across from dorsal to ventral to form the *vocal cords*. Their vibration produces the croaking noise of the male frogs, the *vocal sacs* acting as resonators to increase the volume of sound. These sacs are lateral pouches of the pharynx on either side of the glottis. Female frogs are voiceless.

The Blood Vascular System

The blood system is not single as in the dogfish, where the heart pumps out only deoxygenated blood. On the other hand, it is not a completely double system, but a compromise between the two. The right and left auricles are separated, but the ventricle is single and pumps out a mixture of oxygenated and deoxygenated blood.

The Heart

Seen from the side, the heart has a flattened S shape (*see* Fig. 27.28). Dorsally, there is a thin-walled triangular *sinus venosus* which receives blood from a *vena cava* at each corner (*see* Fig. 27.29). The sinus pumps the blood through a slit-like *sinu-auricular valve* into the *right auricle*. Meanwhile the *left auricle* fills with blood from the lungs brought back by the *pulmonary veins*. The thin-walled auricles contract together and the blood is forced through the *auriculo-ventricular valves* into the *ventricle*. When the ventricle contracts, blood cannot return to the auricles since the valves are attached to the ventricle wall by a number of fibrous strands known as the *chordae tendineae* (*see* Fig. 27.30). They allow the valves to close the openings but will not stretch any further. The ventricle is thick-walled and its internal surface bears numerous projections called *columnae carneae*. Blood from the ventricle is pumped into the tubular *truncus arteriosus* past a set of *semi-lunar valves.* The truncus consists of two distinct parts, a posterior thick-walled *conus* which contains a peculiar fold known as the *spiral valve*, and an anterior thin-walled *ventral aorta.* The junction between the two portions is indicated by a second row of *semi-lunar valves.* Blood from the conus is pumped into the ventral aorta and thence it is forced into three pairs of *arterial arches.* The most posterior are the *pulmocutaneous* arches, the next are the *systemic* arches and the most anterior are the *carotid* arches.

There has been much speculation about the exact nature of the

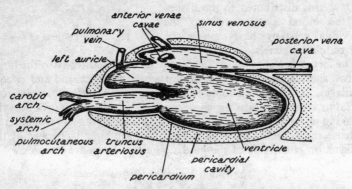

Fig. 27.28. Frog's heart seen from the left side.

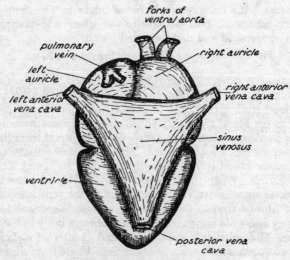

Fig. 27.29. Dorsal view of frog's heart.

circulation from ventricle to arterial arches. It has been postulated that the columnae carneae prevent thorough mixing of two sorts of blood in the ventricle, the deoxygenated blood from the right auricle and the oxygenated blood from the left auricle. However, it has been shown that there is little difference in oxygenation of the blood from either source. In support of this, we know that the lungs are not very efficient and that the musculo-cutaneous veins from the skin return much oxygenated blood to the right auricle. The trabecular nature of

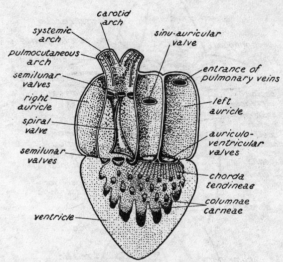

Fig. 27.30. Horizontal L.S. of frog's heart, ventral view.

the ventricle is probably an adaptation to increase the internal surface since the heart itself derives its oxygen from the contained blood; there is no special *coronary* supply such as we find in the mammals.

The function of the spiral valve is not known. It has been supposed to direct the deoxygenated blood to the pulmocutaneous arches, then to shut off this supply, so that increased pressure of the ventricular contraction forces the blood next into the systemic arch, and then lastly, by reason of the resistance of the *carotid labyrinth* (*see* Fig. 27.31), into the carotid arch. Thus it is reasoned that the oxygenated blood from the left side of the ventricle will supply the head. It appears, that all three arches fill simultaneously and that there is little, if any, difference of blood pressure in them. The carotid labyrinth probably functions in the same way as it does in mammals, as a sensory mechanism for perceiving changes in blood pressure.

The Arterial and Venous Systems

The short ventral aorta forks into right and left branches and then the three arterial arches on each side separate. The carotid arch proceeds outward towards the angle of the jaw and sends forward a *lingual artery* along the floor of the mouth. The main branch is then dilated at the labyrinth after which it passes around the side of the head to

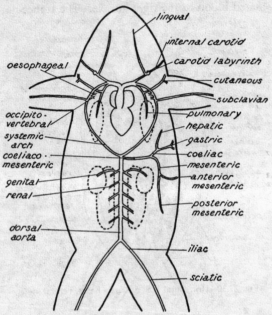

Fig. 27.31. Arterial system of frog, ventral view.

enter the orbit. Smaller branches then supply the roof of the mouth and the brain.

The systemic arch proceeds laterally then dorsally and curves backward in a wide arc to join its fellow in the mid-dorsal line just anterior to the kidneys (*see* Fig. 27.31). Each systemic arch gives off a small *oesophageal artery*, an *occipito-vertebral* to the back of the head and the anterior part of the vertebral column, and a large *subclavian artery* to the front limb. The united systemic arches form the *dorsal aorta* and immediately posterior to the junction, the median *coeliaco-mesenteric artery* proceeds ventrally. It divides into *coeliac* and *mesenteric* branches, the coeliac giving off *hepatic* and *gastric* arteries, and the mesenteric forking into *anterior* and *posterior branches*.

Several small *renal arteries* pass from the dorsal aorta to the kidneys and paired *genital arteries* to the reproductive organs. The latter vessels may arise from the aorta itself or from the most anterior pair of renal arteries. Finally, the aorta forks into paired *iliac arteries*

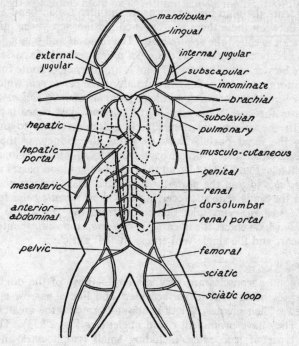

Fig. 27.32. Venous system of frog, ventral view.

which eventually pass into the hind-limbs, where they are called *sciatic arteries*. The pulmo-cutaneous arch forks into a *pulmonary* to the lung and a *cutaneous* which supplies a large area of skin in the dorsal and lateral regions.

The arteries branch repeatedly, and finally end in minute arterioles, which lead to networks of capillaries, from which the blood flows into venules and hence to veins, which return the blood to the heart.

From the anterior regions, blood is returned to the sinus venosus by the *anterior venae cavae*. Each receives three large veins, a *subclavian*, an *innominate* and an *external jugular*. The subclavian receives the *brachial vein* from the arm and the *musculo-cutaneous vein* from the flanks and the back. Entering the innominate are the *subscapular vein* from the shoulder region and the *internal jugular* leads around the angle of the jaw from the dorsal regions of the head. The *mandibular vein* passes back along the inside of the lower jaw and joins the *lingual vein* from the floor of the mouth; both enter the external jugular.

Blood from the hind-limbs returns in an outer *femoral* and an inner *sciatic*. Between these there is a cross-connexion across the middle of the thigh; it is called the *sciatic loop*. The femoral and sciatic join just inside the body cavity to form the *renal portal vein* which passes along the outer border of the kidney. There is an alternative route for blood in the femoral vein, by passing inward along the *pelvic vein* which joins its fellow ventral to the pelvic girdle to form an *anterior abdominal vein*. This passes forward in the mid-line of the body just beneath the skin to join the hepatic portal immediately before its entry to the liver. Entering the renal portal, half-way along the kidney, is the *dorso-lumbar vein* which brings blood back from dorso-lateral regions of the body wall (*see* Fig. 27.32). From the kidneys the blood passes inwards by *renal veins* to join the *posterior vena cava* which returns the blood direct to the sinus venosus, receiving two short *hepatic veins* from the liver. *Mesenteric veins* take the blood from the gut to the *hepatic portal vein* which enters the liver. The two *pulmonary veins* unite dorsal to the heart and the single vein enters the left auricle.

The Blood

The blood corpuscles are very similar to those of the dogfish, the erythrocytes being oval in surface view and like a narrow ellipse in edge view. Their greatest length is about $24\mu m$ and the greatest width $15\mu m$. They have prominent ovoid nuclei (*see* Fig. 27.33). There are several types of leucocytes, including small lymphocytes and poly-morphs similar to those of mammals (*see* Chap. 20). In addition, there

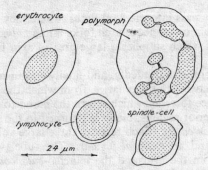

Fig. 27.33. Blood corpuscles of the frog.

are small spindle-shaped cells with large nuclei, which probably act in a similar manner to the thrombocytes of mammals.

The Lymphatic System

The lymph may be regarded as blood without the erythrocytes. It escapes from the capillaries, and circulates in the intercellular channels, nourishing the cells, supplying them with oxygen and taking away their excretory products. Continuous leakage through the capillary walls causes a sluggish flow. The intercellular channels lead into *lymphatic vessels* which are dilated in some regions of the body to form the large *lymph sacs*. They are most pronounced beneath the skin, dorsal to the coelom and in the floor of the mouth. The coelomic fluid is almost identical with lymph; the splanchnocoel communicates with the dorsal lymph sacs by minute pores called *stomata*. Finally, the lymph is pumped into veins by two pairs of *lymph hearts* which are small muscular dilatations with valves. The posterior pair of lymph hearts are situated one on each side of the mid-dorsal line behind the sacrum; their beating can easily be seen. They pump the lymph into the femoral veins. The anterior pair are at the sides of the third vertebra; they drive the lymph into the subscapular veins.

Locomotion

On land, the frog usually moves by jumping, though it can also crawl slowly; in the water it is an expert swimmer.

When the frog jumps, the hind-limb muscles contract so that each successive joint from the pelvic girdle to the foot is straightened. The thrust is transmitted into the vertebral column via the ilium and the sacral vertebra, and the frog leaves the ground at an angle of 45°, which will give the maximum length of leap for the particular effort exerted. The height and the length of the jump at this most favourable angle, reach a maximum of about 23 and 90 cm. Both distances depend on initial velocity, which varies directly as the length of the hind-limbs and inversely as the weight. Thus the frog, with its long legs and light body is well adapted for this mode of locomotion. The short stout fore-limbs, bent outward almost at right angles, and the elasticity of the pectoral girdle, are admirably suited to breaking the shock of landing. Long hind-limbs folded like a spring are characteristic of many jumping animals.

When the frog crawls, diagonally opposite limbs thrust against the ground in successive pairs, so that the body is levered forward with a rolling gait. The right fore-limb works with the left hind-limb and vice versa.

During swimming, the hind-limbs do all the work, thrusting against the water from the folded position, much as in jumping. The large area of foot, with the webbed toes, increases the thrust in the same way as do the flippers of frog-men.

Growth

Rate of growth in the frog is very slow; it takes about three years to become fully mature after metamorphosis is complete. There is very slow growth after this time for two or three years. The maximum length of life recorded for captive frogs is twelve years, but it is probable that few survive to this age under natural conditions. An interesting feature is the ecdysis of the outer layer of skin in one piece.

Urinogenital System

Both male and female frogs have the typical condition associated with anamniotes. The *kidneys* are mesonephric and are situated dorsally above the splanchnocoel, covered by the peritoneum. They are dark red, oval and somewhat flattened. The *Wolffian duct* passes along the outer border of each kidney to open into the cloaca by a small *papilla*. The *bladder* is a thin bilobed sac arising as a ventral outgrowth of the cloaca; its outlet is closed by a sphincter. Since the Wolffian ducts do not open into it, it is not a urinary bladder, but from the manner of its formation it is probably homologous with the *allantois* of embryonic reptiles, birds and mammals, and hence it may be termed an *allantoic bladder* (*see* p. 986). The fluid it contains is probably secreted by the blood-vessels in its walls; it may act as a reserve of water for dry periods.

The *testes* are ovoid cream-coloured objects, each suspended by a double fold of peritoneum, the *mesorchium*. They lie ventrally below the front parts of the kidneys, and from them, a number of fine *vasa efferentia* cross the mesorchium to enter the anterior kidney tubules, which are appropriated for the conveyance of sperm to the Wolffian duct. The *vesiculae seminales* are paired lateral diverticula of the Wolffian duct; sperm are stored there until breeding occurs. The *Mullerian duct* is represented by a pair of coelomic funnels near the lung bases and short solid strands in the dorsal body wall (*see* Fig. 27.34).

In the female, the *ovaries* lie in much the same position as the testes, each suspended by a *mesovarium*. They are irregularly lobed and flattened and numerous half-black and half-white eggs are visible through the epithelium. The *Mullerian ducts* are the *oviducts*, each being dilated in its posterior region to form an *ovisac*, where the eggs are stored until laying in the spring. The Wolffian duct is used solely as a *urinary duct* in the female (*see* Fig. 27.35).

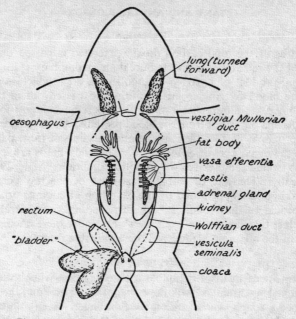

Fig. 27.34. Urinogenital system of male frog, ventral view.

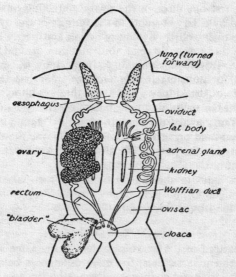

Fig. 27.35. Urinogenital system of female frog, ventra view. Left ovary removed.

Excretion

Four-fifths of the total carbon dioxide excreted is passed out via the skin and the remainder from the buccal and pulmonary epithelia. The main end-product of nitrogen metabolism is urea, which is extracted from the blood by glomerular filtration and passed out in the urine. The glomerular filtrate has essentially the same composition as the blood plasma but is free from the blood proteins. Glucose is reabsorbed in the proximal part of each tubule and certain salt ions, particularly Cl^-, in the distal part of each tubule. The body fluids are hypertonic to fresh water, and hence, in aquatic conditions, water will enter osmotically. The rate of entry is restricted by the low permeability of the skin and compensated by the excretion of copious urine, which is hypotonic to the blood. In dry surroundings, considerable water will be lost by evaporation from the skin; under these conditions, the supply in the allantoic bladder will be a valuable reserve.

Reproduction

The sexes are easily distinguishable at breeding-time when the abdomen of the female is distended with the eggs in the ovisacs, and the male has developed a rough *nuptial pad* on the first finger. Even at other times, the male body is slenderer than that of the female and traces of the patch are visible.

Ripe eggs burst out through the ovary epithelium into the coelom and are wafted by ciliary currents to the funnels of the oviducts. They pass down the ducts, partly by ciliary action and partly by peristalsis. Glands in the ducts deposit gelatinous albumin around the eggs. In early spring, the frogs congregate in shallow ponds, the males croaking loudly. A male mounts a female's back, gripping her under the arm-pits with the fore limbs. The grip is very strong and is a spinal reflex action; even decapitation will not affect it. After several days in this position, the female lays the eggs in a steady stream and the male deposits seminal fluid on them. Approximately one thousand eggs are laid and fertilized in the water. The albumin absorbs water rapidly and swells considerably.

The tadpoles hatch in about a fortnight and then take three months for complete metamorphosis into tiny frogs. Sexual maturity is not attained until the frog is three years old.

The Nervous System

The general pattern of the nervous system is the same as that of the dogfish in all essential respects, the main differences being those connected with the structural changes undergone by the animal in correlation with terrestrial life.

The Brain and Spinal Cord

In the telencephalon, the small *olfactory lobes* project forward and are secondarily united in the mid-line. The *cerebral hemispheres* are clearly defined, the right and left being partially separated by a deep dorsal furrow. Internally the corpora striata are well developed.

The thalamencephalon is narrow, its roof consisting of the *anterior choroid plexus*, behind which is the *pineal stalk*. In the tadpole, the pineal body is attached to its stalk, but in the frog, fronto-parietal ossification has separated them and the pineal body now lies beneath the skin between the eyes. Sometimes it is visible as a pigmented spot.

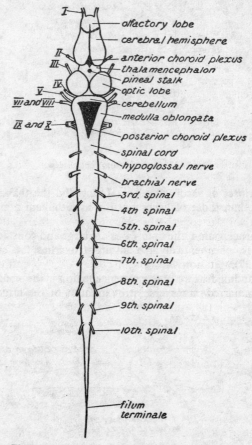

Fig. 27.36. Brain and spinal cord of frog, dorsal view.

In some of the extinct amphibians there was a large fontanelle in the cranium and it is probable that they possessed a pineal eye connected to the brain by the pineal stalk which acted as an optic nerve. Ventrally, there are the usual *pituitary body* and *optic chiasma*. The pituitary consists of the *infundibulum* and the non-nervous *hypophysis*; there are

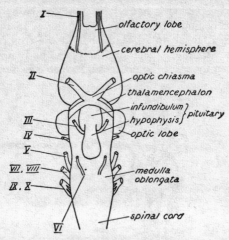

olfactory lobe
cerebral hemisphere
optic chiasma
thalamencephalon
infundibulum } pituitary
hypophysis
optic lobe
medulla oblongata
spinal cord

Fig. 27.37. Brain of frog, ventral view.

no lobi inferiores or sacci vasculosi. Internally, the thalami are relatively larger than those of fishes but the hypothalami are not so well developed.

In the mesencephalon, the *optic lobes* are large and conspicuous ovoid protuberances, and ventrally the pituitary overlies the *crura cerebri* (*see* Fig. 27.37).

The outstanding feature of the metencephalon is the small size of the *cerebellum*, a narrow transverse strip in front of the large triangular

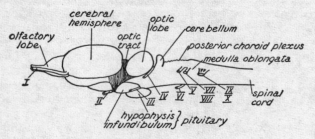

cerebral hemisphere
optic lobe
olfactory lobe
optic tract
cerebellum
posterior choroid plexus
medulla oblongata
spinal cord
hypophysis } pituitary
infundibulum

Fig. 27.38. Brain of frog, lateral view

posterior choroid plexus. Ventrally the *medulla* is thickened and begins to taper posteriorly.

The myelencephalon consists of the *posterior choroid plexus* dorsally and the medulla laterally and ventrally. The latter tapers into the spinal cord and in this region the two are hardly distinguishable.

The spinal cord is not of uniform cross-section, being somewhat swollen where the nerves to the limbs are situated. It begins to taper at the level of the sixth vertebra and ends as the *filum terminale* in the urostyle. In transverse section, it has the same characteristics as are found in the dogfish but it is somewhat more flattened dorso-ventrally.

Cavities of the Central Nervous System

There are two narrow *rhinocoels* in the olfactory lobes which communicate with the two large *lateral ventricles* of the cerebral hemispheres. These lead, by the *foramen of Monro*, into the *third ventricle* which is somewhat reduced by the large lateral thalami. *Optocoels* open into the constricted *aqueduct of Sylvius* which leads into the large *fourth ventricle* beneath the posterior choroid plexus (*see* Fig. 27.39). The narrow *central canal* of the spinal cord is continuous with the cavity of the fourth ventricle.

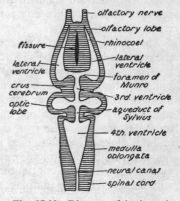

Fig. 27.39. Diagram of horizontal L.S. of frog's brain to show cavities.

Commissures and Correlation Centres

Of the lateral commissures, the *anterior* in the lamina terminalis is well developed, consisting of dorsal and ventral tracts of nerve fibres. The *dorsal tract* connects groups of cells in the cerebral hemispheres, while the *ventral tract* connects cells in the lateral walls of the hemispheres concerned with reception of sensory impulses from the olfactory lobes. The *dorsal commissure* in front of the pineal stalk is less well developed; it connects two small masses of cells again concerned with the olfactory sense. Connecting the antero-ventral region of the two optic lobes is the *posterior commissure* which is more prominent than in fishes. The *crura cerebri* are well developed, containing large tracts of fibres connecting the sensory centres of the hind-brain with those of the fore-brain.

There is less emphasis on the *cerebellum* as a correlation centre compared with its great importance in fishes. Stimuli relating to balance and orientation tend to be diverted into the posterior region of the optic lobes and there is thus a very small cerebellum and a reduced length in the medulla. The *thalamus* is well developed, receiving connexions from all the sensory centres. There is some development of the *pallium*, a dorsal region of superficial grey matter in the cerebrum. It is connected to all parts of the brain but has not yet reached the overriding importance it attains in the mammals. Removal of the cerebral hemispheres seems to have little effect on behaviour except that concerning olfactory stimuli.

Relationship of Brain to Mode of Life

It must be emphasized that when we attempt to correlate the anatomy of the brain with the animal's mode of life, we can do so only by comparison with brain structure in other animals. When we say that the olfactory lobes are small in the frog, indicating less reliance on the sense of smell, we are comparing their relative size with the same structures in the fishes.

The cerebral hemispheres show great development compared with those of the dogfish. This indicates the trend in terrestrial animals of greater centralization of control in this region and hence greater possibilities of more complex behaviour. Relative enlargement of the optic lobes indicates the greater importance of the sense of sight. The great reduction of the cerebellum may be correlated with the decrease of muscular activity. The frog is sluggish by comparison with the fish and it is more or less stationary for the greater part of its life. Its broad body, touching the ground, ensures stable equilibrium without much necessity for fine and continuous adjustment of the muscles concerned with balance. During jumping, the frog has little judgement of distance or direction; it will jump anywhere and it does not choose a spot for landing, it merely falls to the ground. The smaller length and thickness of the medulla are correlated with the loss of the lateral line system, which is so important in the fishes.

Cranial and Spinal Nerves

As in the dogfish, there are ten pairs of cranial nerves, though in some extinct amphibia there were probably twelve pairs. Thus the condition in the frog is secondary, not primitive. The main changes in distribution of the cranial nerves are related to the loss of the lateral line system and of the gill clefts. The nerves which supply these structures in the dogfish are VII, IX and X; these have undergone most change in the frog.

Each olfactory nerve I, leads the fibres from a nasal organ into an olfactory lobe; it is a single small nerve. Nerves II, III, IV, V, VI and

VIII have the same distribution as in the dogfish. In connexion with the distribution of VII, it must be remembered that the Eustachian tube corresponds to the spiracle of the fish. There is a *palatine* branch to the roof of the mouth, a small *pre-tympanic* in front of the Eustachian tube and a large *hyomandibular* behind it. This last branch supplies the muscles attached to the hyoid body and the muscles of the lower jaw. Cranial nerve IX now lives up to its name of glosso-pharyngeal; it passes forward beneath the pharynx to the tongue. Only the visceral branch of the vagus remains, the branchial and lateral line branches having disappeared; it has *laryngeal, cardiac, pulmonary* and *gastric* derivatives (*see* Fig. 27.40).

There are ten pairs of spinal nerves, the first nine emerging from the intervertebral foramina and the tenth pair from small foramina in the urostyle. The dorsal and ventral roots unite outside the vertebral column (*see* Fig. 27.41) the junctions being obscured by white calcareous masses known as the *glands of Schwammerdam*. Each mixed spinal nerve gives off a short dorsal branch to the skin and muscles of the back, a large ventral branch to skin and muscles of the abdomen, and where applicable, to the limbs, and a short ramus communicans to the autonomic chain.

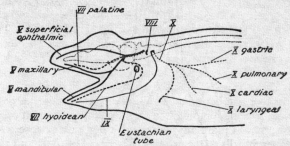

Fig. 27.40. Distribution of cranial nerves of frog, V, VII, IX and X.

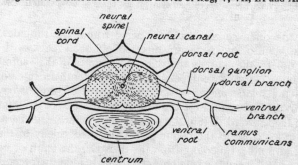

Fig. 27.41. Diagram of T.S. of vertebral column of frog to show spinal cord and segmental nerve roots.

Emerging between the first and second vertebrae is the first spinal nerve, the *hypoglossal*, which curves around the pharynx and proceeds forward ventrally along the floor of the mouth to supply the tongue. The second is the *brachial* nerve, which receives branches from the first and third to form the brachial plexus and then proceeds down the

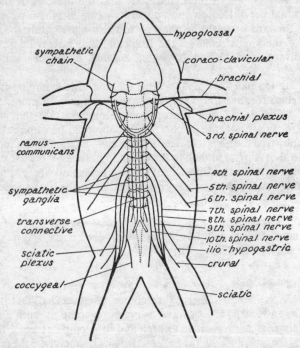

Fig. 27.42. Spinal nerves and sympathetic chain of frog, ventral view.

arm, giving off a *coraco-clavicular* nerve round the shoulder region. The fourth, fifth and sixth are directed obliquely backward parallel to each other; they supply the skin and muscles in the ventral region of the trunk. Nerves seventh, eighth, ninth and tenth are interconnected to form the *sciatic plexus*. The seventh gives off an *iliohypogastric* branch to the intestines, a *crural* to the outer muscles of the thigh, and a small branch inward to join the eighth. The main *sciatic nerve* passes down the leg close to the femur, it is composed chiefly of the joined eighth and ninth. Emerging from the urostyle, the tenth or *coccygeal* nerve is small; it sends a small branch to the bladder before joining the sciatic (*see* Fig. 27.42).

The Autonomic System

There are ten pairs of *sympathetic ganglia* situated at the sides of the dorsal aorta posteriorly, and alongside the systemic arches anteriorly. Each ganglion is joined to its corresponding spinal nerve by a *ramus communicans* and the respective pairs are also joined by *transverse connectives*. Longitudinally each series of ganglia is joined by a *sympathetic chain* which ends blindly posteriorly after its ramus to the coccygeal nerve. Anteriorly, each chain leaves the systemic arch where this bends inward towards the heart. It then proceeds into the cranium, where it is joined to the *vagus ganglion* and it terminates in the *Gasserian ganglion* of the fifth cranial nerve.

There is a *solar plexus* in the mesentery near the dorsal wall of the stomach; it is joined by splanchnic nerves to the third, fourth and fifth sympathetic ganglia. On the auricles, there is a *cardiac plexus* connected to the first pair of sympathetic ganglia. In addition, there are smaller hepatic, renal, genital, intestinal and vesical plexuses in connexion with the liver, kidney, reproductive organs, intestines and bladder respectively.

From the sympathetic ganglia, post-ganglionic motor fibres pass out to the viscera, blood-vessels and skin. Visceral sensory fibres pass through the ganglia into the central nervous system. There are sympathetic and parasympathetic motor fibres which have mutually antagonistic effects (*see* Chap. 26).

Sense Organs

The skin contains numerous receptors of several different kinds. Some are sensitive to touch, some to pressure, some to pain, and there are distinct receptors sensitive to high and low temperatures. The heat receptors are active in the range 39°C to 43°C; and the cold receptors below 10°C.

The eyes have the standard vertebrate pattern but have in addition to the six extrinsic muscles, a pair of *retractor bulbis* muscles which can contract to pull the eyes inwards. The lens is nearly spherical and the focus is fixed; the frog is short-sighted in the air and long-sighted in the water. Rods and cones are scattered evenly over the retina, the absence of a yellow spot indicating that there is little visual acuity. The position of the eyes ensures a wide field of view, but obviates any possibility of stereoscopic vision.

In addition to the inner ear, which has much the same structure as that of the dogfish, a middle ear is developed by conversion of the spiracle into a tympanic chamber connected with the pharynx by the Eustachian tube (*see* Fig. 27.43). Sound vibrations, impinging on the tympanic membrane, are conveyed across the cavity by the columella auris. This articulates with a small plug of cartilage (stapes) which lies against the fenestra ovalis. Vibrations of the latter membrane travel through the perilymph and hence into the endolymph within the membranous labyrinth. The semi-circular canals, utriculus and sacculus, function as in other vertebrates. There is slightly greater development of the lagena which is larger, in connexion with finer sound perception in air, but compared with higher terrestrial vertebrates, the frog's hearing is poor. By comparison with the dogfish, the

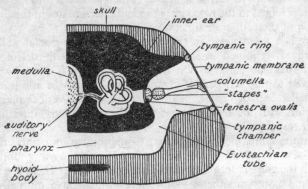

Fig. 27.43. Auditory organ of frog.

ductus endolymphaticus is most peculiar. On each side, it proceeds into the cranium as a narrow tube and there dilates into a vesicle from which a fine duct passes backward inside the vertebral column and lateral to the spinal cord. Dilated sacs protrude through the intervertebral foramina and become filled with a pasty mass of calcium carbonate, forming the glands of Schwammerdam; their function is unknown.

The olfactory organs differ little from those of the dogfish. There are, however, internal openings which enable the frog to perform buccal and pulmonary respiration without opening the mouth. Also, the stream of air passing over the sensory cells gives constant and quicker perception of volatile substances.

Endocrine Glands

The *pituitary gland* consists of four parts, a *pars nervosa* developed from the floor of the infundibulum, and in the hypophysis, three regions are distinguished. They are the *pars anterior*, the *pars intermedia* and the *pars tuberalis*. Pituitary hormones affect skin coloration and egg-laying among other things. The *thyroid* glands are two small spherical pink structures lying beneath the posterior region of the hyoid body near the external jugular veins. Experiments with tadpoles have shown that when the thyroid gland is removed, they do not change into frogs. If, however, such tadpoles are fed on thyroid tissue, even that of another animal, they will then metamorphose. Evidently the thyroid hormone has important effects on growth and development. The *parathyroids*, situated near the thyroids, develop from the ventral regions of the gill slits after they close up; they are concerned with calcium metabolism. *Islets of Langerhans* in the pancreas produce insulin; with other hormones it regulates the blood sugar. *Thymus* glands, beneath the skin behind the angles of the jaws, develop from the dorsal regions of the gill pouches; their hormone is concerned with lymphocyte synthesis and immunity reactions. Longitudinal bands of yellow tissue on the kidneys are the *adrenal* glands. They contain cortical and medullary tissue and it is presumed that they produce hormones with similar effects to those of mammals (*see* Chap. 29). Sex hormones are produced by *interstitial tissue of the gonads*.

Development

The early development of the frog follows the same general pattern as that described for *Amphioxus*, but there are several important differences. Whereas the egg in *Amphioxus* is of the mosaic type, the egg of the frog is described as the *regulation* or *non-mosaic* type. The various cytoplasmic areas (presumptive areas) are not defined until the late blastula stage. It follows that the various organ-forming substances are not distributed by cytoplasmic streaming as in the egg in *Amphioxus*, but by movements of the cells themselves. The embryo hatches as a larva in a much higher state of development. As we ascend the vertebrate series, this trend continues; the larval stage is lost and the embryo emerges almost a replica of the adult. To understand the embryology it is very necessary to make constant reference to the diagrams associated with the text.

The Sperm and the Egg

The sperm is about 30µm in length with a long cylindrical head terminating in a small spherical acrosome. There is a short middle piece, cylindrical like the head, and a long thread-like tail terminating in a fine short flagellum (*see* Fig. 27.44).

The eggs (within the albumin) are spherical and about 1·7 mm in diameter. They are released from the ovary as primary oocytes, the first maturation division taking place in the oviduct, where the thin coating of albumin is deposited outside the vitelline membrane. A first polar body is produced. Slightly more than half the egg is deeply pigmented, with dark granules lying in the superficial cytoplasm; the smaller portion is cream-coloured and bears most of the yolk. Such an egg is said to be moderately *telolecithal*. The axis of symmetry is

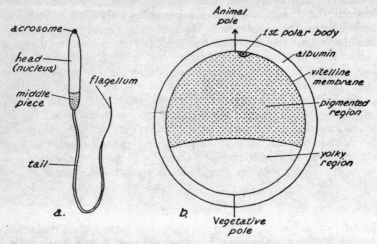

Fig. 27.44. Gametes of frog. (*a*) Sperm. (*b*) Ovum.

from the centre of the pigmented area to the centre of the yolky region, the former being the animal pole and the latter the vegetative pole. There is a large germinal vesicle (nucleus) situated slightly above centre towards the animal pole. In the water, the egg floats with the heavier yolk downward (*see* Fig. 27.45).

Fertilization and its Effects

During mating, the cloaca of the male is very close to that of the female and thus the seminal fluid is deposited near the eggs as soon as they are laid. The sperm penetrate the eggs before the albumin has had time to swell by absorption of water. Penetration occurs in the pigmented area, approximately on the equator of the egg. Normally the sperm enters a spot which becomes marked by a small raised papilla of the egg cytoplasm. The sperm tail does not enter the egg. As the head moves into the cytoplasm, its *penetration path* is marked by dark streaks consisting of pigment granules carried with it from the peripheral region. The route followed by the male nucleus towards the germinal vesicle is the *copulation path*, which is in the same plane as the penetration path, except when the vesicle is abnormally placed.

The penetration of the sperm head has a number of important effects on the egg. Its cytoplasm shrinks owing to the exudation of fluid, which fills a *perivitelline space* between the vitelline membrane and the cytoplasm. There is an increase in viscosity and this is accompanied by greater permeability of the vitelline membrane. The rate of metabolic activity increases and there is greater oxygen uptake. Opposite the point of entry of the sperm, there is withdrawal of pigment from the superficial cytoplasm, thus forming the *grey crescent*. The plane

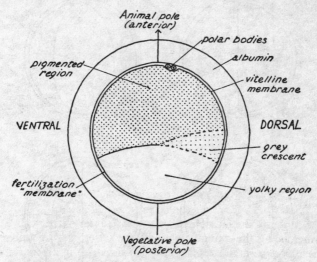

Fig. 27.45. Fertilized egg of frog from the left side.

of the first cleavage coincides with the copulation path and normally it passes through the middle of the grey crescent. Thus the point of entry of the sperm gives the egg bilateral symmetry and the copulation path determines the future right and left halves of the embryo. The second maturation division of the egg takes place and the second polar body is extruded. Finally, the diploid chromosome number, 26, is restored, 13 maternal and 13 paternal.

The first spindle is formed at right angles to the egg axis and the maternal and paternal chromosomes move to the equator. Within two hours of fertilization, the first cleavage has taken place. The albumin swells considerably and serves to protect the egg from predators by its slippery nature and unpleasant taste. It also reduces the effect of large temperature changes. The albumin is not used as food material by the developing embryo (*see* Fig. 27.45).

Cleavage

Cleavage is *holoblastic* but unequal because the concentration of yolk in the vegetative region impedes the passage of the cleavage furrows. The first division is vertical and normally splits the grey crescent into two equal portions (*see* Fig. 27.46 (*a*)). The second division is also vertical and at right angles to the first (*see* Fig. 27.46 (*b*)). This is followed by a horizontal division at right angles to the first two, the

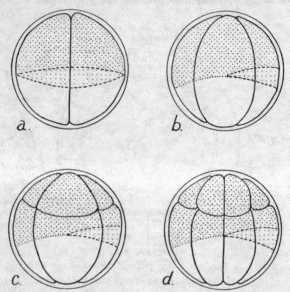

Fig. 27.46. Cleavage stages in egg of frog. (*a*) 2-celled (future dorsal). (*b*) 4-celled, side view from left. (*c*) 8-celled, side view from left. (*d*) 16-celled, side view from left. (*b*), (*c*) and (*d*) drawn as the egg floats.

plane of cleavage lying above the centre of the egg, so that there are four upper *micromeres* and four lower *megameres* (*see* Fig. 27.46 (*c*)). After this eight-cell stage, although vertical and horizontal cleavages follow in sequence, the rate of division of the micromeres outstrips that of the megameres and consequently the animal portion soon consists of many small pigmented blastomeres while the vegetative region consists of fewer large yolky blastomeres (*see* Fig. 27.46 (*d*)).

The Blastula and Presumptive Areas

There is no clearly-marked change from *morula* to *blastula*, the *blastocoel* being present at the eight-cell stage (*see* Fig. 27.47 (*a*)). The completed blastula is taken to be the stage of development at which gastrulation begins. Then, the *blastoderm* is several cells thick at the animal pole and it increases in thickness towards the vegetative pole (*see* Fig. 27.47 (*b*)). The blastocoel is excentric, being situated entirely within the animal half.

Fate-maps showing the presumptive areas on the amphibian blastula have been plotted in great detail by Vogt and others. There is no reason to suppose that *Rana temporaria* differs from these. It is to be noted that cleavage stages and the blastula have thus far been described and illustrated with reference to the egg axis. From now on, development will be discussed in terms of the future animal axis. At the blastula stage, the animal pole indicates the future anterior end, and the

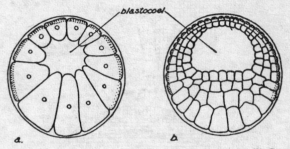

Fig. 27.47. Frog blastula in V.S. (*a*) Early stage, from left. (*b*) Completed from left.

vegetative pole, the posterior end. The middle of the grey crescent is in the mid-dorsal line. Lateral and dorsal views showing the presumptive areas are illustrated in Fig. 27.48. It will be seen that presumptive ectoderm, divisible into epidermis and neural plate, occupies almost all the anterior half, while much of the posterior half consists of the presumptive endoderm. Separating the two is a band consisting of notochord and mesoderm, wider dorsally than ventrally.

Gastrulation

The first sign of gastrulation is the appearance of a small crescentic groove in the mid-dorsal region of the posterior margin of the presumptive *pre-chordal plate* (*see* Fig. 27.49). Along the groove the cells sink inward, while anterior to it, they stream over the lip and are tucked in beneath it. The anterior edge of the groove is the *dorsal lip* of the blastopore and the cells first tucked underneath in the mid-dorsal region are cells of the pre-chordal plate. The lips of the blastopore extend laterally with the streaming and intucking continuing. Dorsally, after all the pre-chordal plate has moved inside, the notochord cells

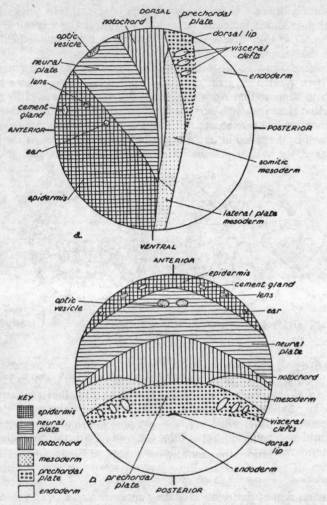

Fig. 27.48. (a) Anuran blastula, presumptive areas, side view. (b) Same, dorsal view.

follow it in the mid-line (*see* Fig. 27.51). On the outer surface, there is convergence of cells towards the lips of the blastopore so that mesoderm begins to be tucked in laterally between epidermis and endoderm (*see* Fig. 27.50 (a)). Meanwhile, streaming continues posteriorly so that the blastopore moves backward, the activity of its lips spreading

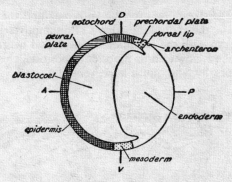

Fig. 27.49. Beginning of gastrulation in frog. V.S.

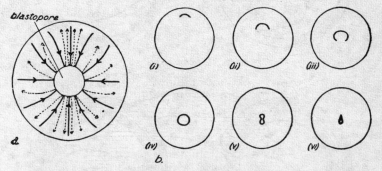

Fig. 27.50. (a) Diagram showing external convergence (heavy lines) of cells towards blastopore and internal divergence (broken line) from blastopore. (b) Changes in position and shape of the blastopore, all posterior view.

ventrally until it appears as a circle enclosing the paler yolky cells (*see* Fig. 27.50 (*b*)). When all the notochord cells and the lateral mesoderm have migrated inside, the neural plate comes to lie as a broad band over the dorsal surface (*see* Fig. 27.56 (*b*)). All the cells which converged towards the blastopore externally, diverge internally. The heavy and more inert yolk-laden cells are not easily invaginated and they block the blastopore as the *yolk-plug*.

The crescentic groove which began gastrulation is the beginning of the archenteron, which as it deepens, gradually obliterates the blastocoel. The slow movement of the yolky cells from posterior to ventral, together with the obliteration of the anterior blastocoel and the formation of the archenteron dorsally, cause a slow change in the centre of gravity and the embryo rotates within its membranes to lie with its anterior-posterior axis horizontal. Gradually the lips of the blastopore contract, the cells streaming over the yolk plug and the last material to be tucked in is the ventral mesoderm. Presumptive epidermis now covers the embryo with the exception of the dorsal neural plate. The blastopore, which is now a slit in a posterior position, closes first in the middle, then dorsally, and, much later, ventrally.

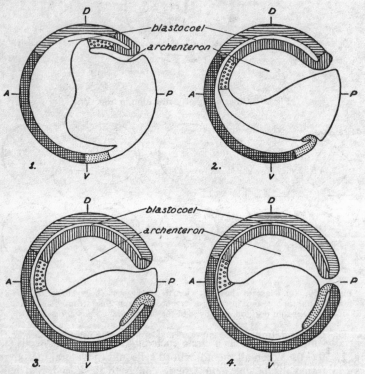

Fig. 27.51. Four stages in gastrulation of frog, all in median V.S.

Gastrulation in the frog is obviously a more complicated process than in *Amphioxus*. The large amount of yolk has made simple invagination impossible and *epiboly* or streaming-over by the pigmented cells has been the main factor. However, it has been assisted by *convergence* externally and *divergence* internally and by the *contraction of the lips of the blastopore*. Throughout gastrulation, the embryo has been elongating slowly. The importance of mass movements of cells must be stressed; there has been little, if any, differential rate of division in particular regions. Resulting from these movements, the presumptive

areas are finally in their definitive positions ready to commence organ
formation. Another important difference from gastrulation in
Amphioxus is the fact that from the commencement of intucking of the
mesoderm, it lies as a middle layer between ectoderm and endoderm
(*see* Fig. 27.51). In the mid-dorsal line, the roof of the archenteron is

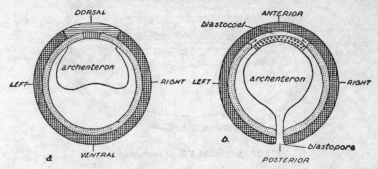

Fig. 27.52. Completed gastrula of frog. (*a*) T.S. (*b*) Horizontal L.S.

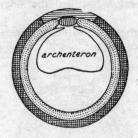

Fig. 27.53. T.S. frog embryo showing endoderm growing beneath notochord.

formed by the notochord and dorso-lateral mesoderm for a time, but
soon the lateral endodermal walls grow up and meet beneath it (*see*
Fig. 27.53).

Gastrulation is completed about three days after fertilization, the
embryo then being 2·5 mm long.

Formation of the Neural Tube

Towards the end of gastrulation, the neural plate lies along the dorsal
surface as a broad band, wide in front and tapering posteriorly (*see*
Fig. 27.56 (*b*)). The sides rise up to form the *neural folds* and the middle
of the plate sinks in to form the *neural groove* (*see* Fig. 27.55). Closure
of the folds begins in front of the mid-point and proceeds anteriorly

and posteriorly. A small opening called the *neuropore* remains for some time at the anterior end. Posteriorly, the folds come together over the remains of the blastopore and thus the neural tube is for a

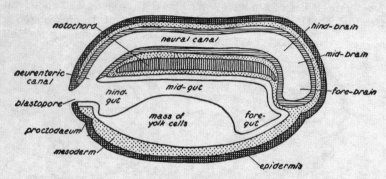

Fig. 27.54. Median V.S. of neurula of frog.

short time continuous with the archenteron via the last vestige of the blastopore. The connexion is called the *neurenteric canal* (*see* Fig. 27.54).

While the neural groove is forming, strips of lateral thickening indicate the appearance of the *neural crests* (*see* Fig. 27.55). The

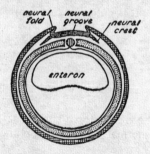

Fig. 27.55. T.S. neurula of frog.

strips will form segmental structures which will give rise to the dorsal ganglia of the sensory nerves.

Meanwhile, two thickened plates of ectoderm on the sides of the anterior region of the neural tube form the *sense plates*. In them will develop the *nasal pits*, the *lenses of the eyes* and the *auditory sacs*. Behind the sense plates are the *gill plates* where the *visceral pouches* will develop.

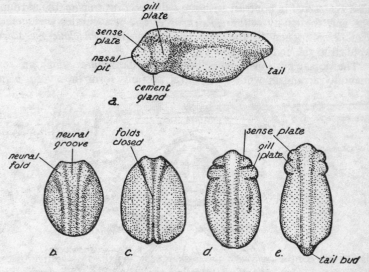

Fig. 27.56. Whole neurula. (*a*) Side view at 3 mm. (*b, c, d* and *e*) Dorsal views of developing neurula.

Further Development of the Notochord and Mesoderm

At first the presumptive notochord cells are not distinct from the mesoderm on either side, but later the cells become rounded up to form a rod and finally each cell assumes a disc-like shape. Eventually, the notochord consists of a single series of these disc-shaped cells with large vacuoles and an external sheath (*see* Fig. 27.57).

A split appears in the mesoderm in the dorso-lateral region and soon extends ventrally. This is the first sign of the coelom, which is described

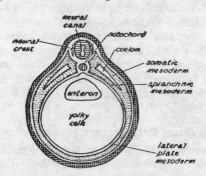

Fig. 27.57. T.S. completed neurula of frog, mid-gut region.

as a *schizocoel* in contrast with the *enterocoel* in *Amphioxus*. Around the gut, the cavity is the *splanchnocoel* and it separates the *somatic mesoderm* applied to the epidermis from the *splanchnic mesoderm* applied to the endoderm (*see* Fig. 27.58).

The dorsal portions of mesoderm form the *somites* which are seg-mentally arranged, while the ventral portions form the *lateral plate*.

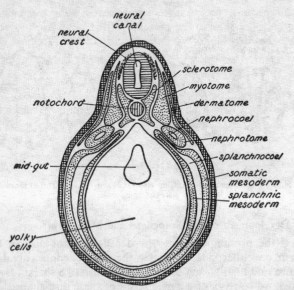

Fig. 27.58. T.S. Young tadpole showing differentiation of the mesoderm.

The somites lie at the sides of the notochord and neural tube and soon each becomes differentiated into three distinct parts, an outer *dermatome* which forms the dermis of the skin, a central *myotome* which forms the segmental voluntary muscles and an inner *sclerotome* from which the vertebral column is developed. Between the somite and the lateral plate is developed the *nephrotome* from which the pronephric kidney and mesonephric kidney are formed. The myotomes and nephrotomes contain small portions of the coelom, *myocoels* and *nephrocoels* respectively (*see* Fig. 27.58).

External Features during Development

Four days after fertilization, the embryo is 4 mm long and shows distinct differentiation into head, trunk and tail. On the head well-marked bulges indicate the future positions of the eyes, each bulge being caused by the outpushing of an *optic vesicle* from the brain. In front of each eye rudiment, a small nasal pit is visible, and behind it, the primordium of the auditory pit. On the ventral surface of the head, two folds of ectoderm arise; they will eventually produce the *oral sucker* or *cement gland*. Between the folds is a slit-like depression, the *stomodaeum*, which will deepen to join the fore-gut and form the mouth and buccal cavity. On the side of the head, a gill plate is prominent though no visceral grooves have yet appeared. The trunk bulges ventrally and laterally due to the presence of the large mass of yolky cells beneath and at the sides of the enteron. In the dorsal region, the neural folds have closed. The tail is a small bud-like structure. Between it

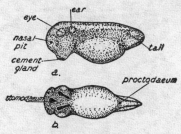

Fig. 27.59. A 4 mm frog embryo.
(*a*) Side. (*b*) Ventral view.

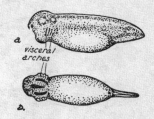

Fig. 27.60. A 5 mm frog embryo.
(*a*) Side. (*b*) Ventral view.

and the trunk, on the ventral surface is the small *proctodaeal invagination* which will form the cloaca and its aperture. Cilia are developed on the epidermis and the embryo frequently wriggles within its membranes (*see* Fig. 27.59).

It must be realized that development is a progressive process, though it is only possible to describe selected stages and to focus attention on major changes. By the time the embryo is 5 mm long, the gill plate shows four faint longitudinal furrows. The fifth and sixth, more posterior furrows, are not visible except in sections. These six furrows separate the developing visceral arches of the embryo, which are, from the front, the *mandibular*, *hyoid* and four *branchial arches* (*see* Fig. 27.60).

At about twelve days old, the embryo is ready to emerge from its membranes. It is 6 mm long, the major part of the increase being due to extension of the length of the tail. The oral sucker is U-shaped, the two lateral grooves having united posteriorly. Delicate branched ectodermal outgrowths on the first three branchial arches form the *external gills* in which capillary circulation can be detected. The stomodaeum is deeper and wider, and the developing eye is indicated by a pale circular patch. Behind it, the auditory pit has closed, indicating that the vesicle has sunk beneath the surface. Movement of the embryo is vigorous and more frequent (*see* Fig. 27.61).

The embryo wriggles free of its membranes to begin its larval life as a tadpole 7 mm long. It swims for a short while and then attaches itself to a water-weed or stone or other object by means of the sticky secretion of glands in the oral sucker. Its tail is now as long as the rest of the body and has wide thin dorsal and ventral extensions acting as *fins*. The mouth is not yet open; the tadpole is still subsisting on yolk in the endoderm cells. Soon, the completion of the eye enables it to see and the frilly external gills reach their maximum development (*see* Fig. 27.62). V-shaped somites are clearly visible in the tail region.

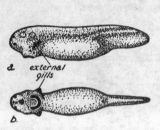

Fig. 27.61. Tadpole at hatching stage, 6 mm. (*a*) Side. (*b*) Ventral view.

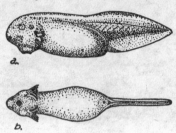

Fig. 27.62. A 7 mm tadpole. (*a*) Side. (*b*) Ventral view.

The oral sucker deteriorates, at first in its posterior region, and the tadpole swims like a fish by lateral movements of the tail with its greatly expanded fins. Ventrally and laterally, a fold of skin develops from the hyoid arch and grows backward over the external gills to form the *operculum*. The stomodaeum perforates through to the fore-gut and the lips develop a fringe of horny outgrowths with which the tadpole rasps algae from stones (*see* Fig. 27.63).

The operculum closes on the right side first, the closure gradually spreading ventrally and finally to the left side until there is only a single opening known as the *opercular spout* on the left (*see* Fig. 27.65). The external gills are slowly absorbed while the four pairs of branchial clefts open and develop internal gills. Thus the water taken in through the mouth passes through the gills into a branchial chamber and out by the opercular spout. The tadpole still feeds on vegetation and has a very long intestine which can be seen as a series of coils through the ventral body wall (*see* Fig. 27.65). From this time until the onset of metamorphosis, there is little change in external features except that the animal grows to a length of about 30 mm.

At this stage, to all intents and purposes, the animal is a fish. It

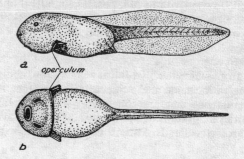

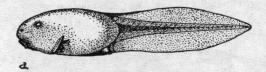

Fig. 27.63. A 9 mm tadpole. (*a*) Side. (*b*) Ventral view.

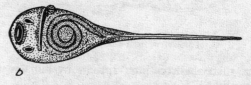

Fig. 27.64. A 10 mm tadpole. (*a*) Side. (*b*) Ventral view.

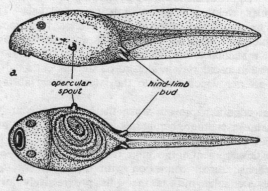

Fig. 27.65. An 11 mm tadpole. (*a*) Side. (*b*) Ventral view.

breathes by gills, swims with its tail, possesses a lateral line system, and cannot live out of water. By the end of the seventh week there are signs that indicate the beginning of metamorphosis.

Metamorphosis

Two buds, from which the hind-limbs will develop, appear at the root of the tail, one on each side of the cloaca. In actual fact, the front-limb buds appear first but they are concealed by the operculum. By the eighth week, the hind-limbs are jointed and the five toes are present. Soon afterwards, the left front-limb emerges through the opercular

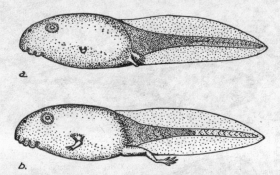

Fig. 27.66. Fully grown tadpole. (*a*) Side view, hind-limb bud appearing. (*b*) Side view, front-limb bud appearing.

spout. Later, the right front-limb appears by bursting through the operculum (*see* Fig. 27.66).

Soon the tadpole comes to the surface frequently and takes a gulp of air. This is a sign that the lungs are developing and the gills atrophying. For a time, it breathes by using both lungs and gills. The gradual transition to pulmonary respiration is necessarily accompanied by vascular changes. When the external gills were present, each received an afferent branchial artery from the short ventral aorta. The blood passed through capillaries in the gills and was collected in efferent branchial arteries which led into the lateral dorsal aortae (*see* Fig. 27.67 (*a*)).

A similar condition prevails when the internal gills are developed. There are, however, more capillaries joining the afferent and efferent vessels (*see* Fig. 27.67 (*b*)).

With the development of the lungs, the afferent and efferent branchial vessels establish direct connexion with one another. At first the connexions are solid but as the gills progressively atrophy they become tubular and more of the blood passes through them, thus

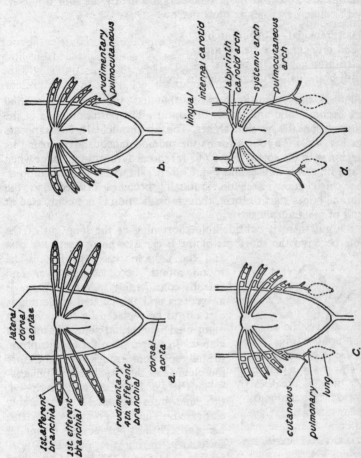

Fig. 27.67. Diagrams to show the arterial arches in frog at successive stages of development. (a) With external gills. (b) With internal gills. (c) With internal gills and developing lungs. (d) With lungs.

a.
lateral
dorsal
aortae
1st afferent branchial
1st efferent branchial
rudimentary 4th afferent branchial
dorsal aorta

b.
rudimentary pulmocutaneous

c.
cutaneous
pulmonary
lung

d.
lingual
internal carotid
labyrinth
carotid arch
systemic arch
pulmocutaneous arch

short-circuiting the gill capillaries. A branch of the fourth efferent branchial artery supplies the lungs. Gradually the gills and gill capillaries are absorbed by phagocytes, and finally the four branchial arches assume new rôles as shown below.

> 1st branchial—Carotid arch
> 2nd branchial—Systemic arch
> 3rd branchial—Disappears
> 4th branchial—Pulmocutaneous arch.

The lateral dorsal aortae between the first and second branchial arches become solid and finally disappear. The posterior parts of the aortae persist as the systemic arches. The third branchial arch disappears altogether while the fourth forms the pulmocutaneous arch, losing its connexion with the aorta. Fig. 27.67 (c) shows a transitional stage when gills and lungs are in use, and Fig. 27.67 (d) shows the final conditions.

The cartilaginous skeleton gradually becomes ossified and the membrane bones start to form, though ossification is not completed at the end of metamorphosis.

In the gut there is considerable shortening as the long gut of the tadpole becomes the short gut of the frog. The horny teeth are cast and the tadpole ceases to feed. The round mouth becomes narrower and extends considerably in width. There is an ecdysis and the ciliated epidermis is cast off, to be replaced by the skin with pigmented patches and numerous mucous glands. In preparation for food-capture, the tongue becomes much larger and more muscular, and the eyes begin to bulge.

Fig. 27.68. Young frog, tail still apparent.

Both sets of limbs are well developed, the hind-limbs becoming considerably elongated. The tail gradually shortens, being absorbed by phagocytes; it supplies sustenance during the period of non-feeding. At about the end of the third month, the little frog leaves the water. It still has a stump of the tail, which slowly disappears, the young frog then being no more than 10 mm long. The physiology of metamorphosis is discussed in Vol. II, Chap. 13.

Adaptation

The dappled pattern of the pigment patches breaks up the shape and acts as camouflage in the grass or in the water. When the frog is swimming, its dark upper surface and light lower surface render it less easily visible from above or below. Its ability to change colour enables it to blend more closely with its background. The adaptations of the limbs and girdles to jumping and swimming have already been described.

In feeding, the tongue and its mechanism are ideally suited to catch insect prey which can move away swiftly. The teeth, with their sharp backward points, render escape of large prey difficult. The protruding eyes give a wide field of view and have an accessory function in assisting swallowing.

The three respiratory surfaces render respiration equally effective on land or in the water, and in this connexion, the suitability of the skin for breathing is to be noted. Hibernation, with considerably reduced metabolism, enables survival when there is no food available. In preparation for it, food is stored in special organs developed for that purpose, as well as in the liver,

There is provision for survival of the race by the comparative certainty of fertilization, by the protection of the embryos in jelly, and by the large number of offspring produced. Careful consideration will reveal many less obvious adaptive features, some of which have been mentioned in the text.

Classification

Phylum: Chordata   Order: Anura
Sub-phylum: Craniata   Family: Ranidae
        [Vertebrata]   Genus: *Rana*
Class: Amphibia   Species: *R. temporaria*

The diagnostic characteristics of the above groupings up to and including Order have been dealt with in the classification tables (*see* Chap. 4).

Members of the family Ranidae are characterized by the absence of cartilaginous discs between the centra of the vertebra. The genus *Rana* contains all the frogs; they are separated from other genera by the largely bony nature of the sternum and by features of the digits. *Rana temporaria* is separated from other species mainly by colour and size differences.

Special Features of Biological Importance

The frog, in company with all the extant amphibians, is a very specialized and modern animal. Extinct members of the class give a truer picture of the animals which made the first vertebrate attempt to colonize the land. The pentadactyl limb was undoubtedly a major feature in the success of this venture and its universal occurrence in all succeeding craniates is adduced as evidence of a common ancestry for amphibians, reptiles, birds and mammals.

The pharynx forms a large and important part of the alimentary canal in fishes; with the loss of gills it has undergone great reduction. These topics are briefly discussed below.

Modern Amphibia

The modern amphibians include the tailed urodeles, the tail-less anurans and the limb-less snake-like Gymnophiona. All the members of the great order Stegocephalia, which flourished in the Carboniferous and Lower Permian periods, became extinct before the Triassic period ended (*see* Fig. 27.69). Urodeles are now represented by the newts and salamanders, anurans by the frogs and toads, and the Gymnophiona by elongated burrowing forms with an exoskeleton of small bony scales. None of these types shows close affinity with the early forms, though some of the Stegocephalia were newt-like in appearance. In general, they were of large size and were covered with

Fig. 27.69. *Cacops*, an extinct stegocephalian amphibian.

bony scales, the head being heavily armoured. The earlier forms had no specialized sacrum, the ilium being quite free of the vertebral column. Some types showed considerable affinity with early reptiles and undoubtedly gave rise to them. Our modern forms must be regarded as very specialized Amphibia, showing, in many respects, great reduction compared with the remote Stegocephalia. In addition, they have developed many new features. The frog, or the newt, must not be regarded as an intermediate stage between fishes and reptiles.

Origin of the Early Amphibia

Evidence collated from the examination of many fossils shows that the earliest amphibians of which we have any record had many features in common with crossopterygian fishes, especially some of the Osteolepidoti. Both had internal as well as external nares and some of the Osteolepidoti had lungs. In both, there was a stout exoskeleton and the head was heavily armoured. We may imagine the transition to land as taking place in the Devonian period when the estuarine shallows and lakes were drying up. Certain fishes may have been able to use their fins as limbs to move from a dried-up pond to one which contained water. It is interesting to speculate that the evolution of tetrapod limbs probably enabled the animal to move to the water and not necessarily to leave it. The land habit may then have become slowly fixed, especially as food would not have been scarce with the presence of vegetation and arthropod species, which were also colonizing the land at that time. However, we must be cautious; so far we have no fossil specimen which shows an intermediate condition between a fin and a pentadactyl limb, though in several extant fishes, the fin skeleton has bones arranged in a linear series rather than a radial one, e.g. *Amia* and *Ceratodus* (*see* Fig. 27.70).

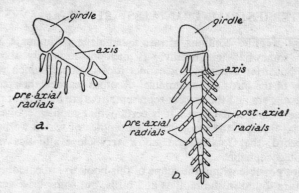

Fig. 27.70. Pectoral fin skeleton of (*a*) *Amia*. (*b*) *Ceratodus*.

Reduction of the Pharynx

Reconsideration of the size, structure and functions of the pharynx in *Amphioxus*, *Scyliorhinus* and *Rana* will show that they present a graded series which probably corresponds to the evolutionary succession which has taken place in this part of the alimentary canal. Originally, the pharynx was primarily a mechanism for food collection, with respiration a secondary function. In the fishes, it becomes essentially a respiratory mechanism while still necessarily being a part of the alimentary canal. In the tadpole larvae of Amphibia, it retains this function though it is considerably reduced in size. As we have seen, in the adult frog, the pharynx has become so small that we recognize it only by means of the structures it contains. These are the glottis and the Eustachian tubes, the one still subserving a respiratory function while the other is concerned with hearing. The evolution of a tympanic membrane was necessarily accompanied by alteration in the form of the spiracular canal, to give a dilated tympanic chamber. The pharynx of the frog might be represented on the dogfish as a narrow strip which includes both spiracles. In the mammals, we shall see some slight increase in the relative size of the pharynx together with the assumption of additional functions. This series of evolutionary transitions in the pharynx gives a good example of a phenomenon of very frequent occurrence, that of putting an "old" organ to new uses.

CHAPTER 28

TERRESTRIAL CRANIATES: REPTILIA; AVES

THE class Reptilia contains a vast assemblage of animals grouped together somewhat unnaturally. It includes not only the extant reptiles, but a large number of extinct forms, among which were the ancestors of the birds and mammals. Reptiles reached their zenith in the Mesozoic era and the present representatives are but a poor remnant of a once-magnificent fauna. It is certain that reptiles evolved from Amphibia; indeed, the most primitive reptiles of which we have any fossil record, the Cotylosauria, show very close affinities with the extinct Stegocephalia.

It is not possible within the scope of this book to indicate the variety of structure found in the reptiles and birds, but some brief account is given of the British sand lizard, *Lacerta agilis*, and the pigeon, *Columba livia*.

LACERTA AGILIS

This lizard is mainly confined to southern England, where it is common in the counties of Dorset, Hampshire, Surrey and Kent. It reaches a

Fig. 28.1. *Lacerta agilis.*

maximum length of about 20 cm and its general background colour is green to brown dorsally and yellow ventrally. On the back and sides are rows of darker spots each with a white centre. It frequents sandy heaths, where it is often to be found basking in the sun or seeking its food, which consists of insects and other small invertebrates. In winter, it hibernates underground or among dead vegetation. The sexes are separate and pairing occurs in May or June. Five to eight soft-shelled eggs are laid in a hole and left to hatch by the heat of the sun. The young lizards emerge in eight to ten weeks and then take two or three years to become sexually mature.

The body form differs from that of the frog in two important respects. In the first place, there is a definite *neck* separating the head and trunk, and secondly, there is a long tail with the cloaca at its root (*see* Fig. 28.1).

Body Wall

Except in the nature of the epidermis, the body wall resembles that of the frog, the skin being, however, firmly attached to the underlying muscle without the intervention of large lymph sacs. Horny scales are

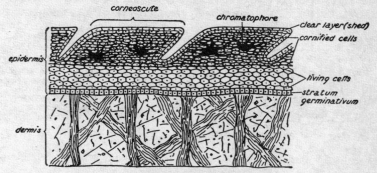

Fig. 28.2. V.S. skin of lizard.

developed from the epidermal layers, forming a complete covering to the body. They are called *corneoscutes* in order to differentiate them from the *osteoscutes* which are formed by dermal ossification in the skull region. Branched chromatophores are plentiful in the epidermis (*see* Fig. 28.2).

The continuous covering of corneoscutes provides an impermeable layer, so that there is practically no loss of water from the external surface, and here we see one of the primary adaptations which made successful the reptilian colonization of the land. There are no glands in the skin.

The coelom shows the same general condition as that of the frog, being represented by the pericardial and perivisceral (splanchnocoelic) cavities.

The Skeleton

The exoskeleton of corneoscutes and the osteoscutes of the head have already been mentioned. The endoskeleton is much more fully ossified than that of the frog. There are a number of additional membrane bones in the skull and an important feature is the *temporal fossa*, a vacuity behind the orbit bounded by the *parietal, supra-temporal, squamosal, post-orbital* and *post-frontal* bones. The number and position of temporal fossae form the basis of classification of the reptiles. In *L. agilis*, the fossa is covered with osteoscutes. There are

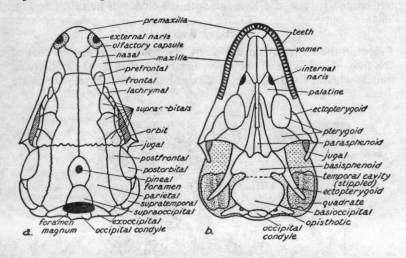

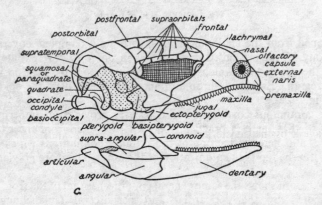

Fig. 28.3. Skull of *Lacerta*. (*a*) Dorsal view. (*b*) Ventral view. (*c*) Side view.

four occipital bones ringing the foramen magnum, a ventral *basioccipital* which bears a single median condyle, two lateral *exoccipitals*, and a dorsal *supraoccipital*. The *quadrate* is ossified and makes a movable joint with the *pterygoid*. Dorsally, the *frontals* and *parietals* are separate ossifications; there is a small *pineal foramen* beneath which is the *pineal eye*. Ventrally, in front of the basioccipital is a large *basisphenoid*, a bone not represented in the frog. The *pterygoids* are long flattened bones forming part of the palatal surface; they articulate with the *quadrate* behind, the *basisphenoid* inwardly and the *palatine* and *transpalatine* in front (*see* Fig. 28.3).

The *olfactory capsule* is covered by the *nasal* bone above and the *vomer* beneath. The more posterior position of the internal nares is noteworthy; the backward displacement of these openings is carried further in the mammals and some reptiles, notably Crocodilia. Apart from the cartilaginous sclerotic, the *optic capsule* is strengthened by a

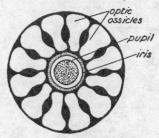

Fig. 28.4. Eyeball of lizard, front view.

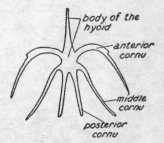

Fig. 28.5. Hyoid body of lizard.

ring of twelve small ossicles in front (*see* Fig. 28.4). Three bones, the *pro-otic*, *epiotic* and *opisthotic*, protect the *auditory capsule*.

The original mandibular arch is represented by the *palatine*, *pterygoid* and *quadrate*, still joined together but now they serve mainly to articulate the upper jaw with the cranium. *Maxillae* and *premaxillae*, bearing pointed homodont teeth, form the upper jaw. There are also small patches of teeth on the palatines. In the lower jaw, Meckel's cartilage is ossified posteriorly to form the *articular* and the rest of the ramus is covered by five membrane bones; the *coronoid*, *supra-angular*, *angular*, *dentary*, and the *splenial* on the inner face of the ramus. The lower teeth are borne only on the dentary. Articulation between the jaws is effected by a joint between articular and quadrate. The type of jaw suspension, with a movable quadrate, is known as *streptostylic*. The hyoid arch is represented by the *columella auris* and the *hyoid skeleton* beneath the tongue (*see* Fig. 28.5). There are anterior, posterior and middle *cornua* which, with the *laryngeal* and *tracheal cartilages*, are the vestiges of the branchial arches.

In the vertebral column, there are eight *cervical*, twenty-two *thoracico-lumbar*, two *sacral* and a large but inconstant number of *caudal* vertebrae. The *atlas* consists of little more than a bony ring with an antero-ventral socket for articulation with the occipital condyle; the dorsal halves of the neural arch do not meet. Turning of the head is accomplished by rotation of the atlas and skull about the *odontoid peg* of the axis; this peg represents the centrum of the atlas (*see* Fig. 28.6). *Ribs* are borne on all the remaining cervical and on the thoracico-lumbar vertebrae, each rib articulating with the centrum. Only the

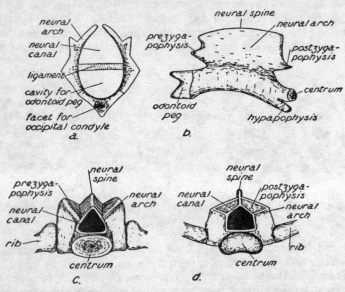

Fig. 28.6. Vertebrae of lizard. (*a*) Atlas, anterior view. (*b*) Axis, side view. (*c*) Thoracic vertebra, anterior view. (*d*) Thoracic vertebra, posterior view.

five anterior thoracic ribs join the *sternum*. Strong transverse processes, possibly ribs, on the sacral vertebrae, form a rigid joint with the *ilia* of the pelvic girdle. The caudal vertebrae gradually diminish in size and differentiation until they become mere splint-like centra. An unusual feature of these tail vertebrae is the central transverse band of unossified tissue. Here *autotomy* occurs when a portion of the tail is shed, but on regeneration, normal vertebrae are not formed.

The ribs which join the sternum consist of vertebral bony and sternal cartilaginous portions. With their intercostal muscles, they play an important part in breathing.

The pectoral girdle and sternum differ from those of the frog mainly in the presence of an *interclavicle*, a *sternal fontanelle*, a *coracoid fora-men*, and, of course, the attachment of five pairs of ribs. In the pelvic

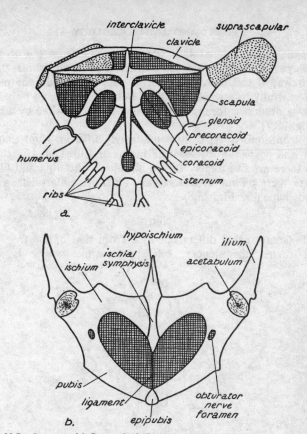

Fig. 28.7. *Lacerta*. (*a*) Pectoral girdle and sternum, ventral view. The left suprascapular straightened. (*b*) Pelvic girdle, ventral view.

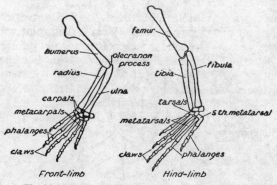

Fig. 28.8. *Lacerta*. Limb skeletons seen from the left.

girdle, the *ischium*, *ilium* and *pubis* all radiate from the *acetabulum*. The ilia pass forward to articulate with the sacral vertebrae, the ischia pass backward and inward to form a symphysis, while the pubes are joined ventrally by a small epipubis. Between ischia and pubes are the two large obturator foramina, separated in the mid-line by a ligament (*see* Fig. 28.7).

The front-limb is typically pentadactyl, differing from that of the frog in the possession of separate radius and ulna, and in the hand, where there are five digits. In the hind-limb, the tibia and fibula are separate, there are but three tarsals and the fifth metatarsal has a peculiar hooked shape (*see* Fig. 28.8).

Nutrition

The alimentary canal differs but little from that of the frog. In the buccal *cavity*, the slender, bifid, protrusible *tongue* is attached

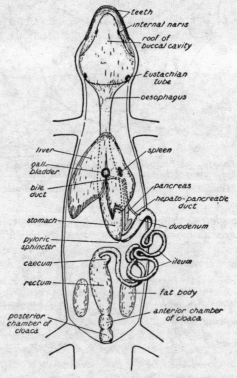

Fig. 28.9. Alimentary canal of lizard, ventral view. Lower jaw removed.

posteriorly. Dorsally, there are lateral *palatal folds*, where the epithelium covers ingrowths of the maxillae. The *stomach* is almost straight and but slightly dilated. At the junction of *ileum* and *rectum* is a small *caecum*. The canal opens into a tubular *cloaca* which has a ventral outgrowth, the *allantoic bladder* (*see* Fig. 28.12).

There are *salivary glands* whose secretion assists in swallowing the dry somewhat prickly insects which form the main part of the diet. The *liver* is large and bilobed, with the *gall-bladder* in a slight groove of the right lobe. From the gall-bladder, the *bile duct* passes through the *pancreas*, forming a common *hepato-pancreatic duct* which enters the duodenum close to the *pyloric sphincter*. The *spleen* is situated in the mesentery near the stomach.

Apart from storage of food in the liver, there is accumulation of material before hibernation in two ovoid *fat bodies* at the sides of the rectum.

Respiration

The sole organs of breathing are the *lungs* which lie laterally, dorsal to the liver. Each lung has a network of internal folds and is highly

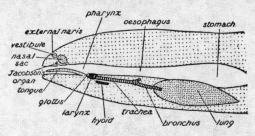

Fig. 28.10. Diagram of median V.S. of lizard showing respiratory organs.

vascular. The *glottis*, behind the root of the tongue, opens into a rounded *laryngeal chamber* which is supported by *cricoid* and *arytenoid* cartilages. From the *larynx*, a long *trachea*, held open by narrow complete cartilaginous rings, leads back and forks into two short *bronchi*, one entering each lung (*see* Fig. 28.10).

Breathing is accomplished by a new mechanism employing the ribs and their *intercostal* muscles. The outer intercostal muscles pull the ribs forward and outward, thus increasing the capacity of the thoracic region and air rushes in to fill the lungs. Exhalation is effected partly by the elasticity of the lungs themselves and partly by pressure exerted on the lungs by the return of the ribs due to the contraction of the inner inter-costal muscles. There is no *diaphragm*.

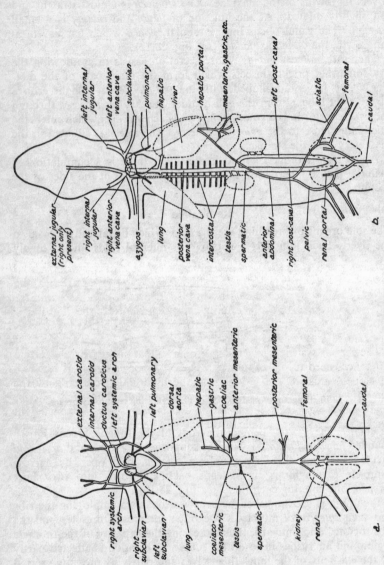

Fig. 28.11. Vascular system of lizard. (a) Arterial system, ventral view. (b) Venous system, ventral view.

(b) labels:

external jugular (right only present), right internal jugular, right anterior vena cava, azygos, lung, posterior vena cava, intercostal, testis, spermatic, anterior abdominal, right post-caval, pelvic, renal portal

left internal jugular, left anterior vena cava, subclavian, pulmonary, hepatic, liver, hepatic portal, mesenteric, gastric, etc., left post-caval, sciatic, femoral, caudal

(a) labels:

external carotid, internal carotid, ductus caroticus, left systemic arch, left pulmonary, dorsal aorta, hepatic, gastric, coeliac, anterior mesenteric, posterior mesenteric, femoral, caudal

right systemic arch, right subclavian, left subclavian, lung, coeliaco-mesenteric, testis, spermatic, kidney, renal

The Blood Vascular System

The heart consists of the *sinus venosus, left* and *right auricles,* and a *single ventricle* partially divided by a *posterior septum* (in the Crocodilia, the septum is complete, giving two ventricles). The *truncus* is split into three to its base, and thus *three aortic arches* lead directly from the ventricle. The most ventral of the three is the single *pulmonary* arch which leads from the right side of the ventricle and thus carries deoxygenated blood. It forks into left and right pulmonary arteries. There are left and right *systemic* arches, both leading from the left side of the ventricle and thus carrying the freshly oxygenated blood from the lungs. The right systemic arch gives off a short *common carotid* forking into right and left carotid arteries, and then proceeds laterally around the gut to join the left systemic arch to form the *dorsal aorta.* The greater part of the blood pumped to the body in the systemic circulation will be freshly oxygenated from the lungs, though there must be some mixing in the ventricle. There is a vestigial solid *ductus caroticus.*

A small *external carotid* artery supplies the floor of the mouth and a larger *internal carotid* supplies the rest of the head. Both *subclavian* arteries arise from the right systemic arch. The first branch of the dorsal aorta is the large *coeliaco-mesenteric* with a distribution similar to that of the frog. There are paired *genital* and *renal* arteries and several small *posterior mesenteric* vessels. The aorta continues into the tail as the *caudal* artery after supplying large *femorals* to the hind-limbs. Along the course of the aorta are paired *intercostal* and *lumbar* arteries (*see* Fig. 28.11).

The venous system is essentially similar to that of the frog but certain differences need to be mentioned. The *renal portal* system is less well developed, most of the blood from the hind-limbs returning by the *anterior abdominal* vein. There is no innominate vein, each *anterior vena cava* being joined by *subclavian* and *jugular* veins. A small right *azygos* vein persists as a relic of the right posterior cardinal; it collects blood from the *intercostal veins* of both sides.

The blood is similar to that of the frog and dogfish, the erythrocytes being ovoid and nucleated. There is a well-developed lymphatic system lacking the large sacs found in the frog.

Locomotion

The approximate equality in length of the front- and hind-limbs precludes jumping, and the angle at which the limbs are set, makes it impossible for the creature to raise the whole body clear of the ground. However, it can run quickly when necessary, by some improvement on the ungainly walking gait of frog and newt. Diagonally opposite limbs work almost together in running, whilst in walking, the sequence is left fore-limb—right hind-limb—right fore-limb—left hind-limb.

Urinogenital Organs

The brown compact kidneys are *metanephric* and situated in the most posterior region of the trunk opposite the hind-limbs. Delicate *ureters* lead backward to open into the *posterior chamber* of the *cloaca*.

The sexes are separate. In the male, the *testes* are paired, ovoid, yellow structures each suspended by a *mesorchium*. The right testis is

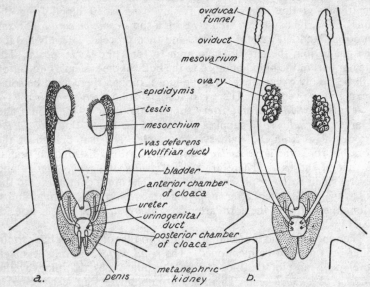

Fig. 28.12. (*a*) Male and (*b*) female urinogenital systems of the lizard.

somewhat anterior to the left, lying under the posterior edge of the liver. *Vasa efferentia* lead the sperm from each testis to a coiled *epididymis* lying along its outer border. The epididymis is composed of the remains of mesonephric tubules and of the coiled Wolffian duct (vas deferens). The ducts pass over the ventral surfaces of the kidneys to open into the posterior chamber near two cylindrical, hollow, protrusible *penes* which effect internal fertilization. There is no trace of the Mullerian duct in the male (*see* Fig. 28.12).

The *ovaries* lie in the same relative positions as the testes, each suspended by a *mesovarium*. Eggs are discharged into the splanchnocoel and wafted by cilia to the wide openings of the *oviduct*, which are dorsally situated opposite the middle of the lungs. The oviducts are thin-walled, wide, twisted tubes in which the albumin and shells are deposited on the eggs. The posterior openings of the oviducts are near those of the ureters.

Excretion

Carbon dioxide is mainly excreted by the lungs, and nitrogenous end-products, chiefly uric acid, by the kidneys. The main function of the kidney is that of osmoregulation. In lizards, water conservation is very important, and both the kidney and rectum resorb most of the water from the excreta and faeces respectively. The nature of the skin precludes any water loss by evaporation.

Reproduction

The sexes are separate and easily distinguished by colour differences, the male having a predominantly greenish background colour while the female is more sombre with a dull brown colour. Mating usually occurs in early June. The protrusible penes of the male penetrate the female cloaca up to the openings of the oviducts before the semen is discharged. Fertilization is internal, an obvious corollary of the development of shelled eggs. The egg-shells are horny and slightly impregnated with calcium carbonate. The eggs are laid in a hole in sand or soil, and hatched by the heat of the sun, and hence the rate of development is dependent upon temperature and may take from six weeks to three months for completion. Young lizards are hatched as replicas of the adult and take about three years to reach sexual maturity. The embryology is essentially similar to that of birds and will not be described here.

Most lizards are *oviparous* but some few are *ovoviviparous*, the female retaining the eggs until hatching occurs. There are also a few instances of true *viviparity* when the young are attached to the oviduct by a placenta-like structure.

The Nervous System

The brain shows little advance on that of the frog, the main development being in the *cerebral hemispheres* where apart from some increase in size, there is an appreciable amount of superficial grey matter. The *olfactory lobes* are long and slender and lie at the end of *olfactory stalks* or *peduncles*. Well-developed *optic lobes* are correlated with the importance of the sense of sight and the small size of the *cerebellum* indicates the somewhat sluggish habit and ease of equilibrium (*see* Fig. 28.13).

The spinal cord is slightly swollen in the regions of the limbs and it tapers rapidly in the tail.

There are twelve cranial nerves, owing to the fact that two further segments have been incorporated into the skull. The eleventh nerve is the *spinal accessory* and the twelfth, the *hypoglossal*. Cranial nerve XII supplies the muscles of the tongue, and XI supplies certain muscles in the neck, and also in the laryngeal region.

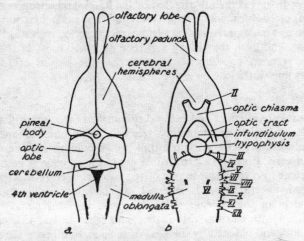

Fig. 28.13. (*a*) Dorsal and (*b*) ventral views of lizard brain.

Sense Organs

The eyes have, in general, the usual vertebrate structure with additional support and protection in the ring of twelve small ossicles surrounding the iris. As in the mammals, the focal length is altered by changing the convexity of the lens. The retina contains mainly cones with few rods, so that there is good daylight vision and probably good colour perception, but little twilight vision. On the inner side of the retina near the optic nerve, there is a small cushion-shaped structure known as the *pecten*, which is better developed in birds. It is pigmented, highly vascular and is said to be concerned either with accommodation or with oxygenation. In addition to movable upper and lower eyelids, there is the *nictitating membrane* in the front corner of the eye. It is really a double fold of the *conjunctiva* and is flicked laterally across the front of the eyeball to wash it. The *Harderian gland* on the anterior side of the eyeball lubricates the nictitating membrane, and the *lachrymal* gland on the posterior side lubricates the exposed surface.

The pineal eye is well developed, consisting of a vesicle with a sensory lower portion and a lens-like upper structure. It could not, however, be of any value since it is covered by an osteoscute, and little, if any, light could penetrate to it.

The internal ear has the same general pattern as that of the frog. The *lagena* is somewhat larger and is sometimes called the *cochlea*; the *ductus endolymphaticus* ends blindly as a small sac in the roof of the cranium. In the middle ear, the *Eustachian tube* is longer and in addition

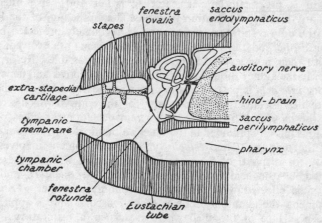

Fig. 28.14. Ear structure of lizard. T.S.

to the *fenestra ovalis* there is a more ventral *fenestra rotunda*. This acts as a safety valve to damp down vibrations in the *perilymph*; when the fenestra ovalis bulges inward, the pressure transmitted through the perilymph causes the fenestra rotunda to bulge outwards. The columella is differentiated into an inner *stapedial* bone and an outer *extrastapedial* cartilage. Apart from the ear there is no trace of the acousticolateralis system (*see* Fig. 28.14).

The nasal cavities are larger than those of the frog and the area of sensory epithelium is increased by the convolutions caused by the *turbinal* bone. An interesting feature in connexion with smell is the presence of *Jacobson's organs*. These are two small pockets in the roof of the mouth beneath the nasal sacs. They serve to smell food in the mouth through the medium of the forked tongue whose tips are placed into the pockets (*see* Vol. II, Chap. 16).

Endocrine Glands

The *adrenal* bodies are collected into two slender elongated masses situated between the gonads and the posterior vena cava. The *thyroid* is an ovoid structure ventral to the larynx and just anterior to the heart

Dorsal to the origin of the two carotids and projecting forward between them, is the crescentic *thymus* gland. The other glands are as previously described.

Adaptation to Environment

Some of the features found in the lizard are concerned with adaptation to terrestrial conditions and are related to water conservation. The skin is practically impermeable to water and hence there is little if any loss by evaporation from it. The epithelium of the lungs is now the only respiratory surface and is adequately protected by its position in the body and new breathing movements are evolved. The ribs with their muscles make these movements possible. Resorption of water in the kidney tubules and rectum is very effective, and hence the excretory *uric acid* is pasty and the faeces are nearly dry. The shelled egg provides an impermeable covering for the embryo which secretes within the *amnion* a private pond wherein development takes place. The fluid is initially provided in the watery albumin deposited round the egg in the oviduct. This *cleidoic* type of development involves the necessity for disposal of the embryo's nitrogenous wastes; these are deposited as uric acid in a special bladder, the *allantois*, and the excretion is effected with the utmost economy of water. Later in development, the allantois becomes highly vascular and is applied to the inner surface of the shell where it acts as a respiratory organ effecting exchange of gases through the shell pores. The type of egg is accompanied by internal fertilization, effected by the protrusible penes.

The possibility of survival is enhanced by hibernation during the cold season, and also by autotomy of the tail when the animal is attacked. This device may serve to detract a predator's attention from the escaping lizard, since the detached portion of the tail wriggles for some time. The long narrow body, low on the ground, has an excellent shape for moving into holes or underneath vegetation; the colouring of the dorsal surface provides effective camouflage.

Movement of the head independently of the body is possible, and the animal can thus follow the movements of its prey. Careful consideration of the various systems will reveal many less obvious adaptations.

Classification

Phylum: Chordata	Sub-order: Lacertilia
Sub-phylum: Craniata [Vertebrata]	Family: Lacertidae
Class: Reptilia	Genus: *Lacerta*
Order: Squamata	Species: *Lacerta agilis*

Reptiles included in the order Squamata are distinguished by the possession of corneoscutes, of protrusible penes and by the movable quadrate-skull joint. There has been secondary loss of one or both temporal vacuities. The order is divided into the lizards, and the snakes (Ophidia). The latter lack both temporal vacuities and there are no limbs or limb girdles except in pythons. Also the eyelids are immovable and the tympanic membrane is lacking. A notable feature of snakes is the extensibility of the mouth, both jaws being freely movable and the rami of the lower jaw can be widely separated. The family Lacertidae is characterized by the pleurodont conical teeth and by the presence of dermal supra-orbital and supra-temporal bones. The corneoscutes are small and the head is covered with osteoscutes. Members of the genus *Lacerta* have large corneoscutes on the head and ventral surface and ring-like rows dorsally, especially on the tail. The claws are pointed and grooved on the ventral surface. Species are distinguished by size and colour differences.

Modern Reptiles

Classification of reptiles is a vexed question; it will suffice to say here that three main sub-classes are recognized on the basis of the number of lateral temporal fossae. In the Anapsida, there are no fossae; the Synapsida have one, and the Diapsida, two. The sub-class Anapsida contains two orders, one of which, the Cotylosauria contains the most primitive reptilian forms, undoubtedly closely related to the stegocephalian amphibians. The other order, Chelonia, is represented now by the tortoises and turtles. They are very distinctive animals, having a horny beak-like mouth with no teeth, and pronounced dorsal and ventral bony shields. In the turtles, which are marine, the pentadactyl limb is modified to form a paddle, while in the tortoises it is a crawling limb. Both groups lay their eggs on land and some species are remarkable for their longevity.

The synapsid reptiles consisted of nine orders, all of which are extinct, but they are of interest since the ancestors of mammals are found in the order Theriodontia.

Most extant reptiles belong to the Diapsida which comprises sixteen orders including the Thecodontia, which are closely related to the ancestors of birds. Other notable diapsid reptiles are the extinct dinosaurs, the largest terrestrial animals evolved, and the pterodactyls, flying reptiles which were not on the avian line of descent. The tuatara of New Zealand, *Sphenodon*, is the sole living representative of the order Rhyncocephalia. It possesses many primitive features including a well-developed and functional pineal eye. *Sphenodon* is on the verge of extinction, but there is news that the line may be preserved by careful laboratory incubation of the eggs. The order Squamata includes the most flourishing groups, the lizards and snakes, both having wide distribution and great variety. Lizards are mainly terrestrial but there are some freshwater species. The chameleons, well known for their rapid colour changes, are adapted for an arboreal existence. Many lizards burrow; one, *Draco volans*, has a plane-like device for gliding; some habitually run bipedally.

Snakes are characterized by the long slender body, mainly due to great elongation of the region between head and tail. Their mode of locomotion is unusual, progression being achieved by horizontal undulations of the body, brought about by concentration of special muscles attached to the ribs. Grip on the substratum is obtained by special transverse ventral scales.

The largest living reptiles, the crocodiles and alligators, belong to the order Crocodilia. They are powerful animals, able to move rapidly through the water by using the strong tail and webbed hind-feet. On land, they are slow and clumsy. They lay large numbers of eggs buried in sand or soil on the shore.

Special Features of Biological Importance

Features of special importance in the reptiles are the temporal fossae, the corollaries of the evolution of the neck, the cleidoic type of development, and the factors which led to success on land. The class also affords an excellent example of adaptive radiation.

Temporal Fossae

In the early amphibians, the Stegocephalia, membrane bones deposited on the skull in the postero-lateral regions, enclose a cavity above and outside the auditory capsule. This is the *temporal cavity*, which is continuous with the

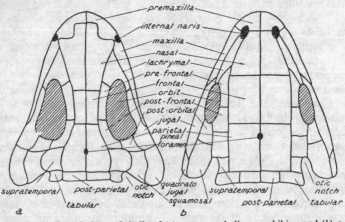

Fig. 28.15. Dorsal views of skulls of (*a*) a stegocephalian amphibian and (*b*) a cotylosaurian reptile.

orbit in front and opens on the posterior face of the skull by the *post-temporal fossa*. In the cavity are housed the muscles which move the lower jaw. The

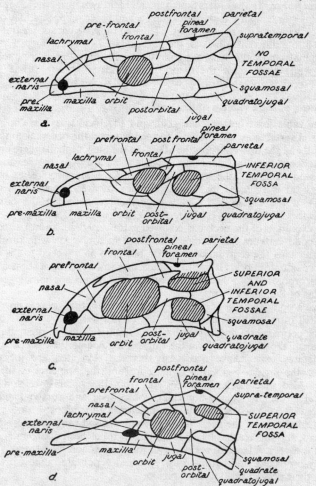

Fig. 28.16. Side views of reptilian skulls. (*a*) Cotylosaurian—anapsid. (*b*) Theromorph—synapsid. (*c*) Rhynchocephalian—diapsid. (*d*) Ichthyosaurian—parapsid.

primitive reptiles, Cotylosauria, show a similar complete roof to the temporal cavity, the anapsid condition, but in the later reptiles, the birds, and the mammals, openings appear between the dermal bones. These openings are called *temporal fossae*; there may be one or two (*see* Fig. 28.16).

The Synapsida, including the mammal-like reptiles, possess only the *inferior temporal fossa*, while the Diapsida have both *superior* and *inferior temporal fossae*. In the orders Squamata and Ichthyosauria, the lower margin of the inferior temporal fossa is incomplete and hence it appears that only the superior temporal fossa is present. Thus some systematists separate these orders into a different sub-class, the Parapsida (*see* Fig. 28.16).

Mammals show the synapsid condition, with only the inferior temporal fossa, while birds show the diapsid condition, with both fossae present though secondarily modified.

Corollaries of the Evolution of the Neck

A movable joint between the skull and the trunk first develops in the terrestrial vertebrates. The joint is formed between the occipital condyles of the skull and the first vertebra, the atlas. In the Stegocephalia there are three occipital condyles; in Anura and Urodela there are two; reptiles and birds possess only one and the mammals two. In the reptiles, greater mobility of the head is achieved by the interpolation of a neck between head and trunk and the degree of mobility is further enhanced in the birds and mammals.

The evolution of the neck has involved extra vertebrae, known as cervical. The second vertebra has become specialized in connexion with turning the head and thus the centrum of the atlas has become attached to the axis to form the odontoid peg. It must be noted that since two extra segments have been incorporated into the skull, the atlas of the frog is not homologous with the atlas of the higher forms.

As an accompaniment of the presence of the neck, the larynx is now widely separated from the lungs and with it the trachea was evolved. To keep this air-tube permanently open, there has been multiplication of the remnants of the branchial cartilages to form the rings strengthening the trachea.

Structures which have necessarily become elongated are the carotid arteries, the jugular veins, the spinal cord and the branches of the vagus nerve. Also the muscles which extend from the visceral skeleton to the pectoral girdle, the coraco-branchial, coraco-hyal and coraco-mandibular, are fitted into the new scheme by having elongated tendons.

The advantage of the neck has been the increased range of movement of the head, and this reaches its height in birds. It has been disadvantageous in that it is a very vulnerable region, with the trachea and blood-vessels inadequately protected, and carnivorous terrestrial vertebrates almost invariably attack their prey in this "throat" region.

Cleidoic Development

The reptiles and birds have evolved a type of embryonic development which takes place within a closed box; such development is known as *cleidoic*. It was an essential step in the reptilian success in a terrestrial environment. The embryo has to be provided with food and water; it has to deal with the problems of respiration and excretion and it is enclosed in a protective covering which prevents water loss and also water absorption. It entails internal fertilization high up the oviduct before the various membranes are deposited on the egg, and in this connexion, various devices for internal fertilization have been evolved. The embryo provides its own aquatic environment by containing fluid around itself in the *amnion*, the fluid being derived from the watery albumin. This also provides a protective cushion which buffers the embryo against jarring, and reduces the effect of temperature changes. The problem of excretion has been solved, by utilizing the almost insoluble uric acid as a vehicle for nitrogenous waste; the uric acid is deposited in the *allantois*, a bladder-like outgrowth of the hind-gut. Although the shell is impermeable to fluids, it is permeable to gases and hence respiratory exchange is effected by placing a vascular surface, the allantois, close against the shell. Within its membranes, the embryo develops until it is a miniature replica of the adult and then it emerges. This process involves some method of breaking the shell, usually accomplished by an egg-tooth on the front of the head.

In birds, cleidoic development is carried to perfection, with incubation at a constant temperature. Furthermore, there is considerable after-care of the young. Three genera of mammals, *Ornithorhyncus* (duckbill platypus), *Zaglossus* and *Echidna* (spiny ant-eaters), lay large yolky eggs and incubate them at body temperature. The remainder of the mammals are placental and the egg is extremely small, but some of the features of cleidoic development are retained.

Success of the Reptiles on Land

The amphibians have never achieved emancipation from the water even though the major part of the adult life is spent on land. They still require the aquatic environment for external fertilization, for development, and for respiration. The reptiles, however, achieved stupendous success on land and attained heights of magnificence only surpassed by the mammals. Their success as terrestrial animals is attributable to a number of factors which are briefly summarized here.

1. Internal fertilization obviates the need for external water.
2. Cleidoic development renders the embryo independent of aquatic surroundings.
3. With no aquatic larval stage there is never need for gill breathing.
4. The skin is impermeable to water.
5. The lungs form an adequate respiratory surface and are well protected from drying. Breathing movements ensure that exchange of gases is rapid enough.
6. Uricotelic excretion minimizes water loss.
7. There is effective resorption of water in the kidneys and rectum.
8. Limbs suitable for running and supporting the body in the less dense medium have been evolved.
9. Loss of the lateral line system and improvement of more necessary sense organs has been achieved.
10. Increased development of the cerebral cortex makes more complex behaviour possible.

11. Large-scale colonization of the land by plants provided constant food for herbivores, and they, in their turn, provided food for carnivores.

Adaptive Radiation

Entering upon the terrestrial scene, the reptiles had little competition from other animals. In such conditions, a dominant group soon extends into a variety of specializations. By such extension, the descendants of one original type are able to exploit all the possibilities of the environment. The process is known as *adaptive radiation*, and while examples of it may be found in any of the larger groups of animals, it is most obvious in insects, reptiles, birds and mammals.

In their Mesozoic heyday, the reptiles branched out into a great variety of forms. They ranged from giants to dwarfs; some of the dinosaurs were the largest terrestrial animals that have existed; *Brachiosaurus* weighed about 50 tonne, and *Diplodocus* was about 26 m long. At the other end of the scale were animals the size of small lizards. There were large carnivores and larger herbivores, swift runners and slow crawlers, burrowers and climbers. The Ichthyopterygia, of fish-like form, became secondarily aquatic and inhabited the seas; the turtles and freshwater tortoises have become aquatic, without such striking adaptation. Flying reptiles, the Pterodactyla, flourished during the Jurassic and Cretaceous periods. The wings were membranous and stretched from a very elongated fourth finger to the hind limb. This brief survey by no means exhausts the variety of lines along which the reptiles evolved, but it serves to illustrate the meaning of adaptive radiation.

COLUMBA LIVIA

All the domestic pigeons are varieties of the wild rock dove, *Columba livia*. By long-continued selection, the various fancy breeds have been produced. *C. livia* is restricted to a few coastal regions of the British Isles, but is common over most of Europe and Asia. It frequents rocky and almost inaccessible places such as coastal cliffs, caves and old ruins. The nest is made of dried seaweed or grass and twigs, and is to be found in a crevice or on a ledge among rocks. Two white eggs are laid in spring or summer, the period of incubation being fourteen to eighteen days. The food of the adult consists of seeds, young green shoots, and occasionally insects and snails are taken. The young are fed by the mother on "pigeon's milk," a white secretion regurgitated from the mother's crop. Other members of the family Columbidae are the stock dove (*C. denas*), the wood pigeon (*C. palumbus*), and the turtle dove (*Streptopelia turtur*). All are serious pests of grain crops.

The type supplied by dealers for class study is usually the domestic pigeon and that particular type will be described here.

There is considerable variety in the colouring, the general background being blue-grey. In the neck region a beautiful blue-green sheen is present. The shape of the body is best compared with a boat, the trunk being plump and tapering forward to the neck and head, but ending rather bluntly posteriorly. Covering the body, and overlapping from front to rear, are the *feathers*, which lie quite flat and afford a smooth contour.

The head has a rounded cranium prolonged in front into a pointed *beak* formed of the upper and lower jaws covered by horny skin. The length of the beak gives a wide gape to the mouth. At the root of the beak the external *nares* are partly concealed by a swollen patch of skin called the *cere*. The eyes, at the sides of the head, have upper and lower *eyelids* and a *nictitating membrane*. Behind the eyes and covered with feathers is the auditory opening which leads by a short tube, the *external auditory meatus*, to the tympanic membrane.

Seen in a plucked bird, the *neck* is almost a cylindrical column, widening slightly towards the trunk. The sharp ventral *keel* is a strongly characteristic feature of the trunk. Posteriorly, the *cloaca* is an opening with transverse lips on the ventral surface. Behind the cloaca is the short stumpy *tail* bearing dorsally a slight papilla on which is the opening of the *uropygial* or oil gland. The bird uses the oil to preen the feathers, during which process they are rendered waterproof.

The front-limbs are modified to form *wings*, and to increase their surface area when extended, they bear the large, broad, *quill* feathers. At rest, the wings are folded against the sides of the body. The bipedal gait is accompanied by considerable alteration in the position of the hind-limbs, so that they are vertical and are not pushed out to the sides as in the frog and lizard. Cover-ing the feet are *corneoscutes* ex-actly homologous with those of the reptiles, thus indicating the relationship of the two groups.

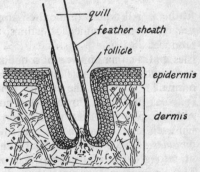

Fig. 28.17. V.S. skin of pigeon.

Body Wall

The body wall has the usual general structure characteristic of vertebrates, namely, an outer skin, consisting of epidermis and dermis, the body wall muscle and the peritoneum. Two fea-tures are distinctive of birds, the possession of feathers and the presence of one solitary gland, the uropygial.

Feathers

Feathers are developed by the epidermis and are arranged in definite tracts called *pterylae*, the non-feathered tracts being *apterylae*. The

spread of the feathers is, however, sufficient to cover the apterylae so
that the whole body is covered. Each feather begins as a papilla of the
epidermis with a dermal core. Later in development the feather is
sunk in a pit known as a *follicle*. The actual material of the feather is
keratin and the whole structure is made up of dead horny cells which
originated in the stratum germinativum. Thus, the feather grows only
from the papilla at its base (*see* Fig. 28.18).

Quill feathers are restricted to the wings and tail; *contour* feathers
cover the body with a smooth layer and fill the gaps between the quill
feathers; *filoplumes* are tiny hair-like structures beneath the contour

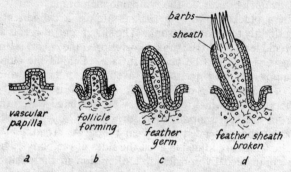

Fig. 28.18. Stages in development of a feather.

feathers. All types are moulted annually, the quill feathers being lost
and replaced in symmetrical pairs so that balance in flight is not affected
(*see* Fig. 28.19).

A quill feather consists of a hollow proximal *quill* and a solid distal
rachis which bears the flattened *vane*. The proximal end is pierced by
a small hole called the *inferior umbilicus*; in life the growing point
(papilla) protrudes through this hole. At the junction of quill and
rachis is a second tiny perforation known as the *superior umbilicus*.
On each side of the rachis is a row of *barbs* which themselves bear
barbules. On any particular barb, the distal barbules bear *hooks* which
fit into *grooves* of the proximal barbules on the next upper barb.
This arrangement ensures that all the barbs on a single vane are
fastened together to form a single surface. The *aftershaft* is a tuft of
separated barbs near the superior umbilicus.

Each wing bears twenty-three quill feathers, called *remiges*, on its
post-axial border. There are twelve *secondaries* attached to the fore-
arm, and eleven *primaries* attached to the *carpo-metacarpus* and digits.
The quill feathers of the tail arise in a semicircle from the uropygium;
they are known as *rectrices*.

The contour feathers have a structure similar to that of the quills except that the barbs are not so strongly joined and can be separated easily. In the tiny filoplumes, the vane is rudimentary and consists of but a few separated barbs at the apex.

Feathers are extremely important in restricting heat loss from the

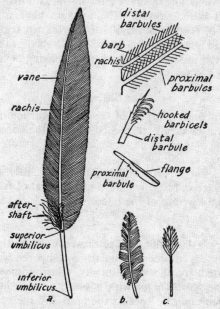

Fig. 28.19. Types of feather. (*a*) Quill. (*b*) Contour. (*c*) Filoplume.

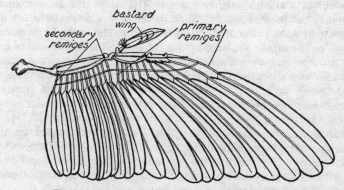

Fig. 28.20. Arrangement of remiges on wing of pigeon.

body surface. The filoplumes form a loose network in which air is retained, while the contour feathers form a layer which reduces escape of this air, and is reasonably wind-proof. It is important to realize that birds are *homoiothermous* with body temperatures averaging 40°C to 43°C. With their relatively large surface area in relation to volume, they would lose heat rapidly by radiation if no conserving mechanism had been evolved. The feathers have muscles at their bases; control of feather position is important in regulation of heat loss, in flight, in preening and in sexual display. Like the hairs of mammals, feathers are also organs of touch, having nerve fibres wound around the bases of the papillae.

The Skeleton

The exoskeleton consists largely of the stratum corneum covering most of the body; it is especially thickened to form the corneoscutes of the legs, the covering of the beak and the claws. Feathers are also epidermal skeletal structures.

The endoskeleton is very well ossified, very little cartilage being present. Characteristic features are the great deal of fusion in various parts and the light weight of the bones.

The Skull

In the skull of the adult, no sutures can be distinguished. The cranium is rounded, considerably enlarged compared with lower forms and characterized by the huge orbits. Surrounding the foramen magnum are the *basioccipital* with a single condyle, the *exoccipitals* and single *supraoccipital*. Roofing the brain are the *parietals*, *frontals* and *prefrontals*, and the floor of the cranium is formed mainly by the *basisphenoid*. Beneath and fused to it are paired *basitemporals* in front of which is a slender median *rostral*. The basitemporals and rostral represent the parasphenoid. Much of the lateral wall of the cranium is formed by the *squamosal*, which is fused to the frontal and parietal above, to the supra- and exoccipitals behind, to the *alisphenoid* in front and to the *auditory capsule* beneath. The cranial cavity continues forward for a short distance above the eyes but not between them, the *orbits* being separated by an *interorbital septum* formed from the *rostral, mesethmoid, presphenoid* and *orbitosphenoid*. In its central region, the orbit is merely a thin plate of cartilage (*see* Fig. 28.21).

The *olfactory capsules* are very small and are supported on their inner and outer aspects by the forked *nasal* bones; *vomers* are vestigial in the pigeon. Representing the *optic capsule* is the sclerotic and on the outer face of the eyeball is a ring of *optic ossicles* similar to those of the lizard (*see* Fig. 28.22). Several bones enclose the *auditory capsule* but they lose their separate identity and fuse to form the *periotic* which is firmly fixed to the side of the cranium.

Each half of the upper jaw consists of an elongated *premaxilla* leading back to a slender bar composed of *maxilla, jugal,* and the

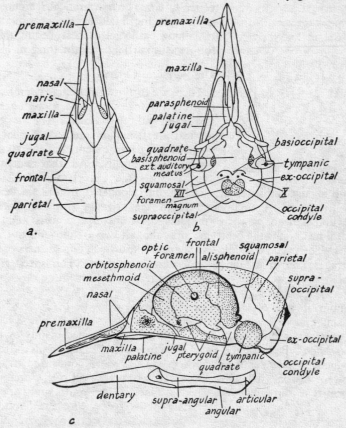

Fig. 28.21. Skull of pigeon. (*a*) Dorsal view. (*b*) Ventral view. (*c*) Lateral view.

quadrato-jugal which is fused to the *quadrate*. Representing the original mandibular arch are the *quadrate, pterygoid* and *palatine*. The quadrate is a tri-radiate bone with its lower arm articulating with the lower jaw, its inner arm forming a movable joint with the *periotic* and its forward arm joining the *pterygoid*. The pterygoids pass forward to join the *basisphenoids* and the *palatines*, which are two slender bones supporting the roof of the buccal cavity. In the lower jaw, the posterior *articular* is an ossified portion of Meckel's cartilage, the remainder of which is invested by four membrane bones, the *angular*, *supra-angular*, *dentary* and *splenial*. These bear the same relation to each other as in the lizard. The hyoid arch is represented by the *columella* and the *body of the hyoid*. The first branchial arch contributes to the hyoid apparatus while the remaining branchial arches are multiplied to form the cartilages of the trachea.

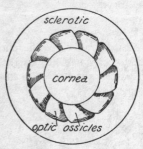

Fig. 28.22. Optic ossicles of eye of pigeon from the front.

The Vertebral Column

There are forty-two vertebrae comprising fourteen *cervical*, five *thoracic*, six *lumbar*, two *sacral* and fifteen *caudal*. The first two cervical are the *atlas* and *axis* similar to those of the lizard except that the atlas is not parted dorsally, All the remaining cervical vertebrae bear two-headed *ribs*, small in the third to the twelfth but elongated in the thirteenth and fourteenth, though none reach the *sternum* (*see* Fig. 28.23). The dorsal head of each rib joins the transverse process and the ventral head joins the centrum; only the last two are movable at these joints. The peculiar saddle-like shape of the articulating surfaces of the centra is known as the *heterocoelous* condition. This gives great

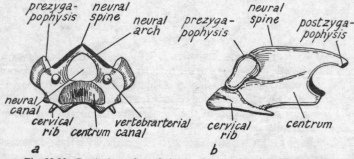

Fig. 28.23. Cervical vertebra of pigeon. (*a*) Anterior view. (*b*) Side view.

flexibility to the neck together with adequate cushioning by the synovial capsules between the centra. The first four thoracic vertebrae are fused together and the fifth is fused to the lumbar region; all have double-headed ribs which join the sternum. Each rib has a dorsal vertebral and a ventral sternal portion, both being ossified. Backward *uncinate processes* from the first four thoracic ribs overlap the vertebral portions from front to rear.

The last thoracic, the six lumbar, the two sacral and the first five caudal are all fused to form a single structure which joins the ilia along its whole length, thus constituting a very elongated *sacrum*. Behind the sacrum are six free caudal vertebrae and a dorsally-projecting *pygostyle* derived from four vertebrae in the embryo.

The Girdles and Limbs

The pectoral girdle is very distinctive in the birds and very different from that of other craniates. The long blade-like *scapula* lies on the ribs close to the vertebral column and extends backward almost to the

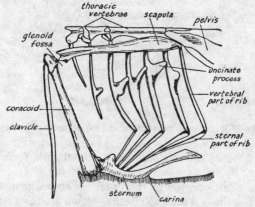

Fig. 28.24. Pectoral girdle and ribs of pigeon, side view.

pelvis. At its front end, it articulates with the stout *coracoid* which slopes downward and backward. Attached by ligaments to both scapula and coracoid is the slender *clavicle* which, with its partner, forms a vertical U-shaped bone nearly reaching the sternum. The *glenoid fossa* for articulation of the humerus is formed by the scapula and clavicle equally (*see* Fig. 28.24).

The *sternum* is a large thin plate curved gently with the convex side outwards. It lies beneath the thorax and most of the abdomen. Ventrally, it is prolonged into a deep keel or *carina* on which the flight muscles are inserted. There are two sets, the *pectoralis minor* which lifts the wing and the *pectoralis major* which pulls the wing down. The five pairs of ribs articulate with the sternum and at the anterior end are two elongated grooves into which the coracoids fit.

The front-limb shows extreme modification in connexion with flight but nevertheless it still shows the main pentadactyl features. When the wing is folded, the short stout *humerus* is almost horizontal and parallel to the vertebral column, with the distal end articulating with the *radius* and *ulna*. The former is slender and straight while the latter is stout and slightly curved. There are two carpals, the *radiale* and *ulnare*, which articulate with the peculiar *carpo-metacarpus*. This is composed of two bones fused at their ends but separated between. The pre-axial is thicker and represents two fused metacarpals. The distal carpals have fused with the metacarpals to form the final structure. There are three digits, the first or thumb bearing one pointed phalanx, the second two phalanges, while the third finger bears only

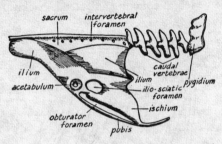

Fig. 28.25. Sacrum, pelvic girdle and tail of pigeon, side view.

one. A small tuft of feathers, inserted on the thumb, form the *bastard wing* (*see* Fig. 28.20).

The pelvic girdle consists of the usual six bones, paired *ilia*, *ischia* and *pubes*. The ilium is attached to the sacrum along its whole length; the rigidity and length of both structures is correlated with the necessity for maintaining the horizontal posture on the posterior limbs. Except for the *ilio-sciatic foramen*, through which the sciatic nerve and artery pass, the ischium is fused to the ilium both above and in front. The pubis is a slender rod joining the ilium below the *acetabulum* and then extending backward beyond the ischium with which it is fused. Between the ischium and pubis is the slit-like obturator foramen. The absence of a pubic symphysis is correlated with the laying of large hard-shelled eggs (*see* Fig. 28.25).

In the hind-limb also there is considerable modification especially in the tarsal and metatarsal regions. The *femur* is short but strong and in the normal standing position the front of its joint with the tibia is open; this weak point is protected by a sesamoid bone, the *patella* (such a bone is developed in a tendon). The *tibia* is long and the proximal *tarsals* are merged with it, while on its outer side, the slender *fibula* is fused to it at several points. There is one small free *metatarsal* but the remainder are fused with the distal tarsals to form a single bone, the *tarso-metatarsus*. The free metatarsal bears a backwardly-directed digit with two phalanges, but the second, third and fourth digits point forward and bear respectively three, four and five phalanges. In each case, the distal phalanx bears a horny claw on its upper surface. With the *hallux* opposed to the other toes, the bird is able to clutch thin branches with a grip which depends on the degree of

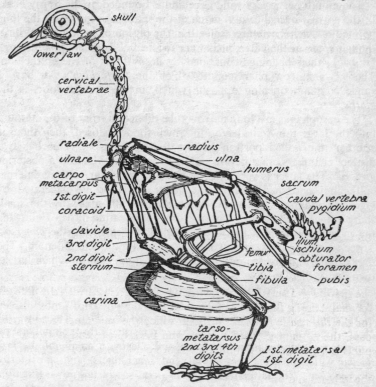

Fig. 28.26. Skeleton of pigeon, side view. The bones of one side only are drawn.

bending in the "knee" and "ankle" joints. The tendons of the toes pass up the back of the tarso-metatarsus, and hence bending of either joint will tighten the grip. Thus the bird sleeps in a squatting position with no danger of falling from the branch.

Almost every bone in a bird's skeleton is highly characteristic. In addition, there are two special features; most of the long bones are hollow, bearing *air-sacs* in communication with the lungs, and the *epiphyses* of most bones are completely ossified.

Nutrition

The alimentary canal consists of the *mouth, buccal cavity, pharynx, oesophagus, stomach, duodenum, ileum, rectum, anus* and *cloaca* (*see* Fig. 28.27).

The mouth has a very wide gape and is bounded by the horny beak. In the narrow buccal cavity, much of the space is occupied by the long pointed *tongue.* There are no teeth in the pigeon or in any extant bird, though some of the early birds were toothed The *internal nares* open far back, their openings concealed by fleshy folds of the epithelium. There is a narrow pharynx into which the *Eustachian tubes* have a single common opening opposite which, in the ventral floor, is the *glottis.*

The oesophagus is a long narrow tube dilated in front of the sternum into the large thin-walled *crop* in which food is stored, then there is another thin-walled portion leading to the stomach. This has two distinct chambers, an anterior glandular *proventriculus* and a posterior *gizzard.* The latter is very thick-walled and muscular, with its internal epithelium hardened and horny. Here the food is macerated by vigorous and powerful contractions of the walls aided by the small sharp stones swallowed by this and other seed-eating birds. Following the *pyloric sphincter* is the looped duodenum enclosing the *pancreas.* Three *pancreatic ducts* and two *bile ducts* lead into the duodenum. The *liver* is large and divided into right and left lobes each of which has its own duct; there is *no gall-bladder* in the pigeon.

The ileum is coiled and very long, reaching about 75 cm in the pigeon. It leads into a short rectum about 4 to 4·5 cm long. At the anterior end of the rectum are two small *caeca*, and posteriorly it leads into the cloaca by the *anal sphincter.* The cloaca consists of three chambers: an anterior *coprodaeum* into which the anus leads, a small middle *urodaeum* which receives the genital and renal ducts, and a posterior *proctodaeum.* The latter has a blind dorsal sac of unknown function, known as the *bursa Fabricii.* It tends to atrophy in adult birds (*see* Fig. 28·27).

The food consists almost entirely of seeds and especially cereal grains, though small insects and snails are occasionally eaten. Each seed is picked up individually by the beak. Glands of the buccal cavity produce a secretion which assists swallowing. In the crop, the food is stored and softened by the glandular secretion of its epithelium. The crop may contain more than five hundred cereal grains. In the proventriculus, the gastric juice is produced, and mastication takes place in the gizzard, the gastric juice being mixed with the food there. Digestion is completed in the duodenum and ileum by the pancreatic juice and the succus entericus. Absorption takes place along the whole length of the small intestine. In the rectum, there is very thorough dehydration of the faeces which are passed out almost dry.

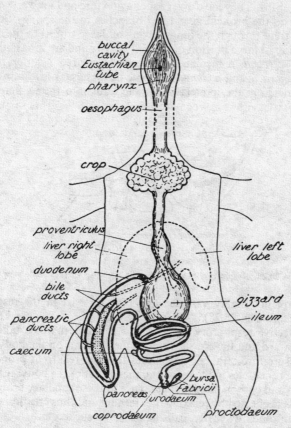

Fig. 28.27. Alimentary canal of pigeon.

Respiration

Respiratory exchange is very efficient in birds. Air enters the body at the external nares and passes through the olfactory sacs into the buccal cavity. The glottis opens behind the root of the tongue and leads into the larynx which is supported by the *cricoid* and *arytenoid* cartilages. The larynx is not the organ of sound in birds. It leads into the long trachea which is supported by complete bony rings. At the base of the neck is a slight dilation, the *syrinx*, where the two bronchi arise. From the point of bifurcation, the *membrana semilunaris* projects into the base of the trachea; by vibrations of this membrane, the bird's song is produced. The bronchi pass into the *lungs* which are pressed dorsally against the ribs. They have a very spongy texture and are very vascular. Not only do the bronchi give a few branches to the spongy tissue but they pass right through the lungs, giving off large trunks to the *air-sacs*. These occupy a large portion of the body cavity and are nine in number; a pair of *cervical*, a median *interclavicular*, paired *anterior thoracic*, *posterior thoracic* and *abdominal*. Some of these sacs lead into cavities in the bones, e.g. the interclavicular sac leads into the humerus. The

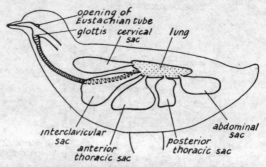

Fig. 28.28. Respiratory organs of pigeon showing air sacs. Side view.

air-sacs are not highly vascular and play no part in the respiratory exchange (*see* Fig. 28.28).

The effective respiratory movement is exhalation which takes place by the upward and inward pressure of the sternum on the body cavity. This pressure forces the air in the sacs through recurrent bronchi into capillary bronchioles in the lungs and thence out of the body. Exchange of oxygen and carbon dioxide takes place in these capillary bronchioles. Inhalation is effected by relaxing the sternum and thus creating negative pressure in the body cavity, causing air to be sucked in.

The structure of the respiratory organs and the methods of inhalation and exhalation ensure that all the air is changed and that there is no reservoir of residual air. This is very important in such metabolically active animals and is partly responsible for their high temperature and their capability for sustained activity. The frequency of breathing at rest is about twenty-five per minute; the maximum in flight is 450 per minute.

The Blood Vascular System

The *heart* consists of four chambers, two *auricles* and two *ventricles*, with no sinus venosus. For the size of the body, it is unusually large and beats about 190 times a minute; both facts are correlated with the high metabolic rate. Deoxygenated blood is brought to the right auricle by the *three venae cavae*. This blood is pumped into the ventricle which it leaves by the *pulmonary arch*. From this, two *pulmonary arteries* take the blood to the lungs whence it returns to the left auricle by four large *pulmonary veins*. From the left ventricle,

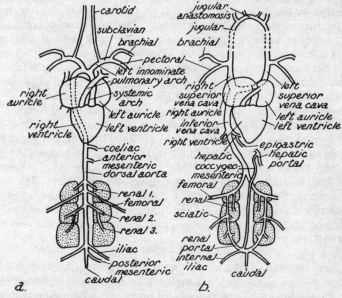

Fig. 28.29. Blood vascular system of pigeon. (*a*) Arterial. (*b*) Venous.

the blood is pumped into the *right systemic arch* to be distributed to the body (*see* Fig. 28.29).

The systemic arch bends over to the right and gives off paired *innominate* arteries, each forking into a *carotid* and a large *subclavian*. High up the neck, the former supplies the *internal* and *external carotids*, while the latter divides into a *brachial* to the wing and a large *pectoral* artery to the flight muscles. The systemic arch curves around the right bronchus, and behind the oesophagus it becomes the *dorsal aorta*. Just below the heart, the *coeliac* leaves the aorta and soon divides into *gastric* and *hepatic* branches. The small intestine is supplied by an *anterior mesenteric* artery. There are three pairs of *renal* arteries, the first pair arising from the aorta, and the second and third pairs from the *sciatic* artery. Between the first and second pairs, the *femoral* arteries pass out to the legs. These arteries to the legs arise well forward, related to the anterior position of the hind-limbs. Behind the kidneys, the paired *iliacs* and the *posterior mesenteric* artery arise at the same level. A small *caudal* artery passes into the tail (*see* Fig. 28.29).

Each *superior vena cava* receives *jugular*, *brachial* and *pectoral* veins. In the anterior part of the neck, the jugulars are joined by an *anastomosis*, a precaution to ensure that if the flexible neck is twisted enough to constrict the jugular on one side, the blood can return to the heart on the other side. Blood from the tail returns in the *caudal* vein which divides into three branches. The two outer branches run ventral to the kidneys, receiving *iliac*, *sciatic* and *femoral* veins and giving a few small branches to the kidneys. These two branches unite above the kidneys to form the *inferior vena cava* which proceeds forward to the right auricle receiving *epigastric* and *hepatic* veins. The middle branch from the caudal proceeds forward in the mesentery as the *coccygeo-mesenteric* vein and joins the *hepatic portal*. Probably the epigastric represents the front portion of the anterior abdominal and the coccygeo-mesenteric the hind portion. Blood from the gut goes to the liver in the hepatic portal, as in all vertebrates. It is noteworthy that the renal portal system is practically eliminated and most of the blood from the posterior regions returns direct to the heart. The large pectoral muscles have necessitated a special and ample supply of blood.

The blood resembles that of the lizard in that the erythrocytes are ovoid and nucleated, but the temperature is maintained at the very high level of 42°C.

Locomotion

The bird can walk, run and also jump, but the main method of locomotion is *flight*. Two distinct methods of flight may be considered; they are gliding and flapping flight. In connexion with either, several accessory factors must be borne in mind; the body is very light, one pound or less; there is a large wing-span; the feathers form a smooth large surface and with the powerful pectoral muscles, the rate of wing-beat can reach eight per second.

If a current of air moves against a wing surface with its front edge tilted upward, then the flow of air over the upper surface will encounter less resistance and have greater velocity. Thus a negative pressure must be created above the wing. Air passing over the lower surface will have greater resistance to overcome and will be retarded and hence exerts a positive pressure upward against the wing. These two forces tend to lift the wing, the suction above and the upward pressure beneath it. There will also be the force exerted by the air tending to sweep the wing backward horizontally. The total force due to the wind on the wing may thus be resolved into "lift" and "drag" components.

The same reasoning applies if the wing is moved against the air instead of the air against the wing. Therefore a bird could glide horizontally in still air for an indefinite period, if its wings were tilted in such a manner as to ensure that the lift and drag forces are equal to the bird's weight and act through its centre of gravity. This is never so, for a bird with rigid wings will always fall in still air at an angle determined by the set of the wings. In moving air, however, both the lift and drag forces are increased and a bird can glide horizontally if the air is rising at the same velocity as the bird is losing height. If the resultant of the bird's own velocity is forward and downward and the air acts with equal velocity upward and backward, then the bird will be stationary. Soaring is achieved by utilizing rising currents of air and is

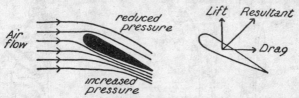

Fig. 28.30. Diagrams showing the lifting power of the air on a wing.

only possible on a large scale for birds with great wing-span, e.g. eagles and vultures.

It is not possible to give a simple analysis of flapping or cruising flight. An important feature of the wing structure, which is a considerable factor in flight, is the difference between the leading and trailing edges. The leading edge is firm, due to the presence of the wing skeleton, while the trailing edge at the ends of the feather vanes is much more yielding and flexible. Considering the simplest case, that of full flight in a horizontal plane, there is a downstroke which gives lift and upstroke which gives forward propulsion. The first part of the downstroke is vertical and gives powerful lift. Then the wing moves forward with the front edge tilted upward; this would develop lift as described above. The upstroke is upward and backward and this gives the forward thrust; it is especially due to the backward movement of the primary remiges. The whole process is considerably complicated and there is great variation in different species.

Steering is effected by the tail and by unequal strokes of the wings on the two sides. The tail and the wings also act as braking devices.

Urinogenital Organs

The *metanephric kidneys* are divided into three lobes in linear series fitting closely into depressions in the pelvis. *Ureters* pass from the middle lobes over the ventral surface to enter the *urodaeum*.

The sexes are separate. In the male, the *testes* are large ovoid structures each attached by a *mesorchium* to the outer border of the kidney. The *vas deferens* (Wolffian duct) leads back alongside the ureter and is dilated posteriorly into a small *vesicula seminalis* which opens into the urodaeum. There are no traces of the Mullerian ducts in the male (*see* Fig. 28.31 (*a*)).

In the female, only the left *ovary* is present, the right becoming atrophied in early life. It is full of *follicles* of various sizes and lies in

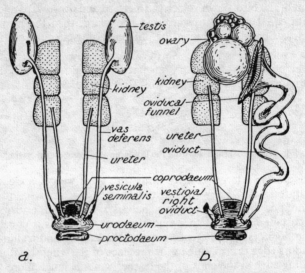

Fig. 28.31. Urinogenital system of pigeon. (*a*) Male. (*b*) Female.

the mid-line just anterior to the kidneys. The right *oviduct* is vestigial but the left is very large, consisting of a wide-mouthed, thin-walled funnel and a convoluted duct leading into the urodaeum on the outer side of the urinary opening. Loss of the right oviduct is correlated with the size of the eggs; if two were passed out simultaneously they would completely block the passage through the pelvic girdle (*see* Fig. 28.31 (*b*)).

Excretion

Carbon dioxide is excreted very efficiently by the lungs, The nitrogenous end-product is *uric acid* which passes down the ureters in saturated solution. In the urodaeum, water is resorbed and the uric acid is precipitated as a pasty white mass. With the faeces this forms a soft half-black, half-white mass which is expelled from the body.

Reproduction

Fertilization is internal. The male "treads" on the female's back gripping the skin and feathers of her neck with his beak. The tail of the female is lifted and the two cloacae are pressed closely together. There is no special copulatory organ in the male; the seminal fluid passes from his cloaca into the female's. Fertilization takes place in the upper thin-walled region of the oviduct.

Two eggs are ovulated in close succession almost directly into the oviducal funnel which is then in a distended condition and applied closely to the ovary. Each egg is the "yolk" only, consisting almost entirely of food reserves with a minute *germinal disc* from which the embryo will develop. After fertilization, successive membranes are deposited on the egg in the thicker part of the oviduct. First there is a thick zone of *albumin*, then two thin but tough *shell membranes*, and finally the *calcareous shell*. The two eggs are laid in the nest and incubated at body temperature, 42°C; this necessitates constant "sitting" by one or other of the parents. The eggs hatch in fourteen to eighteen days, the chick cutting the shell with a special "*egg-tooth*" developed on the end of the beak. At first the chicks are helpless, with closed eyes and bodies covered with fine yellow "down" consisting of filoplumes. They are fed by the mother on "*pigeon's milk*," a mucous secretion of the crop epithelium which includes discharged cells. In three weeks, the contour and flight feathers are developed and the nestlings are said to be fledged. For a few days the mother teaches them to fly, a very interesting spectacle, and soon they leave the nest to fend for themselves.

The Nervous System

The brain is short and broad and remarkable for the size of the *cerebral hemispheres* by comparison with lower forms. Their large size is due mainly to the huge *corpora striata*, the roof being thin with little grey matter. The *olfactory lobes* are extremely small. The cerebral hemispheres extend backward to the *cerebellum*, thus causing the *optic lobes* to be pushed to the sides. The cerebellum shows differentiation into a large central *vermis*, with transverse folding, and two small lateral *flocculi*. Between the posterior ends of the cerebral hemispheres is a well-developed *pineal* body, not, however, functional as an eye. Ventrally, the *optic chiasma* and *optic tracts* are prominent; they almost conceal the small *pituitary* body. There is a marked *cranial flexure* in the *medulla oblongata* (*see* Fig. 28.32).

There is pronounced correlation between the structure of the brain and the habits of the bird. The large optic lobes and tracts indicate the great reliance on the sense of sight, while the small olfactory lobes bear testimony to the comparative unimportance of the sense of smell. The large size of the cerebellum is a measure of the great importance of accurate balance and muscular co-ordination, while the swollen corpora striata are correlated with the high degree to which patterns of instinctive behaviour have been developed.

There are twelve pairs of cranial nerves as in the lizard. A special feature of the spinal nerves is the large *brachial plexus* formed of a

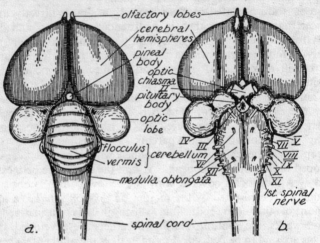

Fig. 28.32. Brain of pigeon. (*a*) Dorsal view. (*b*) Ventral view.

number of segmental nerves from the lower cervical and anterior thoracic regions.

Sense Organs

The *olfactory organs* are small but have their internal sensitive surface increased by scroll-like *turbinals* which are delicate ingrowths of the ecto-ethmoid bones. The olfactory sense does not seem to be of great importance in birds.

The *eyes* are very well developed; in visual acuity and range of accommodation they represent the best type ever evolved. The eyeball is elongated from front to back, and arising from the region of the blind spot is a soft vascular pleated ingrowth of rectangular shape. This *pecten*, found in some reptilian groups also, is of doubtful function. Some have ascribed to it a rôle in focusing, others think that it may be concerned with supplying oxygen to the vitreous chamber and the back of the eye (*see* Fig. 28.33). The lens is very soft and pliable and is adjusted for various distances by changes in its convexity accomplished by combined action of the circular muscle of the iris and the ciliary muscle. Curvature of the cornea and conjunctiva can be adjusted also, by a special muscle (Crampton's) lying within the junction of cornea and sclerotic. In the retina, there is a great preponderance of cones, giving very clear daylight vision both of form and colour. The yellow spot is well developed and there is a large field of vision, about 340°.

The *ear* is very much like that of the lizard, the main features of difference being a tubular *external auditory meatus,* and an elongated

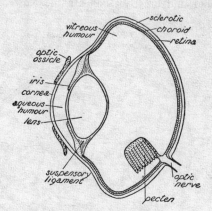

Fig. 28.33. V.S. eye of a bird.

lagena (*cochlea*) which shows the first signs of spiral coiling. Transmission of vibrations across the tympanic cavity still takes place via the *columella.* Hearing is much more acute in birds than in reptiles.

Endocrine Glands

The glands are similar to those of the lizard with minor changes. Paired *thyroids* are situated at the base of the neck and in young birds there is an elongated *thymus* on each side of the neck. It is gradually reduced in size in the adult but its secretion is important with regard to synthesis of lymphocytes in embryos and immunity reactions in adults. The adrenals are paired yellow bodies anterior to the kidneys. Other endocrine glands are similar to those normally found in craniates.

Development

Illustrative of cleidoic development, it is usual to study the embryology of the chick, *Gallus domesticus,* because the eggs are large, easily procured at any time and easily incubated artificially.

The Sperm and the Egg

The sperm is very elongated, 50μm, with a pointed acrosome, a short cylindrical head piece, a longer middle piece and a long tail which tapers to a point (*see* Fig. 28.34).

The egg is spherical, about 40 mm in diameter and of the extreme telolecithal type with the cytoplasmic area as a small disc lying on a great mass of yolk. In the centre is a sphere of white yolk which extends upward as a pillar and fans out beneath the *blastodisc* to form the

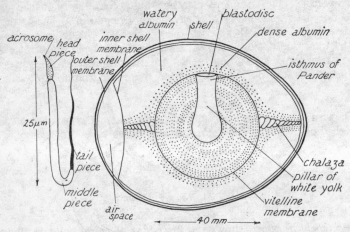

Fig. 28.34. Sperm and egg of *Gallus domesticus*.

isthmus of Pander. Surrounding this central sphere are concentric layers of *yellow* and *white yolk*. The egg is released from the ovary as a primary oocyte, the two maturation divisions taking place after fertilization. The secondary membranes are deposited round the egg in the oviduct. First there is a layer of *dense albumin*. The rotation of the egg as it passes down the oviduct causes the albumin to be twisted on each side of the egg into the two *chalazae* which appear to suspend the ovum in the *softer albumin* deposited later. Two tough *shell membranes* cover the albumin; between them, at the blunter end of the egg is an air space. Finally the oviduct secretes the *calcareous shell* substance which soon hardens. The shell may be pigmented with substances derived from the bile; in many birds there is a constant colour and pattern.

The egg takes twelve to sixteen hours to pass down the oviduct and some degree of development has taken place before it is laid.

Fertilization and its Effects

The sperm swim to the upper part of the oviduct where they may remain viable for several weeks. Often half-a-dozen sperm penetrate the vitelline membrane and enter the blastodisc. There they remain inactive until the maturation divisions are completed. When one sperm nucleus makes contact with the female nucleus, the other sperm migrate to the outer border of the disc and eventually perish.

The entry of the sperm stimulates the maturation divisions of the egg and two polar bodies, which disappear quickly, are extruded. Fusion of the nuclei stimulates cleavage, but point of entry of the sperm does not determine plane of cleavage or orientation. The latter is predetermined and invariable. If the egg is held with the air space to the left and the blastodisc dorsal then the future head develops away from the observer. As usual, the act of fertilization brings the paternal chromosomes into the egg and restores the diploid number.

Cleavage

The cleavage furrows are confined to the blastodisc and do not pass into the yolk. This is known as the *meroblastic* type of cleavage. The

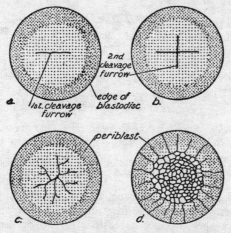

Fig. 28.35. Stages in cleavage of fertilized egg.

first cleavage furrow starts in the centre of the blastodisc and extends outwards on both sides towards the yolk. Its direction with regard to future orientation of the embryo is not constant. The second furrow starts at two points, one on either side of the centre of the first furrow; it grows inwards and outwards at right angles to the first. Cleavage now becomes irregular, furrows being formed in radial and tangential planes with respect to the centre of the blastodisc. On the outer edge, the furrows extend towards the yolk through an undivided zone of cytoplasm known as the *periblast* (*see* Fig. 28.35). Horizontal cleavage furrows begin in the centre and spread radially outwards with the result that the blastodisc becomes converted into a complete layer of cells known as the *blastoderm*. Towards its margins, further cell formation proceeds, utilizing the periblast, until there is a slightly raised lip of cells growing over the yolk.

Beneath the blastoderm, a fluid cavity appears, at first in the central zone, to separate the cell layer from the underlying yolk. This cavity has been called the *subgerminal cavity*; it is possibly homologous with the blastocoel of lower forms.

The Blastula and Presumptive Areas

The subgerminal cavity enlarges towards the edges of the blastoderm and a few yolky cells of uncertain origin appear on its floor. If the

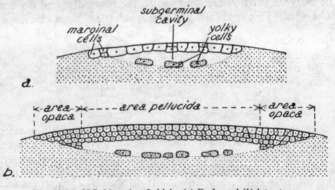

Fig. 28.36. V.S. blastula of chick. (*a*) Early and (*b*) late stage.

cavity corresponds to the blastocoel then these cells will represent the yolky megameres found in the frog and amphioxus. Several further horizontal cleavages produce a blastoderm two or three cells thick. At the margins, the lower cells lie on the yolk which they proceed to digest. Later they form the extra-embryonic endoderm which slowly creeps over the surface of the yolk but takes no part in the formation of the embryo. When a blastoderm in this condition is removed from the yolk and mounted in water on a slide, the central area which overlies the sub-germinal cavity appears transparent. But all round the clear area is an opaque zone due to the granules of yolk which stick to the lower layer of yolky endoderm cells. The central area is the *area pellucida*; it is surrounded by the *area opaca* (*see* Figs. 28.36 and 28.37).

No further mention will be made of cleavage though it must be remembered that cell division continues. The stage of development now achieved is considered to be a completed *blastula*, since gastrulation now commences, and the *presumptive areas* on it are indicated in Fig. 28.37. All these areas lie within the area pellucida; any cells outside this, will form extra-embryonic tissue, not the embryo proper. The *presumptive endoderm* occupies a small posterior disc and in front of it lies the *lateral plate mesoderm*.

Proceeding anteriorly, there are two lateral bands of *somitic mesoderm*, then a strip which will produce the *future notochord*, then a large area of *presumptive neural plate*. These areas from endoderm to neural plate form a broad ellipse towards the future posterior end. The presumptive ectoderm surrounds all the other tissues in a circular plate, except at the posterior end, and outside the embryonic ectoderm is a ring of *extra-embryonic ectoderm* lying over extra-embryonic endoderm formed from the yolky cells.

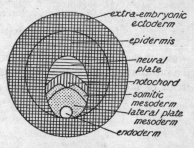

Fig. 28.37. Presumptive areas of blastula. Dorsal view.

Gastrulation

Gastrulation proceeds in three phases though there is some overlapping between them. First, the presumptive endoderm moves to its definitive position, then the presumptive mesoderm, and lastly, the principal axial structures, notochord and neural plate are formed. During all these processes there is cell movement and also cell division.

The presumptive endoderm cells, present as a disc at the posterior region of the area pellucida, sink down and spread out to form a complete floor of endoderm which joins up with the yolky endoderm cells in the extra-embryonic region. The layer of endoderm lies over the yolk and above it is the subgerminal cavity. This precocious formation of endoderm is correlated with the necessity for digesting the yolk and thus providing, as quickly as possible, the materials required for the embryo's growth. At this stage, twelve to twenty hours after fertilization, the egg is laid (*see* Fig. 28.38).

The Primitive Streak. As soon as the presumptive endoderm starts sinking in from the surface, the future lateral plate mesoderm moves backward and inward to take its place, with the result that mesoderm cells become piled up to form a median ridge in this posterior region. The same type of movement gradually spreads forward to the somitic mesoderm, the notochord, and the neural plate cells, so that the lateral

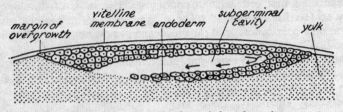

Fig. 28.38. V.S. embryo showing endoderm formation.

wings of each region move backward and inward towards the mid-line, the presumptive epidermis following behind. As a result of this general trend of movement, the *primitive streak*, which began posteriorly, is

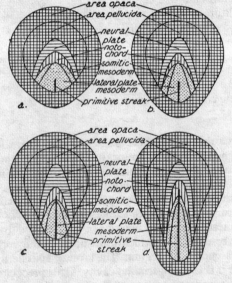

Fig. 28.39. Stages in the formation of the primitive streak.

extended forward to the posterior point of the presumptive notochord cells. Another result is that the area pellucida becomes pear-shaped (*see* Fig. 28.39).

At the anterior end of the primitive streak, a slight depression, the *primitive pit*, is formed, and in front of it is a raised portion called the *primitive knot*, where notochord cells begin to pile up ready for in-tucking. It is considered that the primitive knot represents the dorsal lip of the blastopore, and the primitive streak the fused lateral lips. In the middle of the streak, a narrow gutter, the *primitive groove*, appears (*see* Fig. 28.40).

Notochord and Mesoderm. Notochord cells roll over the edge of the primitive knot, sink down through the pit, and turn forward to form a strip of tissue in the mid-line beneath the surface. As first lateral plate mesoderm, and then somitic mesoderm, sink in through the

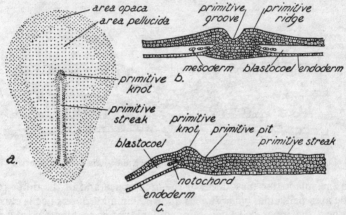

Fig. 28.40. Primitive streak. (*a*) Dorsal view. (*b*) T.S. (*c*) Median L.S.

primitive groove, the knot creeps backward, so that the streak gradually diminishes in length. With the intucking of mesoderm and notochord, the wings of the neural plate gradually close inward and meet on the dorsal surface. It is important to note that differentiation proceeds from anterior to posterior, so that while considerable advance is being made by the head end, at the tail end, the last of the notochord and meso-derm are not tucked in till the end of the second day after laying.

The lateral plate mesoderm streams into the groove, sinks down and fans out to form a third layer in the subgerminal cavity. The movement begins anteriorly and spreads posteriorly. In front, this mesoderm is proliferated forward as two horns with a wide gap between them. The *somitic mesoderm* follows the lateral plate mesoderm but remains as two bands close to the mid-line, separated by the notochord. Soon, the lateral plate splits into an upper *somatic* sheet applied to the ectoderm, (*somatopleur*), and a lower *splanchnic* sheet applied to the endoderm (*splanchnopleur*), separated by the *extra-embryonic coelom*. These sheets spread out and they eventually reach the margin of the colonized area. Gradually the area opaca spreads over the surface of the yolk, carrying with it the three germ layers, ectoderm, mesoderm and endoderm (*see* Figs. 28.41 and 28.42).

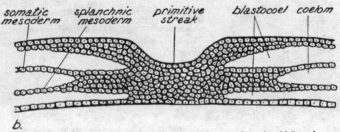

Fig. 28.41. Stages in movement of presumptive mesoderm in chick embryo.

In the splanchnic mesoderm of the area opaca and of the outer part of the area pellucida, *blood islands* appear. Small groups of cells cluster together, the inner cells becoming differentiated as blood corpuscles with haemoglobin, while the outer cells enclose them. These structures

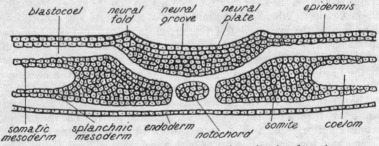

Fig. 28.42. T.S. Chick embryo showing somite and coelom formation.

are the blood islands and the area in which they are developed is the *area vasculosa*. Soon the little islands run together to form small networks of blood vessels, and an extensive circulation is developed on the yolk outside the embryo. By a similar method, two large *vitelline* veins are eventually formed, leading from the general vitelline circulation

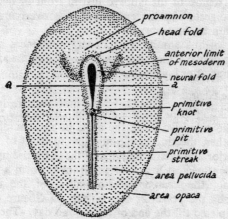

Fig. 28.43. Chick embryo, dorsal view (18 hours).

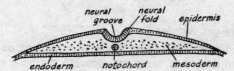

Fig. 28.44. T.S. Chick embryo at *a–a* in Fig. 28.43.

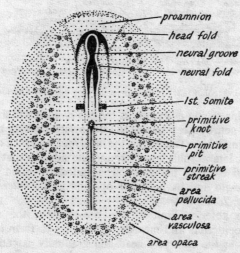

Fig. 28.45. Chick neurula (20 hours). Dorsal view.

into the ventral region of the embryo just in front of the first somite. Now the food digested by the endoderm cells overlying the yolk is carried in solution to the embryo.

Segmentation of the somitic mesoderm commences at about the nineteenth hour and the most anterior pair of *somites* are formed by the twentieth hour after laying (*see* Fig. 28.45).

Formation of the Neural Tube

With the infolding of mesoderm and notochord, and the backward movement of the primitive knot, the arms of the neural plate move towards each other, meeting in the mid-line in front of the primitive knot. The anterior and lateral margins of the plate rise up to form the *neural folds* which meet at first near the front to form a tube with an anterior opening, the *neuropore*. Formation of the tube extends gradually towards the posterior region but the closure of the whole tube is not completed till the end of the second day. The front end of the *neural tube* becomes dilated and by differential growth the three *primary cerebral vesicles, fore-brain, mid-brain* and *hind-brain* are later formed.

Head Fold, Fore-gut, Amnion

In front, the horns of mesoderm come together beyond the embryo, leaving a region devoid of mesoderm beneath the head region and in

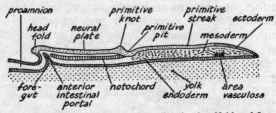

Fig. 28.46. Median L.S. Chick embryo showing headfold and fore-gut.

front of it. This region is known as the *pro-amnion*. A short distance in front of the neuropore, it begins to fold inward beneath the embryo's head, thus lifting it up. This fold is the *head fold*, and by a continuation of the process, lateral folds spread round the sides so that the anterior region is lifted clear of the yolk. The endoderm lifted by the fold forms the *fore-gut* and its posterior opening is the *anterior intestinal portal* (*see* Fig. 28.46).

Beyond the anterior limit of the pro-amnion, the *somatopleur*, consisting of epidermis and mesoderm, rises up to form a fold which grows back over the embryo's head and gradually extends round the sides. The fold consists of two membranes, an outer *chorion*, and an inner *amnion* separated by extra-embryonic coelom. Later, except for a small mid-ventral region, the amnion will completely enclose the embryo in the *amniotic cavity*, within which the "aquatic" phase of development takes place (*see* Fig. 28.63).

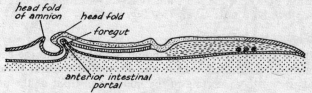

Fig. 28.47. Median L.S. Chick embryo. Amnion formation.

Summary of the First Day

The first day is regarded as beginning when the egg is laid—
1. Endoderm in its definitive position.
2. Primitive streak, groove, knot and pit formed.
3. Area pellucida becomes pear-shaped.
4. Notochord and mesoderm formation begin.
5. Neural folds close anteriorly.
6. Coelom, somatopleur and splanchnopleur formed.
7. Six pairs of mesodermal somites present by the twenty-fourth hour.
8. Area vasculosa and vitelline veins developed.
9. Head fold, fore-gut and amnion begun (*see* Fig. 28.48).

Development of all the tissues and organs proceeds simultaneously and thus without breaking sequence it is not possible to give a description of each part for each day. The following is a summary of the second and third days, but a fuller description of development of some important structures is given later.

Summary of the Second Day

1. Neural folds closed along the whole length. Formation of the three *cerebral vesicles, optic cups, optic stalks* and *lenses* of the eyes. *Auditory vesicles* formed and *cerebral hemispheres* begin to grow forward. *Cranial flexure* develops and torsion to the left follows (*see* Fig. 28.49 (*a*)).

2. Head fold cuts under the embryo to the hind-brain and tail fold begins. Lateral folds develop, more deeply in anterior region (*see* Fig. 28.61).

3. Great development in vascular system. Heart formed and differentiated into *sinus venosus, auricle. ventricle* and *bulbus cordis*. Four pairs of *aortic arches* between the visceral pouches meet above the pharynx to form the *lateral dorsal aortae*. These meet behind the heart

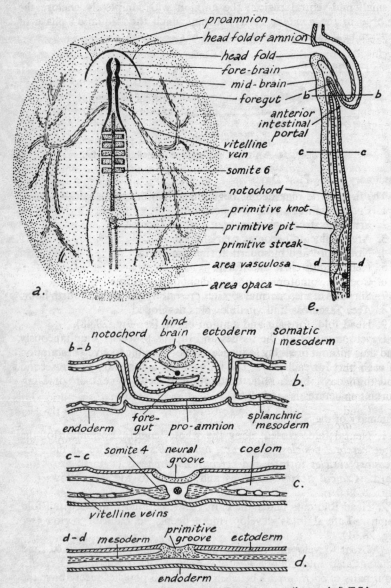

Fig. 28.48. Chick embryo (24 hours). (a) Transparency. (b, c and d) T.S.'s at b–b, c–c, d–d. (e) Median L.S.

forming a single aorta which gives off two *vitelline arteries*. Circulation in the yolk sac is completed and bounded by a circular *sinus terminalis*. Blood goes out to the yolk sac in the vitelline arteries and back to the sinus venosus in the vitelline veins. Anterior and posterior *cardinal* veins develop and flow into *ducti Cuvieri* and hence to the sinus venosus (*see* Fig. 28.49).

4. Head fold of amnion reaches a point beyond the middle of the body, above the sixteenth somite. Tail fold of the amnion begins to overlap the tail. Lateral folds of the amnion start along the whole length (*see* Fig. 28.49 (*a*)).

5. Fifteen pairs of somites at thirty-six hours and twenty-six pairs at forty-eight hours. Anterior somites differentiated into *sclerotome*, *myotome* and *dermatome*. Thickening of mesoderm at junction of somite and lateral plate forms the *nephrotome* outside which the *Wolffian duct* develops as a solid rod and later as a tube. Up to twelve pairs of segmental tubules form the *pronephros*. It probably never has an excretory function in the chick.

Summary of the Third Day

1. The central nervous system is now completely tubular and the cerebral hemispheres form considerable outgrowths. Small invaginations in the anterior region indicate development of the *olfactory pits* (*see* Fig. 28.50 (*a*)).

2. The embryo becomes extremely curved, the front of the head almost touching the heart. Torsion has reached the eighteenth somite so that half the embryo lies on its left side while the other half is still flat on the yolk.

3. The embryonic (fish-like) vascular system reaches its greatest development. There is external indication of division of the auricle into right and left halves. The lateral dorsal aortae continue into the head as the *carotid arteries*.

4. The folds of the amnion have almost closed; there is a hole above the embryo, nearer the tail than the head. It is closed on the fourth day. There is great extension of the yolk sac. The *allantois* begins as a slight saccular outgrowth in front of the hind-limb bud (*see* Fig. 28.55).

5. Thirty-six pairs of somites are formed at seventy-two hours. Beyond the last somite, the *tail bud* is formed from the remains of the primitive streak. The *hind-limb bud* arises in front of it, and the *front-limb bud* arises opposite somites fifteen to twenty (*see* Fig. 28.50 (*a*)).

6. Formation of the tail fold has involved the endoderm as well as ectoderm and thus there is a small tubular *hind-gut* with a *posterior intestinal portal*. In the pharynx, three *visceral clefts* open. The *stomodaeum* perforates through to the fore-gut (*see* Fig. 28.50 (*e*)).

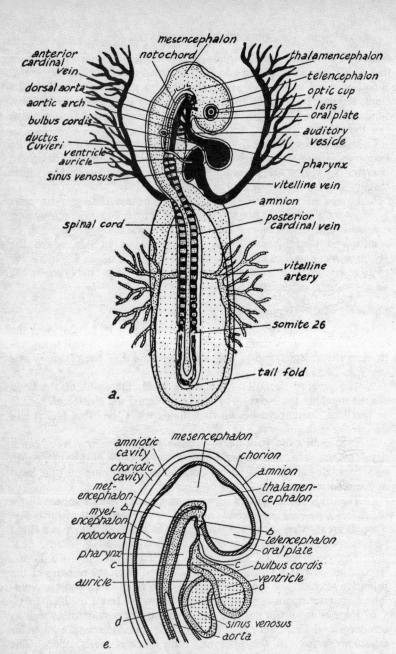

Fig. 28.49. Chick embryo (48 hours). (*a*) Transparency. (*e*) Median L.S.

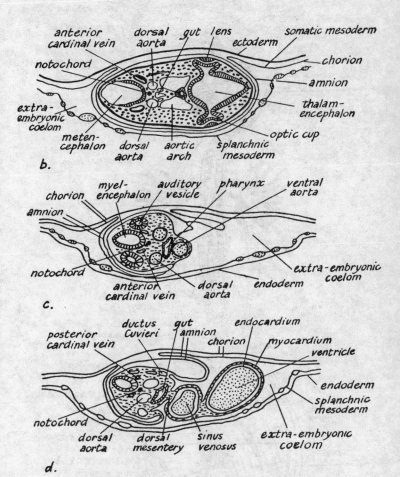

Fig. 28.49.—(*contd.*) Chick embryo (48 hours). (*b, c* and *d*) T.S.'s at planes indicated in (*e*).

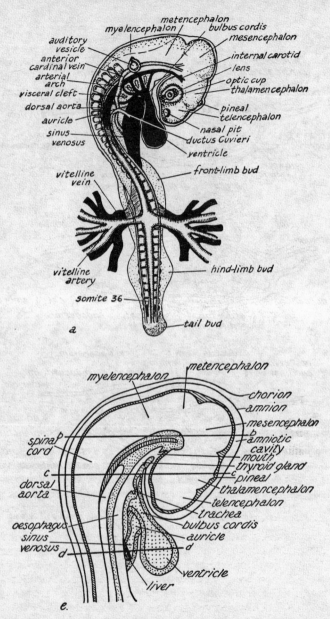

Fig. 28.50. Chick embryo (72 hours). (*a*) Transparency. (*e*) Median L.S.

974

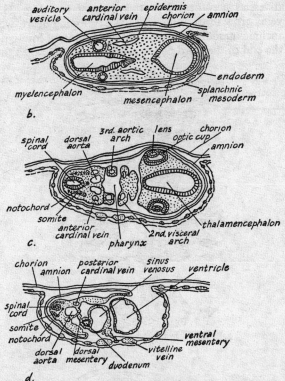

Fig. 28.50.—(contd.) Chick embryo (72 hours). (b, c and d) T.S.'s at planes indicated in (e).

Development of the Main Systems and Organs

An outline of the development of the main systems and organs now follows. The topics are considered in this order: blood vascular system, alimentary canal (including respiratory organs), urinogenital system, nervous system, skeleton and embryonic membranes. They do not develop in this order; all are developing simultaneously after gastrulation is completed.

Blood Vascular System. The whole system is developed from the mesoderm though the spaces it occupies are blastocoelic in origin. The first sign of development is in the area vasculosa where blood islands appear and soon become blood-vessels. There is rapid development of the yolk circulation and the first large vessels to appear are the vitelline veins. They are formed by the flow of blood into tissue spaces and then the gradual formation of an *endothelium* by mesenchyme cells.

All blood-vessels are formed in this manner (*see* Fig. 28.51). The vitelline veins grow in to unite with the developing heart, which arises from splanchnic mesoderm ventral to the junction of fore-gut and mid-gut. By the end of the third day it is beneath the enlarged fore-gut. It

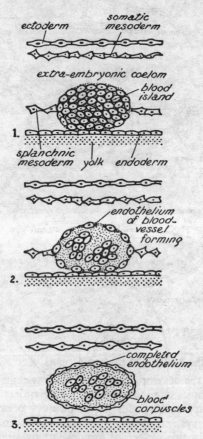

Fig. 28.51. Formation of blood-vessel.

starts as a pair of widely-separated tubes which eventually join in the mid-line to form a single tube. This becomes twisted and bent to form the sinus venosus, auricle, ventricle and bulbus. From the front of the heart, the ventral aorta grows forward and gives off in order of formation, these arterial arches, the *mandibular*, the *hyoid* and four *branchial* arches. By the end of the third day, the first four are present.

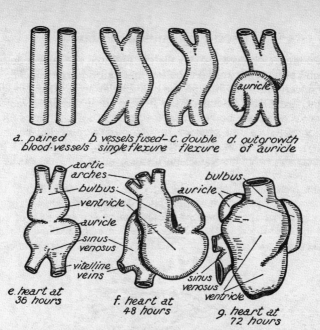

a. paired blood-vessels   b. vessels fused—single flexure   c. double flexure   d. outgrowth of auricle

aortic arches
bulbus
ventricle
auricle
sinus venosus
vitelline veins

e. heart at 36 hours

bulbus
auricle
sinus venosus
ventricle

f. heart at 48 hours

g. heart at 72 hours

Fig. 28.52. Chick embryo. Stages in heart formation.

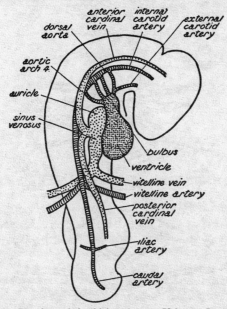

dorsal aorta
anterior cardinal vein
internal carotid artery
external carotid artery
aortic arch 4.
auricle
sinus venosus
bulbus
ventricle
vitelline vein
vitelline artery
posterior cardinal vein
iliac artery
caudal artery

Fig. 28.53. Blood-vessels in chick embryo at 72 hours. Lateral view.

These arches proceed around the gut and join the lateral dosal aortae which continue forward as the internal carotid arteries. The external carotid arteries branch from the mandibular arch. Dorsally, posterior to the heart, the lateral aortae fuse to form the dorsal aorta which proceeds down the body ventral to the notochord. It gives off the two vitelline arteries and proceeds into the developing tail as the *caudal* artery. The anterior and posterior cardinal veins meet at the ducti Cuvieri and enter the sinus venosus in front of the inlet of the vitelline veins (*see* Fig. 28.53).

The heart is an enlarged blood-vessel with a thin lining, the *endocardium*, and a thick muscular coat, the *myocardium*. It begins as a thickening of the splanchnic mesoderm at the junction of fore- and mid-gut (*see* Fig. 28.54). Groups of cells are budded inward from these thickenings and they become arranged to form the *endothelial tubes*.

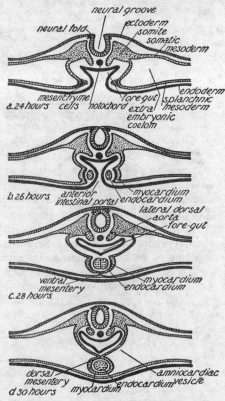

Fig. 28.54. Stages in formation of heart. T.S.

The remainder of the thickened portion will form the myocardium. Gradually, the tubes enlarge and the myocardia become moulded around them. The gut becomes constricted and finally separated from the underlying endoderm, and thus the two endocardial tubes meet to form a single structure. The myocardia close around the tube and the heart is now supported above and below by *mesenteries*. Soon the septum disappears and a single tube is formed. Both the mesenteries disappear except for two small dorsal portions, one each at the front and rear of the heart. Thus the heart arises as two tubes which become a single tube by lateral fusion. This is followed by the bending, twisting and differential growth already described. Later, two lateral *amniocardiac vesicles* fuse to form the *pericardium* and septa appear to divide the auricle and ventricle.

The *lymphatic system* arises as intercellular spaces in mesenchyme. They become confluent and surrounding cells join to form the endothelium.

The Alimentary Canal. All three germ layers contribute to the formation of the alimentary canal. Its front part, the *stomodaeum*, which is an ectodermal invagination with mesoderm as its outer lining, breaks through on the third day. The *hypophysis*, which contributes towards the formation of the pituitary body, develops as an invagination in the dorsal roof of the stomodaeum on the second day and is cut off on the third. The stomodaeum will form the *buccal cavity* and in it will develop the tongue and the palate. On the fourth day, two small buds appear in the floor; they grow and fuse to form the *tongue*.

Behind the stomodaeum, the endodermal part of the gut begins with the pharynx. Five visceral pouches are developed and three open as clefts on the third day. The first cleft closes on the fourth day and the others on the fifth; they are never used as respiratory organs. In the floor of the pharynx, two downgrowths are the primordia of the *thyroid* gland and the *laryngotracheal groove*. The thyroid is separated off on the fourth day and by that time, the lung buds have developed. They branch extensively during the remainder of the first week of incubation.

The *oesophagus* is elongated and its posterior region dilates to form the *crop*, behind which two swellings indicate the commencement of the *proventriculus* and *gizzard*. At the edge of the anterior intestinal portal, two *liver primordia* arise at the end of the third day. They maintain their connexion with the gut by the two *bile ducts*. Immediately behind this, three primordia of the *pancreas* develop, one dorsal and two ventral. The former is present at the end of the third day. Two of the three ducts persist, the ventral ones, opening into the bile duct. All the gut derivatives mentioned so far are derived from the fore-gut of the embryo, up to the edge of the anterior intestinal portal (*see* Fig. 28.55).

The anterior portion of the mid-gut forms the small intestine, and the posterior portion forms the large intestine.

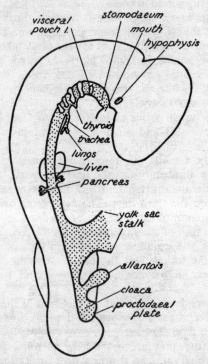

Fig. 28.55. Chick embryo. Alimentary canal derivatives at 72 hours.

From the hind-gut of the embryo, the *proctodaeum*, which becomes the posterior chamber of the cloaca, is formed as an ectodermal invagination. Anterior to it, the allantois begins development at the end of the third day.

The Urinogenital System. Pronephric tubules are formed in the nephrotome at the dorsal junction of somite and lateral plate mesoderm. They are segmental structures and up to twelve pairs may be developed, beginning at somite five. The *pronephric duct* arises outside the ninth somite, first as a solid rod, but later hollowed out. The whole structure of the pronephros is vestigial and it probably never functions as an excretory organ (*see* Fig. 28.56). By the end of the third day, the tubules commence degeneration. *Mesonephric tubules* develop opposite somites twelve to thirty. They open into the pronephric duct which becomes known now as the *Wolffian duct*. The *metanephric* kidney is formed partly as a backgrowth from the posterior region of the Wolffian

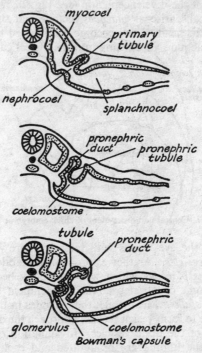

Fig. 28.56. Stages in development of a pronephric tubule.

duct and partly from the nephrotomes of somites twenty-five to thirty-three.

The gonads arise from dorsal genital ridges outside the mesonephros on each side; sex is not distinguishable till the seventh day.

The Nervous System. At the end of the first day, the neural folds have met in the anterior region, leaving an open neuropore, and by the middle of the second day, the three primary cerebral vesicles are distinct. The fore-brain is the most prominent, and from it the optic vesicles stand out laterally. On the floor, a small outgrowth indicates the primordium of the *infundibulum*. By the end of the second day, there is a pronounced cranial flexure and a dorsal evagination which will become the *pineal* stalk and body. At seventy-two hours, a dorsal constriction separates the telencephalon from the thalamencephalon and another constriction separates the mesencephalon from the metencephalon. The cerebral hemispheres have become large outgrowths, the lenses are fitting into the optic cups, and the auditory vesicles lie against the myelencephalon (*see* Fig. 28.57).

The nasal organs arise as *placodes*, ectodermal thickenings at the anterior end of the head. They become invaginated to form the nasal pits which later acquire an opening into the buccal cavity.

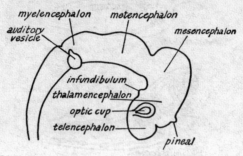

Fig. 28.57. Central nervous system of chick embryo at 72 hours.

Formation of the eye begins with lateral outgrowths of the forebrain, the *optic vesicles*. As they approach the ectoderm, they induce formation of *lens placodes* which will eventually become the lenses. The vesicles become constricted at their attachment to the fore-brain to give the *optic stalks*. Meanwhile, the placodes in the ectoderm sink inward, and close to form vesicles which approach the optic cups formed by invagination of the optic vesicles. Invagination of the optic cups continues until the lumina are obliterated and each cup becomes a double layer. The lens fits into the mouth of the cup which embraces it everywhere except at one point where there is a V-shaped cleft, the *choroid fissure*. The inner layer of the cup becomes the sensory layer of the retina, while the outer coat becomes the pigmented layer. Mesenchyme cells condense around the developing eye and eventually form the *choroid* and *sclerotic* coats and the *extrinsic muscles*. The nervous layer of the retina develops axons which leave the eye at the base of the choroid fissure and unite to form the *optic nerve*. This grows into the brain along the *optic stalk*, which is grooved to receive it. Later the groove closes to imprison the nerve; the edges of the choroid fissure grow towards each other, and the base of the fissure, where the optic nerve leaves the eye, will become the *blind spot* (*see* Fig. 28.58).

The primordium of the ear is an ectodermal invagination opposite the myelencephelon. It sinks inward as a vesicle and for some time maintains an open connexion with the exterior by the *ductus endolymphaticus*. The vesicle becomes pear-shaped, and the ductus closes to become a solid cord: the ductus of the adult is a new structure. Later, the vesicle becomes constricted into a dorsal *utriculus* and a ventral

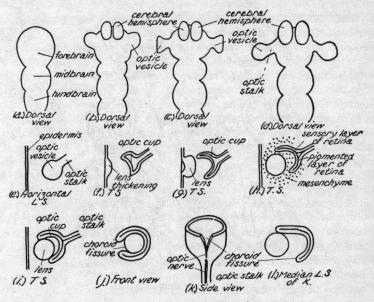

Fig. 28.58. Development of the vertebrate eye.

sacculus from which the *cochlea* grows out. The middle ear is derived from the first visceral pouch (hyoidean pouch). Its outer wall forms the *tympanic membrane* while its cavity forms the *tympanic chamber* and the *Eustachian tube* (*see* Fig. 28.59).

The Skeleton. The skeleton is mesodermal in origin and it arises by chondrification of connective tissue by chondroblasts. Later, most of it becomes ossified in the chick, and, in the skull region, numerous membrane bones are formed from dermal connective tissue. The skull and sense capsules develop as in the tadpole. Around the notochord, the vertebrae are developed as four blocks from the sclerotome of each side. At first each sclerotome produces two dorsal and two ventral blocks, known as *arcualia*. The posterior arcualia of one sclerotome, join with the anterior blocks of the next sclerotome behind, to form a single vertebra. The dorsal arcualia form the neural arches, and the ventral, the centra. Thus each vertebra is intersegmental, half of it developed from one sclerotome and half from another (*see* Fig. 28.60). The ribs are produced as outgrowths of the vertebrae and at their ventral fusion the sternum is formed. With the exception of the clavicles, the skeletal elements of the limbs are formed separately in cartilage and later ossified.

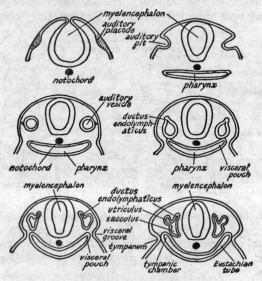

Fig. 28.59. Development of the ear.

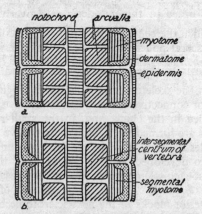

Fig. 28.60. Formation of a vertebra. Horizontal L.S.

The Embryonic Membranes.   The four membranes, *yolk sac*, *amnion*, *chorion* and *allantois* have been evolved in connexion with cleidoic development.

The yolk sac begins, before the egg is laid, by the spreading of ectoderm and endoderm over the yolk.   In the first day, mesoderm joins in, and thus there is, at the limit of the sac, fusion between splanchnopleur and somatopleur.   The sac never quite envelops the yolk, a small hole being left ventrally.   Through this hole the remains

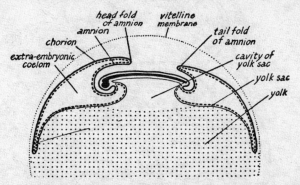

Fig. 28.61.   Embryonic membranes of chick.   Yolk sac and beginning of amnion.

of the albumin are absorbed.   Towards hatching, the yolk sac is drawn up into the mid-gut and when its contents have been absorbed, it degenerates.

The essential function of the yolk sac is the digestion of the food material and the transfer of digested food to the embryo.   Actual digestion is performed by the endoderm cells overlying the yolk.   At first, dissolved food diffuses through the fluid of the sub-germinal cavity to the embryo, but when the area vasculosa and vitelline veins have developed, it moves in the blood-vessels.   The vitelline veins lead directly to the heart and then the food is distributed by the embryonic vascular system.   Thus the yolk sac may be regarded as an extra-embryonic intestine.

The amnion and chorion arise together at the end of the first day, beginning in the region of the pro-amnion.   At that time there is no mesoderm in that region, so the fold which rises up over the head consists of ectoderm alone.   Later, mesoderm moves in to line both layers of ectoderm and they are separated by the extra-embryonic coelom.   The fold extends gradually along each side of the embryo, and by the end of the third day the tail fold has begun.   Thus, the embryo lies in a trough, surrounded by the folds of the amnion which slowly close over it. The folds meet in the fourth day at a point known as the *sero-amniotic connexion*. It is somewhat nearer the posterior than the anterior end of the body. The embryo is now floating in the amniotic cavity, balanced on a pedestal formed by the yolk-sac stalk, but it lies on its left side.

The amniotic cavity is a fluid-filled portion of space outside the embryo. It provides a cushion, giving the embryo protection from shaking and jarring and neutralizing the effects of changes of external

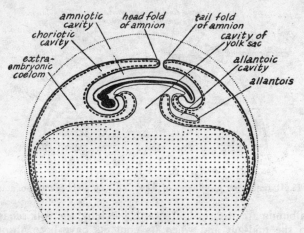

Fig. 28.62. Embryonic membranes of chick. Yolk sac, developing amnion and beginning of allantois.

temperature. Outside the amnion, the choriotic cavity is an extension of the extra-embryonic coelom, bounded by the chorion. It is another fluid protective layer and provides space into which the allantois can grow later. The chorion becomes pressed against the shell membranes and thus plays an important part in absorption of oxygen through the porous shell. Certain parts of the chorion become distended by the great growth of the allantois and they surround the remains of the albumin in an *albumin sac* which is finally drawn into the cavity at the base of the yolk sac, the albumin all being absorbed by the sixteenth day.

The allantois is an outgrowth of the hind-gut consisting of endoderm covered on the outside by mesoderm. It is used as a repository for the nitrogenous excretory product, uric acid, and thus enables this practically insoluble product to be stowed away, outside the embryo proper. Beginning at the end of the third day, the allantois grows eventually to fill the choriotic cavity. The allantoic mesoderm fuses with the cnoriotic mesoderm and is everywhere pressed against the shell membranes. An extensive circulation develops in the allantoic wall, with a main allantoic (umbilical) artery and vein in its stalk. In its later stages, the allantois may be regarded as an extra-embryonic lung.

Towards the end of incubation, all these membranes are attached to the mid-ventral region of the embryo by an *umbilical stalk*. The

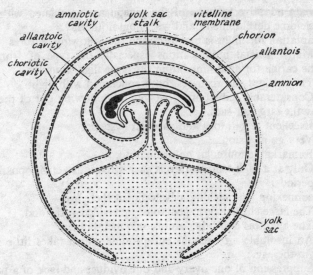

Fig. 28.63. Embryonic membranes of chick. Yolk sac, amnion and allantois developed.

amnion, and chorion and allantois now fused to form an *allanto-chorion*, are left behind in the shell. The yolk sac with some remnants of yolk, is drawn into the body, leaving a permanent scar, the *umbilicus* on the ventral surface.

The relationships of the three germ layers in these membranes must be clearly understood. The amnion consists of ectoderm inside and mesoderm outside; the chorion, of mesoderm inside and ectoderm outside; the yolk sac, of endoderm inside and mesoderm outside; the allantois, of endoderm inside and mesoderm outside. Wherever mesoderm layers come in contact, they fuse. All blood-vessels are developed in mesoderm.

Hatching. On the twentieth day after laying, the yolk sac has been absorbed and the allantois has begun to shrivel. The chick bursts the inner shell membrane abutting on the air chamber and begins to use its lungs. On the same day or the next, it breaks the shell with its *egg-tooth* and emerges. It is able to walk almost immediately and after a short period of drying, it begins to explore its surroundings. For several weeks, the hen mothers the chicks, calling their attention to food and covering them at night.

Adaptation

The main adaptive features of the pigeon are associated with flight, with cleidoic development, and with homoiothermy.

Adaptation for flight is manifested in the following features—

1. Many skeletal modifications especially the type of front-limb, and the carina for accommodating the large flight muscles.

2. The remiges and rectrices, both concerned with flight.

3. Considerable reduction of weight by hollowing out of the bones and by the large air-sacs.

4. Excellent respiratory and vascular systems.

5. Very good vision.

6. Remarkable muscular co-ordination.

7. Only at a high temperature is such strenuous activity possible for long periods.

In connexion with cleidoic development there are—

1. The large shelled eggs, generously provided with food.

2. The allantois and other embryonic membranes.

3. An insoluble nitrogenous end-product which takes little storage space in the egg.

4. Suppression of one ovary and one oviduct and lack of a pubic or ischial symphysis.

Concerned with homoiothermy, there are—

1. The high rate of metabolism, necessitating frequent and large food supplies, efficient digestion and absorption, and rapid respiratory rate.

2. The covering of feathers provides excellent insulation.

3. The lack of glands in the skin prevents loss of heat by evaporation.

Careful consideration will reveal a host of minor modifications which are adaptive.

Classification

Phylum: Chordata   Order: Columbiformes
Sub-phylum: Craniata [Vertebrata]   Family: Columbidae
Class: Aves   Genus: *Columba*
Sub-class: Neornithes   Species: *C. livia*

The Neornithes are distinguished from the Archaeornithes by the presence of a pygostyle at the end of a shortened tail, the possession of a carpo-metacarpus, and the arrangement of the rectrices in a semi-circle. Members of the order Columbiformes are distinguished from those of other orders by many small characteristics. Among them are the large crop, the small caeca and the vestigial vomer. Two families, the Columbidae and the Raphidae belong to the order Columbiformes, the former order being separated by the power of flight whereas the latter includes the dodo and solitaire, two extinct flightless birds. Birds in the genus *Columba* have twelve rectrices. The species are separated by small differences of colour, size, habitat and song.

Special Topics of Biological Importance

Arising out of this cursory study of a reptile and a bird, a number of topics of biological importance remain to be mentioned. Adaptive radiation in the reptiles has been mentioned previously; it is also a notable feature of the birds. The undoubtedly close relationship of birds and reptiles needs to be stressed, and it is also convenient to summarize briefly the various solutions to the problem of flight in the animal kingdom.

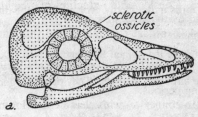

Adaptive Radiation in Birds

The oldest known birds are represented by two fossils found in Jurassic rocks, one of *Archaeopteryx* and one of *Archaeornis*. Since the evolution of feathered flight, they have exploited all its possibilities and the modern birds present a fascinating study in adaptive radiation. In geographical range, they have colonized the fringes of the polar regions and every habitat between, including some few species which spend the greater part of their lives on or above the open sea. There are very large birds and very small birds, with all gradations between. There are carnivores, herbivores and omnivores. There is infinite variety in flight, in song, in colour, and in nesting habits. They have occupied a wide selection of

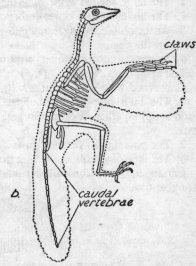

Fig. 28.64. Earliest known fossil birds. (*a*) *Archaeopteryx* (skull, side view showing teeth). (*b*) *Archaeornis* (skeleton, side view, showing long tail).

habitats in the terrestrial environment. Apart from fliers, there are swimmers, divers, waders, walkers, runners, burrowers and climbers. Their vivacity, power of song, grace, beauty, and engaging habits, have excited human interest more than any other group of animals has done.

Relationships of Birds and Reptiles

The birds are so similar to the reptiles in essential structure that it has often been suggested that both classes should be included in one group, the Sauropsida. There are greater differences between certain orders of fishes than there are between the classes Reptilia, Aves and Mammalia. Some zoologists would include reptiles, birds, and mammals in one single class with three sub-classes—

1. Protosauria: including all the primitive amphibian-like reptiles.
2. Theropsida: the mammal-like reptiles and mammals.
3. Sauropsida: the typical reptiles and birds.

Birds undoubtedly evolved from the diapsid stock and appear to be most nearly related to the order Parasuchia, which included a number of bipedal Triassic forms.

Flight in the Animal Kingdom

True flight has been evolved by four groups; the pterosaurs, the insects, the birds and the bats. They present a good example of *convergent evolution,*

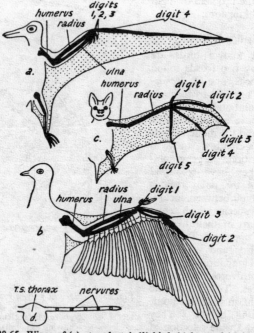

Fig. 28.65. Wings of (*a*) pterodactyl, (*b*) bird, (*c*) bat and (*d*) insect.

which is the development of a similar characteristic independently by different groups. The wings of pterosaurs, birds and bats are modifications of the front pentadactyl limb, though none of these groups evolved from the other. The wings of insects are totally different, being outgrowths of the chitinous integument in the dorso-lateral regions of the meso- and metathorax.

In the pterosaurs (pterodactyls) the fourth finger was enormously elongated to support a membranous wing, which was a double fold of skin attached posteriorly at the ankle. The bird wing consists essentially of the flight feathers, which are epidermal structures. In the bats, the wing is supported not only by the arm but by the digits, which are splayed out like the ribs of an umbrella. The wing extends to the hind-limbs and posteriorly between them.

Other animals have developed some facility in gliding but only these four groups have evolved true flight.

CHAPTER 29

THE HIGHEST TERRESTRIAL CRANIATES: MAMMALIA

THE derivation of the name "Mammalia" from the Latin word "mamma" meaning "breast," refers to the fact that the young of these animals are invariably suckled by the female parent on milk produced in her mammary glands. Undoubtedly of reptilian origin, the mammals include the highest types of animals evolved, in anatomical and physiological complexity as well as in variety of behaviour. The largest animal of all time is a mammal; it is the blue whale, which may achieve a length of about 30 m and a weight of 130 tonne. At the other end of the scale are the tiny shrews of the Mediterranean coast, in length under 4 cm and about 80 g in weight. In between, is a vast variety of forms which provide an excellent illustration of adaptive radiation. At the apex of the animal kingdom is man, the animal with the most complex behaviour, the only one with consciousness of his powers, and the creature with the greatest possibilities of progressive evolution.

In this chapter, the rabbit is described and there are outlines of the special features of the rat. Rabbits are bred for meat and for fur on a large scale; many strains have been produced, but, apart from external differences in size, colour and hair-length, they all exhibit the same anatomical features.

THE RABBIT

The wild rabbit, *Oryctolagus* [*Lepus*] *cuniculus* is described here. It is not a native of Great Britain but was probably introduced by the Romans from Southern Europe.

Habitat and Habits

Rabbits are gregarious animals living in colonies in burrows, which form a network of tunnels known as a warren. In regions where the soil is stiff clay, they make runs among dense vegetation, especially thickets of bramble and blackthorn. They are herbivorous, feeding on a great variety of vegetation. Many carnivores prey on rabbits, which have therefore evolved some counter-measures, among which are their great alertness, their rapid escape, and their habit of feeding at dawn or dusk when their neutral colour makes them very inconspicuous. Breeding four times a year, with up to eight in each litter, they are among the most prolific of mammals. Like all mammals, except the platypus and spiny ant-eater, rabbits are viviparous, the young being born in an underground nesting-chamber. When born, they are naked, blind and helpless.

The introduction of rabbits into Australia and New Zealand, which are both comparatively free from natural carnivores, led to such an enormous increase in their numbers as to constitute almost a plague. It is a good example of lack of foresight by man's interference with natural populations. The propagation of myxomatosis has killed ninety per cent of the rabbits but there are signs that resistant strains are now on the increase.

External Features

The body is covered by greyish-brown *fur* consisting of short fine *hairs* set closely enough together to form a thick pile. On the ventral surface the colour is lighter, and on the underside of the tail, the fur is white. There is distinct division of the body into *head*, *neck*, *trunk* and *tail*.

The head is ovoid in shape, tapering somewhat to the front, where the *mouth* is small and terminal, and bounded by soft *upper* and *lower lips*. A characteristic feature of the group to which the rabbit belongs, is the cleft upper lip which exposes the large incisor teeth. The *nostrils* are oblique slits leading backward from the top of the cleft. Set on the sides of the head, somewhat towards the dorsal surface, are the large *eyes*, with movable *upper* and *lower lids* fringed with *eyelashes*. At the inner (front) corners of the eyes, there are *nictitating membranes* which can be moved across the eye to wash it. At the sides of the mouth and nostrils, and around the eyes are long, stiff, sensitive hairs called *vibrissae*. They are very sensitive to touch and are of great value in the darkness of the burrow. The *ears* have long flexible *pinnae* leading into narrow tubes which end at the ear-drum, each tube being an *external auditory meatus*, which, together with the pinna constitutes the *external ear*, a structure not found in lower groups. The pinnae are movable and reflect sound waves into the canal; they also enable the rabbit to determine accurately the direction from which a sound is coming.

The neck is not as long or as narrow as that of the pigeon; it appears thicker than it really is, because of the loose skin and dense fur which give some protection to this very vulnerable region.

The trunk widens from the neck and though not perceptibly divided into *thorax* and *abdomen*, these two regions are separated by a partition, the *diaphragm*, which appears for the first time in the mammals. Ventrally, the thorax is firm because of the presence of the sternum and ribs, while the abdomen is soft and yielding, being protected only by the body wall. On the ventral surface of the abdomen, are three or four pairs of *teats* which bear the outlets of the *mammary glands*. Beneath the tail is the *anus*, and ventral to it is the *urinogenital opening*. Between these is a hairless patch of skin known as the *perineum*, which has on each side a *perineal gland* producing a secretion which gives the rabbit its characteristic odour. The male opening is borne on a projection, the *penis*, which bears a retractable sheath called the *prepuce*. At the sides of the penis are the *testes* contained in the *scrotal sacs*. The female opening is a longitudinal slit, the *vulva*, which bears a vestigial penis called the *clitoris* on the ventral side. The tail is short and usually bent upward.

The front-limb is short and bears five digits ending in sharp claws. Much of the upper arm is concealed by the skin and fur of the body wall. There are only four toes on the hind-limb; the great toe is missing. It is much longer than the front-limb and there is a considerable area of the foot on the substratum. Again the upper segment, the thigh, is practically concealed by the skin of the body wall. Both pairs of limbs are very typical of jumping animals and bear a skeletal resemblance to those of the frog.

The Body Wall

As is true of all vertebrates, the body wall consists of the skin, comprising epidermis and dermis, a layer of muscle, and then the peritoneum abutting on the coelom. Mammalian skin is very distinctive in three respects; it bears *hair*, *sudoriparous* and *sebaceous* glands. In other respects it differs little from that of any other vertebrate (*see* Fig. 29.1).

On the outside is a *stratum corneum* consisting of flattened, dead, keratinized squames, which are continually being lost from the surface and replaced from beneath. Several layers then form the *stratum lucidum* with the nuclei usually lacking and the cell outlines distinct. It has a distinctly hyaline appearance. Below the stratum lucidum is a thin layer with nucleated cells and clear outlines. The cells are characterized by the presence of abundant granules. This last layer lies on the *stratum germinativum* or *Malpighian layer*. Here the cells are polyhedral and constantly undergo mitosis to produce cells which replace those lost at the surface. Protoplasmic fibrils connecting the cells are well marked. The stratum germinativum lies on a basement membrane secreted by the underlying dermis.

The dermis consists mainly of connective tissue and it is two or three times as thick as the epidermis. Through it, in all directions, pass bundles of white fibres which merge with the basement membrane above and the muscle sheath below. They serve to attach the skin firmly to the body and impose a limit on the amount of stretching, recovery being effected by a network of yellow elastic fibres. In the lower region of the dermis there is usually a considerable amount of adipose tissue, where fat is stored. This layer may reach great thickness in some mammals, particularly in the whale and seal, and also in many hibernating terrestrial animals. Through the dermis ramifies a network of blood-vessels with clusters of capillaries abutting on the epidermis. Normally, blood-vessels do not penetrate into the epidermis. Numerous nerve fibres traverse the dermis, ending either in or beneath the epidermis

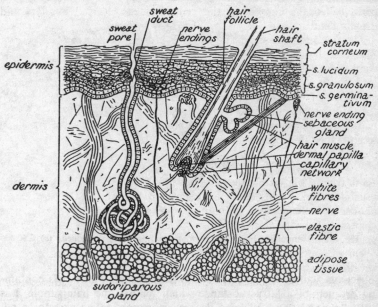

Fig. 29.1. V.S. Mammalian skin.

as terminal arborizations, tactile corpuscles, end-bulbs, Pacinian corpuscles, organs of Ruffini or bulbs of Krause. The nature and structure of these types of endings have been discussed in Chapter 20. They subserve the various divisions of the sense of touch.

Hairs, like feathers, are epidermal structures derived from the stratum germinativum. Each arises as a solid rod of cells proliferated from this germinative layer, which grows into the dermis and the hair pierces the epidermis to appear above the surface. Each hair lies in a *follicle* which is swollen at the base and indented to form a *papilla*. By multiplication of the cells of the epithelium of this papilla, the hair grows to a length determined by the frequency of moulting. The portion within the follicle is the *root* and the exposed portion is the *shaft*. When a hair is shed, it is replaced by a new one which grows from the papilla. Connective tissue and capillaries grow into each papilla. Round the base of each follicle is a spiral nerve-ending; each hair is thus a sense-organ.

Attached to each hair follicle, and sloping in the same general direction but at a still greater angle to the vertical, is an *arrector pili* muscle. It consists of a bundle of involuntary fibres and in the triangle formed by this bundle, the follicle and the epidermis, lies a group of

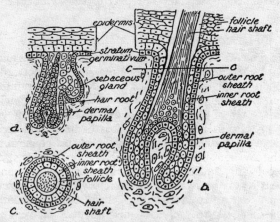

Fig. 29.2. Mammalian hair. (*a*) Growing hair. (*b*) Fully developed. (*c*) T.S. hair in follicle at *c–c* in (*b*).

sebaceous glands. These secrete into their lumina whole cells containing droplets of a fatty substance which renders the hair supple, less likely to break, and in some degree waterproof. The arrectores pili muscles are stimulated to contract by the hormone adrenalin, the effects being erection of the hair, raising of the follicle above the general surface and squeezing of the secretion from the sebaceous glands. The bristling of the hair on a dog's back and the goose-pimples of man are manifestations of the same phenomenon.

The sudoriparous (sudoriferous) or sweat glands are abundant over the whole skin. Each is a coiled tubule developed by downgrowth of the stratum germinativum and invested by connective tissue and a network of capillaries. They are peculiar to mammals and have both excretory and temperature-regulation functions. A fuller description of these glands is given in Chap. 20.

Other glands of the skin are the *Meibomian glands* which open into the follicles of the eyelashes; they are modified sebaceous glands. The *ceruminous glands* of the external auditory meatus secrete a fatty substance which both protects and lubricates the tympanic membrane; they are modified sudoriparous glands. The mammary glands appear, from their mode of formation, to be modified sebaceous glands. In their mature condition, they have a compound racemose structure. The perineal glands appear to be modified sudoriparous glands.

Underlying the skin are also flattened sheets of muscle which serve such purposes as shaking the skin, moving the eyebrows, lips and pinnae. In human beings, the interplay of such muscles gives facial expression.

Functions of Mammalian Skin

The skin provides protection from various hazards; it is an excretory organ; it subserves temperature regulation and sensitivity.

Physical protection from damage is provided by the stratum corneum and the fur, while the colour gives some measure of camouflage. The hair traps a layer of air near the body surface and this acts as an insulating layer, preventing excessive loss of heat. Thickness of the adipose tissue is another important factor in this connexion, though in the rabbit it is not of great significance. In the mammals which have become secondarily aquatic, the blubber is of great importance.

The sweat is, to some extent, an excretory product. It consists of about 95 per cent water, 2 per cent of dissolved salts, mainly sodium chloride, a small quantity of urea, and about 3 per cent of carbon dioxide, all by weight. It is passed from the capillaries into the cells of the tubules and secreted by them into the lumen. Generally, the sweat is evaporated, but in conditions of high temperature or great muscular activity, it may run off the body as fluid.

Regulation of heat loss is a very important function of mammalian skin. Being homoiothermous animals, with temperatures around 35°C (rabbit 36°C), their metabolism is regulated to work best at a particular temperature and therefore it must be constantly regulated. Production of heat is inevitable in every living cell, and is greatest in mammals in muscles and glands, particularly the liver. The heat is more or less equally distributed by the vascular system and regulated mainly by the skin. Heat is lost with any material passed out of the body; such, for example are the faeces, urine and exhaled air. But the greatest quantity of heat is lost by evaporation of sweat from the surface; most of the latent heat necessary for this, comes from the body itself. Therefore, regulation of the amount of sweat will mean regulation of heat loss. It is accomplished by control of the surface blood vessels, including those which supply the sweat glands. Vaso-dilator nerve fibres of the parasympathetic system stimulate enlargement of peripheral vessels, while vaso-constrictor fibres of the sympathetic system stimulate contraction. There is a centre in the brain which correlates these processes.

Nerve endings in the skin are sensitive to a variety of stimuli which are commonly grouped together under the sense of touch. There are endings sensitive to mechanical contact, others for pain, and others for high and low temperatures.

Other special functions of the skin are those associated with special secretions such as milk and ear-wax, erection of the hair to present a more terrifying appearance to a rival or predator, and the shaking or movement of the skin for various purposes.

The Coelom

The splanchnocoel of lower forms is now divided by the transverse diaphragm. In the anterior portion are the central *pericardial cavity* surrounding the heart and the two lateral *pleural cavities* surrounding the lungs. It is important to notice the relationships of the coelomic epithelium to these cavities. Each lung is surrounded by the *pleura* which continues from the root of the lung to line the body wall and the diaphragm and then to meet its fellow in the mid-line as a double fold called the *mediastinum*. The heart is surrounded by coelomic epithelium which doubles back from the roots of the great vessels to enclose the fluid layer between two sheets. The abdominal body cavity surrounds the gut. The peritoneum covers the gut and the body wall and forms

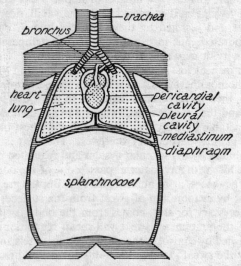

Fig. 29.3. Coelom of a mammal.

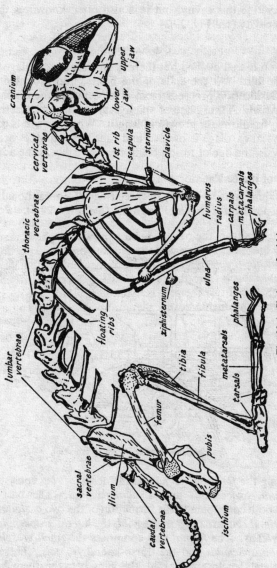

Fig. 29.4. Skeleton of rabbit.

the mesentery as a double fold. The term splanchnocoel may still be used to describe this cavity, but it is also often known as the general peritoneal cavity (*see* Fig. 29.3)

The Skeleton

The skeleton is well ossified but there is much more cartilage persisting than in the bird. At the ends of the bones, thin articular cartilages remain. Ossification proceeds from three centres, one diaphyseal and two epiphyseal. A thin plate of epiphyseal cartilage between epiphysis and diaphysis allows for growth in length. When growth is completed, the epiphyseal cartilage is ossified and thus the epiphyses are fused to the diaphysis, the line of fusion being clearly visible in the adult bones.

The Skull of the Rabbit

The cranium consists mainly of three rings of bones though these do not correspond to segmental regions (*see* Fig. 29.5). Posteriorly,

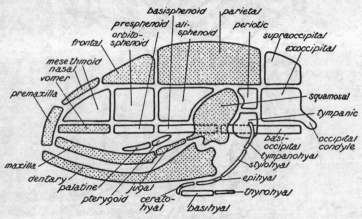

Fig. 29.5. Generalized mammalian skull.

surrounding the *foramen magnum* is the *occipital ring* consisting of the *basioccipital*, *exoccipitals* and a *supraoccipital*. The basi- and ex-occipitals both contribute to the formation of the two *occipital condyles*. In the *parietal ring* are the *basisphenoid*, the lateral *alisphenoids* and the dorsal *parietals*. The *frontal ring* comprises the small *presphenoid*, the lateral *orbitosphenoids* and the dorso-lateral *frontals*. These rings do not completely enclose the brain, the gaps between them being filled by other bones. Between the occipital and parietal rings there is dorsally an *interparietal*, and laterally there are the *squamosal* and the *periotic*.

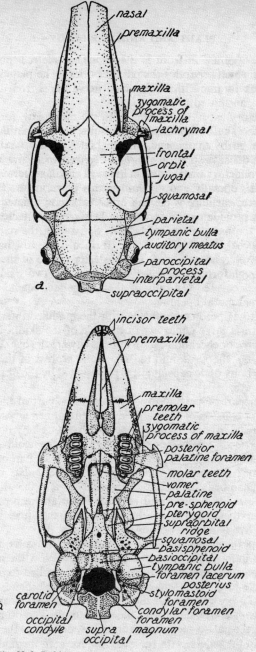

nasal
premaxilla

maxilla
zygomatic
process of
maxilla
lachrymal
frontal
orbit
jugal
squamosal
parietal
tympanic bulla
auditory meatus
paroccipital
process
interparietal
supraoccipital

a.

incisor teeth
premaxilla

maxilla
premolar
teeth
zygomatic
process of maxilla
posterior
palatine foramen
molar teeth
vomer
palatine
pre-sphenoid
pterygoid
supraorbital
ridge
squamosal
basisphenoid
basioccipital
tympanic bulla
foramen lacerum
posterius
stylomastoid
foramen
condylar foramen
foramen
magnum

carotid
foramen

occipital
condyle

supra
occipital

b.

Fig. 29.6. Rabbit skull. (a) Dorsal view. (b) Ventral view.

Closing the cranium in front is the *cribriform plate*, a portion of the *mesethmoid* which separates the nasal cavities. The plate is perforated by many fine foramina through which nerve fibres from the olfactory organs are transmitted to the brain.

The olfactory capsules, together with the upper jaw, form the facial region of the skull. Roofing the capsules are the *nasal* bones; the floor is formed by the *vomers*, and the sides by the *maxillae*. In the cavities are delicate scroll-like *turbinal bones* which give an extensive area to the olfactory epithelium. There are *maxillary turbinals* in front, *naso-turbinals* dorsally and *ethmo-turbinals* posteriorly. The last bear the sensory epithelium, while the other two have ciliated epithelium. The vomers provide partial separation between the olfactory chambers above and the narial passages below. Separating the narial passages from the buccal cavity is the *palate*, formed of ingrowths of the premaxilla, maxilla and palatine. The posterior region of the palate is an inverted trough formed of the *palatine bones* and two small *pterygoids*. In life, this is covered ventrally by the soft palate, behind which is the single internal narial opening.

The orbit has become confluent with the modified inferior *temporal fossa* to form a large concavity in the side of the skull. Forming the *zygomatic arch* or cheekbone across this cavity are the backward portion of the maxilla, the *jugal*, and the *zygomatic process* of the squamosal. There is no bony optic capsule; it is represented by the fibrous sclerotic coat of the eye.

The inner part of the auditory capsule forms part of the wall of the cranium and consists of the *periotic bone*. Its inner or *petrous portion* is a very irregular bone enclosing the membranous labyrinth; its outer *mastoid portion* is visible on the exterior of the skull between the *tympanic* and the exoccipital. The tympanic encloses part of the external auditory meatus, and a swollen portion, the *bulla*, contains the tympanic chamber. Crossing the chamber, are the three *auditory ossicles*, the *malleus*, *incus* and *stapes*. These are respectively homologous with the articular of the lower jaw, the quadrate, and the columella (hyomandibula) of lower vertebrates.

Each upper jaw consists of the premaxilla and maxilla, both bearing teeth. It is immovably fused to the cranium. Below the inner portion of the zygomatic process of the squamosal is a rolled fossa for articulation of the lower jaw, which consists of a single bone, the *dentary*. Its *coronoid process* serves for the insertion of the masticatory muscles, while its *condyle* articulates with the squamosal. The primitive mandibular arch, the palato-pterygo-quadrate bar, persists as the palatine and pterygoid in the palate, with the quadrate forming the middle auditory ossicle, the incus. The hyoid arch is represented by the body of the *hyoid* (basi-hyal) in the floor of the mouth, and the anterior cornua which sweep upward and inward to join the tympanic region. These anterior cornua each consist of a chain of small bones, the *cerato-hyal*, *epi-hyal*, *stylo-hyal* and *tympano-hyal*, which are all probably homologous with the ceratohyal of the dogfish. The posterior cornua are short and fork to the sides of the larynx. They are called *thyro-hyals*

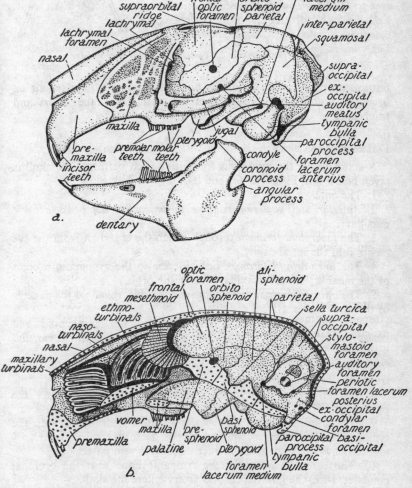

Fig. 29.7. Rabbit skull. (*a*) Lateral view with lower jaw. (*b*) Median L.S.

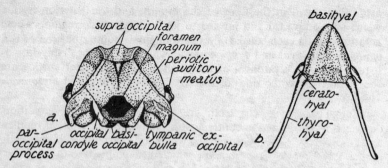

Fig. 29.8. Rabbit skull. (*a*) Posterior view. (*b*) Hyoid body.

but are probably remnants of the first branchial arch. The remaining branchial arches are represented in the cartilages of the larynx and trachea.

Foramina of the Skull

A summary of the numerous foramina which perforate the skull is given below (*see* Figs. 29.7 (*a*) and 29.8 (*a*)).

1. The *anterior nares*.

2. *Anterior* and *posterior palatine foramina* for the passage of V maxillary.

3. The *lachrymal foramen* through which the tear duct from the eye passes into the nasal cavity.

4. The *infra-orbital foramen* just anterior to the zygomatic process of the maxilla; here V maxillary leaves the orbit.

5. The *optic foramen* in the middle of the orbitosphenoid for passage of the optic nerve, II.

6. The *foramen lacerum anterius* between the alisphenoid and basisphenoid; through it pass III, IV, VI and V ophthalmic and maxillary.

7. The *foramen lacerum medium*, between the alisphenoid and periotic, transmits V mandibular.

8. The *stylomastoid foramen*, behind the tympanic, allows the passage of VII.

9. The *foramen lacerum posterius* is situated ventrally between the tympanic bulla and the occipital condyle. Here, cranial nerves IX, X and XI leave the skull and the internal jugular vein passes out.

10. The *carotid foramen* in the tympanic bone near the occipital condyle; here, the internal carotid artery enters the skull.

11. The *external auditory meatus*.

12. The *condylar foramen* in the exoccipital, through which passes the hypoglossal, XII.

13. The *Eustachian foramen* in the anterior and inner portion of the tympanic bone.

14. The *foramen magnum*.

The Teeth of Mammals

In most mammals, the teeth are of different kinds, a condition described as *heterodont* in contrast with the homodont teeth of reptiles and amphibians. There are *incisors*, which are sharp-edged biting teeth in the front of the jaw, *canines*, which are pointed teeth used for tearing, piercing or killing, *premolars* and *molars*, which are chewing teeth. The teeth are replaced once, so that there are two successive sets, *milk teeth* and *permanent teeth*. This is the *diphyodont* condition compared with the *polyphyodont* condition where the teeth are replaced many times. There are no molars in the milk teeth.

It is customary to express the numbers and kinds of teeth by a formula which makes it easier to remember them. Half the upper jaw is taken above the line and half the lower jaw below it; i = incisors, c = canines, p = premolars, m = molars. The typical dental formula is found in the pig and a few other mammals.

$$2 \left\{ \frac{3i.\ 1c.\ 4pm.\ 3m}{3i.\ 1c.\ 4pm.\ 3m} \right\} = 44 \text{ total}$$

When the significance of the various symbols is understood, it is sufficient to learn only the figures in brackets. A few examples, for comparison with the typical complete state are—

$$\text{rabbit} \quad \frac{2033}{1023} = 28 \qquad \text{sheep} \ \frac{0033}{3133} = 32$$

$$\text{dog} \quad \frac{3142}{3143} = 42 \qquad \text{cat} \ \frac{3131}{3121} = 30$$

$$\text{man} \quad \frac{2123}{2123} = 32 \qquad \text{rat} \ \frac{1003}{1003} = 16$$

$$\text{human milk teeth} \ \frac{2120}{2120} = 20$$

The portion of a tooth which projects above the gum is the *crown*, and the part embedded in a socket in the jaw-bone is the *root*. The narrow region between the two is the *neck*. *Enamel* is the hardest substance in the body and forms a covering to the exposed portion of the tooth. It is made of small hexagonal prisms about 5μm in diameter set at right angles to the surface of the crown. The material composing them is mainly calcium phosphate with a small proportion of calcium carbonate. *Cement* is like bone in structure but it lacks Haversian canals. Within the enamel and cement, and constituting the main substance of the tooth, is yellowish *dentine* or *ivory*. It is harder than bone but contains no Haversian canals, lacunae or cells. There are countless fine canaliculi passing into it from the pulp cavity. In life,

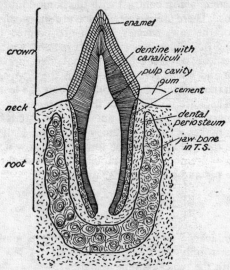

Fig. 29.9. Median L.S. incisor tooth.

these canaliculi are occupied by fine protoplasmic fibrils connected to *odontoblasts* lining the pulp cavity. The cavity is occupied by jelly-like connective tissue containing blood-vessels, lymph channels and nerve fibres, all of which pass through the pulp canal at the base. The tooth is set in an *alveolus* of the jaw-bone, surrounded by the dental periosteum which is a somewhat thickened continuation of the periosteum covering the bone. Connective tissue fibres from the dental periosteum pass into both the cement and the jaw-bone and thus fix the tooth firmly in its socket (*see* Fig. 29.9).

During development, a *dental groove* is formed along the surface of the gum, the groove being due to downward extension of the epidermis with the stratum germinativum leading. The downgrowth is known as the *dental lamina* and soon it forks into an outer branch from which the milk tooth will develop and an inner branch where the permanent tooth will form. The outer branch is invaginated from below to contain a *mesodermal papilla* of connective tissue in which cells accumulate. These cells secrete the dentine, while the enamel organ secretes the enamel. Gradually the tooth grows until it breaks the surface, the enamel organ now forming a thin membrane which is soon worn off. The developing bone forms around it and secretes the cement and thus by growth of both bone and tooth, secure fixation is accomplished.

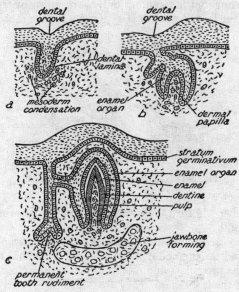

Fig. 29.10. Development of a tooth.

From the other fork of the dental lamina, the permanent tooth develops and gradually pushes the milk tooth out, the process being assisted by osteoclasts which erode the root of the milk tooth.

When the permanent tooth is in position, its root grows down to form a pointed fang, or several fangs in the case of premolar and molar teeth. This growth of the fang almost closes the pulp canal so that the entry of blood is severely restricted. The tooth remains alive, but growth ceases.

The Teeth of the Rabbit. As is the case in most herbivores in which the teeth are subjected to continual hard wear, the pulp canal retains a wide opening and the teeth grow throughout life. They are said to have *persistent pulps*. The incisors have a sharp chisel-like edge with thicker enamel in front than at the back so that they wear into a backward slope with the keen edge at the front. In the upper jaw, there are four incisors, all on the premaxillae. They are arranged in peculiar fashion with two smaller ones lying behind two considerably larger ones. Since the lower incisors pass within the upper, these two small inner teeth serve to stop the lower incisors sliding up too far and damaging the gum. All the larger incisors have very long roots passing a considerable distance into the jaw-bone almost horizontally (*see* Fig. 29.11). Since they grow throughout life and are only worn down by friction against one another, the loss of a tooth is a calamity for the rabbit, because its

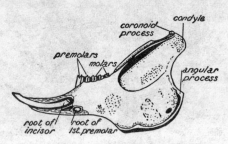

Fig. 29.11. L.S. incisor tooth in jaw of rabbit.

opposite number will then grow without check and prevent the animal closing its mouth.

There are no canines but a wide gap, called the *diastema*, lies between the incisors and the premolars. There is little difference in the mature structure of the premolars and molars which lie in a close group at the hinder ends of the jaw-bones. They are ridged transversely by alternate layers of dentine and enamel and since these wear at different rates, the surface appears serrated. The ridges on the upper teeth fit into the grooves on the lower teeth, the whole arrangement forming an efficient grinding surface (*see* Figs. 29.6 (*b*) and 29.7 (*a*)).

The Skull of the Dog

The cranium is almost entirely composed of three rings of bones, the occipital, parietal and frontal rings. The occipital ring consists of the basi-occipital, paired exoccipitals and the supraoccipital (*see* Fig. 29.12). Enclosed by these bones is the foramen magnum at the sides of which are two occipital condyles for articulation with the atlas. A basi-sphenoid, paired alisphenoids and parietals make up the parietal ring. Between the alisphenoid and the occipital ring the cranium is completed latero-ventrally by the squamosal and the auditory capsule. Dorsally

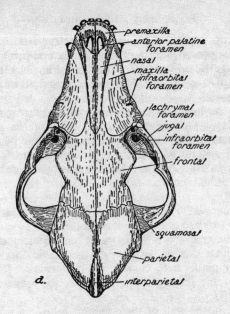

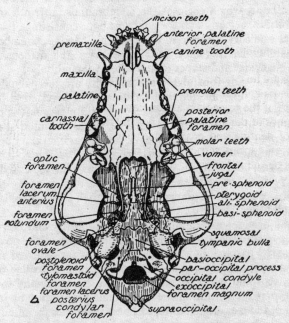

Fig. 29.12. Dog skull. (*a*) Dorsal view. (*b* Ventral view.

the parietals are separated by a narrow interparietal. The frontal ring consists of the presphenoid ventrally, two lateral orbito-sphenoids and two very large dorso-lateral frontals (*see* Fig. 29.13). In front, the cranium is closed by the cribriform plate perforated by openings for the olfactory nerves.

The large nasal cavities are roofed over by narrow nasal bones, the floor consists of the vomers, and the sides, of the premaxillae and maxillae. Separating the cavities is the mesethmoid which is prolonged into cartilage anteriorly. Scroll-like delicate turbinals occupy a large part of each cavity; they are ingrowths of the nasal, maxillary and ethmoid bones and serve to increase the area of the epithelial layer (*see* Fig. 29.13 (*b*)).

The optic capsule is represented by the sclerotic coat of the eye-ball; the eyes face forward and are lodged in the front part of a large cavity formed by the confluence of the orbit and the temporal fossa. Protecting the outer side of the eye and the masticatory muscles behind it, is the zygomatic arch, curved widely outward. It consists of the jugal in front and the zygomatic process of the squamosal behind (*see* Fig. 29.13 (*a*)).

Embedded in the wall of the cranium, below the squamosal, is the periotic bone, which encloses the membranous labyrinth of the inner ear. Outside the periotic is the tympanic bone consisting of a short bony external auditory meatus and a swollen tympanic chamber. Within the chamber lie the three auditory ossicles, the malleus (articular), incus (quadrate) and stapes (columella, hyomandibula).

Forming a new roof to the buccal cavity are the palatal ingrowths of the premaxilla, maxilla and palatine. The inverted gutter formed behind the hard palate by the palatines and pterygoids is covered by flesh during life to form the soft palate. Thus the internal nares open into the pharynx by a single opening, and the animal can now deal with food in the mouth without interference with breathing. The arrangement of the bones in this nasal region has also separated an upper olfactory chamber from the narial passage. From above there is the sequence, olfactory chamber, vomer, narial passage, palate, buccal cavity (*see* Fig. 29.13 (*b*)).

Of the original mandibular arch, the palatines and pterygoids are still in contact with each other, forming the sides of the posterior part of the narial passage, but the quadrate is now far removed as the incus of the middle ear. The upper jaw consists of premaxillae bearing the incisor teeth and maxillae bearing canine, premolar and molar teeth. A large part of the side of the facial region is formed by upward extension of the maxilla. Two fused bones, dentaries form the lower jaw which articulates by articular processes with the glenoid fossae beneath

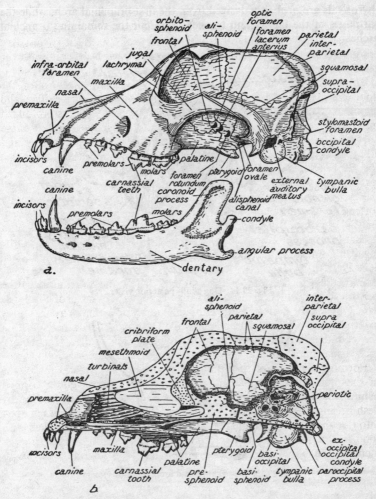

Fig. 29.13. Dog skull. (a) Lateral view with lower jaw. (b) Median L.S.

the squamosals. A flattened coronoid process projects upward within each zygomatic arch. It serves for attachment of the powerful masticatory muscles which are fastened dorsally to the cranium (see Fig. 29.13 (a)).

The hyoid body in the floor of the mouth represents the basihyal, while the anterior cornua, each consisting of ceratohyal, epihyal and stylohyal represent the rest of the arch. The posterior cornua or thyrohyals are probably derived from the first branchial arch, while the cartilages of the larynx and trachea represent the remaining branchial arches.

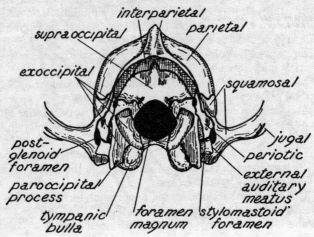

Fig. 29.14. Dog skull, posterior view.

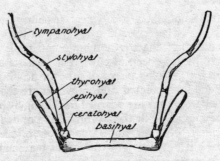

Fig. 29.15. Dog skull, hyoid arch, anterior view

Foramina of the Skull.

1. The *anterior nares.*

2. The *anterior* and *posterior palatine foramina* for the passage of V maxillary.

3. The *lachrymal foramen* for the lachrymal duct which leads from the orbit into the nasal cavity.

4. The *infra-orbital foramen* in front of the zygomatic process of the maxilla; here V maxillary leaves the orbit.

5. The *optic foramen* in the middle of the orbitosphenoid for the passage of the optic nerve, II.

6. The *foramen lacerum anterius* between the alisphenoid and basisphenoid; through it pass III, IV, VI and ophthalmic V.

7. The *foramen rotundum* just behind the foramen lacerum anterius; here V maxillary passes out from the brain.

8. The *foramen ovale* between the alisphenoid and periotic; it transmits V mandibular.

9. The *stylomastoid foramen* behind the tympanic bone for the passage of VII.

10. The *foramen lacerum posterius* ventrally between the tympanic bulla and the occipital condyle; IX, X, XI and the internal jugular vein leave the cranium.

11. The *carotid foramen* in the tympanic bone near the occipital condyle; here, the internal carotid artery enters the skull.

12. The *external auditory meatus.*

13. The *condylar foramen* in the exoccipital through which passes the twelfth cranial nerve, the hypoglossal.

14. The *Eustachian canal* behind the foramen ovale.

15. The *foramen magnum.*

The Teeth of the Dog

The teeth of the dog show the typical structure and arrangement found in carnivores. They cut and tear the food into pieces of a size suitable for swallowing; there is nothing comparable with the masticatory mill of the rabbit, sheep or cow. The incisors are pointed and admirably suited for grasping pieces of food or holding prey. Behind the incisors are the long pointed canines which are the main weapons of attack and defence. They are adapted for killing by piercing, and for tearing. The premolars, with their prominent pointed cusps, form a serrated edge suitable for dividing large pieces of meat or cracking bones. A special characteristic of carnivorous mammals is the possession of *carnassial teeth.* They are the last premolar in the upper jaw and the first molar in the lower jaw. The former has a smooth flat inner surface and the latter a similar outer surface (*see* Fig. 29.13 (*a*)). The carnassial tooth of the upper jaw slides over the corresponding tooth of the lower jaw, thus they constitute a pair of shears. By this device, the dog is able to shear meat from bones and even to cut pieces from the bone itself. The molars of the upper jaw and the last two molars of the lower jaw have inwardly produced crowns with relatively large undulating surfaces. They form a crushing mechanism whereby hard portions of food are broken up.

New Features in the Mammalian Skull. Compared with lower vertebrates, the mammalian skull shows a number of features which make for greater biological efficiency. The cranium is considerably broader and deeper to accommodate the larger brain and certain extra bones are thus included in the cranium wall. Such are the squamosal, the interparietal and the periotic. The rigid fusion to the cranium of the upper jaw, coupled with wide zygomatic arches to accommodate larger masticatory muscles, make for greater efficiency in dealing with the food. Mammals are the only vertebrates which chew and hence there is differentiation of the teeth for various functions. Allied to this is the separation of the respiratory and food passages by the interpolation of the palate so that now the internal narial opening is far enough back to allow of chewing without interference with the breathing. The lower jaw consists of a single bone on each side and this is correlated with the heavy work it has to perform. A jaw with a number of separate bones would be inadequate for this work. The olfactory sense has assumed great importance in terrestrial mammals and hence there is enlargement of the capsule and great increase in area of the internal epithelium by provision of the scroll-like turbinals. In the middle ear, the presence of three jointed ossicles with their ligaments and muscles provides a delicate mechanism for transmission of vibrations and yet guards against damage to the membranous fenestra ovalis by damping violent vibrations. Correlated with the incorporation of the quadrate into the middle ear, there is a new type of jaw suspension which is achieved by the groove on the underside of the zygomatic arch of the squamosal. The rolled articular surface of the lower jaw fits this glenoid fossa and the coronoid process is now inside the arch and thus the large hard-worked masticatory muscles can fill the temporal cavity.

The Vertebral Column (Rabbit)

The vertebral column can be divided into distinct regions with types of vertebrae very characteristic of their particular region. In the neck are seven *cervical vertebrae*, in the thorax, twelve or sometimes thirteen *thoracic vertebrae*, in the loin, seven *lumbar*, in the hip, usually one *sacral*, though three caudal may be fused with it, and finally, in the tail there are about fifteen *caudal vertebrae*. The vertebrae are entirely bony and their centra have flat, smooth, articulating surfaces separated by fibrous *intervertebral discs*. At the centre of each disc is a small soft jelly-like region called the *nucleus pulposus*. It is the sole remnant of the notochord in the adult.

All the cervical vertebrae are characterized by the presence of short double-headed ribs fused laterally to the base of the transverse process. The vertebral artery passes through the foramina so formed. The third, fourth and fifth are the most typical cervical vertebrae. The centra are not very stout, the question of weight in the neck being important. On each articular surface of the centrum is a thin bony plate, the epiphysis, which, after ossification, has fused with the diaphysis. The short cervical ribs enclose the *vertebrarterial canal* and then fork. Above the neural arch is a small neural spine and laterally in front are the upwardly-directed *prezygapophyses* while the downward-facing *postzygapophyses* occupy a similar position posteriorly (*see* Fig. 29.16 (*a*)).

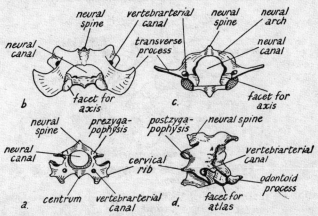

Fig. 29.16. Cervical vertebrae of rabbit. (*a*) Anterior view of 5th. (*b*) Dorsal view of atlas. (*c*) Posterior view of atlas. (*d*) Side view of axis.

The first and second vertebrae, respectively the *atlas* and *axis*, are specially modified. There is no centrum on the atlas and in front, situated latero-ventrally are two large facets for articulation with the occipital condyles of the skull. In life, a ligament divides the neural canal into dorsal and ventral portions, the former occupied by the spinal cord and the latter by the odontoid process of the axis. Broad wing-like cervical ribs provide large surfaces for attachment of the muscles which rock the head up and down. These muscles pass forward both dorsally and ventrally to be inserted on the cranium (*see* Fig. 29.16 (*b*), (*c*), (*d*)).

The odontoid process of the axis represents the centrum of the atlas. Dorsally, there is a ridge-like longitudinal neural spine, to which are attached muscles from the skull and the ribs of the atlas. These muscles produce the turning movements of the head, the skull and atlas rotating on the odontoid process. Laterally, the cervical rib of the axis is longitudinally expanded into a narrow shelf.

The sixth and seventh cervical vertebrae have tall neural spines and begin to approach the condition of the thoracic vertebrae.

All the thoracic vertebrae have tall backward-sloping neural spines and small cylindrical centra. Dorso-laterally placed on the neural arches are short horizontal transverse processes. The ribs articulate at two points, the *capitulum* or head of the rib fitting into a small depression formed of two *demi-facets* at the antero-lateral corner of

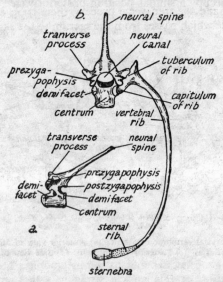

Fig. 29.17. Thoracic vertebra of rabbit. (*a*) Side and (*b*) anterior view showing rib articulation.

the centrum of one vertebra and the postero-lateral corner of the centrum of the next vertebra. The *tuberculum* of the rib articulates with the smooth facet at the end of the transverse process. Movable jointing of the ribs allows breathing movements, but they are also secured to the vertebrae by ligaments. The tall neural spines join the *supra-spinous ligament* which begins at the skull and joins all the vertebrae by their neural spines. Posteriorly, the thoracic vertebrae begin to resemble the lumbar (*see* Fig. 29.4).

The most typical lumbar vertebrae are the second and third (*see* Fig. 29.18). There is a prominent neural spine flanked by strong *meta-pophyses* which rise from the antero-lateral region of the neural arch. The transverse processes are stout and long; they point forward and downward. Below the postzyapophyses, paired pointed *anapophyses* project backward, and ventrally there is a median downward projection of the centrum called a *hypapophysis*. These lumbar vertebrae are the biggest and strongest in the whole column and this is correlated with the fact that a number of the powerful muscles of the back are attached to them. Bending of the vertebral column, which plays a large part in the jumping movements, is mainly performed by muscles passing beneath the centra from the sacrum to all the lumbar and the posterior thoracic vertebrae. Lateral to the lumbar vertebrae between the metapophysis and the transverse process, there is on each side a thick mass of muscle which passes from the sacrum to the skull, narrowing in

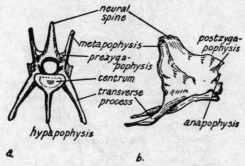

Fig. 29.18. Lumbar vertebra of rabbit. (*a*) Anterior view. (*b*) Side view.

the anterior thoracic and cervical regions. This muscle has branches to the transverse processes and to the metapophyses and also to the ribs. Contraction of this muscle straightens the vertebral column. The relationship of these muscles to locomotion will be considered in the appropriate section.

There is only one true sacral vertebra, but since three or four caudal are fused with it, the whole structure is generally known as the *sacrum* (*see* Fig. 29.19). The thick, strong, transverse processes of the sacral vertebra have a roughened lateral facet for fusion with the ilia of the pelvic girdle. This is a rigid and very strong joint through which the thrust of the hind-limbs is transmitted to the vertebral column. The whole sacrum forms a large triangular bone providing a broad base for posterior attachment of the muscles of the back.

The caudal vertebrae gradually degenerate towards the end of the tail until they become mere small cylindrical centra.

It is important to understand how well the vertebrae are connected together. Each vertebra joins the next behind by three facets; the centrum with the intervertebral disc and the two postzygapophyses which fit over the two prezygapophyses. This three-point contact inter-locks the whole series so that there is more arching possible dorsally than ventrally and a limited amount of lateral bending. The atlas and axis are attached to the skull and each vertebra is joined to the next posterior one by small ligaments. In addition, there are four long ligaments running from the skull to the sacrum, connecting all the vertebrae together. There is a dorsal ligament joining all the neural

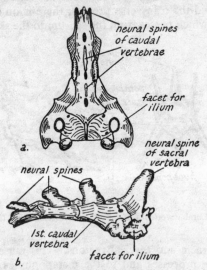

Fig. 29.19. Sacrum of rabbit. (*a*) Side view. (*b*) Dorsal view.

spines, a ventral ligament joining the centra, and two lateral ligaments joining the transverse processes. These bind the whole series together into one unified structure with little bending possible between any two contiguous vertebrae but a considerable degree of curvature possible to the whole column. The ligaments ensure that at no point is the curvature excessive. Power is provided by the complicated muscles of the back. The column plays three important rôles; it protects the spinal cord, is an essential component in locomotion, and axially supports.

Ribs and Sternum

There are normally twelve pairs of ribs articulating by movable joints with the thoracic vertebrae and forming a bony cage which protects the heart and lungs (*see* Fig. 29.20 (*a*)). The first seven ribs are complete half-hoops extending from the vertebral column to the sternum, while the eighth and ninth join the seventh. The last three ribs are sometimes described as "floating," since they make no connexion with the sternum. Each rib has a vertebral bony portion and a cartilaginous sternal portion. Both the dorsal movable joints and the

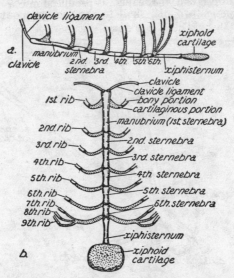

Fig. 29.20. Sternum and ribs of rabbit. (*a*) Side view. (*b*) Ventral view.

flexible ventral cartilage give the elasticity necessary for the breathing movements.

The sternum is a narrow bony rod divided transversely into six *sternebrae*, the first being called the *manubrium*. Beyond the articulation of the seventh rib is a short bony rod, the *xiphisternum*, and a flat round plate, the *xiphoid cartilage* (*see* Fig. 29.20 (*b*)).

Thin flat sheets of muscle join the ribs together. These *intercostal muscles* are in two sets, inner and outer. The former raise the ribs and the latter lower them, aided by muscles which pass forward from the sacrum.

The Girdles and Limbs

As in all mammals except the most primitive, the pectoral girdle is very much reduced. In the rabbit, it is represented by two lateral *scapulo-coracoids* and two ventral *clavicles*. There are no joints between these four components. Each scapula is a flat triangular bone tapering ventrally towards the *glenoid socket* for the humerus. On the outer border is a raised ridge called the spine, which forks at its ventral end to give a small *acromion* process pointing downward and a longer *metacromion* process directed backward. Overhanging the glenoid in front, is a small *coracoid* (probably a pre-coracoid and coracoid fused). At its broad dorsal end. the scapula is produced into a narrow band of cartilage, the *suprascapula*. The clavicle is a short rod-like bone

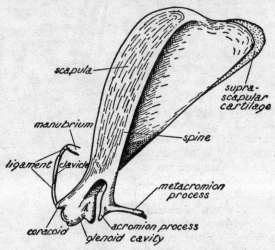

Fig. 29.21. Pectoral girdle of rabbit, left half.

developed in a ligament which joints the coracoid to the top of the sternum (*see* Fig. 29.21).

No part of the pectoral girdle makes a bony joint with the axial skeleton. The scapulo-coracoids are embedded in muscles of the dorsal thoracic region and are only fixed by the muscles attached to them. The clavicles are fastened at both ends by ligaments; indeed, they are in a vestigial condition. These arrangements give the girdle great springiness, which is correlated with the fact that there is little loco-motive work done by the front-limbs; they serve mainly to reduce the impact of landing and this suppleness of the girdle is important in dissipating shock.

In contrast with the pectoral girdle, the pelvic girdle is very strong and rigidly fused to the sacrum. Also, together with the sacrum, it forms a complete girdle. Instead of lying at right angles to the axis, it lies almost parallel to it. The *acetabulum*, for jointing to the head of the femur, is approximately in the middle of the girdle on each side, so that there are large bony surfaces in front of it and behind it, for the attachment of the limb muscles. The *ilium* forms about half the acetabulum and passes forward, being fused with the sacrum at the middle region of its inner side. Proceeding backward in line with the ilium is the *ischium*, forming at its anterior end the larger portion of the posterior half of the acetabulum, which is completed by a small ventral inner bone, the *cotyloid* (*see* Fig. 29.22).

The two *pubes* are joined at the *pubic symphysis* in the ventral mid-line, each having two outwardly-directed arms, the anterior of which is fused to the cotyloid and ilium, and the posterior to the ischium. Between pubis and ischium is the large *obturator foramen*.

The strength and rigidity of the pelvic girdle enable it to sustain the powerful thrust of the hind-limbs during jumping, while its position parallel to the vertebral column and its fusion to the sacrum ensure that the thrust of the limbs is transmitted to the axis of the body. The elastic symphysis in the female is related to parturition, when the girdle separates somewhat to enable passage of the young down the uterus.

The Limbs. There are two important differences between the limbs of mammals and those of the reptiles from which they evolved. Both are concerned with change of position.

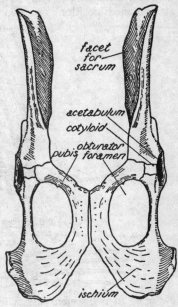

Fig. 29.22. Pelvic girdle of rabbit, ventral view.

Instead of being splayed out laterally from the body, they are now vertically beneath it, so that the body is held clear of the ground. Also both limbs have been rotated, the front in somewhat complicated fashion, so that the original preaxial border is now medial and the fingers and toes face forward. Here they are described as for the resting position. Both limbs, however, retain the pentadactyl plan almost in its entirety.

The humerus has a rounded head which makes a ball-and-socket joint dorsally with the glenoid cavity of the scapula. At the sides of the head are two roughened areas called *tuberosities*, the lesser (which is the larger) on the inner side, and the greater on the outer side. The bone slopes backwards and slightly upwards, tapering somewhat to its articulation with the radius and ulna, where it has a wheel-like end called the *trochlea*. On the ventral surface of the humerus is a knife-like edge, the *deltoid ridge*. Articulating with the trochlea is the *sigmoid notch* of the ulna, which projects beyond the joint as the *olecranon process* (*see* Fig. 29.23 (*a*)). The radius meets the humerus bluntly at a small facet called the *capitellum*, on the inner side of the trochlea. To accommodate the two ends of the sigmoid notch, in either the bent or straightened position, are two shallow depressions, anterior to the

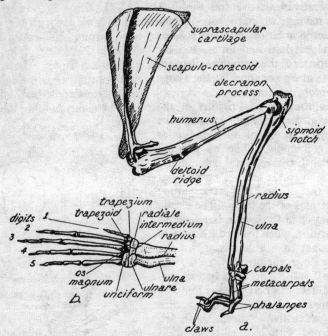

Fig. 29.23. **Fore-limb of rabbit.** (*a*) Side view, natural position. (*b*) Dorsal view of manus.

trochlea. Dorsally there is the *olecranon fossa* and ventrally the *coronoid fossa*; connecting the two is a small foramen, the *supra-trochlear*. The radius and ulna proceed almost vertically downwards, parallel and closely bound together. In the wrist, there are eight carpals arranged 3, 1, 4 from proximal to distal. There are five meta-carpals with digits, the digital formula from inner to outer side being 2, 3, 3, 3, 3. All the distal phalanges bear pointed claws (*see* Fig. 29.23 (*b*)). The rabbit cannot rotate the radius round the ulna as we can, and thus the hand is fixed in the *pronate* position, palm downward and cannot be placed in the *supinate* position with palm upward.

The hand touches the ground with the digits only, the elbow joint cannot be completely straightened and the pectoral girdle is springy. All these features are correlated with impact with the ground at the end of a jump. It is comparable with the way in which we land after a jump, on the ball of the foot with the knees bent.

The hind-limb is very long and in the normal crouching position is shaped like a letter Z from the right; from the left, it has the shape of a laterally inverted Z (*see* Fig. 29.24 (*a*)). The femur is long, directed forward and slightly upward. It articulates inwardly with the acetabulum by a ball-and-socket joint and bears, around its proximal end, three processes called *trochanters* (*see* Fig. 29.24 (*a*)). The great trochanter is a backward extension, the lesser trochanter is in front of the head on the inner aspect and the third trochanter is opposite the lesser on the outer aspect. As with the tuberosities of the humerus, these processes serve for the attachment of ligaments binding the bone

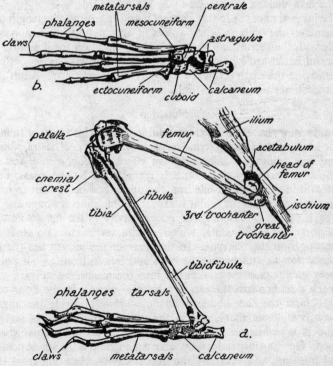

Fig. 29.24. Hind-limb of rabbit. (*a*) Side view, natural position. (*b*) Dorsal view of pes.

to the girdle and also act as stops preventing excessive bending in various directions. At its distal end, the femur bears rounded, lateral condyles separated by an *intercondylar groove*. On the upper surface, the groove narrows to provide a recess in which the *patella* slides. This latter is a disc-like sesamoid bone which serves to protect the open knee-joint. The tibio-fibula proceeds backward and downward at an angle of about 30° with the femur. It has broad facets which fit the femoral condyles and a *cnemial crest*, like the deltoid ridge of the humerus, ventrally. The fibula is a splint-like bone fused with the tibia proximally and at its mid-point but separated between. Distally, the tibio-fibula has a central deep notch and two lateral facets for articulation with the tarsals. The tarsals are six in number, consisting of two large proximal tarsals, the *astragulus* and *calcaneum*, a *centrale*, and three small distal tarsals. The calcaneum is outermost and projects backward as the heel bone. There are four metatarsals, the inner one being absent, and four digits, each having three phalanges with claws on the last phalanx in each case (*see* Fig. 29.24 (*b*)).

The large area of the foot in contact with the ground, the length of the segments of the limb and their angles of articulation, the fusion of the girdle with the sacrum, all show obvious adaptation for jumping. The powerful backward kick of the feet during burrowing is very effective in removing the earth scratched away by the front claws. Adult males will sometimes use the hind-limbs as weapons.

Nutrition

The alimentary canal shows greater differentiation into regions than that of the lower vertebrates. It consists of the *mouth, buccal cavity, pharynx, oesophagus, stomach, duodenum, ileum, caecum, colon, rectum* and *anus*.

The true border of the mouth is represented by the gums, but in front of it are the soft mobile lips, the upper one being cleft to expose the incisors and thus the rabbit is able to nibble short herbage and even the bark of trees. Roofing the buccal cavity is the *hard palate* and posteriorly the *soft palate*, which terminates as the pointed *uvula* projecting into the pharynx. In the floor of the mouth lies the large muscular *tongue* attached at the back and free in front. Four pairs of *salivary glands* pass their secretion into the mouth by salivary ducts. On each side, beneath the ear, is a parotid *gland*; in the floor of the orbit behind the cheek-bone is an *infra-orbital*; inside the angle of the jaw is a *submaxillary*, and in the floor of the mouth beneath the tongue is a *sublingual*. The pharynx is short and somewhat ill defined. Opening into it dorsally, above the uvula, is the single posterior narial opening, and ventrally the buccal cavity. Leading from it are the oesophagus dorsally and the glottis ventrally (*see* Fig. 29.25). At the sides of the pharynx are the openings of the Eustachian tubes and below them are the *tonsils*, two sunken patches of lymphoid tissue. In front of the glottis is a movable flap, the *epiglottis*, which bends over the respiratory opening while food is being swallowed. From the pharynx, a long tube, the oesophagus, leads through the neck and thorax to the stomach. It is muscular and lined internally with stratified epithelium. Longitudinal folds close the lumen except when swallowing is taking place. At the distal end of the oesophagus is a valvular arrangement, the *cardia*, which prevents regurgitation of food from the

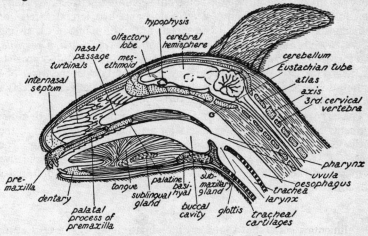

Fig. 29.25. Rabbit head, median L.S.

stomach, a large ovoid sac lying transversely across the abdomen beneath the diaphragm. Its anterior surface is concave and its posterior surface convex. The wall has a plentiful vascular supply and thick bands of unstriated muscle, an outer longitudinal, a middle circular and an inner oblique. Within the muscle is the sub-mucous coat, consisting mainly of connective tissue very well supplied with blood-vessels (*see* Fig. 29.27 (*a*)). The mucous membrane is perforated by numerous minute *gastric pits*; the cells lining these pits produce the gastric juice. Below the mucous membrane is a thin layer of muscle, the *muscularis mucosae*, which sends fine strands to the epithelium between the pits (*see* Fig. 29.27 (*a*)). The contractions of the muscularis mucosae, together with the process of peristalsis, squeeze the gastric juice into the lumen. The gastric pits are simple or branched tubular glands of three functional kinds, *cardiac* near the entrance of the oesophagus, *fundic* throughout most of the stomach and *pyloric* near the exit. Mucus-producing cells line the cardiac and pyloric glands,

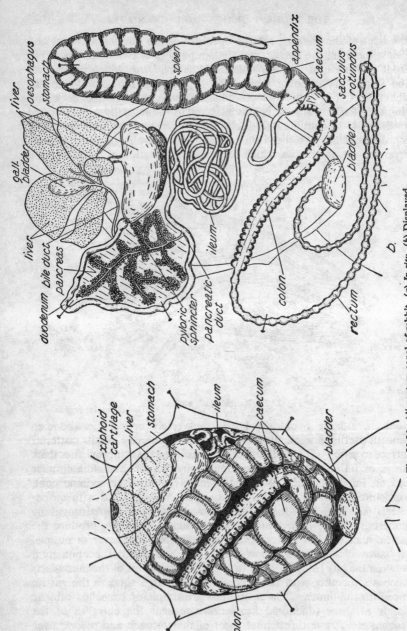

Fig. 29.26. Alimentary canal of rabbit. (a) *In situ.* (b) Displayed.

but the fundic glands have, in addition, *peptic cells* producing the enzymes, and deeper-seated *oxyntic cells* producing H+ and Cl− ions.

The stomach exit is regulated by the pyloric sphincter, which is relaxed at intervals to allow chyme to pass into the small intestine. In the rabbit, two distinct regions can be recognized, the duodenum and the ileum, the total length being about 2·5 m. The duodenum has a backward loop reaching almost the whole length of the body cavity, and then it doubles forward almost to the stomach again. In

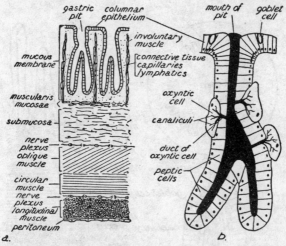

Fig. 29.27. Mammalian stomach. (*a*) V.S. wall. (*b*) Gastric pit, fundus region.

the mesentery between the two loops are numerous small scattered masses of pink tissue which together constitute the pancreas. Its duct opens into the duodenum on the forward loop, about 8 cm from the bend. The bile duct from the liver opens into the duodenum not far from the pyloric sphincter.

Histologically, the duodenum consists of an outer peritoneum, connective tissue, longitudinal and circular muscle, a sub-mucous coat, the muscularis mucosae and then the mucous membrane. The latter has numerous finger-like projections called *villi*, the depressions between the villi being the *crypts of Lieberkühn* (*see* Fig. 29.28 (*a*)). Numerous racemose *Brünner's glands* open into the crypts, their secretion together with that of the crypts constituting the succus entericus (*see* Fig. 29.28). Scattered along the inner lining of the duodenum and ileum are white *Peyer's patches* consisting of lymphoid tissue packed with leucocytes, many of which migrate into the lumen.

The ileum ends at the dilated *sacculus rotundus* where there is further lymphoid tissue and a valvular arrangement, the *ileo-caecal valve*, which directs the food remains into the *caecum*. This is a dilated blind tube with a spiral constriction along it. It ends in the finger-like *appendix* where again there is much lymphoid tissue.

Leading from the junction of caecum and sacculus rotundus, the large intestine continues as the *colon*, which has lateral sacculations, to the *rectum*, a narrow tube dilated at intervals by the faecal pellets. The alimentary canal ends with the *anus*, a sphincter at the root of the tail.

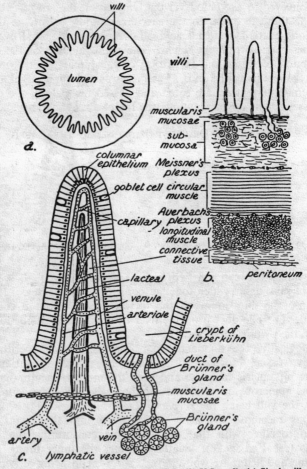

Fig. 29.28. Duodenum of rabbit. (*a*) T.S. (*b*) V.S. wall. (*c*) Single villus.

The mechanical and chemical processes of digestion are fully described in Vol. II. In outline, the food passes along the gut by peristalsis accompanied by segmentation movements in the small intestine. Digestion is accomplished by the digestive juices which are saliva, gastric juice, bile, succus entericus and pancreatic juice. In the rabbit, there is no ptyalin in the saliva, its sole function being to lubricate the passage of food. The products of digestion are absorbed by the villi of the small intestine and carried by the hepatic portal system to the liver, except in the case of fats, which are absorbed by lacteals and conveyed to the blood via the lymphatics, the *receptaculum chyli* and the thoracic duct. In the caecum, cellulose is broken down by symbiotic bacteria and thus any cell contents are digested by residual enzymes carried from the ileum. The main function of the colon is absorption of water and formation of the faecal pellets which pass along the rectum to the anus. The faeces passed out at night are black and semi-liquid; they are eaten and passed through all the digestive processes again. In the daytime, the faeces are almost dry and brown

Summary of Digestive Processes in the Rabbit

Digestive juice	pH	Enzyme precursor	Activator	Enzyme	Substrate	Products
1. SALIVA	6·7	—	—	—	—	Lubricates the food
2. GASTRIC JUICE	1·1 to 1·8	pepsinogen	HCl	pepsin	proteins nucleo-proteins	peptones nucleic acid and peptones
		pro-rennin	HCl	rennin	caseinogen	calcium paracaseinate
3. BILE	8	—	—	—	fat	emulsified fat
4. PANCREATIC JUICE	8·8	trypsinogen	enterokinase	trypsin	peptones	polypeptides
		chymotrypsinogen	trypsin	chymotrypsin	peptones	polypeptides
		—	—	amylase	starch and glycogen	maltose
		—	—	lipase	fat	fatty acids and glycero
5. SUCCUS ENTERICUS	8·3	—	—	enterokinase	—	
		—	—	erepsin complex	polypeptides	amino-acids
		—	—	invertase	sucrose	glucose and fructose
		—	—	maltase	maltose	glucose
		—	—	lactase	lactose	glucose and galactose
		—	—	lipase	fat	fatty acids and glycerol
		—	—	nuclease	nucleic acid	nucleotides
		—	—	nucleotidase	nucleotides	nucleosides
		—	—	nucleosidase	nucleosides	nitrogenous bases plus glycoside

in colour; they are not eaten. The former practice is known as *coprophily*.

Glands Associated with the Alimentary Canal

Apart from the particular glands associated with special digestive secretions, there are glandular cells producing mucus along the whole alimentary tract. The mucus is a colloidal solution of glycoproteins and mucopolysaccharides; it serves in the first place to lubricate the food and prevent abrasion of the delicate mucous membranes, and it

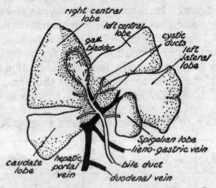

Fig. 29.29. Rabbit liver lobes (turned forward).

also spreads a protective layer, which resists the attack of enzymes, over the entire inner surface.

The salivary glands, the pancreas and Brünner's glands are racemose; the crypts of Lieberkühn are tubular. Both types have been referred to under "glands" in Chap. 20. The spleen, though originally derived from the gut, has lost any connexion with it, and is a lymphatic gland.

The Liver. The liver is the largest gland in the body. It is slung from the diaphragm by a double sheet of peritoneum which also encloses the whole organ. There is partial subdivision into five lobes which are, from right to left, the *caudate* lobe overhanging the right kidney, a *right central* lobe, a small dorsal *Spigelian* lobe, a *left central* lobe and a *left lateral* lobe (*see* Fig. 29.29). Embedded in the right central lobe is the gall-bladder from which the bile duct passes to the duodenum. All the lobes have small cystic ducts from which the bile passes direct to the duodenum while digestion is proceeding, or back to the gall-bladder if there is no digestion

Microscopic structure of the liver can be visualized with reference to

Fig. 29.30. The ground tissue is composed of tightly packed *liver cells* each with a prominent nucleus and sometimes seen to contain glycogen granules and fat droplets. These liver cells form a spongy meshwork separating countless interconnecting spaces or *lacunae*. Through these pass blood capillaries or *sinusoids* whose walls are formed by an often discontinuous squamous epithelium. In the capillary walls may be seen occasional stellate, phagocytic *cells of Küpfer* whose function is to ingest and disorganize effete red blood cells. The capillaries are the ultimate factors of the hepatic portal vein although blood from the hepatic artery will empty into them. Blood which passes through these

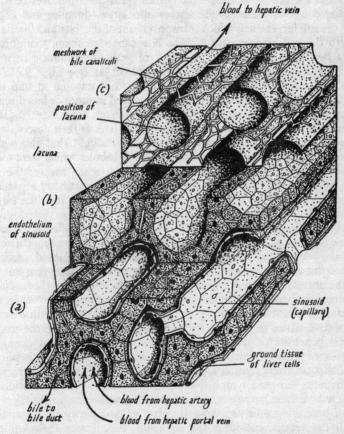

blood to hepatic vein

meshwork of bile canaliculi

(c)

position of lacuna

lacuna

(b)

endothelium of sinusoid

(a)

sinusoid (capillary)

ground tissue of liver cells

bile to bile duct

blood from hepatic artery

blood from hepatic portal vein

Fig. 29.30. Diagram of liver tissue. At (*a*), all cells are represented except blood cells in the sinusoids. At (*b*), sinusoids have been omitted from lacunae. At (*c*), the bile canaliculi are shown in relation to the lacunae.

capillaries is eventually collected up by factors of the hepatic vein which also ramify through the liver tissue. The liver is thus a vast meshwork of microscopic vessels through which blood from the gut must pass before being returned to the main circulatory channels. On its way through the sinusoids it comes into very close relationship with the liver cells which among other things will regulate the form and quantity of food material entering the main circulation. In addition to this function, the liver cells form bile juice and this they secrete into minute *canaliculi* which are formed as intercellular channels between the cytoplasm of adjacent liver cells. These canaliculi have no lining of their own and the bile is secreted directly into them from the liver cells. It is passed out of these minute spaces into larger ductules and finally into the still larger ducts which transport it out of the liver and discharge it into the gall-bladder or gut. The bile canaliculi form, therefore, a most delicate and intricate meshwork of very fine channels between the liver cells, ramifying through the whole organ (*see* Fig. 29.31 (*c*)).

When sections of liver are examined it is not unusual to find that the labyrinth of cells and sinusoids are arranged in more or less discrete masses in which the chains of liver cells (liver cords) are radially arranged around a central blood-vessel. The liver is then described as lobulated and from this appearance it was thought that the whole organ was constructed of prismatic masses or lobules which were more or less permanent and individual formations. In the case of the pig this would appear to be so, for the lobules are distinctly separated from one another by connective tissue through which pass the larger factors of the portal blood system, then described as interlobular veins, and the efferent bile ductules. The connective tissue in this case is continuous with that which forms a sheath, known as *Glisson's capsule*, beneath the peritoneum in which the liver is enclosed. Axially placed in such a prismatic mass is a factor of the hepatic vein known as the intralobular or central vein and into this flow the radially arranged sinusoids (*see* Fig. 29.31 (*a*)). In most mammals, however, the lobulation is much less definite or even absent, there being little or no connective tissue in the interior of the liver except where the major vessels penetrate or find exit. Such connective tissue-lined channels are termed *portal canals* and either house factors of the hepatic portal vein, hepatic artery, lymph and bile ducts in the one case or factors of the hepatic vein and lymph ducts in the other. When lobulation is observed in these latter cases, it would seem to be due to the effect of blood pressure gradients across the liver caused partly by the ability of all the vessels, including the sinusoids, to contract their lumina. When pressure tends to be low in the hepatic portal factors as compared with that in the hepatic factors, lobulation appears, in which the latter

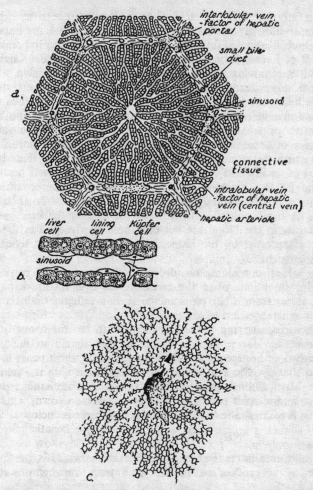

Fig. 29.31. (*a*) T.S. liver lobule of pig. (*b*) Sinusoid. (*c*) Section of rabbit liver, bile canaliculi injected.

are the axes of the lobules. If the pressures are reversed the lobulation is likewise reversed and the hepatic portal factors become axial.

Though primarily a gland for the secretion of bile, the liver, as already mentioned, has other important functions. These include treatment of the digested food entering from the gut and the destruction of effete red corpuscles.

Bile is fully described in Vol. II, Chap. 4. It will suffice to say here that the salts, sodium glycocholate and sodium taurocholate, are important in the emulsification of fats, and that the bile pigments are breakdown products of haemoglobin. Thus the liver, like the spleen, acts as a blood filter, removing effete corpuscles, but retaining the iron.

Hexose sugars, carried in the portal blood stream, are absorbed by the cells lining the sinusoids and converted to glycogen. When this is broken down, it is always glucose that is released into the blood, irrespective of what hexoses were first absorbed. Hence there is conversion of hexoses as well as synthesis of glycogen. The condensation reaction is promoted by a high blood-sugar level, and by the presence of insulin and corticosterone, while the hydrolysis reaction is favoured by low blood-sugar level and the presence of adrenalin, thyroxin and the pituitary diabetogenic hormone. Total lack of insulin, or insufficiency of it, lead to the disease diabetes mellitus, when sugars in the blood are not converted to glycogen in the liver; glucose is excreted by the kidneys and the carbohydrate content is quickly exhausted.

After a meal containing fat, droplets of it are plentiful in the liver cells. In starvation, when the carbohydrate reserves are exhausted, the fat stores from other parts of the body are first mobilized in the liver for general release to the tissues.

Amino-acids arriving at the liver appear to be sorted out, so that those necessary for protein synthesis are distributed to the tissues, while excess or unnecessary acids are deaminated and treated in other ways so that pyruvic acid is formed and oxidized with the release of energy. Much of this energy appears as heat. The ammonia separated from the amino acids enters the *ornithine cycle* (*see* Vol. II, Chap. 15) and urea is formed, the total reaction being expressed thus—

$$2NH_3 + CO_2 = CO(NH_2)_2 + H_2O$$

The soluble urea enters the blood stream and is excreted by the kidneys. Vitamin A is synthesized in the liver from various pro-vitamin carotinoids.

Finally, in the embryo, the liver is, for a period, the site of formation of the blood corpuscles, a marked contrast with its later function of destruction of corpuscles which become useless.

Respiration

Air passes in through the nostrils, where it is filtered by the nasal hairs and warmed and moistened by its passage through the turbinal epithelium and the narial passage. It enters the pharynx, where, except during swallowing, the glottis is open. The larynx and trachea are kept open by cartilages which in the case of the larynx are the *thyroid*, *cricoid* and *arytenoid*, and in the case of the trachea, a long series of rings incomplete dorsally (*see* Fig. 29.32). Stretched across the anterior opening of the larynx are the *vocal cords* by the vibration

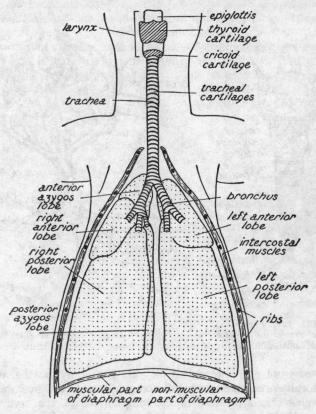

Fig. 29.32. Respiratory organs of rabbit, ventral view.

of which the voice is produced. At the base of the neck, the trachea forks to give the two *bronchi*, one of which enters each lung, and then branches copiously, the ultimate *bronchioles* being minute and lacking cartilaginous support. Each bronchiole finally enters a dilatation somewhat like a very small bunch of grapes, called an *infundibulum*, slightly less than one millimetre in length (*see* Fig. 29.34). Leading from each infundibulum are numerous small *alveoli* or air-cells formed of a delicate squamous epithelium. Tufts of capillary blood-vessels make intimate contact with the air-cells and it is at the regions of contact that respiratory exchange takes place, the blood being separated from the air by two squamous epithelia, that of the air-cells and that of the capillaries. The oxygen is absorbed by the erythrocytes and

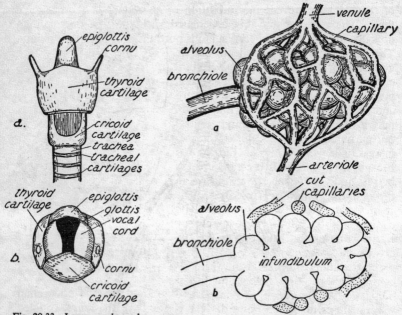

Fig. 29.33. Larynx and vocal cords of rabbit. (*a*) Anterior view. (*b*) Looking into glottis.

Fig. 29.34. Infundibulum of lung. (*a*) Whole. (*b*) L.S.

removed from solution, and as they are constantly moving, there is no difficulty in maintaining a diffusion gradient. In the presence of the relatively-reduced pressure in the lung capillaries, the erythrocytes release the enzyme *carbonic anhydrase* which rapidly catalyses the breakdown of carbonic acid and bicarbonates, thus—

$$H_2CO_3 \rightleftharpoons H_2O + CO_2$$

This ensures a high concentration of CO_2 in the lung capillaries and thus there is a diffusion gradient causing CO_2 to pass from the blood into the air-cells.

To understand the respiratory movements it is necessary to consider carefully the relationships of the lungs, the pleural cavities, the ribs and diaphragm (*see* Fig. 29.32). Each lung is covered by the pleura which continues from the root of the lung and lines the internal surface of the thoracic wall and the diaphragm. Separating the pleurae of the lungs from that of the body wall is coelomic fluid filling the pleural cavities. Thus any movement of the thoracic wall or diaphragm which tends to take these further away from the lungs will entail expansion of the lungs to prevent the formation of a vacuum in the coelomic fluid. The ribs are movably articulated with the vertebral column dorsally, and their sternal cartilaginous portions give ventral flexibility.

The diaphragm has peripheral muscle attached to the ribs and the vertebral column. When the external intercostal muscles contract, the ribs move forward and outward, and when the diaphragm muscle contracts the arching central portion is flattened out. Both processes increase the volume of the thorax and because of the reduced pressure created in the lungs, atmospheric air rushes in through the respiratory passages. The spongy nature of the lung, with all its components bound together mainly by elastic connective tissue, allows for the expansion.

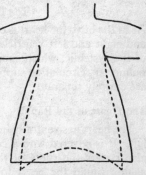

Fig. 29.35. Mammalian thorax during breathing: inhalation (continuous line); exhalation (dotted line).

In exhalation, the ribs are lowered by contraction of the inner intercostal muscles, the diaphragm is relaxed and pressure of the abdominal viscera causes it to arch upward. The elasticity of the lungs, coupled with these two pressures, forces the air out again (*see* Fig. 29.35).

During normal quiet breathing about one-eighth of the gaseous content of the lungs is changed at each inhalation and exhalation. During violent exertion, this may rise to one-half, but there is always 50 per cent of the total lung capacity in which the air is unchanged except by diffusion. Thus, interposed between the changing air and the absorptive surface is still air, which is the actual mediator between atmospheric air and lung epithelium. That the diffusion process is

	Oxygen	Nitrogen	Carbon dioxide	Water vapour
Inhaled	20·96	79·00	0·04	variable
Exhaled	16·5	79·5	4·00	saturated

efficient is shown by comparing the proportions of the gases in inhaled and exhaled air. Roughly, in place of the oxygen absorbed, an equal volume of CO_2 is given out. This is the respiratory exchange, and the ratio CO_2/O_2 is the respiratory quotient; in the case quoted it is $4·16/3·96$ (for interpretation of respiratory ratios *see* Vol. II, Chap. 11).

The large capacity of the lungs, the enormous internal surface, and the efficient respiratory movements, have in no small measure contributed to the success of the mammals as warm-blooded animals.

The Blood Vascular System

As in the bird, the heart is completely divided into right and left auricles and right and left ventricles. There is a double circulation consisting of the systemic, which supplies all the body except the lungs, and the pulmonary circulation supplying the lungs. In the adult the two systems are entirely separate.

The Heart of the Rabbit

The heart lies ventrally in the thorax with its apex slightly tilted to the left. It is covered with a coelomic epithelium, the pericardium, which also covers the roots of the great vessels anteriorly, is then reflexed again around the heart to form a double layer containing coelomic fluid. The space in which it lies, between and ventral to the lungs, is the ventral *mediastinum*. Other portions of the mediastinum are occupied by the thymus gland anteriorly and by the oesophagus, trachea, aorta and posterior vena cava dorsally.

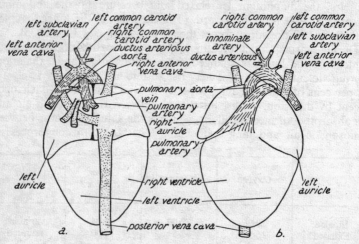

Fig. 29.36. Heart of rabbit. (*a*) Dorsal view. (*b*) Ventral view.

Though the capacity of each of the four chambers is the same, the ventricles appear much larger than the auricles because of their thick muscular walls. Seen in ventral view, it is apparent that the primitive truncus now occurs in two parts, a pulmonary arch opening from the right ventricle and a systemic arch leading from the left ventricle. Joining these two arches is a vestigial *ductus arteriosus*, now a solid strand. Entering the heart dorsally are the great veins; the three venae cavae lead separately into the right auricle, while the pulmonary veins lead into the left auricle by a common aperture (*see* Fig. 29.37).

Internally, the right auricle and ventricle are separated by three membranous flaps made of connective tissue covered by the endocardium. The ventricle contains numerous ridges and projections called

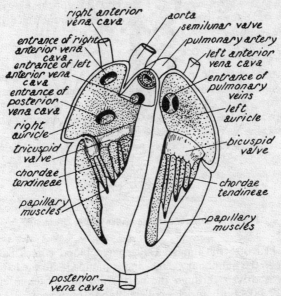

Fig. 29.37. Heart of rabbit. Ventral view dissected.

columnae carneae. To some of these, called *papillary muscles, chordae tendineae* pass from the flaps of the *tricuspid valve.* A similar arrangement exists on the left side of the heart except that the valve has two flaps and hence is called the *bicuspid* or *mitral valve.* At the exit of both pulmonary and systemic arch (aorta) are semi-lunar valves (*see* Fig. 29.37).

The circulation through the heart is fully described in Vol. II, Chap. 9; here a brief outline is given. The auricles contract together and this is followed by simultaneous contraction of the two ventricles. Dealing with the right side of the heart first; blood flows into the right auricle from the venae cavae and at *systole* this blood is pumped into the right ventricle. The chordae tendineae aided by slight contraction of the papillary muscles, prevent reflux into the auricle when the ventricle contracts. Thus the blood is forced into the pulmonary

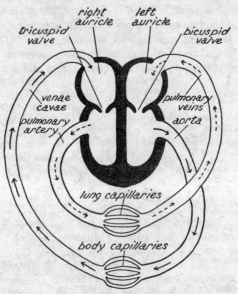

Fig. 29.38. Diagram of mammalian double circulation.

arch and hence to the lungs. Oxygenated blood comes back to the left auricle in the pulmonary veins, and is pumped into the left ventricle. Thence it is driven through the aorta into the systemic circulation (*see* Fig. 29.38). Both auricles collect blood; both ventricles distribute it. The right side of the heart contains only deoxygenated blood, and the left side only oxygenated blood. It is noteworthy that the thicker muscle of the left ventricle compared with that of the right ventricle is correlated with the greater driving force necessary in the systemic circulation than in the pulmonary.

The Heart of the Sheep

Because of the small size of the rabbit's heart, it is customary to examine the heart of a larger animal, usually that of the sheep. While

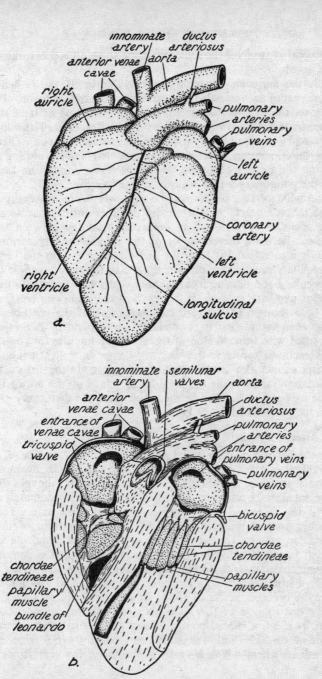

Fig. 29.39. Heart of sheep. (*a*) Ventral view. (*b*) Ventral dissection.

the general anatomy is the same, there are some differences which need to be noted.

Only the auricular appendages are visible in the entire heart, the greater part of each auricle being covered with adipose tissue. There is a groove, the *longitudinal sulcus*, indicating the line of separation of the ventricles; this also, is filled with fat. Branches of the *coronary artery* and *vein* are clearly visible in the surface tissues. There is a single anterior vena cava, the right and left vessels uniting before entering the heart. The solid *ductus arteriosus* connecting the aorta with the pulmonary artery is easily visible (*see* Fig. 29.39).

Internally, certain details can be seen which are not easily visible in the rabbit's heart. A thin area in the inter-auricular septum is the *fossa ovalis*, a remnant of an embryonic passage between the two auricles. Between the entrances of the anterior and posterior venae cavae is a membranous fold, the *Eustachian valve*. In the ventricles, the papillary muscles are prominent, and in the right ventricle there is a muscular band passing from the interventricular septum to the most anterior papillary muscle. It is known as the *moderator band*, since it was once thought that it restricted expansion of the ventricle. Since it has been found that it contains mainly a band of Purkinje tissue concerned with transmission of the myogenic impulse for contraction, it is sometimes known as the *bundle of Leonardo*, a slight tribute to the versatile genius who first drew and described it. In the dissected heart, immediately anterior to the semi-lunar valves of the aorta, the exit of the coronary artery can be discerned. It is the first artery given off from the aorta (*see* Fig. 29.39).

The Arterial System

A comparison of the arterial arches of dogfish, frog, lizard, pigeon and rabbit is given in diagrammatic form across. In mammals, the majority of these arches disappear in the adult, though they are represented in the embryo. The third becomes the carotid arch and the fourth the systemic, only represented on the left side. The right systemic arch is represented by the proximal portion of the right subclavian artery. There is no trace of the fifth arch and the sixth on the left becomes the pulmonary aorta. The original communication between the sixth arch and the lateral dorsal aorta persists on the left as the ductus arteriosus, joining the pulmonary and systemic aortae; its cavity becomes occluded and it remains as a solid strand.

The distribution of the main arteries is shown in Fig. 29.41 and apart from a few special points, it need not be further described. The common carotids and the subclavian usually arise from a short innominate artery which is really a portion of the ventral aorta, and

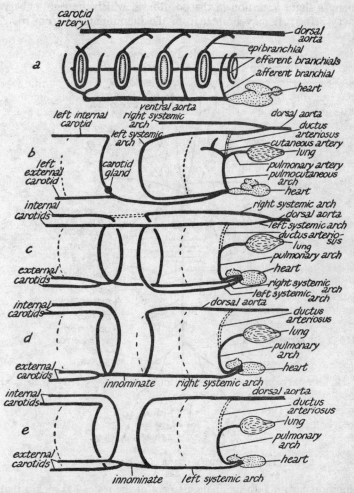

Fig. 29.40. Diagrams of aortic arches. (*a*) Dogfish, left side. (*b*) Frog, left side. (*c*) Lizard, both sides. (*d*) Pigeon, both sides. (*e*) Rabbit, both sides.

owing to the length of the neck, the common carotids extend to the angles of the jaws before forking to give external and internal branches. There is slight variation in the position at which the right subclavian artery arises; it may branch from the innominate or from the right

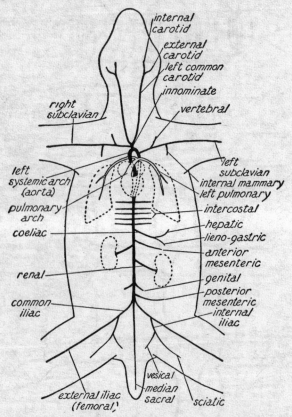

Fig. 29.41. Arterial system of rabbit, ventral view.

common carotid. In the male, descent of the testes has meant that the spermatic arteries become elongated though they still leave the aorta at the same point.

The Venous System

For ease of comparison, the main outlines of the venous systems of craniates are given in diagrammatic form across. In all cases, the hepatic

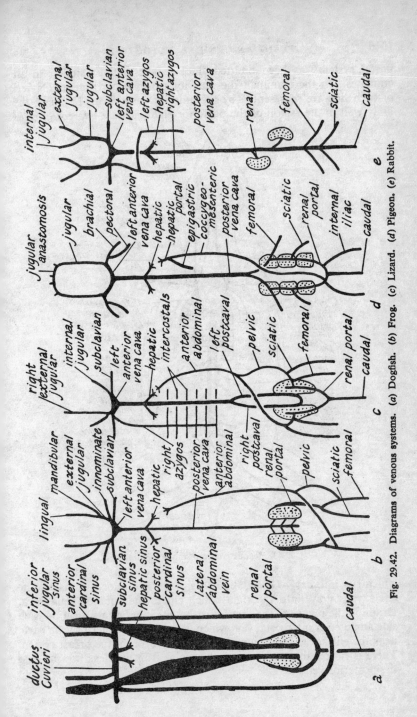

Fig. 29.42. Diagrams of venous systems. (a) Dogfish. (b) Frog. (c) Lizard. (d) Pigeon. (e) Rabbit.

portal system as been omitted since it is essentially similar in all craniates. In the mammal, the anterior cardinal and ductus Cuvieri of each side are represented by the anterior vena cava. Draining the body wall in the region of the posterior eight ribs are *intercostal veins*

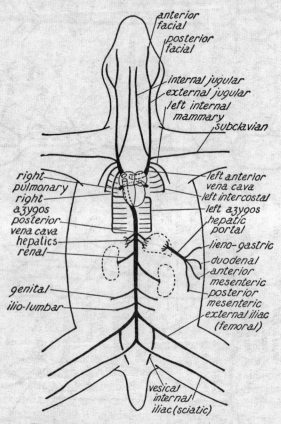

Fig. 29.43. Venous system of rabbit, ventral view.

which run into *azygos veins*, remnants of the posterior cardinals. The left azygos flows into the right which enters the anterior vena cava. Draining the region of the first four ribs, the intercostals form on each side an anterior intercostal vein which flows into the anterior vena cava, near the entrance of an *internal mammary vein* from the breast region. There is no renal portal system, the blood from the legs flowing into the posterior vena cava.

The Blood

Mammalian blood is described in Chap. 20. It is noteworthy that the mammals are the only craniates in which the erythrocytes are non-nucleated. They are also characteristic in their shape, i.e biconcave discs. As in the birds, the blood remains at a constant temperature.

The Lymphatic System

This is more fully described in Vol. II, Chap. 9. In outline, the lymph exudes from blood capillaries and flows from intercellular channels into valved lymphatic vessels which enter the thoracic duct to empty into the blood at the jugular-subclavian junction. Lacteals from the gut enter the *receptaculum chyli* which continues forward as the *thoracic duct*. The lymphatic glands along the course of the vessels are responsible for replenishing the supply of leucocytes and for ridding the lymph of bacteria. The system plays a vitally important part in translocation since it forms the connecting link between the blood-vessels and the tissues and back to the blood system. Lymph directly bathes the tissues, nourishing them and removing their waste products.

Locomotion

The normal method of locomotion is by jumping, though the animal can run swiftly when necessary. It shows the general characteristics associated with all jumping animals; the centre of gravity in the normal resting position is far back, almost over a point mid-way between the hind-limbs; these limbs are long and bent in a spring-like fashion; there is a large area of foot in contact with the ground; the upward curvature of the vertebral column, when straightened by muscular pull, will tend to lift the lighter head end. In addition, the shorter but stout front-limbs with the bend at the elbow, and the springiness of the girdle, will both tend to make landing easier. The running action of the rabbit is really a series of leaps. The body is hurled ahead with the back straight, and during motion through the air the hind-limbs are brought forward so that they actually touch the ground in front of the front-limbs. At that moment the legs are flexed and the back is arched upward ready for the next leap.

Growth

In general, the growth curve for mammals is a series of sigmoid curves at first, with the slowing-down periods at weaning and puberty. At maturity, there is no growth but a steady state in which replacement of cells keeps pace with loss. Eventually, senescence ensues and there is gradual downward slope of the curve and somewhere along this, death will take place (*see* Fig. 29.44).

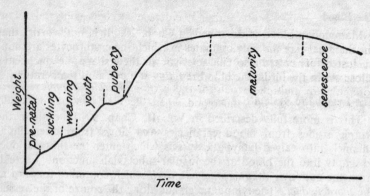

Fig. 29.44. Typical growth curve for a mammal.

Urinogenital System

The kidneys are dark red, bean-shaped structures situated dorsally above the splanchnocoel on either side of the lumbar vertebrae. The right kidney is more anterior than the left, and in ventral view, it is obscured by the caudate lobe of the liver. From the mid-point of the median side of each kidney, a white ureter passes down to the ventral bladder, entering it dorsally in its middle region. At the posterior end of the bladder is a sphincter beyond which the urethra leads the urine from the body via the vestibule and vulva in the female, and via the penis in the male (*see* Figs. 29.47 and 29.51).

Structure and Functions of the Kidney

The kidney is metanephric and hence its duct is a true ureter. It has an outer *cortex* with a granular appearance, then a *medullary zone* which is striated, and at its inner region there is a small cavity known as the *pelvis*, which is formed by the expanded end of the ureter. The whole structure is enclosed in a tough connective tissue capsule. Opening into the pelvis from the medulla is the *pyramid* (*see* Fig. 29.45).

The functional units of the kidney are the uriniferous tubules, of which there are a very large number. Each tubule ends blindly as a small rounded funnel in the cortex; the funnels are known as Bowman's capsules, each consisting of a double layer of squamous epithelium enclosing a small cavity. From the Bowman's capsules, the first convoluted tubule winds about the cortex and then gives rise to the *descending limb of Henlé* which passes into the medulla. It turns back at the *loop of Henlé* and then an *ascending limb of Henlé* re-enters the cortex, where it continues as the second convoluted tubule.

This, with many similar tubules, enters a straight collecting tubule which proceeds through the medulla to open at the apex of the pyramid in the *duct of Bellini* (*see* Fig. 29.46).

Just before entering Bowman's capsule, the afferent arteriole makes close contact with the second convoluted tubule; at this point the cells of both are multiplied to form the *juxta-glomerular complex*. These cells release *renin* into the blood when the Na^+ concentration falls;

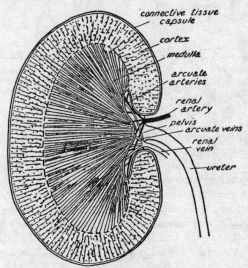

connective tissue
capsule
cortex
medulla
arcuate
arteries
renal
artery
pelvis
arcuate veins
renal
vein
ureter

Fig. 29.45. Kidney of rabbit. Median L.S.

this sets in action a chain of hormonal events which ultimately affect absorption of Na^+ from the second tubule (*see* p. 1084). The afferent arteriole breaks up into a glomerulus of capillaries and the blood leaves the capsule by an efferent arteriole. This divides to give a network of capillaries around both convoluted tubules.

The kidney has two functions; osmoregulation and excretion. Owing to the fact that the efferent arteriole of each glomerulus is smaller than the afferent arteriole, a high blood pressure develops. Under this pressure, ultra-filtration takes place from the glomerular capillaries through the inner epithelium of Bowman's capsule into the lumen of the tubule. The filtrate consists of blood plasma together with all the substances in true solution; colloids such as blood proteins do not pass from the blood. Along the tubule, especially in the convoluted portions, water, glucose, various salt ions and other useful substances are resorbed so that a concentrated urine leaves the kidney. In parts by weight, the urine contains about 95 per cent water, 2 per cent urea and 3 per cent other materials. A more detailed account of kidney filtration and resorption is given in Vol. II, Chap. 15.

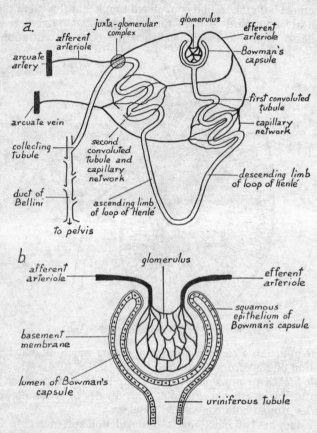

Fig. 29.46. Diagrams showing (*a*) mammalian kidney tubule and blood supply. (*b*) L.S Malpighian corpuscle.

Male Urinogenital Organs

The testes are small ovoid bodies, originally in the abdominal cavity near the kidneys, each being suspended by a mesorchium. But in the adult, they have descended into the *scrotal sacs*, one on each side of the penis. The cavity of each scrotal sac is continuous with the splanchnocoel by the *inguinal canal* through which the testis passed, dragging with it the *spermatic cord* containing the spermatic artery and vein among connective tissue. Each testis is attached to the base of its scrotal sac by a strand called the *gubernaculum*, consisting mainly of elastic tissue. It is by contraction of the gubernaculum that the testis is pulled down. Along the inner border of the testis is a much coiled mass of tubules, the *epididymis*, which represents the remains of the mesonephros; it is aggregated chiefly into an anterior *caput* epididymis

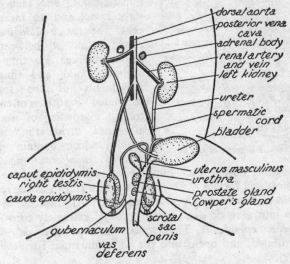

Fig. 29.47. Urinogenital system of rabbit (male).

and a posterior *cauda* epididymis. From the cauda epididymis, the vas deferens (Wolffian duct) passes up through the inguinal canal, curls over the ureter and opens dorsally below the bladder sphincter into the urethra. Posterior to the openings of the vasa deferentia is a small dorsal sac, the *uterus masculinus*, which represents the sole trace of the Mullerian ducts in the male. The urethra, now a urinogenital duct, passes through the penis to open at its tip (*see* Fig. 29.47).

At each side of the urethra, near the uterus masculinus, is a *prostate gland* whose secretion activates the sperm, and just at the root of the penis are *Cowper's glands*. They produce a fluid whose exact function is unknown, though it is suggested that it may wash out traces of urine in the urethra before ejaculation of the seminal fluid.

The penis is elongated and has a retractible skin, the *prepuce*, covering the end region which is known as the *glans penis*. In the penis are three longitudinal cavities filled with spongy tissue, the paired *corpora cavernosa* and the single *corpus spongiosum* (*see* Fig. 29.48). The spaces in these corpora become engorged with blood prior to copulation and thus the penis becomes swollen and stiff and is said to be erected. Blood from small arteries flows into the spaces and eventually drains away into small veins.

Structure and Functions of the Testis. The testis is enclosed by two coats, an outer serous *tunica vaginalis* which is continued over the

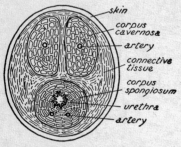

skin
corpus cavernosa
artery
connective tissue
corpus spongiosum
urethra
artery

Fig. 29.48. T.S. penis of rabbit.

gubernaculum and then lines the scrotal sac, and an inner fibrous coat, the *tunica albuginea*. Surrounding the testis between the two serous surfaces is a thin layer of coelomic fluid, and thus sliding movements of the testis are facilitated. Partitions of connective tissue, ingrowths of the tunica albuginea, divide the testis into lobules which contain the convoluted *seminiferous tubules*. Towards the inner border, each tubule becomes straight and then all the tubules meet and form a network of passages known as the *rete testis*. A number of fine *vasa efferentia* lead anteriorly from the rete testis, and open into a single duct which becomes extremely convoluted to form the *caput epididymis*. The duct continues to the *cauda epididymis*, also convoluted, and opens into the wider muscular *vas deferens* (*see* Fig. 29.49).

Each seminiferous tubule is circular in transverse section, though owing to their convoluted nature, various shapes will be seen in any section. Surrounding each tubule is loose connective tissue with its cells flattened against the basement membrane. On this are the cells of the germinal epithelium, which are cubical in shape. The majority of the cells are destined to form gametes but some will become *cells of Sertoli*, whose function is to nourish the developing sperm. These Sertoli or sustentacular cells are pyramidal with the wide end on the basement membrane and the apex projecting into the lumen. The *germinative cells* multiply by mitosis, forming rounded *spermatogonia*. By further division, these form somewhat smaller cells which then undergo a phase of growth to become *primary spermatocytes*. From each of these, by a first meiotic division, two haploid *secondary spermatocytes* are produced, and then, by the second meiotic division, four haploid *spermatids*. These become attached to the inner end of a Sertoli cell and metamorphose into *spermatozoa* which lie with their

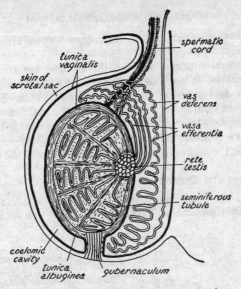

Fig. 29.49. Median L.S. of rabbit testis in scrotal sac.

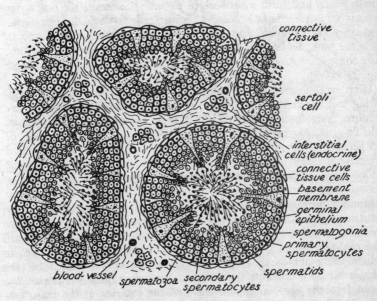

Fig. 29.50. T.S. testis of rabbit.

tails pointing towards the centre; later, they become free in the lumen (*see* Fig. 29.50).

In the connective tissue between the tubules are small groups of rounded *interstitial cells* which produce the male hormones, *androgens*. The secretion is endocrine and is distributed in the blood system. These hormones initiate the development of the male secondary sexual characteristics and also maintain them after development.

The primary function of the testes is the production of the male gametes, while the second function is the secretion of the androgens.

Female Urinogenital Organs

The *ovaries* are small ovoid bodies lying in the dorsal wall of the abdomen below the kidneys. Close to each ovary, and actually wrapped

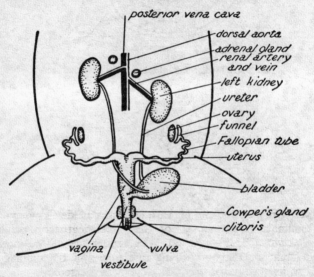

Fig. 29.51. Urinogenital system of rabbit (female).

around it during ovulation, is the wide, thin-walled, fimbriated *funnel* of the oviduct. The ducts themselves have somewhat convoluted portions, known as the *Fallopian tubes*, which lead inward toward the mid-line where they become dilated to form the paired *uteri*, in which the embryos develop. The uteri lead into a wide tube, the *vagina*, which is dorsal to the bladder. Both the vagina and the *urethra* open into the *vestibule* which leads to the exterior at the *vulva* (*see* Fig. 29.51). Immediately within the vestibule on its ventral surface is a small rod-like organ, the *clitoris*. This contains two corpora cavernosa and is erectile; thus it is homologous with the penis in the male. There are no prostate glands in the female, and Cowper's glands are reduced.

Structure and Functions of the Ovary. The ovary is covered by the peritoneum. In its outer region it has clear cubical cells constituting a germinal epithelium. Inside the ovary is a dense weft of connective tissue consisting mainly of collagen fibres among which is a little unstriated muscle. In the stroma are blood-vessels, lymphatic vessels,

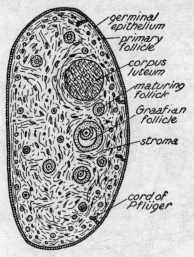

Fig. 29.52. Median L.S. ovary of rabbit.

nerve fibres, *Graafian follicles* in various stages of development, and in older animals, *corpora lutea* or their final regression products, *corpora albicantia* (*see* Fig. 29.52). The appearance of the ovary is subject to great variation according to the age of the animal, and according to its stage in the oestrous cycle or in pregnancy.

Cells are proliferated into the stroma by the germinal epithelium, to form the *egg-tubes of Pflüger*. All the cells are capable of becoming oogonia, but in fact, only one in each egg-tube does. The cells become rounded up to form *nests* with one future ovum in the centre surrounded by follicle cells with a nutritive function. By a series of divisions, the follicle becomes larger and the cells become separated into an inner layer attached to the outer layer in one region. The fluid separating the cells is secreted by them and is known as the *liquor folliculi*. A ripe Graafian follicle contains a *discus proligerus* surrounding the ovum, the whole discus being attached by a follicle stalk to the *membrana granulosa* which is the inner layer of follicle cells (*see* Fig. 29.53). The discus proligerus is almost surrounded by the liquor folliculi which eventually distends the follicle considerably. When it is near the outer side of the ovary, the follicle bursts by increasing turgidity, perhaps aided by contraction of unstriated muscle fibres

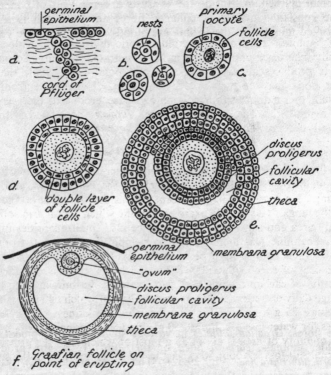

Fig. 29.53. Developmental stages of Graafian follicle.

around it. The force of ejection carries the discus proligerus with its contained ovum into the oviducal funnel.

The cavity remaining in the ovary after ovulation becomes a corpus luteum, consisting of chains of cells and connective tissue. These chains of cells contain yellowish fat droplets and they secrete the hormone *progesterone* which stimulates preparation of the uterus, embedding of the fertilized ovum, the formation of the placenta and the inhibition of ovulation during pregnancy. During birth, the hormone *relaxin*, from the corpus luteum, stimulates widening of the pelvic girdle.

Besides producing the ova, the ovary is an important endocrine gland, secreting the *oestrogens* which stimulate the development of the female secondary sexual characteristics. The tissue which produces these hormones is probably the follicular tissue, the whole process being under the control of the follicle-stimulating hormone from the pituitary.

Gametogenesis follows the same stages as in the male, namely, *oogonia → primary oocytes → secondary oocytes → ova*, but at the first meiotic division, the products are one large cell and a polar body, both haploid. Then at the second meiotic division, which does not usually take place until the sperm has penetrated, the large secondary oocyte produces an ovum and a second polar body, while the first polar body may or may not divide again. Thus, while from one primary spermatocyte, four spermatozoa are produced, there is only one ovum from one primary oocyte. This is correlated with the necessity for providing food for the embryo in the ovum.

Excretion

In the mammal there are three principal excretory organs, apart from the gut, through which waste products of the bile, mucus, and used enzymes, are passed. The important organs are the kidneys, the skin and the lungs. The kidneys excrete the urine which contains in solution mainly urea and salt ions. There may be also small quantities of uric acid, creatinine and ammonia. The perspiration escaping from the skin contains about 2 to 3 per cent of salts (mainly NaCl) and about 3 per cent of carbon dioxide. From the lungs, there is considerable excretion of carbon dioxide and water vapour. In human beings, the average daily excretion of CO_2 is about 670 g of which 640 g pass from the lungs, 25 g from the skin and 5 g from the kidney. The relevant figures for water loss are, lungs 250 g, skin 650 g, kidneys 1,500 g. The total quantity of urea is about 35 g most of which is in the urine, and the total salt loss is about 50 g, 35 g in the urine and 15 g in the sweat.

Reproduction

Mammals undoubtedly evolved from reptiles which laid large heavily-yolked eggs. The evolution of viviparity and the placenta led to the minute *microlecithal* egg. Hence, fertilization is necessarily internal and the external genitalia are suitably adapted. Mature Graafian follicles are only present in the ovary at the heat periods, which occur three or four times a year in the rabbit. Copulation takes place by the male mounting the female's back with his front limbs and then the erected penis is passed into the vestibule, the prepuce being pushed back during entry to expose the glans penis. Friction of this sensitive region with the sides of the vestibule is the stimulus for ejaculation of the seminal fluid. In the rabbit, ovulation takes place immediately after copulation, five or six eggs from each ovary passing almost simultaneously into the respective oviducts. Fertilization takes place high in the oviducts and the embryos are at the blastocyst stage when they arrive at the uteri ready for implantation. The period of gestation is about thirty days and when the young are born, they are blind and helpless and still enclosed in the true amnion, which is removed by the mother. They are fed on milk from the mammary glands, and in three to four weeks, they begin to make short excursions from the burrow and can soon find their own food.

The Nervous System

It is in the brain that the most remarkable advances in the nervous system are to be found, and here perhaps lies the main key to the success of the mammals.

The Brain

In the telencephalon, the cerebral hemispheres are very large, almost obscuring the small olfactory lobes and reaching back to touch the cerebellum. There is a thick cortex consisting of grey matter mainly, and developed largely by increase in area of the dorsal part of the roof,

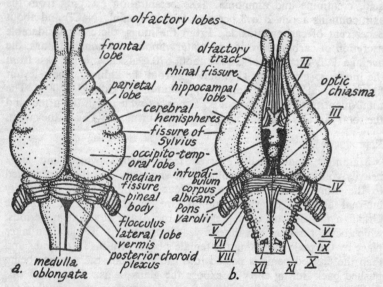

Fig. 29.54. Brain of rabbit. (a) Dorsal view. (b) Ventral view.

the *neopallium*. Further increase in area is effected by the folding of the surface into sulci, though these are poorly represented in the rabbit. Fissures divide the hemispheres into *frontal, parietal* and *occipito-temporal lobes*. The median fissure is deep, but the two hemispheres are connected by the *corpus callosum*, a broad tract of fibres peculiar to mammals. In front, the small olfactory lobes continue

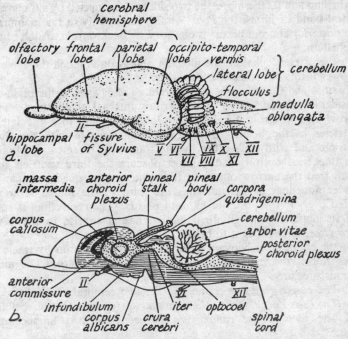

Fig. 29.55. Brain of rabbit. (*a*) Side view. (*b*) Median L.S.

ventrally into the olfactory tracts which terminate in the *hippocampal lobes* at the sides of the optic chiasma (*see* Fig. 29.54).

Dorsally, the thalamencephalon is covered by the cerebral hemispheres. The pineal stalk projects between the hemispheres. On the ventral surface, the infundibulum has a backward protrusion, the *corpus albicans*. The optic thalami are so thickened that they touch across the third ventricle, forming the *soft commissure* or *massa intermedia*. The anterior choroid plexus is a thin vascular fold which dips downwards into the ventricle (*see* Fig. 29.55.) The hypothalami are of exceeding importance in neurosecretion (*see* p. 1081).

The mesencephalon also, is almost obscured by the cerebral hemispheres; beneath their posterior portions are the optic lobes, now divided into four *corpora quadrigemina*. The crura cerebri are considerably thickened.

In the metencephalon, the cerebellum is large and considerably folded. It is divided into a central *vermis* and two lateral lobes each ending in a twirled *flocculus*. There is considerable grey matter in the cerebellum and furthermore, the two sides are connected by a transverse ventral band of fibres, the *Pons Varolii*, found only in the mammals. The posterior choroid plexus is obscured by backward extension of the cerebellum.

In the myelencephalon, the medulla oblongata is much the same as in lower forms but somewhat thickened.

Cavities and Commissures of the Brain. The cavities of the brain are considerably constricted by the various internal thickenings. Two narrow rhinocoels in the olfactory lobes continue into the lateral ventricles in the hemispheres. These communicate with the third ventricle and with each other by the transverse foramen of Monro. The thickened optic thalami almost obscure the third ventricle into which lead the narrow optocoels from the corpora quadrigemina. A slender aqueduct of Sylvius joins the third to the fourth ventricle, roofed over by the posterior choroid plexus. The cerebellum is solid and its pattern in longitudinal section has given rise to the name *arbor vitae*, once thought to be the seat of the soul.

In the connexions between different parts of the brain by tracts of nerve fibres, the mammals show considerable advance. The main commissures are—

1. The *corpus callosum* connecting the two cerebral hemispheres.
2. The *Pons Varolii* joining the right and left regions of the cerebellum.
3. The *hippocampal commissure* between the two hippocampal lobes.
4. The *anterior commissure* connecting the corpora striata.
5. The *habenular commissure* between the optic thalami.
6. The *posterior commissure* in the roof of the mid-brain joining the two anterior corpora quadrigemina.
7. The *inferior commissure* across the floor of the third ventricle near the optic chiasma.
8. The *anterior peduncles* from the cerebellum to the posterior corpora quadrigemina.
9. The *middle peduncle* from the cerebellum to the Pons Varolii.
10. The *posterior peduncles* from the cerebellum to the dorsal region of the medulla oblongata.
11. The *crura cerebri* from the hind-brain to the thalamencephalon.

Relationship of Brain Structure to Mode of Life

Throughout our study of the vertebrates, reference has been made to some degree of correlation between the important senses and activities of an animal, and the major structure of the brain. In the mammal, we find that though the main sensory and motor areas show comparatively little advance on those of lower animals, there has been vast improvement in the size and extent of correlation and co-ordination centres.

In the telencephalon, these centres are the corpora striata and the cerebral hemispheres. The corpora striata are not as well-developed as are those of birds, indicating less reliance on instinctive behaviour. The pattern of nervous connexions between sensory and motor areas in these corpora striata is undoubtedly more or less fixed by heredity, since it is constant in any particular species. It is noticeable that while in young mammals behaviour is largely instinctive, much of it is modified as the animals become adult.

It is in the cerebral hemispheres that the outstanding advance has been made by the mammals. In the fish, the hemispheres consist largely of the corpora striata with a small roof, the pallium, almost entirely devoted to olfactory correlation. The grey matter for the most part, retains its primitive position around the central cavity as in the spinal cord, though some few nerve cells migrate to the cortical position. In the amphibians, the dorsal region of the hemispheres becomes the neopallium and the olfactory pallium is separated into two middle-lateral and outer-lateral positions, respectively termed the *archipallium* and *palaeopallium* (*see* Fig. 29.57). The neopallium is concerned with over-riding correlation between all types of sensory impulse and co-ordinated response through effector organs, but it is little developed and the great majority of the cell bodies still line the central cavity. There is slightly more development of the neopallium in birds and reptiles, but the greater emphasis, especially in birds, is on the corpora striata. It is in the mammals that the neopallium reaches its greatest development and there is very considerable migration of cell bodies to the surface, thus forming a cortex of grey matter whose area is increased by two means. First, there is enormous increase in the size of the hemispheres, and secondly, there is folding into sulci to increase the surface area further. Thus various areas of the body and various activities are, as it were, represented by areas of nerve cells with a specific pattern. All the sensory impulses are relayed to the neopallium; all the neurones seem to be interconnected; the probable number of neurones in the human cerebral cortex is over ten million, hence the number of possible combinations is incalculable. In the neopallium lies the physical basis of mind, the ability to learn and to show intelligent

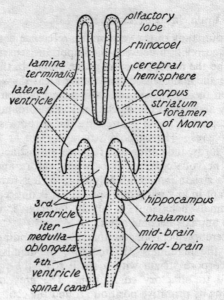

Fig. 29.56. Diagram of mammalian brain showing ventricles in horizontal section.

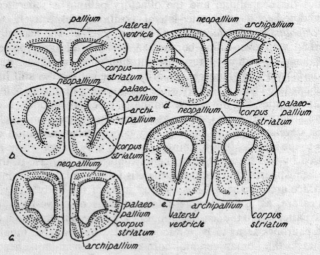

Fig. 29.57. Diagrams of cerebral hemispheres of vertebrates. T.S. (a) Fish. (b) Amphibian. (c) Reptile. (d) Bird. (e) Mammal. The stippling shows density and location of main groups of neurones.

behaviour, which is the consideration of a situation in the light of past experience and the making of the correct response. It is in the neopallium that memory, thought, imagination, reasoning and judgement are located. We do not know how these abilities are manifested by a set of interconnected nerve cells, but we do know that they are largely inherited. It must be clearly understood that learning in man, is quite different from learning in the lower animals. For example, an earthworm can learn to negotiate a maze, but it is a conditioned reflex and

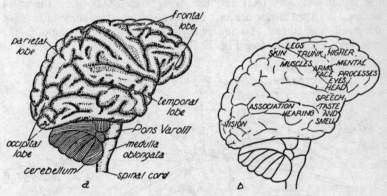

Fig. 29.58. (a) Human brain, side view from the right. (b) Human brain, correlation areas.

not intelligent behaviour. If the maze is altered slightly, the worm has to learn the new route by trial and error.

Co-ordination between the two hemispheres is effected by fibres running transversely in the corpus callosum.

The thalamencephalon has two correlation centres, the thalamus and hypothalamus. The former receives sensory impulses before they are passed to the neopallium; it is thought to be the seat of that consciousness or awareness which distinguishes man from other animals; here, sensations seem to be analysed into pleasant and painful, possibly having great survival value in evolution. Many optic fibres terminate in the thalamus, hence the usual name, optic thalamus. The hypothalamus is small; it controls most of the endocrine system, and plays an important part in regulation or *homeostasis*.

In the mesencephalon, the two anterior corpora quadrigemina are sight sensory centres, while the posterior lobes are concerned mainly with hearing. Ventro-laterally, the crura cerebri contain fibres carrying sensory impulses from the hind-brain and spinal cord to the thalami, and thence to the neopallium. They also carry many motor fibres emanating from the neopallium.

The cerebellum retains its primary function of co-ordinating motor activity in relation to balance and orientation. As in all animals on the reptilian line of descent, the medulla oblongata is thickened and shortened in correlation with the loss of the lateral line system and the branchial components of the cranial nerves.

The Cranial and Spinal Nerves

As in the lizard and pigeon, there are twelve pairs of cranial nerves, the *spinal accessory* (XI) and the *hypoglossal* (XII) being the extra nerves. Both are motor nerves. The former innervates some muscles of the neck, the larynx and the pharynx, while the latter supplies the muscle of the tongue (*see* Fig. 29.59).

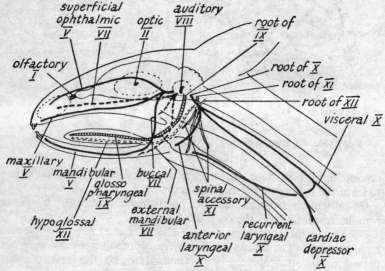

Fig. 29.59. Cranial nerves of rabbit, side view.

The development of the neck has entailed certain changes in the distribution of the branches of cranial nerve X. The posterior laryngeal branch is looped around the subclavian artery on the right and round the ductus arteriosus on the left. Both nerves then pass forward as *recurrent laryngeal* nerves. Other nerves of the neck are shown in Fig. 29.60.

With two exceptions, the spinal nerves are typical. The third, in the neck, sends a large branch called the great *auricular* nerve to the pinna of the ear. Portions of the fourth, fifth and sixth spinal nerves contribute to the formation of the *phrenic* nerve which supplies the diaphragm.

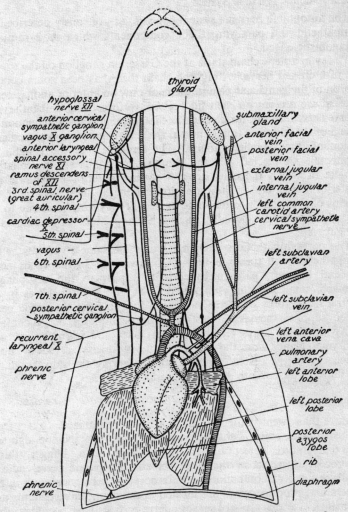

Fig. 29.60. Ventral dissection, neck of rabbit: veins shown only on left; spinal nerves and cranial XI and XII only on right.

The Autonomic Nervous System

The autonomic nervous system consists, as previously described, of sympathetic and parasympathetic components which have mutually antagonistic effects.

The sympathetic chain starts at the Gasserian ganglion on the root of the fifth cranial nerve. Along the chain there has been some concentration of the ganglia so that in the neck only an anterior and posterior cervical are present on each side. Rami to these ganglia from several spinal nerves of the neck indicate that there has been reduction by fusion of the ganglia. In the thorax, the stellate ganglion represents the fusion of three smaller ganglia. The remainder of the ganglia are segmental. Connected with the sympathetic ganglia are the collateral ganglia of which the chief are the coeliac, anterior mesenteric and posterior mesenteric. They are situated in the mesentery near the origins of the arteries of the same name. From them, fibres run to the viscera, supplying especially Auerbach's and Meissner's plexuses of the gut wall.

The parasympathetic system innervates the same structures as the sympathetic, with the exception of the oviduct. In the vagus nerve (visceral branch), parasympathetic fibres pass to the oesophagus, stomach, small intestine, lungs and heart. Posteriorly, fibres in the ventral nerve roots of the sacral region fuse to form the pelvic nerve which supplies the large intestine. The oculomotor nerve contains parasympathetic fibres leading to the ciliary and iris muscles. The lachrymal glands and the glands of the nose are served by fibres which run in the seventh cranial nerve. Serving the salivary glands are fibres in the seventh and ninth cranial nerves.

Sense Organs

More than twenty different senses are now recognized. Apart from the usual taste, smell, sight, hearing and touch, they include high and low temperature detection, texture, pressure, pain, hunger, thirst. Exteroceptors are sense organs, or sometimes separate nerve-endings, which perceive external stimuli. Enteroceptors perceive stimuli in the viscera and proprioceptors are located in muscles, joints, tendons and ligaments. Various types of sensory nerve-endings have been described in Chapter 20. Here, brief accounts of the main exteroceptors, the tongue, nose, eye and ear are given.

The Tongue. The tongue is the organ of taste, though it is also important in connexion with the movement of food in the buccal cavity, with swallowing, with mixing food with the saliva and with speech in human beings. It consists mainly of voluntary muscle fibres running in

three directions, longitudinally, transversely and vertically. These
fibres are bound together by connective tissue and a strong band of
the same tissue runs antero-posteriorly dividing the tongue into halves.
The surface is covered by mucous membrane, consisting of stratified
epithelium overlying connective tissue, among which are the tubular
Ebner's glands which secrete a fluid to keep the surface moist. They are
probably modified sudoriparous glands and in some animals evaporation of their secretion has a cooling effect, e.g. the lolling tongue of the
dog in hot weather. The lower surface is smooth, but the upper surface
has a large number of *papillae* which give it a roughened appearance.
Most plentiful are the small *filiform* papillae; there are less *fungiform*
papillae, while the large *circumvallate* papillae are few in number.
On the sides of the pits between the papillae, especially of the circumvallate type, are *taste buds*, each consisting of an ovoid cluster of long
columnar cells (*see* Fig. 29.61). Some have a supporting function, and

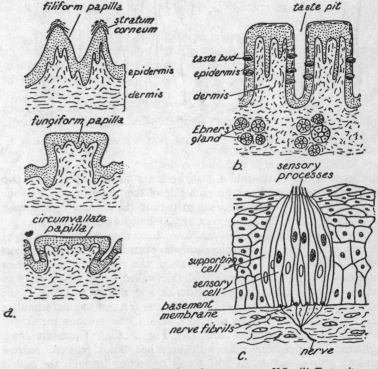

Fig. 29.61. (*a*) Types of papillae from human tongue. V.S. (*b*) Taste pits.
V.S. from papilla foliata of rabbit. (*c*) Taste bud. V.S.

some are sensory and are characterized by an apical protoplasmic fibril which projects through the taste pore into the pit. Nerve fibrils which ramify among the cells are factors of the glossopharyngeal (IX) cranial nerve. Chemical substances in the mouth dissolve in the fluid which fills the pits and set up disturbances in the protoplasmic fibrils. Resultant impulses pass along the nerve to the "taste brain." After correlation with olfactory impulses, interpretation of taste is located in

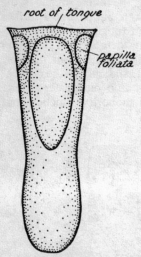

Fig. 29.62. Rabbit tongue,
entire, dorsal view.

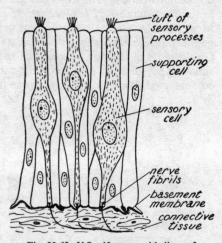

Fig. 29.63. V.S. olfactory epithelium of
mammal.

the neopallium. In the rabbit, taste buds are most plentiful in the two *papilla foliata* situated one on each side of the posterior region of the tongue (*see* Fig. 29.62). In many mammals, there are also taste buds on the soft palate, in the pharynx and sometimes on the gums.

The Olfactory Epithelium of the Nose. Each nasal passage consists of three regions. First there is the *vestibular* portion containing long hairs which act as filters. The next part, in the region of the anterior turbinals has numerous superficial thin-walled veins which serve to warm the air. Overlying the posterior and middle turbinals is the olfactory epithelium where chemicals in the form of vapour stimulate the sensory cells. In this olfactory region, the mucous membrane consists of three types of cells (*see* Fig. 29.63). There are long, cylindrical, supporting cells with branched basal regions, narrow sensory cells with tufts of stiff fibrils projecting through the cuticle into the lumen, and small basal cells which help in support. Vapours stimulate the fibrils of the sensory cells, and nerve impulses are carried into the brain through the cribriform plate by olfactory nerves. Interpretation is in the brain.

The Eye. The eye is the sense organ concerned with perception of stimuli due to light, but it is far more than a collection of photo-sensitive cells. Apart from the actual sensory cells, there are various refinements which render the sense more acute, certain structures for protecting the eye, and muscles for moving it.

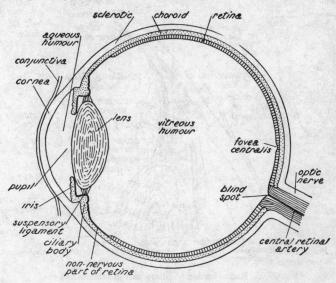

Fig. 29.64. Mammalian eye, horizontal section.

The eyeball itself resembles a camera in that it is light-tight except for one aperture for admission of the rays; there is a lens which focuses the light on a sensitive screen; it is adjustable for various object distances; also, there is a diaphragm which regulates the amount of light entering the system. The light-tight box consists of the three coats, the *sclerotic*, *choroid* and *retina*; the *lens* is held in position by the *suspensory ligament* and adjusted for convexity by the *ciliary muscle*; the *pupil* is the aperture in front of the lens, and its size is regulated by movement of the *iris* (*see* Fig. 29.64).

The eyeball is spherical except for an outward bulge in the front. It is divided by the lens and suspensory ligament into anterior and posterior chambers, the former containing the *aqueous humour* and the latter the jelly-like *vitreous humour*. These two fluids, which are perfectly transparent, serve to maintain the shape of the eyeball. Enclosing the fluids are the three coats, none of which is complete. The outer coat is the sclerotic, white and opaque, and made mainly of white fibrous connective tissue. In front, the sclerotic bulges outward to form the transparent *cornea*. At the back of the eyeball, slightly on the inner side, the sclerotic is perforated for the exit of the optic nerve along which the fibrous coat continues for some little distance.

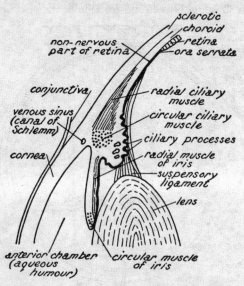

Fig. 29.65. Radial section of ciliary part of mammalian eye.

Within the sclerotic is the choroid, a highly vascular membrane consisting of loose connective tissue among which are many large branched chromatophores containing melanin. The choroid is black in many animals, but is brown in human beings. In front, the choroid is thickened to form a ring, the ciliary body, from which it continues inward as the suspensory ligament which suspends the lens. The choroid terminates in the coloured iris in front of the lens. The third and innermost coat of the eyeball is the retina, which is the sensitive layer. It extends to the margin of the pupil behind the choroid, but its nervous region ends at the *ora serrata*, somewhat behind the ciliary body. The outline of the ora serrata is marked by a wavy line around the inner surface of the eyeball. The retina is interrupted by the optic nerve, the region being known as the *blind spot*. In the middle of the retina, immediately opposite the optical axis of the lens, is the yellow spot (*macula lutea*).

The middle region of the yellow spot (*fovea centralis*) is the area of clearest vision.

STRUCTURE OF THE RETINA. From outside to inside, the retina consists of the following layers—

1. A cubical epithelium pigmented by melanin. This layer lies against the choroid coat and is the only part of the retina which continues beyond the ora serrata to form a backing for the iris. Processes of the cubical cells are produced inward among the next layer.

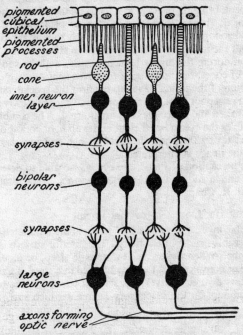

Fig. 29.66. Retina of mammal. V.S.

2. Specialized bi-polar neurones called the rods and cones, the former containing the pigment rhodopsin and the latter iodopsin. These rods and cones are the specialized outer dendrons of nerve cells whose inner dendrons make synapses with the third layer.

3. A layer of bi-polar neurones which make synapses with the second and fourth layers.

4. A layer of large nerve cells which make synapses with the third layer and send their axons inward to form the fifth layer.

5. A layer of axons which converge to form the optic nerve (*see* Fig. 29.66).

The only cells stimulated by the light are the rods and cones, and since, to reach these, the rays have to pass through three other layers first, the retina is known as inverted, by contrast with the direct retina of most invertebrate eyes.

FORMATION OF THE IMAGE ON THE RETINA

Light reaching the retina has been refracted four times; by the cornea, the aqueous humour, the lens and the vitreous humour. The greatest refraction takes place at the cornea and the least through the humours. The lens acts as a fine adjustment, bringing the rays to a focus on the retina, where an inverted image is formed. Image formation is due to bleaching of the pigments rhodopsin and iodopsin. The rhodopsin in the rods is rapidly bleached in strong light but the iodopsin is far less photosensitive. Hence, it is the cones which function during the higher light intensities and the rods in the lower. The presence of cones, but no rods, in the fovea centralis, which is by far the most-used region of the retina, tends to confirm the special value of cones in good light. In very poor light, the rhodopsin is bleached slowly and the iodopsin scarcely affected and hence the rods are utilized. The combination of rods and cones enables the eye to be efficient under all light conditions. An action potential is set up by the photochemical change and impulses travel to the brain, where the image is interpreted.

Apart from perception of shape, the eye is also able to detect variation in light intensity and in addition there is colour vision. Some discussion of these is given in Vol. II, Chap. 16.

ADJUSTMENT OF THE LENS AND OF THE PUPIL

The lens is biconvex and consists of transparent laminated fibrous tissue with a considerable degree of elasticity. The interior surface is more convex than the exterior. When the eye is at rest, as in sleep, or focused on distant objects, it is least convex and is thus maintained in a state of tension by forces acting against its own elasticity. This state of tension is due to the pressure of the two humours on the suspensory ligament which surrounds the lens. When the eye is focused for near objects, the lens becomes more convex, the process being effected by the ciliary muscles, of which there are two sets. The circular fibres contract and thus narrow the radius of the suspensory ligament. The meridional fibres contract and pull the choroid forward. Both forces reduce the tension of the suspensory ligament and thus the lens, by its own elasticity, increases in thickness but becomes narrower in diameter. The curvature of the outer surface is now uneven, with considerable convexity in the middle region. It is no longer part of a sphere, because the edges are much less convex than the middle. Therefore to reduce distortion of images which could be caused by such unequal curvature, the pupil contracts. Suitable adjustment in the degree of contraction of the ciliary muscles alters the convexity of the lens so that objects at various distances are focused clearly. The whole process is known as *accommodation*, and it is to be noted that while in the fish it is accomplished by moving the whole lens in relation to the retina, in the mammal it is the convexity of the lens which is altered.

The amount of light passing through the lens is controlled by the iris, which has circular and radial muscles. Contraction of the circular muscle fibres will reduce the size of the pupil, while contraction of the radial muscle

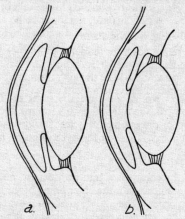

Fig. 29.67. Positions of lens. (*a*) Focused at infinity. (*b*) Near point.

fibres will increase it. Unlike most involuntary muscle, these fibres have the power of rapid contraction.

MOVEMENT OF THE EYE

In the mammals, as in all craniates, there are six muscles which move the eyeball; they are known as the *extrinsic* muscles and include *four rectus* and

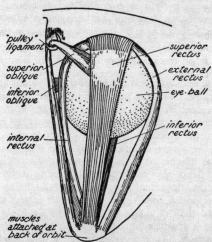

Fig. 29.68. Mammalian eye, extrinsic muscles from above.

two oblique. The eyeball is embedded in fat at the back and round the sides and the muscles move the ball on the fat. Above and below are the superior and inferior rectus, while at the sides are the internal and external rectus muscles. The oblique muscles are attached to the sclerotic above and below and then they pass transversely inward, the lower being attached to the inner side of the orbit, while the upper traverses a pulley-like loop of ligament and then proceeds towards the back of the orbit with the rectus muscles. These four rectus muscles and the superior oblique are attached to the bone of the orbit around the optic foramen (*see* Fig. 29.68).

By contraction of these muscles, movement of the eye in any direction is possible. The superior rectus will turn the front of the eye upward, the inferior rectus downward, the internal rectus inward and the external rectus outward. The action of the oblique muscles is somewhat more complicated but their general tendency is to roll the eyeball on its axis.

STRUCTURES PROTECTING THE EYE

Over the front of the cornea is a thin transparent mucous membrane, the *conjunctiva*. It is continuous with the inner lining of the eyelids and serves to protect the sensitive cornea. The eyelids are both movable and can be closed to protect the eye; they are also used for blinking at short intervals for the purpose of washing the surface. They bear the stiff eyelashes and a row of *Meibomian glands* which produce a greasy secretion enabling frictionless blinking. Above the eyes are the eyebrows which usually have the long sensitive vibrissae, which are absent in man. At the inner corner of the eye is the nictitating membrane which can be moved sideways across the surface. It lubricates the conjunctiva, and may protect the eye from damage by dust or foliage. In man it is a vestigial structure. Situated above the outer and upper region of each eyeball is a compound racemose *lachrymal gland* which secretes a slightly saline fluid to keep the conjunctiva moist. The secretion is drained into the nose by the *lachrymal duct* at the inner corner of the conjunctiva.

DEFECTS OF THE EYE

There are a number of common defects of the eye, apart from many caused by damage or disease. Perhaps the most prevalent are *myopia* and *hypermetropia*, known respectively as short and long sight. Both are due to variation in the distance from the front of the cornea to the macula lutea and unequal growth of the eyeball or inherited distortion may account for this. In human beings, the normal distance, though this is in fact rare, is taken to be 24 mm. In the myopic condition, the eyeball is slightly elongated from front to back and hence rays are brought to a focus in the vitreous humour in front of the retina, the actual image on the retina being blurred. Hypermetropia is the opposite condition; the eyeball is too short and images are focused behind the retina (*see* Fig. 29.69). *Presbyopia* is an almost invariable concomitant of advancing age; it is due to hardening of the lens and hence loss of elasticity. Thus there is inability to accommodate for near objects, giving the condition of long sight, but from another cause. In *astigmatism*, the rays of light are not all focused at the same point. It may be due to many causes, the principal being unequal curvature of the cornea. *Cataract* is the condition in which there are opacities in the lens; it may

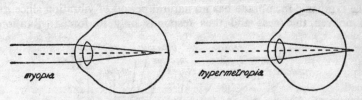

Fig. 29.69. Diagrams showing image formation in short and long sight.

become completely opaque, resulting in almost total blindness. Squinting is the inability to direct both eyes on the same object; one of the most common causes is variation in the length or power of contraction of the extrinsic muscles.

The Ear. In the mammals, the ear consists of three distinct parts, outer, middle and inner. The outer ear consists of the pinna and the external auditory meatus; the middle ear comprises the tympanic chamber with the three auditory ossicles, and in the inner ear are the membranous and bony labyrinths. The advances made by the mammals are three in number; there is a well-developed outer ear; there are three auditory ossicles, and the lagena has been transformed into the spirally coiled cochlea.

The pinna consists of elastic cartilage and certain muscles used in moving it. Since its dimensions are considerably smaller than the wavelengths of ordinary sound (e.g. with a frequency of 1,000 cycles per sec the wavelength is about 30 cm), it cannot scatter sound waves but will collect them like a funnel so that some enter the meatus and reach the tympanic membrane. Its most valuable function is the detection of the direction of the sound source. The meatus is supported by cartilage in its outer portion and bone in its inner portion. It is lined by stratified epithelium bearing hairs in the outer region and *ceruminous* glands further in. The tympanic membrane is thin and consists mainly of fibres radiating from the central region, covered on the outer side by thin stratified epithelium and on the inner side by mucous membrane continuous with that which lines the tympanic cavity.

In the middle ear, the tympanic chamber is enclosed by the tympanic bone, perforated at the base by a small foramen for the passage of the Eustachian tube, which leads into the pharynx. The pharyngeal opening is closed except during swallowing, when air enters or leaves the tube to equate the pressure on both sides of the membrane. A person in an aeroplane which is either rising or diving rapidly, has to swallow frequently to equate the internal pressure with the changing external pressure. Transmitting vibrations across the chamber from the tympanic membrane to the *fenestra ovalis*, are the *auditory ossicles*. The tympanic membrane has no natural period of vibration since it is of uneven thickness and thus responds only to forced vibrations,

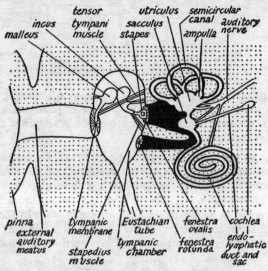

Fig. 29.70. Diagram of mammalian ear structure.

coming to rest when they cease. The ossicles which transmit the vibrations are the *malleus*, *incus* and *stapes* (hammer, anvil and stirrup), derived respectively from the articular, the quadrate and the columella auris (hyomandibula) (*see* Fig. 29.71). They are small bones sheathed in cartilage and make typical joints with each other. Between the malleus and incus is a synovial joint, and between the incus and stapes, there is a ball-and-socket joint. The *tensor tympani* muscle from the malleus to the inner wall of the chamber, adjusts the tension on the membrane. Attached to the stapes, where it joins the incus, is the tiny *stapedius* muscle, its other insertion being on the bony inner wall between the fenestra ovalis and the fenestra rotunda. Together, these two muscles appear to be a kind of volume control, so that very loud noises, which would damage the delicate membranous labyrinth, are automatically damped down. An animal's hearing is acute when they are relaxed and less acute when they are contracted.

The inner ear is enclosed in the very hard periotic bone, It consists of a membranous labyrinth containing endolymph, surrounded by a

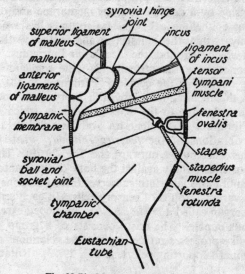

Fig. 29.71. Mammalian middle ear.

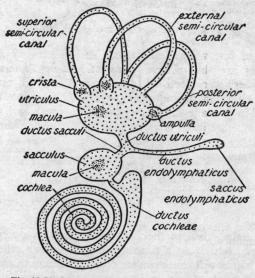

Fig. 29.72. Membranous labyrinth of mammalian ear.

bony labyrinth containing perilymph. The oval end of the stapes abuts on the fenestra ovalis composed of thin connective tissue, covered on the outside by a delicate mucous membrane and on the inside by a squamous epithelium; the fenestra rotunda has a similar structure. Immediately within the fenestra ovalis is the vestibule containing perilymph which surrounds the sacculus and utriculus. Enclosed in the periotic bone above the utriculus, are the semicircular canals, and below the sacculus is the cochlea. Perilymph in the bony labyrinth surrounds the membranous labyrinth everywhere and finally has a small channel leading to the fenestra rotunda, which acts as a safety device. Vibrations of the fenestra ovalis are followed by similar but opposite vibrations of the *fenestra rotunda*; when the one bulges inward, the other bulges outward (*see* Fig. 29.70). The ductus endolymphaticus ends blindly against the bone of the cranium.

The membranous labyrinth subserves three functions by detection of stimuli in various groups of sensory cells. In each semicircular canal is a small organ called a *crista acustica*, enveloped except at its base in a gelatinous cupule. The crista consists of a group of sensory cells with hair-like processes projecting into the gelatinous mass; there are also columnar supporting cells (*see* Fig. 29.73). Rotation of the head

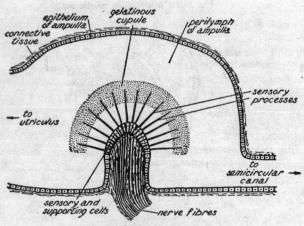

Fig. 29.73. V.S. single crista acustica.

will cause the crista in the horizontal canal to sweep through the endolymph, setting up a pressure on the sensory cells. Movements in other planes will cause similar pressure stimuli in the other canals. Action-potentials set up in the nerve-endings elicit reflex responses tending to restore equilibrium. Thus the cristae in the ampullae subserve the sense of balance.

In the utriculus and sacculus are similar sense organs known respectively as the *macula utriculi* and the *macula sacculi*. Minute calcareous otoliths rest among the sensory processes and on any change in posture they exert pressure on the sensory cells. Similar reflex actions are evoked to restore normal posture or to maintain abnormal posture.

Sound perception is located in the *cochlea*. In man, there is sensitivity to vibrations in the frequency range of 16 to 20,000 cycles per

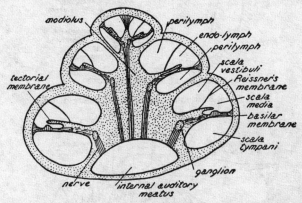

Fig. 29.74. V.S. cochlea.

second, though many mammals are sensitive to higher frequencies, e.g. the dog over 25,000, and the bat almost 100,000 cycles per second.

The cochlea consists essentially of a spiral tube divided into three channels. It is shaped like a snail's shell with the apex downward and is surrounded by the periotic bone. The upper channel is the *scala vestibuli* and the lower the *scala tympani*, both containing perilymph and connected at the apex of the coil by a small canal, the *helicotrema* (*see* Fig. 29.77). Between these upper and lower channels is a middle channel, the *scala media*, enclosed in a membrane which is continuous with the saccule and contains endolymph. The upper and lower membranes of the scala media have special names, the upper being *Reissner's membrane* and the lower the *basilar membrane* (*see* Fig. 29.75). On its inner half towards the bony *modiolus* or central column of the cochlea, it bears, along its whole spiral length, five rows of receptor cells which, with supporting cells, form the *organ of Corti* (*see* Fig. 29.76). Each receptor cell bears a tuft of stiff hair-like processes embedded in the *tectorial membrane*, a smooth, gelatinous,

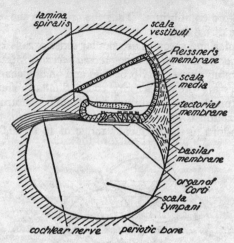

Fig. 29.75. Portion of cochlear canal, enlarged. V.S.

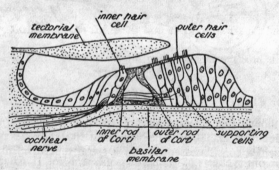

Fig. 29.76. Organ of Corti. V.S.

longitudinal shelf anchored internally to the modiolus. The outer portion of the basilar membrane, where it is not overlain by the organ of Corti, bears parallel fibres, at right angles to the canal wall.

If we imagine the cochlea to be uncoiled, as shown in the figure opposite, it would resemble a piano keyboard with the organ of Corti representing the keys and the fibres of the basilar membrane representing the strings.

Vibrations of the fenestra ovalis pass through the fluid of the scala vestibuli and agitate Reissner's membrane. By means of the endolymph in the scala media, the vibrations next affect the basilar membrane, causing it to undergo rocking movements which distort the sensory cells of the organ of Corti. The fibres of the basilar membrane show a gradual transition from the short taut fibres at the base of the cochlea to the long slack fibres at its apex. It is known that damage to the fibres in one region will cause inability to appreciate sound of a certain pitch, and hence we may perhaps infer that the whole basilar membrane together with the organ of Corti corresponds to a whole range in pitch. Though vibrational stimulus will affect the whole length, there will be maximum effect in a particular region. Impulses along the cochlear branch of the auditory nerve are interpreted by the brain in terms of pitch, loudness and timbre. The first of these depends on the frequency,

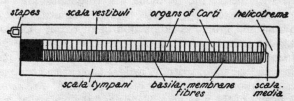

Fig. 29.77. Diagram of cochlea, unrolled.

the second on the amplitude and the third on the nature of the wave form.

There is no generally-accepted interpretation of the mode of action of the organ of Corti and the basilar fibres.

Endocrine Glands

All endocrine structures develop from epithelia or nervous tissue, or from both. It is noteworthy that some structures described here have other important functions, e.g. kidney, gonads, pancreas. Detailed discussion of the effects of hormones is given in Vol. II, Chaps. 6 and 8.

1. *The hypothalami* are paired thickenings in the thalamencephalon (*see* p. 830) and thus nervous in origin. They control most of the endocrine structures, acting through the pituitary and autonomic system. Groups of cells produce *neurosecretions;* droplets produced in the cells traverse the axons into the pars nervosa, to be stored and later released into the blood. Other neurosecretions (releasing factors) pass in the blood of the hypothalamo-hypophyseal portal system into the pars anterior where they stimulate production of other hormones. Two hormones plus a number of releasing factors are produced. *Oxytocin* stimulates contractions of the uterus during birth, and promotes secretion of milk during suckling. *Vasopressin* causes a rise in blood-pressure by contraction of arterioles, and is also *anti-diuretic*, favouring resorption of water and Na$^+$ ions from the renal tubules.

Specific *releasing factors* affect the secretion of all hormones produced in the pars anterior and pars intermedia.

2. *The pituitary body* lies beneath the thalamencephalon. It is formed by fusion of a hollow down-growth from the brain, the infundibulum, with a dorsal invagination from the stomodaeum, the hypophysis, and is thus nervous and epithelial in origin. The infundibulum becomes the pars nervosa; the endocrine parts of the hypophysis are the pars anterior and pars intermedia. The former secretes six hormones. *Somatotropin* (STH or growth hormone) stimulates rate of protein synthesis, excess producing gigantism, and deficiency, dwarfness; the hormone also promotes production of glucagon in the pancreas. *Thyrotropic hormone* stimulates development of the thyroid and promotes production of thyroxin. *Adrenocorticotropic hormone* induces production of corticoids from the adrenals. *Follicle-stimulating hormone* promotes development of Graafian follicles in females, and of sperm in males. *Luteinizing hormone* (LTH) stimulates ovulation and formation of corpora lutea. *Prolactin* affects the development of the mammary glands and the maintenance of milk secretion. The pars intermedia produces two hormones, both *melanocyte-stimulating;* they affect formation and distribution of melanin granules in the chromatophores.

3. *The thyroid gland* is a mass of soft, red, vesicular tissue on each side of the larynx. It develops from epithelium in the floor of the pharynx and is homologous with the endostyle of lower chordates. The hormone *thyroxin* regulates the basic rate of metabolism (BRM); deficiency lowers the BRM and leads to *hypothyroidism*. In the young, this causes retardation of development, a condition known as *cretinism*, or mentally retarded dwarfness; in adults, deficiency leads to sluggish metabolism, atrophy of the gland and swelling of the neck—the condition of *myxoedema*. Excess of thyroxin causes *hyperthyroidism;* there is a high BRM, restless activity, rapid heart-beat and general wasting of the body. The gland becomes enlarged and the eye-balls protrude; a condition known as *exophthalmic goitre*. Deficiency of iodine may cause simple goitre. The effects of thyroxin in promoting metamorphosis in amphibia and some fishes are notable.

4. *The suprarenal glands* are small, yellow, ovoid structures, one anterior to each kidney. The cortex is derived from neural crests and the medulla from coelomic epithelium. The medulla secretes *adrenalin* and *nor-adrenalin* after sympathetic stimulation. These produce dramatic changes in the body in response to fear, stress and shock. The three zones of the cortex (*see* Fig. 20.52) secrete different hormones; the outer zone produces *mineralocorticoids* called *aldosterone* and *deoxycorticosterone* which play a vital part in osmoregulation; the

middle zone secretes the *glucocorticoids*, *cortisone* and *cortisol*, which affect carbohydrate metabolism; the inner zone produces *androgens* and *oestrogens* which promote development of the secondary sexual characteristics.

5. *The parathyroids* are two pairs of small glandular masses, lateral to the thyroid, and derived from epithelium of the third and fourth visceral clefts. The secretion, *parathormone* affects Ca^{++} metabolism, playing a large part in exchange of Ca^{++} and PO_4^{---} ions between bones and blood; it also affects excretion and resorption of these ions.

6. *The thymus gland*, derived from epithelium dorsal to the visceral clefts, is a large, soft, pink mass above the heart; it degenerates considerably with age. In the young, it is the main source of lymphocytes and is important in immunological reactions. The hormone, *thymosin*, stimulates lymphocyte production in the lymphatic glands.

7. *The pineal body* is a hollow dorsal outgrowth of the thalamencephalon. In lamprey larvae and some reptiles, it has a complete eyelike structure, and in the former, it has an undoubted effect on skin colour. In amphibians, the hormone *melatonin* causes blanching of the skin; the same effect may occur in mammals. Melatonin certainly stimulates maturation of the gonads, probably by stimulating secretion of gonadotropic releasing factors from the hypothalamus.

8. *The pancreas* is derived from endodermal epithelium. The *islets of Langerhans* contain two types of cells; large β cells which secrete *insulin*, and smaller α cells which secrete *glucagon*. The former promotes synthesis of glycogen in the liver from blood hexoses; the latter favours breakdown of liver glycogen to glucose. β cells are sensitive to blood sugar level, and α cells are stimulated by STH. Deficiency of insulin results in *diabetes mellitus*.

9. *The ovaries*, like the testes, are derived from coelomic epithelium. The follicular phase of the oestrous cycle is activated by FSH; this induces development of the follicles, stimulating them to produce *oestrogens*, the most potent being *oestradiol*. These activate the reproductive tract in preparation for pregnancy and stimulate development of mammary glands and secondary sexual characteristics. The luteal phase is activated by LH which induces repair of the ruptured follicles and growth of corpora lutea; the latter, activated by prolactin, secrete *progesterone* which inhibits further ovulation, prepares the uterus for implantation and induces further development of the mammae. *Relaxin*, from the corpora lutea, promotes dilation of the cervix and relaxation of the pubic symphysis during birth.

10. *The placenta* is epithelial in origin, part from the uterine lining, and part from the trophoblast (*see* p. 1091). Three hormones are secreted; a *gonadotropin*, an *oestrogen* and *progesterone;* they

influence growth of the uterus and mammae after ovarian secretions have waned, and assist in maintenance of corpora lutea until birth.

11. *The testes*, after stimulation by FSH, produce at least two *androgens*, *androsterone* and *testosterone*, which play a part in spermatogenesis, control activity of the seminal vesicles and prostate glands and help in the formation of the male secondary sexual characteristics.

12. *The kidneys* are derived from coelomic epithelium. A thickened pad of cells on each tubule, the *juxtaglomerular complex* (*see* Vol. II, Chap. 8), secretes *renin* in response to falling concentration of Na^+ in the blood. Renin converts a plasma globulin, *hypertensinogen*, into hypertensin, which then causes vasoconstriction and stimulates release of mineralocorticoids; these raise the level of Na^+ resorption from the tubules.

13. *The alimentary canal*. The gastric mucosa secretes *gastrin*, which induces continued flow of gastric juice; *enterocrinin*, which starts enzyme secretion in the duodenum, and *gastric secretin*, which promotes secretion of salt solution from the pancreas. The duodenal mucosa produces *secretin*, which stimulates further flow of pancreatic salt solution; *pancreomysin* induces secretion of pancreatic enzymes; *cholecystokinin* causes contraction of the gall bladder, and *enterogastrone* inhibits acid secretion by the stomach.

14. *Nerve-endings* secrete hormones which excite adjacent cells. Sympathetic fibres secrete *sympathin*, identical in effects with adrenalin; parasympathetic and somatic motor fibres produce *acetylcholine*, which also facilitates transmission of impulses across synapses.

15. *Tissue hormones*. *Histamine* and *acetylcholine*, both powerful depressors, are probably present in inactive form in all cells. They are activated when cells are damaged and play an important part in the process of healing (*see* Vol. II, Chap. 8).

The Early Development of the Rabbit

Apart from the monotremes, which lay yolky telolecithal eggs about 5 mm in diameter, the mammals produce tiny eggs ranging between 0·1 and 0·3 mm. The eggs are secondarily microlecithal since the mammals undoubtedly evolved from reptiles which laid large yolky eggs, though there is the possibility that the later mammal-like reptiles may have been viviparous. One of the most important evolutionary advantages achieved by mammals is the development of the *placenta*, by means of which the embryo is attached to the uterus wall and through which it is supplied with all its needs from the mother's blood.

The Sperm and the Ovum

The ovum is about 0·15 mm in diameter and is released from the ovary at the secondary oocyte stage. Its nucleus is large and excentrically situated. Scattered throughout the egg, are minute granules of yolk. Outside the thin vitelline membrane is a thicker *zona pellucida* which has numerous fine radial striations which may be minute canals. This zona pellucida seems to be secreted by the follicle cells; if so, it is a secondary membrane. Outside the zona pellucida, a number of follicle cells, still attached to the ovum, constitute the *corona radiata*. After fertilization, they disappear and the egg is coated with a thin layer of dense albumin secreted by the oviduct wall. This constitutes a tertiary membrane.

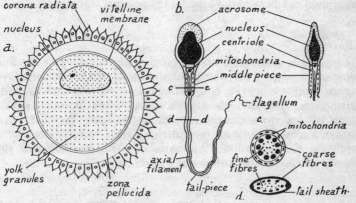

Fig. 29.78. Rabbit gametes. (*a*) Ovum. (*b*) Two views of sperm. (*c*) T.S. at *c–c*. (*d*) T.S. at *d–d*.

The sperm is about 50μm in length and consists of a head-piece, middle-piece and tail. The head-piece contains the nucleus, sheathed in a minute quantity of cytoplasm. Over the nucleus and partly covering it, is the *acrosome*, which is flattened and tapers to a rounded edge at its apex. The middle-piece is short and cylindrical; it contains centrosomes and a number of rod-like mitochondria embedded in a small quantity of cytoplasm. Axial fibres with complex arrangement (*see* Fig. 29.78) persist from the middle piece to the end of the long, tapering tail-piece and into the flagellum.

Fertilization and its Effects

Fertilization occurs high up the oviduct, the whole sperm penetrating the egg, though the tail soon disintegrates. At the time of entry of the sperm, the ovum nucleus is usually at the metaphase stage of its second maturation division. This is speedily completed and the second polar body is extruded. The female nucleus passes into a short inter-phase and is now called the female pronucleus. At the same time, the sperm nucleus swells to form the male pronucleus and the two nuclei lie close together. The centrosome of the sperm now divides and the two centrioles induce the formation of the asters and soon the spindle begins to form. The nuclear membranes of both pronuclei disappear and the two sets of chromosomes arrange themselves around the equator of the spindle ready for the first mitotic division of the zygote. It is noteworthy that the two nuclei do not fuse in their interphase condition, though this does happen in many animals and plants, including most flowering plants. The entry of the sperm has restored the diploid number and has brought the paternal chromosomes into the zygote.

Cleavage

Cleavage is holoblastic and approximately equal, both conditions being secondary and correlated with the loss of yolk. The first cleavage occurs about twenty-two hours after coitus and produces two equal blastomeres. One of these divides again, before the other, and the planes of cleavage are at right angles so that four blastomeres in the form of a cross are formed. Thereafter cleavage becomes irregular and results in the formation of a morula, which is completed about seventy-two hours after coitus (*see* Fig. 29.79).

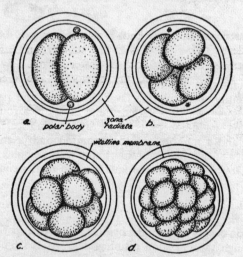

Fig. 29.79. Stages in cleavage of fertilized egg of rabbit. (*a*) 2 cells. (*b*) 4 cells. (*c*) 8 cells. (*d*) Morula.

The Blastocyst

In the morula, a cavity appears, separating an outer layer of cells from an inner mass. The fluid which fills this cavity is derived from a milky secretion of the oviduct wall. Besides providing the fluid, it also contains nutriment for the embryo. The outer layer of cells is called the *trophoblast* since later it plays an important part in nutrition of the embryo. Attached to it at one region is the inner cell mass, now known as the *embryonal knob*; from it, the whole of the embryo will be formed.

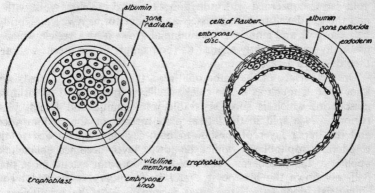

Fig. 29.80. Rabbit blastocyst. V.S.

Fig. 29.81. Three layered blastocyst of rabbit. V.S.

The complete structure is now known as a *blastocyst* and its cavity may be considered homologous with the sub-germinal cavity of the chick and possibly the blastocoel of lower forms. By continued absorption of the uterine fluid, the blastocyst swells considerably (*see* Fig. 29.81).

There is no certainty that the presumptive areas are yet formed and that they resemble those of the chick, but since the general pattern of future development follows the same lines, it is permissible to consider that the presumptive areas are similar.

Gastrulation

The blastocyst continues to swell by absorption of the uterine fluid, and the zona pellucida becomes very attenuated. Soon, together with the albumin, it is cast off. The embryonal knob becomes stretched and gradually forms a flattened *embryonal disc* which consists of several layers of cells. From the lower layer, cells spread out laterally to form the endoderm which grows round the inside of the trophoblast to enclose the fluid. The cells of the trophoblast above the embryo (*cells of Rauber*), become separated by the stretching and soon disappear. Thus the embryonal disc lies on the surface of the blastocyst and is continuous all round with the trophoblast (*see* Fig. 29.81). At this stage, implantation in the wall of the uterus begins, and the embryo now can be compared with a similar stage in the chick.

The embryonal disc corresponds with the area pellucida, and the trophoblast at its margins, with the area opaca. Together with the trophoblast, the endoderm forms a precociously-developed yolk sac, enclosing not yolk but fluid. In both the bird and the mammal, the yolk sac is concerned with nutrition; the bird envelops yolk with it and the sac develops blood-vessels and hence forms a vascular bridge between yolk and embryo; the mammal grows it as a vesicle which is gradually pushed tightly against its food supply in the uterus wall and then develops a vascular bridge.

On the surface of the embryonal disc, the primitive pit, streak and knot appear, much as in the chick. Cells migrate inward to form the mesoderm, which is soon separable into somitic and lateral plate regions. By a split in the lateral plate mesoderm, the coelom arises and the upper layer of mesoderm becomes somatic, applied to the ectoderm (trophoblast), while the lower layer becomes splanchnic, applied to the endoderm. The mesoderm does not extend more than half-way down the blastocyst; later its boundary is marked by an equatorial blood-vessel, the sinus terminalis. At the primitive pit, cells sink in and are turned forward to form the notochord. Neural plate and neural groove formation follow, much as in the chick. Later, the head fold, tail fold and lateral folds, lift the embryo above the yolk sac and the fore-gut and hind-gut are formed. While these developments are taking place, the embryo becomes implanted in the wall of the uterus.

Implantation

When the blastocyst reaches the uterus and becomes distended enough to press against the uterus wall, small villi grow out from the trophoblast in the region diametrically opposite the embryonal disc. These *trophoblastic villi* grow into corresponding depressions in the uterine wall and probably even digest some of the epithelium. In any case, secretions of the uterine glands are passed through the villi into the yolk sac fluid and thence by diffusion to the embryo.

This temporary implantation of the embryo is soon succeeded by permanent attachment almost diametrically opposite, where the placenta is developed, and later the lower half of the yolk sac including the trophoblastic villi, disintegrates, and the embryo lies exposed ventrally to the uterine cavity.

The Embryonic Membranes

The embryonic membranes are the same as those of the chick, namely, the yolk sac, amnion, chorion and allantois.

The Yolk Sac. The yolk sac began with the formation of the trophoblast after the morula stage of cleavage. Before implantation, the endoderm grew into it and later the mesoderm, and thus the sac consists of endoderm overlaid on the outside with mesoderm in the upper (embryonic) half, and of endoderm and ectoderm (trophoblast) in the lower half. It is from this lower half of the yolk sac that the early

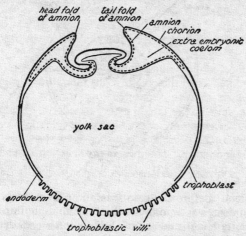

Fig. 29.82. Embryonic membranes of rabbit, early stage of development.

trophoblastic villi grow to absorb nutriment from the uterine epithelium, and when it disintegrates, nutritive secretions of the uterus have an open pathway to the embryonic gut. The portion of yolk sac immediately beneath the embryo, forms the fore-gut and hind-gut when the head fold and tail fold appear.

The vascular system of the embryo begins with blood islands in the splanchnic mesoderm of the yolk sac and the first blood-vessels develop there, to convey uterine secretions to the embryo via the vitelline circulation.

The Amnion and Chorion. The amnion and chorion arise together as a fold of the somatopleur (mesoderm and trophoblast) around the edge of the embryonal disc. In mammals, the tail fold develops more rapidly than the head fold and thus the sero-amniotic connexion is near the anterior end of the embryo. The amnion consists of ectoderm (trophoblast) inside and mesoderm outside; the chorion has these layers reversed, with ectoderm outside and mesoderm inside, its cavity being extra-embryonic coelom. As soon as the chorion is completed, it forms villi which burrow into the uterine epithelium.

Not only do these membranes enclose fluid layers for protection of the embryo, but the chorion provides a large space into which the allantois can grow, and later, a portion of the chorion partakes in formation of the placenta.

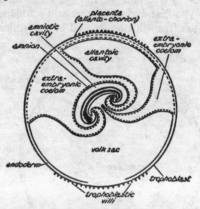

Fig. 29.83. Embryonic membranes of rabbit, later development.

The Allantois. Before the sero-amniotic connexion is formed, the allantois commences as an outgrowth of the hind-gut into the choriotic cavity. Its outer layer is mesoderm and its inner endoderm. It grows around the tail of the embryo and dorsal to the posterior region it fuses with the chorion over a small disc-shaped area. This structure, the *allanto-chorion*, forms the embryonic part of the placenta (*see* Fig. 29.83). The allantois soon develops an efficient blood supply connecting the placenta with the embryo. The vessels in the umbilical stalk are the allantoic (umbilical) artery and vein. As in the bird, the allantois is concerned with excretion and respiration, and it has an additional function, that of nutrition. All exchanges take place between maternal and embryonic blood in the placenta.

The Placenta

The placenta is formed at the area of attachment of the allanto-chorion to the uterus. This area is always opposite the *mesometrium*, the fold of peritoneum by which the uterus is suspended. A longitudinal groove develops in the uterus wall and on either side of the groove two thickened placental folds develop. Corresponding thickenings arise in the trophoblast, which later consists of two zones, an outer coenocytic *syncytio-trophoblast* and an inner *cyto-trophoblast*. The syncytio-trophoblast invades the uterus wall by its villi and destroys the epithelial tissues, until finally the walls of the maternal capillaries are dissolved and the maternal blood circulates through large lacunae. With the arrival of the allantois in this placental area, there is rapid multiplication of embryonic blood-capillaries.

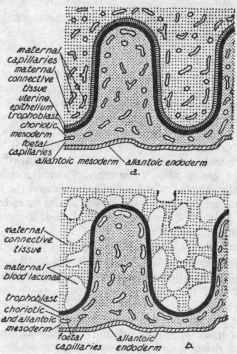

Fig. 29.84. Placenta of rabbit. (*a*) Details of layers before erosion. (*b*) Final state after erosion.

In the early placenta, six different tissue layers separate the maternal from the embryonic blood (*see* Fig. 29.84). They are: the uterine capillary walls, the uterine connective tissue and epithelium, the trophoblast, the embryonic connective tissue (mesoderm of the allanto-chorion), and the embryo's capillary walls. In succession, the uterine epithelium, connective tissue and capillary walls are eroded by the trophoblastic villi. Some of the embryonic connective tissue also breaks down, so that finally, the maternal blood circulates in lacunae, bathing the trophoblast, close to which are the embryonic capillaries (*see* Fig. 29.84 (*b*)).

By diffusion, food materials and oxygen pass from the blood of the mother to that of the embryo, and in the reverse direction, embryonic excretory products pass into the maternal blood. The two sorts of blood being incompatible, are never in direct contact. In the first place, the pressure of the maternal blood would be far too great for the embryo's vessels, and secondly, there must be a barrier against the passage of harmful substances from the maternal blood. Such, for example are the blood proteins, and the sex hormones, which would affect normal sexual development of the embryo.

Birth

When the period of *gestation*, thirty days in the rabbit, is completed, rhythmical contractions of the uterus take place, eventually rupturing the embryonic membranes, and causing what is known in human parturition as the "breaking of the waters." The placental connexion between embryo and mother is loosened, and gradually the foetus is expelled from the mother's body. The umbilical stalk is bitten through by the mother and it shrivels up to leave a scar called the *umbilicus* or navel on the young rabbit's abdomen. Later, the embryonic membranes, with the remains of the umbilical stalk and the foetal portion of the placenta, are expelled as the *afterbirth* and eaten by the mother. The maternal portion of the placenta is resorbed, so that there is only the loss of a little blood.

The young rabbits are blind and helpless when born and are fed from the mother's mammary glands. The hair and teeth develop quickly and they begin to feed themselves after about four weeks.

Adaptation

The most obvious adaptations in the rabbit are to be found in connexion with homoiothermy, viviparity, the herbivorous feeding, the relative lack of defence, and the mode of locomotion.

The maintenance of a constant body temperature depends on many factors, among which are a sufficient supply of energy-producing foodstuffs, an adequate respiratory mechanism, an efficient circulatory system and some means of regulating heat loss. In all these respects, the rabbit is suitably adapted. It will eat almost any kind of plant material and possesses hard-wearing teeth suitable for biting the food and grinding it up. The great length of the gut enables maximum absorption, and the bacterial colonies of the caecum release extra sustenance. The practice of coprophily finally enables it to extract the maximum amount of nourishment from its food. There is great efficiency in the respiratory and circulatory systems and the structure of the skin is admirably adapted to control heat loss.

Viviparity entails internal fertilization and provision for attachment of the embryo, through which it receives all necessary supplies. In the reproductive organs, the mechanism for internal fertilization is present and co-ordinated to occur at the heat periods. The placenta provides an ideal means of exchange between the mother's and embryo's blood with the necessary safeguards against dangerous materials. The birth process and lactation at the correct period, show further adaptation for care of the young until they are able to fend for themselves.

The burrowing habit arises in connexion with the lack of means for active defence. In the limbs, we see the front adapted for scratching away the earth and the hind-limbs for throwing it back. The nictitating membrane protects the eye in dusty conditions and the vibrissae gauge the width of the burrow in its darkest depths. The neutral colour is excellent camouflage when the rabbit emerges in the twilight. The white scut is raised as a warning signal and the young follow it when scampering to the shelter of the burrow.

In connexion with jumping the main adaptive features have already been mentioned (*see* p. 1024). Careful consideration will reveal numerous minor adaptations.

Classification

Phylum: Chordata
Sub-phylum: Craniata [Vertebrata]
Class: Mammalia
Order: Lagomorpha [Duplicidentata]

Family: Leporidae
Genus: *Oryctolagus* [*Lepus*]
Species: *O. cuniculus*

The rabbits and hares have been formerly placed in the large order Rodentia, but it is now usual to separate them into the Lagomorpha, which they share only with the pikas (tail-less hares). The main characteristic by which they are separated from the rodents, Simplicidentata, is their possession of the second pair of smaller incisors in the upper jaw. In the Lagomorpha are two families, the Leporidae and the Ochotonidae. The Leporidae are distinguished by their elongated hind-limbs, their long ears, the short recurved tail and the vestigial clavicles. The hares, *Lepus*, are distinguished from the rabbits by their longer hind-limbs and longer black-tipped ears. There are also many differences in habits; hares are solitary and do not burrow; their young are born in a more advanced state. Species of the genus *Oryctolagus* are distinguished by small differences of size, colour and length of hair.

Special Features of Biological Importance

The mammals, and particularly the Eutheria, constitute the dominant group of modern terrestrial craniates. Both physiological and anatomical advances in their evolution have combined to give them their dominance. That the mammals evolved from reptiles is undoubted and since the beginning of their separation in the Permian period, they have radiated successfully into a great variety of habitats and modes of life. From the point of view of "intelligence," the Primates are the most advanced mammals; they include man.

The Success of the Mammals

It must be remembered that apart from evolutionary changes in structure and function, the rise of the mammals practically coincides with the rise of the insects and spermatophytes, the latter providing through the agency of the former an inexhaustible supply of nutriment in the form of foliage, fruits and seeds. The main advances in physiology and anatomy which led to mammalian success are listed below.

1. The development of homoiothermy, accompanied by a high rate of metabolism and structures such as the hair and sweat glands to control body temperature.

2. Efficient organs of respiration to provide the oxygen necessary for rapid metabolism; here are many accessory structures such as the diaphragm, the intercostal muscles, and the separation of the food and breathing passages.

3. Viviparity, with fewer young produced, but greater parental care; the placenta and mammary glands and many physiological processes are involved here.

4. The great development of the cerebral hemispheres and particularly the neopallium with the corpus callosum allowed better co-ordination, retention of past sensations, and finally intelligent behaviour.

5. Improved muscular co-ordination and control of posture and locomotion are associated with the more complicated cerebellum and the Pons Varolii.

6. Elaboration and improvement in acuity of sight, hearing and smell.

7. Heterodont dentition; a variety of teeth for a variety of purposes.

8. Complete separation of blood in the heart so that the arterial blood is subjected to a separate and stronger pressure in the systemic circulation. This has been accompanied by the high rate of metabolism.

9. Numerous skeletal features including the position of the limbs with respect to the body axis, and the three centres of ossification which allow long periods of bone growth.

There are a great many minor and less obvious features, not to be discerned in the examination of one animal but by consideration of the whole class. Every order, indeed every species, has undergone specialization to a greater or lesser extent, and hence only the more general advances are listed above.

The Origin of Mammals

The mammals undoubtedly had their origin in the reptilian order Theriodontia, members of which flourished from the Permian to the upper Triassic periods. In the higher theriodonts, especially the Cynodontia, a number of definitely mammalian characteristics appeared. Such, for example, were the presence of two occipital condyles, heterodont teeth, a large dentary, a false palate and jaw articulation by means of the squamosal. The limb girdles resembled those of mammals in the presence of an acromion process and a large ilium and obturator foramen. The limbs approached the mammalian condition and lifted the body clear of the ground. In the digits, the formula was 2, 3, 3, 3, 3 (as in man).

The transition from reptile to mammal seems to have taken place in the late Permian period and by the Eocene, the monotreme stock had separated from the main line. In the Jurassic period, mammals existed which could equally well be placed with the marsupials or the eutherian mammals, but in the Cretaceous, the two groups appear to have been already separated. Owing to geographical changes, the monotremes were isolated in Australasia, and the marsupials in Australasia and South America.

Adaptive Radiation in the Mammals

The mammals show the phenomenon of adaptive radiation to a marked degree. They have not only thoroughly conquered the land, they have burrowed into it, flown and climbed above it, and some have even become secondarily aquatic, with conspicuous success in a few cases. In the matter of diet, there are omnivores, carnivores, herbivores and insectivores.

On land, there is a range from the mighty elephant to the tiny shrew and between these two extremes is a vast variety of forms. Moles, badgers and rabbits make their homes in the earth, while monkeys, lemurs and opossums are quite at home in the trees. The bats are expert fliers, and planing devices are seen in the flying squirrels and flying phalangers. The largest mammal, indeed the largest animal of all time, is the whale; it is completely aquatic and does not leave the water even to bear its young. The seal and walrus are not quite so completely aquatic; their young are born on land. Almost equally at home in both media are the water-rat, the otter and beaver. The camel excels in the hot deserts and the goat on precipitous hills, while the polar bear thrives within the Arctic circle.

THE RAT

The rat is frequently used to illustrate mammalian anatomy, the species employed in nearly all cases being *Rattus norvegicus*. There are no native rats in Great Britain; both the black rat, *R. rattus*, and the brown rat, *R. norvegicus*, have been brought in by shipping. The brown rat is much commoner, and at one time it had almost ousted the black rat, though there are signs that the latter is now on the increase. It must be clearly understood that the colours are very variable, the black rat being very dark only in the northernmost countries of its range. *R. norvegicus* varies in colour from nearly black to pale grey-brown, and all the tame rats, white, brown and variegated, belong to this species. Its original home seems to have been in temperate Asia and it was known to have crossed the Volga in great numbers after an earthquake in 1727. They were first recorded in England in 1728, probably brought in by timber ships. They soon spread over Europe and reached the United States in 1775.

In this short account, only those features in which it differs from the rabbit will be mentioned.

Habitat and Habits

R. norvegicus has become closely associated with man and has become known as the sewer-rat. In the British Isles, the rat population probably exceeds the number of human beings. They are expert swimmers and prefer to live near water, and hence the greatest concentrations of them are found near docks, canals, rivers and sewers. In country districts, they burrow and form colonies near farm buildings. They show great cunning and are very adaptable, being found even in cold stores. Both sexes are mature in about eight weeks, and then the female heat periods occur every ten days. On average, ten to eleven young are produced in each litter, the period of gestation being twenty-one days. They will take a great variety of food materials, preferring grain. Having typical rodent teeth with persistent pulps, they must gnaw hard materials to wear the teeth down; this habit has led to considerable damage of materials such as wooden piles, water and gas pipes, electrical conduits and even brick and cement. As carriers of disease, they constitute a serious menace.

External Features

The body averages about 25 cm in length, the long scaly tail being somewhat shorter, nearer to 20 cm. On the head, there are prominent vibrissae around the mouth and nose, with a few above the eyes. The pinnae of the ears are small, rounded, and covered with very fine short hair. In the females, there are six pairs of mammary glands,

Fig. 29.85. *Rattus norvegicus.*

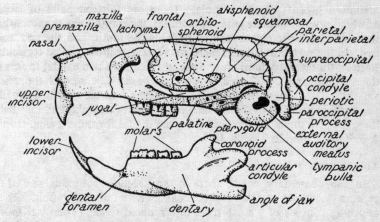

Fig. 29.86. Skull of rat, side view with lower jaw.

three on the thorax and three on the abdomen. The anus and the urinogenital apertures are separate, and in the female, the urethra traverses the clitoris which opens in front of the vulva. Perineal glands are found only in old males.

The Skeleton

The skeleton is very similar to that of the rabbit, differing only in small details. The dental formula is $\frac{1003}{1003}$. In the pectoral girdle, the clavicle is a complete bone, articulating with the sternum and the

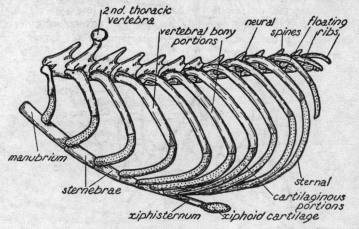

Fig. 29.87. Rat skeleton. Sternum and ribs, side view.

acromion process of the scapula. There are thirteen pairs of ribs, of which seven articulate with the sternum, the eighth joins the seventh, the ninth joins the eighth, the tenth joins the ninth, and the rest are free. In the vertebral column there are 57–60 vertebrae; seven cervical, thirteen thoracic, six lumbar, two sacral fused with two caudal to form the sacrum, and 27–30 free caudal vertebrae. The second thoracic vertebra has a long neural spine articulating distally with a small sesamoid bone. The limbs are similar to those of the rabbit except that there are five digits on the hind-foot, the digital formulae being, front 2, 3, 3, 3, 3, hind 2, 3, 3, 3, 3.

The Alimentary Canal

In the alimentary canal, there is no sacculus rotundus and the caecum lacks the spiral groove characteristic of the rabbit. The appendix consists of a small mass of lymphoid tissue. There are four liver lobes, two on the right, one in the centre and one on the left. There is no gall-bladder, the cystic ducts from the liver lobes joining to form the bile duct. Numerous small pancreatic ducts enter the duodenum.

Blood Vascular System

In the arterial system, the posterior region is somewhat different from that of the rabbit (see Fig. 29.88). The left spermatic and ovarian

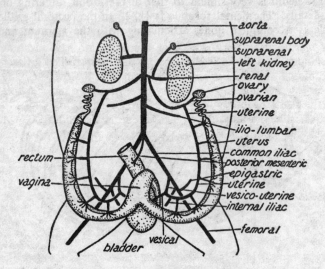

Fig. 29.88. Posterior arterial system of female rat.

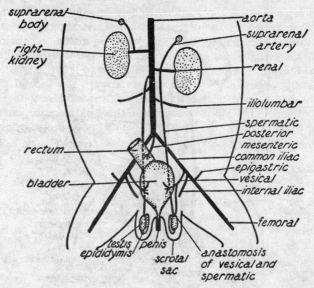

Fig. 29.89. Posterior arterial system of male rat.

arteries leave the renal, the latter supplying also the Fallopian tube. The iliac arteries from the dorsal aorta continue into the legs as the femoral arteries. Just below the kidneys, the ilio-lumbar arteries leave the aorta to supply the dorso-lateral regions of the body wall. A *vesico-uterine* artery from each iliac branches into a vesical supplying the bladder, and the large uterine to the uterus. The latter branch anastomoses with the Fallopian tube branch of the ovarian.

Each external jugular vein is very large, draining most of the blood from the head, the internal jugulars being small and close to the trachea. On each side, the anterior vena cava enters the thorax between the clavicle and the first rib. The azygos vein is present on the left side; it opens into the left anterior vena cava. Supplying the reproductive organs, the venous system is similar to the arterial, with an anastomosis between the ovarian and vesico-uterine veins. The excellent blood supply to the uteri is correlated with the large size of these organs, the frequency of breeding, and the large number of young borne.

Urinogenital System

In the male urinogenital system, there are considerable differences from that of the rabbit. The epididymis is very large, being almost

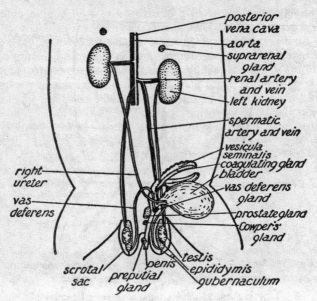

Fig. 29.90. Urinogenital system of rat. Male, ventral dissection.

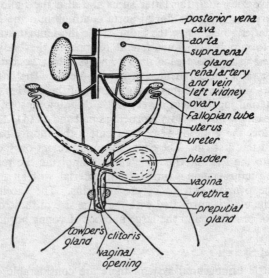

Fig. 29.91. Urinogenital system of rat. Female, ventral dissection.

twice the length of the testis. Where the vasa deferentia enter the urethra are small paired pink glands, each known as a *vas deferens gland*. Immediately dorsal to these is the forked seminal vesicle, bearing on each fork a *coagulating gland*; the whole structure corresponds to the uterus masculinus of the rabbit and represents the joined posterior portions of the Mullerian ducts. At each side of the urethra is a lobed prostate gland and at the root of the penis are small ovoid Cowper's glands. The penis contains a cartilaginous process in its ventral wall and near its tip are paired *preputial glands* (*see* Fig. 29.90).

In the female, the urethra opens at the tip of the clitoris, the vagina having a separate opening, no vestibule being present. Each ovary is small and embedded in fat; the Fallopian tubes are single tiny undulating coils (*see* Fig. 29.91).

Nervous System

In the brain there is little difference from that of the rabbit except that the olfactory lobes are much larger. The cervical sympathetic system of the neck contains three ganglia, anterior, middle and posterior.

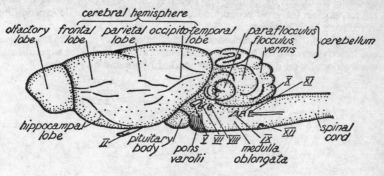

Fig. 29.92. Brain of rat. Side view.

Classification

Phylum: Chordata
Sub-phylum: Craniata [Vertebrata]
Class: Mammalia
Order: Rodentia

Family: Muridae
Genus: *Rattus*
Species: *R. norvegicus*

The Order Rodentia is distinguished from the Lagomorpha by the lack of the two inner small incisors in the upper jaw. The family

Muridae includes the rats, mice and jerboas, all having hairless scaly tails, and naked soles. Distinguishing the genus *Rattus* from the genus *Mus* are the larger size, and differences in the molar teeth. *R. norvegicus* is larger than *R. rattus* but has a smaller tail and ears.

Rats as Pests

Rats carry a number of diseases which have devastating effects on human populations. The worst of these diseases is bubonic plague, due to the bacillus *Pasteurella pestis*. It is carried by rat-fleas which leave the dead rodent hosts and attack man, thus infecting him with the disease. In addition, rats may cause trichinosis indirectly through the pig. If a rat is infected with the parasitic worm *Trichina spiralis* and then eaten by a pig, man may be infected by eating trichinous pork. The worms may also be conveyed from rat to pig in faeces or in rat-soiled food. Various spirochaetal diseases may also be transmitted from the rat to man by insects or by the consumption of food or water fouled by rats. Food-poisoning due to *Salmonella spp.* is undoubtedly often due to rats.

Man suffers enormous loss from rats, by damage to his property and consumption of food stores. The gnawing habits of these rodents cause considerable damage to buildings and their foundations, to pipes of all kinds and to wooden structures. Their depredations into food supplies, not only by eating them, but by spoiling and infecting them with dangerous parasites, are responsible for great economic loss and considerable public expenditure in reducing their numbers.

Perhaps a little may be reckoned in their favour; they are good scavengers and latterly have proved to be very useful laboratory animals for experimental work especially on dietary problems, on hormones and on genetics.

CHAPTER 30

SPECIAL MODES OF LIFE

DISTINCTIONS were drawn in an early chapter between the ways in which organisms may "make a living" and, based on a natural system of classifying them, examples of many of the major groups of the free-living plants and animals have been described. The tremendous range in form and function needs no stressing but the range must be extended still further, for within many of these natural divisions into which organisms fall, we can find representatives whose characteristics are such that, whilst indicating a fundamental relationship with the free-living types, they also exhibit certain obvious differences which make them distinctive. Such organisms have become adapted to some other mode of life. Both in structure and function they reflect this difference. There is every reason to suppose that they are forms derived from free-living ancestors and that the differences they exhibit from the general condition existing among members of their group, are due to the accumulation of the many special features by which they have become adapted to their ways of living.

In this chapter attention is drawn to the specialized characteristics of parasites, saprophytes and symbionts, with some small mention of the commensal and insectivorous conditions. In the following chapters, selected examples of plants and animals are described to illustrate some of the structural and functional adaptations by which these organisms have become fitted to their modes of life.

PARASITISM

Parasitism is a relationship between two organisms, generally of different species, in which one, the parasite, clearly obtains advantages from its association with the other, the host, which as a result suffers some injurious effects. The relationship may be between one animal and another, between one plant and another, between a parasitic animal and a plant host or vice versa, between a bacterium and a plant or animal, between a virus and a plant or animal, or finally, between a bacteriophage and a bacterium. In rare cases in animals, one sex may be parasitic on the other sex within the same species, e.g. some angler fish males parasitize the females.

The condition of parasitism may take many forms and can occur in so many graded conditions of relationship between the one organism and the other, that it is not always easy to recognize it or to distinguish it clearly from some other relationship such as symbiosis or commensalism. A parasite need not necessarily live all its life in such a condition. There are many cases of parasitic animals in which a free-living larval stage precedes an adult parasitic mode of life, e.g. the hookworm of man. Similarly an early parasitic development may be followed by the release of adult free-living forms, e.g. the swan-mussel, *Anodonta cygnea*. Sometimes the parasitic condition is confined to one sex of a species only, e.g. only the female of the copepod species *Lernaea branchialis* parasitizes the haddock and then only after mating. In its association with the host, the parasite may be situated externally upon it, either affixed to the superficial tissues, e.g. the tick on a rabbit, or wandering about on its surface, e.g. the flea on a dog or the aphis on the bean. Such parasites may be termed *ectoparasites* in contrast to the *endoparasites* which live entirely surrounded by the tissues of the host, e.g. the malaria parasite, *Plasmodium*, or the wheat rust, *Puccinia*. Between these two conditions, again it is not always easy to decide. How far are gut parasites such as tapeworms actually within the host's tissues and how deep into the skin must a parasite burrow before it becomes an endoparasite?

When all the possible conditions of parasitism and the wide variety of the forms of parasitic plants and animals are taken into account, it becomes clear that great care should be taken to distinguish between them. So far, a loose usage of the term parasite has tended to neglect this, and has clouded the concept of parasitism to such an extent that included within the range of parasitic organisms on an equal footing, we may find every grade between the purely parasitic *Plasmodium* for example, and the almost free-living predatory flea. A clarification of the concept might be made if greater attention were focused on the host's body by regarding it as merely another environment, organic as opposed to inorganic, and classifying the so-called parasites by the ways they have become adapted to it.

There is no doubt that parasites have been derived from free-living ancestors. In animals, there is no group of parasites which does not show clear relationship with free-living forms. Even in those most profoundly modified, such as some protozoans and the Cestoda, we still see clearly the characteristics of their phylum which also includes free-living animals. In plants, excluding the Fungi for the moment, there are very few parasitic representatives. The few outstanding cases, such as *Cuscuta* and *Lathraea*, show very clear relationship to a particular family. The Fungi constitute a special case. We can find evidence which appears to relate them to both the Algae and the Protozoa. On the other hand, they may have diverged from a common stock which gave rise also to both plants and animals. It is obvious, however, that parasitic fungi have their saprophytic counterparts.

The differences which exist between free-living organisms and their parasitic relatives may be regarded as due to the adaptations necessary for the conquest of a new environment. In what way the conquest has been made is debatable. There are two possibilities, the direct path from the free-living condition by adaptive changes to the purely parasitic condition, or the indirect path through commensalism to symbiosis and thence to the one-sided association of parasite and host. Either case can be argued, but however parasitism arose, certain inter-organism relationships have arisen in which the one has become adjusted to the other with varying degrees of success. In the parasitic relationship, we find the condition in which the adjustments have been made principally by the parasite, so that its host is at a disadvantage. The major adjustments from the free-living condition shown by parasites in general, may be summarized as follows—

1. The parasite has to be able to find all its nutritional requirements in the materials of the host's body or in the food which the host acquires for itself. In some cases a parasite may utilize a variety of hosts for this purpose; in others, the parasite is so exacting that only a single species can supply the requirements. Generally, the parasite is able to extract its own requirements without killing the host before its own reproductive cycle is completed.

2. The parasite has to be able to form a more or less permanent attachment to the host from which it cannot be dislodged easily either by physical or other means. Internal parasites achieve this constant physical attachment automatically by gaining entry to the tissues or body fluids, but run the risk of being killed by a physiological resistance offered by the host. External parasites, and the gut parasites can be included among these, usually achieve the physical attachment either by affixing themselves to, or burrowing into the superficial tissues, or by being so independently active that they can quickly find a host with which they need form only a temporary attachment during the feeding process.

3. The parasite has to be able to ensure that succeeding generations can find new hosts. This is essential to success on the part of the parasite, particularly where the host is specific to the parasite.

Characteristics of Parasites

In achieving these major adjustments to living conditions in the organic environment, parasites have evolved into types which show numerous divergences from their free-living counterparts. This is particularly noticeable in animals. These variations we may survey under three headings, namely, structural, physiological or metabolic, and reproductive.

Structural Modifications of Parasites

These are of many kinds and may be summarized thus—

(*a*) Associated with a specialized manner of obtaining food.

(i) Loss or reduction of powers of locomotion by some parasitic animals, e.g. *Fasciola, Taenia, Sacculina.*

(ii) Absence or degeneration of feeding organs and sometimes even of the alimentary canal, where feeding is saprozoic, e.g. *Taenia, Monocystis, Plasmodium.*

(iii) Development of highly specialized mouth parts in some ectoparasitic animals, particularly the fluid feeders, e.g. *Pulex, Aphis, Pediculus, Glossina.*

(iv) Development of highly specialized haustorial structures by some parasitic plants, e.g. *Cuscuta, Erysiphe*, and by a few parasitic animals, e.g. *Sacculina.*

(*b*) Associated with penetrating or maintaining contact with the host.

(i) Development of boring devices to effect entry, e.g. hexacanth tapeworm embryos, many nematodes, many fungi.

(ii) Development of organs of attachment by which to cling securely, e.g. hooks and suckers of *Taenia*, suckers of *Fasciola*, "teeth" of the hookworm, tight spirals of *Cuscuta*, suckers of leeches, claws of biting lice.

(*c*) Associated with offering resistance to host reactions.

(i) Development of thick resistant outer coverings in some parasitic animals, e.g. *Taenia, Fasciola*, nematodes.

(ii) Very rapid means of escape, e.g. *Pulex.*

(*d*) Associated with great constancy of the parasite's environment.

(i) Tendency for the degeneracy of the sensory organs, e.g. *Taenia.*

Note that whilst it is not always the case, parasites as a whole show a tendency towards degeneracy in many directions and this may be bound up with the comparatively permanent and good nutritional conditions and great constancy of the environment from the chemical and physical aspects. Thus feeding mechanisms and digestive tracts are often poorly developed or even absent, osmoregulatory, excretory and respiratory systems under-developed, and the sense-organs of their free-living relatives lost.

Physiological or Metabolic Modifications

(a) Associated with nutritional processes.

(i) Production of exo-enzymes by parasitic plants and animals which digest host tissues external to the parasite, e.g. fungi, *Plasmodium*.

(ii) Failure to develop photosynthetic pigments in some parasitic plants, e.g. *Cuscuta, Lathraea*.

(iii) Production of anti-coagulants by blood-feeding parasitic animals, e.g. *Pulex, Hirudo*.

(iv) Pronounced chemosensitivity in order to reach the right place in the host's body, e.g. *Monocystis, Plasmodium* in the mosquito, liver-fluke.

(b) Associated with effecting penetration of the host.

(i) Production of cytolytic (cell dissolving) substances by some parasitic plants, e.g. fungi, *Cuscuta*.
(Note that the most recent investigation indicates that penetration of a cuticularized surface by fungal hyphae is mechanical not chemical.)

(c) Associated with resistance to host reactions.

(i) Production of anti-enzymes by some parasitic animals, e.g. gut parasites.

(d) Associated with conditions of low oxygen tension.

(i) Increased ability to respire efficiently in comparatively low oxygen concentrations, e.g. gut parasites.
(Note that no parasitic animal has been conclusively proved to be anaerobic.)

Modifications to Reproductive Processes and Variations in the Continuity of the Life Cycle

(a) Associated with effecting fertilization.

(i) The hermaphrodite condition, with possible self-fertilization, in many parasitic animals and plants, e.g. *Taenia, Fasciola*, many fungi.

(ii) Prolonged association of the sexes in parasitic animals where the female may carry the male or vice versa, e.g. *Bilharzia*.

(iii) Union of two sexes in permanent coition in some parasitic animals, e.g. *Diplozoon* (trematode worm).

(iv) Release of sexually mature forms as free-living organisms in some parasitic animals, e.g. horse-hair worms.

(b) Associated with increased chances of successful dissemination of offspring among new hosts.

(i) Enormous numbers of reproductive bodies (eggs, cysts, spores, etc.) produced by nearly all parasitic organisms, e.g. a single tape-worm may produce over 70,000,000 fertile eggs per year.

(ii) High degree of resistance of the reproductive bodies external to the host, e.g. cysts of *Monocystis*, spores of *Phytophthora*.

(iii) Employment of specialized reproductive phases in the life cycle, e.g. parthenogenesis in *Aphis*, polyembryony in *Fasciola* and in chalcid wasps.

(iv) Use of secondary hosts as vectors, e.g. *Plasmodium* in the mosquito, *Taenia* in the pig.

Not all parasites are entirely parasitic for the whole life cycle. Instances have already been mentioned where a parasite may be free-living for part of its life cycle. There are other conditions, notably in plants, where parasitism is only one of two possible modes of life. We may recognize among the fungi, for example, the condition in which the fungus is well able to continue its existence after the death of the host by living as a saprophyte on the dead organic remains. Such fungi are termed *facultative* or *non-specialized parasites* as distinct from *obligate* or *specialized parasites*. The latter are characterized by the fact that they can live only in or on living host tissue. Among the higher parasitic plants we find cases where the parasite is known to flourish at its best only when it has formed some organic attachment to another living plant. It may be able to develop from seed, produce chlorophyll and make some kind of autotrophic existence, but if presented with the opportunity, it rapidly establishes contact via its own roots with the roots of neighbouring plants, and from that time flourishes more successfully. Such plants are termed *partial parasites* and include the eyebright (*Euphrasia*), lousewort (*Pedicularis*), yellow rattle (*Rhinanthus*) and cow-wheat (*Melampyrum*). The mistletoe (*Viscum*) is another familiar example, but in its case, continued development from seed can only continue if early penetration of the host tissues is accomplished by the young root.

Control of Parasites

One of the more obvious results of an organism living parasitically on another is the development of a diseased condition in the host, and frequently its ultimate death. The diseased condition can take many forms such as structural malformations, poisoning due to toxic substances released by the parasite, and other physiological disturbances. In nature there is the inevitable balancing out of the effects since complete mastery by the parasite must lead to its own extinction through lack of hosts. To man, where the health of his own body and that of his livestock and crops are of utmost importance, the incidence of disease even without death constitutes a serious problem. He has been at some pains to devise methods of extermination of the parasites which affect him. In most cases he has been unsuccessful but in many others he has achieved a high degree of control over the parasites, which enables him to reduce their effects. The study of parasites and the nature and effects of parasitism is known as *parasitology*.

Control of any particular parasite involves adherence to a strict application of measures worked out logically from a knowledge of the parasite and its activities. They may be designed to kill directly or to kill indirectly by preventing it from reaching a new host or by preventing it from reproducing. Such measures can be worked out on a logical plan only if an intimate knowledge of the structure, physiology, reproductive processes and life cycle of the parasite has been gained. Without this knowledge any control measures can be no more effective than the swipes of a blindfold boxer. At no time is it more necessary to "know your adversary" than when waging war on a parasite. Hence much time and money have been spent in improving our knowledge of parasites, the effects of which can prove so economically disastrous.

Control measures likely to be effective can be worked out for general cases as shown below—

1. *Measures taken to safeguard or to eliminate susceptible hosts.*

(*a*) Breeding or cultivation of susceptible hosts only under the best conditions. Poor conditions for livestock and crops invariably lead to general low state of health and a lessening of any natural resistance the host may possess. Dirty, ill-lit and badly ventilated places are ideal breeding grounds for some parasites.

(*b*) Breeding or cultivation of only the most naturally resistant strains of livestock or crops. Many immune or highly resistant strains of plants and animals have been developed as a result of breeding experiments, and the use of them in place of less resistant varieties has done much to reduce the incidence of disease. The greatest difficulty has always been to couple immunity with a high yield but many good results have been achieved.

(*c*) Conferring artificial immunity on a susceptible host by the use of vaccines, etc. This is a normal method of control in modern medicine.

(*d*) Prevention of contamination of healthy stock or crops by infected members.

This can be done in several ways. Importation of certain species into an area can be completely restricted or some system of inspection worked out. The quarantine laws of most countries are designed for this purpose and vary from an immediate inspection, from which a warranty of freedom from certain diseases may be given, to a long period of confinement, during which disease symptoms are carefully sought.

(e) Framing of laws which make certain diseases compulsorily notifiable. Prompt action in such cases as foot-and-mouth disease of cattle, fowl pest, and smallpox in human beings, can prevent serious epidemics.

(f) Restriction of the breeding or cultivation of animals or crops in areas where no effective control measures can be taken.

2. *Measures Taken to Destroy the Parasites on or in the Host.*

(a) Breaking the physical contact with the host where this is possible. Numerous methods can be employed according to the parasite. Surgery may be the only effective means sometimes.

(b) Using chemical substances which can kill the parasites without affecting the host.

Many specific drugs, fungicides, antibiotics, etc., have been found useful.

(c) Destruction by burning of all diseased, dead or removed tissue.

(d) Finding other organisms which are harmless to the host but which prey on the parasites (*see* Biological Control, Chap. 23).

3. *Measures Taken to Destroy the Parasite During its Transmission from Host to Host.*

(a) Taking measures to control or destroy any vector which may carry the parasite.

(b) Sterilization of soil in the case of soil-inhabiting plant parasites.

(c) Starving out of soil-inhabiting plant parasites by not growing susceptible crops until sufficient time has elapsed to ensure the death of the parasites.

(d) Isolation of diseased plants or animals until control measures have proved effective, or destruction of them by burning, if this is not possible.

Consideration of these general measures will make it obvious that many of them can only be applied in particular cases. Which ones to apply and when to apply them will only be known if a full detailed knowledge of the habits of parasite and host are at the disposal of the controllers.

Tolerance of the Host

It has been pointed out that the pathological effects of parasites on their hosts vary greatly. Thus many species of *Trypanosoma* cause serious effects to man and his domestic animals, while wild game are comparatively unaffected though heavily parasitized. *Monocystis* is almost always present in earthworms but they seem to suffer little from the infection. Hence it has been suggested that those parasites which cause marked pathological effects are either recently evolved or have but recently infected a new type of host. Where a parasitic relationship is of very long duration, the host seems to have evolved some degree of tolerance to it. Perhaps non-tolerant species were exterminated by activity of the parasites. Furthermore, we know from modern studies of bacteria and viruses that new strains can arise quickly. Such new strains are often able to resist previously successful control. Herein may lie an explanation of the virulent epidemics of disease which afflict both man and his animals and plants.

SAPROPHYTISM

This is a mode of life exhibited by some fungi and bacteria in which their energy-giving and body-building requirements are derived from the products of, or the dead remains of, other organisms. Before such remains can be absorbed by the saprophyte, they must be rendered soluble, and the saprophyte is thus often instrumental in initiating the conversion. Therefore it must live in or on the organic material. The conversion process from the complex organic condition to the more simple diffusible condition is generally known as *putrefaction* or *decay*. It is a digestive process. Saprophytes are therefore of paramount importance in nature in maintaining the circulation of materials throughout the living world, since by their putrefactive activity they eventually release into the inorganic environment all the materials taken from it by other living things. They may also be of some economic importance to man in two ways. They may have deleterious effects by causing deterioration in many of his carefully harvested food reserves. On the other hand, they may be put to useful service in synthesizing complex substances valuable to the human race, e.g. organic acids of many kinds, alcohol, vitamins and antibiotics.

The saprophytes must obviously have originated from free-living organisms somewhere along the evolutionary line but connexions are nowhere clear. This is due to the fact that the fungi and bacteria are difficult to derive from any known living things. Some would derive the fungi from the filamentous green and red algae on grounds of structure and reproductive processes and thus would indicate that the saprophytic mode of life is a corollary of the loss of photosynthetic pigments. Others would find the origin of the fungi among the more lowly protozoan animals, in which case the structural and reproductive likenesses to the algae are merely examples of parallel evolution, and the heterotrophic condition inherited. In the past the bacteria have been considered as simple or degenerate fungi. One interpretation tends to separate them from all other classes of living things and to regard them as a third kingdom. In this case, they cannot be linked with any other extant living organisms.

Characteristics of the Saprophytes

The major common characteristic of all saprophytes is a physiological one. They are able to produce and exude the enzymes by which they render their substrate soluble and diffusible. This is of course a characteristic of many parasites as well, but the distinction between the two with regard to the nature of the substrate has already been drawn.

Structurally also, the two groups of saprophytes have each their common characteristics. The fungi are nearly all of microscopic filamentous nature and well adapted to permeating a suitable substrate and coming into the necessary intimate contact with it. The yeasts and bacteria are still more minute, unicellular structures, which can also make the most intimate of contacts with organic substrates. The filamentous fungi appear to have the advantage over the bacteria in many cases in that they can radiate more successfully from an initial starting point. They can survive longer by growing away from any toxic products which they may produce as a result of their putrefying activity. Bacteria often achieve their own destruction by producing, in very high concentration, toxic substances from which they are unable to escape.

Motility in water is a feature of many bacteria and some fungal reproductive bodies (zoospores) and many of these show a high degree of ability to make chemotactic responses. In this way, suitable new substrates are quickly found and unsuitable ones avoided. Fungal hyphae are capable of making chemotropic responses to serve the same ends.

In reproductive capacity, the bacteria are unrivalled but most fungi are likewise able to produce enormous numbers of reproductive cells. This is essential to the mode of living if new substrates are to be exploited and the race to continue. Bacterial and fungal spores are among the most highly resistant of all living structures and are small enough and light enough to be disseminated over prodigious areas by almost every known agency.

Some biologists would include among the saprophytes a few higher plant genera such as *Monotropa* and *Neottia* which enter into associations with saprophytic fungi. It is true that such higher plants, lacking chlorophyll, can only survive if sufficient organic matter is available. This they obtain through the agency of a fungus and not by their own putrefying activities. Such cases are, therefore, best considered as symbiotic mycorrhizal relationships.

SYMBIOSIS

This is the condition in which two living organisms derive mutual benefit from their association with one another. The partners are referred to as symbionts and may be plant and plant, plant and animal, animal and animal or either plant or animal and a bacterium. Such association usually confers nutritional benefits upon the participants, the capabilities of one often being augmented by the capabilities of the other. Other benefits may also be derived, including the sheltering of the one by the other and increased chances of reproduction and dispersal.

It is just as difficult to trace the origin of symbiosis as it is of parasitism and saprophytism. In fact it can be argued that each could be the starting point for the others. Some parasites could have evolved from saprophytes which became adapted to living organic environments, whilst equally well, some saprophytes could have come from parasites which gradually became facultative parasites and later saprophytes. Symbiosis could have resulted from a controlled parasitism in which the host gradually became able to take advantage of the presence of the parasite, whilst parasitism could be a symbiosis "gone wrong," to the advantage of one partner. The fact that some symbiotic unions, as for instance those of the lichens, can be artificially created, points to an accidental incidence of the situation in that instance, and this may well have been the case in many others.

Characteristics of Symbionts

Symbionts are so widely represented in the plant and animal worlds that it is not possible to generalize their characteristics any more definitely than is the case for parasites. There are numerous structural and physiological modifications of free-living forms which enable the two organisms to become mutually compatible. Many of these have already been described but there is one in particular which needs mention. For a symbiotic union to be permanent, reproductive bodies produced by the partners must consist partly of the one organism and partly of the other. There can, of course, be no sexual union between the partners, but in many instances of symbiotic partnerships the normal reproductive bodies of one partner are infested with cells of the other, so that from the commencement of development the two are united. Failing such mechanisms, it is frequently the case that one symbiont alone cannot survive unless it is able to find its partner in its early stages of growth.

COMMENSALISM

This term has been used by biologists in at least three senses. It was applied originally to include all associations between two organisms since the word means literally "feeding at the same table." When the conditions of parasitism and symbiosis (mutualism) were more clearly recognized, the remaining condition of relationship in which partners had no apparent physiological effects on one another, was known as *inquilinism,* and the term commensalism went out of use. It seems to have come into use again later to mean only those relationships between organisms which were of a non-physiological kind but which did give definite benefit to both partners such as some kind of shelter-association. The more modern usage of the term commensalism is to apply it only to those cases in which one organism lives in association with another so that neither is subject to harmful effects nor able to gain an advantage. In some instances, both associates could be considered commensals but since the union is generally one in which a lesser organism has as its natural habitat the body of a higher one, only the former is called the commensal. A good example is the association of animals and some of their gut bacteria. As far as is known, the animal suffers no harm nor derives beneficial effects from the union. It merely offers the bacteria a perfect organic substrate on which they can live saprophytically. The bacteria could live equally as well in a comparable substrate elsewhere.

Another condition bordering on commensalism, if not wholly so, is that of the organism which uses the body of another from which to gain a positional advantage only. Such organisms may be termed *epiphytic* or *epizoic* according to whether they use plants or animals for their purpose. They undoubtedly gain some positional advantage but whether at the expense of the organism on which they grow, is not easy to decide. It is doubtful if the forest tree suffers any harm as a result of the growth of lichens and mosses on its bark or even of orchids on its upper branches. Should, however, the condition arise in which the epiphyte were so successful in its position as to encroach over much larger areas including leaves, the tree might run the risk of suffering severe harm. The commensal would then be a positional but not a nutritional parasite.

It seems possible that some parasitic and symbiotic unions may have been initiated as commensal associations.

INSECTIVOROUS PLANTS

The insectivorous plants are a small but unique group of organisms which have become adapted to augmenting the nutritional substances synthesized in the normal way for green plants, with others derived from the digestion of small animals which they are able to catch. They couple autotrophism with heterotrophism and the holophytic and holozoic methods of feeding. From this, they gain advantage over other plants in regions where certain soil nutrients, particularly nitrogen, may be scarce.

They are characterized by possessing special structural adaptations for the capture of prey and the ability to secrete enzymes capable of digesting them externally.

In the following chapters will be found descriptions of representatives of all these modes of life. They serve to illustrate still further the immense diversity of living things.

CHAPTER 31

PARASITIC PLANTS

THE majority of parasitic plants are fungi. They form a group of organisms showing many unique features, not least being their total lack of ability to produce chlorophyll or any other photosynthetic pigment. For convenience, they are regarded as plants, although this may be disputed and a relationship with the protozoan animals has been suggested. They have been studied in much detail, partly because of their own great interest to botanists, and partly because they are of great economic importance. Those which are not parasites live saprophytically and many of both forms can exert great influence on the activities of man. Some can be put to useful work, others can cause serious damage to man's property.

The study of the fungi is known as *mycology* and might almost be said to form a separate subject outside the sphere of botany. Mycologists have built up a terminology peculiar to the subject, in keeping with the distinctness of the fungi from other groups of plants. The vegetative body of any fungus is known as the *mycelium* and is composed of an intricately branched system of delicate filaments known as *hyphae*. Other terms applied to fungal structures only, will become apparent in the following sections.

The fungal parasites to be described belong to the genera *Phytophthora*, *Pythium*, *Peronospora*, *Albugo* [*Cystopus*] and *Puccinia*. The first four fungi belong to the Phycomycetes and the last to the Basidiomycetes. The general characteristics of these groups can be found in the plant classification table. The flowering plant parasites will be the genus *Cuscuta* and the species *Viscum album* (mistletoe).

PHYTOPHTHORA

The genus includes a number of species known to cause soft rots in a variety of higher plants. The majority are obligate parasites but some can be grown on artificial culture media and the details of their life history are thus more conveniently studied. Most parasitize specific hosts and are often recognizable by the disease symptoms which they produce. Among the commoner species, causing diseases as indicated, are—

P. cactorum: soft rot of apples and pears.
P. syringae: soft rot of lilac buds.

1116

P. erythroseptica: pink rot of potato.
P. fragariae: red core of strawberry.
P. parasitica and *P. cryptogae*: stem rot of tomato.
P. porri: white tip of leek.
P. infestans: potato blight and tomato rot.
Only *P. infestans* will be further described.

Structure, Reproduction and Life Cycle

The well-developed mycelium of *P. infestans* is to be found in the tissues of infected potato plants, particularly leaves and stems, and if the attack is heavy, the tubers as well. Within the aerial parts, the hyphae ramify between the cells, filling intercellular spaces and sending out sac-like protrusions to surround individual host cells. Internal contact with the host cells is also made by means of extremely fine hyphal outgrowths which penetrate the cell wall and then enlarge within the cell to form *haustoria*. Each hypha is of very fine dimensions, measuring no more than 10μm in diameter. Cross-walls in the hyphae are not developed except in connexion with reproductive structures and so the mycelium is *coenocytic*. The very delicate wall is of cellulose with an outer deposit of fatty substance and pectic compounds, the whole impregnated with chitin, and the protoplast lining the periphery is made up of granular cytoplasm containing stored food substances and numerous nuclei. Growth of the hyphae is at the tips and under good conditions is very rapid, spreading from a point of infection through a whole leaf in a few days. Enzymes such as pectinases and cellulase are extruded and aid in separating and destroying host cells. The fungus seems to be unable to digest starch.

After absorbing sufficient nourishment through the haustoria or from the digested cell contents, and if atmospheric moisture conditions are suitable, the fungus enters a phase of asexual reproduction.

Branches of the mycelium are produced externally on the host, usually through stomata, and these hyphae become modified to produce *sporangia*. Each such branch or *sporangiophore*, after growing outwards, branches considerably again and at the tip of each branch, a single, oval, multinucleate structure is cut off. Below it, the hypha grows on again leaving the sporangium in a lateral position. At its new tip, again it cuts off another sporangium. The sporangiophore may eventually bear large numbers of these reproductive bodies, which, when mature, are easily shed and carried away on air currents. The extent to which these aerial sporangia are produced depends upon the humidity of the atmosphere. It has been found that in conditions of less than 85 per cent humidity, the sporangiophores are seldom formed, whilst sporangia cannot be produced successfully in less than 95 per

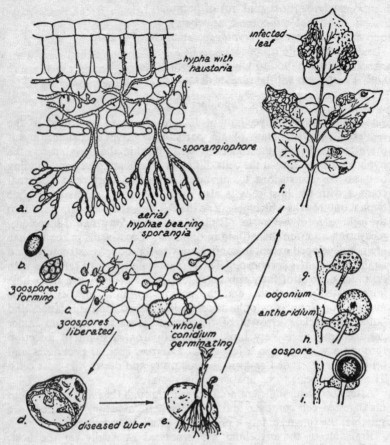

Fig. 31.1. *Phytophthora infestans.* Structure and reproductive cycles. (*a* to *f*) Asexual reproduction by zoospores and overwintering in tubers. (*g* to *i*) Sexual reproductive stages; oospore formation.

cent humidity. Very rainy conditions are therefore necessary to the spread of the fungus by asexual means. When shed, the sporangia develop in one of two ways. Under very wet conditions, each sporangium develops a number of biflagellate *zoospores* which are released to swim through water films and effect new attacks, either on tubers in the soil, or on foliage and stems not yet infected. Under drier conditions, the whole sporangium may develop as a single spore and in such cases it is called a *conidium*. In either case, the zoospore or the conidium quickly develops a delicate germ tube which penetrates the host through a stomate, lenticel, wound or even directly through the epidermal tissues. Once inside, the mycelium develops and disease symptoms are soon apparent.

Sexual reproduction may also occur but has been studied chiefly in artificial cultures. It has been observed in some infected tubers, but there is no doubt that the most rapid means of reproduction is asexual. The sex organs are club-shaped *antheridia* and globose *oogonia*. An antheridium commences development at the apex of an internal hypha and a separate oogonial branch grows up to it and proceeds to grow right through it. On emergence at the far side, the oogonial branch tip enlarges to form the oogonium so that the two organs are closely applied to one another. Such relationship of the antheridium to the oogonium is referred to as *amphigynous*. Fertilization is effected by the passage of a male nucleus into the oogonium through a conjugation tube which forms between the two. Fusion of this male nucleus with the single oosphere nucleus results in a zygote which develops into a thick-walled resting *oospore*. Within the tuber, oospore formation often occurs, apparently without male organs being produced, i.e. is parthenogenetic. Such structures can winter in the ground in old tubers and may therefore cause renewed outbreaks of the disease subsequently. On germination, an oospore may either develop directly into a new mycelium or may grow a sporangiophore which produces zoospores from its sporangia, according to the conditions of moisture. Meiosis most probably occurs at the first divisions of the oospore so that the mycelium is haploid.

Fig. 31.1 illustrates the various stages in development of the fungus and the diagram below summarizes the life cycle.

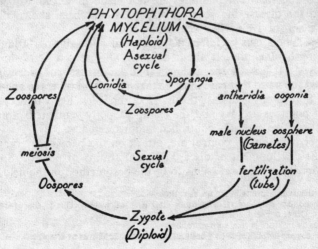

Effect on the Host

The first signs of infection of a potato crop are usually to be seen on the leaves. Here small brown patches appear. These may not spread much in dry weather, but in wet weather they spread rapidly, extending into stems and further downwards. If the attack is very heavy, the whole plant may quickly become a blackened soggy, stinking mass, though this is also due to the presence of other organisms, particularly bacteria, which invade the infected tissues secondarily. Before such devastation has been effected, often within three or four days following infection, the fungus develops its aerial reproductive structures and these can be seen as whitish patches chiefly on the undersides of the leaves. In the tubers, the disease symptoms are somewhat different. Regions of infection show as a form of dry rot, in which the tissues are discoloured a rusty brown under the skin and inwards irregularly towards the centre of the tuber. If such tubers are stored dry, the infection shows up little more than this and may not spread, but if left in wet conditions, other organisms may attack and the whole tuber may rot away.

Control Measures

The chief source of new epidemics of the disease from year to year is the planting of infected tubers. It has been shown that the mycelium may infect new sprouts as they develop and so give rise to the aerial reproductive bodies. Under wet conditions, a single infected plant can spread the disease via the air-borne or water-borne spores over a wide area. Great care must therefore be taken to see that no infected tubers are planted and that new plantings are not made in soil known to have carried the disease the year previously. It has been shown that the fungus can survive up to a year in the soil.

Since tubers can be infected from aerial parts during lifting if the decaying haulms are left about unburnt, all diseased parts should be destroyed. It has also been shown that the disease can over-winter in unlifted tubers so that care must be taken to lift all tubers in an infected field. Spread of the disease through a clamp is less likely to occur if the stored potatoes are dry and the clamp properly ventilated. Imported seed should be carefully controlled and inspected.

Other measures of control are, attack on the parasite by fungicides and the development of disease-resistant strains of potato. Spraying with *Bordeaux mixture*[1] seems to be the best method in the field, but it

---

[1] Bordeaux mixture is made up as follows—

2·7 kg copper sulphate; 1·8 kg lime; 180 litres of water. This is the 6:4:40 composition. Other concentrations such as 5:5:50 can be made.

Burgundy mixture is made up as follows—

4·5 kg copper sulphate; 5·6 kg sodium carbonate; 225 litres of water.

must be carried out at the correct times to prevent an attack, since infected plants cannot be saved. It is usual to spray at roughly fort-nightly intervals, from the time when the plants are a few inches high until they are well-matured. Weather forecasting may help in settling the exact day for spraying, since the spread of the disease is most rapid in wet weather. Spraying with corrosive solutions such as sulphuric acid, to kill the mature haulm, has been employed to prevent tuber infection during lifting. Tubers intended for seed can be sterilized externally by immersion in a 0·1 per cent mercuric chloride solution.

Breeding for resistance to the blight has been going on for some years. The wild potato, *Solanum demissum*, is known to be immune and some of its hybrids have yielded promising material, but one great obstruction to producing the required immunity lies in the fact that the fungus exists as many strains and no potato has been found to be resistant to all of them.

Other hosts of the parasite include the tomato and it is thus necessary to watch carefully that the disease is not transmitted from one to the other when both are grown in close proximity.

General Remarks

By reason of its manner of taking the host substance, i.e. largely by digesting whole cells, the fungus is a killer and to that extent not a successful parasite. It is found in general that the fungi best adapted to feeding haustorially can do so without killing the cells and may live for much longer periods. *Phytophthora spp.* rely to a great extent on the rapid development of reproductive bodies, which are easily disseminated in wet or dry weather once they have been formed. By over-wintering in tubers or as oospores, their year by year incidence is fairly well assured, particularly where no measures of control are employed.

The disease first reached economically important proportions in 1845, when it swept through the European potato fields and from there across England and into Ireland, where it caused such devastation to the potato crops as to cause a widespread famine. It is estimated that the attack cost Ireland over one million and a half of her population due to death and emigration in the following few years.

PYTHIUM

This genus includes a number of soil-inhabiting species where undoubtedly most of them can thrive quite successfully as saprophytes on the organic matter. Several cause disease symptoms and ultimately death of higher plants and are therefore parasitic, but they can also live for some time on the host remains. They are therefore facultative parasites. Most species of *Pythium* will take advantage of the successful attack by another parasite and enter already infected host tissue. Thus many rotting conditions of crop plants are not primarily due to *Pythium spp.* but to other parasites in whose wake they follow. Two species of importance are *P. ultimum*, causing watery wound rot of potato tubers, and *P. debaryanum* infecting a wide variety of young seedlings, cuttings, etc., to cause "damping off" disease. It is also associated with more specific diseases known by the name of the host, e.g. conifer root rot, stem rot of *Pelargonium*, black leg of sugar beet. *P. debaryanum* will be described here.

Structure, Reproduction and Life Cycle

The mycelium is initially coenocytic, ramifying through the host tissue or organic matter as exceedingly fine hyphae (up to 4μm diameter) which fill intercellular spaces and may grow into and through host cells without producing any clearly-defined haustoria. As the mycelium ages and if nutritional conditions are poor, parts may be cut off by crosswalls, but in the early stages these are formed only in connexion with reproductive structures. The wall is of cellulose covered by pectic and fatty compounds and impregnated with chitin, and the multinucleate protoplast is densely granular, showing fat and glycogen in abundance when nutrition is good.

Asexual and sexual reproductive phases are developed as the mycelium ages. Asexually, the fungus produces *sporangia* borne on *sporangiophores* external to the host. The sporangia are spherical organs arising most often in the terminal position on the hyphae. They may function as single air-borne spores and are then *conidia*, or may develop as sporangia by producing *zoospores* from their contents. When conditions are dry, the former is the case, but if the sporangia are wetted copiously, they open and the contents are extruded into a very delicate vesicle within which a number of reniform biflagellate zoospores are formed. These are released on rupture of the vesicle and swim freely before settling down to round off and invest themselves in an outer membrane. They may rest for short periods only, but conidia have been known to retain their vitality for many months in the soil. A conidium or settled zoospore, if in suitable surroundings, develops a very fine germ tube with which to penetrate a new host.

Sex organs usually appear on the mycelium in later stages, but there is no definite time relationship with the sporangia, and they may be developed on either the internal or the external hyphae. The globose female *oogonia* are usually produced terminally on the hyphae, and one or several club-shaped *antheridia* may be developed from the same hypha just below an oogonium, or on adjacent separate hyphae. The antheridium applies itself to the oogonium, i.e. is *paragynous*

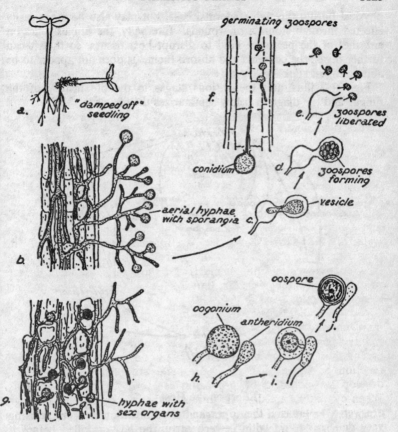

Fig. 31.2. *Pythium debaryanum.* Structure and reproductive cycles. (*a* to *f*) Asexual reproduction by zoospores. (*g* to *j*) Sexual reproductive stages; oospore formation.

(cf. amphigynous), and a short conjugation tube between the two is formed. Fertilization is effected by the passage of the antheridial contents into the oogonium and a single *oospore* results. This is spherical with a smooth thick wall. When host and fungus decay, the oospores are released into the soil, where they can over-winter successfully. On germination, germ tubes may be produced directly, or alternatively the oospore may give rise to numerous zoospores which are comparable with those from asexual sporangia. It is probable that the first divisions of the oospore are meiotic.

Penetration by germ tubes seems to be purely mechanical, i.e.

physical boring through epidermal cells, but may also be more easily
effected through stomata or wounds. Internally, the fungus relies on
enzymes of the pectinase kind to disrupt host tissues, so that it can
further digest the contents and absorb them. It does not appear to be
able to digest starch.

Fig. 31.2 illustrates the various stages in the life history of the
fungus and the diagram below summarizes the life cycle.

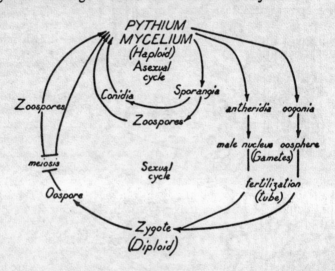

Effect on the Host

Hosts may be infected at any stage after germination until the seedling
stage is past. If infection is very early, the host is killed before it
emerges above ground. On seedlings, the first signs of infection are
watery spots at or just below soil level. They eventually become brown
and finally black in colour. If infection penetrates deeply, the seedling
wilts and finally topples over, bending at the infected region. Sometimes the fungus is prevented from getting beyond the cortex into the
vascular tissues and the wound may heal. After death of the host, the
fungus ramifies more rapidly through the tissues as a saprophyte and
may be aided by other organisms in completing the whole decay of the
host.

Control Measures

Pythium spp. are inhabitants of the soil for much of their time either as
oospores or conidia, and thus an effective method of destruction would

be to steam-sterilize the soil. Such a measure is often impracticable on a large scale. Treatment of seed with sterilizing compounds such as mercuric chloride can be effective in preventing transmission by contaminated seed. Perhaps the greatest check on "damping off" is to grow susceptible plants from seed of known healthy parents under the best possible conditions, avoiding over-crowding, over-watering and poor ventilation. Seedlings forced under higher temperatures are more prone to attack than those grown under colder conditions. This is because higher temperatures favour the growth of the fungus, and the seedlings are weaker and less resistant. Destruction of all infected seedlings and cuttings by burning is essential.

General Remarks

By combining the saprophytic with the parasitic mode of life *Pythium spp.* are remarkably successful. As parasites alone, however, they are not among the more fully adapted. Lack of haustoria as absorbing structures which do not kill the host cells, is looked upon as a simple condition, but by living on the dead host, the fungus partly rectifies this position in its favour. By over-wintering in the resting stages and by an ability to attack a fairly wide variety of hosts, it is difficult to control. Economically it can be very destructive, but reasonable precautions go a long way towards reducing its incidence.

PERONOSPORA

This is a genus of strictly parasitic fungi causing the so-called "downy-mildew" diseases of a wide variety of hosts. Some members are highly specific in their choice of hosts and can live in no other, whilst a few are less exacting in their requirements. The former are said to exhibit *selective parasitism*. Some species apparently exist as a number of physiological strains or races since sometimes the fungus is known to attack only a particular variety of a higher plant species and not all its sub-species, whilst they in their turn may be attacked by other strains of the same parasite.

Among the commoner species are: *P. destructor*—downy mildew of onion; *P. schachti*—downy mildew of beet; *P. effusa*—downy mildew of spinach; *P. parasitica*—downy mildew of cabbage and other cruciferous plants.

Structure, Reproduction and Life Cycle

Peronospora parasitica is an obligate parasite. The delicate non-septate mycelium is to be found at first ramifying profusely through the intercellular spaces of the leaves of the host. It sends finger-like haustoria into the adjacent cells from whence its nourishment is extracted. If very young seedling plants are attacked, the fungus may penetrate into stems and eventually into the roots. Each hypha possesses a wall of "fungal-cellulose," i.e. cellulose impregnated with chitin, enclosing the multinucleate and highly granular protoplast.

After a period of development within the host, the parasite sends out aerial hyphae through the stomata. It is these which give the whitish, downy appearance to patches of the lower surface of the infested leaf. Each aerial hypha, on emergence, becomes repeatedly dichotomously branched and occasionally cross-walls may appear. Each small branch cuts off a delicate spore at its tip. The whole hypha is a *conidiophore* and each short piece bearing a spore is called a *sterigma*. Each spore is formed by the swelling of the tip of the sterigma to include some cytoplasm and a single nucleus. A constriction across the hypha below the swelling, then cuts off the swollen tip as a *conidiospore*. Such a spore is adapted only to an air-borne method of transference and unlike the comparable structures of *Phytophthora* and *Pythium*, it does not produce zoospores even in the wettest conditions. On reaching a new host, it germinates by producing a germ tube which wanders over the surface of the leaf until it finds a stomate through which to penetrate. Sometimes the germ tube may penetrate the epidermal cells directly. The fact that the sterigmata are water-soluble and therefore release the spores in wet periods, partly ensures that the conidiospores will have favourable conditions for germination.

Sexual reproduction is carried out within the host tissue and is markedly oogamous. Frequently, the sex organs, male *antheridia* and female *oogonia*, are produced only in deeper parts such as the pith of stems, at the apices of the same or separate hyphae. Each antheridium is a club-shaped multinucleate cell and the oogonium is a globose structure, which at first is multinucleate but later changes its form as it becomes ready for fertilization. At first, in the developing oogonium, the numerous nuclei are evenly scattered but gradually all except one migrate to a peripheral position into a region of clear cytoplasm (*periplasm*) where they eventually abort. The remaining nucleus takes up the central position in the cell and with the granular cytoplasm forms the *oosphere*. The antheridium now effects union with the oogonium by pushing into it a fine, short, fertilization tube and through this, a single male nucleus and some cytoplasm pass into the oogonium. The male and female nuclei now fuse so that a zygote is formed. The zygote develops a thick wall to enclose itself and becomes an *oospore* of a yellowish-brown colour. The oospores are resistant and remain in the host tissues till these rot, at which point they are released into the soil. Under favourable conditions, each oospore germinates by the development of a germ tube capable of penetrating the host as described

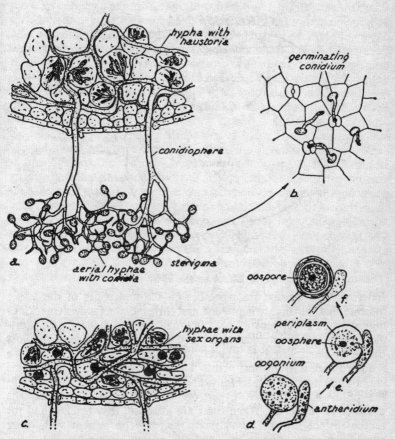

Fig. 31.3. *Peronospora parasitica*. Structure and reproductive cycles. (*a* to *b*) Asexual reproduction by conidia. (*c* to *f*) Sexual reproductive stages; oospore formation

for conidiospores. The first divisions of the oospore are probably meiotic.

Fig. 31.3 illustrates the various stages in the life history of the fungus and the diagram below summarizes the life cycle.

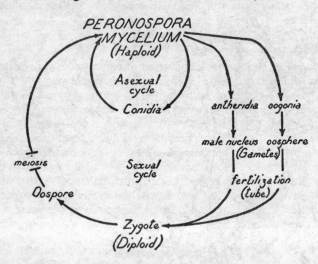

Effect on the Host

Externally the downy white patches on the undersides of the leaves indicate that the disease is present, and corresponding greyish markings may show on the upper surfaces. Internally, although feeding haustorially, the fungus is very destructive and cellular breakdown of the host tissues is usual. In bad attacks, whole leaves may shrivel and be rendered useless to the host plant. The presence of the fungus in stems is not often noticeable externally, and the mycelium may be confined to the pith which becomes hypertrophied and eventually shows the presence of oospores. When roots are attacked, they blacken and rot in the surface layers. *Peronospora spp.* may be present with other parasites such as *Albugo spp.* and the effects of one are not easily discernible from the effects of the other.

Control Measures

The fungus appears to survive from season to season as oospores in the soil. Short of complete sterilization which is usually quite impracticable, little can be done to eradicate the fungus when it is present in the soil, except to "starve it out." This would mean a rotation in the soil of crucifers with non-cruciferous crops, and the removal of all cruciferous weeds which might carry the parasite. All cruciferous crop refuse should be burnt to get rid of oospores which might be present.

Spraying with fungicides such as Bordeaux mixture is useful in preventing attacks via the conidiospores which are killed when they germinate on the sprayed leaf surface.

General Remarks

Peronospora species form a collection of very successful parasites and are very difficult to control. Unlike the *Phytophthora* and *Pythium* species, the members are much less reliant on the presence of water for rapid spread. No zoospores are produced, the asexual spore functioning purely as an air-borne infective structure, i.e. a conidium. Assuming that the production of zoospores is a primitive condition, since it is exhibited by the water-inhabiting saprophytic fungi such as *Saprolegnia*, *Achlya*, etc., the species of *Peronospora* represent the end of an evolutionary trend towards reproductive structures more suited to dissemination on the land. In *Phytophthora* and *Pythium*, the zoosporangia can function in this way under dry conditions and represent a transitional stage in the evolution of a conidium from a zoosporangium.

ALBUGO [CYSTOPUS]

This genus is closely similar to *Peronospora* in many respects and contains only species which are strict parasites. These cause the so-called "white-rusts" of a number of hosts, chiefly members of the Cruciferae. The use of the term "rust" in this connexion must not lead to confusion with some genera of basidiomycete fungi, which are more usually termed "rusts," e.g. *Puccinia*. There are about twenty-five species of *Albugo* and some of these are known to exist as several physiological strains. They include *A. portulacae*, on purslane, *A. bliti* on *Amaranthus spp.*, and *A. tragopogonis* on several *Tragopogon spp.* and other members of the Compositae. The most well-known species is *A. candida*, which causes white rust or blister of cabbage, shepherd's purse, candytuft and other crucifers. The genus is most frequently known by the name *Cystopus*, but rules of nomenclature demand that the earlier name shall be applied.

Structure, Reproduction and Life Cycle

The mycelium consists of delicate hyphae which may be found ramifying through the intercellular spaces of the host tissue, particularly those of the flowers and inflorescences. Contact with the host cells is established by means of numerous small spherical *haustoria*, and through these the fungus obtains its nourishment, eventually killing the host in the process. The hyphae are characteristically those of a phycomycete fungus, being non-septate and with walls composed of fungal cellulose.

After a period of vegetative development, the fungus enters a phase of asexual reproduction. It is then that its presence in the host becomes most apparent because of the visible pustules or blisters which are formed. Branches of the mycelium collect in patches just beneath the host epidermis and develop into what may be termed *sporangia beds*. These reproductive branches arise in large numbers, closely packed, and as the reproductive bodies are formed in succession from their tips, the epidermis is ruptured and lifted clear of the fungus. The products of the reproductive branches may be considered as *zoosporangia* or *conidiospores*, since under different conditions they develop in different ways. The branches which produce them, can be called *sporangiophores* or *conidiophores*, likewise. The sporangia or conidia, by whatever term they are known, are budded off in chains at the apices of the short, thick-walled branches. Each is a multinucleate structure, roughly spherical in shape and separated from its neighbours in the series by pads of callose, known as *disjunctors*, which, on dissolution, allow the sporangia to be scattered freely by air currents. The first-formed sporangium is said not to germinate and may be concerned only in effecting a break through the host epidermis. If the sporangia fall into water, their contents divide to form four to eight uninucleate, bi-flagellate, reniform *zoospores*, which are released on rupture of the parent wall. When a zoospore comes to rest, it secretes a cell wall and forms a germ tube. If the water, into which the sporangium fell, is on a suitable host plant, penetration of the tissues is rapidly effected through stomata or other openings. It has been shown, in some species, that the reproductive structures act as conidia, and on encountering a suitable host, germinate directly without zoospore formation.

Sexual reproduction occurs within the host tissues. At the tips of branches are formed spherical *oogonia*, each cut off by a septum, and containing many nuclei. The *antheridia* are small, club-shaped multi-nucleate structures; each is terminal and separated by a cross-wall from the rest of the hypha. Fertilization is effected by the application of the antheridium to the oogonium, i.e. *paragynous*, and the development of a fertilization-tube by the former, which penetrates the latter. Details of nuclear fusions differ in different species. In some, the oogonium contains originally two hundred or more nuclei. Of these, all but one pass to a peripheral position, i.e. into the periplasm, but in a number of cases, some of these nuclei, or their products by division, pass back into the egg cytoplasm, forming a multinucleate female

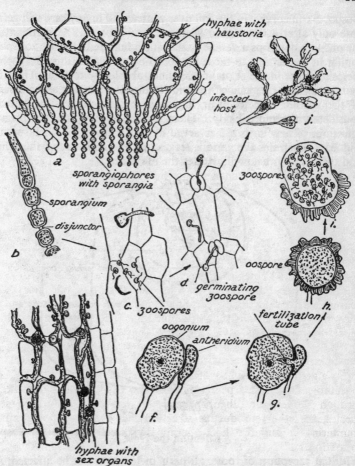

Fig. 31.4. *Albugo (Cystopus) candida.* Structure and reproductive cycles. (*a* to *d*) Asexual reproduction by zoospores. (*f* to *i*) Sexual reproductive stages. (*j*) Infected *Capsella* inflorescence.

structure. In such cases, many nuclei pass from the antheridium into the oogonium and the male and female nuclei then fuse in pairs. When only one nucleus occurs in the egg, only one nucleus leaves the antheridium and the zygote is formed by a single fusion. *A. candida* acts in this way. The fertilized egg produces a thick wall consisting of two layers, a thin endosporium and a thick exosporium which is characteristically bluntly ridged. When a single zygotic nucleus has been formed, there is repeated division of this to form a multinucleate *oospore*.

Oospores can survive in the soil over winter, and in any case will germinate only after a rest period lasting several months. At germination, the oospore develops a vesicle containing a hundred or more zoospores similar in all respects to those produced by asexual means. Just where meiosis occurs in the sexual cycle is not absolutely certain. There are two possibilities, at gamete formation in the sex organs or at the division of the zygotic nucleus prior to zoospore formation. The latter is considered the more likely. There is little doubt that the primary infections of new hosts are achieved by zoospores of the sexual source. Fig. 31.4 illustrates the various stages in the life history of the fungus and the diagram below illustrates the life cycle.

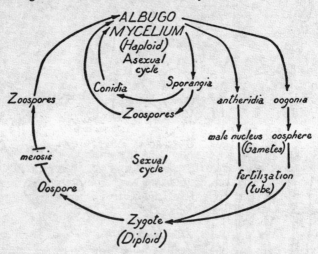

Effect on the Host

With the exception of roots, all parts of the host can be affected, and they show presence of the fungus by bearing the sporangia beds and by considerable swelling and distortion. Inflorescences and flowers are particularly prone to attack, and they become swollen and fleshy with sometimes unusual greenish colouring. There is a general tendency in the flowers for abnormal development in that the perianth is all leaf-like and the stamens may be similar to carpels. Ovules never reach maturity and no fertile pollen is produced. The parasite has profound effects on the host vegetative tissues also. Leaves do not develop normal mesophyll. The cortex and pith of stems may develop considerably, i.e. hypertrophy. Lignified tissues, such as sclerenchyma, may fail to mature, remaining as thin-walled parenchyma. The cambium may become over-active and increase further the fleshiness and girth of stems. The general tendency is to cause development of much nutritive, loose-celled parenchyma which, at first, becomes heavily stored with starch. Even cells of the cambium may be starch-filled, an unusual condition. As the fungus reaches reproductive maturity, this excess food is removed and the host suffers. Its tissues gradually dry up and turn brown, eventually disintegrating. It is not unusual for species of *Albugo* and *Peronospora* to be associated together in an attack on the same host.

Control Measures

Since the fungus over-winters in the soil as oospores and since these are almost impossible to eliminate by any other means, "starving them out" is the only real solution. A rotation of cruciferous crops with non-cruciferous, on the same soil, is the control measure generally adopted, Coupled with this must be the eradication of all cruciferous weeds. and the destruction of all infected material which might harbour the parasite, including the underground parts of biennials. Spraying with a suitable fungicide, to coincide with release of zoospores, can be employed to prevent the spread of an attack through a crop.

General Remarks

The fungus is not of tremendous economic importance since control measures can be adequate if properly applied. In producing asexual structures which can germinate in wet conditions to produce zoospores, or directly in drier conditions, the fungus is comparable with the genera *Phytophthora* and *Pythium*.

PUCCINIA

This genus is one of the fungal parasite forms known as "rusts," so named because of the rusty spore-forming streaks or patches which erupt through the epidermis of the infected host. The rust order, Uredinales, includes other common genera such as *Uromyces* and *Phragmidium*, which infect peas and beans and wild and cultivated roses respectively. *Puccinia* includes a number of species, attacking hosts as shown: *P. malvacearum* (hollyhock), *P. antirrhini* (antirrhinum), *P. pringsheimiana* (gooseberry), *P. prunispinosae*, (plum) and three species, *P. glumarum*, *P. triticina* and *P. graminis* which cause yellow, brown and black or stem rusts respectively of cereals and wild grasses. Some of the rusts are *heteroecious*, requiring two host species on which to complete the life cycle; *autoecious* forms infect only one. *P. graminis* lives part of its life on a member of the Gramineae and part on the common barberry, *Berberis vulgaris*, although other barberry species and a relative, *Mahonia*, may be infected.

P. graminis occurs as different sub-species, identical morphologically but distinguishable by their capacity for infecting certain host species or varieties only. A trinomial system of naming is used to designate these different sub-species. For example, *P. graminis tritici*, described below attacks wheat, *P. graminis avenae* attacks oat and *P. graminis secalis* attacks rye and barley. Each of these can also infect wild grasses. Owing to the range of varieties among the hosts, particularly the cultivated ones, there exists within each fungal sub-species a series of physiological races, recognisable by their capacities to attack different host varieties with differing effects. So far, over 200 races of *P. graminis tritici* have been recorded, each given a number. Thus *Puccinia graminis tritici* 19 indicates physiological race No. 19 of the sub-species for which wheat is the most important host. The rusts are basidiomycete fungi.

Structure, Reproduction and Life History

The mycelium in the stem and leaf tissues of the wheat, resulting from spores formed in spring on the barberry, is intercellular and composed of fine hyphae which send small rounded or branched haustoria into the host cells. These extract requirements without any apparent destructive effects. The fungal cells are binucleate or *dikaryotic* and each nucleus is haploid. After a period of growth, the fungus enters its first reproductive phase. This is effected by rapid concentration of localized sub-epidermal mycelial beds which form erect stalk cells each bearing one spiny, thickwalled, oval, brown, binucleate spore (*see* Fig. 31.5). Due to rapid growth of the fungus, the host epidermis is pushed outwards and eventually disrupts to expose the spore clusters or sori, which appear as rusty brown streaks. The spores are called *uredospores* and the clusters, *uredosori*. When shed, these spores can infect neighbouring wheat plants, spreading the disease rapidly. Penetration, through a stomate, is effected by a germ tube which develops from one or other of the four germ pores in the uredospore wall. From such an infection, the new mycelium can produce another crop of uredospores within about fourteen days. This method of reproduction and dissemination continues throughout the summer, but as the wheat ripens the form of reproductive spore changes.

Towards the end of summer, *teleutospores* are formed, at first intermingled with uredospores, but finally in separate *teleutosori*. These spores are produced in much the same way as uredospores, but are distinct in form and colour. Each is composed of two smooth, thickwalled, dark brown cells, each with a germ pore (*see* Fig. 31.5). Initially, each cell contains two haploid nuclei but as the spore ripens, these fuse in what corresponds to a sexual act. The ripe teleutospore

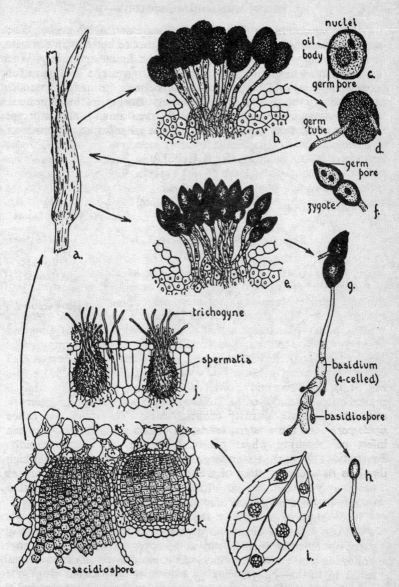

nuclei

oil body

germ pore

c.

germ tube

d.

germ pore

zygote

f.

g.

trichogyne

spermatia

j.

basidium (4-celled)

basidiospore

h.

aecidiospore

k.

b.

e.

i.

a.

Fig. 31.5. *Puccinia graminis tritici.* Reproductive cycles. (*a*) "Rust" patches on stem and leaf of wheat. (*b*) Uredosorus. (*c*) Uredospore in section. (*d*) Uredospore germinating. (*e*) Teleutosorus. (*f*) Teleutospore in section. (*g*) Teleutospore germinating. (*h*) Basidiospore germinating. (*i*) "Cluster cups" on barberry leaf. (*j*) and (*k*) Spermagonia and aecidia on barberry.

therefore *represents the diploid zygotic phase in the life cycle.* When shed, the teleutospores do not germinate at once but remain dormant, over-wintering on soil and stubble until the following spring. When activity commences one or both spore cells gives rise to a germ tube which elongates and becomes a *pro-mycelium.* From its subsequent development, this is clearly a *basidium.* During its formation, the diploid nucleus of the teleutospore cell passes along it and undergoes meiosis to form four haploid nuclei. These are separated by crosswalls

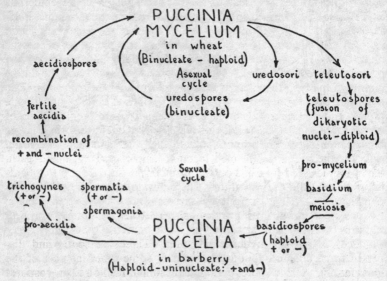

Life cycle diagram of Puccinia.

and from each of the newly formed cells there arises a narrow sterigma terminating in a swelling. Into this, the nucleus with some cytoplasm passes and is eventually cut off as yet a third type of spore, a *basidiospore.* This can germinate only on the second host, the barberry.

When airborne to its host, the basidiospore puts out a germ tube which can penetrate directly through the cuticle of any young exposed parts, but most infections occur via the upper surfaces of young leaves. Following penetration, a uninucleate haploid mycelium is soon established in the mesophyll, making haustorial connections from intercellular hyphae. Shortly, two types of fructifications are formed at the leaf surfaces, *spermagonia* or *pycnidia* on the upper and *aecidia,* usually in clusters called "cluster cups," on the lower. The spermagonia are tiny, narrow-necked, flask-shaped structures, lined with fine hyphae which bud off countless minute spores called *spermatia* or *pycnospores*. These are extruded through the outlet ostioles of the spermagonia in globules of sugary fluid. Whilst the spermagonia are becoming functional, the early stages of the aecidia or pro-aecidia are formed from the same infecting mycelium. Each is initially a loose bed of uninucleate hyphae near the lower side of the host leaf. So long as these cells remain uninucleate, the formation of an aecidium goes no further. However, in connection with each pro-aecidium, uninucleate hyphae are produced across the leaf to emerge through the upper epidermis either close to or even through the ostiole of a spermagonium. Each such hypha is called a *trichogyne* and is capable of accepting through its wall the contents of a spermatium, so that some cells become binucleate. In some way, this binucleate condition is passed to the pro-aecidial cells from which the trichogynes originated and these now multiply rapidly in the dikaryotic state to form a fertile *hymenium*. The hymenial cells form into a group in close lateral contact and divide rapidly and continuously parallel to the leaf surface to produce series of *aecidiospore mother cells*. Each of these divides again to form a larger binucleate *aecidiospore* proper and a smaller, flat binucleate *interstitial cell*. As the spores are formed in rapid succession from underneath, the host epidermis is pushed outwards under pressure from the elongating mass of spore chains within. The outermost layer of aecidial cells remains sterile and constitutes a surface rind over the spore mass. Eventually, the whole erupts through the lower epidermis; the rind ruptures, curling back at the edges, to expose the oldest and ripest rounded, orange-coloured aecidiospores. These are soon wind dispersed to germinate only on the wheat or some other member of the grass family. Aecidiospores germinate in similar fashion to uredospores and thus, early in summer, the cycle is commenced once more by the introduction of a dikaryotic mycelium into the wheat.

The significance of the events in the barberry is now clearly understood. *P. graminis* is *heterothallic* and the four basidiospores produced from a teleutospore are of two kinds. Two are designated + and two —. Infections by any one of these on the barberry can produce functional spermagonia of either + or — but only immature pro-aecidia. In order to be made fertile the pro-aecidial cells must be rendered binucleate with one each of the + and — nuclei. The reconstitution of this "opposite sign" dikaryotic condition is effected by the acceptance of a spermatium of one or other sign by a trichogyne of the opposite sign. This means that the formation of mature aecidia necessitates the infection of the barberry by both kinds of basidiospores and the necessary transference of spermatia. The exudation of nectar from the spermagonia may attract insects which effect this "cross-fertilization."

It appears that the dikaryotic condition can sometimes arise merely by the intermingling of + and − mycelia in the pro-aecidium, but the result is the same.

In the full life cycle, the bringing together of + and − nuclei is effected during the phase in the barberry, but the actual fusion resulting in a diploid zygote, is delayed until the ripening of teleutospores. When these germinate, the necessary meiosis, to produce haploid basidiospores, separates the + and − nuclei once more. Uredospore formation spreads the parasite during the period when the wheat is most susceptible, but uredospores will over-winter in warm climates and the fungus may persist from year to year without any sexual process.

Effect on the Host

P. graminis tritici kills neither of its hosts. In the wheat, its main effect is on the final size of the grain which does not fill out normally.

Control Measures

Eradication of barberry plants in colder regions where uredospores cannot over-winter is an obvious means of eliminating the disease but is quite ineffective in warmer climates. The breeding of wheat strains with resistance to the disease has been tried many times but the existence of so many races of the parasite which can hybridize to produce new races makes very difficult the task of developing a wheat wholly immune. The use of copper and sulphur dusts on a wide scale is hardly practicable. Infected straw and stubble should be burnt.

General Remarks

Puccinia spp. are very successful parasites with an enormous capacity for air-borne spore production. Some can live on a range of hosts, wild as well as cultivated, making control very difficult. The decline of sexuality is a feature common to many of the advanced fungi.

CUSCUTA

Cuscuta is a genus of flowering plants in the family Convolvulaceae. There are about 100 species and sub-species widely represented in temperate and warmer climates. All have the characteristic of being without chlorophyll and parasitize a wide variety of higher plants. There are three species found in Great Britain, namely, *C. europaea* (greater dodder), using chiefly nettles and hops as hosts, *C. epithymum* (lesser dodder), using chiefly leguminous plants such as gorse, broom and clovers but occasionally heather, as the hosts, and *C. epilinum*, parasitic on the flax. The last named is not a native. It can be recognized by the host and by its yellowish flowers. The other two species have pinkish flowers. All are obligate parasites.

Cuscuta europaea: Structure, Reproduction, Life Cycle

When fully developed, the parasite may be seen twining vigorously around the stems, leaves and other aerial parts of the nettle (*Urtica dioica*) or the hop (*Humulus lupulus*) in great profusion. The twining

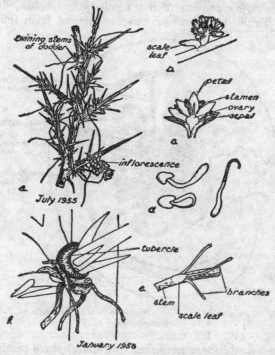

Fig. 31.6. *Cuscuta.* (*a*) *C. epithymum* on gorse (summer condition). (*b*) Inflorescence. (*c*) Single flower. (*d*) Seeds of *C. europaea* germinating (after Verdcourt). (*e*) Portion of stem with scale leaf and branches. (*f*) Tubercle of *C. epithymum* on gorse (winter condition).

parts are stems and these are slender, whitish to yellow or red in colour, bearing tiny scale leaves from the axils of which branches, or in later stages, inflorescences arise. The stem has no connexion with the ground and a root system is never developed. At intervals along the stem, contact is established with the internal tissues of the host. This is achieved by penetration of haustorial growths through the host's outer tissues to effect a union with the vascular tissues within (*see* Fig. 31.7). The haustoria develop from pad-like *appressoria* on the stem of the parasite, and as they penetrate inwards, vascular tissues differentiate within them to become continuous with the phloem and xylem of the host. By this means, the parasite is able to tap the supplies of food and water moving through the host.

From about July, flowering commences and large numbers of pinkish flowers in tightly arranged spikes develop in the axils of scale leaves. The flower consists of five sepals, joined below, five petals forming a corolla tube, and on this are inserted from four to five

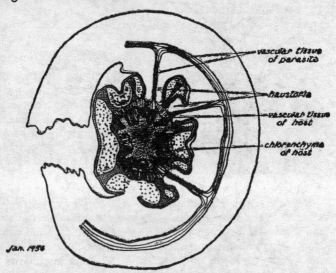

Fig. 31.7. *Cuscuta epithymum.* Attachment to host by haustoria. L.P. plan of tissue layout.

stamens, below which are from four to five very small petaloid scales which do not close the tube. (These may be used in identification since the comparable scales in *Cuscuta epithymum* are large and close the tube.) The ovary is two-celled and bears two styles. Pollination appears to be by insects but self-pollination may occur. Two small angular seeds are produced in each of the two loculi of the capsule. These are shed by a transverse split in the capsule and the parent dodder plant dies during the autumn. The scattered seed may be dispersed partly by water since the parasite is often found on hosts near river banks. In spring of the following season (April–May) the seeds germinate and it becomes evident that the embryo is not constructed in the usual way. There is no differentiation into radicle, plumule and cotyledons. There is instead only a single, straight axis which functions as a shoot (*see* Fig. 31.6 (*d*)). This elongates rapidly at the expense of food stored in the seed and grows upwards, nutating very strongly in an anti-clockwise direction. If it does not find a suitable host, it dies very quickly. If it finds a nettle or hop seedling, it twines about it very vigorously and quickly makes its first haustorial connexion. It may twine on other non-host species but is incapable of making use of them and no haustoria are developed. Once established, vigorous growth is made over neighbouring hosts and more and more contacts are made until one plant covers a wide area.

The species is clearly an annual and over-winters as seed.

Cuscuta epithymum: Structure, Reproduction, Life Cycle

From the wide variety of hosts used, it is probably the case that a number of physiological strains of the species exist but this has not been investigated fully. One of the commonest hosts is the gorse (*Ulex europaeus*) over which very profuse growth is made. In general the characteristics of the species are similar to those of *C. europaea*, but the plant parts are smaller, the stems being very slender by comparison. The small floral differences have been noted. One other very great difference is in the life history. *C. epithymum* has been shown to be able to perennate on any of its hosts. This is possibly because the hosts themselves perennate above ground whereas the hosts of *C. europaea* do not perennate to the same degree. The parasite forms along its stem, at intervals, small fleshy *tubercles* which remain adpressed and attached to the host whilst the other stems die back in winter (*see* Fig. 31.6 (*f*)). In spring, renewed growth of stems from the tubercles follows new growth by the host and haustoria quickly establish themselves on the young host tissues.

Effect on the Host

Injury done by the parasite can sometimes be great, particularly on the softer hosts such as flax, clover and hop. Growth of the host is never very vigorous and with crop plants, yield is severely cut down. On the more woody hosts such as gorse, the effect is much less pronounced.

Control Measures

The parasite can be "starved out" at any time by removal of suitable hosts from areas where it is known to occur. Destruction of weeds which can act as hosts must also be effected to make extermination complete. Careful inspection of crop seeds ensures that the parasite is not reintroduced.

General Remarks

The genus *Cuscuta* illustrates well the adaptation of a free-living higher plant to a parasitic mode of life. Other members of the same family such as *Convolvulus* and *Calystegia* (bindweeds) show the same climbing characteristics but produce normal green leaves and never develop haustorial connexions with the plants over which they twine.

VISCUM

This is the only British genus of the family Loranthaceae. *V. album* is the well-known European mistletoe, and like all other nineteen species of the genus, is a partial parasite on branches of deciduous trees such as apple (most commonly), poplar, hawthorn, willow and oak (less so). It occurs still more rarely on conifers and other evergreens. A well-grown specimen forms an evergreen bush possessing somewhat woody but green stems 60 to 90 cm in length, apparently dichotomously branched and bearing narrow obovate, yellowish green leaves, thick and coarse-textured. Chlorophyll is amply present, indicating that food manufacture can be carried on. Contact with the host is established

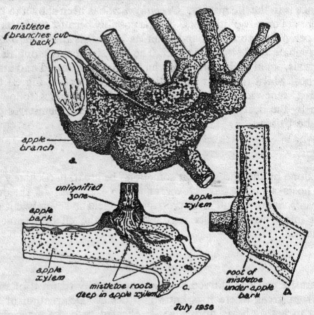

Fig. 31.8. *Viscum album* on apple branch. (*a*) Parasite and host relationship. (*b*) Bark of host removed to show parasite roots spreading over apple xylem. (*c*) V.S. of parasite-host tissue connexions.

through the root system which ramifies into the host xylem to establish tissue contact through which water and mineral salts can be obtained (*see* Fig. 31.9). The mistletoe is dioecious and the unisexual flowers are produced in February–March. They are small with no sepals (male) or four very reduced sepals (female), and four small yellowish sepaloid petals. The stamens are without filaments and open by pores. The fruit is a white translucent berry filled with viscous pulp and containing several seeds. It is eaten by birds which disseminate the seeds by ejecting them from their crops on to surrounding branches. Here they adhere and are protected by the sticky mass which soon hardens. On germination, the young root penetrates the host bark and establishes the first tissue contact. Subsequent growth is slow but the mistletoe is a persistent parasite which usually lives as long as its host. Year by year, root growth keeps pace with the gradually thickening host branch so that the parasite is always in contact with the functional host xylem.

Effect on the Host and Control Measures

The parasite appears to do little damage to the host and because of its commercial value at Christmas no control measures appear to be levelled against it. It can be effectively destroyed by chopping out the stem below bark level and applying a tar preparation over the host wound.

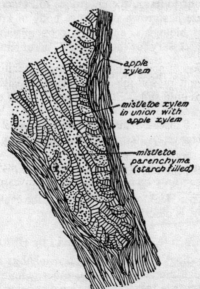

Fig. 31.9. *Viscum album.* Tissue connexions with apple. L.P. plan of tissue layout.

CHAPTER 32

PARASITIC ANIMALS

THERE are parasitic animals in most of the major phyla, but while parasitism is of unusual occurrence in some groups, in others it is widespread. The chief phyla which contain parasitic animals are the Protozoa, the Nematoda, the Platyhelminthes and the Arthropoda.

From the outset, it must be realized that parasitism is not an uncommon mode of life. The great majority of plants and animals harbour parasites, and in a number of species they may even exceed free-living forms. Under natural conditions, the parasite and its host have settled down to a condition which approaches amicable equilibrium. The devastating effects of parasitic diseases are mainly due to man's interference with the natural state, in which widely differing animal species have evolved mutual tolerance. Nevertheless, since man's migrations, together with his domesticated animals and plants, have reached the stage at which there is no possibility of return to natural conditions, he must endeavour to lessen the enormous toll taken by the parasites. To this end, there has grown up a huge body of knowledge, and the united efforts of biologists, engineers, economists, geographers and others are now necessary for the waging of an unremitting war against parasitic disease.

The parasites described here belong to the genera *Entamoeba*, *Trypanosoma*, *Monocystis*, *Plasmodium*, *Trichinella*, *Fasciola*, *Taenia* and *Pulex*.

ENTAMOEBA

This genus includes a large number of species found in the alimentary canal of various craniates. There are at least three species in man: *E. gingivalis* in the mouth, *E. coli* and *E. histolytica* in the colon and rectum. One species, *E. invadens*, is a serious pathogen in reptiles, particularly snakes. Here, only *E. histolytica*, the causative organism of *amoebic dysentery*, is described.

Structure, Reproduction and Life History

In its *trophic* (feeding) form, *E. histolytica* inhabits the human colon and rectum, though monkeys, rats and other mammals may be alternative hosts. It exists in two forms, the smaller being harmless, feeding on bacteria, the larger ingesting portions of the gut epithelium and blood corpuscles. The smaller form is about 10μm to 20μm in diameter with definite plasmagel and plasmasol, a spherical nucleus with a delicate layer of chromatin granules beneath its membrane, and a central karyosome (*see* Fig. 32.1). Normally it projects only one large blunt pseudopodium with an extensive clear region of plasmagel. Its food vacuoles contain bacteria in various stages of digestion.

It is not known under what conditions this smaller form passes into the larger aggressive form which is 40μm to 50μm in diameter and has,

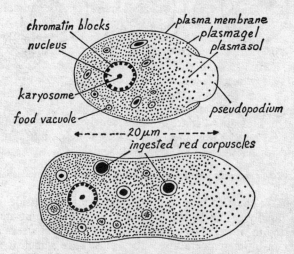

Fig. 32.1. *Entamoeba histolytica.* Small and large forms.

in its food vacuoles, ingested cells and blood corpuscles. In both forms, reproduction is by binary fission, and under certain conditions, cysts are formed. Before their formation, food particles in the vacuoles are either digested or egested, and two or three large *chromatoid bodies* are formed. These are so-called because they stain easily with dyes which show up chromatin, but they probably contain reserve food materials. There are also granules of glycogen scattered throughout the plasmasol. The nucleus divides twice so that there are four small nuclei, and finally the amoeba secretes a delicate, shining, transparent wall, to form the completed cyst, measuring about 10μm in diameter. These cysts are passed out with the faeces and may gain entry to another host in water or contaminated food. In the gut of another host, a further nuclear division takes place after liberation from the cyst wall, and then cytoplasmic cleavage follows, so that eight amoebulae result. The cyst wall may be dissolved by alkaline juices of the small intestine, but in cultures, the amoeba emerges by dissolving a small portion of the wall with enzymes secreted from the tip of a pseudopodium (*see* Fig. 32.2).

This is an example of a *direct* life history since it does not necessarily involve the use of a *vector* for carrying the parasite from host to host.

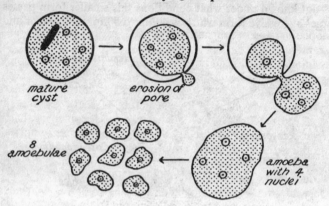

Fig. 32.2. *Entamoeba histolytica*. Erosion of cyst wall and reproduction.

Apart from the encysted form, the amoeba cannot live outside the host, perishing rapidly in the higher oxygen content, and dying quickly if not immersed in water. The cysts are viable for several weeks at 15°C but longer at lower temperatures; they must have sufficient external moisture. The life history is summarized below.

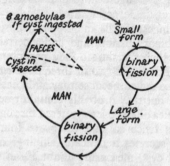

Structural, Physiological and Reproductive Modifications

Though all parasites show structural modifications compared with their free-living relatives, in the case of *E. histolytica*, these relatives are the pond amoebae, which show very little differentiation in any case. In *Entamoeba* there is no contractile vacuole, signifying that the fluid contents of the gut must be more or less isotonic with its cytoplasm. It seems normally to produce but one pseudopodium, whereas the pond amoebae are constantly exploring the environment with many pseudopodia, produced in response to favourable and unfavourable stimuli. Living in an environment where it is surrounded by its food supply, there are practically constant conditions and only one large pseudopodium for movement is produced, apart from those used for food capture.

Physiologically, it is modified in that it can live in a situation where the oxygen content must be extremely low, except when it has destroyed a blood-vessel and ingested the erythrocytes. Having little need for locomotion, there will be little expenditure of energy compared with that used by free-living forms. It has not yet been shown that it can respire anaerobically. It can vary its diet from bacteria to animal cells and produces the enzymes for coping with each. The resistance of the cyst wall to acid digestion in the stomach but not to alkaline digestion in the duodenum is another physiological adaptation.

A very important characteristic of animal parasites is their ability to produce large numbers of potential offspring so that some may survive the hazards of transfer from host to host. In *Entamoeba histolytica*, there is rapid binary fission and large numbers of cysts are produced, each capable of giving rise to eight amoebulae. The viability of the cysts under various conditions, together with the ability to survive in a number of alternative hosts, give enhanced possibilities of survival. As mentioned, a further reproductive adaptation is shown in the ability of the cysts to resist acid digestion in the stomach through which they must pass to arrive at the large intestine.

Effect on the Host

Infection with *E. histolytica* does not necessarily mean that the host will show pathological symptoms, though it is probable that the majority of cases will have slight ulceration. Most human beings are tolerant and act as carriers. It is estimated that between four and five million people in Great Britain carry these amoebae, but an acute case of amoebic dysentery is a rarity. In some tropical and sub-tropical areas, at least two-thirds of the population are infected. Serious cases show very obvious symptoms and the disease is painful, wasting and very dangerous. Tissue of the gut epithelium is destroyed and blood capillaries are eroded. Ulceration always ensues and blood is released into the intestine. There are frequent motions which contain blood and mucus; these are accompanied by abdominal pain, nausea, vomiting and fever. A very serious condition arises if the amoebae effect entry into the blood stream. They may then set up infection in any part of the body; such infections are most serious in the liver, kidney and brain.

Control Measures

These may be grouped into three categories; the safeguarding of susceptible hosts, the treatment of the disease in an acute case, and the destruction of the parasites during transmission.

In the first place, it is extremely difficult to find out which human beings are susceptible and which are carriers. It would involve regular faecal examination of the whole population, a stupendous task. Much, however, can be done by proper disposal of faeces, safe-guarding of water supplies and prevention of food contamination. In certain countries where hygienic precautions are almost negligible, where night soil is used as fertilizer, and where flies and rodents abound, it is almost impossible to do anything except by education of the populace.

Treatment of the disease, except in the most advanced cases, results in complete recovery. Colonic irrigation with solutions of various drugs will eventually result in the death of all the parasites, and then by careful convalescence, the ulcerated colon is soon repaired. In larger scale treatment, certain drugs are given by mouth and generally result in cure.

Destruction of the cysts passed out with the faeces seems to be the best method of large-scale control. Proper sewage disposal will destroy the cysts without necessarily losing the manurial value of the faeces. The warfare against flies, rats and mice must be continued. Special precautions must be taken against contamination of drinking water and of food. Perhaps the most important factor of all would be the education of the people in simple hygiene.

General Remarks

Study of the incidence of amoebic dysentery, as indeed of any disease, reveals many aspects which cannot yet be explained. We do not know why some hosts are merely carriers though there may be very heavy infection; neither do we know under what conditions the larger forms are developed from the smaller, nor what causes the formation of cysts.

In localities where such diseases are most prevalent, the population is usually ignorant, underfed, badly housed and often there are racial and religious taboos or ancient custom which present very serious obstacles to progress in health as in other matters.

TRYPANOSOMA

The genus *Trypanosoma* includes a number of species which are dangerous parasites of man and domestic animals, though many of the same and other species are non-pathogenic in wild animals. The trypanosomes belong to the family Trypanosomidae of the order Protomonadina and are flagellates with a single flagellum. Some of the more important pathogenic species are listed below. The species

Species	Country	Host	Vector	Disease
T. gambiense	West and Central Africa	Man	*G. palpalis*	Sleeping sickness
T. rhodesiense	South and Central Africa	Man	*G. palpalis*	Sleeping sickness
T. brucei	South and Central Africa	Cattle	*G. morsitans*	Nagana
T. evans	Asia, Eastern Europe, N. Africa	Cattle	Tabanid flies	Surra
T. cruzi	S. America	Man	Triatomid bugs	Chagas' disease

further described is *T. gambiense*, the causative organism of the more serious of the two forms of *sleeping sickness*.

Structure, Reproduction and Life History

In its slender form, found in the blood of man after infection by the tsetse fly, *Glossina palpalis* (*see* Chap. 23), *T. gambiense* is about 15µm

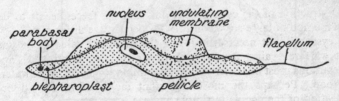

Fig. 32.3. *Trypanosoma gambiense*. Slender form.

long and 1µm wide. This form is pointed at both ends and bears a prominent ovoid nucleus in the central region. It is enclosed in a strong pellicle which is instrumental in maintaining body shape and which is drawn out along most of the length to form the wavy *undulating membrane*. Along the edge of the membrane is the flagellum, attached posteriorly to a small granule known as a *blepharoplast*. Anteriorly, the flagellum projects in front of the body as a short, fine lash. Immediately posterior to the blepharoplast, there is a prominent granule, the *parabasal body*, whose function is not known (*see* Fig. 32.3).

In the blood of man, there are usually several polymorphic types which are derived by longitudinal binary fission. The different types

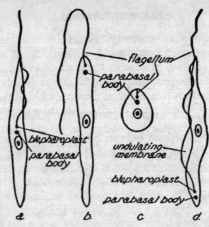

Fig. 32.4. Haemoflagellate forms. (*a*) *Crithidia.* (*b*) *Leptomonas.* (*c*) *Leishmania.*
(*d*) *Trypanosoma.*

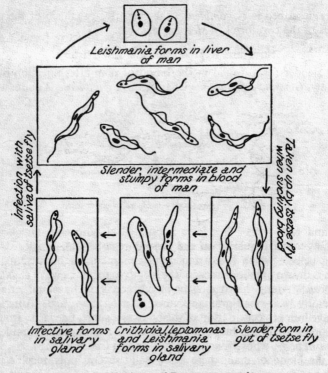

Leishmania forms in liver of man

Slender, intermediate and stumpy forms in blood of man

Infection with saliva of tsetse fly

Taken up by tsetse fly when sucking blood

Infective forms in salivary gland

Crithidial, leptomonas and Leishmania forms in salivary gland

Slender form in gut of tsetse fly

Fig. 32.5. Life history of *Trypanosoma gambiense.*

show three main body shapes namely, slender, intermediate and stumpy, all probably due to the unequal fission of the body. There is a fourth ovoid form which is often present in the liver, spleen and lungs of the host. It is known as the *leishmania* form and is probably a latent body for replacing the losses which occur in the host's blood stream. During binary fission, the blepharoplast divides first, then the parabasal body and then the nucleus.

If the blood of an infected human being is taken in by the blood-sucking fly *Glossina palpalis*, the trypanosomes undergo multiplication in the mid-gut and within twenty days, *crithidial* forms are found in the insect's salivary glands. Further multiplication takes place in the cells of the salivary glands and both *leptomonas* and *leishmania* forms may be produced (*see* Fig. 32.4). Finally, within thirty days from the time the blood was sucked, infective trypanosome forms are present in the lumina of the glands among the saliva. These infective forms are injected into the wound with the saliva, the specific purpose of which is to prevent the blood from clotting.

The life cycle (*see* below) thus involves two hosts, the human being and the tsetse fly, and since the latter carries the infective forms from man to man, it is known as the *vector*.

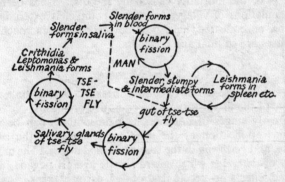

Structural, Physiological and Reproductive Modifications

By comparison with the more highly differentiated free-living flagellates such as *Euglena*, the trypanosomes are structurally simplified. They do not possess either the gullet or the contractile vacuole.

Physiologically, it is isotonic with the blood plasma, as the lack of the contractile vacuole shows, and having a large surface area in relation to its volume, respiratory exchange in an oxygen-rich medium is of no difficulty. The large surface area also serves its purpose in nutrition and excretion; both of which can only take place by diffusion.

In its reproductive process, the rapid rate of binary fission ensures quick growth of the population under favourable conditions, and even when host resistance is high, resting forms can remain alive in the cells of the spleen and lungs. Further multiplicative phases in the insect vector provide a constant reservoir of infective forms. No sexual process has yet been discovered in trypanosomes.

Effect on the Host

In its epidemic form, human *trypanosomiasis* is a devastating and terrible disease. Large areas of West and Central Africa have been rendered uninhabitable by this scourge. Considering *T. gambiense* alone, the disease is known as Gambia fever while the parasites remain in the blood stream; it is characterized by headaches, fever and general lethargy. Later, the trypanosomes penetrate into the lymphatic glands which show swelling, particularly in the neck and in the axillae. Finally, the parasites find their way into the cerebro-spinal fluid and the fatal sleeping-sickness ensues. The sufferer becomes progressively more lethargic and the body more wasted, though the appetite is voracious. Eventually there is not enough energy even to eat and the living skeleton sleeps into oblivion.

In the past, the mortality caused by the disease has been terrible. Entire populations of villages have been completely exterminated and wide areas, once cleared, have been covered by the encroaching bush. Few diseases are so final and merciless.

Control Measures

As is always the case, effective control measures depend on a thorough knowledge of the life history of the causative organism.

In the early stages of infection, trypanosomiasis can be cured by intravenous application of the drug *tryparsamide* in the case of *T. gambiense*, and *germanin* in the case of *T. rhodesiense*. The more recent discovery of *antrycide* which guards cattle against nagana, may have widespread effects in recolonization of pasture areas. As yet, no drug has been found which will confer lasting immunity. Further, there is an inexhaustible reservoir of trypanosomes in the wild game, in which they are not pathogenic.

It is usual, in the case of insect-borne infections, to expect some success in attack on the vectors, but in the case of the tsetse fly, this has not been the case. Indeed, the insects seem to be extending their range. They cannot live in treeless country, since they shelter in trees and bushes during the hot periods of the day and in the very dry seasons. The adult female is viviparous and the larvae are deposited near trees or at the edges of permanent bodies of water. They pupate in cracks in the ground or in trees. Natural enemies, such as insectivorous birds and parasitic insects, seem to have little effect on the tsetse population.

The main method of control now employed, is that of clearing forest and bush around settled areas; this would neither be desirable nor possible over the whole enormous area of the fly belt. In some areas, a "scorched earth" policy has been tried with some success. It has been seriously suggested that the wild game of Africa should be completely exterminated; this would involve not only the large mammals, but all terrestrial vertebrates, since several species of tsetse feed readily on reptiles. If carried out, the scheme might have serious repercussions. At the present time, the main policy is a combination of clearing and the use of drugs; both are methods of avoiding rather than eradicating the disease.

General Remarks

The trypanosomes seem to have been evolved from parasites of invertebrates, particularly of insects. That they are recent parasites of man and his animals, is indicated by the severity of their effects. The various forms which they pass through during the complete life cycle are given the names of other genera which resemble those forms. There are genera called *Leptomonas*, *Crithidia* and *Leishmania*, the first two being mainly parasitic in insects and the third transmitted to vertebrates by an insect vector. Of all the polymorphic forms, the trypanosome may be assumed to be the adult, while the others are young stages spent in the insect's body. In their ontogeny, trypanosomes may be repeating their phylogeny.

MONOCYSTIS

Several species of *Monocystis* are parasitic in the seminal vesicles of the earthworm. They belong to the class Sporozoa and are placed in the order Gregarinida because the adults are extracellular and produce merogametes. The species described is *Monocystis lumbrici* [*M. agilis*].

Structure, Reproduction and Life History

The adults or mature trophozoites are spindle-shaped and are very commonly present in the seminal vesicles of the worm. There is a thick pellicle, beneath which, in the plasmagel, are longitudinal myonemes. In the granular plasmasol, there are paramylum granules and an ovoid nucleus with a prominent nucleolus (*see* Fig. 32.6). The organism feeds on the cytoplasm of a sperm morula by extruding enzymes and absorbing the digested products through the pellicle. It may move to another morula and likewise consume the cytoplasm, before it is fully grown. The locomotion is characterized by changes of shape brought about by contraction of the myonemes during wriggling; it is known as *gregarine* motion. Often, numerous sperm tails adhere to the pellicle, giving the monocystis a ciliated appearance. Excretion and respiratory exchange are accomplished by diffusion.

There is no multiplication by fission in the trophozoite stage, i.e. there are no *schizozoites*, but when two mature adults come together, they secrete a common wall, the whole structure being a *conjugation*

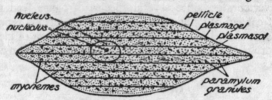

Fig. 32.6. *Monocystis lumbrici*. Adult form.

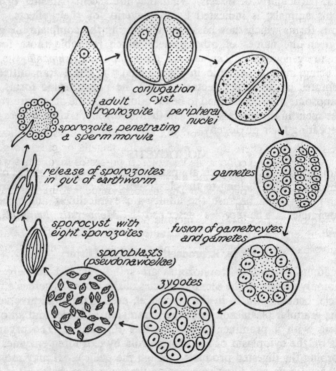

Fig. 32.7. Life History of *Monocystis lumbrici*.

cyst. Within the cyst, each *gametocyte* nucleus undergoes numerous mitotic divisions so that a large number of nuclei are formed. These migrate to the periphery and each nucleus becomes invested with a thin layer of cytoplasm. Then the two gametocytes fuse and the gametes, recognizably of two sizes, fuse in pairs, leaving a certain amount of vacuolated residual cytoplasm. Each zygote, now diploid, secretes a rigid wall and has a boat-shaped appearance resembling that in the diatom *Navicella.* Hence, these *sporocysts* are sometimes known as *pseudonavicellae.* After a short resting-period, the zygote divides three times to produce eight sickle-shaped *sporozoites,* the first nuclear division being meiotic. There is no further development until the cysts are swallowed by another earthworm, which first entails liberation of the cysts into the soil. This may be accomplished by birds or other animals which, after eating the earthworm, are unable to digest the cysts, which are voided with the faeces. Alternatively, the earthworm may die and rot in the soil. If the cyst is now swallowed by a worm, the cyst coat is digested and the pseudonavicellae are freed in the gut of the worm. Each dehisces by a small pore at one end and the tiny sporozoites wriggle out. They find their way to the vesiculae seminales, probably by boring through the gut wall into the coelom. Each penetrates and consumes the cytoplasm of a sperm morula and proceeds to grow into the adult form. It is noteworthy that there is but a short diploid phase in the life cycle.

Structural, Physiological and Reproductive Modifications

Compared with free-living protozoa, *Monocystis* shows reduction in several respects. There are no pseudopodia, flagella or cilia, no gullet or cytostome and no contractile vacuole. It possesses myonemes which enable the wriggling gregarine movement and its tough pellicle is an important protective organelle. The fusiform shape favours insinuation of the body into sperm morulae.

Physiological modifications include power of osmotic regulation in several different environments, resistance to enzymes, and pronounced chemotaxis which enables the organism to locate its natural habitat in the body of the worm.

The possibility of transfer to another host during the period of viability of the sporozoites must be remote and hence there are two multiplicative phases in the life history. Each gametocyte may produce up to sixty-four gametes, so that a cyst may contain sixty-four sporocysts (in some species, many more are present). Thus with eight sporozoites in each pseudonavicella, each cyst will contain over five hundred potential parasites, so that if an earthworm swallows but one, there will be a heavy infection and the probability of numerous progeny.

Other reproductive adaptations are seen in the resistance of the cysts to digestion by animals other than the earthworm and the certainty of digestion by the earthworm. The cysts appear to be viable in the soil for a considerable period.

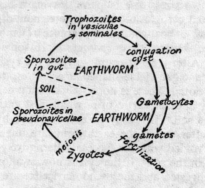

Effect on the Host

Although the great majority of earthworms are infected, and often quite heavily, the parasites seem to cause little, if any inconvenience. In any case, sperm are produced in such numbers, that destruction of large quantities would have little effect on the earthworm's reproductive capacity. Yet, by strict definition, we must consider *Monocystis spp.* to be parasites since they do definite damage to the worm. However, a state of tolerance has been evolved in which the worm does not destroy the parasite, and neither does it cause appreciable harm to the worm.

PLASMODIUM

Malaria probably accounts for more deaths than any other disease caused by parasites. In India alone, more than one hundred million people contract the disease every year; of these, at least one million die of it. The name is derived from the Italian mal (bad) and aria (air); it arose originally because the citizens of Rome thought that the disease was contracted by breathing the bad air of the Pontine marshes. There are many species of *Plasmodium* which infect mammals and birds, and in the case of man, at least three species cause pathological effects. They are *P. vivax*, *P. malariae* and *P. falciparum*; the last has the most severe effects. This account will be confined mainly to *P. vivax*.

Structure, Reproduction and Life History

The parasites enter the blood-stream of man with the saliva of an anopheline mosquito when it pierces the skin, as minute sickle-shaped *sporozoites* about 2μm long. For approximately the next hour, they are to be found in the blood, but after that period there is no trace of them in any part of the vascular system. Recent discovery has shown that they have penetrated the liver cells. Each of these minute sporozoites enters a liver cell and proceeds to grow at the expense of the glycogen, fat and cytoplasm of the cell, to form a large roughly spherical *schizont* (*meront*). Then, by repeated mitotic division a large number of nuclei are produced, probably over one thousand (1,024 if the division has

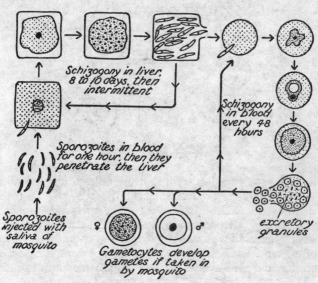

Fig. 32.8. *Plasmodium vivax.* Stages in man.

been regular). Each nucleus is then invested with a portion of cytoplasm and eventually the liver cell bursts, releasing these *schizozoites* into a blood sinusoid. This process of growth and *schizogony* in the liver takes eight to ten days, after which the parasites will again be found in the blood. Some may continue to enter liver cells but the majority enter the circulation as small schizozoites (merozoites) about 3μm to 4μm long (*see* Fig. 32.8); these enter the red corpuscles.

In a red corpuscle, a schizozoite proceeds to feed and grow, losing its elongated shape and becoming amoeboid. Eventually, a large vacuole appears in the central region, pushing the nucleus to one side and giving the parasite the characteristic "signet-ring" appearance. By continued growth, it almost fills the corpuscle, having consumed practically all its cytoplasm, and then proceeds by division to form about twenty to thirty further schizozoites. There is a small quantity of residual cytoplasm which contains light brown excretory granules. The envelope of the corpuscle bursts, releasing the schizozoites and the excretory granules into the plasma. It is the toxic effect of these excretory granules which causes the fever characteristic of malaria, and since the development and division in a red corpuscle takes about forty-eight hours, so, on their liberation, the fever will recur at regular

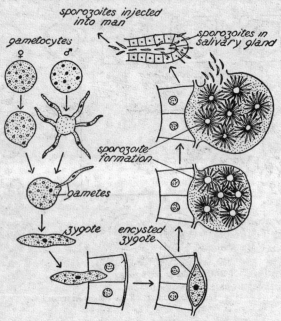

Fig. 32.9. *Plasmodium vivax*. Stages in mosquito.

intervals. The liberated schizozoites infect new corpuscles and the schizogony cycle is repeated. Eventually, some cease division and grow as larger single cells within the corpuscle, constituting *gametocytes*, which will produce gametes if taken up by a mosquito. The female gametocyte has a small nucleus and the cytoplasm contains numerous granules of food materiaı; the male gametocyte has a large nucleus and clear cytoplasm. If they are not ingested by a mosquito, they will eventually disintegrate or will be engulfed by phagocytes.

It is only the female mosquito which sucks blood and during this feeding operation, all stages of the parasite will arrive in the crop, where, together with the blood corpuscles, they will all be digested except the gametocytes. The membranes of the corpuscles containing these, are dissolved, and the gametocytes are set free. In the female gametocyte, there is little change, except that the nucleus migrates towards the periphery, and at that point, a cytoplasmic papilla projects. In the male gametocyte, the nucleus divides, and by repeated division of the daughter nuclei, four, and then eight are formed. They migrate to the periphery, and surrounded by a small portion of cytoplasm, each becomes free and elongates to form a minute male gamete. A male gamete penetrates a female gamete at the papilla, the nuclei fuse, and thus a zygote is formed. After a short resting period, the zygote becomes spindle-shaped and motile. It moves through the contents of the crop and penetrates the epithelium, coming to rest in the connective tissue between this and the outer tissues. There, it secretes a cyst wall which is soon reinforced by connective tissue of the host, and gradually the cyst enlarges until it forms a prominent swelling bulging into the haemocoel. Repeated nuclear division and the appearance of vacuoles ensue, and each nucleus is invested with some cytoplasm to form a sickle-shaped sporozoite. Enormous numbers of these are produced and arranged around the vacuoles, the whole multiplicative process being called *sporogony*. Eventually the *sporocyst* bursts and the sporozoites are liberated into the haemocoel, from which the majority make their way into the salivary glands. When the infected mosquito pierces human skin, the parasite-laden saliva is injected into the blood and the life cycle begins again.

Structural, Physiological and Reproductive Modifications

The extreme simplicity of structure of *Plasmodium* is correlated with the sheltered life it leads within the bodies of the two hosts. It never comes into contact with the outside world and thus elaborate protective structures are unnecessary. It must possess considerable osmotic adaptability so that it can adjust its water relationships to the conditions in mammalian blood, in the mosquito's crop, haemocoel, and salivary glands, and the gametocytes must have some means of resisting the mosquito's digestive enzymes. Chemotaxis is pronounced, since all the parasites find their way to the liver cells, and later to the corpuscles, and in the insect host to the site of encystment and finally to the salivary glands. Penetration of liver cells, red corpuscles, mosquito gut epithelium, and salivary glands indicates some unknown physical method, or special enzymes.

The most spectacular modification is seen in the reproductive phases, which consist of schizogony in the liver cells, repeated schizogony in the blood, and sporogony in the mosquito. These multiplicative phases, coupled with the reservoir of latent forms in the liver, ensure that enough parasites will survive to enable the species to continue.

Effect on the Host

P. vivax causes *tertian* fever, recurring at three-day intervals; *P. malariae* causes *quartan* fever, recurring at four-day intervals, and with *P. falciparum* there is more or less continuous fever. There is often mixed infection by two or even more species.

After man has been infected by the mosquito "bite," there are no signs of disease for eight to ten days, while the parasites are in the liver. This is known as the *incubation* period, and after it, the recurrent bouts of fever begin. Malarial fevers are characterized by successive cold, hot and sweating stages. At first there is pronounced shivering and the patient complains of feeling cold, then the temperature rises rapidly and is followed by copious sweating. Before the next fever, the patient will have shown signs of recovery, except for some weakness, but each fresh attack has an increasing debilitating effect and in many cases, death ensues. In tropical and sub-tropical countries where malaria is rife, there is often acquired tolerance in a large percentage of the population, but even in these cases there is considerable debilitation, and the wastage of human effort must be very great. Tropical races suffer considerably from the weakening effects of such diseases as malaria. *P. falciparum* is the most lethal of these parasites and *P. vivax*, the least, and hence we speak of malignant *quotidian* malaria and benign *tertian*.

Control Measures

Here again we recognize the importance of a knowledge of the life history of the parasite and of its vector. The essential relationships of *Plasmodium*, man, and mosquito were established in 1897 by Dr. Ross of the Indian Army Medical Corps.

Susceptible hosts, and particularly white men who have no acquired immunity, can be adequately protected by a number of measures. In the first place, the mosquitoes can be prevented from making contact with the human host by netting of windows and beds, since the insects are nocturnal. A number of drugs such as *quinine, mepacrin, plasmaquine* and *paludrine* are prophylactic and small regular doses will usually ensure immunity. The same drugs are used in effecting cure; paludrin is particularly effective as it will kill all stages of the parasite with the exception of the intracellular forms in the liver.

Large-scale methods of control of the mosquitoes are now increasingly used so that more natives of the endemic areas shall be saved. In British Guiana, an experimental spraying of huts with DDT in kerosene, resulted in almost total extermination of the insects. Methods such as this, coupled with clearing of vegetation round the villages, and travel by day, should go far towards greater success in the campaign against malaria. The aquatic larvae are most vulnerable and thus draining of ponds and marshes and covering of water storage tanks are routine practice in many districts. On a larger scale, lakes are sprayed with paraffin, which blocks the breathing tubes of the larvae and pupae and so kills them. The use of fish and birds which eat the larvae is also practised. The life history of the anopheline mosquito is described in Chap. 23.

General Remarks

There is disagreement over the question of the position of a meiotic division in *Plasmodium*. Some authorities state that it occurs during development of the gametocytes, and others aver that the first division of the zygote nucleus is meiotic. On the latter view, it follows that the greater part of the life cycle is haploid, the diploid phase being confined to the short period of existence of the zygote before its first division. This opinion is in agreement with the condition found in many of the Telosporidia.

TRICHINELLA

The members of this genus belong to the phylum Nematoda, among which are some of the most serious parasites of man and domestic animals. The species *Trichinella spiralis*, described here, is parasitic in man, the pig, the rat and other mammals, and is found practically all over the world, particularly in the United States, in Europe and in northern and eastern Asia.

Structure, Reproduction and Life History

These small cylindrical worms are pointed anteriorly and rounded posteriorly, the female being about 3 mm long and 80μm wide, while the smaller male is but 1·5 mm long and 40μm wide. There is a smooth tough cuticle of protein material beneath which is a coenocytic hypodermis. Four quadrants of thin longitudinal muscle traverse the body, which is acoelomate and unsegmented. The alimentary canal consists of a short buccal cavity, a muscular pharynx, a long and slender oesophagus enclosed by large granular cells, and a simple intestine which leads to a terminal anus. There is a pharyngeal nerve ring and two main longitudinal nerves. There does not seem to be an excretory system.

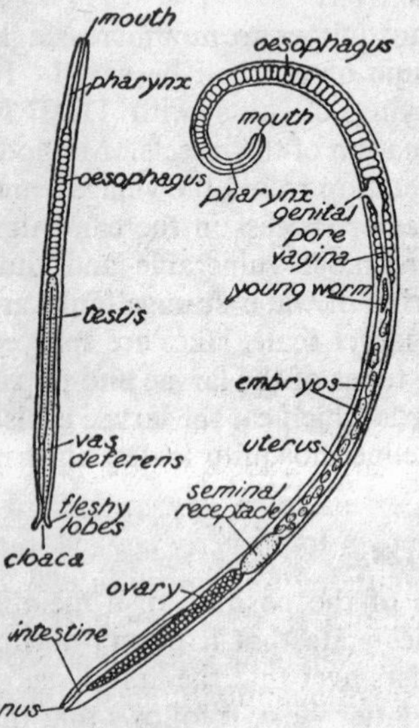

In the male, there is a large testis which occupies most of the posterior half of the body and bends abruptly into the vas deferens, which passes back to an ejaculatory duct opening into the cloaca near the anus. The cloaca can be everted during copulation and is guarded by two fleshy lobes which play some part in the mating process (see Fig. 32.10).

In the female there is a long cylindrical posterior ovary which leads forward to a narrow oviduct; this joins the large uterus, the first part of which is the seminal receptacle. The uterus narrows to the vagina, which opens at the genital pore in the mid-oesophageal region.

Fig. 32.10. *Trichinella spiralis*.
Adult male and female.

Fertilization is internal and takes place in the intestine of a mammal. The small thin-shelled eggs are fertilized as they pass through the seminal receptacle and proceed to develop rapidly, and within five or six days, the female releases minute wormlike larvae from her genital pore.

The host is infected by eating flesh which contains viable cysts, the walls of which are digested in the intestine, releasing young worms. Three or four days later, the young females are impregnated by the males, which subsequently die and are passed out with the host's faeces. In the next few days, the females burrow into the intestinal wall, and about five days after impregnation, they begin to produce tiny worms which are liberated into lymphatic or blood vessels. Over a period of several months, each female will produce more than one thousand young which are deposited in the host's circulatory system. These young worms, 100μm by 5μm, burrow into the voluntary muscles especially in the intercostal region, the diaphragm, the tongue, the shoulders and the back. Nine or ten days after liberation, each worm penetrates a muscle fibre and grows to about 1 mm in length. Then it coils itself up and becomes enclosed in a spindle-shaped cyst produced around it by the host. The cyst is fully formed in nine or ten weeks and then its size is about 0·5 mm by 0·2 mm (*see* Fig. 32.11). Later, the young cysts become calcified and the worms lie dormant in the host's muscle, remaining viable for about ten years. It has been

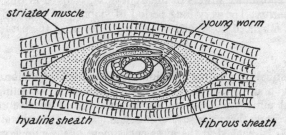

Fig. 32.11. *Trichinella spiralis.* Cyst.

shown that infected pork may contain as many as 80,000 cysts in one ounce of meat. No further development takes place until the meat of the infected animal, alive or dead, is eaten by a susceptible host. Thus a rat may be eaten by a pig, and pork, improperly cooked, may be eaten by man. Some idea of the magnitude of an infection may be gained from the following figures. One ounce of trichinous pork may contain 40,000 males and 40,000 females; each female will produce over one thousand young and thus from this small quantity of meat, a mass infection of muscle by over 40,000,000 worms will occur. The life cycle of *Trichinella spiralis* is illustrated diagrammatically below.

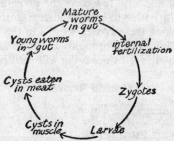

Structural, Physiological and Reproductive Modifications

Except for certain special organs for attachment and rasping in forms such as the hookworms, most parasitic nematodes show comparatively little structural modification compared with free-living forms. The only obvious features of *T. spiralis* are the very pointed anterior end of the female for boring, and the forward position of the genital pore. Physiological adaptations include resistance to the host's enzymes, and chemotaxis in the adult female, and in the young, so that they shall locate voluntary muscle.

In reproduction, we find that very common feature of parasites, namely, enormous powers of multiplication, coupled in this case with ovoviviparity. The very long period of viability of encysted juveniles gives an enhanced possibility of survival of some of the parasites.

Effect on the Host

The intestinal phase of an infection is characterized by abdominal pain, vomiting and diarrhoea, and is often mistaken for other gastrointestinal afflictions. During the migration and penetration of the young worms, there are severe muscular pains. The critical phase of *trichinosis* is reached at the mass encystment of juvenile worms in the muscles, and in severe cases, death rapidly follows, due to toxaemia, cardiac disturbance and in some cases, pneumonia and kidney disorders.

Control Measures

As far as human beings are concerned, the most effective control measures lie in thorough inspection of meat and proper cooking. It is perhaps ironical that although governments and local authorities are particular about official inspection of foodstuffs, there is little attempt to educate the general public on simple measures for the prevention of parasitic diseases.

There is little possibility of treating the intestinal phase, since diagnosis is difficult and in a few days the juveniles are in the blood. Various vermifuges are used to lessen the degree of infection. There is no method of attacking the encysted worms in the muscle.

The food of pigs should be thoroughly cooked and every effort should be made to exterminate rats, since a pig will readily eat a dead rat.

General Remarks

A complete list of nematode parasites of man which cause serious pathological conditions, would be formidable. Some of the more important parasites are listed below.

1. Hookworms: *Ancylostoma duodenale* (Old World) and *Necator americanus* (New World). Severe intestinal parasites with wandering larvae.

2. *Filaria bancroftii* A blood parasite with the mosquito as vector.

3. *Dracunculus* [*Filaria*] *medinensis:* The dreaded Guinea-worm; length up to 2 m; it inhabits the subcutaneous tissues of the legs and causes elephantiasis.

4. *Ascaris lumbricoides:* 30 to 40 cm long; a common intestinal parasite. Most serious if it bores through the gut wall and wanders in the body.

5. *Oxyuris vermicularis:* The threadworm of children.

Other common nematodes parasitic in living organisms are: *Rhabditis* in earthworm nephridia; *Rhabdonema* in frog lungs; *Proleptus* in the dogfish gut; eelworms in many plants, e.g. *Tylenchus tritici* in wheat; many parasites of insects, e.g. *Spherularia* in humble bees. A great many nematodes are free-living; the vinegar worm, *Anguillula aceti* is particularly interesting because of its unusual substrate; large numbers of nematodes live in the soil, in fresh and salt water.

FASCIOLA [DISTOMUM]

A number of flukes are parasitic in the bodies of vertebrates, the species described here being the liver-fluke of the sheep, *Fasciola hepatica* [*Distomum hepaticum*]. It is also found in other mammals, particularly in cattle, and occasionally in man. Its life history was elucidated by Thomas in 1883.

Structure, Reproduction and Life History

The adult fluke has a flattened, oval shape and is about 2·5 cm long and 1·2 to 1·3 cm wide. In the anterior region, there is a triangular projection at the apex of which lies the mouth, surrounded by the *oral sucker*. Ventrally, at the base of the projection, there is a rounded *ventral sucker*, and between the two suckers there is a shallow depression, the *genital atrium* (*see* Fig. 32.12). Posteriorly, there is a minute, terminal *excretory pore*.

The body is invested by a tough cuticle prolonged into numerous short backwardly-directed spines. There is

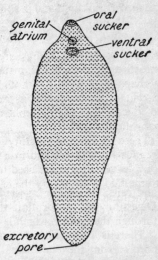

Fig. 32.12. *Fasciola hepatica.*
Ventral view of adult.

no coherent epidermis, the cells of which have become separated and sunk into the deeper parts. A thin layer of outer circular muscle fibres is followed by a layer of longitudinal fibres. Among these muscle fibres are unicellular glands which send minute ducts to the surface through the cuticle. Packed around the various organs are the stellate parenchyma cells characteristic of the Platyhelminthes (*see* Fig. 32.15).

The mouth leads into a short buccal cavity, following which are the muscular pharynx and the narrow oesophagus which forks into two blind branches leading to the posterior region and giving off numerous lobed *caeca* (*see* Fig. 32.13). The animal feeds in the liver on blood

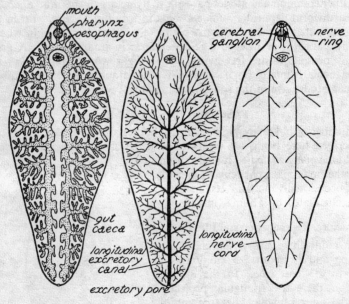

Fig. 32.13. *Fasciola hepatica.* Diagrams of gut, excretory and nervous systems.

and cells, which are ingested by the pumping action of the pharynx. Digestion and absorption take place in the caeca, and egestion is through the mouth, which is the only aperture of the gut.

There is a posterior median excretory canal opening at the terminal pore. From the main canal, numerous branches ramify all through the body, terminating in *flame cells* (*see* Fig. 19.7). For such a thoroughgoing parasite, there is a well-developed nervous system consisting of two lateral cerebral ganglia joined by a nerve ring, and two main longitudinal cords which give off numerous branches (*see* Fig. 32.10 (*a*)).

The liver fluke is hermaphrodite and the reproductive organs are very complicated. There are two much-branched testes, one behind the other, mainly in the posterior half of the body (*see* Fig. 32.14). From the centre of each branched mass, a fine vas deferens leads forward, the two vasa deferentia uniting close to the ventral sucker to form a wider vesicula seminalis. This passes forward as an ejaculatory

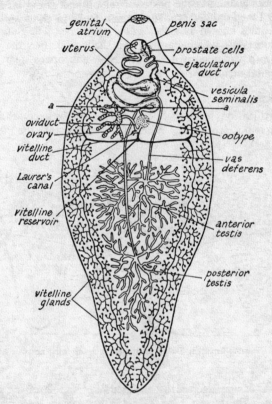

Fig. 32.14. *Fasciola hepatica.* Diagram of reproductive organs.

duct through the protrusible penis which is housed in a muscular sac. Where the duct enters the penis sac, it is surrounded by prostate cells. The ovary, like the testis, is much-branched, but the branches are thicker. It lies anteriorly on the right-hand side of the body and from it, a short oviduct leads into the mid-line. Numerous vitelline glands lie laterally and their products, yolk cells and shell substance, are collected by a series of fine canals which all lead eventually to two main ducts. These pass inward and meet centrally in a small vitelline reservoir from which a short duct passes forward to join the oviduct. At their junction, a narrow *Laurer's canal* leads dorsally and opens on the body surface. Its function is doubtful but it has been suggested that excess yolk is passed out there. From the junction of oviduct, vitelline duct and Laurer's canal, the eggs pass forward into a small reservoir surrounded by the glandular *cells of Mehlis*, the whole spherical structure being sometimes known as a *shell gland* or *ootype*. The glandular cells secrete a substance which hardens the shells and then the eggs pass forward into a wider convoluted uterus, which opens near the penis into the genital atrium.

Reproduction

Cross-fertilization in liver flukes has been observed, though self-fertilization is not precluded. When the eggs pass into the uterus, each

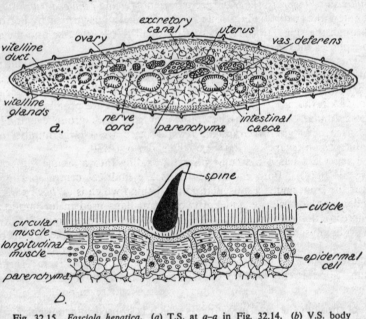

Fig. 32.15. *Fasciola hepatica*. (a) T.S. at *a–a* in Fig. 32.14. (b) V.S. body wall.

contains a zygote and a number of yolk-filled cells. The first cleavage of the zygote separates a small *propagative cell* from a larger cell which divides rapidly to form the ectoderm. Later, the propagative cell divides into two, one of which forms the endoderm and mesoderm of the embryo while the other is destined to form a mass of *germ-cells* in the larva. The eggs pass out at the genital atrium and are carried into the duodenum by the bile. They leave the body of the host in the faeces and their development is completed if they are deposited in water. A *miracidium* larva hatches by pushing a lid off one end of the shell.

The miracidium is conical in shape, tapering toward the posterior end, while in front there is a small pointed projection terminating in the mouth (*see* Fig. 32.16 (*a*)). It consists of large ciliated cells, one of which bears two pigmented eye-spots. There is a small sac-like penetration gland and a single pair of flame cells packed around with loose mesenchyme, while posteriorly there is a small mass of rounded germ cells derived from the propagative cell of the embryo. The miracidium swims in water and is attracted to a water snail of the genera *Limnaea*, *Bulinus* or *Planorbis*, the usual secondary host being *Limnaea truncatula*. It enters the snail's body through the pulmonary aperture or by boring through the skin. In the tissues of the snail it loses its cilia and metamorphoses into a *sporocyst*.

This is a simple immobile closed sac with a thin cellular wall and a large germinal cavity (*see* Fig. 32.16 (*b*)). The cells of the wall are small and cubical and appear to be derived entirely from the germ-cells present in the miracidium. Small groups of cells are proliferated into the germinal cavity from the epithelium, and each group eventually forms a new type of larva, the *redia*. There are a large number of rediae which escape by rupture of the sporocyst wall.

Each redia has a muscular pharynx leading into a simple gut (*see* Fig. 32.16 (*c*)). Both ends taper from a cylindrical central portion; near the front end is a muscular collar, behind which is a "*birth pore*," and near the posterior end are two lateral flaps used in locomotion. There is a thin cellular body wall which encloses a large germinal cavity. With its muscular pharynx, the redia can suck fluids or take in cells of its host. It is a very active little creature and soon it migrates into the digestive gland of the snail where it grows and produces from "germ-balls" about twenty *secondary rediae*, or the final larval forms, *cercariae*. These leave the body of the primary redia by the birth-pore.

The cercaria has a rounded body and a tapering tail; it possesses some of the features of the adult fluke. There are oral and ventral suckers, a muscular pharynx and a forked gut. Rudiments of the reproductive system are present and there are flame cells whose tubules lead to an excretory duct with a median posterior pore (*see* Fig. 32.16 (*d*)). All the organs are packed in with mesenchyme cells among which are many rounded *cystogenous* cells. The cercariae leave the snail by the pulmonary aperture and swim in the water with which they may enter a sheep while it is drinking. Alternatively, in a drier situation the cercariae encyst on vegetation.

The *cyst* is a small transparent object with a yellow or brownish tint; it is about 0·18 mm in diameter. Within it, the small cercaria can be

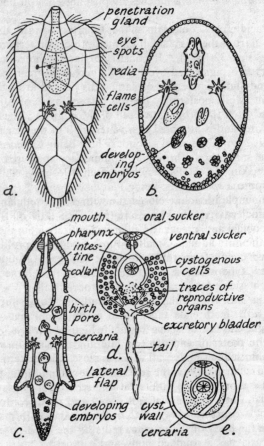

Fig. 32.16. *Fasciola hepatica.* Young stages. (*a*) Miracidium. (*b*) Sporocyst. (*c*) Redia. (*d*) Cercaria. (*e*) Cyst.

seen (*see* Fig. 32.16 (*e*)). If an encysted cercaria is taken in by a sheep or other mammal, it will be freed in the stomach and will make its way through the wall into the splanchnocoel and then be attracted to the liver. Eventually, by traversing the liver tissue, it will find its way to a bile duct and will grow into the adult form.

The life history therefore entails a primary host, the sheep or other mammal, and a secondary host, the water snail. It is further complicated by the four distinct larval stages.

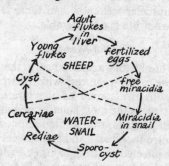

Structural, Physiological and Reproductive Modifications

When compared with the free-living Platyhelminthes, *Fasciola hepatica* illustrates how parasites have evolved new modifications and have lost certain characteristics. The suckers provide a method of fixation in the bile ducts, while the backwardly directed spines both erode the liver cells in the manner of a rasp and also prevent the creature from being washed down the ducts with the bile. The thick cuticle and the secretion of the gland cells protect it from the effects of the host's anti-toxins. On the debit side, the parasite has lost the cilia and also the well-developed anterior sense organs of the free-living flatworms.

Physiological modifications include enzymes for penetration of various tissues at various stages in the life history, pronounced chemotaxis, both in the snail and the mammal, and resistance to the host's enzymes in both cases.

The powers of reproduction and the different multiplicative phases balance the enormous mortality in the young stages. The adult produces very large numbers of eggs; each egg may produce a sporocyst; each sporocyst will produce a large number of rediae. There may be secondary rediae and each redia will finally release about twenty cercaria. An infected snail may release more than twenty thousand cercariae in one hour.

Effect on the Host

Although a sheep may be able to tolerate a few flukes, a heavy infection sets up a very serious condition and usually results in death. The migration of the cercariae through the liver and erosion of the cells by the adults, interfere seriously with liver metabolism. The blockage of the bile ducts affects digestion, and the excretory products of the flukes have a poisoning effect. In a serious infection, the condition of "liver rot" results; the liver is eroded into a broken mass of tissue, the sheep suffers from great muscular weakness and there is severe dropsy. In some regions, the loss of life is considerable.

Control Measures

A knowledge of the life history again indicates the best point at which to attack the parasite. Wet pastures, which harbour the snails, are obviously conducive to the spread of the infection, and therefore, draining of sheep pasture is the most suitable measure of protection for the flocks. In the hill pastures, this is often impossible and it has been found profitable to introduce ducks and geese to eat the snails. Various drugs are used on the infected animals, but they do not have considerable effect. It has been found that the "eggs" of *F. hepatica* will not hatch in water which is more alkaline than pH 7·5 and therefore the plentiful use of lime on pastures might have a beneficial effect.

General Remarks

Although man may be infected with liver flukes by drinking water which contains the cercariae, such cases are rare. There are several flukes which have more serious consequences. Among them are the blood flukes of the genus *Schistosoma*, and the Chinese liver flukes, *Clonorchis* [*Opisthorchis*] *sinensis*. Adult schistosomes live in the abdominal veins of man, the female being carried permanently in ventral folds of the male body. The eggs are laid in capillaries of the bladder; each possesses a sharp spine which lacerates the wall and thus it is liberated into the urine and passed out of the body. The young stages are passed in a water snail, and man is infected by the cercariae in drinking water or through the skin. *Schistosomiasis* is a serious disease in the rice-eating people of the East, where the flooded paddy-fields provide ideal conditions for continuous infection. That it is an ancient human disease is proved by the fact that schistosome eggs have been found in Egyptian mummies of a period three thousand years ago. It is estimated that over two hundred million people are seriously affected at the present time.

Clonorchis sinensis has three hosts in its life history. The primary host is a mammal, often man, the secondary host is a water-snail and the tertiary host is a freshwater fish. The cercariae from the snail burrow into the muscle of the fish, usually a carp or goldfish, and man is infected by eating raw or insufficiently cooked fish. There is an endless source of infection in the fish-ponds of China and Japan.

The interpretation of the multiplicative stages in the young forms of

Fasciola has been the subject of some controversy, and the development of rediae and cercariae from "germ-cells" has been variously described as *polyembryony*, *parthenogenesis* and *paedogenesis*. These topics are discussed in Vol. II, Chap. 17. If it is correct that a portion of the zygote is set aside in the early stages to give rise to "germ-cells" later, then the phenomenon is undoubtedly polyembryony for part of the substance of the fertilized egg gives rise to the rediae and cercariae.

TAENIA

Two species of *Taenia* are well-known parasites of man: they are *T. solium*, the pork tapeworm, and *T. saginata*, the commoner beef tapeworm. In this account, *T. solium* is described, though the general features apply also to the larger *T. saginata*.

Structure, Reproduction and Life History

Taenia solium is a flattened ribbon-like animal, white in colour, and tapering anteriorly. It may attain a length of 2·5 to 3·5 m, a width of 6 mm and thickness 1·5 mm. The anterior is marked by a tiny knob called the *scolex*, which bears a rounded protrusible projection known as the *rostellum*. Behind the rostellum is a double row of curved

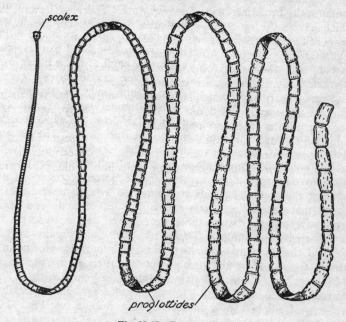

Fig. 32.17. *Taenia solium.*

chitinous *hooks*, which, together with the four *suckers*, form the means of attachment in the intestine (*see* Fig. 32.18). When the rostellum is withdrawn, the hooks point straight ahead and are plunged into the gut wall; then the rostellum is protruded and the hooks are bent outward and backward, thus locking the scolex securely in position. Behind the scolex, there is a narrow *region of proliferation*, and a little farther back, the faint outlines of transverse septa are to be seen. The portions between the transverse septa are known as *proglottides*; they are not to be confused with true segments such as we find in the

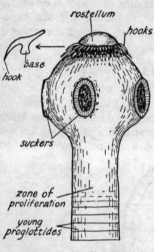

Fig. 32.18. *Taenia solium.*
Anterior portion.

earthworm or in the chordates. As they are pushed further away by growth in the region of proliferation, the proglottides become longer and wider, until they are almost square in outline. In the fully-grown tapeworm, there are about eight hundred proglottides, the posterior of which are cast off in groups of four or five, while proliferation in front continues at the rate of seven or eight every day.

There is no mouth or alimentary canal; the animal absorbs the digested food of its host over its whole surface. There are two ill-defined ganglia, joined by a broad band of nerve fibres, in the scolex. These ganglia supply nerves to the rostellum and the suckers, and two longitudinal nerve cords, lying laterally, pass down the whole length of the body and give off fine branches to each proglottis. The excretory system consists of flame cells united by fine ducts to two longitudinal excretory canals which pass along the whole length of the body slightly median to the longitudinal nerves. In the posterior region of each proglottis, the excretory canals are connected by a transverse canal.

Every mature proglottis contains a full set of male and female reproductive organs, though these are not well developed in the first two hundred proglottides. Thereafter, the male organs are first functional, then the female organs become functional as well, and in the posterior region, all are absorbed except the distended uterus, which is full of "eggs" and almost fills the proglottis (*see* Fig. 32.20).

As seen in a transverse section through a mature proglottis, the shape is a flattened ellipse with a somewhat wavy outline (*see* Fig. 32.21). Externally there is a thick, laminated cuticle made of protein and chitin impregnated with calcium carbonate. This cuticle is perforated by minute pits, at the bases of which lie unicellular glands or nerve-endings. Beneath the cuticle, there is a thin layer of circular muscle followed by longitudinal muscle, within which are to be found the

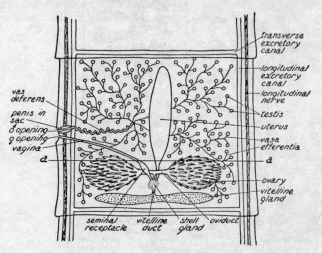

Fig. 32.19. *Taenia solium.* Sexually mature proglottis.

epidermal cells, which have sunk in from their original position. They make contact with the cuticle by fine fibres passing between the muscle cells (*see* Fig. 32.21). There are two prominent bands of transverse muscle, one upper and one lower, which appear to divide the body into an outer cortical region and an inner medulla. Occasional strands of transverse muscle pass from the upper to the lower region. With this muscle equipment, the tapeworm is able to wriggle fairly actively in the intestine. Within the medulla, all the reproductive organs are located.

The testis is sub-divided into a large number of small lobules which are scattered in the anterior and middle regions of a proglottis. Fine vasa efferentia from the lobules, unite to enter the narrow, coiled vas deferens, which opens at the tip of a protrusible penis situated in a muscular sac. The penis opens into the lateral genital atrium. These genital atria alternate on the right and left sides in successive proglottides. There are paired ovaries posteriorly situated, the ducts meeting in the mid-line to form a common oviduct. Behind the ovaries is a small vitelline gland from which a duct leads forward to join the oviduct in the shell gland. From this junction, a simple saccular

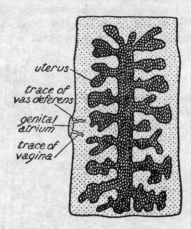

Fig. 32.20. *Taenia solium.* Proglottis just before casting.

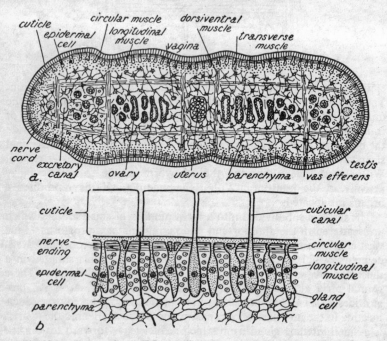

Fig. 32.21. *Taenia solium.* T.S. sexually mature proglottis at *a–a* in Fig. 32.19.

uterus passes forward almost the whole length of the proglottis. A narrow vagina leads in from the genital atrium, dilates to form a seminal receptacle and then joins the oviduct shortly before its junction with the vitelline duct (*see* Fig. 32.19).

Reproduction

Fertilization is internal, the penis passing into the vagina and ejaculating seminal fluid there. It may occur between male and female organs of the same proglottis or, by folding of the body, between the male of one region and the female organs of another region. There can

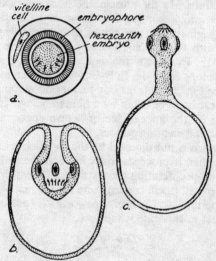

Fig. 32.22. *Taenia solium*, life history. (*a*) Onchosphere. (*b*) Cysticercus inverted. (*c*) Cysticercus everted.

hardly be cross-fertilization since two mature tapeworms could scarcely exist in the same intestine. Besides, infection with one *T. solium* seems to give immunity against a further infection. The eggs are fertilized in the oviduct at its confluence with the vagina and then they receive yolk and shell substance. As they pass through the glandular ootype, the chitinous shell hardens and the egg passes forward into the uterus.

Development proceeds in the uterus and by the time the proglottis is cast off, it may contain thirty- to forty-thousand *onchospheres*, each about 40μm in diameter. An onchosphere contains within its chitinous shell, a *hexacanth* (six-hooked) embryo enclosed within a secondary radially striated membrane, the *embryophore* (*see* Fig. 32.22 (*a*)). A few proglottides at a time are cast off and passed out with the host's faeces. No further development takes place until the onchospheres are swallowed by the secondary host, the pig.

Life History

If the onchospheres are swallowed by the pig, the shells and embryo-phores are digested in the duodenum after previous immersion in the acid juices of the stomach, and the hexacanth embryos are freed. With their sharp hooks, they bore into the gut wall and enter blood or lymphatic vessels in which they are carried round the body. They soon leave the circulation and enter voluntary muscle, particularly in the tongue and the limbs. In the muscle, the hooks are cast off, and the embryo develops into a sac-like *bladder-worm* or *cysticercus*, 10 mm by 6 mm. An invagination at one end of the cysticercus gives rise to an inverted scolex with the suckers, hooks and rostellum on the inside (*see* Fig. 32.22 (*b*)). Eventually the scolex is everted, a short region of proliferation develops, and the fully-formed cysticercus lies passively in the muscle (*see* Fig. 32.22 (*c*)). For further development the raw or under-cooked meat must be eaten by a human being. Infected pork is readily discerned by the appearance of brown spots; it is known as "measly pork" to the meat inspectors.

The bladder-worm is not digested by the stomach juices of man and in the small intestine, it proceeds to fix itself to the wall, casts off the bladder, and starts proliferating proglottides. Unless drastic measures are taken to remove it, it will remain there for the rest of the host's life. A similar cycle pertains to the beef tapeworm, *T. saginata*, except that the secondary host in this case is the cow.

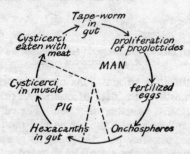

Structural, Physiological and Reproductive Modifications

The tapeworms show adaptations related to parasitism much more so than do trematodes. The lack of the alimentary canal can be correlated with the fact that the trophic stage is perpetually bathed in a solution of digested food. The suckers and hooks have evolved in connexion with fixation to the gut wall. Compared with free-living platyhelminthes there is reduction of the nervous system and of the sense organs of parasitic forms.

Physiologically, the tapeworm is adapted for life in an environment with very little oxygen and it is known that some tapeworms can respire anaerobically, breaking down glycogen to fatty acids and carbon dioxide, though they will use oxygen if it is available. There is some mechanism by which it is able to resist the host's enzymes, both in man and in the pig, though it is not known with certainty if anti-enzymes are produced by the secretion of the gland cells. There is precise physiological adaptation in the structure of the onchosphere in that the protective structures are not digested by either the stomach juices or duodenal juices alone, but by the latter, after previous immersion in the former. During its life history, there are changing osmotic conditions to which it can adapt itself, but no mechanism is known by which this is achieved.

It is in reproduction that the tapeworm excels. In the first place, there is proliferation of proglottides at the rate of seven or eight a day, and each proglottis will develop complete male and female organs. During one year, a single tapeworm will cast off more than 2,500 proglottides each containing 30,000 to 40,000 onchospheres. If a man harbours a tapeworm for thirty years, and periods longer than that are known, he will pass out with his faeces, over two thousand million onchospheres. These will remain viable for several months on the soil and probably longer in fresh water. The cysticerci can remain alive in muscle for five or six years before they die, and are then calcified by the host.

Effect on the Host

In a human being in good health, there is comparatively little pathological effect due to a single tapeworm, but in less robust individuals, the condition may become severe enough to merit the special name of the disease, *taeniasis*. It is characterized by abdominal pain, indigestion and vomiting, constipation, loss of appetite and nervous disorders. In children especially, there is considerable debilitating effect. Perhaps the main danger of taeniasis is that it renders the sufferer less resistant to other diseases. Nevertheless, human beings have been known to harbour a tapeworm for many years without serious effect.

More important than taeniasis is *cysticercosis*, the condition caused by bladder-worm infection. If a human being ingests onchospheres in contaminated water or food, or by infection carried on the fingers, the hexacanths follow much the same course as they do in the pig, but unfortunately they often show predilection for the eye and the brain. In the former case blindness may result, and in the latter, there may be epilepsy, paralysis or even death. If they lie dormant in the muscles, there is some muscular pain, but after a few years they die and are then calcified.

Control Measures

In urban communities with good sewage systems and piped water-supply, there is little danger of infection by tapeworms, but in rural areas, there may be considerable incidence of disease. Thorough cooking of meat will remove the chief danger. In countries where pickled pork and underdone beef are gastronomic delicacies, there is considerable taeniasis; it is estimated that 90 per cent of the population of Abyssinia are infected by *T. saginata* while in certain Northern European countries from 5 to 10 per cent harbour *T. solium*.

Treatment of taeniasis in bad cases is carried out by administration of vermifuges which paralyse the worm and cause it to cast off much of the body. Unfortunately, they rarely remove the scolex as well. The vermifuges most commonly used are oil of male fern (*Dryopteris*) and oil of *Chenopodium*. Usually, the complete removal of a tapeworm entails surgical operation.

The only method of ensuring that the onchospheres do not reach the secondary host is by ensuring that pigs (or cattle) do not have access to human faeces. In backward communities, this is rarely possible; sometimes the pig is almost a member of the family.

General Remarks

The majority of mammalian species harbour tapeworms, one of the commonest being *Dipylidium caninum* in which the primary host is the dog, and the secondary host, the dog flea. The dog also harbours *T. serrata*, the bladder-worms existing in the muscles of rabbits and hares. Another tapeworm of man, *Diphyllobothrium latum*, has two secondary hosts, the first a water-flea, and the second, a freshwater fish. Cysticerci of *Echinococcus granulosus*, a small and relatively harmless tapeworm of the dog, set up a serious pathological condition in man and other mammals. The bladder-worm stage is represented by a huge *hydatid cyst* which may become 10 to 12 cm in diameter. Within this primary cyst, secondary and tertiary cysts are produced, and from the walls of all grades of cyst, *brood capsules* are developed. Each of these contains a number of scolices, and it is possible for one large cyst to produce over a million. Such cysts cause severe derangement of internal organs and their removal entails surgical operation, otherwise death frequently ensues. Dogs are infected by eating raw meat containing cysts, and man ingests the hexacanths in food or water contaminated by dogs' faeces.

There has been considerable speculation as to whether tapeworms are animals or colonies of animals produced by budding. Each mature proglottis is much the same as a liver-fluke, containing a complete set of all the organs necessary for continued existence. It is, however, significant that the rudimentary brain and the organs of attachment are in the scolex, and there is only one scolex per tapeworm.

The difference between true metameric segmentation and proliferation of proglottides can be appreciated by a careful comparison of the conditions in a chordate embryo on the one hand and a tapeworm on the other.

True segments	*Proglottides*
1. Within narrow limits a definite and comparatively small number.	1. An indefinite and very large number.
2. No region capable of permanent proliferation of segments.	2. A definite proliferating region which remains permanently "young."
3. The oldest segment is the most anterior.	3. The oldest proglottis is the most posterior.
4. Segments are pre-formed in the embryonic somites.	4. Proglottides are not preformed in somites.
5. If segments are removed there is not complete regeneration.	5. Removal of any number of proglottides makes no difference.
6. Segments are not "voluntarily" cast off.	6. Proglottides are "voluntarily" cast off.
7. Though essentially alike some segments are very specialized.	7. All proglottides are almost identical.

There is obviously only a superficial resemblance between the two types of structures.

PULEX

Fleas are ectoparasites of birds and mammals, "making their living" by sucking the blood of their homoiothermous hosts. More than one thousand species are known, the one described here being the flea of man, *Pulex irritans*. They form a very compact insect order and a description of one will show the general features of all.

Structure, Reproduction and Life History

The body is laterally compressed, pale brown to yellow in colour and there are no wings or compound eyes. The legs are modified for jumping and the mouth parts for sucking (*see* Chap. 23). When on the host, the front pair of legs are used for parting the fur or feathers and the animal walks on the other four. When there are no obstacles, it will use all six legs, but contrary to popular belief, a flea rarely jumps. It will jump to its first host and it will jump in response to mechanical stimuli, but in this latter case, there is not directional response; it lands anywhere. The sucking tube is formed of three stylets, the anterior one being smooth while the two lateral stylets have serrated tips. This tube is held in position by the labial palps and then thrust into the skin up to the hilt. Saliva injected into the host has an anti-coagulating property and causes irritation to the recipient. Fleas are wasteful feeders, much of the blood they suck is passed out with the faeces, possibly to provide food for the larvae.

The sexes are separate and after fertilization the female cannot produce eggs until she has fed on blood. After the meal, a few eggs will be laid singly, normally in the nest or sleeping-place of the host or on clothing or in debris. Then no more eggs will be laid until after the next blood meal. The eggs are very small, about 0·5 mm long, oval in shape and white in colour. They are coated with a sticky substance which fastens them to the substratum. Fleas are holometabolous insects and the larva moults twice before pupating. It is narrow and

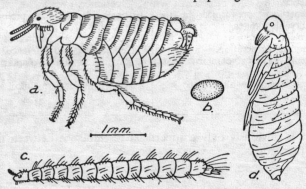

Fig. 32.23. *Pulex irritans*, life history. (*a*) Adult. (*b*) Egg. (*c*) Larva. (*d*) Pupa.

elongated, with a brown head and thirteen white segments; it feeds on faeces of the adults and it is stated that the dried blood in the faeces is necessary for proper development. Unlike the adult, there are biting mouth parts, no eyes and no legs. Shortly after its second moult, the larva makes a silken cocoon within which it pupates (*see* Fig. 32.23). Metamorphosis takes four or five days, but the imagines may remain motionless in the cocoon for a long period, emerging when disturbed. The life history is thus that of a typical holometabolous insect, i.e. egg → larva → pupa → imago. Some further details of structure and life history are given in Chap. 23.

Structural, Physiological and Reproductive Modifications

The laterally compressed body is an adaptation to creeping among fur and feathers and in this connexion the special use of the front-limbs for parting the hair is another modification. There is a very tough cuticle which ensures that brushing or scratching by the host will have little effect on the flea. In connexion with the feeding method, the mouth parts are modified to form a sucking mechanism with serrated stylets for piercing the skin. The legs are adapted for a number of purposes, walking on four legs or on six legs, jumping and separating hairs. Reduction, when compared with the probable nearest relatives, the Diptera, is shown in the loss of wings and compound eyes.

In common with other blood-sucking ectoparasites, the saliva contains an anti-coagulant. Blood is absolutely essential for the continuance of the race; if it is not obtained, the eggs may not be produced, and even if they are produced, they are not viable.

The eggs are laid singly so that there is greater possibility of some of the progeny finding a host, and they are deposited in positions where the host is likely to come in contact with the offspring, e.g. nests of birds and rodents, or in the case of *P. irritans*, in the clothing or in cracks in the floor. Blood seems to be essential for larval development and the habit of excessive feeding by the female imagines, ensures that there is dried blood in the faeces which constitute the principal food of the larvae. A strong adaptation for survival under difficult conditions is seen in the ability of the newly-formed imagines to remain motionless in the cocoon for as long as twelve months. If an infected house has been empty for some time and is then occupied, fleas may appear in swarms.

Effect on the Host

Beyond a certain amount of skin irritation due to the injected saliva, *P. irritans* has no effect on the human host, and does not transmit disease. But *Xenopsylla cheopis*, the common flea of the black rat (*Rattus rattus*), is now known to transmit plague both in its bubonic and pneumonic forms. Bubonic plague is characterized by swellings called buboes in the lymphatic glands, and in pneumonic plague the lungs are infected, but there are no buboes. The causative organism is a bacterium, *Pasteurella pestis*. Throughout history, there have been devastating epidemics of plague, the Black Death being one of the most notable. The disease has spread with the black rat, in ships, and cases have been recorded from most parts of the world. Plague is peculiar in that it waxes and wanes; epidemics appear and have devastating effects and then for a long period there are few cases. It seems almost as if there are mild and virulent strains. Its spread, from China in the latter half of the nineteenth century, has left foci of infection in many parts of the world and though it has virtually died out in the great ports, there is undoubtedly a reservoir of infection in the wild rodents of many countries. In their virulent form, bubonic and pneumonic plague kill in a few days. Cases occurred in Glasgow and London in the early part of the twentieth century, and the last British outbreak was in 1918, in Suffolk. The rat dies from the disease and then the flea leaves the cooling body and may attack man. It is known that apart from rural infection of rodents, almost all ports harbour *Rattus rattus*, and the rodent supports *Xenopsylla cheopis*. The same flea is the vector in a type of typhus in the U.S.A.; the causative organism is a species of *Rickettsia* (*see* Chap. 36). There is little that can be done to cure patients suffering from the disease in its virulent form. The only control measure that seems likely to be effective is the use of vigorous measures against the rat.

Parasitism is a way of life which under natural conditions always seems to lead to a state of tolerance between the two organisms concerned. Parasitic disease is a symptom of a new and recent association and tolerance has not been achieved. Hence, the parasite causes pathogenic disturbance in the host and may even cause death, thus encompassing its own destruction. Since man has colonized the earth, parasites have found in him a new host, and rarely has the condition become non-virulent. With him, man has taken his plants and animals, highly inbred and artificially produced, with little natural resistance to "foreign" parasites. There is no road back; the position must be accepted and we must make every effort to reduce the depredations caused by parasitic disease. The greatest advances will undoubtedly be made by universal education in biological matters.

CHAPTER 33

SAPROPHYTIC PLANTS

THE saprophytic plants are all fungi and have the same primary characteristic as their parasitic relatives, that is, they lack any means of manufacturing their own food supplies. Unlike the parasites, however, instead of obtaining them from living tissues, they utilize the dead remains of other organisms, being responsible with the bacteria for their ultimate degradation and decay.

This chapter deals with the saprophytic genera *Mucor*, *Eurotium*, *Penicillium*, *Saccharomyces* and *Psalliota*. The first is an aflagellate member of the fungal class Phycomycetes, the middle three are members of the Ascomycetes and the last is a basidiomycete fungus. Their characters may not only be taken to illustrate the saprophytic mode of life but also the general taxonomic features of these three main classes of fungi.

(Note that flagellate representatives of the Phycomycetes have already been described under *Phytophthora*, *Pythium*, *Peronospora* and *Albugo*.)

MUCOR

The genus contains many species found commonly on a wide variety of substrates such as the litter and its humus derivatives in the soil, dung, particularly of horses and cattle, spoiling human food of wide variety including bread, cooked potato and other vegetables, cooked cereals, etc. A few species, because of the special enzymes possessed, can be used commercially, e.g. *M. javanicus* will ferment sugar to alcohol. The species most usually encountered and easiest to grow in culture are *M. hiemalis* on horse dung and *M. mucedo* on damp bread, porridge, etc. The last mentioned will be described here.

Structure, Reproduction and Life Cycle

The mycelium is very evident even from its early stages of development as a white growth like cotton-wool over the surface of its substrate. It is composed of long, slender non-septate hyphae and is therefore coenocytic in structure. Only in older parts, and during development of reproductive structures, are there any cross-walls formed. As well as ramifying profusely outside the substrate, the fungus sends countless fine, branching hyphae into the food material from which it derives its nourishment. These establish close contact with the substance, in order to digest and absorb it.

After the development of the mycelium has commenced, a reproductive phase soon follows. This is at first only asexual by means of spores, but under suitable conditions reproduction may be by sexual means as well.

Asexual reproduction is initiated by the development of hyphae which grow away from the substrate and into the air. These are the *sporangiophores* each of which will bear a single *sporangium* at its extremity. A sporangium begins as a swelling of the sporangiophore tip and ultimately becomes a spherical head enclosing a multinucleate mass of the protoplasm. This head is cut off from the sporangiophore below, by the development of a dome-shaped cross-wall at the base of the sporangium. This cross-wall pushes up into the sporangium from below and is called the *columella*. During ripening, the contents of the sporangium are divided into a large number of uninucleate masses, each of which develops a clear resistant wall which gradually becomes brown or black in colour. Each such structure is a *spore*. When these are ripe, the sporangium wall becomes brittle and black. Externally, it may bear deposits of crystalline calcium oxalate, products of the metabolism within.

Liberation of the spores is effected by deliquescence of the sporangium wall, its broken lower part remaining attached to the sporangiophore. It is noticeable that just before the sporangium disrupts, a drop of water is secreted around it by the sporangiophore. It is possible that the rupture is finally effected by the pressure exerted by the columella within the sporangium. There is little doubt that in some species where deliquescence does not occur, a fully ripened sporangium may be burst open by a slight pressure from external sources. Such a pressure might be caused by insects alighting on the mycelium. In any event, the spores are finally liberated as a closely adhering mass, and on drying out they separate, to be dispersed as individuals. Each is a very small structure and is easily air-borne or they can be carried in large numbers on the bodies of insects. If such a spore reaches a suitable substrate, it can germinate immediately to produce a new mycelium. Spores may retain their viability for several months, so that chances of ultimate success are thereby increased.

Sexual reproduction in *Mucor mucedo* is not often observed in the wild state, but the process can readily be seen in cultures, provided that the right conditions obtain. One essential condition is that the fungus shall be present in both the forms in which it is known to exist. The existence of the two forms was discovered by Blakeslee who described the fungus as *heterothallic*, that is, it exists in two morphologically identical forms which differ from one another physiologically. A sexual union can come about only between the different physiological forms. Two mycelia of the same physiological kind are not compatible sexually and will not

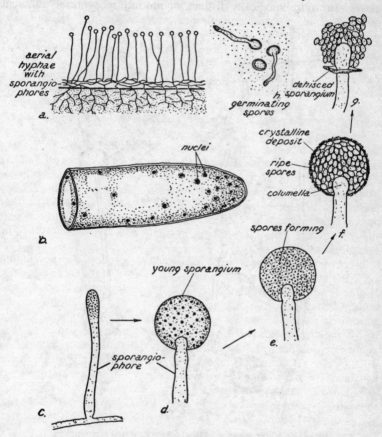

Fig. 33.1. *Mucor mucedo*. Structure and asexual reproduction. (*a*) "Pinheads" on nutritive substrate. (*b*) Tip of hypha (enlarged). (*c* to *h*) Formation, ripening and dehiscence of sporangium.

even intermingle very successfully on the same substratum. We may regard the condition as being one of unisexuality within the species, but since there is no morphological distinction between the gametes or the organs which produce them, we cannot call one of the mycelia male and the other female as we do in more evident cases of unisexuality. Instead we refer to one as "plus" (+) and the other as "minus" (−), for convenience. This condition of heterothallism seems to be a very primitive form of sexuality, true sexuality only becoming completely evident when the physiologically distinct forms of a species are themselves also morphologically distinct, or produce recognizably different

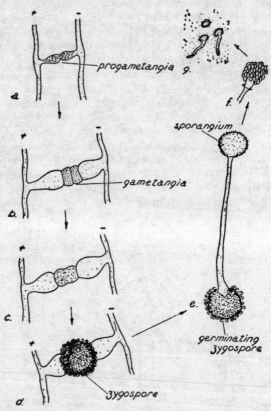

Fig. 33.2. *Mucor mucedo*. (*a* to *g*) Stages in sexual reproduction.

gametes. Heterothallism is very widespread in the fungi, but may be encountered in many of the lower algae also (*see* Chaps. 5 and 9). Some species of *Mucor* exist in the *homothallic* condition and regularly reproduce sexually from gametes developed on a single form of the mycelium. In such cases, there is not even any physiological difference between the mycelia. Other homothallic species show distinct differences in the sizes of the gamete-producing organs. In these cases the mycelium is described as *heterogamic homothallic*, really a hermaphrodite condition, if the larger organ is considered female and the smaller male.

Sexual reproduction between the two strains of *M. mucedo* commences by the development of short side branches from two laterally placed hyphae. These branches are called *progametangia* and they grow towards one another until their tips adhere. After touching, each gradually swells and a cross-wall is formed to cut off a terminal, rounded cell, a *gametangium*. The lower part of each branch is termed the *suspensor*. Each gametangium is multinucleate and the two are equal in every respect. As maturity is reached, the cell-walls where the two are adherent break down, so that the two gametangia fuse into a single structure. Very soon, the wall of this fusion cell thickens, with a rough exterior coat, and darkens in colour. It is known as the *zygospore*, but the precise behaviour of the nuclei in the gametangia prior to, during, or after its formation, is uncertain. Some suggest that the nuclei from the conjugating gametangia fuse in pairs at some time during its development. Another suggestion is that only one pair of nuclei fuse and that the others play no part in the sexual act. When fully formed, the zygospore breaks away from the suspensors as a separate highly-resistant reproductive body. It can retain its viability for many months, and after an initial long period of rest, once it is deposited on a suitable substrate, its germination is rapid. The zygospore wall is burst open and from the contents a single hypha develops.

This is known as a *promycelial hypha* because instead of developing into a new mycelium directly, it gives rise to a single sporangium which develops spores exactly as in asexual reproduction. There is reason to believe that the spores contain nuclei derived from the zygotic nucleus (or nuclei) by meiotic divisions and are therefore haploid. Every spore produced by the sporangium is either plus or minus; there is never a mixture of spores of the two strains. This shows that the differentiation of strains must have occurred in some nuclear division in the zygospore prior to its germination and that the spores have developed from the products of division of only one of these nuclei. This is contrary to what happens in some related heterothallic genera (e.g. *Phycomyces*) in which one half of the spores develop as plus strains and the other half as minus strains. Figs. 33.1 and 33.2 illustrate the various stages in the life history of the fungus and the diagram on p. 1189 summarizes the life cycle.

Physiology

Apart from the existence of two distinct physiological races of the species giving rise to its heterothallism, the fungus exhibits in common with other saprophytic fungi very interesting physiological characteristics concerned with its mode of living. Strictly speaking, all organisms have comparable requirements with regard to nutritional substances. They must all have a source of carbon, nitrogen, water, mineral salts (ions) and usually certain organic compounds known as vitamins or accessory growth substances. From these they build their protoplasmic constituents. They differ only in the sources from which these requirements are obtained and in the methods of obtaining them. Whereas the chlorophyll-containing plants can trap energy and synthesize all their nutritional substances from simple inorganic sources, organisms without the necessary pigments must obtain supplies by other means. The saprophytic fungi use the dead remains of other organisms. As a source of carbon, they use either the carbohydrates or the fats or both, as a source of nitrogen, the proteins, amino-acids, ammonium compounds or nitrates which are found there. The necessary water and some of the mineral salts and accessory growth substances are usual components of both animal and plant protoplasm and therefore will also be present in the dead remains. The particular form of carbohydrate, protein or fat and the precise nature of the accessory growth-substances present in a particular dead organic environment will depend upon its kind and many saprophytic fungi are therefore restricted to a substrate containing their own particular requirements. They will be restricted to substrates in which both the carbon and nitrogen source offered and the accessory growth substances suit their requirements by being capable of being metabolized. This depends entirely on the enzyme systems which they possess. First, they must be able to render the nutrient sources soluble and diffusible, if not already in this condition, and secondly, they must be able to synthesize their own protoplasmic and storage substances from the absorbed products of digestion. Therefore the saprophyte must first secrete into the substrate the enzymes necessary to hydrolyse polysaccharides to monosaccharides, proteins to amino-acids and so on. If it lacks the necessary enzymes, then it is unable to do this and must rely on finding a source in which its requirements are already in diffusible form. Many saprophytes can produce only a limited range of enzymes so that their carbon source may be restricted to one carbohydrate only, such as cellulose, starch, glycogen or sugars. Some may be able to produce fat-splitting enzymes only, so that the carbon source must be a fat. This wide variation in the capability of saprophytes to produce specific enzymes accounts partly for their wide range of substrates and the fact that one saprophyte may be able to grow only on one particular kind of medium. For example, the fungus *Onygena equina* can grow only on horn or bone, and species of *Gymnoascus* and *Ctenomyces* can grow only on feathers. Another factor which may restrict the ability of the fungus to grow on other than one kind of substrate is the presence of its requirements of accessory growth substances. Such substances as thiamin (vitamin B_1), biotin (vitamin H), riboflavin (vitamin B_2), pyridoxine (vitamin B_6) and pantothenic acid are known to be essential for certain fungi since they are unable to synthesize them from simpler compounds. Hence they can grow only where the substances are to be found.

The nutritional activities of the genus *Mucor* have not been studied very deeply, chiefly because no members are of great economic importance. Nutrient requirements are known to include a source of glucose, and starch seems to provide this, since the fungus can rapidly hydrolyse it by diastatic enzymes. The nitrogen source is provided from proteins, amino-acids or ammonium compounds such as ammonium sulphate. The minerals necessary for growth include sulphur (sulphate), potassium, iron, sodium, magnesium and phosphorus (phosphates). *Mucor spp.* do not seem to be very exacting with regard to accessory growth substances and seem to be able to manufacture their own. *M. ramannianus* is reported to require small quantities of thiamin.

Several species of *Mucor* are able to bring about the fermentation of sugar to ethyl alcohol and therefore must possess the full complement of enzymes known to make up the enzyme complex, zymase. If the species *M. racemosus* and *M. javanicus* are grown in sugar solution, they undergo a change of form in which the mycelium becomes broken up into small rounded segments known as *sprout cells* (*see* Fig. 33.3). These bud continuously, rather like yeast cells under similar conditions, and are capable of the same alcoholic fermentation process.

The sporangiophores of *Mucor* species exhibit very clear tropic responses (*see* Vol. II, Chap. 16). Initially all tend to grow away from the substrate in which the sterile hyphae are ramifying and this may be

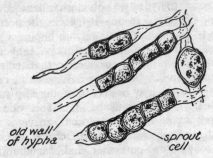

Fig. 33.3. Sprout cells of *Mucor sp.*

a negative chemotropic response. If grown in total darkness, they tend to take a vertical position, indicating a negative geotropism, but if developed in conditions of unequal lighting on different sides, they make very strong positive phototropic responses by setting themselves along the line of the incident beam and growing vigorously towards the greatest light intensity.

ASPERGILLUS [EUROTIUM]

This is a genus of the Ascomycete fungi, the majority of the species being saprophytes on various substrates. A few species parasitic on animals are known. The commonest belong in the *A. glaucus* group, greenish moulds found on a variety of preserved foods, sugary substances and vegetable remains. Species within the group are difficult to define. The one described here is *Aspergillus repens.* Owing to the fact that the asexual and sexual phases of reproduction may occur on separate mycelia, and the fungus continue to exist indefinitely by reproduction by one or other process only, the two stages were not originally connected as being parts of the same life history. The two phases were independently named, the sexual phase was called *Eurotium* and the asexual phase *Aspergillus.* The latter was then placed in the indeterminate group, the Fungi Imperfecti, since it showed no special characters by which it could be further identified. There are many fungal species still so classified since the sexual or perfect phase has never been found.

Structure, Reproduction and Life Cycle

The mycelium is made up of hyphae of multinucleate cells, and prior to reproductive activity, forms a whitish growth like cotton-wool, spreading over its substrate. Rate of spread often does not seem to be very rapid and individual mycelia may be seen on the same food source as fairly clearly-defined areas for some time before they merge into one another. As the asexual reproductive phase commences, the area of contamination by the fungus turns bluish-green as millions of coloured spores are produced. These are developed on branches growing out from the main mycelium into the atmosphere. Each such branch is a *conidiophore*, is thicker than the other hyphae and is non-septate. Its apex swells into a spherical mass containing cytoplasm and many nuclei. Radiating from this head are developed short fine branches termed *sterigmata*. These bud off, in rapid succession, long chains of *conidiospores* or *phialospores*. A conidiospore is produced by the passage of a nucleus into the sterigma where it quickly divides. One of the products moves to the extreme tip and behind it a delicate wall is formed, cutting it off with a little cytoplasm. Within this terminal cell on the sterigma, the contents round off and secrete another thicker wall which may become adherent to the outer one (*see* Fig. 33.4 (*c*)). Immediately one cell is cut off at the sterigma tip, another is quickly formed behind it (acropetal succession). This continues until long chains are produced, the oldest spores furthest from the sterigma. Since each conidiospore is formed within the old cell wall, the production is termed *endogenous.* When ripe, the conidiospores are greenish in colour and owing to the rounding up of each, they are easily dislodged from one another by air currents or physical contact. They are very minute and readily dispersed. On reaching a new substrate, germination is rapid.

Sexual reproduction follows in older mycelia and the process results in the development of *ascospores*. The sex organs are produced together as short, lateral branches on the main hyphae. The female organ is a composite structure of several cells; a lower multicellular *stalk*, a middle unicellular *ascogonium* and an upper unicellular *trichogyne*. All these cells are multinucleate. The whole structure is sometimes called an *archicarp* and is tightly coiled. The *antheridium* usually arises from the same hypha and is a multinucleate, unicellular branch which grows up on the outside of the coiled archicarp. Fusion has been reported between the trichogyne and the antheridium but this is doubtful and, even if cellular fusion occurs, it is very doubtful whether the antheridial nuclei play any fertilization rôle. In some cases, antheridia are never produced, but the ascogonium still functions normally. It divides into a number of binucleate cells, each of which develops septate outgrowths called *ascogenous hyphae*, several cells long. In the penultimate cell of each ascogenous hypha, there are two nuclei which fuse and the cell enlarges to form a club-shaped *ascus*. The fusion nucleus undergoes meiotic division into four and each then divides

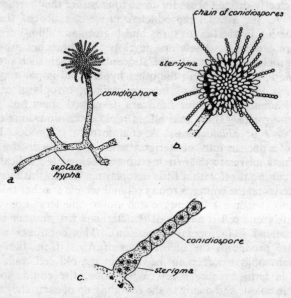

Fig. 33.4. *Aspergillus repens.* Structure and asexual reproduction. (*a*) Hypha bearing conidiophore. (*b*) Conidium (enlarged). (*c*) Formation of conidiospores.

mitotically to give eight nuclei in all. Each nucleus with a little cytoplasm rounds up and secretes its own wall to become an ascospore within the ascus.

Whilst the ascospores have been developing, from the neighbouring hyphae, many multicellular sterile branches are developed. They grow up around the archicarp, and by lateral fusion into a sheet, completely enclose it in a two-layered wall. The whole structure is termed an *ascocarp* and the outer wall is the *peridium* or rind. The inner layer of this peridium serves a nutritive function and eventually breaks down as do all the other cells inside, often including the asci themselves, so that the ascospores may lie free in the interior. The outer wall layer secretes a bright yellow substance and serves a protective function. It does not dehisce or open in any way and the whole ascocarp is shed. Because the outer wall does not open, the ascocarp is sometimes referred to as a *cleistothecium* to distinguish it from comparable structures called *perithecium* and *apothecium* in other ascomycete fungi. In those, the

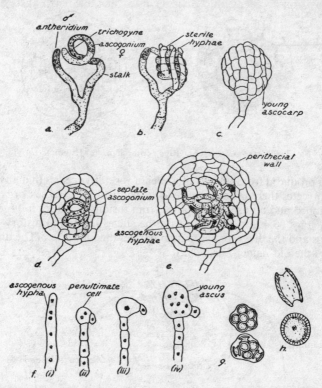

Fig. 33.5. *Aspergillus repens.* Sexual reproduction. (*a* to *e*) Sex organs and formation of ascocarp. (*f* (i) to (iv)) Formation of ascus by ascogenous hypha. (*g*) Ascospores in ascus. (*h*) Ascospores (enlarged).

peridium may split open to uncover the asci and ascospores before their dispersal. On decay of the cleistothecial wall, the ascospores are liberated. If they reach new substrates, each can germinate into a new mycelium.

The whole procedure represents a stage in the gradual decline of sexuality which is evident in the Ascomycetes. In some representatives the sexual process is clear-cut and involves nuclear fusion by specially-produced gametic nuclei in specialized sex organs. In *Aspergillus*, sex organs are clearly formed but it is doubtful if the fusion of their nuclei ever occurs, the zygotic nuclei being produced by fusion of two vegetative nuclei. In *Erysiphe polygoni*, the sex organs produced appear to go through the preliminaries and then abort, the ascospores eventually

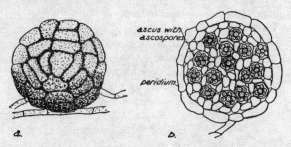

Fig. 33.6. *Aspergillus repens*. Ripe perithecium. (*a*) External. (*b*) V.S.

being produced from fusions of nuclei in vegetative cells. In many other ascomycetes there is no pretence at sexuality at all. No sex organs are developed and all ascospores arise from fusions of nuclei in vegetative cells. Figs 33.4 and 33.5 illustrate the stages in the life history of the fungus and the diagram below summarizes the life cycle. (The diagram shows the old name, *Eurotium*.)

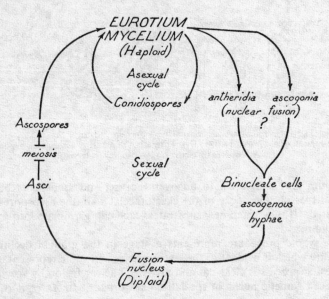

Physiology

The nutritional activities of *Aspergillus spp.* have never been deeply studied and little detail is available. Their special saprophytic character has been summed up in the text relating to *Mucor*. They undoubtedly absorb nutritional substances in soluble form, after digesting the substrate with suitable extracellular enzymes. Some species of *Aspergillus* have been used successfully in alcoholic fermentation.

One interesting feature in the physiology of *Aspergillus* is its ability to change its form, i.e. mutate. In culture, variants can be deliberately induced by heat treatment of the spores (sowing with too hot a needle), but the corresponding changes known as *saltations* which occur in some cultures, apparently quite naturally, are not readily explicable. The changes often involve weaker growth and inability to develop the normal pigmentation, browns replacing the normal greenish colours.

PENICILLIUM

This is an Ascomycete genus very closely related to *Aspergillus* and exhibiting the same structural and reproductive characters. Species occur on equally varied substrates and to the unaided eye usually no distinction between the two moulds can be seen. *Penicillium* has become world-renowned as the first fungus group containing species producing antibiotic substances to be discovered. Penicillin is now a word in every language. There are a large number of species including several put to useful work by man besides *P. notatum*, the penicillin producer. Several are used in cheese ripening such as *P. camemberti* and *P. roqueforti*.

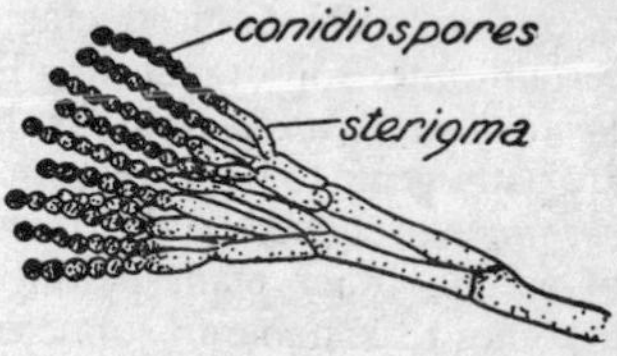

Structure, Reproduction and Life Cycle

The mycelium is very similar to that in *Aspergillus*, but when in the asexual phase, it can be distinguished by the structure of the conidiophores. The conidiospores are developed on sterig-

Fig. 33.7. *Penicillium sp.* Conidiospore formation.

mata in the same way but the sterigmata themselves are developed as short outgrowths from branches at the end of the conidiophore. The whole structure has a brush-like, tufted appearance (*see* Fig. 33.7).

The details of sexual reproduction are also very similar to those in *Aspergillus*. Definite sex organs are produced but the same doubt is present as to whether there are true gametic unions or whether the ascospores develop as a result of vegetative nuclear fusions.

Physiology

Penicillium species live saprophytically on their substrates and produce a series of extracellular enzymes by which to digest it.

The most interesting feature of the physiology of the genus is the ability of some species, particularly *P. notatum*, to produce substances which inhibit the growth of other organisms. These substances are known as antibiotics, and the story of Sir Alexander Fleming's famous discovery and Florey's subsequent extraction of the active *penicillin*, is too well known to need repeating. The discovery led to the production on a large scale of the life-saving drug and encouraged the search for others with occasional satisfactory results. Most work has been done on elucidating the nature and action of antibiotics useful in human and animal medicine. Among those now in regular use besides penicillin are *streptomycin*, toxic to many bacteria and produced by the actinomycete fungus *Streptomyces griseus*, *aureomycin* produced by *Streptomyces aureofaciens* and *chloromycetin* (chloramphenicol) produced by *Streptomyces venezuelae* and used against typhoid fever. Many others are known, but owing to a much less specific action than those mentioned, they prove toxic to man and animals as well as to the disease-causing organisms and therefore cannot be used in medicine.

Note on Antibiosis (Antonym of Symbiosis)

In nature, the production of antibiotics by a wide variety of organisms must have profound effects, but these are not as yet well known except in a few cases. One such effect concerns soil fertility and it is known that the presence of certain antibiotic-producing organisms in the soil, inhibits the presence of certain other soil organisms. For example, the presence of the green mould *Penicillium expansum* inhibits the development of "damping off" fungi which are pathogenic to higher plants. The antibiotic is known as *patulin*. Another, *viridin*, is produced by the fungus *Trichoderma viride*, and inhibits the growth of certain other plant pathogens in the soil. From such information, it becomes reasonable to suppose that the balance of the soil population, and therefore soil fertility, must be to a great extent dependent on the numbers and kinds of antibiotic producers present. Careful and exhaustive examination of the position may lead one day to the exact control of soil fertility from the soil population standpoint, by the encouragement of useful micro-organisms and discouragement of others.

Several problems and possibilities have become clear since the first general use of antibiotics. It has been shown that use of such substances leads to the development of resistant strains or "persisters" of the organism which it was intended to kill. In medicine, if the antibiotic is not toxic to man, as in the case of penicillin, this can be overcome by dosing in such large amounts as to prevent it. In other cases, such as with streptomycin, this cannot be done, and its use therefore must be very carefully controlled. Use of antibiotics also leads to the increased development of organisms not destroyed by the antibiotic since much of the competition will be removed. Use of a substance such as aureomycin, has led to the rapid increase of other yeast-like organisms which have proved themselves toxic to the patient. Such possibilities must be clearly recognized and guarded against.

Apart from its use in fighting disease, a knowledge of antibiosis is proving useful in other spheres. For example, certain antibiotic substances which are very powerful, but not specific enough to be useful in medicine, can be put to other useful work. *Subtilin*, a product of *Bacillus subtilis*, is a very powerful sterilizing agent and may prove valuable in the field of food preservation. *Nisin*, from *Streptococcus lactis*, although probably present in milk, can be added to assist in preventing the growth of unwanted organisms in cheese-making processes.

Another use for antibiotics has been found in the raising of young animals and poultry. Aureomycin greatly increases the growth rate in pigs. Penicillin is used in turkey rearing. The increase in the growth rate is proved due to the presence of extra quantities of vitamin B_{12} in the food. This apparently arises in the gut itself, due to the fact that the antibiotic encourages the development of the gut micro-organisms which produce vitamin B_{12}, and destroys others which do not.

Lastly, the antibiotics may prove valuable in pest control. Some antibiotics in sufficiently high concentrations may prove efficient rat exterminators, for instance, whilst another possibility lies in developing antibiotics which may be taken up from the soil by higher plants, and prove effective preventers of fungal or insect attacks.

SACCHAROMYCES

This is a genus of the ascomycete fungi which with other related genera forms a group which are in the main unicellular. There is little doubt that these unicellular fungi are not exhibiting a primitive structural condition but rather have been derived from multicellular forms, since it is well known that many otherwise multicellular fungi can exist as unicells under certain abnormal conditions, e.g. *Mucor* sprout cells. In the genus *Saccharomyces*, the condition is normal and permanent. The species of the genus, with others, are collectively described as the *yeasts*, and of them *S. cerevisiae* is by far the best known because of its use in bread-making and beer-brewing. It will be described here. *S. ellipsoideus* is used in wine-making. Both are typical saprophytes living in substrates with a high sugar content.

Structure, Reproduction and Life Cycle

Each cell is an ovoid to spherical structure, very small (about 10μm in diameter) with a delicate wall not of the usual fungal type but said to be of polysaccharide compounds of phosphoric acid. The protoplast fills the cell except for small vacuoles and the cytoplasm is dense and granular. Glycogen is a normal food reserve inclusion and volutin (ribo-nucleic acid or one of its salts), may be detected as small granules in the vacuoles. The nucleus seems to be of a peculiar structure and in fixed and stained preparations appears to be vacuolate with the chromatin condensed on delicate threads.

Reproduction is chiefly by asexual means and the process is known as "budding." This distinguishes it from a related genus, *Schizosaccharomyces*, in which the process is one of transverse fission. The

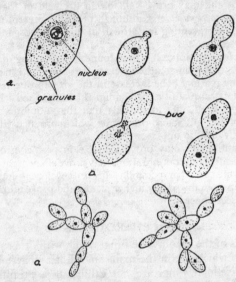

Fig. 33.8. *Saccharomyces cerevisiae*. (a) Fixed and stained cell. (b) Stages in bud formation. (c) Colonies formed as a result of rapid budding.

reproducing cell starts to develop a small protrusion, near one end as a rule, and this rapidly enlarges and fills with cytoplasm. When the protrusion approaches the size of the parent, the nucleus of the parent migrates to the entrance to the "bud" as it may now be called, and there divides by mitosis. One of the nuclei passes into the bud and the join between parent and bud is constricted to become a narrow neck. Eventually, this becomes sealed off and the bud will break away. However, in rapid budding conditions, the parent cell may produce several buds in succession and each of these may bud again several times before any separation occurs, so that colonies of cells may be developed (*see* Fig. 33.8).

Sexual reproduction, if it may be thus called, results in the production of *ascospores*. These are formed in slightly enlarged vegetative cells which may therefore be called *asci*. Vegetative cells undergo ascospore production when food conditions are poor and there is a tendency to dryness. The contents of the ascus round off and divide into four pieces, each of which contains a nucleus and develops a thick wall. When the ascus disrupts, these are released and if conditions are satisfactory they germinate into small rounded cells. If they germinate close to one another, the resulting cells immediately fuse together in pairs to form single cells which may be called zygotes. Each has the property of repeated budding to produce the normal vegetative cells which can continue the budding indefinitely as long as conditions are

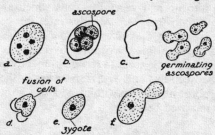

Fig. 33.9. *Saccharomyces cerevisiae*. Sexual reproduction. (*a*) and (*b*) Ascospore formation. (*c*) Germination of ascospores. (*d*) and (*e*) Fusion of cells to form the zygote. (*f*) Normal vegetative cell budding.

favourable. They are eventually able to become asci again. It has been shown in culture that fusions only occur between certain pairings of the ascospores, indicating that they possess certain physiological distinctions, two being of one kind and two of another, i.e. heterothallic. If the four spores from a single ascus are germinated separately, they may produce colonies of small rounded cells and it has been observed that occasionally two of these may conjugate to form a larger and apparently normal vegetative cell. This continues to bud and its descendants may even produce ascospores, but usually only two instead of four and these are incapable of germination. If the colonies of small cells from the separated ascospores are intermingled, many conjugations between cells occur, giving rise to perfectly normal vegetative cells.

All these facts can be explained in terms of the nuclear condition of the cells. The normal vegetative cell is diploid and by budding it produces a continuous succession of diploid cells, but when converted into an ascus, it produces its ascospores as a result of meiosis. When the ascospores germinate, the small round cells are haploid and exist as two strains which must fuse to reconstitute the normal vegetative diploid cell.

It can be regarded as an alternation of generations in which the diploid sporophyte, the vegetative cell, produces spores which are haploid and these then germinate to give the gametophyte generation, which by fusion of two cells once more produces the sporophyte generation. A similar condition arises in some other fungi.

Not all the yeasts exhibit the condition shown by *S. cerevisiae*. In many, the vegetative cells are haploid and ascospores are only produced by the conjugation of two such cells. A short conjugation tube unites the two cells and the two nuclei come together and fuse. This is immediately followed by meiosis to produce four nuclei (sometimes eight), and these then become ascospores. The released ascospores then germinate into normal vegetative cells which are haploid. The yeast *Schizosaccharomyces octosporus* illustrates this condition.

In other cases, such as *Saccharomyces ludwigi*, the vegetative cells are diploid and produce four ascospores by meiosis. These immediately fuse in pairs within the ascus to reconstitute the diploid generation. The difference between this and *S. cerevisiae* lies in the fact that in the latter, the ascospores never fuse within the ascus. The life cycle of *S. cerevisiae* is summarized below.

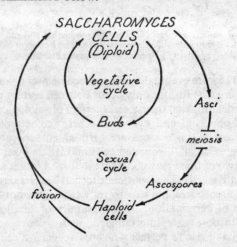

A proper understanding of the life histories of the yeasts has led to the artificial breeding of new strains, more suitable for their particular work in industry.

Physiology

Nutritional materials are obtained from non-living organic sources and growth is best made in solutions containing sugars, small quantities of nitrogenous materials and mineral salts, particularly phosphates. Pasteur's solution contains the following and will be found useful in growing yeast cultures—

Cane sugar	15·0 g
Ammonium tartrate	1·0 g
Dipotassium hydrogen phosphate	0·2 g
Calcium phosphate	0·02 g
Magnesium sulphate	0·02 g
Distilled water	100 cm³

The main storage product of metabolism is glycogen, not starch as is the case with most plants. Simple monosaccharide sugars can be absorbed by the yeast cells directly from the solution, but more complicated carbohydrates must be converted to this state by enzymes. Invertase, produced by yeasts, converts cane sugar to glucose and fructose.

The yeasts are among the comparatively few organisms which can exist for lengthy periods in the absence of oxygen. For most living things the presence of oxygen is an essential to their respiratory activities and in its absence they quickly die; they are obligate aerobes. A few bacteria, on the other hand, are quickly killed in the presence of oxygen; they are obligate anaerobes. The yeasts, whilst living normally as aerobes and obtaining their energy by processes involving the use of atmospheric oxygen, can, if the substrate is rich in carbohydrate, derive enough energy from its breakdown without resorting to the use of oxygen; they are facultative anaerobes.

The normal course of energy release by aerobic organisms can be summed up briefly as—

carbohydrate (monosaccharide sugar) $\rightarrow$ pyruvic acid $\rightarrow$
carbon dioxide+water $+ 2·87 \times 10^3$kJ

Only the breakdown of the pyruvic acid necessitates the use of oxygen. The whole may be represented by the equation

$$C_6H_{12}O_6 + 6O_2 = 6CO_2 + 6H_2O + 2·87 \times 10^3 kJ$$

In the absence of oxygen, yeasts can bring about the breakdown of carbohydrate as follows—

sugar $\rightarrow$ pyruvic acid $\rightarrow$ carbon dioxide + ethyl alcohol $+ 1·09 \times 10^3$kJ

This may be represented by the equation

$$C_6H_{12}O_6 = 2CO_2 + 2C_2H_5OH + 109 \times 10^3 kJ$$

Careful investigation of the two processes has shown that in all probability the breakdown (glycolysis) of carbohydrate to pyruvic acid follows identical steps and that most organisms are capable of carrying them out. How the pyruvic acid is subsequently dealt with depends upon the nature of the organism and the conditions obtaining. In the absence of oxygen, most animals convert the pyruvic acid to lactic acid which accumulates and brings about death quickly. In the presence of oxygen, animals eventually release carbon dioxide and water as a result of operating a cycle of oxidation-reduction reactions in which pyruvic acid is the key substance. A great deal more energy is released and the animal comes to no harm as the carbon dioxide is quickly eliminated in its external respiratory gaseous exchanges.

In the presence of oxygen, green plants and yeasts perform the same process, but in the absence of oxygen, the pyruvic acid is converted first to acetaldehyde with the evolution of carbon dioxide, and then to ethyl alcohol. To the ordinary green plant such products are toxic even in small quantities, and the organism soon dies. The yeast, however, is able to survive successfully in high concentrations of ethyl alcohol and will thus continue to live for long periods in the absence of oxygen as long as carbohydrate is in plentiful supply.

The enzyme complex known to be associated with the production of ethyl alcohol from sugar was first extracted from yeast and thought to be a single enzyme. It was called *zymase*. This is now known to be a mixture of numerous enzymes, each of which is specifically associated with a single step in the glycolytic process. Details of these enzymes and their activities in the anaerobic and aerobic respiratory processes will be found in Vol. II, Chap. 11.

The conversion of sugars to carbon dioxide and ethyl alcohol by yeast was once known by the name *alcoholic fermentation* and originally the term fermentation was applied to this process only. It is now used in a much wider sense to embrace any chemical change induced by a micro-organism.

The industrial use of yeasts depends upon their fermenting properties under anaerobic conditions. The alcohol is of value to the brewers and the carbon dioxide is of value to the bakers in causing bread to "rise."

In addition to its use as a fermenting organism, yeast is known to be a rich source of certain vitamins, and yeast extracts are used with great success in many disease conditions.

Wild Yeasts

Many species of *Saccharomyces* and allied genera exist in the wild state as soil micro-organisms where they obtain the necessary nutritional substances from dead remains of other plants and animals. Not infrequently, they are carried on to the surfaces of other organisms where they may be found in large numbers obtaining nourishment presumably from dead outer cells.

AGARICUS [PSALLIOTA]

This genus is representative of the basidiomycete fungi and has species among the best known of all fungi. The edible "mushrooms" are familiar examples. The species *A. campestris* (the field or common mushroom) is the one most prized, but the more coarsely growing *A. arvensis* (the horse mushroom) is also favoured. Mushroom cultivation is extensively practised and the species is *A. bisporus* although this may be only another form of *A. campestris*. Altogether there are some twenty recognized British species, differing largely in size, colour and form. The gigantic mushroom reported occasionally is *A. villatica*. The genus has been known for some time by the name *Psalliota* but by rules of nomenclature is now *Agaricus*. All the species are terrestrial and saprophytic in the soil. *A. campestris* will be described here.

Structure, Reproduction and Life History

The mycelium most frequently inhabits the soil of pastures in which horses have grazed, although this is not essential to its presence as long as the soil has a high organic content of the right kind. The separate hyphae are minute multicellular branching threads and the cells are multinucleate. The cell-wall material is fungal cellulose. The presence of the fungus only becomes apparent above ground, apart from its effect on other vegetation by the formation of "fairy rings," when the hyphae become tightly packed into solid masses to form the aerial spore-producing parts or *sporophores* ("*fructifications*"). These are the edible mushrooms and occur only at certain periods, usually in early autumn of each year. Close examination of the mycelium below ground shows that cells of adjacent hyphae very readily fuse together so that the whole mycelium forms an intricate meshwork. In most corresponding basidiomycete genera, there is a special system of intercellular connexions developed, whereby successive cells in the same hypha are in communication by short tubes. These are known as clamp-connexions (*see* Fig. 33.10 (*c*)). They do not occur in *Agaricus spp.* In most septate fungal hyphae, the cells are also in communication by a central pore in the septum through which there is cytoplasmic continuity. This is the condition in the species of *Agaricus*.

When sporophores are to be produced, the mycelium aggregates very densely at a few points and the hyphae become welded together into a pseudo-parenchymatous mass from which the sporophore parts quickly differentiate. Leading to this aggregation, and visible to the unaided eye, are numerous white strands known as *rhizomorphs*.

These are formed by the lateral union of numerous hyphae to form a thick cylindrical thread. The hyphae forming it lead in from all parts of the mycelium and undoubtedly serve to concentrate the food and growth substances necessary to the sporophore formation.

Reproduction is effected in nature only by the production of *basidio-spores*. The mushroom or sporophore is the only part of the mycelium

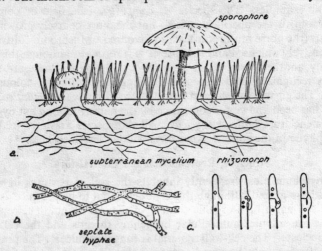

Fig. 33.10. *Agaricus campestris*. Vegetative and reproductive structures. (*a*) V.S. of mycelium bearing sporophores. (*b*) Portion of mycelium. (*c*) Formation of clamp connexions as seen in some basidiomycete fungi.

concerned with spore production and each year the energy of the fungus is concentrated into developing countless millions of spores.

The ripe sporophore appears as in Fig. 33.10 (*a*). There are two main parts, the *pileus* or cap and the *stipe* or stalk. The former is a circular disc turned down at the edges, about 10 cm across and supported at its centre on the underside by the latter. The whole forms an umbrella-like construction. The stipe is about 15 or so mm in diameter and may be hollow inside. It bears a distinct ring of tissue called the *annulus*, about half-way along. This is the broken edge of the cap still connected to the stipe, showing that in the early stages of development the two were united by a ring of tissue called the *veil*. In this stage the mushrooms are known to collectors as "buttons." On the upper surface, the cap is fairly smooth, often silky and whitish with tints of pinks or browns. On its under-surface, it is seen to suspend vertically a large number of individual sheets of tissue, known as *gills* or *lamellae*, radially arranged about the stalk (*see* Fig. 33.11 (*b*)). These vary in colour with age, turning from pale pink to deep purplish-brown or black. The gills are arranged so that all have a common starting point at the circumference of the cap, but only some extend fully in to the stipe. Those that do, are not joined to the stipe, a condition described as *free*. The gill relations with the stipe, and spore colour, are useful identification points in many of the basidiomycete fungi. Between the gills forming full radii, are shorter ones extending only about half- or

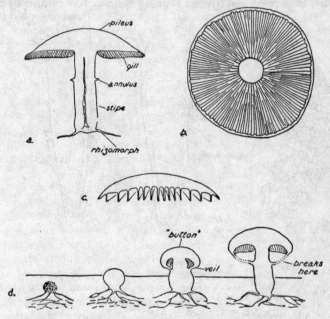

Fig. 33.11. *Agaricus campestris.* Morphology of the sporophore. (*a*) V.S. sporophore. (*b*) View of pileus from below. (*c*) Tangential V.S. of pileus. (*d*) Stages in formation of a sporophore.

quarter-way inwards from the edge. This is consistent with maximum gill production with all the gills more or less equally spaced.

Development of the sporophore is shown in Fig. 33.11 (*d*). From a pseudo-parenchymatous mass, the stipe and cap are rapidly differentiated, the two being in one piece joined by the veil. Inside the cap region, some tissue in the gill chamber called the *hymenial tissue*, gives rise to the gills. Full size is reached very rapidly (24–36 hours) and rapid elongation of the stipe, coupled with expansion of the cap, ruptures the veil to form the annulus on the stipe and leave the cap with a broken edge.

Microscopic examination of any part of the stipe and cap, except the gills, shows its pseudoparenchymatous construction throughout (*see* Fig. 33.12 (*a*)). The outermost layers are more densely compacted, thicker walled and form a protective rind over the whole structure except the gills.

A vertical section through a gill shows a different construction (*see* Fig. 33.12 (*b*)). The central part or *trama* of each gill is composed of somewhat loosely-packed hyphae running more or less parallel to one

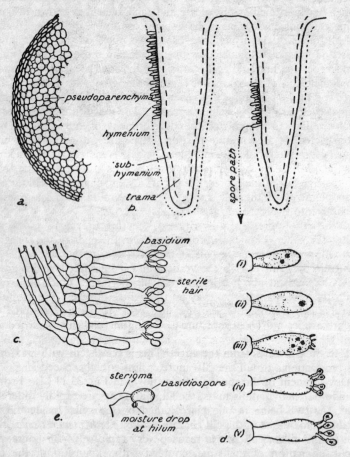

Fig. 33.12. *Agaricus campestris.* Anatomy of the sporophore and basidiospore formation. (*a*) T.S. stipe. (*b*) V.S. gills (L.P. plan). (*c*) Hymenium. (*d* (i) to (v)) Stages in formation of batidiospores. (*e*) Spore at discharge.

another but turning outwards towards the lateral surfaces where the cells are smaller, binucleate and more closely packed to form a *subhymenial layer*. On this layer are produced sterile *paraphyses* or hairs intermingled with club-shaped, binucleate, spore-producing *basidia*. Each of the latter eventually produces at its distal end, four *basidiospores*, each on a short *sterigma*. The cultivated mushroom produces two spores per basidium only.

A basidium produces spores as a result of nuclear fusion within the cell and subsequent division of the fusion nucleus. Each basidium, when newly formed, is binucleate and each nucleus is known to possess nine chromosomes. This is the haploid condition and is the condition of all nuclei of the mycelium. These two nuclei in the basidium now fuse to form a diploid nucleus with eighteen chromosomes. This quickly undergoes the first and second meiotic divisions to produce four haploid nuclei and at the same time four fine sterigmata are developed at the free end of the basidium. Into each of these a nucleus passes and at the tip of each a rounded swelling appears. The nucleus finally moves into the swelling to commence the development of the spore. This is constricted off as a minute pyriform structure with a purplish-brown outer pigmented wall. To one side at its base is a small projection known as the *hilum*. The change in colour of the gills as a whole is partly due to the ripening of the spores, but in part also, to changes in colour of the sap pigments of the gill trama. The nucleus in each spore usually divides into two before it is shed.

When the spores are fully ripened, they are shot away quickly one after the other, like small projectiles, from the ends of the sterigmata into the space between the gills. Gradually, as a spore loses momentum, its trajectory moves into the vertical and it falls freely under gravity. This happens at about 0·1 mm from the sterigma. Once clear of the gills the spores are borne away on the lightest breeze. The propulsion mechanism is not fully clear, but just prior to being discharged each spore exudes a drop of moisture at the hilum, and this is carried away with the spore. The discharge mechanism may be the sudden rounding off of the flat cross-walls between the sterigma and the spore. A single sporophore may produce thousands of millions of spores over the very large hymenial surface of the gills.

The success of the whole spore-dispersal mechanism depends upon the gills being perfectly vertical, being spaced sufficiently apart so that the spores fall free, and in being elevated enough for them to clear surrounding vegetation. If this were not so, many of the spores would be caught up in the gills as they fell. The gills are kept vertical by geotropic responses made by themselves and the stipe. They are elevated by growth of the stipe and are also protected by being on the underside of the cap, a condition which is necessary since the basidia are easily destroyed by too much moisture.

Of the many millions of spores produced, only a few can develop after being shed. How they establish themselves as mycelia in nature is not understood, but from culture experiments it is known that they will germinate only after a period of some days and best in the presence of another mushroom mycelium. It is known that the fungus is homothallic since a mycelium produced from a single spore is capable of developing fructifications. There is no doubt that the mycelia produced by different spores intermingle and unions between them are readily effected. The homothallic condition is not usual in basidiomycete fungi; they are generally heterothallic. In species of the genus *Coprinus* for example, the mycelium produced by one spore must unite with that of another spore of a different strain with which it is compatible, before sporophores can be developed. The life cycle of *A. campestris* is summarized below. (The diagram shows the old name, *Psalliota*.)

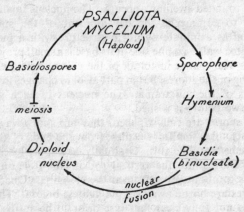

Physiology

The fungus lives saprophytically on the organic matter in the soil but can be grown, although only vegetatively, on a suitable culture medium. This must include a source of carbon, glucose, a source of nitrogen, urea, and various inorganic substances including the sulphates and phosphates of calcium, potassium and magnesium, with traces of iron, zinc, copper and manganese also.

The effects of the presence of the mycelium in a pasture can be seen as "fairy rings." These show up as regions of vigorous growth of the grasses against a less vigorous background. If a ring is examined, it can be seen to show a zonation. Centrally, growth of the grass is normal, then follows a zone of depressed or even no growth of the grasses and immediately outside this occurs the luxuriant growth zone which merges into the region outside the ring. The ring is caused by the continual outward advance of the mycelium through the soil and its subsequent death in the more internal parts. The vigorous growth ring is due to the presence of the young mycelium actively breaking down organic matter to release ammonia on which nitrifying bacteria can work. This increases the nitrate content of the soil to the advantage of the grasses. The region of depressed growth inside is probably due to

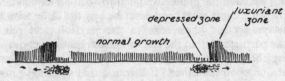

Fig. 33.13. V.S. of soil in region of "fairy ring."

the older mycelium having robbed the soil of much of its nutriment and having upset the water relations of the soil so that it becomes very dry in times of drought. If the speed of advance of a mycelium through the soil is measured, the diameter of the ring will give its age. Some fairy rings on Salisbury Plain are estimated to be several hundreds of years old.

Light seems to play no part in the life of the fungus, but some parts, particularly the stipe and gills, show very marked geotropic responses. The stipe is strongly negatively geotropic, and grows vertically from any position during development. Since the cap is set in a plane at right angles to the stipe, the gills are roughly vertical in any case, but each shows strong positive geotropism, and by differential growth at its junction with the cap, will set itself perfectly in the vertical plane. These responses ensure that the spores are free to fall into the air below the cap. It is possible that the growth curvatures of both stipe and gills are due to redistribution of auxins in the tissues as in higher plants, but there is no definite information available as is the case for some lower fungi, which are known to produce β-indolyl acetic acid (*see* Vol. II, Chap. 16).

CHAPTER 34

SYMBIOTIC UNIONS

THE study of lichens by Schwendener, Rees and others first led de Bary to his conception of a mutually beneficial association between two organisms. He gave the name *symbiosis* to such an association. Since then, many other cases have been described by the same term but there is not always a clear knowledge of the physiological relationships between the partners. Often the test of mutual benefit can only be made by growing the partners separately and by judging the effects of the absence of one upon the other. It is found that within the many cases of co-existence usually referred to as symbiotic, there is a wide degree of variation in the interdependence of the partners. Many cases border on commensalism, others on parasitism by one partner under control of the other, whilst many show so complete an interdependence as to be inseparable.

Here will be described a number of examples of the condition, illustrating the wide variety of organisms which may be involved.

THE LICHENS: AN ALGA–FUNGUS PARTNERSHIP

The lichens are the most universally distributed of all plants and may grow naturally in cold, exposed and dry positions which cannot be inhabited by other living things. Enormous tracts of mountain and arctic regions may be populated by nothing else, whilst in warmer regions, the lichens are well able to maintain an existence on bare rock, stones, bark of trees, sandy wastes and even on pebbles of the sea shore.

Morphologically, the thallus or vegetative body may be described as being of one of three kinds (*see* Fig. 34.1). The *crustaceous* lichens are the encrusting, flattened structures found chiefly on rocks, soil surfaces and tree bark. Examples include the genera *Xanthoria*, *Lecanora*, *Physcia* and *Rhizocarpon*. The *foliose* or leafy lichens are more spreading, with often many lobed leaf-like expansions. They include the common genera *Peltigera*, *Parmelia* and *Cladonia*. The *fruticose* or shrubby lichens show an upright habit of many branches rising from a single attachment. Typical examples are *Usnea* and *Ramalina*. Most lichens never attain great size, the thallus dimensions usually not more than a few centimetres, but some tropical epiphytic fruticose forms, hanging from trees, can reach a few metres in length.

Internal structure is variable in showing a dorsi-ventral arrangement of parts in the crustaceous and foliose lichens and a radial arrangement in the fruticose forms. There are always present both algal cells, termed *gonidia*, and fungal hyphae. A section through the thallus of

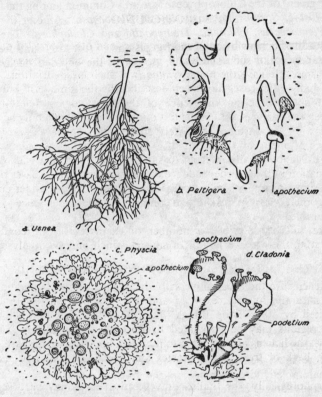

Fig. 34.1. Lichen forms. (*a*) Fruticose, *Usnea*. (*b*) Foliose, *Peltigera*. (*c*) Crustaceous, *Physcia*. (*d*) Foliose, *Cladonia*.

Physcia is shown in Fig. 34.2. The structure is described as *heteromerous* since the algal cells are more or less confined to a distinct layer among the fungal hyphae. In some cases the algal cells are evenly distributed and the structure is then said to be *homoiomerous* as in *Collema*.

The fungal partner in British lichens is always an ascomycete fungus, not identifiable as a free-living species. The fungus has undergone some change in nature, and attempts to isolate and grow the fungus under natural conditions away from its algal partner have not succeeded. In one instance with the tropical lichen, *Cora*, the fungus has been grown independently and was proved to be a normally saprophytic basidiomycete, *Thelephora sp.*

The algal partner belongs to one of two groups, the Cyanophyceae (blue-green) or the Chlorophyceae (green). Common among the former are *Nostoc*, *Scytonema*, *Rivularia* and *Gloeocapsa*. Among the latter are *Pleurococcus*, *Chlorella*, *Trentepohlia* and *Cladophora*. The algae can readily be grown free of the fungus and in fact are found free, but can rarely make such successful growth in the exposed positions in

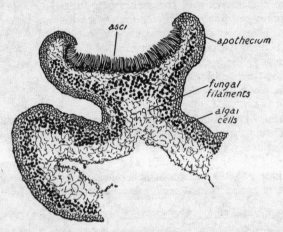

Fig. 34.2. Lichen anatomy. Heteromerous structure of *Physcia* with apothecium.

which they are found as lichen elements. The fungus and the alga therefore must benefit mutually to be able to co-exist in otherwise uninhabitable environments.

The advantages conferred one upon the other are nutritional and in conservation of water supplies in the exposed positions. The green cells function photosynthetically and can produce carbohydrate. The fungal hyphae are able to absorb water and minerals from the substratum, where they can penetrate it, or from the atmosphere where they cannot. The fungus can also conserve water supplies because of its thick-walled, sometimes gelatinous nature, and the compactness of its growth. That the fungus withdraws food material from the alga is borne out by the fact that lichen-fungi sometimes develop haustorial intracellular growths and will digest the contents of dead algal cells.

Reproduction in the lichens is of two kinds. There is a common vegetative process in which small bodies called *soredia* are developed in large numbers. These consist of a few algal cells invested by some fungal filaments and form the greyish, dusty powder so easily removed from lichen surfaces. Each soredium, possessing both alga and fungus can give rise to a new plant under suitable conditions. Sometimes the lichen thallus is differentiated into structures specially concerned with soredium development.

Sexual reproduction occurs in the fungal partner only. In British lichens, asci are developed usually containing eight ascospores, and these may be enclosed by a perithecium or apothecium characteristic of the ascomycete fungi. The ascospores germinate readily enough when dispersed but unless contact is quickly made with the correct algal partner, the hyphae soon die. Very frequently, the spore-bearing structures form characteristic fructifications on the lichen thallus as in *Cladonia*, where the *podetia* are easily recognized (*see* Fig. 34.1 (*d*)).

Fig. 34.3. Lichen soredium.

The lichens have assumed some economic importance for several reasons. They may form a valuable human food source as in *Cetraria islandica* (Iceland moss). Reindeer feed very largely on the species *Cladonia rangiferina*, whilst snails and slugs will readily eat many different kinds. The extraction of lichen-acids is also important. The dye, litmus, extracted from *Rocella tinctoria* is universally known.

CONVOLUTA–ALGA: AN ANIMAL–PLANT RELATIONSHIP

Convoluta roscoffensis is a small marine turbellarian, 3 mm long and 0·25 mm broad. It is found on the sandy beaches of Normandy and Brittany where the olive-green colonies are conspicuous on the sand just above low-water mark. At low tide, the animals lie exposed on the surface, but they bury themselves in the sand as soon as it is covered by the incoming tide. The green colour is due to regular rows of unicellular green algae which lie just beneath the surface (*see* Fig. 34.4).

The worms are hermaphrodite but cross-fertilized. They produce transparent egg-capsules about the size of a pin's head, each containing eight to twelve eggs. These capsules are manufactured of slime secreted by epidermal glands around the region where the eggs are extruded. Neither the capsules nor the eggs contain algae at this stage. The larvae hatch in twenty-four to thirty-six hours and move around inside the capsule. Within four days, they possess the algal cells and finally emerge from the capsule in five or six days.

The algae belong to the genus *Carteria* of the Chlamydomonadineae. They possess four flagella, a reticulate chloroplast, a pyrenoid, and a red pigment spot. The main storage product resulting from their photosynthesis is starch; it can be demonstrated as a sheath surrounding the pigment spot (*see* Fig. 34.5). It seems that these algae are attracted by traces of nitrogenous substances present in the egg capsule. They penetrate into it and form cysts within which multiplication takes place. When the cysts burst, the tiny flagellate cells are taken up by the larvae and thenceforward they multiply in its body by binary fission.

For the animal, the partnership is an obligate symbiosis, but the plant cells can exist free in the water. They secrete droplets of fat and

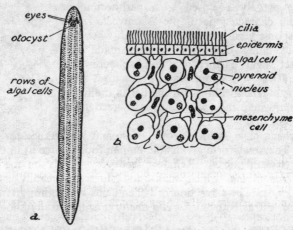

Fig. 34.4. *Convoluta roscoffensis.* (*a*) Dorsal view. (*b*) V.S. showing algal cells.

possibly protein also, into the body of the worm, and the oxygen they produce during photosynthesis is also of benefit to the animal. Unlike all other turbellarian genera, *Convoluta* has no organs for nitrogenous excretion but the algal cells provide an excellent substitute. It may be recalled that nitrogen compounds are in short supply in the sea, and these symbiotic algae find in these animals an adequate supply. The excretory carbon dioxide of the animal is also utilized for photosynthesis by the plants.

During its larval stages, the animal ingests a variety of solid food particles, though no true gut is ever present, the mouth and gullet leading into a series of intercellular spaces which serve as digestive vacuoles. When mature, it loses the ability to feed itself and thenceforward it relies entirely upon the algae. In the last phase of existence, it digests its partners and then dies. There is therefore, a true symbiotic union for a limited period during which the animal reproduces prolifically. All the plant cells are inevitably destroyed and thus derive no ultimate benefit from the association.

Another turbellarian, *Convoluta paradoxa*, is found in the same regions as *C. roscoffensis*, clinging to seaweeds in and near the low-water mark. They are solitary animals, golden-brown in colour, about 2·75 mm long and 0·75 mm wide (*see* Fig. 34.6). Living symbiotically

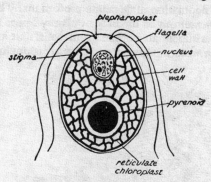

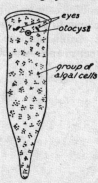

Fig. 34.5. *Carteria sp.* symbiotic with *C. roscoffensis*.

Fig. 34.6. *Convoluta paradoxa*. Dorsal view.

in their bodies, are small brown algal cells, also able to exist independently. Their arrangement in the body of the worm is rather more irregular than that found in *C. roscoffensis*. Here, the general sequence of events and the nature of the union are much the same except that the worms do not appear to digest the algal cells in natural conditions. Also, *C. paradoxa*, even when mature, does take in solid food particles. The worm's dependence on the algae has not advanced as far as the condition found in *C. roscoffensis*.

TERMITE–TRICHONYMPHID: AN ANIMAL–ANIMAL RELATIONSHIP

The termites, which constitute the insect order Isoptera, are remarkable in two respects. In the first place, they have evolved a degree of social organization which exceeds even that of the hive bees, and secondly, although the major part of their diet consists of wood, they are unable to digest it. The main constituent of wood is cellulose, but there are also small quantities of sugars and nitrogenous substances. It has been pointed out previously (*see* Chap. 29) that very few living organisms are able to digest cellulose. Its breakdown involves the following two stages—

$$\underset{\text{cellulose}}{2(C_6H_{10}O_5)_n} + n.H_2O \overset{\text{enzyme cytase}}{\rightleftharpoons} \underset{\text{cellobiose}}{n.C_{12}H_{22}O_{11}}$$

$$\underset{\text{cellobiose}}{C_{12}H_{22}O_{11}} + H_2O \overset{\text{enzyme cellobiase}}{\rightleftharpoons} \underset{\text{glucose}}{2C_6H_{12}O_6}$$

The two enzymes occur together in most cases. Termites will thrive o[n]
a diet of cotton-wool, but not if the last traces of nitrogenous substance[s]
are removed.

It is now known that the termites can exist only by reason of th[e]
presence of a flourishing gut population of flagellate protozoans. Thes[e]
all belong to the genus *Trichonympha* of the order Polymastigina, an[d]
are probably the most highly differentiated of the Protozoa. There are [a]
number of species of *Trichonympha*, ranging from 50μm to 360μm long.

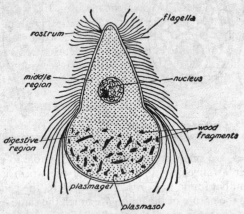

Fig. 34.7. Optical section of a trichonymphid.

all are pear-shaped. The body is divisible into three regions; a taperin[g]
anterior rostrum, a middle bell-like region, and a swollen bulbo[us]
posterior portion. There are numerous flagella of various length[s]
arranged in longitudinal grooves. The posterior bears none but it [is]
overlapped by a fringe of long flagella originating in the middle zo[ne]
(*see* Fig. 34.7). Longitudinal ridges traverse the firm pellicle beneat[h]
which the plasmagel consists of five successive layers. First, there is [a]
layer of basal granules of the flagella and then a series of obliqu[e]
myonemes. Beneath this is a layer which appears to consist of minu[te]
foamy bubbles, followed by a transverse series of myonemes. Finall[y]
abutting on the plasmasol are the longitudinal myonemes. The so[ft]
central region contains the nucleus and ventrally there are ma[ny]
vacuoles containing minute portions of wood. There is no gullet, t[he]
particles being engulfed posteriorly by temporary cup-like indentatio[ns]
produced by the action of the myonemes. In this posterior region, t[he]
plasmagel has a very simple structure.

The exact nature of the relationship between termite and trich[o]
nymphid is not certain, but both are obligate symbionts, and neith[er]

an live without the other. If the termites are heated to a temperature of 40°C, they are not harmed but the trichonymphids are destroyed. Thereafter, though the termites continue to ingest food, they cannot digest it and eventually die.

From the symbiosis, the termites obtain their essential dietary requirements, probably by digesting the trichonymphids. The protozoa get their food from the termite's gut and have, in addition, shelter and a suitable environment. They reproduce there, both by binary fission, and in some cases at least, by sexual means also. It is worthy of note that only the worker termites ingest such obstinate pabulum as wood and paper. All other adults and the larvae are fed by the workers on regurgitated and partly-digested material. During ecdysis, the workers lose most if not all of the trichonymphids, whereupon they replenish the supply by anal feeding from other termites.

LEGUMINOUS PLANT–BACTERIA RELATIONSHIP: ROOT NODULES

Reference is made in Vol. II, Chap. 10, to this symbiotic union in connexion with its effect on soil fertility. This has been recognized and utilized by man for many hundreds of years. The early Greeks knew the value of rotating legumes with other crops. The true nature of the effect has been worked out only within the last seventy-five years.

The partners concerned are members of the flowering plant family Papilionaceae [Leguminosae] and the bacterium *Rhizobium leguminosarum* [*Bacillus radicicola*] [*Pseudomonas radicicola*]. Only certain strains of the bacterium can unite with a particular species of legume and altogether there are about seven groups of legumes recognized as forming effective unions with seven different strains of the bacterium.

The micro-organism exists freely in the soil in a non-motile coccoid (spherical) form for most of its time, but when in proximity with the roots of a leguminous plant, an oval uniflagellate motile condition is formed which effects penetration of the root. It appears that the changes undergone by the bacterium are in response to some substance secreted by the roots. Penetration is made through root-hairs but from the numbers of recognizable infections, it is obvious that the event must be comparatively rare. After entry, the bacterium rapidly multiplies and changes form yet again to become multiflagellate and a deeper invasion into the cortical cells of the root occurs.

The effect of the presence of the bacterium in the root cortex is to stimulate the cells to very active division and in the immediate vicinity of infection a tuberous swelling or nodule appears on the root (*see* Fig. 34 8). The bacteria possibly secrete a substance of the nature of β-indolyl acetic acid to cause this rapid proliferation of cells by the root. Internally, the nodule can be seen to be composed of a central mass of large cortical cells containing great numbers of the bacteria in still yet another form. This is the "banded-rod" form of various Y and T shapes and the structures are known as *bacteroids*. The banded appearance becomes apparent only in stained preparations and as yet there is no clear explanation of the condition. Surrounding the central

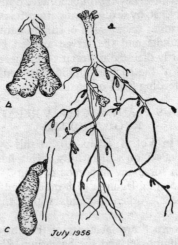

July 1956

Fig. 34.8. Root nodules on clover. (*a*) Root system. (*b*) and (*c*) Nodules (enlarged).

mass is a layer of uninfected tissue, some parts of which are differentiate into vascular tissues continuous with those of the main root (*se* Fig. 34.9). At the distal end of the nodule, a zone of cells retains it meristematic activity for some time and the nodule gradually increase in size. As more cells from this region differentiate, they becom infected by the bacteria. As a nodule ages, each bacterium-infecte cell vacuolates and the bacteroids become densely crowded at the ce periphery. They then digest the cell contents and attack the cell wal The nodule gradually breaks away from the root to disintegrate an release the bacteria into the soil.

The alliance is undoubtedly beneficial to both participants from nutritional standpoint. The higher plant is able to assimilate carbo dioxide and the bacterium benefits from this by obtaining carbohydrate from the root cells. The bacterium is able to fix atmospheric nitroge into an organic form some of which becomes available to the legume For the nitrogen fixation mechanism *see* Vol. II, Chap. 10.

The effect of cutting off the carbohydrate supply to the bacteria by growing the legume in the dark, is to convert the bacteria into active parasites, which dissolve the cell walls of the host and obtain

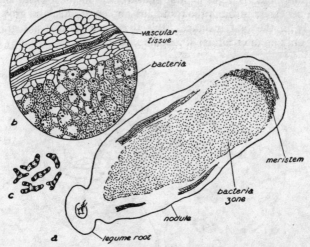

Fig. 34.9. Structure of root nodule and symbiotic bacterium. (*a*) T.S. root and nodule (L.P. plan). (*b*) Portion of nodule (H.P. drawing). (*c*) Banded rod form of bacterium.

carbohydrate in that way. From such observations it might be conjectured that the association could originally have been a parasitic one, but under natural conditions has become one of almost perfect symbiosis.

HIGHER PLANT—FUNGUS PARTNERSHIPS: MYCORRHIZAL ASSOCIATIONS

The term mycorrhiza describes the association between the roots of a higher plant and a fungal mycelium. Such associations exist almost invariably between fungi and the roots of deciduous and coniferous forest trees, quite commonly between a fungus and a herbaceous plant, and is the permanent condition in some orchids and heath plants. In the case of the trees, the fungal growth is always restricted to the roots, but in others the fungus frequently spreads through all parts of the plant, a condition which is then termed *mycotrophic*. A mycorrhiza may be described as *ectotrophic* (*ectophytic* fungus) when the roots are merely enveloped in a covering of fungal hyphae, and *endotrophic* (*endophytic* fungus) when the hyphae actually persist inside the root cortical cells. The ectotrophic mycorrhizae of the forest trees are clearly recognizable as variations from normal root development. The lateral rootlets lose their ability to elongate and assume a stunted swollen appearance referred to as "coralloid" (*see* Fig. 34.10). The ectotrophic mycorrhiza is at first endotrophic in most cases since the hyphae penetrate through the root hairs and epidermis, and grow intracellularly in the first instance. But these are soon disintegrated to remain only as intercellular filaments in the cortex, where they form a

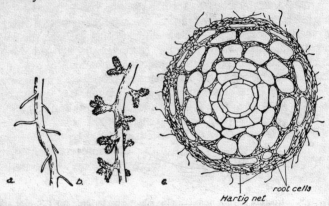

Fig. 34.10. Mycorrhizal association. (*a*) Normal root. (*b*) Root with ectophytic fungus. (*c*) T.S. root with ectotrophic mycorrhiza.

close meshwork between the cells referred to as the *Hartig net* (*see* Fig. 34.10). It is from this that the external hyphae are then developed to encase the root.

The endotrophic mycorrhizae of some orchids and heathers show less readily on the outer surfaces, but internally the fungal hyphae enter the cells of the root cortex where they persist as tightly massed coils or *pelotons* which may give rise to vesicular structures known as *arbuscules*. These eventually break down into shapeless masses. It is noticeable that in many endotrophic cases, the fungal penetration is restricted to a distinct zone of the outer cortex beyond which the fungus cannot penetrate successfully (*see* Fig. 34.11). The root cells internal to this are called "digestive" and have the ability to destroy the fungus as soon as it penetrates them.

The fungi forming ectotrophic mycorrhizae with the forest trees are chiefly saprophytic basidiomycetes and include most, if not all, the woodland gill- and pore-bearing toadstools. The genera *Russula*, *Amanita*, *Boletus*, *Lactarius*, *Clitocybe* and *Rhizopogon* are typical examples. An ascomycete, *Tuber* (truffle), is also known to be associated with oak and beech trees.

The fungi forming endotrophic mycorrhizae with the orchids are usually sterile species of *Rhizoctonia* (a genus called *Corticium* in its fertile stages) but a peculiar condition arises in the Japanese orchid, *Gastroda elata*, in which the association is with the otherwise serious parasite *Armillaria mellea*, the honey agaric. The parasite seems to be under control in the orchid which reacts to its presence by producing

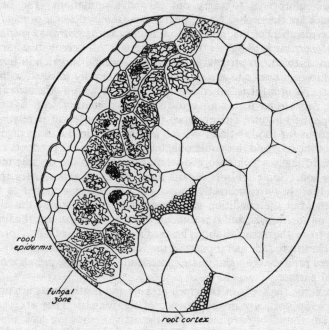

Fig. 34.11. Mycorrhizal association. Endophytic fungus in root cells. H.P. drawing.

a flowering shoot, something it is unable to do in the absence of the fungus.

The heathers and lings are generally associated with species of *Phoma*, and in most such cases the fungus extends throughout the plant even into the fruits. Some of the orchids also show this mycotrophic condition.

Other plants are sometimes involved with the fungi in partnerships and attention is drawn to the condition of the gametophytes of some of the species of *Lycopodium*, which cannot develop in the absence of the appropriate fungus.

It is not always easy to account for the physiological relationships between the partners of a mycorrhiza. The precise effects of the association differ in different cases but the general concensus of opinion is to regard them as symbiotic unions. The higher plant at least, appears to benefit almost invariably in those cases investigated. The most outstanding cases of the reliance of the higher plant on the fungus are to be seen in those instances in which the higher plant is unable through lack of chlorophyll to carry out carbon assimilation. The British examples are the orchid *Neottia nidus-avis* (the bird's-nest orchid) and the two members of the family, Monotropaceae, *Monotropa hypopithys*, and *Monotropa hypophegea* (the bird's-nests). All perennate as underground rhizomatous structures in moist woodland soil rich in humus. The rhizomes bear clusters of stumpy roots heavily infected with the fungus. *Neottia* forms an endotrophic alliance with a *Rhizoctonia sp.* whilst *Monotropa* forms an ectotrophic combination with a similar saprophytic fungus. The evidence that the higher plant is relying on the fungus for food is clear. Starch accumulates in the inner digestive zone of the root and this could only have come from the products of the digested fungus which absorbed its nutriment from the organic matter in the soil. Some authors regard these plants as saprophytes in the sense that they are indirectly converting dead organic matter to their own use, but the condition is one nearer to parasitism by the higher plant on the fungus, and it is difficult to see what advantage the fungus gains from the association. The bird's-nests and bird's-nest orchid are able to produce aerial parts in the form of inflorescences only, and the seed produced can germinate successfully only in the presence of the fungal partner.

Similarly, the seeds of the green orchids and heath plants are unable to develop normally in the absence of the fungus. They are usually very small and often undeveloped themselves, showing lack of food reserves. The fungi undoubtedly supply some of the nutritional requirements in the early stages of the germination. The same seed can be grown normally in the absence of the fungus, in specially prepared culture media containing sugars, among other organic substances. In the case of the orchids, the fungal association is restricted to the roots and new associations must be formed when the seeds germinate but in the case of the heathers such as *Calluna*, the fungus may even extend into the seed coats so that the germinating seeds are almost automatically infected from their earliest development. This is certainly the case in *Vaccinium* (whortleberry), in which the embryo itself may contain the fungus.

In the case of the forest trees the evidence shows an advantage gained by the higher plant. Digested fungal hyphae would undoubtedly add to the food material available to the tree, and some experiments have shown conclusively that without the fungus young conifer seedlings often fail to make normal healthy growth, or may even fail to establish themselves.

Another way in which a higher plant may be nutritionally aided by the fungus could be by nitrogen fixation on the part of the latter. Whilst the evidence for this at the moment is inconclusive it is not outside the bounds of possibility. The fungus *Phoma radicus-callunae* in association with *Calluna vulgaris* (common ling) has long been thought to be a nitrogen-fixing fungus. Still another possibility lies in the direct absorption by the higher plant of simple breakdown products of humus as a result of the saprophytic activity of the fungus, whilst still another may be that the presence of the fungal mycelium increases the rate of mineral salt absorption by the root by greatly increasing the absorptive area.

If the union is symbiotic, then some advantage must be gained by the fungus but this is often less easy to understand than the converse. It is generally held that the fungi receive carbohydrates in a suitable from from their partners and also very possibly certain accessory growth substances which many fungi are known to need. It is certainly the case that most of the fungi in association with trees form their fructifications profusely only in the near neighbourhood of the trees.

A rather different view of the relationship is that the mycorrhizae are unions of parasitic fungi with other plants in which the parasite is under strict control of the host. There are several indications that this may be so. Entrance to the host tissues by the fungus is usually by normal parasitic methods and often the host may show typical reaction and resistance to the infection. The ectotrophic mycorrhizae of forest trees afford examples. The fungus first invades the root hairs and outer cells of the root just as would a normal parasite, but the host rapidly destroys any intracellular hyphae, allowing only those between the cells to remain. The host cells also contain abnormal amounts of tannins, a condition often associated with fungal attacks in many plants. In the endotrophic cases, the fungus cannot penetrate the digestive zone without being destroyed and here again it may seem that the host is carefully regulating the advance of the fungus into the tissues.

OTHER SYMBIOTIC UNIONS

Apart from those previously described, there are many other examples of symbiosis. In certain groups, it is a very common phenomenon. Many protozoa have formed such partnerships with either green algae (Zoochlorellae) or brown algae (Zooxanthellae). In the Rhizopoda, many radiolarians and foraminiferans have such symbiotic unions with algal cells. The case of the phosphorescent flagellate *Noctiluca* is interesting. In tropical waters it always has algal partners and is green, but in colder water it is usually without them and is transparent. The case of *Chlorohydra* [*Hydra*] has been discussed in Chap. 10. Many coelenterates, especially the corals, show a similar condition.

None of the chordate animals possess the enzymes cytase and cellobiase and therefore they cannot digest cellulose which forms a large part of the diet of herbivores. It is doubtful whether they would survive without a flourishing gut flora and fauna consisting mainly of bacteria and flagellates which possess the requisite enzymes. The large caecum of the rabbit and the specialized paunch and rumen of cattle are examples of organs concerned with the activities of these micro-organisms. It is doubtful whether any cellulose is digested in the human gut.

CHAPTER 35

INSECTIVOROUS PLANTS: COMMENSALS; EPIPHYTES; EPIZOITES

THERE are several hundreds of species of plants of world-wide distribution which are able to trap, digest and absorb nutritive compounds from the bodies of insects and other small animals. This method of obtaining food is an addition to the normal photosynthetic process since the insectivorous plants possess chlorophyll. The mechanisms by which the prey is captured and subsequently treated show some variation and are among the most fascinating of all plant adaptations. All the species are included in a small number of flowering plant families and a few representative genera will be described here.

DROSERA: THE SUNDEW

This is a genus of the family Droseraceae with three British species, namely, *D. rotundifolia*, *D. anglica* and *D. intermedia* [*D. longifolia*]. All are inhabitants of damp, peaty localities. The plant has a rosette habit and each leaf forms an organ by which the insect is trapped and digested. Its upper surface bears a number of multicellular glandular hairs or tentacles which are long at the leaf margins and shorter in the centre (*see* Fig. 35.1). The whole leaf surface is always sticky due to secretory activity of other smaller glands, and the knob-like glandular ends of the tentacles secrete proteolytic enzymes capable of digesting the animal body. The same glands function also to absorb the decomposition products.

The reaction of the leaf on being stimulated by the presence of an insect is to bring about curvature of all the outer tentacles inwards towards the leaf centre, so that the insect is completely enmeshed. All the glands then vigorously secrete to form a large drop of fluid in which the animal is submerged. Charles Darwin showed that the curvature is partly chemonastic since it can be induced by liquid substances which contain nitrogenous material, but comparatively few others. But response to contact is also observed and similar results are obtained when a whole variety of solids are touched against the tentacles. The movements are growth curvatures of the tentacles and are caused by increased growth rate of the outer side of a tentacle, causing bending towards the leaf centre. The stimulus can be transmitted through the leaf, since if only one tentacle in the centre of the leaf is stimulated,

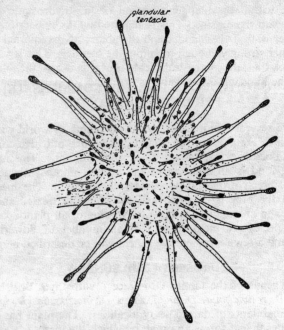

Fig. 35.1. Leaf of *Drosera rotundifolia*. Upper surface.

the more distantly-situated tentacles curve inwards. It is probable that the conduction of the excitation is hormonal and that an auxin is involved.

UTRICULARIA: THE BLADDERWORT

This is a genus of the family Lentibulariaceae and the four British species, *U. vulgaris*, *U. neglecta*, *U. intermedia* and *U. minor* are all rootless aquatics. Certain segments of the very finely-divided leaves become modified to form hair-lined bladders or utricles which are roughly ovoid and up to 3 mm in length (*see* Fig. 35.2). It is in these that tiny water animals are trapped and digested. Each bladder is on a short stalk and at the distal end there is an opening to the inside of the bladder, guarded by a door-like valve, which is hinged on one margin so that it can open inwards, but tends to remain closed to seal the aperture from the inside. From the outer surface of the valve arise a number of long fine hairs. If the bladder is ready to accept prey, pressure from outside on the valve or on its hairs, triggers open the valve, and the inflowing current of water carries with it small objects in the vicinity of the opening. In order that the mechanism can operate, there must be created within the bladder a region of low hydrostatic pressure compared with the outside. This is achieved by the impervious nature of the outer wall of the bladder and the ability of the internal hairs to absorb water strongly enough to empty the bladder. This is borne out by the fact that the outer walls cave inwards when the bladder is empty. The hingeing of the valve is arranged so that it remains shut

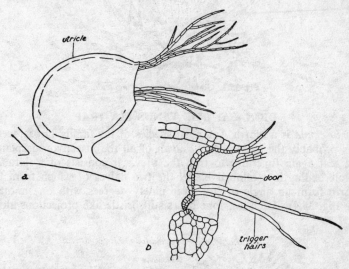

Fig. 35.2. (*a*) Bladder of *Utricularia sp.* (*b*) V.S. through "door."

unless subjected to inward pressure; it is made watertight by a membrane or velum which develops behind it.

Whether the prey captured by a bladder is killed and digested by the secretion of enzymes, is doubtful. It is more probable that the animal dies of starvation and is then decomposed by bacterial activity. The plant would still be able to benefit by absorbing some of the bacterial digestion products.

PINGUICULA: THE BUTTERWORT

This is another genus of the Lentibulariaceae with three British species, *P. vulgaris*, *P. lusitanica* and *P. grandiflora*. In these plants, the leaves are all more or less radical and form a rosette. Each leaf is roughly oval in shape with inrolled margins. On the upper surfaces are borne long-stalked multicellular glands which secrete a sticky fluid, to which small animals adhere on contact. Interspersed with these hairs are short-stalked glands with usually about eight cells forming the head (*see* Fig. 35.3). These secrete a digestive fluid and the products of digestion of the animal's body are absorbed through the leaf surface.

Fig. 35.3. Glands on leaf of *Pinguicula*.

DIONAEA: THE VENUS FLY-TRAP

D. muscipula is a North American species of the family Droseraceae. It is probably the most widely known of all the insectivorous plants. The leaf again functions to trap the prey. It consists of a flattened petiole ending in a bilobed blade, the two halves of which from the midrib form an angle of just over ninety degrees with one another (*see* Fig. 35.4). Each leaf lobe bears stiff bristle-like projections along

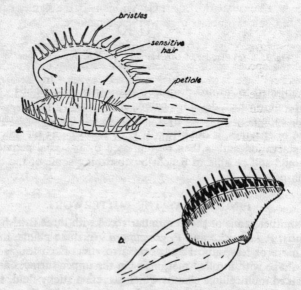

Fig. 35.4. Leaf of *Dionaea*. (*a*) Open. (*b*) Closed.

its margin and on its upper surface three sensitive hair-like processes standing stiffly upwards. The upper surface also bears other smaller glandular structures which give it a reddish colour.

When one of the sensitive hairs is touched by a small animal it serves as a stimulus to cause a rapid folding together of the two leaf lobes whose marginal spines interlock to form a tightly-closed trap. Normally a double stimulus is required to set the trap in motion, either two hairs must be touched or one touched twice within a period of about fifteen seconds. After the first rapid movement the leaf lobes squeeze together more slowly. The small glandular hairs on the surface discharge a digestive fluid which decomposes the animal so that absorption can be effected, and the leaf remains closed until this is complete. The leaf can also be stimulated by touch with other solid objects but the closing mechanism is fully effective only if the object contains nitrogenous materials, so that the response is in part chemonastic (see Vol. II, Chap. 16). A touch with a pencil, for instance, results in only partial closure of the trap followed by quick reopening, whereas a piece of meat induces a full response. The mechanism of closure is at first due to osmotic changes in the cells in the midrib region, and these changes can occur only as a result of the conduction of the excitation caused by the stimulus, from the sensitive hairs to the midrib. What form this conducting mechanism takes is not known. The later and slower part of the reaction, namely the tighter squeezing together of the leaf lobes, is a growth phenomenon.

NEPENTHES AND SARRACENIA: THE PITCHER-PLANTS

None of the species of these genera occur naturally in Great Britain. The "pitchers" are formed from modified leaves. In the *Nepenthes* species, only the terminal portion of the leaf is so modified. From a lowermost blade the midrib is continued as a tendril-like organ which then expands into a hollow container, closed when young by the ultimate tip of the leaf, but open when fully mature (see Fig. 35.5). The midrib subtending the pitcher may act as a tendril, and by coiling around neighbouring vegetation, support the pitcher and keep it upright. In the *Sarracenia* species, the whole leaf is modified into a long conical container, also closed by a lid when young (see Fig. 35.6).

In the lower half of a pitcher in *Nepenthes* is a watery fluid secreted by hairs on the walls, but above this, the wall is quite smooth and covered by minute waxy scales. The insect prey is presumably attracted by a sugary secretion of the lid, outer walls and mouth of the vessel, and having once crawled over the rim is unable to find foothold on the waxy scales which slide freely over one another, and so it drops into the fluid. Here, enzymes secreted by the pitcher, aided possibly by bacteria, digest the animal and nutritive compounds are absorbed. The pitchers of the *Sarracenia* plants function in a comparable way, as do those of the species *Cephalotus follicularis*, a native of Australia.

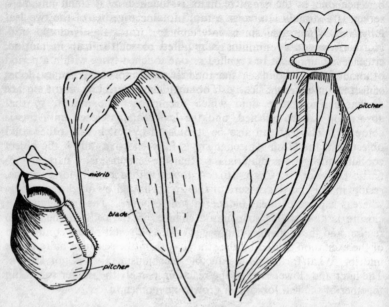

Fig. 35.5. Pitcher of *Nepenthes*.   Fig. 35.6. Pitcher of *Sarracenia*.

COMMENSALS

It was pointed out in Chap. 30, that organisms are to be regarded as commensals when, although habitually found in some spatial sort of alliance, they neither benefit nor harm one another physiologically. There are very numerous cases of commensalism in the animal kingdom; a few of the more familiar examples will be mentioned here.

Hermit-crabs inhabiting molluscan shells almost invariably carry commensals on the shells. There may be a group of sea-anemones which afford concealment and protection for the crab and themselves obtain transport, better oxygenation and possible particles of food floating up while the crab is feeding (*see* Fig. 35.7).

The colonial coelenterate *Hydractinia* favours whelk shells inhabited by hermit-crabs. Here, the zoophyte forms an encrusting mass on the carapace with the feeding polyps at the ends of short upright branches. The same benefits accrue to the partners as in the case of the sea-anemone.

Some species of sponge grow only on the carapace or larger appendages of certain crabs. The crab is somewhat concealed by the encrusting masses while the sponge obtains better oxygenation and possibly better feeding by change of habitat as the crab moves. The glass-rope sponge *Hyalonema* is always found in association with the zoophyte *Palythoa*. Commensalism is very common in sponges and the paragastric cavity often contains a great variety of small animals, principally crustaceans, annelids and molluscs.

Some large species of sea-anemone always contain a particular species of fish in the enteron. The fish obtains ideal protection and food but

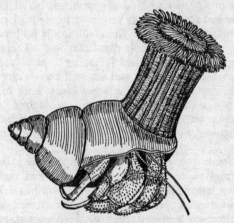

Fig. 35.7. Hermit crab and sea anemone.

the anemone does not seem to benefit in any way. Several small species of annelid worms normally live attached to the gills of crustaceans. *Histriobdella* utilizes the lobster and *Stratiodrilus* is found only in Australasian crayfishes. The worms have plenty of oxygen and a good supply of minute food particles in the respiratory current. In return, perhaps they clear some of the debris from the gills.

The mantle cavities of the larger bivalve molluscs often form the normal habitat for a variety of creatures. An example is found in the mussel, the commensal being the little pea-crab which finds ample food and shelter in its peculiar abode.

In addition to those mentioned, very large numbers of organisms must live commensally with one another, but many of these so regarded at the present time may well eventually be proved to be forming a relationship bordering more closely on parasitism or symbiosis. Such a case is that of the gut bacteria which occur in most animals. Exactly how far these intestinal organisms and the animals influence one another physiologically is not known in most cases, but from the use of antibiotic substances in animal rearing, it has become plain that interference with the relative numbers of the micro-organisms in the gut can have profound physiological effects on the young animal.

EPIPHYTES AND EPIZOITES

These are organisms which grow attached to and supported by other plant or animal bodies but which in no way establish relationships other than by external attachment; nor do they show any marked preference for one particular kind of supporting body. Such organisms are usually able to develop on any structure, dead or alive, which presents a satisfactory surface. The condition is well marked in many plants ranging through the whole plant kingdom. There are numerous instances of epiphytic algae in which smaller forms inhabit the surfaces of larger ones. Lichens and mosses are well-known epiphytes on trees and many pteridophytes, including some ferns, both in Great Britain and the tropics, use the same kind of support. Among flowering plants the best examples are the tropical epiphytic orchids which without any contact whatsoever with the soil, form a thickening to the overhead canopy.

Among animals the condition is perhaps rarer. Barnacles often establish themselves on crustacean carapaces and molluscan shells, though the association appears to be purely fortuitous. *Obelia* hydroids are almost invariably present on *Laminaria* fronds, and *Convoluta paradoxa* on fine seaweeds attached to the brown alga, *Pycnophycus*. The sucker-fish, *Remora*, is often associated with sharks, but perhaps just as frequently it may be found on any moving object including ships and more rarely, on human divers.

Associations between two types of organisms range through all grades, from the obviously accidental to the purposive and obligate. Often it is difficult to distinguish between commensalism, parasitism and symbiosis.

CHAPTER 36

BACTERIA, VIRUSES AND MYCOPLASMATALES

OF all living things, none are so small, so widely distributed or so numerous as the collection of microbes which form the subject of this chapter. Their influence on the affairs of the rest of the living world is unparalleled. If numbers and distribution are the criteria then the bacteria and their allies have long since out-stripped all others in the battle for supremacy.

The bacteria possess the characteristics common to all other living things. They are cellular, have a comparable metabolism and are large enough to be seen with a light microscope. It should be noted though that they form a heterogeneous collection of microbes and that the term *bacterium* should be applied to one group of them only. The bacteriophages and the viruses are units of organic substance of molecular dimensions, invisible with an ordinary light microscope and capable of passing through filters whose pores are small enough to stop all other living things. The terms "ultra-microbes" and "filter-passers" are often used to describe them. To continue their existence, the bacteriophages and viruses must have access to living cells and the former are distinguishable from the latter by reason of the fact that they multiply only in the protoplasm of bacterial cells, whereas the viruses inhabit a wide variety of plant and animal cells. It is only because they are self-perpetuating in the presence of the appropriate protoplasm that these ultra-microbes have been considered to be alive at all. It may well be that in fact they do not grow and reproduce themselves, but rather, by their presence, induce living protoplasm to duplicate their molecular structure by interfering with its normal metabolism. It is debatable therefore whether they should be considered as living things or merely as organic molecules with particularly striking influences on living protoplasm.

THE BACTERIA

It has been pointed out that the organisms usually called the bacteria and placed together in one class of the plant kingdom, the Schizomycetes, are a mixture of types. They may be classified into six orders, namely, the Eubacteriales (true bacteria), the Actinomycetales (the actinomycetes), the Chlamydobacteriales (the "iron-bacteria" and the colourless sulphur bacteria), the Myxobacteriales (slime bacteria), the Spirochaetales (the spirochaetes) and the Rickettsiales (the rickettsiae). In this section, only the true bacteria will be fully described.

There is little doubt that the first man to record the observation of such organisms was Leeuwenhoek, one of the earliest microscopists, who in the period 1676–83, described as minute "animalcules" certain motile bacteria which came to his notice in many of his preparations. He had no conception of their significance and was nearly two hundred years ahead of the eventual elucidation of their nature and origin. Pasteur, Koch and others succeeded in proving them to be living organisms in their own right, descended from organisms like themselves, and showed that they were the causative agents of putrefaction, fermentation and disease. It was also shown that their origin was not the result of a "spontaneous generation" due to chemical activity in dead protoplasm, an idea which had long been held.

Within the last seventy-five years, a tremendous amount of knowledge has been gained concerning the chemical activities of the bacteria in connexion with disease and other phenomena, but much less about their physical make-up. This is partly due to the influence of Pasteur, primarily a chemist, on later research workers, and partly because of the inability to improve the resolution of the light microscope so that they could be seen clearly. There is still much to be discovered concerning their true characteristics and relationships in many cases, but the subject of bacteriology has expanded so rapidly in this century that despite constant revision of opinion on many matters, the over-all picture has become fairly clear. As is always the case, new experimental techniques open up the way to new discoveries and no doubt within a few years much of what seems unaccountable at the present time will be explained.

Structure, Physiology and Reproduction

The bacteria are nearly all unicellular, of a variety of shapes and sizes, but always extremely small. The smallest spherical types measure as little as $0 \cdot 1 \mu m$ in diameter, whilst the largest of the rod forms measure no more than $20 \mu m$ long with a width of $1 \cdot 5 \mu m$.

The structure of the true bacterial cell is comparable with the plant cell. Surrounding the protoplast is a rigid cell wall, largely of polysaccharide substance, but rarely, if ever, pure cellulose. Fatty materials and proteins are often constituents and chitin occasionally occurs. This outer wall is sometimes modified to form a mucilaginous capsular structure which possibly serves to protect against desiccation. In certain instances, the capsules of many cells may run together to form a composite structure termed a *zoogloea*, in which many bacterial cells are cemented together by their gummy walls. In *Azotobacter*, as each generation of cells succeeds the previous one, the old capsules remain to enclose the ever-increasing mass in a slimy outer covering. It is not unlikely that all bacterial cells have some kind of moist outer envelope, but it is visible only in those instances where it is thick.

The cytoplasm does not appear to be of similar chemical constitution to that of plant cells, having much greater affinity for the basic dyes and thus resembling more closely the condition of a plant-cell nucleus. Within this background substance there may be granules of a material which has been described as true chromatin and this is regarded as the nuclear substance of the cell. There is seldom a single aggregate of chromatin material and thus the cell cannot be said to possess a normal nucleus. During fission of a cell, these granules have been observed in division and thus may be regarded as functioning in the same way as chromosomes. Other granular inclusions are chiefly food stores and include the polysaccharides, of which glycogen is the commonest, fats and protein compounds, and even sulphur particles in a few cases. The substance volutin, a compound of ribo-nucleic acid, is a common inclusion and indeed derives its name from the bacterium *Spirillum volutans* in which it occurs in great abundance. Pigmentation is not uncommon, though the majority are colourless. Bright red (*Serratia marcescens*), yellow (*Sarcina lutea*) and violet (*Bacillus violaceous*) tints, are due to carotenoid pigments which may serve a protective function by absorbing the shorter wavelengths (ultra-violet) of the radiations reaching the earth. The colourless bacteria are extremely susceptible to short-wave radiation and a short exposure to direct sunlight often proves lethal. Other pigments occurring in a few cases are the bacteriochlorophyll substances, one of which is purplish red and the other greenish. These are related to the chlorophyll pigments of the higher plants and function in the same way, but they are not located in plastids. They are evenly distributed in the cytoplasm, a condition similar to that found in the blue-green algae.

The protoplast is surrounded by a cell membrane which seems to be comparable with that of higher organisms. Bacterial cells can be plasmolysed in the same way as plant cells and in such a condition the protoplast is seen clearly separated from the cell wall.

When bacteria are viewed, they usually appear to be moving, but in many cases it is due to Brownian movement, as would be the case for any small suspended particles. Thus caution must be exercised in observation for motility. Those which are freely motile develop extremely fine, tenuous flagella often of considerable length in comparison with the cell size. These are protoplasmic and execute co-ordinated flexures similar to those observed in other flagellate organisms. The location of flagella is often a group characteristic. A bacterial cell is described as *monotrichous* when possessing a single flagellum at one end of the cell, *lophotrichous* when it has a single tuft of flagella at one end, and *peritrichous* when the flagella are distributed all over the cell surface. In many cases, only young cells are actively motile and as they age, the flagella may be shed.

To deal with the physiology of the bacteria comprehensively would need far more space than can be allowed here. A brief survey will be given, but attention is paid to the more important aspects of bacterial metabolism in later sections. They are chiefly heterotrophic, living either as saprophytes or as parasites, but a few are autotrophic and can synthesize their own protoplasm from simple raw materials, using energy derived from one of the two sources available. The photo-autotrophes utilize light energy and the chemo-autotrophes utilize energy released from chemical reactions. The former are the photo-synthesizers and the latter the chemosynthesizers. The heterotrophes have widely varying requirements of nutrients. They range from those needing comparatively simple materials, which may sometimes be inorganic substances in part, to those which are so exacting that only one particular organic environment providing highly complex organic compounds, will support their growth. These latter are chiefly the disease-causing parasites. The ability to use atmospheric nitrogen as a nitrogen source is a feature of a few groups of bacteria, and with the other organisms known to possess the same ability, these nitrogen-fixers play an outstanding part in the lives of other organisms.

In broad outline, the respiratory activity of bacterial cells seems to be comparable with that of all other organisms (*see* Vol. II, Chap. 11). There are those which can function in this respect only in the presence of oxygen; they are the obligate aerobes. Others can live only in the total absence of oxygen; they are the obligate anaerobes. Facultative anaerobes can live equally well with or without oxygen, whilst a few *micro-aerophilous* types can exist only under conditions of very low oxygen concentration, or none at all. The products of the fermenting activity of bacteria are often of commercial importance since many such compounds have never been artificially synthesized. Certain bacteria therefore are of use in industry and are employed in such processes as cheese and butter making, vinegar manufacture and in the production of butyl alcohol, acetone, glycerine and lactic and butyric acids. Their putrefactive ability makes them equally useful to man in such processes as hemp and flax retting in which the pectic compounds cementing the useful fibres together are broken down by bacterial activity.

The production of toxins, substances capable of poisonous effects on other living things, is characteristic of many types of bacteria. In many instances, the effects of these toxins produce the disease symptoms associated with parasitic attacks. Some of the products of metabolism of saprophytic bacteria are equally poisonous. The toxin produced by *Clostridium botulinum* in some decaying foods is the most potent poison known to man, whilst the substance secreted from *Micrococcus aureus* is a frequent cause of "food-poisoning."

Growth of the bacterial cell occurs by the synthesis of more protoplasm until a limiting size is reached, whereupon the organism divides by binary fission into two smaller freely existing cells. Bacteria fall into three groups with regard to the temperature conditions at which they can make best growth. The great majority behave as most other organisms do and grow best between 30–37°C. A few, commonly isolated from cold water, have an optimum growth temperature of about 15–20°C, whilst a few others can make reasonable growth at temperatures down to freezing-point, or below if the freezing point is depressed. Some species however, can make growth only when the temperature is high enough to cook most other organisms. These are the thermophilous bacteria found only in hot springs and in piles of rotting vegetation and manure. Their optimum growth temperature may be as high as 60°C.

Binary fission is the only method of reproduction known to occur in all species. It is achieved by the separation of the cytoplasm in the cell into two portions by a delicate septum and the eventual deposition of wall material on this until the two new cells are separated. In rod bacteria, the division is always transverse. Some of the spherical forms elongate prior to division, whilst others divide into hemispheres which round off on separation. In a few cases, the separation of the daughter cells may be delayed for some time and by continuous fission, chains of cells may arise, giving a filamentous appearance. Sometimes the cells of such chains may remain in continuity with one another by delicate cytoplasmic plasmodesmata. The rapidity with which this binary fission occurs under the best growth conditions is phenomenal. Cell division can be repeated every 20 to 30 min. Assuming the slowest of these rates, this means that a single organism in 15 hours would have multiplied to produce about 1 000 000 000. If the bacteria were of average size, this would be a bulk of about 1 mm³. On a suitably prepared plate of nutrient material, this bulk would appear as a small patch called a *colony*. The appearance of such colonies on inoculated plates gives a guide to the number of organisms occurring in the liquid with which the plate was inoculated. If the bacteria continue to multiply at this rate it can be calculated that in less than 36 hours the progeny of a single cell would occupy a volume of about 1000 m³.

Naturally, such a condition never arises, since many of the bacteria die without reproducing themselves and the general rate of multiplication slowly falls away to nothing. The growth of the population follows the sigmoid curve explained in Vol. II, Chap. 13. There are two main reasons for this. First, the supply of nutrient materials becomes depleted, and secondly, the by-products of bacterial metabolism are often acid enough to cause unfavourable growth conditions. It is fortunate for man and all other living things that the growth conditions for bacteria never remain favourable for long periods. Nevertheless, the numbers of bacteria occurring naturally in various habitats are colossal. For example, 1 g of good fertile soil may contain 10^9 bacteria, whilst comparatively clean milk may contain up to 10 000 per cm^3. In sour milk, the fantastic number of 32 000 million organisms per cm^3 has been counted. This helps us to comprehend the minuteness of the bacteria.

Some bacteriologists hold that some form of inter-breeding between the strains of a species can occur. There is no clear cytological evidence to support this view. It is true that some strains of a species appear as large and small cells, possibly indicating sexual difference, and also that some bacterial cells appear to undergo a fusion process. But the fusion of cells alone does not necessarily mean that the process is essentially a blending of inheritable characters and no one has recorded any observation of the fusion of nuclear material in bacteria. Nevertheless, the strongest evidence for such a method of reproduction comes from studies of the mixing of inheritable characters when two colonies possessing different properties are blended together. Only physiological characters can be studied in this way. For example, when a strain of the bacterium *Escherichia coli*, which is unable to synthesize biotin and methionine but able to synthesize proline and threonine, was mixed with a strain able to synthesize the first two but not the others, there arose a few forms in the mixture which could synthesize all four substances. Such an occurrence could be interpreted as the result of some sexual fusion process but recent researches into the ways in which bacterial cells develop new inheritable potentialities indicate that a sexual fusion is not a necessity. For instance, bacteria of the *Pneumococcus* type occur showing variability in the chemical nature of the capsules which they form. There is a "smooth" form possessing capsular polysaccharides and a "rough" form lacking them. The "rough" form can produce "smooth" forms if treated with a filtrate taken from *dead* "smooth" organisms. The interpretation put upon this is that the filtrate contains a substance called a "transforming principle" derived from the "smooth" forms, which if taken up by the "rough" forms, induces them to manufacture the molecules necessary to make the capsular polysaccharides previously lacking. So do the descendants of the cells which took up the transforming principle and thus an inheritable character has been passed from one bacterium to another merely as a chemical substance. The transforming principle in this case has been shown to be pure desoxyribonucleic acid, the substance of which genes are believed to be composed.

A characteristic of some of the rod-form bacteria is that they are able to form highly-resistant resting bodies known as *spores*. These are not strictly reproductive bodies but serve to carry the organism over periods of bad conditions such as shortage of nutrients. A spore may be formed from the contents of a whole cell or sometimes a single cell may give rise to several spores. With or without division, the small mass of bacterial protoplasm rounds off and an extremely resistant wall is deposited around it. In order to penetrate this wall with stains it is necessary to use heat. Carbol fuchsin at about 60°C will penetrate fairly well in about ten minutes. Treatment with hydrochloric acid at 60°C will eventually change the nature of the wall so that ordinary stains may be used. The spores are so tenacious of life that many of them can withstand boiling for hours and are not killed at the lowest of temperatures reached. Some of the more dangerous disease-causing organisms are spore-formers, e.g. *Clostridium tetani* and *Bacillus anthracis*. Some bacilli form protective walls to become cysts.

Identification of the Bacteria

Identification of the bacteria, in view of their small size, is often a tedious business and cannot be carried out in purely morphological terms as is the practice with plants and animals. Two bacteria may look so much alike as to be inseparable under the microscope, but have quite different physiological characters. Thus a number of characteristics must be used and these include morphology and sporing ability, reactions with certain stains, metabolic activities, i.e. nutrient requirements, oxygen requirements, products of metabolism, etc., serological characteristics and pathogenicity.

It has been mentioned that bacterial cells may have characteristic shapes (*see* Fig. 36.1). The earliest descriptions and classifications were based on this. All rod forms were termed *bacilli*, the rounded forms, *cocci*, the spirally twisted, *spirilla*, and the comma-shaped, *vibrios*. The bacillus forms vary considerably in shape, size and motility with almost every conceivable intermediate condition, so that little can be gained by merely looking at them. The coccus forms may occur singly (*Micrococcus*), in indeterminate groups (*Staphylococcus*), in pairs (*Diplococcus*), in chains (*Streptococcus*) or in cubical packets (*Sarcina*). The spirilla show true spiral twisting and there may be several twists to the spiral. The vibrios are only slightly curved without being fully twisted into a spiral. In some of these cases form can be a useful preliminary guide to identification. In addition to the shapes of individual cells, the form and colour of a whole colony on a suitable growth medium can also be useful, but long experience in handling bacteria is necessary. If the organism is a sporer, the position of the spore (one only in each cell) can also be a useful identification guide. The size, form and position of its spore is often characteristic of a species. A spore may be formed at one end of a cell only, to give a characteristic "drumstick" appearance as in *Clostridium tetani*, slightly sub-terminal as in *Bacillus subtilis*, or centrally placed as in *Bacillus mycoides* (*see* Fig. 36.1).

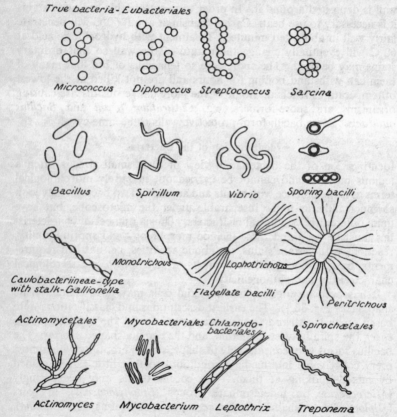

Fig. 36.1. Forms of bacterial cells and allied micro-organisms.

The staining of bacteria is usually quite simply achieved by treating an air-dried smear on a slide with one of a variety of common stains. Methylene blue, carbol fuchsin and gentian violet are among the easiest to use. Many years of experience have resulted in techniques designed to show up particular organisms to the best advantage. A staining technique first used by Gram has for long proved useful in distinguishing between two clearly different kinds of organisms with respect to their staining reactions. A smear is first stained with gentian violet and then treated with iodine solution. The whole preparation is then washed with alcohol until no more stain is released and then counter-stained with a red dye such as carbol fuchsin. Organisms treated in this manner react in one of two ways. They either retain the violet dye despite vigorous washing and show no traces of redness, or they lose all the violet dye on washing and appear bright red owing to the counter-stain. The former are called "Gram-positive" organisms and the latter "Gram-negative." The difference between them must lie in the differences of their protoplasmic constitution and it is interesting to note that the majority of Gram-positive organisms differ from the Gram-negative types in several physiological ways.

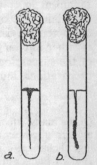

Fig. 36.2. "Stab" cultures. (a) Showing aerobic growth. (b) Anaerobic growth.

They are generally much more exacting in their nutritional requirements, less chemically active and more easily destroyed by drugs and antibiotics.

Bacteria can be distinguished from one another in terms of their nutrient and oxygen requirements. As will be described more fully later, the nutritional requirements of the bacteria are widely variable. Certain organisms can be discerned from closely-related ones purely in terms of the substances which form the carbon and nitrogen sources required for their normal metabolism. Inability to make growth in the absence of certain accessory growth substances can sometimes be a useful identification guide. Similarly, the aerobes can be distinguished from the anaerobes. A simple method of demonstrating this distinction is to make a "stab-culture," in which an agar medium in a tube is inoculated with the organism under test to some depth, by stabbing the loop into it. The differences in the position of growth of the colonies on the medium of the two types is shown in Fig. 36.2. The aerobe can grow only at the surface of the stab; the anaerobe only deeply in the medium.

One of the effects of injecting bacteria (or other foreign substances of protein nature) into the blood of animals is to stimulate the formation of substances called *antibodies* in the blood. Such antibodies are specific to the foreign substance or *antigen* which induced their formation, i.e. they will tend to eliminate or destroy that particular antigen but no other. The antibodies constitute one of the major resistance reactions of an animal body to infection by other organisms or foreign substances. If the blood serum of an animal artificially infected by a known organism is collected, it will contain the antibody specific to that organism and it can be used *in vitro* to test for the presence of the organism in cultures. If the serum is introduced into a suspension containing the organism which caused the antibody to be formed, a characteristic visible effect results such as the agglutination or running together in clumps of the organisms and their subsequent settling out of the suspension. By testing unknown organisms with known serum preparations, much can be learned as to their identity.

Classification of the Bacteria

Of the many attempts to classify the bacteria only two incorporate sufficient modern discovery to be of any value. The early attempts based on morphological characters have long since gone out of use. The system put forward in 1941 by Stanier and van Niel sought to collect together all the bacteria-like organisms into one group, the Schizomycetae, and with the blue-green algae, the Myxophyta, form them into a third living kingdom, the Monera, on the grounds that they were all micro-organisms without true nuclei or plastids and lacking any sexual reproductive process. The scheme does not seem to have been widely adopted.

The Society of American Microbiologists has periodically attempted to classify bacteria and allied organisms, incorporating the most recent discoveries concerning them. A recent scheme, based on Bergey's Manual of Determinative Bacteriology is given below. It includes only those organisms that have been fully and properly described. The old idea of regarding the bacteria as plants is still adhered to and with other microbes they make up the division Protophyta with three classes, the Schizophyceae (blue-green algae), the Schizomycetes (bacteria and related forms) and the Microtatobiotes (rickettsias and viruses).

DIVISION: **Protophyta**

CLASS: Schizophyceae. These are most commonly regarded as algae and described under Cyanophyta (*see* p. 66).

CLASS: Schizomycetes

ORDER: Eubacteriales (the true bacteria). Simple unicells with rigid walls. Coccus or rod forms. Peritrichate flagellation when motile. Probably some genetic interchange between individuals but reproduction by binary fission only most common. Some form endospores.

FAMILY: Azotobacteriaceae. Large rods, often motile. Free-living in the soil. Nitrogen fixers. Gram —ve. For example, *Azotobacter*.

FAMILY: Rhizobiaceae. Rod-shaped, often motile. Some symbiotic nitrogen-fixers. Some cause gall diseases of plants. Some contain a violet pigment. Mostly Gram −ve. For example, *Rhizobium, Agrobacterium, Chromobacterium.*

FAMILY: Micrococcaceae. Spherical cells occurring singly, in clusters or packets but not in chains. Mostly Gram +ve. For example, *Micrococcus, Staphylococcus, Sarcina.*

FAMILY: Lactobacillaceae. Some rods, some cocci either in pairs or chains. The rods, Lactobacilleae, are important as fermenters. The cocci, Streptococceae, are frequent disease organisms. Gram +ve. For example, *Lactobacillus, Streptococcus, Diplococcus, Leuconostoc.*

FAMILY: Enterobacteriaceae. Large group of rod forms, some motile. Can ferment sugars to various organic acids, etc. Many are normal gut inhabitants. Some cause disease in man, e.g. typhoid fever. Some are plant parasites. Many are soil saprophytes. Gram −ve. For example *Escherichia, Salmonella, Erwinia, Serratia, Proteus.*

FAMILY: Neisseriaceae. Diplococci, essentially parasites of mucous membranes. Gram +ve. For example, *Neisseria.*

FAMILY: Corynebacteriaceae. Branched, non-motile rods causing diseases such as diphtheria. Gram +ve. For example, *Corynebacterium, Erysipelothrix.*

FAMILY: Achromobacteriaceae. Rod forms, some motile. Mostly unimportant saprophytes of soil and water. Gram −ve. For example, *Achromobacter, Flavobacterium, Alcaligenes.*

FAMILY: Brucellaceae [Parvobacteriaceae]. Short oval rod forms non-motile. Many important disease agents with some saprophytes. Gram −ve. For example, *Pasteurella, Brucella, Malleomyces.*

FAMILY: Bacillaceae. Relatively large straight rods, mostly motile. Mainly soil saprophytes but a few disease agents. The only family to form endospores. Gram +ve (at least in early growth stages). For example, *Bacillus, Clostridium.*

FAMILY: Propionibacteriaceae. Rod forms, non-motile. Fermentation products propionic acid, butyric acid or ethanol, producing carbon dioxide. Gram +ve. For example, *Butyribacterium, Proprionibacterium.*

FAMILY: Brevibacteriaceae. Rod forms, motile and non-motile. Gram +ve. For example, *Brevibacterium, Kurthia.*

FAMILY: Bacteroidaceae. Rods, some filterable (very small); motile and non-motile. Gram −ve. For example, *Bacteroides, Streptobacillus.*

ORDER: Pseudomonadales. Straight, curved or spirally twisted rods with polar flagellation. Some photosynthesizers, some chemosynthesizers. Gram −ve.

SUB-ORDER: Rhodobacteriineae. Cells with red, purple, brown or green photosynthetic pigments and may enclose free granules of sulphur. Abundant in waters containing hydrogen sulphide and lacking oxygen. Many are concerned in the sulphur cycle in nature (*see* Vo.l II, Chap. 10). For example, *Chromatium* (purple "sulphur" bacteria), *Thiospirillum, Chlorobium* (green "sulphur" bacteria).

SUB-ORDER: Pseudomonadineae. May be pigmented but not photosynthesizers. Free sulphur granules occur in some and ferric hydroxide is deposited by others. Include the nitrifying bacteria such as *Nitrobacter* and *Nitrosomonas*, the colourless "sulphur" bacteria such as *Thiobacillus*, the "hydrogen" bacteria such as *Hydrogenomonas*, the "methane" bacteria such as *Methanomonas*, the stalked "iron" bacteria such as *Gallionella* and sulphate reducers such as *Desulphovibrio*, the only genus to form endospores outside the Bacillaceae.

ORDER: Actinomycetales. Contains some representatives very much like true bacteria and others more like fungi. The first are the Mycobacteriaceae differing only from true bacteria in physiological respects which show up as acid-fastness, i.e. dyes cannot be washed out by acids. The bacterium causing tuberculosis belongs to this family. The remainder are filamentous, at least at some time in the life cycle. Those which are permanently filamentous and produce spores resembling fungal conidia, are members of the family Streptomycetaceae. The members of the other family, the Actinomycetaceae, are at first filamentous but break up into bacterium-like cells. These last two families are the organisms usually termed the actinomycetes and they play a large part in soil fertility.

ORDER: Chlamydobacteriales. Colourless chains of cells, sometimes branched and often ensheathed in a layer of organic substance that may be impregnated with iron or manganese oxides. Gram −ve. For example, *Leptothrix*, *Crenothrix*.

ORDER: Beggiatoales. Mostly chains of cells, some motile but never flagellate, showing a gliding motion not so far explained. Contains some colourless "sulphur" bacteria that are often found in waters rich in hydrogen sulphide where they exist as chemosynthesizers. *Beggiatoa* is possibly a colourless form of blue-green alga.

ORDER: Myxobacteriales. A clearly distinct collection since although the cells are usually of rod form, they have no rigid walls and thus in a mass appear slimy. The naked cells are motile, without flagella or other locomotive parts. They show creeping movements similar to those of the blue-green algae. As a colony of them develops and ages, the cells aggregate into characteristically shaped "fruiting bodies." In these, resting bodies known as microcysts, are developed from the vegetative cells. Many are soil saprophytes and figure largely in cellulose decomposition.

ORDER: Spirochaetales. This is a group of spirally twisted organisms also lacking rigid walls. They move by sinuous twisting movements of the whole body. Many are saprophytic and harmless whilst a few are blood parasites of higher animals. *Treponema macrodentium* lives harmlessly in the human mouth whilst a close relative *T. pallidum* is the causative organism of syphilis in man. The order possesses some physiological resemblances to the animal trypanosomes.

OTHER ORDERS: Mycoplasmatales (PPLO) (*see* p. 1267); Caryophanales (filamentous, sheathed bacteria); Hyphomicrobiales (budding bacteria). The class Microtatobiotes is not treated further here but *see* p. 1261 for viruses.

The Metabolism of Bacteria

The bacteria possess all the characteristics of living things and can perform all the same functions in comparable ways. Because of their importance as disease-causing, putrefying and synthesizing agents, many of them have been studied in detail. It has been found, as might be expected, that all their metabolic activities are controlled by the enzymes which they produce. These enzyme systems correspond very closely to those produced by higher organisms and may be classified in the same way (*see* Vol. II, Chap. 5).

Nutrition

Within the bacteria, we find the same range of differences in nutritional activities as is found in other living things. Some are autotrophic and make use of light or chemical energy to build simple inorganic substances into their complicated organic food requirements. They are termed photo-autotrophic or chemo-autotrophic respectively. The remainder are heterotrophic and must rely for at least some of their organic requirements on the material which they can derive from the bodies of other living things. They have adopted either the parasitic or saprophytic mode of life. In either case, autotrophe or heterotrophe, the chemical substances from which their protoplasm is composed are much the same, but both the energy source by which the synthesis is accomplished, and the type of nutrient required as a starting point in the chain of synthetic reactions, are different. The protoplasmic substances which have to be synthesized by any organism include carbohydrates, proteins and fats and a wide variety of other organic substances. The difference between the autotrophe and the heterotrophe, lies in the ability of the former to make use of a source of energy other than that of the potential energy of organic compounds, with which to build these from simple inorganic substances. It is not unusual to find bacteria capable of existing as both autotrophe and heterotrophe according to environmental conditions.

Photo-autotrophic Bacteria. Light energy can be made to perform chemical work by living things only in the presence of the necessary pigments. These pigments are possessed by three groups of bacteria only. They are the green sulphur bacteria (Chlorobacteriaceae) the purple sulphur bacteria (Thiorhodaceae) and the purple and brown bacteria (Athiorhodaceae).

The green sulphur bacteria can assimilate carbon dioxide in essentially the same way as can higher plants, but instead of using water as the reducing agent or hydrogen donor for the reduction of the carbon dioxide, hydrogen sulphide is used. The overall synthesizing reactions of green plants and the green sulphur bacteria can be compared thus—

Green plant: $2H_2O + CO_2 \rightarrow (CH_2O) + O_2 + H_2O$

Green bacterium: $2H_2S + CO_2 \rightarrow (CH_2O) + 2S + H_2O$

The strictly anaerobic bacterium *Chlorobium*, abundant in soil, mud and sulphuretted waters, is able to perform this synthesis. In the equations as written, (CH_2O) merely represents a starting point for further carbohydrate synthesis. Nitrogen requirements are filled by ammonia or nitrate.

The purple sulphur bacteria perform the same reaction as the green bacteria but in this case the sulphur appears as visible granules within the cells. Should the organisms be deprived of H_2S they can use the elemental sulphur stored in the cells to reduce more carbon dioxide. This reaction may be written—

$$2S + 8H_2O + 3CO_2 \rightarrow 2H_2SO_4 + 3(CH_2O) + 3H_2O$$

It is an oxidation–reduction process which may be split into two parts as below—

$$2S + 8H_2O - 12H \rightarrow 2H_2SO_4$$
$$3CO_2 + 12H \rightarrow 3(CH_2O) + 3H_2O$$

Starting from H_2S as the reducing agent, the carbon dioxide reduction may be written—

$$2H_2S + 8H_2O + 4CO_2 \rightarrow 2H_2SO_4 + 4(CH_2O) + 4H_2O$$

These sulphur bacteria can use other sulphur compounds such as thiosulphate for a similar purpose. An example of such a bacterium is *Chromatium*.

The purple and brown bacteria do not use sulphur compounds as the hydrogen donators in the carbon dioxide reduction process. They are not "sulphur bacteria." Instead they use organic acids and may be confused with the heterotrophic bacteria because of this. However, they can be distinguished because they grow only anaerobically and in the presence of light. An example of a synthetic reaction involving carbon dioxide may be represented—

$$2\underset{\substack{isopropyl \\ alcohol}}{CH_3CHOHCH_3} + CO_2 \rightarrow 2\underset{acetone}{CH_3COCH_3} + (CH_2O) + H_2O$$

Chemo-autotrophic Bacteria. These organisms synthesize all their protoplasmic constituents from inorganic substances such as carbon dioxide, water, ammonia or nitrates and obtain the initial energy for the syntheses from the oxidation of inorganic substrates. The substrates which they use are specific to the organisms concerned and can be used in their identification.

Among the best-known and important examples are the nitrifying bacteria of the soil such as species of *Nitrosomonas*, *Nitrosococcus*, *Nitrosospira*, *Nitrosocystis* and *Nitrosogloea* which can oxidize ammonia to nitrite, and species of *Nitrobacter* and *Nitrocystis* which can oxidize nitrite to nitrate. The former reaction may be represented—

$$2NH_3 + 3O_2 = 2HNO_2 + 2H_2O + 3\cdot31 \times 10^3 kJ$$

and the latter—

$$HNO_2 + O = HNO_3 + 9\cdot5 \times 10^3 kJ$$

Both these groups of organisms are obviously strictly aerobic. They are mentioned in Vol. II, Chap. 10, as playing a great part in the cycle of nitrogen in nature.

Besides nitrogen compounds, a wide variety of substances can be used by other organisms as oxidizable substrates. Among the more interesting chemo-autotrophic organisms besides those mentioned above are the following:

1. The colourless sulphur bacteria: these oxidize hydrogen sulphide thus—

$$2H_2S + O_2 = 2S + 2H_2O + 5\cdot28 \times 10^3 kJ$$

The sulphur is stored in the cells as granules and the energy released is used to assimilate carbon dioxide. The sulphur can later be used as a reserve oxidizable substrate when H_2S is not available, thus—

$$2S + 2H_2O + 3O_2 = 2H_2SO_4 + 5\cdot94 \times 10^3 kJ$$

Examples of organisms able to perform these reactions are the genera *Beggiatoa*, *Thiothrix* and *Thiospirillopsis* of the order Chlamydobacteriales and the genera *Thiospira* and *Thiobacillus* of the true bacteria. The species *Thiobacillus thio-oxidans* is a well-known oxidizer of sulphur to sulphates.

2. The hydrogen bacteria: these organisms use the energy derived from the oxidation of molecular hydrogen using nitrates, sulphates or even carbon dioxide as oxidizing agents. A typical reaction may be written—

$$4H_2 + H_2SO_4 = 4H_2O + H_2S + 4\cdot09 \times 10^3 kJ$$

and another—

$$4H_2 + CO_2 = 2H_2O + CH_4 + 2\cdot60 \times 10^3 kJ$$

Organisms of the genus *Desulphovibrio* perform the first of these reactions whilst a mixed collection of species designated the "methane bacteria" perform the second.

Most of these organisms are not obligatory chemo-autotrophes since they can be grown in the absence of hydrogen on media containing the correct organic substances. This means that they can substitute a suitable organic compound for inorganic hydrogen if the need arises, and carry on a heterotrophic existence.

3. The iron bacteria: these were once regarded as chemo-autotrophes which obtained energy by the oxidation of ferrous compounds to ferric hydroxide, thus—

$$4FeCO_3 + O_2 + 6H_2O = 4Fe(OH)_3 + 4CO_2 + 3.39 \times 10^3 kJ$$

Members of the genus *Leptothrix* were believed to perform this reaction as their sole means of obtaining energy, but it has recently been proved that some at least, can live heterotrophically in organic media alone and are quite unable to grow in purely mineral media containing reduced iron. The presence of the ferric hydroxide deposited around the bacterial cells in nature is now believed to be the result of the spontaneous conversion of ferrous iron to the ferric condition on exposure to air, if the water, pH, and other conditions are correct. The bacteria possibly play some part in producing the correct conditions for the spontaneous reaction to occur.

Heterotrophic Bacteria. These form much too variable a collection for treatment in great detail here. Their common characteristic is that they can utilize for their own purposes, only the energy which has been incorporated into organic compounds by other living things. The range of such energy-yielding substances is extremely wide, but for convenience we may group the heterotrophes according to their requirements of energy-supplying and body-building substances as follows—

1. Those which must have organic carbon such as carbohydrate, but are able to make use of gaseous nitrogen as a nitrogen source. With water and certain mineral ions they can then synthesize all their requirements including accessory growth factors. Such organisms are the nitrogen-fixing bacteria such as the free-living *Azotobacter* species, *chroococcum*, *agile*, *beijerincki* and *indicum*, the free-living species *Clostridium pastorianum* and the symbiotic *Rhizobium leguminosarum*.

2. As above but unable to use gaseous nitrogen. They use nitrate or ammonia as a nitrogen source instead. Many saprophytic bacteria growing on a wide variety of substrates are in this category.

3. Those which must have organic carbon and are unable to utilize

any form of inorganic nitrogen. Certain amino-acids are therefore essential. From a limited number of these, together with the carbohydrate, water and necessary mineral ions, all protoplasmic constituents can be synthesized including the accessory growth substances. Saprophytic bacteria occurring on a limited range of substrates are in this group.

4. Those which must have organic carbon, certain amino-acids and accessory growth substances. In this group are all the parasitic bacteria and the saprophytic organisms which will grow in only one particular kind of medium, e.g. milk.

From this brief summary of the heterotrophic bacteria it must not be concluded that even the most thorough-going saprophyte or parasite cannot utilize inorganic materials. It must be remembered that we have used the term heterotrophe to mean an organism which cannot tap for itself sources of energy in the physical environment external to the living world. As long as some other source is available to provide the energy for synthetic reactions, inorganic materials can be incorporated into the system quite readily. Indeed, this seems to be the universal condition, since the presence of water and mineral ions is essential to all protoplasmic processes in both plants and animals. It will also be seen in Chaps. 10 and 11 of Vol. II that carbon dioxide may be utilized for the building of the dicarboxylic acids in the Krebs' cycle of metabolism. In assessing the position of the heterotrophe in the scheme of living things, two factors must be taken into account. First, it must rely on the energy-fixing ability of other organisms for its supply of energy with which to accomplish its own syntheses. A carbohydrate respired in its own cells suffices for most heterotrophic organisms in this respect. Secondly, different heterotrophes possess different enzyme systems and therefore all cannot use the same starting substances from which to build their protoplasm. When supplied with the substances with which their enzymes can cope, they can then build protoplasm, using the energy released in their respiratory activity. The autotrophe, on the other hand, possesses the complete range of enzymes necessary to the synthesis of all protoplasmic substance from carbon dioxide, an inorganic nitrogen source, water and some mineral ions. In the form of proteins, some synthesized compounds perform the enzymic function of catalysing the formation of the others and once the system is in full operation, it becomes self-increasing, as long as raw materials and energy source last out. The heterotrophes, in varying degree, lack the ability to synthesize all these compounds and at fewer or more places, gaps must be filled by direct access to the substances which cannot be built from smaller units. Hence they are restricted to those nutritional substrates which can supply their individual needs.

Respiration

It has been mentioned that some bacteria respire aerobically, some anaerobically, and that some are facultative anaerobes.

The aerobic organisms use oxygen in oxidative reactions on suitable substrates and the oxidation may be fully complete or only partially so. This use of oxygen in respiratory activity may be looked upon as a particular case of a biological oxidation which is effected by the transfer of hydrogen from the substrate to a suitable hydrogen acceptor which is thereby reduced (*see* Vol. II, Chap. 11). In this case, oxygen acts as the hydrogen acceptor and is reduced to water. If the oxidation of a substrate is complete, then carbon dioxide is formed as well. Such a complete oxidation of a carbohydrate substrate can be represented by the equation—

$$C_6H_{12}O_6 + 6O_2 \rightleftharpoons 6CO_2 + 6H_2O + 2\cdot87 \times 10^3 kJ$$

Reference to Vol. II, Chap. 11, will show that this merely represents a long series of reactions, only the last of which involves the use of molecular oxygen. In some cases aerobic bacteria are unable to oxidize their substrates completely, and substances other than carbon dioxide may accumulate as by-products of the reactions. An incomplete oxidation of this kind is the one in which glucose is converted to gluconic acid as follows—

$$CH_2OH(CHOH)_4CHO + \tfrac{1}{2}O_2 \rightleftharpoons CH_2OH(CHOH)_4COOH$$

The vinegar bacterium, *Acetobacter*, performs the incomplete oxidation of ethyl alcohol to acetic acid so—

$$CH_3CH_2OH + O_2 \rightleftharpoons CH_3COOH + H_2O + energy$$

This property of the bacterium is used commercially in the production of vinegar.

Some anaerobic bacteria can release energy from organic compounds by using an inorganic substance other than oxygen to accept the hydrogen from the substrate to be oxidized. Such substances may be nitrates, sulphates or carbonates and the processes are referred to as reductions of nitrate, sulphate or carbonate accordingly. The so-called hydrogen bacteria, mentioned previously, are really doing this when they use organic compounds as substrates from which to obtain energy, instead of hydrogen. Nitrate and sulphate reduction can have considerable effect on the fertility of the soil. Many bacteria which are normally aerobic can use nitrates for respiratory purposes when oxygen is lacking. Some may reduce nitrates only to nitrites. This is not so important, since the nitrites under acid conditions often prove toxic to the bacteria producing them, and when oxygen is once more available, the nitrites can be readily converted back into nitrates by other organisms. More serious are the bacteria which reduce nitrates to nitrous oxide or molecular nitrogen. These are the denitrifying bacteria of which species of the genus *Pseudomonas* and the species *Thiobacillus denitrificans* are examples. Sulphate reduction to sulphides seems to be carried out only by the members of the genus *Desulphovibrio*. They are strict anaerobes.

Carbonate reduction by bacteria results in the formation of methane and the process is sometimes called methane fermentation. It is a very special case of anaerobic respiration in which carbon dioxide acts as the hydrogen acceptor. A variety of respiratory substrates may be used and an example is ethyl alcohol—

$$2CH_3CH_2OH + CO_2 \rightleftharpoons 2CH_3COOH + CH_4 + \text{energy}$$

In some cases, the bacteria are further able to oxidize the acetic acid thus formed, to carbon dioxide and water. This seems peculiar since carbon dioxide is acting not only as oxidizing agent but appears as an end-product as well. By the use of radioactive carbon it has been shown to be the case and the reaction may be represented as follows—

$$CH_3COOH + 2H_2O + CO_2 \rightleftharpoons 2CO_2 + CH_4 + 2H_2O + \text{energy}$$

It is well known that methane or "marsh gas" is liberated from the mud in marshes, bogs and lakes where there is a good deal of decomposition of organic matter proceeding. The organisms concerned are species of *Methanobacter*. Bacteria of the same kind are inhabitants of the gut of ruminants like the cow and such activity may cause the animal to produce large quantities of methane per day.

A large number of bacteria can live anaerobically by deriving energy from fermenting activities. Many of these are facultative anaerobes and the fermentation products are those substances which accumulate only in the absence of oxygen. When oxygen is available they can be further oxidized to carbon dioxide and water and more energy is released. It is also the case that some obligate aerobes can survive for short periods without oxygen by the same means. This is strictly comparable with the cases of higher plants and animals in which the respiratory metabolism involves a long series of reactions with many intermediates, and in which only the last oxidative step involves molecular oxygen as the final hydrogen acceptor (*see* Vol. II, Chap. 11). There are numerous substances which can act as fermentable substrates and the by-products are equally varied according to the type of microorganism concerned. The products are often of industrial importance. The better known fermentation processes include—

(*a*) ethyl alcohol and CO_2 from sugars by many species of bacteria, yeasts and fungi;

(*b*) lactic acid from sugars by species of *Lactobacillus* and *Streptococcus*;

(*c*) mixtures of lactic, acetic and formic acids from sugars by species of *Escherichia* and *Salmonella*;

(*d*) butyric acid and butyl alcohol from sugars by species of *Clostridium* and *Butyribacterium*.

Whilst these fermentations serve to provide the energy for the life processes of the organisms concerned, it must be remembered that the energy released during fermentations cannot compare with the quantity released by complete oxidation in which molecular oxygen is involved. Further, the end-products often accumulate, and in high enough concentration interfere with environmental conditions, particularly pH; thus the only organisms able to survive in nature by such methods of releasing energy are the small ones in a liquid medium, through which the toxic products are quickly dispersed.

Putrefactive or Digestive Activity

The saprophytic micro-organisms find their food requirements in plant and animal excretions and their dead remains. Such matter is largely in the form of complex molecules such as polysaccharides, proteins and fats and cannot be absorbed in this form any more readily than they can by the higher animals. They have first to be digested to a soluble, absorbable form. Such digestion is carried out by the production of exo-enzymes secreted by the micro-organisms. The enzymes hydrolyse the polysaccharides to hexoses, the proteins to amino-acids and the fats to fatty acids and glycerol. This digestive or putrefactive activity proceeds on a tremendous scale in places such as the soil, where organic matter accumulates. It results in the eventual disintegration of all dead material, so that it is reduced to a form available for circulation among living things once more. The details of these digestive processes appear not to vary from those employed by other larger organisms, and the range of enzymes is generally the same. It is interesting to note that the digestion of the commonest of all plant products, cellulose, is almost entirely achieved by the micro-organisms, including some of the true bacteria, fungi, actinomycetes and protozoa. Few animals, if any, are able to secrete the enzyme cellulase and although many of them take in large quantities of cellulose in their food, they rely on microbes in the gut to digest it for them. The rabbit and the cow are familiar examples.

Bacteria in Relation to Other Living Things

Because of their widespread occurrence and the great range of their activities, there are no living things which do not come under the influence of the bacteria in one way or another. Their important effects are summarized below.

1. They have a tremendous influence on soil fertility in several ways—

(i) By their putrefying effects, so causing the decomposition of organic matter, to yield up the raw materials of metabolism for other living things, e.g. carbon dioxide, ammonia, mineral salts, water.

(ii) By their formation of humus, the organic colloid, which influences the nature of a soil in many ways.

(iii) By the ability of some to metabolize free nitrogen and so add to the pool of nitrogenous material in living things.

(iv) By the ability of others to influence the state of nitrogen and sulphur compounds, e.g. by nitrification, denitrification, and oxidation and reduction of sulphur compounds.

2. They cause disease in many plants and animals, including man.

3. They can be useful in man's industry.

4. They can destroy the products of man's industry.

Bacteria and Disease

It must be emphasized that all bacteria do not cause disease; all are not pathogenic, and indeed, the great majority are not. Not even all the bacterial parasites are pathogenic. Many of them can live externally or internally on the body surfaces and cause no ill effects. Some of these, even if they enter the tissues, are unable to cause injury. Most of the organisms which are pathogenic are strictly so and are never found other than in association with a particular diseased condition. Such bacteria are nearly always highly specialized parasites and rely on a continual transfer from host to host for their perpetuation. The disease-producing power of a bacterium is called its *virulence*. A few virulent organisms may not produce a diseased condition in some hosts, whilst they do in others. The host which can harbour a potentially pathogenic organism and itself remain healthy, is known as a *carrier*. Such carriers often prove to be the greatest spreaders of epidemics of disease.

As a result of medical research, by far the greatest accumulation of knowledge is centred around those organisms causing disease in human beings. Below is a short list of human diseases with the causative organisms—

Tuberculosis (*Mycobacterium tuberculosis* var. *hominis*), pneumonia (*Diplococcus pneumoniae* or *Pneumococcus*), diphtheria (*Corynebacterium diphtheriae*), typhoid fever (*Salmonella typhosa*), cholera (*Vibrio comma*), boils (*Micrococcus aureus*), meningitis (*Neisseria intracellularis* or *Meningococcus*), gonorrhoea (*Neisseria gonorrhoeae* or *Gonococcus*,) scarlet fever, "blood-poisoning," puerperal fever and others (various strains of *Streptococcus pyogenes*), bubonic plague (*Pasteurella pestis*), "botulism" (*Clostridium botulinum*,) tetanus (*Clostridium tetani*), anthrax (*Bacillus anthracis*), leprosy (*Mycobacterium leprae*), syphilis (*Treponema pallidum*), gas gangrene (*Clostridium perfringens* or *C. welchi*).

From a study of such diseases, certain general principles which underly the diagnosis and treatment of bacterial infection have been developed.

Virulence of an organism depends on its ability to penetrate and reproduce within the host's tissues or body fluids and to injure these by the secretion of toxins. Both properties vary widely in different organisms so that different diseases show lesser or greater effects on the host.

Bacteria can invade only by breaking through the epithelial coverings of the body. Most of the bacteria which are able to live on the epithelial surfaces cannot freely penetrate them. Most pathogenic bacteria can enter only through breaks in the skin or mucous membranes, and in many cases only certain places can be penetrated even then. For example, the meningococcus can enter only through the mucous membrane of the nasal cavities, the diphtheria bacillus only through the tonsils, pneumococcus only through the respiratory tract, the typhoid organism only through the gut.

Pathogenic bacteria, once they have invaded or infected, must be able to offer resistance to the defence mechanisms of the host. Structural and physiological characters may help them in this way. Capsular secretions prove protective, for instance.

Infection may be spread in the body by continuous growth in the tissues or by transport in the fluids of the vascular and lymphatic systems. Presence of bacteria in the lymphatic ducts is often revealed by swelling of the lymph glands. If the bacteria are able to live and reproduce in the blood stream they may set up the condition known as *septicaemia*.

The ability of the bacteria to cause injury when they have invaded the tissues is largely due to their ability to produce *toxins*. These are of two kinds. *Exotoxins* are secreted externally by the bacteria into the surroundings. *Endotoxins* are substances secreted internally and released only on death and break-up of the bacterial cell. In some cases, as in diphtheria, the disease symptoms are due to the absorption by the blood of exotoxins secreted by bacteria which do not penetrate deeply into the body, and practically never into the blood stream. Diphtheria is therefore said to be a local infection followed by *toxemia*. Other diseases caused by exotoxins are gas gangrene, tetanus, botulism and scarlet fever. These exotoxins are nearly all similar to the venom of certain snakes. They are unstable protein substances which can be destroyed by the usual protein-destroying methods such as heating, coagulation and use of proteolytic enzymes. The toxin of botulism has been found to be a complete protein containing the ten amino-acids essential to animal nutrition. Endotoxins differ from the exotoxins in several respects. They do not diffuse out of the living bacteria. They are more stable and heat-resistant, but less poisonous. There is some variety in their chemical nature; some are conjugated proteins and some are complex polysaccharides and phospholipides.

Another factor affecting spread through the host is the ability of some bacteria to produce the enzyme hyaluronidase which hydrolyses the cementing substance, hyaluronic acid, between the cells of the host tissues.

Some organisms, leading a normal saprophytic existence in the soil or elsewhere, can prove pathogenic if they gain entry to the human body. Typical are the organisms of gas gangrene and tetanus. They cannot themselves gain access to or live in healthy living tissue. If wounds cause the death of tissue, then these organisms can live saprophytically on the dead cells and in turn kill more cells by their exotoxins.

Many diseases show an incubation period, that is, a period of time elapses between the bacterial invasion and the development of disease symptoms by the host. This may be due to several causes. Exotoxins may diffuse only very slowly or the rate of reproduction of the bacteria may be slow, so that only small quantities of either toxin are at first produced.

Virulence may fluctuate in the same organism. Continuous culture in artificial media often leads to decreased virulence in a bacterium whilst rapid transfer from host to host may have the opposite effect. Such fluctuation is most probably due to the mutation of the bacterium and the selecting out of less or more virulent strains according to the environment.

These observations have all been concerned with the disease-causing nature of some bacteria. We must also regard the condition from the point of view of the effect of bacterial invasion upon the host. Hosts vary greatly in their proneness to become diseased, that is, they have different susceptibilities. They offer varying degrees of resistance to an attack. If an attack by some organism, ordinarily disease-producing, results in no symptoms being developed, the subject of the attack is said to be *immune* to that disease organism. Such immunity may be partial or complete and often reflects the previous experiences of the subject's body with respect to that particular disease. It was discovered that at least partial immunity can be induced by exposure to mild attacks of disease. Jenner showed that dairy-maids who had contracted cowpox or vaccinia, did not catch smallpox. When cowpox was deliberately caused in a subject by inoculation from fresh cowpox blisters, that subject automatically became immune to smallpox. The process of deliberately infecting a host with disease organisms is known as *vaccination* and the inoculated substance is a *vaccine*. It is true that smallpox is caused by a virus but the same principle is true for some bacteria. The immunizing effect is really due to using organisms said to be attenuated in virulence, that is, organisms which have lost their powers of producing extreme symptoms in a host. Attenuation may be achieved by passing an organism through a host other than the true host, as in the case of smallpox, in which the cow acts as the intermediate. Continuous culture in artificial media, growth in abnormal conditions of temperature, e.g. anthrax bacilli grown at 42°C, and drying, e.g. hydrophobia, are other methods of attenuating organisms which cause disease. Pasteur discovered several of these immunizing methods and several others have been discovered since. The term vaccine is now used to describe any of these immunizing agents containing attenuated strains of bacteria. They are used to immunize artificially and can be used preventively or prophylactically before the disease has developed. They are rarely of use after symptoms are discovered.

This kind of immunity is the result of active resistance by the host to the invaders. Vaccination brings about the development in the blood of the host, substances which can counteract the activities of the bacteria. These resisting substances are found in the blood serum, the liquid which is expressed by the blood on clotting. They neutralize toxins and are called *antitoxins*. They do not kill the bacteria but merely neutralize their effects.

From the discovery of the presence of these neutralizing substances, otherwise known as *antibodies*, in blood serum, the method was developed of using activated blood serum itself to counteract the effects of bacteria after they have attacked. This is known as *passive immunization* since the host's body plays no part in the process, as distinct from *active immunization* in the case of vaccines where the host's body produces its own antibodies. Several kinds of *serum* have been developed which give passive immunity against diseases such as diphtheria, tetanus, scarlet fever, gas gangrene and botulism. They confer only transient effects and have been found most useful in counteracting the action of bacteria, if applied quickly after the invasion has occurred. They can seldom be used preventively and are not much use when the disease symptoms are well advanced. The distinction between the vaccine and the serum is that the former contains the causative organism of the disease or its products, whereas the latter contains the resistant substances or antibodies produced by the host when invaded by the bacterium concerned. The vaccine can actively immunize, its effects are fairly slow to develop but long lasting; the serum can passively immunize, its effects are immediate but only short-lived.

Investigation into the properties of antibodies in blood serum showed that they possess characters other than that of merely neutralizing the exotoxins of some bacteria. They are described according to the effects they have on various organisms. For instance, *antitoxins* neutralize toxins, *agglutinins* cause bacterial suspensions to clump together or agglutinate and so settle out of suspension, *lysins* dissolve or disintegrate bacterial cells, *precipitins* react with foreign substances in solution to form a precipitate, *opsonins* enable white corpuscles of the blood to ingest bacteria more readily, i.e. hasten phagocytosis, *bactericides* kill bacteria or prevent their growth. The exact chemical nature of the antibodies is not known, or even if individual types have individual effects, but they seem to be large protein molecules of the globulin variety. In addition to being active against bacteria, antibodies are capable of reacting with all kinds of protein substances foreign to an animal's body. Such foreign substances may range from whole red blood cells to egg albumin. Any substance which, when injected into an animal's blood or tissues, causes the formation of antibodies, is called an *antigen*. Each antigen produces a specific antibody which will react with it but no other. The method of identifying particular organisms or protein substances by the action of specific antibodies upon them is known as *serology*. It has been referred to previously. On the assumption that related organisms develop closely similar protein antigens, serology is now sometimes used in solving classification problems in both botany and zoology.

Phagocytosis, mentioned above, is another resistance method used by hosts against invading bacteria. This is the process by which the bacteria are literally devoured, in the same way as an amoeba devours small organisms, by certain of the leucocytes of the blood. Such white corpuscles are termed *phagocytes* and have the power of amoeboid motion, by which they can find their way out of the blood vessels by wriggling their way through interstices of the capillary walls into the surrounding spaces; there they meet the invaders. They show chemotactic responses by moving towards chemical substances excreted by the bacteria. Thus large numbers of them appear in the neighbourhood of an infected wound or opening in the skin. A battle then commences between the phagocytes and the bacteria. Some of both die. The dead leucocytes liberate proteolytic enzymes which will digest dead bacteria, dead tissue cells and dead leucocytes alike. The result is an accumulation of a yellowish creamy fluid called *pus*. Enclosed pus under the skin forms an abscess. When the skin finally ruptures to release the pus, the abscess empties and the wound heals.

When it was first realized that bacteria could be the cause of disease, and that often they were responsible for most of the awful consequences of the primitive surgical methods employed at the time, attempts were made to control the incidence of wound infection. Lister was the first to show results in this field. What he really demonstrated was that certain substances killed or inhibited the growth of bacteria in a wound without harming the patient. These substances used in surgery are *antiseptics*. When all his instruments, the patient's skin and the wound dressings were soaked in carbolic acid, Lister had put up a lethal barrier between the wound and the bacteria, so that even if any succeeded in entering, they must die in the antiseptic substance before they could become active. Many such bactericidal substances have been discovered since. Drugs like the sulphadrugs, and antibiotics such as penicillin, can do the work much more efficiently than carbolic acid. Modern surgery no longer involves such crude antiseptic methods but favours the *aseptic* technique, which is aimed at protecting instruments, dressings, patients and the surgeon by sterilization, so that unwanted bacteria are never present to interfere with the surgeon's work.

The above few paragraphs represent no more than the very briefest of introductions to *pathology*, the study of disease; a subject of ever-increasing scope. Bacterial diseases of plants have not been mentioned at all, but there is no more space available other than to remind the student that many plants are as equally susceptible to bacterial attack by specific organisms, as are animals.

Bacteria in Industry

The best and oldest of the industrial uses of bacteria is that of the manufacture of milk foods, chiefly butter and cheese. Butter-making involves the use of bacteria to sour the cream or "ripen" it. The ripening effect is to cause the fat globules of the cream to run together more readily during the churning process. This is in part due to the digestion of protein substances between the fat globules which tend to hold them apart. Under modern dairy conditions the whole process is carefully controlled by regulation of the organisms which effect the ripening, and the temperature and other conditions, such as pH, at which they work. Cultures of organisms specially bred for the purpose are called "starters." Not only do these ripen the cream, but they produce just the right acidity to prevent unwanted organisms from attacking the butter. "Farm-house" butter is made from cream accidentally infected with suitable organisms and tends to differ from that produced in large milk-processing plants by being less uniform in character from day to day, and having poorer keeping qualities. The starting organisms are *Streptococcus lactis* which ferments the milk sugars to lactic acid, and *Leuconostoc citrovorum* which produces diacetyl from citric acid. The diacetyl gives the butter its aroma, Rancid butter results from the conversion of lactic acid to butyric acid by species of *Butyribacterium*.

Cheese-making involves first the formation of a curd from milk by the action of rennet. The curd is subsequently ripened under the influence of bacteria of the acid-forming type. Artificial "starters" can be employed. These vary according to the process used. Cheddar cheese is ripened chiefly by *Lactobacillus* species. *Penicillium* species of fungi are also used extensively in cheese-ripening processes and these are responsible for the "blue-vinny" cheeses.

As producers of other commercially valuable substances, the bacteria are used occasionally. Vinegar (acetic acid) manufacture is the most widely occurring example. The organisms concerned are species of *Acetobacter*, the vinegar bacteria. Other fermentation products of bacteria have been mentioned previously in this chapter.

Sewage disposal is essential to human life in crowded communities. The bacteria are natural disposers of unwanted organic material and they are harnessed by man to solve his problem. Between them the aerobic and anaerobic organisms mineralize completely all the sewage substances by their putrefactions and fermentations. Filter beds and septic tanks are specially constructed to allow each kind of organism to play its part until an effluent liquid is produced which contains only harmless soluble substances. The whole process can be paralleled by what normally goes on in a healthy, fertile soil. Dead organic remains are put back into circulation as inorganic materials by the soil population.

As well as being useful to man, bacteria can also prove to be destructive in many of his industrial enterprises. Destruction of his carefully gathered food stores in particular, must be guarded against. Rotting of textiles and corrosion or clogging of his machinery are too often encountered and traced to bacterial interference. Iron bacteria can cause partial and even complete blockage of pipes.

In their multitudinous millions, these tiny organisms industriously pursue their appointed labours. On balance, we are mightily in their debt, for without them, the whole complex cycle of life, death and decay would inevitably cease.

VIRUSES

The existence of viruses was first demonstrated in 1892, when Iwanovsky showed that tobacco mosaic disease was caused by a transmissible material. Since that time, a very considerable amount of research work has revealed the existence of many viruses which attack animals, plants and bacteria. All viruses seem to consist essentially of two components, protein and nucleic acid. The protein encloses the nucleic acid, which may be either RNA or DNA. It has been shown that the protein and nucleic acid portions can be separated and that later the virus can be reconstituted from the portions. In 1935, it was shown that virus nucleoprotein could be crystallized and stored for long periods and that it still retained its power of attacking the right type of cell. The bacteriophages are large viruses, specific in that they only attack bacteria. They were first described by Twort in 1915, and D'Herelle gave them their present name in 1917. Both scientists found that they were able to lyse bacteria, and D'Herelle claimed to have had some success with bacteriophages as prophylactic agents against bacterial diseases. He experimented with their use in cholera, plague and other diseases, and his work was extended with some success by the Indian Medical Service. These bacteriolytic agents attack beneficial as well as harmful bacteria; they will destroy the root nodule bacteria of legumes or the lactic acid bacteria used in cheese factories. Nowadays they are chiefly important as a source of material for the study of viruses. They appear to be of very widespread occurrence and can flourish in almost any situation where bacteria are present. Thus they are prolific in sewage and plentiful in the alimentary canal.

Nature of Viruses

The results of many studies on the nature of viruses indicate that they all consist of a protein coat enclosing RNA or DNA. No case has yet been discovered of a virus containing both RNA and DNA. It may be significant that most viruses which attack plants contain RNA, while most which attack bacteria and animals contain DNA. Sometimes the nucleic acid core is present as a helix, and sometimes as a folded thread (see Fig. 36.3). The outer coat in most cases consists of protein alone, but there are a few examples such as the influenza virus where the protein envelops the helix of nucleic acid and is itself enclosed in another coat of fat and protein. This second coat contains not only virus protein but is formed partly from the membrane of the infected cell (see Fig. 36.3).

In size, the viruses show a great range of variation from the 6 nm of turnip yellows to the rods of tobacco mosaic which are 400 nm long. Some indeed are not as large as certain protein molecules, e.g. haemocyanin, 33 nm × 30 nm. There are three main shapes, spheres, rods, and the tadpole-like bacteriophages (see Fig. 36.4). In many cases, the shapes conform with standard geometric figures.

Life Cycle of Viruses

An important characteristic of all viruses is that they can multiply only in living cells, and in most cases, each particular virus is specific in its

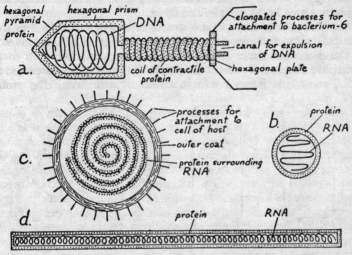

Fig. 36.3. Diagrammatic structure of (*a*) a bacteriophage, (*b*) poliomyelitis virus (*c*) influenza virus (*d*) tobacco mosaic virus.

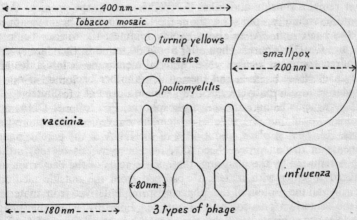

Fig. 36.4. Sizes and shapes of some viruses, all drawn to the same scale.

host and even of the type of cell within its host. Within the cell, the virus proceeds to cause the synthesis of more of its own substance from the materials available in the cell. The process often causes destruction of the host cells and sets up a pathological condition, and in such cases the virus may be regarded as being parasitic. Outside the host, many viruses can exist in a completely desiccated state, still capable of becoming fully active in the right environment.

The life cycles of many of the viruses have been worked out in great detail. Fig. 36.5 shows diagrammatically the cycle of the 'phage T, in the bacterium *Escherichia coli*. The 'phage attaches itself to the bacterial membrane by its tail end; the membrane is punctured and the DNA content is injected into the bacterial cytoplasm; the protein

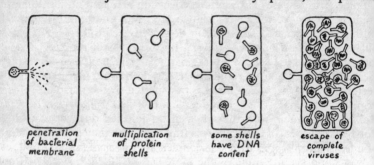

penetration of bacterial membrane   multiplication of protein shells   some shells have DNA content   escape of complete viruses

Fig. 36.5. Reproduction of a bacteriophage, (diagrammatic).

coat remains outside and takes no further part in the process. After about ten minutes, 'phages without the DNA content, begin to appear in the bacterium. After about twenty minutes, the viruses begin to acquire the DNA core. Then after about 30 minutes, there are several hundred complete 'phages; the bacterial membrane disintegrates and they are released. Each can then attack another bacterium if one is available, or alternatively, each can remain dormant indefinitely.

Experiments using radioactive phosphorus, P^{32}, to label DNA, and radioactive sulphur, S^{35}, to label protein, have revealed some interesting facts. In the first place, about 40% of the DNA of the parent 'phage appears in the offspring. Secondly, for the synthesis of the further DNA required by the offspring, the nucleic acids of the bacterium are utilized together with materials absorbed from the outside medium. Thirdly, all the protein of the 'phage offspring is derived from materials in the bacterium plus some from outside. Fourthly, when the 'phage particles are subjected to "osmotic shock" e.g. by addition of distilled water, they lose their DNA to the surrounding medium, leaving only the protein envelopes. In this condition, the 'phage particles can still attack and destroy bacteria but cannot replicate themselves.

Viruses and Disease

is now certain that a very large number of plant and animal diseases e caused by viruses. Some of the commoner plant diseases are: af mosaic disease of many plants, especially potato, tobacco, and mato; petal mosaic disease in many flowers, e.g. tulip, sugarbeet d turnip yellows; swollen shoot disease of cocoa trees. In many of e plant virus infections, it is known that the vector is an insect. phides, flea-beetles, leaf-hoppers and many others are known to ansmit virus disease. There are also instances of seed-borne infection. Some virus diseases have serious effects on man and on his domestic imals. A few of the better known are: foot-and-mouth disease of ttle; distemper and hard pad in dogs; polyhedral disease of cater- llars; fowl pest and swine fever; myxomatosis in rabbits; and, in an, poliomyelitis, yellow fever, smallpox, influenza, measles, rabies, erman measles and the common cold. For some of these, definite ctors are known; yellow fever is transmitted by the mosquito, *Aedes gypti*; myxomatosis is spread by the rabbit-flea, *Spilopsyllus cuniculi*. abies virus enters with the saliva of an infected dog when it bites. lyhedral disease of caterpillars is transmitted in the eggs. Inhalation infected droplets or direct skin contact, are sufficient in some diseases. Protection against some of the more serious diseases is carried out using an attenuated strain of the virus or by vaccination with a nilar but harmless strain. The former is used against foot-and-mouth ease and distemper, while the latter is used against smallpox.

liomyelitis

Three types of virus are known and it is comforting to realize that proximately 80 per cent of human beings have natural protection ainst all three. The virus appears to enter by the mouth and hence ntaminated food and dirty hands are suspect. In the first place, it acks the epithelium of the alimentary canal and later may appear in e blood. If it penetrates into the nervous system, then it proceeds to ack the motor cells; if sufficient are destroyed, paralysis results, and extreme cases, death. There are approximately 10 000 motor cells pplying each limb; destruction of more than 80 per cent will mean rmanent paralysis. When the organs of breathing or of swallowing e affected, there is a critical condition; in the former case, the iron g assists breathing; in the latter case it is very essential that the tient shall lie face downward, otherwise vomiting may cause choking d possibly autolysis of the lungs.

n several countries, vaccines which have been developed, seem to mise a large measure of immunity.

Evolution of Viruses

There are three current theories as to the possible origin of viruses.
The first, that they were precursors of living cells, can be discarded as
unlikely in view of their very simple structure, and the fact that they
can only multiply in living cells. The second theory, that they are
degenerate descendants of bacteria, has more to commend it, especially
in view of the fact that the Rickettsia and Psittacosis bacteria, themselves
somewhat degenerate, are also of very small size. But it must be noted
that unlike bacteria, viruses cannot be cultured on artificial media, they
show no binary fission, they do not respond to anti-biotics, and they
do not contain both DNA and RNA. In all these respects, they differ
from bacteria, whereas the Rickettsia and Psittacosis groups differ
from bacteria only in the fact that they cannot be grown in artificial
media.

The third theory postulates that viruses are "rogue genes," detached
portions of nucleic acid or nucleo-protein from the chromosomes, or
errant lengths of RNA from the cytoplasm. In favour of this view, we
have the fact of their specificity. They can only multiply in specific
types of cells and it may be that their DNA or RNA fits only into certain codes and there elicits replication. In other types of cells they can
not fit into the scheme of things.

The question is undecided but is interesting to contemplate in view
of the fact that some types of cancer are apparently caused by viruses.

The viruses change; the changes are in the nucleic acid; such
changes may be called mutations. A mild strain can give rise to a
virulent strain, such as, for example, the Spanish influenza after the
1914–18 war, the Asian 'flu of more recent times, and the various
poliomyelitis peaks. There is also some evidence in favour of the
development of tolerance by the hosts. In the King Edward potato
plant, there is a virus which is quite harmless and is never transmitted
to other kinds of potato plant under natural conditions. But if a
portion of a King Edward plant is grafted on a potato plant of a
susceptible strain, the virus multiplies, and symptoms of disease soon
appear. The myxoma virus, which caused the epidemics of myxomatosis
in rabbits, is transmitted by fleas in England and by mosquitos in
Australia. The virus is able to multiply in both hosts; in the insect
without apparent harm; in the rabbits with serious disease. Strains
of rabbits with genetic resistance to myxomatosis survived the epidemic
and are now increasing rapidly. Similarly it appears that many human
beings are resistant to the polio virus or tolerant of it. The common
cold virus is lethal in some parts of the world, but in others such as
Western Europe, its effects are comparatively mild.

INTERFERON

In 1937, it was discovered that monkeys infected by one virus were thereby protected against another. By 1943, "killed virus" was being used as an *interfering agent* in animal tissues. In 1957, such killed virus was mixed with cells and both were incubated. Later, a protein, given the name of *interferon*, was extracted. It seems that this substance is produced by the cells of many species infected by various viruses. Interferon affects glycolytic activity, preventing the formation of ATP and thus possibly there is insufficient energy for virus replication. Interferon has certain important properties. Firstly, it is non-toxic in doses sufficient to suppress a virus; secondly, it has no antigenic effect in the body, and thirdly, it has a wide range of action.

There has been some success in pioneer experiments with human subjects. The experiments were performed with use of the interferon in conjunction with the vaccinia virus. The subjects who were first injected with interferon showed no "take" with the normal vaccination process in the great majority of cases. There seems to be some possibility of stimulating human subjects to make their own interferon. It is early to prophesy, but here may lie the remedy against some of the worst scourges of mankind.

MYCOPLASMATALES (PPLO)

The smallest known organisms, all parasitic, are placed in this group, sometimes called PPLO (i.e. pleuro-pneumonia-like organisms) because they resemble the microbes causing bovine pleuropneumonia. Many types have been isolated from soil, sewage, plants and animals. One, the *Eaton agent*, causes a common type of human pneumonia; one causes "witches broom" disease in potatoes, and several cause various "yellows" diseases in plants.

The spherical *Mycoplasma laidlawi*, with a diameter of about 100 nm at one stage, is the smallest known. These *elementary bodies*, as they are called, grow through an intermediate stage into larger bodies about 300 nm in diameter. Then follows one of two courses; each large body may undergo fission to produce intermediate stages, or may undergo sporulation to produce a number of elementary bodies.

These organisms grow, reproduce, possess lipoid-protein membranes; they have a double DNA helix and ribosomes with RNA. Theoretical calculations suggest that the lower limit of size for living organisms is about 50 nm diameter with possibly 150 large molecules. The smallest PPLO are about twice this diameter ($8 \times$ mass) and possess about 1200 large molecules. It is possible that there may be even smaller organisms.

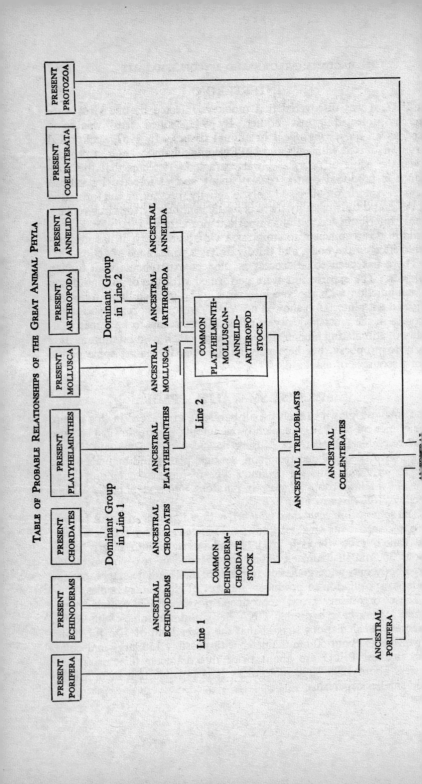

TABLE OF PROBABLE RELATIONSHIPS OF THE GREAT ANIMAL PHYLA

COELOMATE ANIMALS 5: MOLLUSCA

The phylum Mollusca, containing over 100,000 living and probably a greater number of fossil species, is one of the largest and most important in the animal kingdom. There is a vast range in size from minute snails

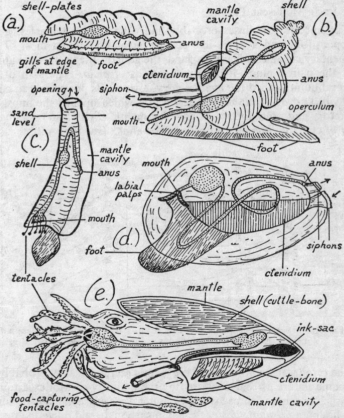

Fig. A.1. Diagrammatic representations of the five molluscan classes. (a) *Chiton*; Amphineura. (b) Whelk; Gastropoda. (c) *Dentalium*; Scaphopoda (d) Swan Mussel; Lamellibranchiata. (e) Cuttle-fish; Cephalopoda.

and clams a few millimetres long to the giant squids, 15 m long exclusive of the tentacles, 6 metres in maximum circumference and weighing two or three tonne. There is an equally wide range in body form including the small flattened chitons which creep about on the rocks of the seashore, a staggering variety of bivalves, the snails, slugs, and their marine relatives, the peculiar burrowing tooth-shells of sandy or muddy substrata, and the most highly evolved are the predatory cephalopods such as the octopus, squid and cuttle-fish (*see* Fig. A.1). In spite of this great variety of form, it is not too difficult to relate them all to one standard type which the chitons of today resemble and which the ancestral forms may have possessed.

The Basic Molluscan Pattern

The ancestral molluscs probably had a head with tentacles, a flat creeping foot and a dome-like *visceral hump* containing most of the alimentary canal, the digestive gland, the gonads, the heart, the kidneys and the paired plume-like gills known as *ctenidia*. The skin of the visceral hump, called the *mantle*, grew downwards posteriorly to cover a cavity known as the *mantle cavity* into which opened the anus, the excretory and reproductive ducts. The mantle cavity also contained a pair of ctenidia, one on each side of the anus. (*see* Fig. A.2).

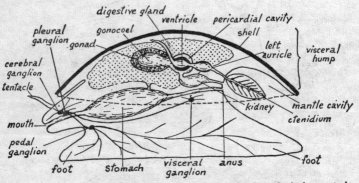

Fig. A.2. Diagram illustrating the main features of a hypothetical ancestral mollusc, much like modern chitons and pre-torsion gastropods.

The ectodermal epithelium of the mantle secreted a shell probably of the same nature as that possessed by the majority of Mollusca today. The shell consists of three layers; an outer *periostracum*, made of horny conchiolin, a *prismatic layer* of calcium carbonate laid down in crystals at right angles to the shell surface, and a smooth *nacreous layer* also of calcium carbonate (*see* Fig. A.3). The periostracum is produced by the cells in the fold at the edge of the mantle, the prismatic layer by the thickened edge, and the nacre by the whole upper surface.

As in the modern chitons, the heart probably consisted of a median ventricle with two lateral auricles. Blood pumped from the ventricle

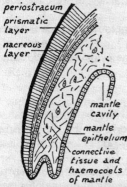

periostracum
prismatic layer
nacreous layer
mantle cavity
mantle epithelium
connective tissue and haemocoels of mantle

Fig. A.3. Vertical section through shell and edge of mantle.

passed through an extensive haemocoel and was returned via the auricles, the coelom being reduced by this haemocoel to the pericardium, the cavities of the gonads, and of the kidneys.

In the nervous system there were probably *cerebral* and *pleural ganglia* above the gut, *pedal ganglia* below it and even more posterior *visceral ganglia*, all these ganglia being connected by commissures on each side.

The *buccal mass* behind the mouth, in most modern forms, contains a highly characteristic structure called the *radula*, a strip of horny basement membrane in the centre of the floor of the buccal cavity. On this membrane are fastened many rows of minute recurved teeth (*see*

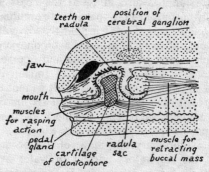

teeth on radula
position of cerebral ganglion
jaw
mouth
muscles for rasping action
pedal gland
cartilage of odontophore
radula sac
muscle for retracting buccal mass

Fig. A.4. Sagittal vertical section through the head of a snail.

Fig. A.4) constantly proliferated from a *radula sac*. In the buccal mass are so-called cartilages which form firm bases for the radula muscles which move the organ so that it rasps against a transverse bar in the roof of the mouth, and thus forms a feeding mechanism. The most ancient molluscan forms of which we have any knowledge possessed a radula.

Assuming that our ancestral form was marine, it probably had a trochophore larva in its life history, as indeed most marine molluscs have today. This is some evidence of relationship with Annelida (*see* p. 1301).

The Class Gastropoda

Although retaining all the basic molluscan characteristics outlined previously, the gastropods exhibit in varying degrees two unusual features not found in any other class of mollusca. They are *coiling* and *torsion*.

In the alimentary canal, digestion and absorption are almost entirely restricted to a dorsal diverticulum which develops into the digestive gland. The growth of this forms the major part of the visceral hump; it grows until it falls over, the first step in coiling. Growth is then continued with one side growing faster than the other and thus the whole structure becomes twisted into a compact spiral. If growth had been symmetrical, a long cone would be produced which would have made locomotion very difficult. The compact spiral offers less interference with locomotion.

Torsion is a strange process whereby the visceral hump, at a particular stage in development, rotates through 180°. The mantle cavity containing the ctenidia, anus, reproductive and excretory apertures, is at first in the posterior position. With torsion, the mantle cavity is in front, above the head, and the structures associated with it are also anterior. The torsion has also involved the heart so that the two auricles, originally posterior to the ventricle are eventually in front of it. The nervous system is also affected in that the visceral connectives on each side from pleural to visceral ganglia become crossed over each other, one passing dorsal to the intestine and one ventral to it, thus forming a figure 8. The whole process of torsion is usually rapid taking but a few minutes in some species. It cannot therefore be due to differential growth, but is brought about by muscular action, the only region actually twisted being the neck of tissue between the visceral hump and the rest of the body (*see* Fig. A.5).

The probable evolutionary advantage of torsion is concerned with the direction of the respiratory current of water over the ctenidia. With the ctenidia in the mantle cavity in the posterior position, the cilia would have to draw in a respiratory current in opposition to the flow of the water and the direction of movement. With the mantle cavity in the anterior position the work of the cilia is augmented by the

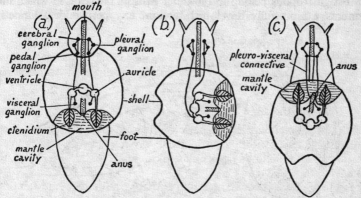

Fig. A.5. Diagram illustrating torsion. (a) Before torsion. (b) 90° torsion. (c) 180° torsion.

flow of the water and the mantle cavity is continually flushed with fresh sea-water (*see* Fig. A.6).

Torsion has however also brought the anus to the anterior position. To prevent contamination of the respiratory current by faecal material, three different types of adaptation have been evolved—

1. The shell develops a hole or a series of holes; the anus is retracted behind the ctenidia and water passes in through the mantle opening

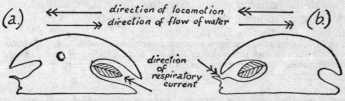

Fig. A.6. Diagram showing the respiratory advantages of torsion.

over the gills then out through the holes carrying faecal material with it, e.g. *Haliotis*, the ormer (*see* Fig. A.7 (*a* and *b*)).

2. One of the ctenidia is lost and the respiratory current sweeps laterally through the mantle cavity, e.g. *Buccinum*, the whelk (*see* Fig. A.7(*c*)).

3. The ctenidia are reduced or lost and the whole mantle cavity becomes respiratory, in some cases as in *Patella*, the limpet, developing pallial gills at the mantle edges (*see* Fig. A.7(*d*)).

Most gastropods belong to the order Prosobranchiata, in which the members exhibit fully developed torsion, e.g. periwinkles, limpets,

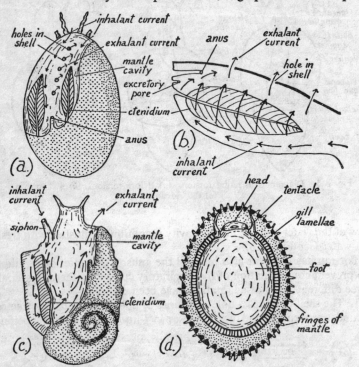

Fig. A.7. Respiratory currents in some prosobranch molluscs. (*a*) *Haliotis;* dorsal view with shell removed. (*b*) *Haliotis;* vertical section of mantle cavity. (*c*) *Buccinum;* dorsal view with shell removed. (*d*) *Patella;* ventral view.

ormers, whelks and the peculiar heteropods, which are predatory pelagic prosobranchs using the laterally compressed foot as a fin, e.g. *Carinaria* (*see* Fig. A.8(*a*)). The second order, Opisthobranchiata, contains forms which have undergone varying degrees of detorsion always associated with the partial or complete loss of the shell and uncoiling and shortening of the visceral hump. The mantle cavity becomes posterior, the ctenidia tend to disappear and accessory respiratory organs develop, e.g. Doris, a slug-like nudibranch (*see*

Fig. A.8(*b*)). This order also includes the numerous pteropods or sea-butterflies e.g. *Cavolinia* (*see* Fig. A.8(*c*)). Members of the third order, the Pulmonata, have the anterior mantle cavity modified to

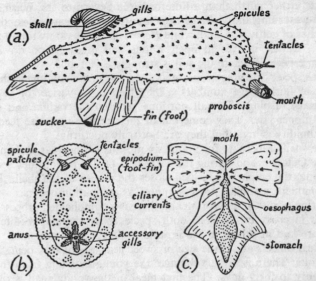

Fig. A.8. (*a*) Side view of *Carinaria*, a heteropod prosobranch, shown in the upside-down swimming position. (*b*) Dorsal view of *Doris*, a nudibranch opisthobranch. (*c*) Dorsal view of *Cavolinia*, a pteropod opisthobranch (sea-butterfly).

form a lung with a vascular roof and a small external opening. There are a few sea-shore forms which breathe air, but the vast majority are water-snails and land-snails.

THE GARDEN SNAIL

The common British garden snail, *Helix aspersa*, is distributed widely in the northern hemisphere. The larger edible snail, *Helix pomatia*, is less common in Great Britain but is quite plentiful on the European mainland where in many localities it is bred and reared for use as food. *Helix pomatia*, which is larger and better for dissection, is described here. The differences between the two species are relatively insignificant.

Habitat and Habits

Both *Helix aspersa* and *Helix pomatia* are entirely terrestrial. The former is widely distributed in the British Isles except for Northern

Scotland and is also a common species in Western Europe and in the Mediterranean region. It is also found in some of the Atlantic islands. *Helix pomatia* is much more localized in the British Isles and is not found further north than a line from the Severn to the Wash, nor in south-west England. *Helix aspersa* frequents gardens and other stretches of cultivated land, while *Helix pomatia* is rarely found in such areas. Rather it lives in open woods and quarries, on downs and banks, especially where the soil is strongly calcareous.

Both species are gregarious, tending to rest in the daytime in sheltered spots in fairly large numbers. They feed on a variety of vegetable materials, rasping off small portions between the radula and the so-called upper jaw. They come out of their resting-places to feed when the humidity is high, but they are not truly nocturnal.

The snails hibernate for about six months of the year, commencing in late October, and during the early part of this period they secrete a covering, the epiphragm, which closes the mouth of the shell. In hot, dry summers, a similar process known as aestivation occurs.

Pairing occurs in late spring and there is a complicated process which results in cross-fertilization, both species being hermaphrodite. The eggs are laid in a hole in the ground in July. They are small, white, spherical objects about the size of sweet peas, about fifty being laid in one hole. There is no larval stage, the young hatching from the eggs in twenty to forty days. The first meal of the young snail is the egg-shell. Length of life in both species is five or six years.

External Features

Although the body can be completely withdrawn into the shell, it is described here in the fully extended condition. (*See* Fig. A.9). The body of a well-grown specimen is 8 to 9 cm in length from the front of

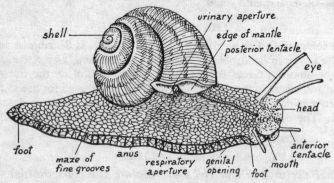

Fig. A.9. Side view of *Helix pomatia* shown fully extended.

the head to the end of the foot; the height from the base of the foot to the top of the shell is about 3·8 to 5·2 cm. The shell is balanced in the middle of the body. Three regions are obvious, the head, the foot and the visceral hump entirely contained within the shell. There is no clear line of demarcation between the head and the foot. The body has a rough texture due to a maze of slight grooves: the colour is a pale yellow to grey, except in the area of the mantle where it is yellowish.

The head and foot are flattened dorsoventrally with a blunt anterior end and a pointed posterior end. Almost at the base of the front of the head is the mouth, a transverse slit with slightly thickened lateral and ventral lips. Above the mouth on each side are the short anterior tentacles and almost on the top of the head are the much longer posterior tentacles bearing the small black eyes at their tips. The skin of these tentacles is quite transparent and within, the strands of muscle which turn the tentacles outside-in can be seen (*see* Fig. A.21).

Between the edge of the shell and the body, the thick yellowish edge of the mantle can be seen. It is fused to the body everywhere except for the round respiratory aperture on the right side. Immediately behind this aperture, in the thickened edge of the mantle, is the anus and above the anus lies the urinary aperture, barely to be seen. The common reproductive aperture is below the posterior tentacles; from it a prominent line goes back under the mantle.

The shell consists of four or five turns and is usually coiled to the right or *dextral*, though occasional *sinistral* specimens are found. These two terms are quite arbitrary, but since they are often used as

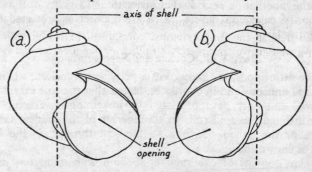

Fig. A.10. (*a*) Dextral, and (*b*) sinistral shells of *Helix pomatia*.

distinguishing characteristics in classification, their origin is described here. The shell is held with its mouth facing the observer and the apex upward; if the mouth of the shell is then to the right of the vertical axis, the shell is termed dextral; if to the left, it is termed sinistral (*see*

Fig. A.10). This direction of coiling seems to be controlled by a single pair of Mendelian factors, the sinistral being double recessive.

The shell is thick and strong with a background colour of yellow or cream with several pale brown bands following the direction of coiling. These bands are interrupted by yellow or white streaks at right angles to the bands. The shell is supported internally by a hollow axis called the *columella* to which the snail is anchored by a *columella muscle*. The contraction of this muscle pulls the head and foot into the shell. At the base of the columella is a small round hole, the *umbilicus* (*see* Fig. A.11). The shell has the typical three layers, outer conchiolin, the

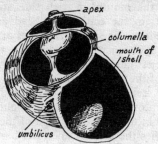

Fig. A.11. Vertical section of shell.

prismatic and nacreous calcareous layers. In fresh-water snails particularly, the conchiolin prevents the dissolving of the calcareous layers by acids in the water. This also applies to terrestrial snails especially during the hibernating period. The strength and rigidity of the shell is given by the calcareous layers which are themselves protected by the outer horny layer.

Body Wall, Coelom and Segmentation

As in the arthropods, the absence of a perivisceral coelom, which is so obvious in annelids and in chordates, means that the true extent of the body wall can only be appreciated by imagining a vertical section cutting through the epidermis to the interior of the kidney, the pericardium or the gonad. Such a section, cut through to the kidney coelom is shown in Fig. A.12.

The skin consists of columnar epithelium with numerous mucous cells and scattered sensory cells all secured to the basement membrane. The connective tissue of the dermis is like a meshwork with the spaces constituting haemocoels. There is little unstriated muscle in the kidney wall but a greater concentration of connective tissue, then the internal epithelium or peritoneum is thrown into folds. Beyond this epithelium is the kidney cavity, the renocoel.

The coelom arises in development as three pairs of sacs probably all originally interconnected. In the snail, the renocoel remains connected to the pericardial cavity, while the gonocoel never has any such connexion. The loss of all three coelomic sacs on one side is associated with coiling.

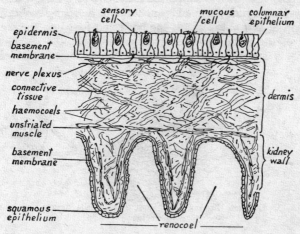

Fig. A.12. Diagrammatic section of body wall in the kidney region.

The only sign of metameric segmentation is that of the presence of three pairs of coelomic sacs in the embryo. There is no segmentation to be seen in the nervous system or the vascular system. Indeed, the only mollusc which shows signs of segmentation which are at all convincing is Neopilina, discovered in 1957 (*see* p. 1301).

The Skeleton

The lack of the arthropod exoskeleton or the vertebrate endoskeleton has probably been responsible for the name of the phylum and one of its main characteristics, i.e. soft-bodied. There is certainly no external cuticle but the shell may be considered an exoskeletal structure although it is only adherent to the animal at the mantle edge and at the columella muscle (*see* Fig. A.13). In the bivalves, the shell also provides for the insertion of important muscles concerned with closing the valves and protruding and retracting the foot. Since the shell provides protection and attachment for muscles, it may be considered a skeletal structure. The only other hard structures which may be regarded as skeletal are the jaw, a horny plate in the roof of the buccal cavity, and the so-called cartilage of the odontophore (*see* p. 1271) which supports muscles concerned with the movement of the radula (*see* Fig. A.4).

As in all soft-bodied coelomates, the fluid cavities provide a hydrostatic skeleton. In this case, the main cavities are the extensive haemocoels, and changes of shape are effected by the contraction of muscles

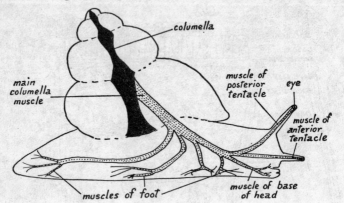

Fig. A.13. Diagram showing attachment of columella muscle and its main branches.

which squeeze the blood from one region to another. It is similar to the process by which we can alter the shape of a small elongated balloon by squeezing with the hands at one or two points.

The connective tissue always has a skeletal function in binding all parts of the body together; also its elasticity helps recovery of normal shape after distortion by muscular activity.

Nutrition

The alimentary canal consists of the mouth, buccal cavity, pharynx, crop, stomach, intestine and anus. The mouth is a transverse slit with a prominent dorsal lip and two slight lateral lips. On the roof of the buccal cavity is a curved horny plate with nine slight longitudinal ridges. This plate is often called the jaw. Behind and below the jaw is a large raised mass, the *odontophore*, which bears on its upper surface a broad longitudinal strip of horny basement membrane, the radula. In a full-grown specimen the radula has about 145 transverse rows of small pointed recurved teeth with 107 in each row (*see* Fig. A.14). The teeth are all of the same type, unlike the highly differentiated teeth found in many other molluscs (*see* Fig. A.14). Behind the odontophore is a blind caecum, the radula sac, where both the horny membrane

ınd the teeth are produced (*see* Fig. A.4). As the front teeth are pro-
ɡressively worn down, they are loosened and swallowed with the food.
Ƀlunted teeth can often be found in the faeces. The slow production
ɔf new teeth and the gradual moving forward of the membrane ensure

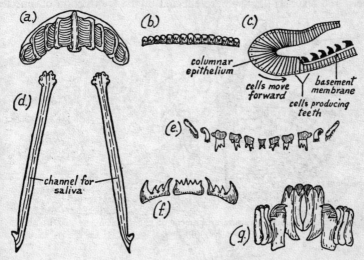

Fig. A.14. (*a*) Jaw of *Helix*, seen ventrally. (*b*) Teeth of *Helix*, portion of one
transverse row. (*c*) V.S. radula sac of *Helix*. (*d*) Teeth of *Conus;* only two in
each transverse row; they act as poisonous daggers. (*e*) Representative teeth
from one transverse row of *Planorbis*, modified for rasping algae from stones.
(*f*) Teeth of *Buccinum*, the whelk, carnivorous. (*g*) Teeth of *Patella*, the limpet,
for browsing on sea-weeds.

that the teeth in contact with food material are always sharp enough for
rasping. The entrances of the two salivary ducts are dorsolateral,
opposite the posterior end of the odontophore.

Behind the pharynx a fairly wide oesophagus leads into a dilated crop
where food is stored temporarily. A narrower extension of the crop
passes below the mantle up into the digestive gland where the true
stomach appears as a small dilatation which receives two ducts from
the gland. The intestine then proceeds forward over the roof of the
mantle cavity to open at the anus just behind the respiratory aperture.
There is very little muscle in the gut wall, the movement of food being
accomplished mainly by cilia. There are paired salivary glands (*see*
Fig. A.15) flattened laterally against the oesophagus and crop. The
ducts pass forward laterally and then dorsally to open into the pharynx
near the odontophore.

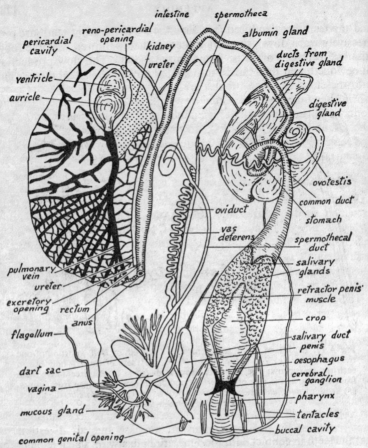

Fig. A.15. Dorsal dissection of *H. pomatia* with viscera displayed.

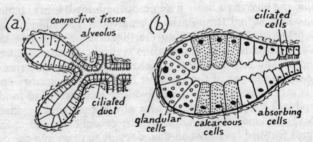

Fig. A.16. (*a*) Section of portion of the digestive gland. (*b*) Section of one alveolus.

The digestive gland, often called the liver, occupies most of the visceral hump. It is brown in colour, and in nature it is a very solid mass of tubules constituting a racemose gland. From it, two main ducts, one upper and one lower, and a number of smaller ducts open into the stomach. The tubules are ciliated except at their extremities where they form slightly dilated alveoli (*see* Fig. A.16). Each alveolus contains cells of three kinds: glandular cells which produce a digestive juice, absorbing cells which take in small particles by amoeboid action, and calcareous cells which produce calcium hydroxide, $Ca(OH)_2$, to neutralize the organic acids in the food material.

Digestion, Absorption and Storage

The minute teeth rasping against the horny jaw ensure that only extremely small particles enter the pharynx. The food consists mainly of leaves, though fruits, shoots, berries, fungi and decayed vegetation may be eaten. Small portions are seized by the lips and dragged by the radula against the jaw-plate. There the backward-pointing teeth tear off small fragments, the mass accumulating on the radula being pushed backward into the pharynx and mixed with the saliva.

The saliva contains mucus and an amylase which digests starch released from broken cells. The food mass, with a great deal of mucus, is passed along the oesophagus by a mixture of weak peristalsis and strong ciliary action. The brown secretion of the digestive gland is found in the crop and in the stomach. It contains calcium hydroxide to render the contents slightly alkaline and a further amylase. It was formerly supposed that this juice also contained enzymes capable of digesting cellulose but it has been shown, by Florkin and his colleagues in France, that cellulose digestion is accomplished by bacteria. The juice does contain an amylase but all digestion of lipides and proteins takes place intracellularly in vacuoles in the amoeboid cells found in the alveoli of the digestive gland. The gland has ebb and flow periods, the cilia being capable of reversal of beat. Thus at one period there is active secretion and the brown liquid is passed into the gut. Then secretion ceases, the ciliary beat is reversed and liquid containing minute food fragments is driven into the alveoli. There is absorption of monosaccharide sugars and water all along the intestine. The faecal material, brown in colour, contains largely undigested cellulose.

The food absorbed and digested in the alveoli is passed in solution into the blood and circulated by the vascular system. There is little food storage when the animal is in an active period but during hibernation and aestivation, there is storage of fat and glycogen in the digestive gland and in the muscles.

Respiration

The mantle cavity has been transformed into a lung by the fusion of
the edge of the mantle with the body everywhere except at the respiratory opening or *pneumostome*. There is thus a large enclosed chamber
with an external opening controlled by a valve (*see* Fig. A.17). The

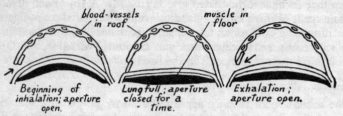

Fig. A.17. Three stages in the breathing of a snail.

floor of the cavity is arched upward and plentifully supplied with
muscles. The roof is thin and ridged on the inner surface by large
dilated blood-vessels forming a branched system. All the lateral
blood-vessels lead into a central one, the pulmonary vein, in which
the blood flows directly into the auricle of the heart (*see* Fig. A.18). It
is worthy of note that in molluscs with paired ctenidia, each has a
branchial vein in which the blood flows into the auricle of that particular side.

In inhalation, the muscles below the floor of the lung contract, thus
flattening the floor. This causes a reduced pressure on the air inside the
lung compared with the atmospheric air. There is therefore a flow of
air into the lung cavity. The pneumostome is then closed. The muscles
of the floor are relaxed and haemocoelic pressure from beneath causes
them to arch upward. The pneumostome is opened and some of the
air is expelled (*see* Fig. A.17).

Breathing is not regular or rhythmical; it varies considerably
according to the degree of activity. During hibernation it may cease
altogether. It is estimated that on average 10 per cent of the oxygen in
the enclosed air is absorbed into the veins and replaced by an equal
amount of carbon dioxide. The blood pigment haemocyanin has an
affinity for oxygen under high tension forming oxyhaemocyanin. This
is distributed to the tissues by the vascular system. Under the lower
oxygen tension in the tissues, oxygen is released from the haemocyanin.

The Blood Vascular System

As in the arthropods, the blood system is an open one as opposed to the
closed blood system of annelids and chordates, in which the blood is

all contained in vessels. There are arteries, which distribute the blood from the ventricle, no capillaries, but a series of spaces in the connective tissue known as haemocoels. From these the blood is collected into veins which lead to the auricle. The haemocoels are not coelomic cavities but relics of the blastocoel; they are not blood-vessels because they have no endothelial lining and no muscle.

The heart lies somewhat posteriorly to the left of the mid-line with the auricle in front of the ventricle. Both chambers have the same capacity and are connected by a valved passage which allows flow of the blood in one direction. The muscular wall of the auricle is about half as thick as that of the ventricle. The rate of heart beat depends largely on temperature; at 30°C it is 50 to 60 beats per minute, at 15°C it is about 10, and during hibernation about 5.

From the ventricle, the blood enters a single aorta which immediately divides into two, one branch supplying all the organs of the visceral hump and the other taking the blood forward to the head region and then turning backward ventrally almost to the end of the foot (*see*

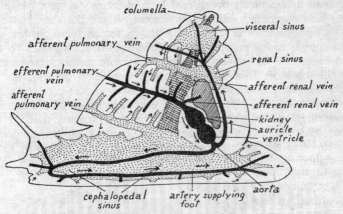

Fig. A.18. Blood vascular system of *H. pomatia*.

Fig. A.18). These two aortae give off many branches, which, after subdivision, have open ends, and the blood then passes into the haemocoels.

From the smaller haemocoels, the blood passes into three larger ones: the *cephalopedal sinus* which drains the head and foot, the *visceral sinus* which collects blood from the visceral hump, and a *renal sinus* at the side of the columella muscle. From these three large sinuses, the blood flows into a looped afferent pulmonary vein which passes forward along the left side of the mantle, around the collar and backward along the right side of the mantle. Blood from this afferent pulmonary vein is distributed in small spaces in the roof of the mantle cavity and also to the kidney. From the kidney, it is collected into an efferent renal vein which joins the efferent pulmonary vein just before it joins the auricle. There is thus a renal portal system.

The aortic blood pressure is very low, about 1 kN m^{-2} (compare man, 20 kN m^{-2}), but it must be remembered that the snail is a relatively inactive mollusc. The circulation is aided considerably by any change of body shape when the muscles squeeze the blood from one region to another.

The blood contains haemocyanin in solution and numerous stellate amoebocytes which have considerable powers of phagocytosis. They may assist nutrition, they certainly play a part in excretion (see p. 1288), they cluster together in enormous numbers in clotted blood, and they are responsible for repair to a broken portion of the shell.

Locomotion

The snail moves on its broad foot by a gliding movement which has often been compared with the movement of turbellarians. However, the foot of the snail is not ciliated. In its search for food, the snail often crosses rough ground and will climb walls and fences. To ease its passage and to prevent damage to its soft surface, it secretes a mucoid substance from a pedal gland just beneath the mouth. The gland is a simple invagination bearing many mucus-producing cells (see Fig. A.4). The slime is spread out by pressure of the flattened anterior region and thus a carpet of mucus forms a trail, at first rather sticky but soon hardening. The speed of movement is very slow for such a relatively large animal, rarely exceeding 10 to 13 cm per minute.

Fig. A.19. Ridges and furrows on the ventral surface during crawling.

The apparent steadiness is due to the rapid succession of waves of contraction with small amplitude which pass from anterior to posterior. The foot is almost entirely made of a loose muscular network with numerous blood spaces. The muscle fibres run in three directions, longitudinal, transverse, and dorso-ventral. The method of movement can best be described by considering one particular small portion of the foot. The dorso-ventral fibres contract, raising the region above the slime and then the transverse fibres contract squeezing the blood forward and thus the region of foot in front of this point is elongated. Both these sets of fibres then relax and the region is again flat on the slime trail. Then the longitudinal fibres contract, pulling the posterior region towards this fixed point. Thus the movement is essentially a succession of pushing and pulling. If the foot is examined from beneath when the snail is creeping on a glass plate, about thirty transverse ridges and furrows can be seen (*see* Fig. A.19). The ridges are the regions in contact with the substratum while the furrows are the regions which are temporarily raised. The rippling of these ridges and furrows along the body can also be seen.

When the snail withdraws into its shell after some obnoxious stimulus, the movement is rapid. It is caused by the contraction of the columellar muscle so that first the head and then the foot are rapidly withdrawn (*see* Fig. A.13). On emergence, the movement is very much slower and is due to the squeezing of blood from the main sinuses into the foot which emerges first and then the head.

Growth

Growth is normal and ceases in the third year, hence only two or three annual rings can be seen on the shell. There is little power of regeneration of damaged tissue because the very fluid contents of the body easily escape and become dispersed. Small wounds are first sealed by a clotting mechanism due to large numbers of amoebocytes which quickly appear at the site of damage. Later, the superficial body layers are regenerated beneath the clot. Broken parts of the shell are also repaired by these amoebocytes which form a dense sheet on the surface at the site of damage. This sheet then becomes calcified with calcium carbonate transported from the digestive gland by the amoebocytes.

Excretion

Carbon dioxide is excreted largely from the network of blood sinuses in the roof of the mantle cavity from whence it passes out of the body at the pneumostome. A certain amount of carbon dioxide also passes into the atmosphere from the skin.

The organ of nitrogenous excretion is the single kidney which represents the right side of bilateral forms. It is a large yellow structure situated in the roof of the mantle with its posterior region alongside the pericardium (*see* Fig. A.15). There are numerous internal folds covered by cells which contain uric acid. The cavity of the kidney, which is coelomic, is connected to the pericardial cavity by a very narrow reno-pericardial canal. The ureter is a thin-walled, narrow tube which follows the course of the rectum to open on the lip of the pneumostome just above the anus.

The kidney deals with excretory material from blood sinuses of the renal portal system and from the coelomic fluid. The endothelial cells contain uric acid derived from the blood; this accumulates in the renocoel as small white spherules which pass down the ureter by ciliary action; they are discharged at about five-week intervals in *H. pomatia*. The coelomic fluid contains the filtrate exuded under high hydrostatic pressure from the heart. It contains mainly excess salts and glucose. Osmoregulation occurs by resorption of glucose, salts and water into the blood sinuses around the kidney and ureter. Very little fluid is finally discharged, conservation of water being an important factor for terrestrial success. Amoebocytes convey particles from the blood into the gut lumen, into the pericardial cavity and renocoel and possibly through the body wall to the external surface.

Sensitivity, Co-ordination and Behaviour

In the central nervous system, the ganglia are mainly concentrated in a ring around the oesophagus, all tightly bound up in strong connective tissue. The only ganglia outside this so-called brain are the buccal ganglia.

Above the oesophagus, immediately behind the pharynx are the paired cerebral ganglia. From these, two pairs of commissures, cerebropedal and cerebropleural, pass backward and downward underneath the oesophagus to join the pedal and pleural ganglia respectively. In this sub-oesophageal complex, paired pedal, pleural and visceral ganglia form a compact ring-like mass with the anterior aorta passing through the centre of the ring (*see* Fig. A.20). The small buccal ganglia are situated near the ends of the salivary ducts and are connected to the cerebral ganglia by paired cerebro-buccal commissures.

Peripheral Nervous System

From the cerebral ganglia, there are paired nerves extending forward to the anterior tentacles, to the lips, to the posterior tentacles, to the integument of the anterior region of the body behind the head. From the pedal ganglia, there are several pairs of nerves branching among the musculature of the foot. From the pleural ganglia, nerves pass to the mantle and to the integument of the anterior region of the body behind the head. The visceral ganglia supply single large nerves to the visceral hump, the columella muscle, and the lung, and paired tegumentary

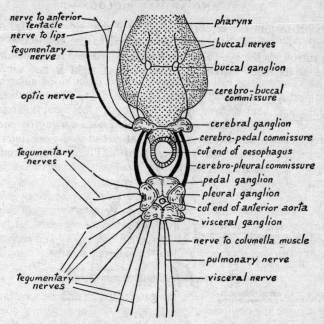

nerve to anterior tentacle
nerve to lips
Tegumentary nerve

optic nerve

Tegumentary nerves

Tegumentary nerves

pharynx
buccal nerves
buccal ganglion
cerebro-buccal commissure

cerebral ganglion
cerebro-pedal commissure
cut end of oesophagus
cerebro-pleural commissure
pedal ganglion
pleural ganglion
cut end of anterior aorta
visceral ganglion
nerve to columella muscle
pulmonary nerve
visceral nerve

Fig. A.20. Dorsal view of central nervous system and anterior part of peripheral nervous system (paired nerves are shown only on the left).

nerves to the posterior region. From the buccal ganglia, paired nerves pass to the buccal mass.

Sense Organs

The major sense organs are the eyes and the statocysts. Apart from these, there are tactile sensory cells all over the exposed parts of the body except the sole of the foot, and olfactory cells on the tentacles, on the lips, on the front region of the foot, and, more widely scattered, all round the edges of the foot.

The eyes are situated at the ends of the anterior tentacles and can easily be seen as small black spots. They are fairly simple structures compared with the complex eyes of cephalopods. Above each eye, there is a transparent epidermis and a transparent layer of connective tissue. A horny spherical lens almost fills the optic cup, the lens lying in a thin clear gelatinous layer of fluid. The optic cup itself consists of a layer of pigmented cells, then the retina. From all parts of the retina, nerve fibres converge to form the optic nerve which traverses the haemocoel to join the cerebral ganglion of that side (*see* Fig. A.21). The retractor muscle of the eye is attached to the connective tissue which surrounds the eye-ball; this muscle is fastened to the columellar muscle at its inner extremity. The sense of sight is not very well

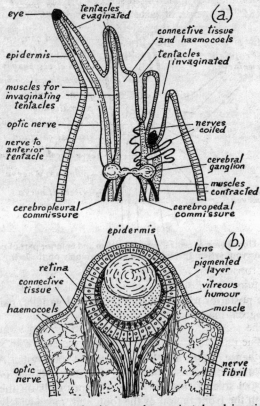

Fig. A.21. (*a*) Diagram showing tentacles evaginated and invaginated. (*b*) Vertical section of posterior tentacle and the eye.

developed; the eye perceives intensity and up to a distance of about 10 cm, there is perception of form.

The statocysts, or otocysts, are minute paired spherical sacs buried in the tissues of the foot behind the oesophagus. Each vesicle consists of an epithelium containing supporting cells, and cells with hair-like sensory processes; from these sensory cells, nerve fibres converge to form the statocyst nerve which is connected to the cerebral ganglion.

Resting on the floor of the sac is a small spherical granule of calcium carbonate. The whole structure is obviously an organ concerned with balance, any movement from the normal position will disturb the sphere so that other sensory cells are affected.

Tactile and olfactory sensory cells are all essentially similar, being elongated columnar cells, each with sensory processes embedded in the surface mucus. The sense of taste is present on the lips, on the front of the foot and all round the sides; a few drops of sugar solution placed in any of these regions will cause the snail to orientate itself so that it can drink the liquid. Olfactory cells are probably present on both sets of tentacles.

Co-ordination and Behaviour

The cerebral ganglia seem to be entirely concerned with the reception of anterior stimuli; from these ganglia, there is transmission of impulses via the commissures to muscles or glands. The snail is almost entirely a creature of reflex behaviour, though some reactions appear to be instinctive, and some show learned behaviour.

Sensitivity to light is easily demonstrated by casting a shadow on the snail. If a group is placed in a box with several openings, each snail will traverse a more or less direct line to one of the openings. Sensitivity to temperature change can be seen when they seek shade on a hot day and aestivate in summer; both reactions are also associated with humidity and loss of water from the skin. The taste sense can be demonstrated by placing drops of various liquids in a snail's path: e.g. sugar, saccharine, weak quinine, acid or alkali. It will recoil from all except sugar, and move in a different path. The other aspect of the olfactory sense, smell, is also obvious. *H. pomatia* can perceive lettuce and celery at 60 cm; some snails can perceive favourite fungi from much greater distances. The tactile sense is well marked; the snail will shrink from a slight touch, and repetition will cause withdrawal into the shell.

Snails have a well-developed homing instinct. Personal observation on a number of specimens has shown that they return night after night to a box with an opening of 50 cm^2. The individual slime trails show that they rarely follow the same outward and inward path. This behaviour implies memory, which may be associated with light, tactile and olfactory recognition of the environment. Experiments with mazes show clearly that there is some power of memory. Mating behaviour is extremely complex and is entirely instinctive once the initial stimulus has been applied. The whole sequence can be initiated by stroking the body with a soft brush. Once started, it continues with almost total disregard of environmental changes. Similar instinctive behaviour is observed in the egg-laying process. In general, coordination is very good and there is often complex behaviour; these are difficult to explain in terms of the relatively few neurones present in the body.

Hormones

The great majority of molluscs have small groups of neurosecretory cells in all the ganglia and sometimes these are associated with minute neurohaemal organs into which they discharge. The only definite endocrine glands so far discovered are anterior to the eye-stalks in cephalopods; these organs control sexual maturation; their secretion is inhibited in juveniles by neurosecretion from the brain.

Reproduction and Development

The snails are hermaphrodite, the single gonad being called an *ovotestis*, which produces sperm for most of the year but ova for a short period in summer. There is a complex array of accessory reproductive organs and glands.

Reproductive Organs

The ovotestis is a small cream-coloured gland lying on the surface of the liver near the uppermost coil of the spiral. It consists of numerous tubules each ending in a slightly dilated follicle. Each follicle produces both eggs and sperms, but it must be noted that both are not passed out at the same time (*see* Fig. A.22). From the ovotestis, a common or hermaphrodite duct coils its way to a junction between a small seminal receptacle, where the ova await fertilization, and a large albumin gland. Fertilization occurs at the mouth of the receptacle by sperm from another snail and then the ova receive a coat of albumin from the albumin gland (*see* Fig. A.22). The snail's own sperm will pass by this point from which the oviduct and vas deferens become partly or completely separate. Considering the oviduct first, it is a large convoluted tube along which the outer layer of albumin is first hardened and further along the duct is calcified. The oviduct passes into the vagina at the junction of several branched mucous glands, a swollen muscular *dart sac*, and a fine tube, the spermathecal duct, leading to a small spherical spermotheca which lies near the albumin gland. Here the sperm obtained from the partner during copulation are stored. The dart sac produces the calcareous dart which stimulates impregnation (*see* later). The mucous glands produce sticky slime which assists impregnation. From this junction point, the vagina leads to the common genital opening beneath the right posterior tentacle. The complex nature of the female organs provides for the deposition of the various coatings of the ovum and it also ensures the separation of the snails own sperm from that of its partner.

From the anterior region of the albumin gland, the vas deferens passes forward, bound to the oviduct by connective tissue. It is a slender duct and its cavity is at first in communication with the cavity of the oviduct. Farther forward, near the anterior portion of the crop,

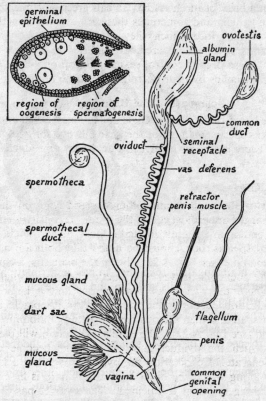

Fig. A.22. The reproductive system of *H. pomatia* dissected out. (*inset*) A single follicle of the ovotestis.

the vas deferens becomes completely separate from the oviduct and leads into a thick muscular penis which can be partly everted and so protruded during copulation; it is withdrawn to its normal position by a *retractor penis muscle*. Shortly before the junction of the vas deferens with the penis, there is a long slender closed tube called the *flagellum*, in which the spermatophores are shaped. The vas deferens finally joins the vagina behind the common genital opening.

Mating and Fertilization

Pairing occurs, normally at night, in late spring or early summer. The conjugants approach each other and each applies the broad sole of its foot to the other snail, the posterior part of the foot being spread out to form a base (*see* Fig. A.23). In this erect position, the anterior

Fig. A.23. Courtship in *H. pomatia*.

tentacles become elongated, then they quiver and finally are bent to touch the partner. The snails slide up and down each other, rubbing the partner with the lips. Throughout the whole process the pulmonary aperture opens widely and closes rapidly. After about 15 minutes, both snails become exhausted and crouch back into their shells but do not completely release each other, the anterior regions of the feet remaining in contact. There is a brief rest and then a continuation of the former ecstatic movements. Their bodies glide on each other and sway from side to side, the tentacles bend and move in various directions, and eventually the margins of the genital openings become very swollen.

The stimulus to actual impregnation is provided by the "love-dart" which is discharged from the dart sac to penetrate the integument of the partner snail. The dart is almost 1 cm long, made of calcium carbonate, sharp-pointed at one end and blunt at the other with four or five ridges arranged longitudinally (*see* Fig. A.24(*a*)). It takes the snail about a week to produce another dart. Normally they penetrate into the body of the partner about 1 or 2 mm but often they fall to the ground having merely touched the partner.

Having received this somewhat violent stimulus, each snail protrudes its penis and mutual impregnation occurs. Close observation reveals that this is alternate, not simultaneous. From the penis an elongated spermatophore, containing myriads of the thread-like sperm, passes into the partner. The act is repeated a number of times, with short

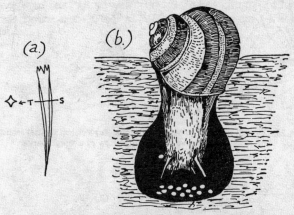

Fig. A.24. (*a*) Dart of *H. pomatia*. (*b*) Egg-laying.

resting periods, the whole process of courtship and mating having taken 2 to 3 hours. It is carried out with almost complete indifference to the environment. After the consummation, the snails separate and each goes its own way.

The spermatophores are squeezed into the spermatheca where their chitinous envelopes are dissolved. When the ova are passed to the receptaculum seminis, the sperm swim down the spermathecal duct to the vagina, then up to the seminal receptacle where fertilization occurs.

Development

In midsummer, the snail digs a pit in loose earth by movement of its head and the anterior region of the foot. With the shell clamped tightly to the soil and the head extended to the bottom of the cavity, about 30 to 50 small white eggs about the size of sweet pea seeds are laid, one by one (*see* Fig. A.24(*b*)). Finally, the snail pushes soil over the cavity and the eggs are left; there is no maternal care of the offspring. After about 25 days, tiny snails, about 6 to 8 mm long, emerge.

In the more typical marine gastropods, there is a free-swimming larva, the trochophore, followed by a veliger larva (*see* Fig. A.25). In the terrestrial snails, a modified trochophore and veliger are also developed but the organs of locomotion are vestigial. The main stages in cleavage and development are shown in Fig. A.26.

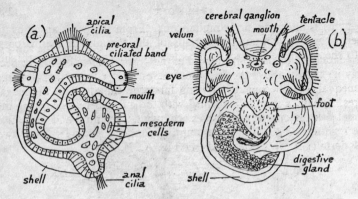

Fig. A.25. Typical larvae of marine gastropods. (a) Vertical sagittal section of a late trochophore larva. (b) Ventral view of a veliger larva.

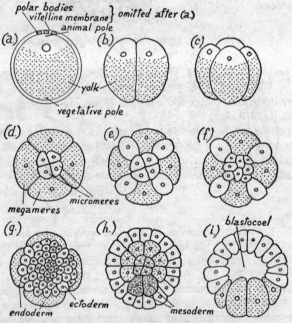

Fig. A.26. Cleavage stages in development. (a) Vertical section of an egg. (b) First cleavage, lateral view. (c) Second cleavage, lateral view. (d) (e) (f) Third, fourth and fifth cleavages, from the animal pole. (g) Morula stage, from the animal pole. (h) View from the vegetative pole. (i) Vertical section of the completed blastula.

The eggs are telolecithal, the yolk occupying somewhat more than the vegetative half. The first two cleavages are vertical and the third is horizontal and of the spiral type, i.e. the 4 micromeres do not respectively lie exactly above the four megameres. After this stage, cleavage is unequal, the micromeres dividing far more rapidly than the megameres. Finally a morula is formed with the micromeres occupying the animal pole region, the megameres occupying the central and vegetative pole regions. At this stage presumptive ectoderm, endoderm and two mesoderm cells can be detected (*see* Fig. A.27).

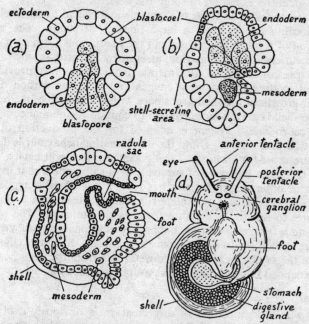

Fig. A.27. (*a*) Transverse section showing beginning of gastrulation. (*b*) Sagittal vertical section showing completion of gastrulation. (*c*) Sagittal vertical section showing completion of the modified trochophore. (*d*) Ventral view of the modified veliger stage.

Secretion of jelly produces a blastula from which gastrulation proceeds by invagination and epiboly. The trochophore stage is produced and a modified veliger stage. In typical veliger larvae, the preoral ciliated band of the trochophore is drawn out laterally into two flaps which provide organs of locomotion. This phase is not present in terrestrial snails nor even in freshwater snails. The shell is present from the late trochophore stage.

Adaptation, Survival and Dispersal

The most striking adaptations are those associated with success in terrestrial environment. One of the most important dangers of ter restrial life is that of loss of moisture from the body. In this connexion the land snails have evolved the protective shell with its broken pattern the habit of aestivation with a protective epiphragm and a predilectio for damp shady habitats. They come out to feed when weather condi tions are humid and temperature is not high, and they choose "roostin places" which are shaded and protected. Conservation of water i further aided by excretion of solid uric acid.

The diet includes all types of vegetable matter and hence a relativel small locality can support a large number of snails. The efficien shredding of food by the radula and the continuous formation of new sharp teeth ensure that digestion, assisted by bacteria, is efficient.

The transformation of the mantle into a lung has provided a excellent method of obtaining oxygen and excreting carbon dioxide Regular growth of the shell keeps pace with the growth of the body, s that the shell is always large enough to contain the animal completely

The reproductive system is adapted for the production of larg yolky, well-protected eggs, and the whole mating behaviour is designe to ensure cross-fertilization. Laying the eggs in a soil cavity, alway damp, favours a high rate of survival. It is to be noted that in this a well as in other features, there has been a considerable tendency t use the properties of a suitable environment rather than to fabricat structures to isolate the creature from its environment. The eggs ar not immune from evaporation, but in the conditions where they develo they are not likely to suffer from evaporation. Similarly, the who body of the snail is very subject to water loss from the skin, hence it only expanded in conditions where evaporation is unlikely.

Survival

The whole organization of any creature is obviously evolved f survival, at least until a suitable rate of reproduction has been achieve Special features of garden snails which aid survival in unfavourab conditions are the processes of hibernation during winter and aestiva tion in high summer. Several species of *Helix* have shown themselv to be remarkably tenacious of life, existing for several years in captivi without food. The most outstanding case on record is that of a spec men of *Helix desertorum*, from Egypt, which was presented to th British Museum in 1846 and fixed on a display tablet. One of th curators noticed in 1950 that it was showing signs of life. Whe moistened with warm water, it began to feed and lived satisfactorily f more than a year. It became torpid in late 1951 and died in 1952.

It is interesting to note that from the point of view of survival, there
e considerable modifications to shell structure under different
vironments. Snails kept all their lives under very moist conditions,
roduce large thin shells; those kept in dry conditions, produce small
ick shells. High temperatures are conducive to thick shells and low
mperatures to small thin shells. Bright light favours bright coloura-
on and dim light produces dark and dingy colours.

ispersal

The eggs are laid normally a fair distance from the roosting-place
d the young snails do not show any instinct to return to the parental
me. Instead, those that survive tend to establish new colonies. A
all area of vegetation can support many snails; there are snail
rdens of small area in France and Spain, where thousands are reared
r market every year. Migration must not be ruled out; there are
ports of marked *Helix aspersa* establishing themselves many metres
om the roosting-places where they were marked.

Classification

he main phylum and class characteristics have been given in Chap. 4
d in the earlier part of this appendix (*see* pp. 1269–75). *Helix spp.*
long to the order Pulmonata which are hermaphrodite gastropods
ith the mantle cavity modified to form a lung and without ctenidia.
here is a single kidney and there are no larvae. The ganglia are
ncentrated into a circumoesophageal ring. The order includes
rrestrial snails and slugs and the fresh-water snails.

The order Pulmonata is divided into two sub-orders solely on the
sition of the eyes. In the Basommatophora, the eyes are at the
ses of the posterior tentacles; in the Stylommatophora they are at
e tips. *Helix spp.* belong to the latter sub-order. Members of the
mily Helicidae are characterized by a dextral shell which is more or
ss globose in shape, and has a great range of colour and pattern.
he jaw is arched and ridged and the teeth on the radula are all of the
me shape. There is no pedal gland round the edge of the foot. There
a dart sac elaborating the dart used during mating. In the genus
elix, the shells are large, rounded and thick-walled; the lowest
horl or body whorl makes up four-fifths of the shell. The umbilicus
present as a narrow cleft or may be completely closed in the adult.
he members of the genus *Helix* are distinguished by size, by shell
attern and by habitat.

PHYLUM: Mollusca
CLASS: Gastropoda
ORDER: Pulmonata
SUB-ORDER: Stylommatophora
FAMILY: Helicidae
GENUS: *Helix*
SPECIES: *Helix pomatia*

Special Features of Biological Importance

In number of species, ranking second to the phylum Arthropoda, the phylum
Mollusca is a very successful one. It shows, as do all successful phyla,
marked degree of adaptive radiation. The question of molluscan relationship
is not solved but certain suggestions are made here. Finally some facets c
their economic importance are mentioned.

Success of Molluscs

The phylum has been a very successful and important one since the Uppe
Cambrian period, about 450 million years ago. Indeed, with the possibl
exception of cephalopods, the numbers of molluscs are greater now than the
have ever been throughout their long history. It is difficult to point to an
special features which have contributed to their success, such features als
being possessed by other phyla. One factor, undoubtedly, is the productio
of large numbers of eggs, e.g. *Tethys*, a nudibranch gastropod, lays 50
million eggs per annum; *Ostrea edulis*, the common oyster, 60 million pe
annum; the squid, *Loligo vulgare*, produces hundreds of egg capsules, eac
containing 200 eggs; the common octopus, *Octopus vulgare*, lays thousand
of eggs etc. These high reproductive rates have evidently compensated fc
the hazards of the environment, especially to young molluscs.

There is very pronounced resistance to changes of environment especiall
in the case of those molluscs which have left the equable marine environmen
Many terrestrial pulmonates can withstand extremes of temperature, wate
availability, water loss and even shortage of food, passing into a state whic
has sometimes been called "suspended animation."

In general, molluscs exhibit a high degree of evolutionary plasticity.
seems that the process of evolution has, in this group, plenty of responsiv
material to act upon.

Adaptive Radiation

This phenomenon, the evolution of types from some common anceste
which can occupy every niche in the environment has been pointed ot
previously in this book in connexion with arthropods and chordates. In th
sea, molluscs are found which are planktonic, pelagic and benthic, the latte
either fixed to the sea bed, or creeping on it, or burrowing into it. Th
abyssal depths, the neritic zone whether sandy, rocky or muddy, the intertid
zone, freshwater lakes and streams, the forests, the deserts and the se
itself, have all been successfully colonized by molluscs. There are carnivore
some of which are swift predators while others lurk watchfully; there a
herbivores which graze on algae or rasp leaves; there are omnivores wit

filter-feeding mechanisms. There are numerous ecto- and endoparasitic forms in Gastropoda and Lamellibranchiata.

There is truly a very wide range of form and of modes of life, but nevertheless all can be referred to a fairly standard pattern.

Relationships of Mollusca

Broadly speaking, molluscs have characteristics which may show affinity with platyhelminths, with brachiopods and with annelids. With platyhelminths they share, in the classes Amphineura and Gastropoda, the broad creeping surface, the simplified nervous system and the similarity of locomotion; with annelids they share the trochophore and, in *Neopilina*, what appears to be serial repetition of organs which, at least superficially resembles metameric segmentation. With brachiopods they share the trochophore, the shell and the mantle.

In 1957, a Danish expedition, dredging at 4,000 metres off the Pacific coast of Mexico, found specimens of a mollusc which they named *Neopilina galatheae*, after their ship, Galathea. This creature is strikingly similar to forms previously found only in fossils of Cambrian and Devonian rocks.

Neopilina (*see* Fig. A.28) has a saucer-shaped shell about 4 cm in diameter, a flat oval ventral foot with a mouth at one end and an anus at the opposite

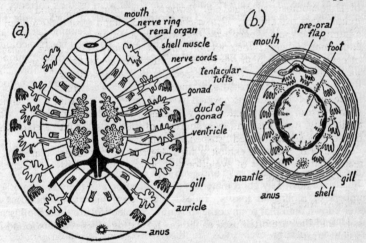

Fig. A.28. *Neopilina galatheae.* (*a*) Schematic diagram showing the paired structures (after Lemche and Wingstrand). (*b*) Ventral view.

end. There are five pairs of gills, eight pairs of shell muscles, two pairs of gonads, each with a separate duct, two pairs of auricles and a median ventricle, and six pairs of renal organs. The nervous system resembles that of the chitons. All these paired structures suggest segmentation, but nevertheless until details are available of the coelomic development it would be u wise to place too much emphasis on the structures found in these adult animals. At present there is really insufficient evidence to link the molluscs with annelids or brachiopods and perhaps eventually it may be shown that all three of the groups evolved from some early turbellarian ancestors.

Economic Importance

Molluscs are widely used as human food, the best-known examples are the oyster (*Ostrea*), cockle (*Cardium*), mussel (*Mytilus*), winkle (*Littorina*), ormer (*Haliotis*) and land-snails or escargots (*Helix pomatia*). Some of the larger clams (*Mya*) and conches (*Strombus*) are widely eaten in chowder, a stew made, in this case, of shellfish, pork, biscuit and onions. At the height of the Roman Empire, special gardens called *cochlearia* were used for breeding *Helix pomatia*.

Molluscan larvae are plentiful in the plankton in early summer and form an appreciable part of the diet of plankton feeders. Numerous marine animals are predators on larger molluscs and along the sea-shore many birds will eat them (oyster-catcher). On land, snails form the major part of the diet of some birds (thrush). On land, in fresh-water and in the sea, molluscs provide a most important link in many food-chains.

Shells have, from very ancient times, been used for jewellery and for articles of value. Until very recently cowrie shells were used as currency on the Pacific coasts and islands. The mother-of-pearl of thick shells has provided buttons, rings, pins, earrings and inlay work. Genuine cameos are cut from the shells of *Carcis rufa* from the Red Sea. The shell has two coloured layers; the figure is cut in the light inner layer and the red background is supplied by the outer layer. Pearls are manufactured by Lamellibranchs, especially oysters, to isolate sources of irritation, particularly trematode larvae.

Freshwater snails of many species harbour the larval stages of trematode parasites, e.g. *Fasciola*, *Clonorchis* and *Schistosoma*, and are thus partly responsible for the spread of certain diseases.

Wooden piles, pier supports and wooden boats suffer severely from the boring of bivalves, particularly the shipworm (*Teredo navalis*). Numerous other bivalves bore into rocks and even into concrete.

Shells are obviously good material for fossilization and there are countless numbers of molluscan fossils; indeed the ancient history of molluscs is better known than that of any other phylum. So plentiful are these molluscan fossils, that they are often used as indices for dating other remains found in the same strata.

Neritic shellfish of various kinds are used all over the world as bait by fisherman. Two items of artistic interest may be included here. The imperial dye, Tyrian purple, highly prized in the Roman Empire, was, and is, extracted from the horny whelk, *Murex sp.* found in the Mediterranean. The ink from the ink-sac of the cuttlefish (*Sepia*) was once widely used for writing and is still extracted for making the artists' pigment, sepia.

QUESTIONS

CHAPTER 1

Units of Living Substance: Cells

1. What inclusions are found within plant cells? Give a brief account of their importance.   *O.B.*

2. Make a labelled diagram of a typical animal cell with its contents. How much of this is visible in life? What do you know of the functions of the various components of the cell?   *O.Z.*

3. Discuss the definition of a cell as "an organized and more or less independent mass of protoplasm constituting the structural unit of an organism."   *L.B.(S.)*

CHAPTER 2

The Formation of New Protoplasmic Units: Cell Division

4. Describe in detail an animal cell and the way in which it divides.   *L.Z.*

5. Give a detailed illustrated account of the process of nuclear and cell division in a plant meristem.   *B.Bi.*

6. Give an account of mitosis in *either* a plant cell *or* an animal cell.   *L.Bi.*

7. What are the chief functions of the cell nucleus? Describe in detail the changes that occur in the nucleus during mitotic division.   *B.B.(S.)*

8. Describe, with illustrations, the behaviour of the nucleus in the formation of pollen grains from a pollen-mother-cell in a plant such as the broad bean (*Vicia faba*) which has a diploid (2 n) chromosome number of 14.   *O.B.*

9. Give an illustrated account of mitosis. State *briefly* in what important ways mitosis differs from meiosis.   *L.Bi.*

10. By means of labelled diagrams, compare and contrast mitosis with meiosis.
                                                                              C.B.

11. What are chromosomes and how do they behave in the animal body?
                                                                            O.C.Z.

12. Describe with the aid of diagrams, the following: chromatid; chiasma; nuclear spindle; prophase; metaphase; anaphase. Why is the second division in meiosis not regarded as mitotic?   *O.B.*

CHAPTER 4

The Principles of Classification: Classification Tables

13. Explain concisely the principles upon which plant classification is based.   *L.B*

14. What do you understand by a "natural" system of classification? Outline a classification of any large group of organisms; to what extent may this classification be considered a natural one?   *B.Bi.(S.)*

15. Describe the use of the terms, family, genus, species by reference to Raspberry (*Rubus idaeus*); Blackberry (*Rubus fruticosus*); Apple (*Malus sp.*); Strawberry (*Fragaria vesca*); Creeping buttercup (*Ranunculus repens*); and Cocksfoot (*Dactylis glomerata*).   *O.C.B*

16. "A classification table of the animal kingdom represents much more than a means of identifying animals." Discuss this statement, outlining the basis of such a table and giving examples.   *C.Z.(S.)*

16(a). Devise a simple scheme or key which could enable a student starting a VIth form biology course to distinguish either the individual classes of the Arthropoda or the major divisions of the plant kingdom.   *A.E.B.Bi.*

CHAPTER 5

Unicellular Green Plants: Chlamydomonas, Pleurococcus

17. Describe the structure, mode of life, and reproduction of any one species of *Chlamydomonas*. Indicate the range of difference in the form and behaviour of the gametes to be met with in different species of *Chlamydomonas*.   *W.B.*

CHAPTER 6

A Simple Protozoan: Amoeba

18. What are the characteristics of living matter? Illustrate your answers by reference to *Amoeba*.   *C.Z.*

CHAPTER 7

An Indeterminate Organism: Euglena

19. Which is the more primitive, *Amoeba* or *Euglena*? Support your decision by evidence from the anatomy and physiology of these and other animals.   *B.Z.*

CHAPTER 8

A Complex Protozoan: Paramecium

20. Describe in detail the methods of reproduction in *Paramecium*, and comment on their importance.   *C.Z.*

21. Show how *Paramecium* may be said to show specialization in organization as compared with *Amoeba*.   *W.Z.*

22. Which of the activities and processes of life of either *Amoeba* or *Paramecium* can be related to structures visible under the microscope? Give an account of the structures concerned.   *O.C.Z.*

CHAPTER 9

Simple Multicellular Green Plants: Pandorina, Eudorina; Volvox; Ulothrix, Oedogonium; Spirogyra; Vaucheria; Ulva; Fucus

23. Briefly compare *Chlamydomonas*, *Pandorina*, *Eudorina* and *Volvox* as regards their vegetative organization and methods of reproduction. Do these comparisons provide information concerning the evolutionary relationships of these organisms?   *O.C.B.*

24. Describe the vegetative structure and reproduction of *Vaucheria*. State concisely how *Oedogonium* differs from *Vaucheria*. *L.B.*

25. Give an account of the method of reproduction in *Fucus*, and describe how the new plants establish themselves. *C.B.*

26. Describe the ways in which *Fucus* appear to be adapted to its environment. Describe, with the aid of diagrams, the method of reproduction of this alga. *L.B.*

27. Compare the reproduction of *Chlamydomonas* with that of *Fucus*. *L.B.*

28. Compare the mode of life and reproduction of a marine alga such as *Fucus*, with those of a freshwater alga, such as *Spirogyra*. How far may the differences between these forms be related to differences in the environment. *C.B.(S.)*

29. Give a comparative account of the methods of sexual reproduction in *Vaucheria* *Spirogyra* and *Fucus*, stating which you regard as the most highly evolved in this respect and why. *W.B.*

30. Compare and contrast the vegetative structure and mode of growth of *Spirogyra* and *Fucus*. *W.B.*

31. Illustrate by reference to specific examples, the different types of sexual reproduction found in algae. *L.B.*

32. What do you understand by an alga? Illustrate your answer by reference to any algae you have studied. *W.B.(S.)*

CHAPTER 10

Simple Multicellular Animals: Sponges; Hydra; Obelia

33. Give an account of the movements, feeding and behaviour of *Hydra*. Illustrate your answer with diagrams to show the position and arrangement of the structures involved. *B.Z.*

34. Give an account of the life-history of *Hydra*. How do you know it is an animal? *C.Z.*

35. Define the terms "tissue" and "organ." Illustrate your answer with special reference to *Hydra*. *N.Z.*

36. Give an illustrated account of the structure of *Hydra* and describe its method of feeding. *B.Bi.*

37. Give an illustrated account of the types of cells found in *Hydra* and describe the part which each plays in the life and life-history of the animal. *L.Z.*

38. Describe concisely the structure of the main phases in the life-history of *Obelia* and point out how each is adapted to its rôle in the life-history of the animal. *L.Z.*

39. Describe the origin, development and structure of the medusa of *Obelia*. What part does it play in the life-history of the animal? *L.Z.*

40. Give an account of those characteristics which enable you to distinguish between animals and plants, using *Amoeba*, *Euglena* and *Obelia* (hydroid colony) as examples. *L.Z.*

CHAPTER 11

Simple Terrestrial Green Plants: Bryophyta

41. Give an illustrated account of the structure of the gametophyte of a *named* liverwort *or* moss. Why should liverworts or mosses be considered more highly evolved than thalloid algae? *B.Bi.*

42. On what grounds may mosses be considered to be closely related to liverworts? To what extent are these plants water-loving? *B.B.(S.)*

43. Give an account of the structure and life-history of *either* any named liverwort *or Fucus*. *N.B.*

44. Compare and contrast the sporophyte of *Pellia* with that of *Funaria* (or other

named moss) in respect of structure and mode of nutrition. Why are these plants classified together as members of the Bryophyta? *W.B.*

45. Compare and contrast the life-cycles of *Spirogyra*, *Fucus* and *Pellia*. *L.B.*

46. Compare the structure and mode of reproduction of *Fucus* and *Funaria*. In what ways do these two plants appear to be adapted to their environments? *L.B.*

Chapter 12

Histology of Vascular Plants

47. Describe the structure of a young meristematic cell. Trace the changes undergone by such a cell during the differentiation of (a) a parenchyma cell of the pith, (b) a xylem vessel. *W.B.*

48. Describe in detail the development and structure of the tissues (a) sclerenchyma, and (b) collenchyma. What are the functions of these tissues and where do they occur in plants? State briefly your procedure in order to identify them in freshly cut sections of plant material. *W.B.*

49. Describe with the aid of diagrams, the structure of a living parenchymatous plant cell. What changes occur during the formation of xylem vessels from meristematic cells? *O.C.Bi.*

50. List the principal types of lignified cells found in angiosperms and indicate where they occur in the plant. Make careful drawings to show the structure of three of these types and state their functions. *L.B.*

51. Give an illustrated account of the structure and distribution of the phloem in an herbaceous dicotyledon. What functions are attributed to this tissue? *L.B.*

52. With the aid of diagrams and examples distinguish between (a) tracheid and vessel; (b) phloem and sieve tube; (c) vascular cambium and cork cambium. What functions are attributed to these cells or tissues? *O.C.B.*

Chapter 13

Vascular Terrestrial Green Plants: Pteridophyta

53. Give an illustrated description of the structure of the sporophyte of a *named* fern (anatomical detail not required). Contrast the life-cycle of this plant with that of a *named* moss *or* liverwort. *B.B.*

54. Describe the method of spore dispersal in (a) *Funaria* (or other named moss), (b) *Dryopteris* (or other named fern). Describe and contrast the gametophytes produced by the germination of the spores of the two named plants you have chosen. N.B. Details of minute structure and of reproductive organs are not required. *W.B.*

55. Compare and contrast the life-cycles of *Pellia* and *Dryopteris*. Which plant do you consider to be better adapted for life on land? Give reasons for your answer. *L.B.*

56. Describe the development of the gametophyte generation of *Selaginella* (or *Lycopodium*) from spore germination up to and including the formation of the embryo sporophyte. *W.B.*

57. Compare and contrast the sporophyte of *Funaria* (or another named moss) with that of *Selaginella*. *L.B.*

58. Compare and contrast the sporophyte generations of *Pellia*, *Dryopteris*, and *Selaginella*. *L.B.*

Chapter 15

Spermatophytes with Naked Seeds: Gymnospermae; Pinus; Taxus; Cycas

59. Draw a diagram of a two-year-old stem of *Pinus* as seen in transverse section, fully labelling all the tissues. Draw diagrams to show the appearance of medullary

rays as seen in radial and in tangential longitudinal sections. Describe the detailed structure of (*a*) a xylem tracheid, (*b*) a sieve tube. *W.B.*

60. Why do you think that *Pinus* is included in the Botany syllabus of this examination? *L.B.*

61. Compare the sexual reproduction of *Fucus* and *Pinus*. Emphasize those features which appear to be related to the environmental conditions in which these plants are found. *L.B.*

62. What is a gametophyte? Compare the gametophyte of *Dryopteris* with those of *Selaginella* and *Pinus*. *L.B.*

CHAPTER 16

Spermatophytes with Enclosed Seeds: Angiospermae

63. Make carefully labelled diagrams of the organs which are essential for reproduction in any *named* flower. Give a full description of how pollination is effected in this flower. *L.Bi.*

64. Describe and illustrate the structure of a *named* flower which is wind pollinated. In what ways is the structure of the flower related to its mode of pollination? By what means is cross-pollination favoured in wind-pollinated flowers? *B.B.*

65. Give an account of the development and structure of the stamen of an angiosperm (e.g. lily), including the method by which dehiscence of the anther is brought about. *W.B.*

66. Make a *large*, labelled diagram of a transverse section of an anther to show its structure immediately preceding dehiscence. Describe the growth and development of the pollen grain after pollination. *L.B.*

67. Make *one* labelled drawing to show the detailed structure of the ovule of an angiosperm just before fertilization. Describe concisely the changes which occur after fertilization in the development of such an ovule into a seed. *L.B.*

68. What is "fertilization"? Describe the structure of the gynaecium of any *named* flowering plant at the time of fertilization, and give a concise account of the changes which take place resulting in the formation of the mature fruit. *B.B.*

69. Distinguish between pollination and fertilization in an Angiosperm flower and describe what happens as a result of fertilization. How may seedless fruits be produced artificially? *O.C.Bi.*

70. Compare the structure and functions of the stamen of a flowering plant with those of the sporangium of a fern. *L.Bi.*

71. Describe and discuss the mechanisms by which the male gamete reaches the female gamete in both flowering and non-flowering plants. *B.B.(S.)*

72. Compare by means of clear diagrams the gametophytes of a fern, a conifer and an angiosperm and describe the fertilization process in each example. *N.B.*

73. What do you understand by a gametophytic generation? Compare and contrast this generation in *Pinus* and a typical angiosperm. *W.B.*

CHAPTER 17

Vegetative Morphology and Anatomy of Angiosperms

74. What are (*a*) the two main types of dicotyledonous seeds, (*b*) the two main types of germination? Briefly explain the terms you use, and name *one* example of each. List the conditions that are necessary for seed germination, and describe how you would demonstrate the necessity of *two* of these conditions. *C.B.*

75. Describe briefly the external features of a herbaceous stem of an Angiosperm. What peculiarities of stem form may be associated with vegetative reproduction? *N.B.*

76. Illustrate by reference to named examples four different modifications which adapt the stems of plants to perform special functions. *N.B.(S.)*

77. Give an account of the origin, development and structure of protoxylem. Make suitable labelled diagrams to show its position relative to the other vascular tissues in an herbaceous dicotyledon. *L.B.*

78. Distinguish clearly between monopodial and sympodial growth, illustrating your answer by reference to the growth of (a) rhizomes, (b) shoots of trees and (c) inflorescences. *L.B.*

79. Give a concise account of secondary thickening in the stem of a named woody dicot. Describe the structure of the cells of the various elements comprising the wood of this stem, and indicate briefly their functions. *B.B.*

80. Describe the origin, development, and structure of cork in the stem of a dicotyledon. How does the structure of cork fit it for the functions it serves in the plant? *W.B.*

81. Where would you expect to find cambial tissue in a woody stem during the fourth year of growth? Describe the structure of cambial cells and indicate the nature of the tissues which they may produce. *N.B.*

82. Give an illustrated account of the structure of a foliage leaf of a *named* dicotyledon. How is this structure fitted to serve the functional requirements of the plant? *B.Bi.*

83. Give an illustrated account of the structure of a green leaf of a *named* mesophyte. List the differences between this leaf and that of *Pinus*. *L.B.*

84. Describe the processes by which a stem grows in length and new leaves develop upon it. *C.B.(S.)*

85. Illustrate and describe the external appearance and internal structure of a root of a named higher plant. How is this structure related to the functions of the root? *B.B.*

86. Compare the development of the primary vascular systems of roots with that of stems in flowering plants. *O.C.Bi.*

87. Explain how secondary thickening takes place in the root of a dicotyledon. Indicate any differences between the mode of secondary thickening of such a root and that of the stem of a dicotyledon. *L.B.*

88. Give a comparative account of the apical meristems in the stem and root of a flowering plant. *W.Bi.*

89. Describe the development of lateral branches from (a) stems and (b) roots. *L.B.*

90. Name *four* commonly grown food-plants in which the edible parts are morphologically different. Make large, labelled drawings to show the exact morphological nature of these edible regions. *L.Bi.*

91. Compare the main anatomical and morphological features of a named monocotyledon with those of a named dicotyledon. *O.B.*

92. What are meristems? Give an illustrated account of the structure, occurrence and function of these tissues in dicotyledons. *L.B.*

93. Briefly compare the morphology and anatomy of a *named* water plant with that of a *named* xerophytic plant. Discuss the significance of the differences in the plants in relation to the differences in the environments. *O.C.B.*

CHAPTER 18

Floral Morphology and Anatomy of Angiosperms

94. Compare chiefly by means of labelled diagrams a *named* insect-pollinated flower and a *named* wind-pollinated flower. In what respects do you consider them to be adapted to their methods of pollination? *L.B.*

95. With the aid of drawings, indicate the range of structure of the gynaecium among the flowering plants you have studied. *N.B.(S.)*

96. What types of mechanism favouring cross-pollination do flowers show? Describe in detail, with reference to a *named* flower, *one* such mechanism. Why is cross-pollination considered biologically more advantageous than self-pollination? *B.Bi.*

97. For any *one* named dicotyledonous plant describe (*a*) the flower structure, (*b*) the method of pollination, (*c*) the development and dispersal of fruits and seeds. Microscopic details are not required. *C.B.*

98. Define the term *fruit*. Make large, labelled accurate diagrams *only* to illustrate the structure of an apple, an orange and a blackberry. *L.B.*

99. Give an illustrated account of the external appearance and structure of *one named* example of each of the following types of fruit: berry, follicle, achene, caryopsis, nut. *L.B.*

100. Explain the terms "pericarp" and "testa," illustrating your answer by reference to four of the following fruits: apple; plum; orange; raspberry; strawberry; tomato. *O.C.Bi.*

101. With the aid of large, labelled drawings describe the structure of (*a*) a simple fruit; (*b*) a compound fruit and (*c*) a false fruit. Indicate clearly the origin of each part of the fruit. *O.C.Bi.*

102. Write short illustrated accounts of the structure of *three* British wild plants which possess different mechanisms by which their seeds are dispersed. Indicate how the structure of each fruit or seed is related to its mode of dispersal. *O.C.B.*

103. In what ways may seeds be dispersed? Give examples of plants showing any three of the ways you mention and indicate their suitability to the habit and habitat of each plant. *B.Bi.*

104. Making reference to two families of flowering plants, discuss the use of floral and vegetative characters in classification. *B.B.*

105. Describe with the aid of large labelled diagrams, the inflorescence, flower and fruit of any *one* member of *either* the Labiatae *or* the Scrophulariaceae. *List* those characters which enable you to refer this plant to its family. *L.B.*

106. Compare the range of floral and vegetative structure in the Rosaceae with that in the Leguminosae. *O.C.B.*

107. Referring to *named* examples describe the mechanisms of fruit and seed dispersal in the Rosaceae. *N.B.*

108. Summarize the characteristics of the *Compositae* and indicate the differences between the *Liguliflorae* and *Tubuliflorae*. Give an illustrated description of the structure of a hermaphrodite floret of *one named* example of this family. Why are the Compositae considered to represent the highest development among flowering plants? *L.B.*

109. *Gramineae* and *Compositae* are regarded as being among the most successful of angiosperm families. What do you understand by "successful" in this connexion? Choose one of the above-named families and indicate the principal features which may have contributed to its success. *W.B.*

110. Describe the floral structure of any *one named* species of grass. In what ways are members of the grass family of value to man? *O.C.B.*

111. Describe with the aid of annotated diagrams the chief similarities and differences between the floral and vegetative characters of a grass and of a named member of the Liliaceae. *C.B.*

112. Survey the evidence for believing that evolution of the flower has involved (*a*) reduction, (*b*) fusion, of floral parts. *C.B.(S.)*

113. Discuss the main lines of evolution of the flower in angiosperms. *O.B.(S.)*

CHAPTER 20

Histology of Animals

114. Show how the structure of the epithelial tissues known to you reflect the functions which they serve. *O.Z.*

115. Give an illustrated account of areolar connective tissue. In what ways does this tissue differ from (*a*) yellow elastic cartilage; (*b*) tendon tissue, and (*c*) bone. Give a brief account of the functions of these four tissues. *W.Z.*

116. Give an illustrated account of the histology of the skeletal tissues of a mammal. *L.Z.*

117. Describe the structure of a mammalian long bone and the process of its formation. *L.Z.*

118. Describe the structure of mammalian blood, and give an account of the functions. *B.Bi.*

119. Make a large labelled diagram showing the parts commonly present in animal cells. Show how the cells of (*a*) the blood, (*b*) medullated nerve, and (*c*) striated muscle, differ from this generalized cell and from each other, and discuss why such differences in cells occur. *O.C.Bi.*

120. In what circumstances is it important to have a knowledge of human blood groups?

Explain concisely the inheritance of the ABO series of blood groups. *W.Z.*

121. How do the characteristic cells of the following tissues differ from the typical animal cell: stomach wall, pancreas. striped muscle, ciliated epithelium, blood? What have you yourself actually seen of these tissues with the microscope? *O.C.Z.(S.)*

122. Draw the gross general arrangement of the tissues which might be seen in a transverse section of the human forearm somewhere between the elbow and the wrist. (Histological detail not required.) Describe in detail the histology of any *two* of the tissues you have described relating structure to function. *A.E.B.Bi.*

123. Write an essay on "tissues in animals." *C.Z.*

CHAPTER 21

Coelomate Animals I: Annelida

124. Make a large, fully labelled diagram of a transverse section through the body of an earthworm, (*a*) in the region of the cerebral ganglia, (*b*) in the region of the vesiculae seminales, (*c*) behind the reproductive region. *O.C.Bi.(S.)*

125. Describe the blood vascular system of the earthworm, indicating the direction of blood flow in the vessels you describe. Give some account of the method by which circulation is maintained. *O.C.Bi.*

126. Give an account of the life-history of the earthworm (including a description of copulation but not of the internal reproductive organs). In what ways are earthworms considered to be beneficial to man? *B.Bi.*

127. Give an account of movement in the earthworm and describe the body structure and organs concerned. Say how the movement of earthworms helps to maintain soil condition. *B.Bi.*

128. Show how the cells in the body wall of an earthworm receive from the external environment (*a*) a supply of food, and (*b*) a supply of oxygen. *W.Z.*

129. Describe the reproductive organs of the earthworms and state what you know of the way in which reproduction occurs. *L.Z.*

130. Write a general account of the natural history and habits of the earthworm. How do earthworms affect the fertility of the soil? *C.Z.*

131. Show how the earthworm illustrates, when compared with *Hydra*, the specialization of cells into tissues, tissues into organs, and organs into systems.

W.Z.(S)

132. Illustrate by reference to an earthworm, the meanings of the terms "coelomate" and "metamerism." Discuss the general differences in organization of coelomate and acoelomate animals.

B.Z.

133. What do you understand by the terms "bilateral symmetry," "the coelom," and "metameric segmentation"? Illustrate your answer by reference to the earthworm.

L.Z.

134. Enumerate the external features of *Nereis* and discuss the possible adaptations of this animal to its life in the sea.

W.Z.

135. What are the basic distinguishing characters of the Annelida? Illustrate your answer by reference to the earthworm and to *Nereis*. How far can the differences in their external features be correlated with their environment?

C.Z.

CHAPTER 22
Coelomate Animals II: Arthropoda; Crustacea

136. Describe how the crayfish feeds and provides itself with oxygen, including a description of the structures concerned.

O.C.Z.

137. Describe the structure and functioning of the alimentary canal in a crayfish.

W.Z.

138. Describe the structure of the eye of the crayfish and the method of functioning of such eyes.

L.Z.

139. Define respiration and state the characteristics of an efficient respiratory surface. Briefly describe *one* respiratory organ of a crayfish, and explain how the muscles of the chela are kept continually supplied with oxygen. (Details of tissue respiration are *not* required.)

L.Z.

140. To what extent may a crayfish be regarded as exhibiting (a) metameric segmentation and, (b) adaptation to environment.

W.Z.

141. The crayfish is a triploblastic, metamerically segmented, coelomate animal. Explain fully what is meant by this statement.

L.Z.

142. "A crayfish is more highly organized than an earthworm." Discuss this statement as fully as you can.

W.Z.

CHAPTER 23
Coelomate Animals III: Arthropoda; Insecta

143. State briefly what you regard as the major features of social organization in a colony of honey bees. Give a detailed account of the methods by which information is communicated. How does social organization in a bee colony (a) resemble, and (b) differ from that in human societies?

N.Bi.

144. Compare by means of large fully labelled drawings, the mouth-parts of the cockroach, the butterfly and the honey-bee. Do you consider these mouth-parts well adapted for the particular method of feeding employed by these insects?

O.C.Bi.

145. Compare the life-history of the cockroach with that of the butterfly. Do you consider these insects to be of any economic significance?

O.C.Bi.

146. Some insects exist in a variety of forms in the adult stage. Describe the forms occurring in *two* species you have studied, referring to the life-histories of the forms you mention.

B.Z.

147. Write an essay on the importance of insects to man.

B.Bi.

148. Review, with named examples, some of the methods used to control destructive insects.

C.Z.

149. What are the outstanding features of the habits and life-history of the honey-bee? In what respects does the life-history of the house-fly (or blow-fly) differ from that of the honey-bee? *C.Z.*

150. Compare the body cavity of the earthworm with that of the cockroach. *C.Z.(S.)*

151. Give examples of different feeding habits of insects. What relation is there between insects and food production? *C.Z.*

152. Describe the external features of a typical insect and indicate the part played by insects in transmitting disease. *W.Z.*

153. What is a "sense organ"? Give an account of the sense organs of an insect. *N.Z.*

154. Write an account of any harmful Coleoptera (beetles) and Diptera (flies) with which you are acquainted. *N.Z.*

155. Describe the life-history of one species of *Aphis*. Discuss methods for its control. *O.C.Z.*

Chapter 24
Coelomate Animals IV: Chordata

156. Give an outline classification of the Chordata, with one or more examples of each group you mention. In enumerating the main features of each group, give those characters which enable you to distinguish clearly that group from any other. *N.Z.*

Chapter 25
A Primitive Chordate: Amphioxus

157. Write a general account of the structure, habitat and mode of life of *Amphioxus*. *N.Z.*

158. Describe, with diagrams the method of feeding in *Branchiostoma* (*Amphioxus*) and the passage of food through the gut. (Details of digestion are not required.) *O.Z.*

159. Give a comparative account of nitrogenous excretion in *Amphioxus* and the earthworm. *N.Z.*

Chapter 26
An Aquatic Craniate: Scyliorhinus

160. Give a short account of any *four* of the following systems in the dogfish: fins, gills, alimentary canal, circulation, scales, skeleton. *O.C.Z.*

161. Describe the characteristic organization of the vertebrates, with particular reference to the dogfish. *C.Z.*

162. Make labelled sketches to show what you would expect to see in a transverse section through a whole dogfish at the level of (*a*) the mid-brain, (*b*) the gills, (*c*) the heart. *O.C.Z.*

163. List the cranial nerves of the dogfish and briefly describe their various functions. Which of them do you consider to be comparable with dorsal and ventral roots? *O.C.Bi.(S.)*

164. Draw a vertical longitudinal section of the heart of a dogfish and compare this heart with that of a crayfish. Discuss the nature of the blood vascular system shown by these two water-living animals. *W.Z.*

165. Give an account of the ways in which you consider a fish to be adapted to an aquatic existence. *B.Bi.*

166. State clearly the evidence for believing that the vertebrate head is a segmental structure. *O.C.Z.*

CHAPTER 27

An Amphibious Craniate: Rana

167. Show, by reference to as many features of its anatomy, physiology and life-history as you can, whether the frog may be described correctly as amphibious.
L.Z.

168. To what extent may the frog be regarded as showing progressive adaptations to a terrestrial habitat from an aquatic one? *W.Z.(S.)*

169. Along which blood-vessels will a molecule of glucose absorbed from the intestine have to pass in order to reach a muscle in the frog's hind-leg, and along which vessels would the CO_2 released therefrom be likely to pass in order to reach the lung? *N.Z.*

170. Describe briefly the structures concerned with *breathing* in a frog and give an account of the mechanical and chemical processes concerned (details of tissue respiration are not required). *B.Bi.*

171. What is excretion? Give a detailed description of the excretory structures found in a frog. *W.Z.*

172. Give an account of the process of fertilization of the egg and of the development of the embryo of the frog up to the blastula stage. *W.Z.*

173. Show how the mass migrations of the cells (formative movements) in the blastula of a frog result in the formation of a gastrula. *W.Z.*

174. Write an illustrated account of the development of the frog from the blastula stage to the formation of the myotomes and coelom. Compare the formation of the coelom in the frog with its formation in *Amphioxus*. *N.Z.(S.)*

175. Give an account, with a time-table, of the life of a frog from the time the egg hatches until the young frog leaves the pond. Describe in detail any one selected stage which occurs during this period. *N.Z.*

176. What are the characteristic features of (*a*) the Fishes, (*b*) the Amphibia? What is the evolutionary relationship between these two groups of animals? *C.Z.*

CHAPTER 28

Terrestrial Craniates: Reptilia; Aves

177. What structural features of a bird are associated with flight? How has flight contributed to the success of birds? *C.Z.*

178. Briefly describe the unfertilized egg of the fowl and give a short account of fertilization and the subsequent changes which occur up to the establishment of an embryo with three germ layers. *L.Z.*

179. Compare and contrast the main stages of development from fertilized eggs of a frog and a chick. *C.Z.*

180. Describe the formation and functions of the foetal membranes of the chick. *L.Z.*

181. Describe the formation of the central nervous system in the embryonic frog and chick. *C.Z.*

182. Describe how cleavage and gastrulation in *Amphioxus*, frog and chick illustrate the effects which the amount of yolk present in the egg has upon these processes. *L.Z.*

183. "Birds are little more than glorified reptiles." This implies that the mammals have progressed much farther from the reptilian condition. Discuss the statement and its implication. *O.Z.*

CHAPTER 29

The Highest Terrestrial Craniates: Mammalia

184. Give an account of the skin of a fish, a frog, and of a mammal. Say how
each is adapted to the mode of life of the animal.   *B.Bi*

185. What is a skull? Show how the skulls of the animals you have studied are
based on a common pattern.   *L.Z*

186. What are the functions of a vertebral column in a mammal? Give an account
of the various types of vertebrae and their functions in the vertebral column of a
rodent.   *W.Z*

187. Discuss the structures involved in standing and moving in any mammal
you have studied.   *O.C.Z*

188. Describe the dentition of a named mammal. Do you regard this dentition a
typical of the mammals?   *C.Z*

189. Make a large labelled diagram of the alimentary canal of any mammal with
which you are familiar. Give some account of the functions of each part you have
labelled.   *O.C.B*

190. Describe the structure and function of the mammalian liver and pancreas.
                                                                     C.Z

191. Describe all the kinds of cell that can be seen in a section through (*a*) the
stomach wall (*b*) the liver.   *O.C.Z*

192. Compare the arrangement of the heart and arterial system in the dogfish
frog and mammal, relating the arrangements as far as possible to their modes of life
                                                                     O.C.B.

193. By means of coloured diagrams indicate the relationship of the liver to its
blood supply. Indicate the direction of the blood-flow by arrows and give an account
of the composition of the blood in the vessels indicated in your diagrams.   *W.Z*

194. Describe the vascular supply of the kidneys, liver and lungs in a mammal
What differences would be observed in the composition of the blood entering and
leaving these organs?   *L.Z*

195. How is respiration carried out in (*a*) *Hydra*, (*b*) the cockroach, (*c*) a mammal
Discuss the relative merits of each type of respiratory mechanism.   *O.C.B*

196. Write a descriptive account of the mechanism of movement in the wing of
bird and the limb of a terrestrial mammal.   *C.Z*

197. By means of annotated diagrams *only*, compare the excretory and reproduc
tive systems of a named male and female mammal.   *C.Z*

198. Compare the male urinogenital system of the frog with that of a mammal
Do you consider the latter system to be more efficient than the former? State you
reasons.   *O.C.B*

199. Make diagrams to illustrate the structure of the mammalian brain. What
are the functions of the main regions?   *C.Z*

200. With the aid of diagrams contrast the external features of the brain of
frog with those of the brain of a mammal. Relate the differences to the mode of life
of these animals.   *W.Z*

201. Give an account of the microscopic structure of the spinal cord and of
spinal nerve in a mammal. Show by means of a simple diagram how the disposition
of the nervous tissue in these structures allows for what is known as a "simple
reflex."   *N.Z*

202. Name and indicate the main functions of the organs which occur within the
body cavity of a female mammal.   *B.E*

203. Draw and label a diagram of the mammalian eye. Describe how accommoda
tion is brought about.   *B.*

204. Show how the structure and mechanism of the mammalian ear are related to its functions. *W.Bi.*

205. Give an account of the fertilization of the mammalian ovum and discuss the means whereby the developing embryo receives protection and nutritional requirements. *O.C.Bi.*

206. Give an account of

(a) the development of a mammalian egg following fertilization and its implantation;

(b) the functions of the embryonic (foetal) membranes, and

(c) the formation of the placenta.

What functions does the placenta serve? List the main differences between the development of a mammal and that of a fish or an amphibian. *N.Bi.*

207. Compare the nutrition and respiration of the embryonic chick and foetal rabbit. *C.Z.*

208. Terrestrial animals face problems in reproduction not met by those which are aquatic. Discuss these problems and the means by which terrestrial vertebrates have overcome them. *B.Z.*

209. What do you understand by the term *homology*? Illustrate your answer by reference to the limbs of vertebrates. *C.Z.*

210. Zoologists often refer to one animal as being "higher" than another. What do you understand by the term "higher" as used in this respect? What are the chief factors that have made for success in mammals? *O.C.Bi.(S.)*

211. *Either:* discuss and explain the likely consequences of the elimination of all wild rabbits from Great Britain, *or:* write an essay on "The Brown Rat." *O.C.Z.*

CHAPTER 31

Parasitic Plants

212. Describe the life cycles of *Pythium* and *Peronospora*. Comment on the biological significance of the differences between these fungi. *O.C.B.*

213. Write a concise, illustrated account of the life-cycles of *Erysiphe* and *Cystopus* dealing particularly with their adaptations to a parasitic existence. *N.B.*

214. Write an account of a disease of plants caused by a parasitic fungus. Describe the life cycle of the infecting organism and the measures necessary for the control of the disease. *B.Bi.*

215. Outline the life history and give a detailed illustrated account of the mode of reproduction of any one named parasitic fungus. Describe briefly by what means this fungus: (i) infects its host (ii) may be controlled. *B.B.*

216. Give an illustrated account of the structure and of the reproductive organs of *one named* parasitic fungus. In what ways can it be said that your selected fungus is adapted to its mode of life? *L.B.*

217. Describe the life history of *one* named parasitic fungus. What effects does it produce on its host? What are the general principles underlying the control of plant diseases caused by parasitic fungi? *C.B.*

218. Name five parasitic, or partially parasitic, flowering plants, indicating which are completely parasitic and which partially parasitic. Referring as necessary to the plants cited, discuss the characteristics of parasitic flowering plants and in particular the host-parasite relationships. *N.B.(S.)*

219. Give *five* examples of native British parasitic flowering plants. Choosing from your list *one* total parasite and *one* partial parasite, give an account of the adaptations they show to their peculiar mode of life. *C.B.*

220. Describe the vegetative structure of a *named* parasitic fungus and compare its mode of nutrition with that of a *named* parasitic flowering plant. *L.B.*

CHAPTER 32
Parasitic Animals

221. How would you demonstrate practically, the presence of *Monocystis* in an earthworm? How would you distinguish the typical (named) stages that you might expect to find?
C.Z

222. Construct a labelled diagram illustrating the life-history of the malaria parasite. Write an account of how the life-history of the mosquito affects the spread and incidence of malaria.
N.Z

223. Give an account of the life-history of a named parasitic protozoan and discuss the differences between its life history and that of a free-living species. *C.Z*

224. Give an illustrated account of the life-history of the liver-fluke, indicating clearly those features which can be ascribed to its parasitic mode of life. *L.Z*

225. State what you know of the nematode worms, and write an account of one *named* nematode worm which is known to be harmful. *N.Z.(S.*

226. Give labelled diagrams illustrating the life-histories of (a) the malarial parasite, (b) a tapeworm. Discuss the details of the processes whereby the parasites are transferred from host to host.
N.Z

227. By comparing free-living and parasitic members of the phylum Protozoa describe those features of structure and life-history which are associated with the parasitic mode of life.
L.Z

228. List the chief characteristics of the parasitic mode of life. Describe the life-history of one parasite of economic importance (e.g. *Heterodera*), point out the effects it has upon its host, and give a reasoned opinion as to whether you think it a successful parasite.
O.C.B.

229. Give an account of any animal parasite which affects food production. Explain its importance and the methods used for control. *B.Z*

230. Give a brief account of the various ways in which parasites are transmitted from host to host.
L.Z

231. Describe those features of animals which have resulted in their being vectors of disease. Illustrate your answer with named examples.
C.Z

CHAPTER 33
Saprophytic Plants

232. Describe the structure and life-history of a named saprophytic fungus. State concisely in what important features fungi resemble and differ from algae.
B.B

233. Describe the structure and mode of life and reproduction of *Mucor*. Briefly state the outstanding resemblances and differences between *Mucor* and *Vaucheria*.
W.I

234. Give an illustrated account of the structure and life-history of EITHER *Eurotium* OR *Erysiphe*.
L.I

235. Describe the structure, mode of life and nutrition of *Saccharomyces*. Explain how its life processes are made use of by man.
W.I

236. Compare nutrition in *Chlamydomonas* with that in Yeast and with that in *Mucor*.
L.I

237. Write a concise description of the structure and life-history of the Common Mushroom, and account for the relatively widespread distribution of this fungus.
W.I

238. Describe the modes of nutrition of a named parasitic fungus (e.g. *Phytophthora*) and a named saprophytic fungus (e.g. *Mucor*), pointing out the main similarities and differences between the mode of nutrition of the two organisms. *O.C.B*

239. Compare and contrast, with respect to nutrition and reproduction, a *named* parasitic fungus and a *named* saprophytic fungus. *L.B.*

Chapter 34
Symbiotic Unions

240. Give some account of the interrelations of fungi and bacteria with the roots of higher plants. *W.B.(S.)*

241. Give an account of the differences between parasitism and symbiosis. Illustrate your answer by reference to animals with which you are familiar. *L.Z.*

Chapter 35
Insectivorous Plants; Commensals; Epiphytes; Epizoites

242. Write a short essay on insectivorous plants. *N.B.*

243. Give a concise account of the different ways in which plants trap insects. Do you consider that such plants should be regarded as parasites? *O.C.B.*

Chapter 36
Bacteria; Bacteriophages; Viruses

244. Write a concise account of the structure and life-history of the Bacteria. Discuss the importance of this group in the economy of Nature. *W.B.(S.)*

245. Discuss the biological importance of bacteria, making special reference to *one* of the following elements: nitrogen, carbon, sulphur. *B.B.*

246. Give an account of those activities of Bacteria known to be of benefit to plant life. *L.B.*

247. "If Bacteria were to become extinct, all other forms of life would cease to exist." Explain and discuss this statement. *W B.(S.)*

248. The yeasts are considered to be fungi and not bacteria. State arguments for and against this situation. *O.C.B.*

249. Compare viruses and bacteria. *L.B.*

250. Describe the structure of a named virus. Discuss the ways in which virus diseases of plants and animals are transmitted. *N.Bi.*

251. Discuss the following statement: "To a great extent the whole of human nutrition is built on food chains in which micro-organisms play an essential role." *N.Bi.*

252. Write a short essay on "Viruses and their importance". *A.E.B.Bi.*

253. What are the characteristics of a virus? Illustrate your answer by reference to one named plant virus, and one named animal virus.
How would you classify a virus? *C.Bi.*

Appendix
Coelomate Animals V: Mollusca

1. State precisely in what habitats you would expect to find a turbellarian worm, an earthworm and a land mollusc. Point out the problems that have to be overcome to enable survival in these habitats, and show how the animals are adapted to their habitats. *O.C.Z.*

2. Contrast the type of food and feeding habits of a turbellarian worm and a snail, explaining how these animals detect, move towards and ingest their food. *C.Z.*

3. "An animal can only propel itself forward by pushing backwards against its surroundings." Show how this is brought about by *Paramecium*, a planarian, a snail and a bird. *S.Z.*

4. Classify with reasons: (*a*) *Paramecium*, (*b*) *Ascaris*, (*c*) earthworm, (*d*) crayfish, (*e*) snail, (*f*) salmon. Briefly comment on the purposes served by classifying animals.
N.Z.

5. Compare and contrast from a functional point of view the circulatory systems of a mammal and a snail.
O.C.Z.

6. Write short notes on *four* of the following: pupa, radula, gonotheca, bastard wing, gastrula.
S.Z.

NOTE

General questions, especially those of a comparative nature, will be found at the end of the question sequences in Volume II.

Parasite, facultative—
(*contd.*)
  host relations—(*contd.*)
    plant—
      Albugo, 1132
      Cuscuta, 1141
      Peronospora, 1128
      Phytophthora, 1120
      Puccinia, 1138
      Pythium, 1124
      Viscum, 1143
  host tolerance, 1110
  modifications, 1106
  obligate, 45, 1108
  partial, 46, 1108
  specialized, 1108
Parasitic animals—
  Entamoeba, 1144
  Fasciola, 1165
  flukes, 1172
  Monocystis, 1153
  nematodes, 1164
  Plasmodium, 1156
  Pulex, 1181
  Taenia, 1173
  tapeworms, 1180
  Trichinella, 1161
  Trypanosoma, 1149
Parasitic plants—
  Albugo, 1129
  bacteria, 1238
  Cuscuta, 1138
  Peronospora, 1125
  Phytophthora, 1116
  Puccinia, 133
  Pythium, 1121
  Viscum, 1142
Parasitology, 1109
Parasympathetic system, 834
Parenchyma, 230
Parichnos, 283, 289
Parthenocarpy, 371
Parthenogenesis, 271, 371, 720
Patella, 1024
Pathology, 1260
Pecten, 958
Pediastrum, 128–31
Pedicel, 481, 489
Peduncle, 481
Pellia, 72, 206
Pellicle, 102, 109, 1153
Peloton, 1222
Penetration path, 900
Penicillium, 70, 1197
Penis, 825, 1051, 1167, 1177
Pentadactyl limb, 873
Pepsin, 1029

Pereiopod, 644, 684
Perennial, 375
Perianth, 516, 545
Periblem, 400, 462
Pericardial cavity of—
  Astacus, 658
  Helix, 1279
  Oryctolagus, 998
  Periplaneta, 696
  Rana, 863
  Scyliorhinus, 808
Pericardio-peritoneal septum, 808
Pericardium, *see* Pericardial cavity
Pericarp, 497
Perichaetium, 217
Perichondrium, 572
Periclinal, 400
Pericycle, 234
  of angiosperm, 402, 464
  Dryopteris, 262, 266
  Lycopodium, 281, 283
  Pinus, 314
  Selaginella, 291
Periderm, 253
  of angiosperm, 411, 468
  Cycas, 340
  Pinus, 311
Peridium, 1194
Perigonium, 217
Perigynium, 217
Perigyny, 486
Perilymph, 845
Perimysium, 587
Perineurium, 592
Periosteum, 574
Peripharyngeal bands, 766
Periplaneta, 679
Periplasm, 1126
Perisarc, 193
Perisperm, 367, 523
Peristome, 222
Peristomium, 603
Perithecium, 1195
Peronospora, 69, 1125
Persistent pulps, 1007
Petal, 349, 490
Petiole, 256, 431, 446–7
  tendril, 441
Peyer's patch, 1027
Phaeophyceae, 67, 156–66
Phagocyte, 1259
Phalanges of—
  Columba, 948
  Lacerta, 925
  Oryctolagus, 1022
  Rana, 874
Phanerogamia, 76

Pharynx, importance of, 790
  of *Amphioxus*, 764, 790
  chick, 979
  Columba, 950–1
  Fasciola, 1166
  Helix, 1281
  Lacerta, 927
  Lumbricus, 607
  Nereis, 629
  Orvctolagus, 1024
  Periplaneta, 689
  Planaria, 552
  Rana, 876
  Scyliorhinus, 809, 812
  reduction of, 919
Phellem, 253, 412
Phelloderm, 253, 412
Phellogen, 253, 411
Phelloid, 254
Phlobaphene, 267
Phloem, 262
  of angiosperm, 403, 405, 410, 444, 465, 468
  Dryopteris, 262
  Lycopodium, 281
  Pinus, 310
  Selaginella, 291
Phloem fibres, 248
Phloem parenchyma, 248
Phloem sclereids, 248
Photoreceptor, 79, 105
Phototaxis, 80, 121, 128
Phototropism, 150
Phragmoplast, 26
Phycomycetes, 68, 1116
Phylloclade, 384
Phyllode, 439
Phyllopodium, 641
Phyllotaxis, 434
Phylogeny, 51, 543
Phylum, 52
Physalia, 57, 204
Physiological race, 1134
Physiology, 40
Phytophthora, 69, 1116
Pigeon, 64, 940
Pigeon's milk, 957
Pigment—
  animal, 568, 797, 861
  bacterial, 1237
Pileus, 1206
Piliferous layer, 461
Pinacocyte, 174
Pineal body, 830, 891, 932, 957, 1059
Pineal eye, 830, 932
Pineal foramen, 923
Pinguicula, 1229